* *For a summary of general treatment categories, see the Chapter 16 Summary. For a summary of research techniques, see Tables 7-1 and 7-2.*

An Introduction to Brain and Behavior

An Introduction to Brain and Behavior

Bryan Kolb
University of Lethbridge

Ian Q. Whishaw
University of Lethbridge

G. Campbell Teskey
University of Calgary

Fifth Edition

worth publishers
Macmillan Learning
New York

This book is dedicated to Cornelius H. "Case" Vanderwolf (1935–2015), with whom each of us studied. Case did his Ph.D. with Donald O. Hebb and postdoctoral research with Konrad Ackert and Roger Sperry, figures whose research is featured prominently in this book. He was an advocate of the theory that the study of behavior provided the window to the organization of the brain, and he was especially encouraging of our first attempt at book writing.

Publisher, Psychology and Sociology: Rachel Losh
Senior Acquisitions Editor: Daniel DeBonis
Development Editor: Barbara Brooks
Assistant Editor: Katie Pachnos
Senior Marketing Manager: Lindsay Johnson
Marketing Assistant: Morgan Ratner
Executive Media Editor: Rachel Comerford
Associate Media Editor: Jessica Lauffer
Director, Content Management Enhancement: Tracey Kuehn
Managing Editor, Sciences and Social Sciences: Lisa Kinne
Project Editor: Edgar Doolan
Media Producer: Elizabeth Dougherty
Copy Editor: Kate Daly
Senior Photo Editor: Cecilia Varas
Photo Researcher: Richard Fox
Senior Production Manager: Paul Rohloff
Director of Design, Content Management Enhancement: Diana Blume
Design Manager: Blake Logan
Interior Design: Charles Yuen
Art Manager: Matthew McAdams
Illustration Coordinator: Janice Donnola
New Illustrations: Evelyn Pence, Matthew McAdams
Composition: codeMantra
Printing and Binding: RR Donelley
Cover Art: ALFRED PASIEKA/SCIENCE PHOTO LIBRARY/Getty Images
Chapter Opener Illustrations: Katherine Streeter

Library of Congress Control Number: 2015957301

ISBN-13: 978-1-4641-0601-9
ISBN-10: 1-4641-0601-0

Copyright © 2016, 2014, 2011, 2006 by Worth Publishers
All rights reserved.
Printed in the United States of America

First printing

Worth Publishers
One New York Plaza
Suite 4500
New York, New York 10004-1562
www.macmillanhighered.com

Deborah Muirhead

Bryan Kolb received his Ph.D. from The Pennsylvania State University in 1973. He conducted postdoctoral work at the University of Western Ontario and the Montreal Neurological Institute. He moved to the University of Lethbridge in 1976, where he is Professor of Neuroscience and holds a Board of Governors Chair in Neuroscience. His current research examines how neurons of the cerebral cortex change in response to various factors, including hormones, experience, psychoactive drugs, neurotrophins, and injury, and how these changes are related to behavior in the normal and diseased brain. Kolb has received the distinguished teaching medal from the University of Lethbridge. He is a Fellow of the Royal Society of Canada and of the Canadian Psychological Association (CPA), the American Psychological Association, and the Association of Psychological Science. He is a recipient of the Hebb Prize from CPA and from the Canadian Society for Brain, Behaviour, and Cognitive Science and has received four honorary doctorates. He is a Senior Fellow of the Experience-Based Brain and Behavioral Development program of the Canadian Institute for Advanced Research. He and his wife train and show horses in Western riding performance events.

David Benard

Ian Q. Whishaw received his Ph.D. from Western University and is a Professor of Neuroscience at the University of Lethbridge. He has held visiting appointments at the University of Texas, University of Michigan, Cambridge University, and the University of Strasbourg. He is a fellow of Clair Hall, Cambridge, and of the Canadian Psychological Association, the American Psychological Association, and the Royal Society of Canada. He is a recipient of the Canadian Humane Society Bronze Medal for bravery, the Ingrid Speaker Gold Medal for research, and the distinguished teaching medal from the University of Lethbridge. He has received the Key to the City of Lethbridge and has honorary doctorates from Thompson Rivers University and the University of Lethbridge. His research addresses the neural basis of skilled movement and the neural basis of brain disease, and the Institute for Scientific Information includes him in its list of most cited neuroscientists. His hobby is training horses for Western performance events.

Tannis Teskey

G. Campbell Teskey received his Ph.D. from Western University in 1990 and then conducted postdoctoral work at McMaster University. In 1992 he relocated to the University of Calgary, where he is a professor in the Department of Cell Biology and Anatomy and the Hotchkiss Brain Institute. His current research program examines the development, organization, and plasticity of the motor cortex, as well as how seizures alter brain function. Teskey has won numerous teaching awards, has developed new courses, and is a founder of the Bachelor's of Science in Neuroscience program at his home university. He serves as Education Director for the Hotchkiss Brain Institute and chairs the Education Committee of Campus Alberta Neuroscience. His hobbies include hiking, biking, kayaking, and skiing.

CHAPTER 1

What Are the Origins of Brain and Behavior? 1

CHAPTER 2

What Is the Nervous System's Functional Anatomy? 33

CHAPTER 3

What Are the Nervous System's Functional Units?
73

CHAPTER 4

How Do Neurons Use Electrical Signals to Transmit Information?
107

Katherine Streeter

CHAPTER 8

How Does the Nervous System Develop and Adapt?

Katherine Streeter

CHAPTER 9

How Do We Sense, Perceive, and See the World?

Katherine Streeter

CHAPTER 10

Katherine Streeter

How Do We Hear, Speak, and Make Music? 321

CHAPTER 11

Katherine Streeter

How Does the Nervous System Respond to Stimulation and Produce Movement? 355

CHAPTER 12

What Causes Emotional and Motivated Behavior?

CHAPTER 13

Why Do We Sleep and Dream?

Katherine Streeter

How Do We Learn and Remember? 479

CHAPTER 15

Katherine Streeter

How Does the Brain Think?

The Fifth Edition of *An Introduction to Brain and Behavior* continues to reflect the evolution of behavioral neuroscience. In keeping with this evolution, we welcome G. Campbell Teskey, whose fresh perspective—especially on topics related to neurophysiology and nervous system disorders—enhances our author team.

Other major changes in this edition include a deeper emphasis on genetics and epigenetics throughout. Epigenetics is especially important for understanding brain and behavior because environmentally induced modifications in gene expression alter the brain and ultimately behavioral development. Thus, experience—especially early experience—modifies how brain development unfolds. These modifications—of at least some behavioral traits—can be transferred across generations, a process known as epigenetic inheritance. We introduce it in the case study at the end of Section 3-3.

This edition fully addresses advances in imaging technology, including techniques that are fueling the burgeoning field of connectomics and progress toward a comprehensive map of neural connections—a brain connectome. These exciting advances are especially relevant in the second half of the book, where we review higher-level functions.

Imaging advances and epigenetics concepts and research continue as a prime focus in this revision but are not our sole focus. In Chapter 2 we introduce the enteric nervous system, which controls the gut, and later chapters elaborate on ENS functioning. Section 7-1 introduces the emerging field of synthetic neurobiology, elaborated in Section 16-2. Section 5-2 adds new research on lipid neurotransmitters and detail on receptor subtypes.

The range of updates and new coverage in the Fifth Edition text and Focus features is listed, chapter by chapter, in the margins of these Preface pages. See for yourself the breadth and scope of the revision; then read on to learn more about the big-picture improvements in the Fifth Edition.

With encouraging feedback from readers, the book's learning apparatus continues to feature sets of self-test questions at the end of the major sections in each chapter. These Section Reviews help students track their understanding as they progress. Answers appear at the back of the book.

We continue to expand the popular margin notes. Beyond offering useful asides to the text narrative, these marginalia increase the reader's ease in finding information, especially when related concepts are introduced early in the text then elaborated on in later chapters. Readers can return quickly to an earlier discussion to refresh their knowledge or jump ahead to learn more. The margin notes also help instructors move through the book to preview later discussions.

The illustrated Experiments, one of the book's most popular features, show readers how researchers design experiments, that is, how they approach the study of brain–behavior relationships. The Basics features let students brush up or get up to speed on their science foundation—knowledge that helps them comprehend behavioral neuroscience.

We have made some big changes, yet much of the book remains familiar. In shaping content throughout, we continue to examine the nervous system with a focus on function, on how our behavior and our brain interact, by asking key questions that students and neuroscientists ask:

- Why do we have a brain?
- How is the nervous system organized, functionally as well as anatomically?
- How do drugs and hormones affect our behavior?
- How does the brain learn?
- How does the brain think?

FIFTH EDITION UPDATES

CHAPTER 1: ORIGINS

NEW: **locked-in syndrome** in §1-1 features the case of Martin Pistorius.

NEW: Figure 1-12, Neanderthal Woman, and NEW text describes *H. sapiens sapiens–H. neanderthalis* intermingling.

NEW discussion in §1-4 and Comparative Focus 1-3 explain brain cell *packing density*.

UPDATED coverage, Altered Maturation, in §1-4, simplifies the concept **neoteny**.

NEW section, Acquisition of Culture, in §1-5, introduces the concept **memes**.

CHAPTER 2: NEUROANATOMY

NEW: Research Focus 2-1, Agenesis of the Cerebellum.

UPDATED Figure 2-2 charts ENS in anatomic *and* functional nervous system organization.

NEW: §2-5 introduces the **enteric nervous system**, diagrammed in NEW Figure 2-31.

CHAPTER 3: NEURONAL ANATOMY

UPDATED Focus 3-3 describes chlorotoxin-based methods for identifying and treating brain tumors.

NEW photos: social roboticist Heather Knight with Marilyn Monrobot, Figure 3-6; Woody Guthrie, Focus 3-4; Chris Burke, Figure 3-22.

CHAPTER 4: NERVOUS SYSTEM ELECTRICAL ACTIVITY

UPDATED Focus 4-1, Epilepsy, details **electrographic seizure** and alternatives to drug treatments.

UPDATED: Multiple Sclerosis now Focus 4-2; Focus 4-4, ALS: Lou Gehrig's Disease, profiles Stephen Hawking's 50-year-plus battle with ALS.

CONDENSED: Myasthenia gravis coverage and photos conclude §4-4.

FIFTH EDITION UPDATES

CHAPTER 5: NEUROTRANSMISSION

NEW in §5-2: Lipid Transmitters focuses on **endocannabinoids**; Varieties of Receptors introduces **subunits** plus NEW Table 5-3, Small-Molecule Transmitter Receptors.

NEW in §5-3: enteric nervous system–CNS autonomy.

REVAMPED: neural bases of habituation and sensitization responses in *Aplysia*, in §5-4.

CHAPTER 6: DRUGS AND HORMONES

STREAMLINED Table 6-1, Grouping Psychoactive Drugs.

UPDATED coverage: endogenous opioid peptides and anandamide psychedelics in §6-2.

UPDATED statistics in Figure 6-16, Drug Use in the United States.

REVAMPED: Glucocorticoids and Stress in §6-5 features discrete sections on Activating a Stress Response and on Ending one.

CHAPTER 7: RESEARCH METHODS

REFOCUSED: Figure 7-5, Pathology in Parkinson Disease, accompanies discussion of Brain Lesions in §7-1.

NEW coverage: **synthetic biology** and **chemogenetics**, including *DREADD,* and temporary and reversible lesion techniques in §7-1.

REVAMPED: Single-Cell Recording begins §7-2, including NEW Figure 7-8, Spatially Related Cells.

NEW: Tables 7-1 and 7-2 summarize neuroscience research methods that Measure and Manipulate Brain–Behavior Relations, in §7-6.

UPDATED in §7-7: Animal Models of Disease and Animal Welfare and Scientific Experimentation.

CHAPTER 8: DEVELOPMENT

NEW Clinical Focus 8-1, Linking SES to Cortical Development, sets a chapterwide theme.

NEW in §8-4: infant sexual differentiation now introduces Hormones and Brain Development; Gut Bacteria and Brain Development reveals the microbiome's influence.

UPDATED in §8-4: fetal exposure statistics in Drugs and Brain Development; coverage of SIDS.

Every chapter's central question highlights the brain–behavior relationship. When we first describe how neurons communicate in Section 5-4, for example, we also describe how synaptic plasticity serves as the basis of learning. Later, in Section 14-4, we expand on plasticity as we explore learning and memory.

As it was when we wrote the First Edition, our goal in this new edition is to bring coherence to a vast subject by helping students understand the big picture. Asking fundamental questions about the brain has another benefit: it piques students' interest and challenges them to join us on the journey of discovery that is brain science.

Scientific understanding of the human brain and human behavior continues to grow at an exponential pace. We want to communicate the excitement of recent breakthroughs in brain science and to relate some of our own experiences from a combined 120+ years of studying brain and behavior, both to make the field's developing core concepts and latest revelations understandable and to transport uninitiated students to the frontiers of physiological psychology.

Areas of Emphasis

To convey the excitement of neuroscience as researchers understand it, we interweave evolution, genetics, and epigenetics; psychopharmacology; and neural plasticity and connectivity, including CNS and ENS interactions, throughout the book.

EVOLUTION Our perspective—neuroscience in an evolutionary context—recurs in almost every chapter. By focusing on comparative behavior and anatomy, we address nervous system evolution in depth in Chapters 1 and 2, evolution of the synapse in Section 5-1, and evolution of visual pathways in Section 9-2. We add ideas about how natural selection might promote overeating in Section 12-5 and evolutionary theories of sleeping and dreaming in Section 13-3. We describe the evolution of sex differences in spatial cognition and language in Section 15-5 and links between our evolved reactions to stress and anxiety disorders in Section 16-4.

GENETICS AND EPIGENETICS We introduce the foundations of genetic and epigenetic research in Sections 1-3 and 2-1 and begin to elaborate on them in Section 3-3. Chapter 5 includes discussions of metabotropic receptors and DNA and of learning and genes. The interplay of genes and drug action is integral to Chapter 6, as are the developmental roles of genes and gene methylation to Chapter 8. Section 9-4 explains the genetics of color vision, and the genetics of sleep disorders anchors Section 13-6. Section 14-4 now includes the role of epigenetics in memory. Sections 16-1 and 16-3 consider the roles of genetics and of prions in understanding the causes of behavioral disorders.

PSYCHOPHARMACOLOGY Chapter 6 investigates how drugs and hormones affect behavior, topics we revisit often through the book. You will find coverage of drugs and information transfer in Section 4-3, drugs and cellular communication in Section 5-3, and synthetic neurobiology in Section 7-1. Section 12-6 covers drugs and motivation; Section 13-6, drugs and sleep disorders; and Section 14-4, neuronal changes with drug use. Section 16-2 discusses the promise of the liposome as a delivery vehicle in pharmacological treatments, and Section 16-4, drugs used as treatments for a range of behavioral disorders.

CONNECTIVITY Neural plasticity is a hallmark of this book. We introduce the concept in Section 1-5, define it in Section 2-1, develop it in Section 2-6, and expand on it throughout. At the conclusion of Section 14-4, we elaborate seven Guiding Principles of Brain Plasticity. We describe the expanding boundaries of connectomics in Section 15-3. The new field of psychotropics, which identifies the connection between the gut microbiome and its effects on the enteric nervous system—as well as on the central nervous system—appears in Sections 2-5 and 12-5.

Scientific Background Provided

We describe the journey of discovery that is neuroscience in a way that students just beginning to study the brain and behavior can understand; then they can use our clinical examples to tie its relevance to the real world. Our approach provides the background students need to understand introductory brain science. Multiple illustrated Experiments in 13 chapters help them visualize the scientific method and how scientists think. The Basics features in 6 chapters address the fact that understanding brain function requires understanding information from all the basic sciences.

These encounters can prove both a surprise and a shock to students who come to the course without the necessary background. The Basics features in Chapters 1 and 2 address the relevant evolutionary and anatomical background. In Chapter 3, The Basics provides a short introduction to chemistry before the text describes the brain's chemical activities. In Chapter 4 The Basics addresses electricity before exploring the brain's electrical activity.

Readers already comfortable with the material can easily skip it; less experienced readers can learn it and use it as a context for neuroscience. Students with this background can tackle brain science with greater confidence. Similarly, for students with limited knowledge of basic psychology, we review such facts as stages of behavioral development in Chapter 8 and forms of learning and memory in Chapter 14.

Students in social science disciplines often remark on the amount of biology and chemistry in the book, whereas an equal number of students in biological sciences remark on the amount of psychology. More than half the students enrolled in the Bachelor's of Science in Neuroscience program at the University of Lethbridge have switched from a biochemistry or psychology major after taking this course. We must be doing something right!

Chapter 7 showcases the range of methods behavioral neuroscientists use to measure and manipulate brain and behavior—traditional methods and such cutting-edge techniques as optical tomography, resting-state fMRI, chemogenetics, and DREADD. Expanded discussions of techniques appear where appropriate, especially in Research Focus features, including Focus 3-2, Brainbow: Rainbow Neurons; Focus 4-3, Optogenetics and Light-Sensitive Channels; and Focus 16-1, Posttraumatic Stress Disorder, which includes treatments based on virtual reality exposure therapies.

Finally, because critical thinking is vital to progress in science, select discussions throughout the book center on relevant aspects. Section 1-2 concludes with The Separate Realms of Science and Belief. Focus 15-3, The Rise and Fall of Mirror Neurons, demonstrates how the media—and even scientists—can fail to question the validity of research results. Section 12-5 introduces the idea that gender identity comprises a broad spectrum rather than a female–male dichotomy. Section 7-7 considers issues of animal welfare in scientific research and the use of laboratory animal models to mimic human neurologic and psychiatric disorders.

Clinical Focus Maintained

Neuroscience is a human science. Everything in this book is relevant to our lives, and everything in our lives is relevant to neuroscience. Understanding neuroscience helps us understand how we learn, how we develop, and how we can help people with brain and behavioral disorders. Knowledge of how we learn, how we develop, and the symptoms of brain and behavioral disorders offer insights into neuroscience.

Clinical material also helps to make neurobiology particularly relevant to students who are going on to a career in psychology, social work, or another profession related to mental health, as well as to students of the biological sciences. We integrate clinical information throughout the text and Clinical Focus features, and we expand on it in Chapter 16, the book's capstone, as well.

CHAPTER 12: EMOTION, MOTIVATION, CHEMICAL SENSES

UPDATED estimates of the number of smells humans can discriminate in §12-2.

UPDATED: Stimulating and Expressing Emotion in §12-4 explains how the ENS interacts with other neural systems.

NEW: mindfulness training as a treatment strategy for anxiety disorders in Clinical Focus 12-3.

UPDATED: Clinical Focus 12-4 includes a high-fiber food component in any weight loss strategy; Figure 12-24 charts the ENS, hormones, and cognition as major factors in controlling eating.

UPDATED in §12-5: the spectrum of gender identity, including **transgender** identity, illustrated by Bruce Jenner's transition to Caitlyn Jenner.

NEW Figure 12-30: mapped by rs-fMRI, areas affected by nicotine illustrate the breadth of the brain's reward system.

CHAPTER 13: SLEEP

NEW photo: schoolchildren using light treatment to combat SAD in Focus 13-2.

NEW table: Recommended Sleep Duration times, by age group, in §13-3.

UPDATED: REM Sleep Disorders in §13-6 includes NEW subsections: Sleep Paralysis, Cataplexy, and REM Sleep Behavioral Disorder.

CHAPTER 14: LEARNING AND MEMORY

NEW discussion: *highly superior autobiographical memory* (HSAM) in §14-1.

NEW: Figure 14-12 illustrates EXPANDED discussion of spatially related cells that constitute our neural GPS.

NEW neuroimages: Figure 14-6, impaired autobiographical memory; Focus 14-3, neurofibrillary tangle formed by misfolded tau proteins; Figure 14-26, brain sections show cortical stroke and repair via induced neurogenesis.

In *An Introduction to Brain and Behavior*, the placement of some topics is novel relative to traditional treatments. We include brief descriptions of brain diseases close to discussions of basic associated processes, as exemplified in the integrated coverage of Parkinson disease through Chapter 5, How Do Neurons Communicate and Adapt? This strategy helps first-time students repeatedly forge close links between what they are learning and real-life issues.

To provide a consistent disease nomenclature, the Fifth Edition follows the system advocated by the World Health Organization for diseases named after their putative discoverers. Down syndrome, for example, has largely replaced Down's syndrome in the popular and scientific literature. We extend that convention to Parkinson disease and Alzheimer disease, among other eponymous diseases and disorders.

The nearly 150 disorders we cover are cross-referenced in the Index of Disorders inside the book's front cover. Chapter 16 expands on the nature of neuroscience research and the multidisciplinary treatment methods for neurological and psychiatric disorders described in preceding chapters. Its discussion of causes and classifications of abnormal behavior includes updated Table 16-3, now thoroughly revised to conform to the DSM-5 classification.

We emphasize questions that relate to the biological bases of behavior. For us, the excitement of neuroscience lies in understanding how the brain explains what we do, whether it is talking, sleeping, seeing, or learning. Readers will therefore find nearly as many illustrations about behavior as illustrations about the brain. This emphasis on explaining the biological foundation of behavior is another reason that we include a mix of Clinical, Research, and Comparative Focus features throughout the text.

Abundant Chapter Pedagogy

Building on the innovative teaching devices described so far, numerous in-text pedagogical aids adorn every chapter, beginning with an outline and an opening Focus feature that draws students into the chapter's topic. Focus features dot each chapter to connect brain and behavior to relevant clinical or research experience. Within chapters, definitions of boldface key terms introduced in the text appear in the margins as reinforcement, margin notes link topics together, and end-of-section Review self-tests help students check their grasp of major points.

Each chapter ends with a Summary—several include summarizing tables or illustrations to help students visualize or review big-picture concepts—and a list of Key Terms, each referenced to the page number on which the term is defined. Following this Preface, the Media and Supplements section describes the wide array of supplemental materials designed exclusively for students and teachers using the Fifth Edition.

Superb Visual Reinforcement

Our most important learning aid appears on nearly every page in the book: an expansive and, we believe, exceptional set of illustrations. Overwhelmingly, readers agree that, hand in hand with our words, the diagrams describe and illuminate the nervous system. Important anatomical illustrations are large-format to ease perusal. We have retained applications photos that range from a dance class for Parkinson patients in Section 5-3 to a seniors' bridge game in Section 16-3. New photos include, to illustrate color constancy in Section 9-4, the dress that inspired a social media controversy.

Illustrations are consistent from chapter to chapter so as to reinforce one another. We consistently color-code diagrams that illustrate each aspect of the neuron, depict each structural region in the brain, and demark nervous system divisions. We include many varieties of micrographic images to show what a particular neural structure actually looks like. These illustrations and images are included on our PowerPoint presentations and integrated as labeling exercises in our Study Guide and Testing materials.

Teaching Through Metaphors, Examples, and Principles

If a textbook is not enjoyable, it has little chance of teaching well. We heighten students' interest through abundant use of metaphors and examples. Students read about patients whose brain injuries offer insights into brain function, and we examine car engines, robots, and prehistoric flutes for the same purpose. Frequent illustrated Experiments, comparative biology examples, and representative Comparative Focus features help students understand how much we humans have in common with creatures as far distant from us as sea slugs and as close to us as chimpanzees.

We also facilitate learning by reemphasizing main points and by distilling sets of principles about brain function that offer a framework to guide students' thinking. Thus, Section 2-6 introduces ten key principles that explain how the parts of the nervous system work together. Section 14-4 summarizes seven guiding principles of neuroplasticity. These sets of principles form the basis of many discussions throughout the book. Frequently, marginal notes remind readers when they encounter these principles again—and where to review them in depth.

Big-Picture Emphasis

One challenge in writing an introductory book on any topic is deciding what to include and what to exclude. We organize discussions to focus on the bigger picture—a focus exemplified by the ten principles of nervous system function introduced in Section 2-6 and echoed throughout the book. Any set of principles may be arbitrary yet nevertheless afford students a useful framework for understanding the brain's activities.

In Chapters 8 through 16 we tackle behavioral topics in a more general way than most contemporary books do. In Chapter 12, for instance, we revisit experiments and ideas from the 1960s to understand why animals behave as they do, then we consider emotional and motivated behaviors as diverse as eating and anxiety attacks in humans. In Chapter 14, the larger picture of learning and memory is presented alongside a discussion of recovery from traumatic brain injury.

This broad focus helps students grasp the big picture that behavioral neuroscience paints. While broadening our focus requires us to leave out some details, our experience with students and teachers through four earlier editions confirms that discussing the larger problems and issues in brain and behavior is of greater interest to students, especially those new to this field, and is more often remembered than are myriad details without context.

As in preceding editions, we are selective in our citation of the truly massive literature on the brain and behavior because we believe that too many citations can disrupt the text's flow and distract students from the task of mastering concepts. We provide citations to classic works by including the names of the researchers and by mentioning where the research was performed. In areas where controversy or new breakthroughs predominate, we also include detailed citations—177 in all—to papers (especially reviews) from the years 2013 to 2016. An end-of-book References section lists, by chapter, all the literature used in developing the book, reflecting the addition of about 200 new citations total in this edition and elimination of other, now superseded, research.

CHAPTER 15: COGNITION

NEW: Hebb's cell assembly diagram concludes §15-1.

NEW: Research Focus 15-3, The Rise and Fall of Mirror Neurons.

UPDATED discussions: connectomics and the Human Connectome Project in §15-3.

NEW research: Cognition and the Cerebellum in §15-3.

NEW: Figure 15-20 maps sex differences in female–male hemispheric connectivity.

UPDATED: research in §15-5 on brain networks and gender identity.

NEW research on bilingual brain connectivity concludes §15-6.

CHAPTER 16: DISORDERS AND DYSFUNCTION

UPDATED Focus 16-1, PTSD, illustrates increasingly effective **VR exposure therapies**.

UPDATED Table 16-3 thoroughly revised to conform to DSM-5.

NEW coverage, §16-2, diagrams a liposome for drug delivery.

NEW chart: in §16-3 F.A.S.T. test for spotting stroke.

NEW discussion in §16-3: Are All Degenerative Dementias Aspects of a Single Disease? outlines prion theory and its implications, and Figure 16-13 diagrams healthy and misfolded proteins.

Acknowledgements

As in past editions of this text and *Fundamentals of Human Neuropsychology*, we have a special debt to Barbara Brooks, our long-time development editor, who has left a strong imprint on both books.

We sincerely thank as well the many people who also contributed to the development of this edition. The staff at Worth Publishers is remarkable and makes revisions a joy to do. We thank our sponsoring editor, Daniel DeBonis, more than ably assisted by Katie Pachnos; our project editor, Edgar Doolan; and production manager Paul Rohloff.

We thank design manager Blake Logan for a striking cover and Charles Yuen for a fresh, inviting, accessible new interior design. Thanks also to Cecilia Varas for coordinating photo research and to Richard Fox, who found photographs and other illustrative materials that we would not have found on our own. We are indebted to Macmillan art manager Matt McAdams, illustration coordinator Janice Donnola, and medical illustrator Evelyn Pence for their excellent work in creating new illustrations.

Our colleagues, too, have helped in the development of every edition. For their contributions in shaping the Fifth Edition, we are especially indebted to the reviewers who provided extensive comments on selected chapters and illustrations: Nancy Blum, *California State University, Northridge*; Kelly Bordner, *Southern Connecticut State University*; Benjamin Clark, *University of New Mexico*; Roslyn Fitch, *University of Connecticut*; Trevor Gilbert, *University of Calgary*; Nicholas Grahame, *Indiana University–Purdue University Indianapolis*; Kenneth Troy Harker, *University of New Brunswick*; Jason Ivanoff, *St. Mary's University*; Dwight Kravitz, *The George Washington University*; Ralph Lydic, *University of Tennessee, Knoxville*; Paul Meyer, *The State University of New York at Buffalo*; Jaime Olavarria, *University of Washington*; Christopher Robison, *Florida State University*; Claire Scavuzzo, *University of Alberta*; Sarah Schock, *University of Ottawa*; Robert Stackman, *Florida Atlantic University*; Sandra Trafalis, *San Jose State University*; Douglas Wallace, *Northern Illinois University*; Matthew Will, *University of Missouri, Columbia*; and Harris Philip Zeigler, *Hunter College*.

Likewise, we continue to be indebted to the colleagues who provided extensive comments on selected chapters and illustrations during the development of the Fourth Edition: Mark Basham, *Regis University*; Pam Costa, *Tacoma Community College*; Russ Costa, *Westminster College*; Renee Countryman, *Austin College*; Kristen D'Anci, *Salem State University*; Trevor James Hamilton, *Grant MacGewn University*; Christian Hart, *Texas Woman's University*; Matthew Holahan, *Carleton University*; Chris Jones, *College of the Desert*; Joy Kannarkat, *Norfolk State University*; Jennifer Koontz, *Orange Coast College*; Kate Makerec, *William Paterson University of New Jersey*; Daniel Montoya, *Fayetteville State University*; Barbara Oswald, *Miami University of Ohio*; Gabriel Radvansky, *University of Notre Dame*; Jackie Rose, *Western Washington University*; Steven Schandler, *Chapman University*; Maharaj Singh, *Marquette University*; Manda Williamson, *University of Nebraska—Lincoln*.

We'd also like to thank the reviewers who contributed their thoughts to the Third Edition: Chana Akins, *University of Kentucky*; Michael Anch, *Saint Louis University*; Maura Mitrushina, *California State University, Northridge*; Paul Wellman, *Texas A&M University*; and Ilsun White, *Morehead State University*. The methods chapter was new to the Third Edition and posed the additional challenge of taking what easily could read like a seed catalog and making it engaging to readers. We therefore are indebted to Margaret G. Ruddy, *The College of New Jersey*, and Ann Voorhies, *University of Washington*, for providing extensive advice on the initial version of Chapter 7.

In addition, we thank the reviewers who provided their thoughts on the Second Edition: Barry Anton, *University of Puget Sound*; R. Bruce Bolster, *University of Winnipeg*; James Canfield, *University of Washington*; Edward Castañeda, *University of New Mexico*; Darragh P. Devine, *University of Florida*; Kenneth Green, *California State University, Long Beach*; Eric Jackson, *University of New Mexico*; Michael Nelson, *University of Missouri, Rolla*; Joshua

S. Rodefer, *University of Iowa*; Charlene Wages, *Francis Marion University*; Doug Wallace, *Northern Illinois University*; Patricia Wallace, *Northern Illinois University*; and Edie Woods, *Madonna University*. Sheri Mizumori, *University of Washington*, deserves special thanks for reading the entire manuscript for accuracy and providing fresh ideas that proved invaluable.

Finally, we must thank our tolerant wives for putting up with sudden changes in plans as chapters returned, in manuscript or in proof, with hopes for quick turnarounds. We also thank our colleague Robbin Gibb, who uses the book and has provided much feedback, in addition to our undergraduate and graduate students, technicians, and postdoctoral fellows who kept our research programs moving forward when we were engaged in revising the book.

Bryan Kolb, Ian Q. Whishaw, G. Campbell Teskey

An *Introduction to Brain and Behavior*, Fifth Edition, features a wide array of supplemental materials designed exclusively for students and teachers of the text. For more information about any of the items, please visit Worth Publishers' catalog at www.macmillanhighered.com.

For Students

LaunchPad with LearningCurve Quizzing

A comprehensive Web resource for teaching and learning psychology

LaunchPad combines Worth Publishers' award-winning media with an innovative platform for easy navigation. For students, it is the ultimate online study guide, with rich interactive tutorials, videos, interactive e-Book, and the LearningCurve adaptive quizzing system. For instructors, LaunchPad is a full-course space where class documents can be posted, quizzes are easily assigned and graded, and students' progress can be assessed and recorded. Whether you are looking for the most effective study tools or a robust platform for an online course, LaunchPad is a powerful way to enhance your class.

LaunchPad for *An Introduction to Brain and Behavior*, Fifth Edition, includes the following resources:

- **THE LEARNINGCURVE** quizzing system, written by Carolyn Ensley of Wilfrid Laurier University, is a new media component for this edition. LearningCurve combines adaptive question selection, immediate and valuable feedback, and a gamelike interface to engage students in a learning experience that is unique to them. Each LearningCurve quiz is fully integrated with other resources in LaunchPad through the Personalized Study Plan, so that students will be able to review with Worth's extensive library of videos and activities. And state-of-the-art question analysis reports allow instructors to track the progress of individual students as well as their class as a whole.

- **SUMMATIVE QUIZZES,** another new media component to this edition, were written by Linda Lockwood of the Metropolitan State University. Each quiz is written on the topics discussed throughout each chapter and features a variety of multiple-choice questions presented to students randomly from question pools. Valuable to both student and instructor, the summative quizzes are a useful learning tool to propel students' understanding of the information introduced in the book.

- **AN INTERACTIVE E-BOOK** allows students to highlight, bookmark, and make notes, just as they would with a printed textbook. The search function and in-text glossary definitions make the text ready for the digital age.

- **STUDENT VIDEO ACTIVITIES** include engaging modules that instructors can easily assign for student assessment. Videos cover a variety of topics and are sure to spark discussion and encourage critical thinking.

- **THE *SCIENTIFIC AMERICAN* NEWSFEED** delivers weekly articles, podcasts, and news briefs on the very latest developments in psychology from the first name in popular science journalism.

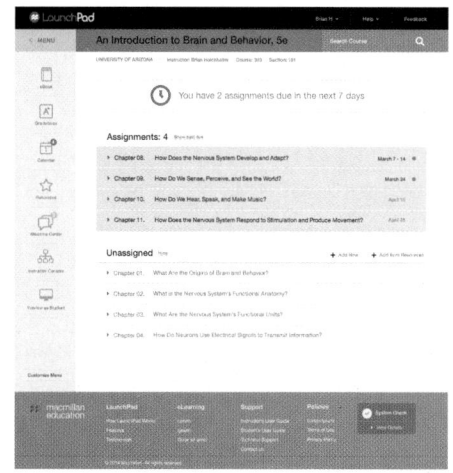

LaunchPad macmillan learning to Accompany *An Introduction to Brain and Behavior*, Fifth Edition, can be previewed and purchased at http://www.macmillanhighered.com/launchpad/kolbintro5e.

An Introduction to Brain and Behavior, Fifth Edition, and LaunchPad macmillan learning can be ordered together with
ISBN 10: 1-319-06192-3
ISBN-13: 978-1-319-06192-0

- **THE NEUROSCIENCE TOOL KIT** is a powerful Web-based tool for learning the core concepts of behavioral neuroscience—by witnessing them firsthand. These 30 interactive tutorials allow students to see the nervous system in action via dynamic illustrations, animations, and models that demystify the neural mechanisms behind behavior. Carefully crafted multiple-choice assessments make it easy to assign and assess each activity. Based on Worth Publishers' groundbreaking CD-ROM, *Foundations of Behavioral Neuroscience*, the Neuroscience Tool Kit is a valuable accompaniment to any biopsychology course.

- *PSYCHOLOGY AND THE REAL WORLD: ESSAYS ILLUSTRATING FUNDAMENTAL CONTRIBUTIONS TO SOCIETY,* **SECOND EDITION** is a superb collection of essays by major researchers describing their landmark studies. Published in association with the not-for-profit FABBS Foundation, this engaging reader includes Bruce McEwen's work on the neurobiology of stress and adaptation, Jeremy Wolfe's look at the importance of visual search, Elizabeth Loftus's reflections on her study of false memories, and Daniel Wegner's study of thought suppression. A portion of the proceeds is donated to FABBS to support societies of cognitive, psychological, behavioral, and brain sciences.

For Instructors

REVISED! INSTRUCTOR'S RESOURCES This invaluable tool, for new and experienced instructors alike, was revised by Catherine Smith of Carleton University. It includes chapter-by-chapter learning objectives and chapter overviews, detailed lecture outlines, thorough chapter summaries, chapter key terms, in-class demonstrations and activities, springboard topics for discussion and debate, ideas for research and term paper projects, homework assignments and exercises, and suggested readings from journals and periodicals. Course-planning suggestions and a guide to videos and Internet resources also are included. The Instructor's Resources can be downloaded from Worth's online catalog at www.macmillanhighered.com.

Assessment Tools

Downloadable Diploma Computerized Test Bank Prepared and revised by Christopher Striemer of Grant MacEwan University, the Test Bank includes a battery of more than 1300 multiple-choice and short-answer test questions, as well as diagram exercises. Each item is keyed to the page in the textbook on which the answer can be found. All the questions have been thoroughly reviewed and edited for accuracy and clarity. The Diploma software allows users to add, edit, scramble, or reorder items. The Test Bank also allows you to export into a variety of formats that are compatible with many Internet-based testing products. For more information on Diploma, please visit https://blackboard.secure.force.com. The Test Bank files can be downloaded from Worth's online catalog at www.macmillanhighered.com.

Presentation

Illustration Slides and Lecture Slides Available for download from www.macmillanhighered.com, these slides can either be used as they are or customized to fit the needs of your course. There are two sets of slides for each chapter. The Illustration slides feature all the figures, photos, and tables. The Lecture slides, prepared and revised by Matthew Holahan of Carleton University, feature main points of the chapter with selected figures and illustrations.

CHAPTER 1

What Are the Origins of Brain and Behavior?

Katherine Streeter

1

Living with Traumatic Brain Injury

Fred Linge, a clinical psychologist with a degree in brain research, wrote this description 12 years after his head injury occurred:

> In the second it took for my car to crash head-on, my life was permanently changed, and I became another statistic in what has been called "the silent epidemic."
>
> During the next months, my family and I began to understand something of the reality of the experience of head injury. I had begun the painful task of recognizing and accepting my physical, mental, and emotional deficits. I couldn't taste or smell. I couldn't read even the simplest sentence without forgetting the beginning before I got to the end. I had a hair-trigger temper that could ignite instantly into rage over the most trivial incident. . . .
>
> Two years after my injury, I wrote a short article: "What Does It Feel Like to Be Brain Damaged?" At that time, I was still intensely focusing on myself and my own struggle. (Every head-injured survivor I have met seems to go through this stage of narcissistic preoccupation, which creates a necessary shield to protect them from the painful realities of the situation until they have a chance to heal.) I had very little sense of anything beyond the material world and could only write about things that could be described in factual terms. I wrote, for example, about my various impairments and how I learned to compensate for them by a variety of methods.
>
> At this point in my life, I began to involve myself with other brain-damaged people. This came about in part after the publication of my article. To my surprise, it was reprinted in many different publications, copied, and handed out to thousands of survivors and families. It brought me an enormous outpouring of letters, phone calls, and personal visits that continue to this day. Many were struggling as I had struggled, with no diagnosis, no planning, no rehabilitation, and most of all, no hope. . . . The catastrophic effect of my injury was such that I was shattered and then remolded by the experience, and I emerged from it a profoundly different person with a different set of convictions, values, and priorities. (Linge, 1990)

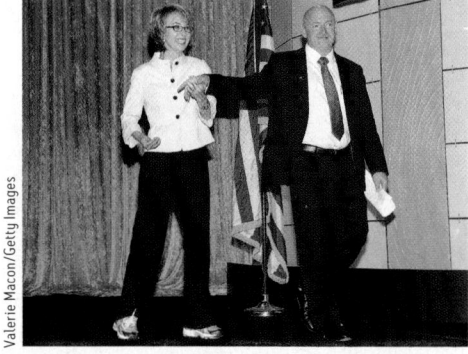

Left: U.S. Representative Gabrielle Giffords (D-AZ) reenacts her swearing-in with House Speaker John Boehner in January 2011, days before a gunshot through the left side of her brain left her near death.
Right: Giffords and husband, astronaut Mark Kelly, 16 months later: she had regained limited speech, but mobility on her right side remained limited.

In the years after his **traumatic brain injury** (TBI)—a wound to the brain that results from a blow to the head—Fred Linge made a journey. Before the car crash, he gave little thought to the relation between his brain and his behavior. After the crash, adapting to his injured brain and behavior dominated his life. On his journey, Linge learned how his injured brain affected his behavior, he relearned many skills, and he learned to compensate for the impairments his changed brain imposed on him.

1-1 Neuroscience in the Twenty-First Century

Illustrated Experiments through the book reveal how neuroscientists conduct research, beginning with Experiment 1-1 in Section 1-2.

Fred Linge emerged profoundly changed from his journey of learning to live with **traumatic brain injury** (TBI). The purpose of this book is to take *you* on a journey toward understanding the link between brain and behavior: how the brain is organized to produce behavior. Evidence comes from studying three sources: (1) the evolution of brain and behavior in diverse animal species, (2) how the brain is related to behavior in typical people, and (3) how the brain changes in people with brain damage or other brain dysfunction. The knowledge emerging from these three lines of study is changing how we think about ourselves, how we structure education and our social interactions, and how we aid those with brain injury, disease, and disorder.

We will marvel at the potential for future discoveries. We will begin to understand how genes influence the brain's structure and activity. We will learn how our experience in turn changes our genes. We will review developments in brain imaging techniques that allow us to watch our own brain in action as we think and solve problems or sleep. We will consider the goals of brain–behavior research in arresting the progress of brain disease and finding cures for brain disease and injury. We will marvel at the injured brain interacting with machines that serve as prosthetics. We will consider the possibility of repairing and even replacing malfunctioning brains. We will also consider the possibility of interacting with artificial brains—brains of our making that can, in principle, match our intelligence or perhaps even surpass it. Our journey will broaden your understanding of what makes us human.

Why Study Brain and Behavior?

The *brain* is a physical object, a living tissue, a body organ. *Behavior* is action, momentarily observable but fleeting. Brain and behavior differ greatly but are linked. They have evolved together: one is responsible for the other, which is responsible for the other, and so on. There are three reasons for linking the study of the brain to the study of behavior:

1. *How the brain produces behavior is a major unanswered scientific question.* Scientists and students study the brain to understand humanity. Understanding brain function will allow improvements in many aspects of our world, including educational systems, economic systems, and social systems. Many chapters in this book touch on the relation between psychological questions related to brain and behavior and philosophical questions related to humanity. For example, in Chapters 14 and 15, we address how we become conscious, how we speak, and how we remember.

2. *The brain is the most complex living organ on Earth and is found in many groups of animals.* Students of the brain want to understand its place in the biological order of our planet. This chapter describes the basic structure and evolution of brains, especially the human brain. Chapter 2 surveys its functional anatomy, and Chapters 3 through 5 describe the functioning of brain cells—the building blocks of every animal's brain.

3. *A growing list of behavioral disorders can be explained and treated as we increase our understanding of the brain.* More than 2000 disorders may in some way be related to brain abnormalities. As indexed inside the front cover of this book, we detail relations between brain disorders and behavioral disorders in every chapter, especially in the Focus features.

None of us can predict how the knowledge we gain about the brain and behavior may prove useful. A former psychology major wrote to tell us that she took our course because she was unable to register in a preferred course. She felt that, although our course was interesting, it was "biology, not psychology." After graduating and getting a job in a social service agency, she has found to her delight that understanding the links between brain and behavior is in fact a source of insight into many of her clients' disorders and the treatment options available for them.

What Is the Brain?

Brain, the Anglo-Saxon word for the tissue found within the skull, is but a part of the human nervous system (**Figure 1-1**). Most connections between the brain and the rest of the body are made through the **spinal cord**, which descends from the brainstem through a canal in the backbone.

Together, the brain and spinal cord make up the **central nervous system** (CNS). The CNS is encased in bone, the brain by the skull and the spinal cord by the backbone, or vertebrae. The CNS is called central both because it is physically the nervous system's core and is as well the core structure mediating behavior. All of the processes radiating out beyond the brain and spinal cord constitute the **peripheral nervous system** (PNS).

The human nervous system is composed of cells, as is the rest of the body, and these nerve cells, or **neurons**, control behavior most directly. Neurons in the brain communicate with one another, with

traumatic brain injury (TBI) Wound to the brain that results from a blow to the head.

spinal cord Part of the central nervous system encased within the vertebrae (spinal column); provides most of the connections between the brain and the rest of the body.

central nervous system (CNS) The brain and spinal cord, which together mediate behavior.

peripheral nervous system (PNS) All of the neurons in the body outside the brain and spinal cord; provides sensory and motor connections to and from the central nervous system.

neuron Specialized nerve cell engaged in information processing.

FIGURE 1-1 Major Divisions of the Human Nervous System The brain and spinal cord together make up the central nervous system. All of the nerve processes radiating out beyond the brain and spinal cord and all of the neurons outside the CNS connect to sensory receptors, muscles, and internal body organs to form the peripheral nervous system.

(A) Cerebrum (forebrain)

Right
hemisphere

Left
hemisphere

Brainstem

(B) Right hemisphere of cerebrum

Brainstem

Cerebellum

FIGURE 1-2 The Human Brain **(A)** Shown head-on, as oriented within the human skull, are the nearly symmetrical left and right hemispheres of the cerebrum. **(B)** A cut through the middle of the brain from back to front reveals the right hemispheres of the cerebrum and cerebellum and the right side of the brainstem. The spinal cord (not shown) emerges from the base of the brainstem. Chapter 2 describes the brain's functional anatomy.

Focus 2-1 elaborates cerebellar function by describing a man born without one.

sensory receptors in the skin, with muscles, and with internal body organs. As shown in **Figure 1-2**, the human brain comprises two major sets of structures. The **cerebrum (forebrain)**, shown in Figure 1-2A, has two nearly symmetrical halves, called **hemispheres**, one on the left and one on the right. The cerebrum is responsible for most of our conscious behaviors. It enfolds the **brainstem** (Figure 1-2B), a set of structures responsible for most of our unconscious behaviors. The second major brainstem structure, the **cerebellum**, is specialized for learning and coordinating our movements. Its conjoint evolution with the cerebrum suggests that it assists the cerebrum in generating many behaviors.

For his postgraduate research, our friend Harvey chose to study the electrical activity given off by the brain. He had decided that he wanted to live on as a brain in a bottle after his body died. He expected that his research would allow his bottled brain to communicate with others who could read its electrical signals. Harvey mastered the techniques used to study the brain's electrical activity but failed in his objective, not only because the goal was technically impossible but also because he lacked a full understanding of what *brain* means.

Harvey clearly wanted to preserve not just his brain but his *self*—his consciousness, his language, and his memory. This meaning of *brain* refers to something other than the organ found inside the skull. It refers to the brain as the body organ that exerts control over behavior. It is what we intend when we talk of someone smart being a brain or speak of the computer that guides a spacecraft as being the vessel's brain. The term *brain*, then, signifies both the organ itself and the fact that this organ produces behavior.

To return to Harvey's experiment, the effect of placing even the entire CNS in a bottle would be to separate it from the PNS and thus from the sensations and movements the PNS mediates. Could the brain function without sensory information and without the ability to move? Some evidence suggests that it could not.

One line of research and philosophical argument, called **embodied behavior**, proposes that the movements we make and the movements we perceive in others are central to our behavior (Prinz, 2008). That is, we understand one another not only by listening to words but also by observing gestures and other body language. We think not only with silent language but also with overt gestures and body language. Thus, the brain as an intelligent entity cannot be divorced from the body's activities.

In the 1920s, Edmond Jacobson wondered what would happen if our muscles completely stopped moving, a question relevant to Harvey's experiment. Jacobson believed that, even when we think we are entirely motionless, we still make subliminal movements related to our thoughts. The muscles of the larynx subliminally move when we think in words, for instance, and we make subliminal eye movements when we imagine or visualize some action or a person, place, or thing. In Jacobson's experiment, then, people practiced "total" relaxation and were later asked what the experience was like. They reported a condition of mental emptiness, as if the brain had gone blank (Jacobson, 1932).

In 1957, Woodburn Heron investigated another question related to Harvey's experiment: How would the brain cope without sensory input? He examined the effects of *sensory deprivation*, including feedback from movement, by having participants each lie on a bed in a bare, soundproof room and remain completely still. Padded tubes covered their arms so that they had no sense of touch, and translucent goggles cut off their vision. The participants reported that the experience was extremely unpleasant, not just because of the social isolation but also because they lost their focus. Some even hallucinated, as if their brain was somehow trying to create the sensory experiences that they suddenly lacked. Most asked to be released from the study before it ended.

Findings from these lines of research suggest that (1) the CNS needs ongoing sensory stimulation from the environment and from its own body's movement and (2) the brain communicates by producing movement and observing others' movements. Thus, when we use the term *brain* to mean an intelligent, functioning organ, we are referring to an active brain that is connected to the rest of the nervous system and producing behavior.

Yet other evidence suggests that the brain can produce levels of consciousness with greatly reduced sensory and motor stimulation. When Martin Pistorius was 12 years old, his health began to deteriorate. Eventually, he lapsed into a coma. His parents placed Martin in a nursing home, where over a number of years he became conscious of his condition, **locked-in syndrome**, although he remained completely paralyzed and unable to communicate.

Martin's condition persisted until, when he was 25, a nurse noticed him making some small facial movements. He seemed to be trying to communicate. With rehabilitation, he made excellent progress toward recovering movement, including using a voice synthesizer. Pistorius has since married. His book *Ghost Boy* describes his frustration and helplessness during years of enduring locked-in syndrome. We return to this idea of the nature of consciousness in Section 1-2.

Patients such as Martin Pistorius reveal that the brain can be conscious to a great extent in the absence of overt behavior. Whether it can maintain consciousness in the absence of all movement and sensory experience, the goal of Harvey's brain in a bottle experiment, remains unknown.

What Is Behavior?

Irenäus Eibl-Eibesfeldt began his textbook *Ethology: The Biology of Behavior,* published in 1970, with the following definition: "Behavior consists of patterns in time." These patterns can be made up of movements, vocalizations, or changes in appearance, such as the facial movements associated with smiling. The expression *patterns in time* includes thinking. We cannot directly observe someone's thoughts. The changes in the brain's electrical and biochemical activity that are associated with thought show, however, that thinking, too, is a behavior that forms patterns in time.

The behavioral patterns of animals vary enormously. Animals produce behaviors that consist of inherited responses, and they also produce learned behaviors. Most behaviors

Figure 12-1 illustrates Heron's experimental setting. *Note*: we refer to healthy people who take part in research studies as *participants* and to those with brain or behavioral impairments as *subjects* or as *patients*.

cerebrum (forebrain) Major structure of the forebrain that consists of two mirror-image hemispheres (left and right) and is responsible for most conscious behavior.

hemisphere Literally, half a sphere, referring to one side of the cerebrum.

brainstem Central structure of the brain; responsible for most unconscious behavior.

cerebellum Major brainstem structure specialized for learning and coordinating movements; assists the cerebrum in generating many behaviors.

embodied behavior Theory that the movements we make and the movements we perceive in others are central to communication with others.

locked-in syndrome Condition in which a patient is aware and awake but cannot move or communicate verbally because of complete paralysis of nearly all voluntary muscles except the eyes.

A crossbill's beak is specifically designed to open pine cones. This behavior is innate.

A baby roof rat must learn from its mother how to eat pine cones. This behavior is learned.

FIGURE 1-3 Innate and Learned Behaviors Some animal behaviors are largely innate and fixed (top). Others are largely learned (bottom). Learning is a form of cultural transmission. Top: Information from J. Weiner (1995). *The beak of the finch* (p. 183). New York: Vintage. Bottom: Information from J. Terkel (1995). Cultural transmission in the black rat: Pinecone feeding. *Advances in the Study of Behavior, 24,* p. 122.

consist of a mix of inherited and learned actions. **Figure 1-3** illustrates the contributions of mainly inherited and mainly learned behavior in the eating behavior of two animal species, crossbills and roof rats.

A crossbill beak seems awkwardly crossed at the tip, yet it is exquisitely evolved to eat pine cones. If its shape is changed even slightly, the bird is unable to eat the pine cones it prefers until its beak grows back. For crossbills, eating is largely a fixed behavioral pattern: it is inherited and does not require much modification through learning. Roof rats, in contrast, are rodents with sharp incisor teeth that appear to have evolved to cut into anything. Pine cones are an unusual food for the rats, although they have been found to eat them. But roof rats can eat pine cones efficiently only if an experienced mother teaches them to do so. This eating is not only learned, it is *cultural* in that parents teach it to offspring. We expand on the concept of culture in Section 1-5.

The mixture of inherited and learned constraints on behavior varies considerably from species to species. Generally, animals with smaller, simpler nervous systems exhibit a narrow range of behaviors that depend mainly on *heredity*. Animals with complex nervous systems have more behavioral options that depend on *learning*. We humans believe that we are the animal species with the most complex nervous system and the greatest capacity for learning new responses. Most of our most complex behaviors, including reading, writing, mathematics, and using smartphones, were learned long after our brain evolved its present form.

But most human behaviors retain some mixture of inheritance and learning, because we humans have not thrown away our simpler nervous systems. Like other animals, we retain many inherited ways of responding. The sucking response of a newborn human infant, for example, is an inherited eating pattern, but later in life eating is strongly influenced by learning and by culture.

1-1 REVIEW

Neuroscience in the Twenty-First Century

Before you continue, check your understanding.

1. _____ is a wound to the brain that results from a blow to the head.

2. The brain and spinal cord together make up the _____. All of the nerve fibers radiating out beyond the brain and spinal cord as well as all of the neurons outside the brain and spinal cord form the _____.

3. One major set of brain structures, the _____, or _____, has nearly symmetrical left and right _____ enfolding the _____, which connects to the spinal cord.

4. A simple definition of behavior is any kind of movement in a living organism. All behaviors have both a cause and a function, but they vary in complexity and in the degree to which they are _____, or automatic, and the degree to which they depend on _____.

5. Explain the concept of *embodied behavior* in a statement or brief paragraph.

Answers appear at the back of the book.

For additional study tools, visit **LaunchPad:**
www.macmillanhighered.com/launchpad/kolb5e

1-2 Perspectives on Brain and Behavior

Back to our central topic, how the study of brain and behavior are related. Many philosophers have reasoned about the causes of behavior. Their speculations can be classified into three broad approaches: mentalism, dualism, and materialism. After describing each, we explain why contemporary brain investigators subscribe to the materialist view. In reviewing these theories, you will recognize that some familiar "commonsense" ideas about behavior derive from these long-standing perspectives.

Aristotle and Mentalism

The hypothesis that the mind (or soul or psyche) controls behavior can be traced back more than 2000 years to ancient Greece. In classical mythology, Psyche, a mortal, became the wife of the young god Cupid. Venus, Cupid's mother, opposed his marriage, so she harassed Psyche with almost impossible tasks.

Psyche performed the tasks with such dedication, intelligence, and compassion that she was made immortal, thus removing Venus's objection to her. The ancient Greek philosopher Aristotle was alluding to this story when he suggested that all human intellectual functions are produced by a person's **psyche**. The psyche, Aristotle argued, is responsible for life, and its departure from the body results in death.

Aristotle's account of behavior marks the beginning of modern psychology, but the brain played no role in it. Aristotle thought the brain existed to cool the blood. Even if he had thought that the brain ruled behavior, as did some other philosophers and physicians of his time, it would have made little difference in the absence of any idea of how a body organ could produce behavior (Gross, 1995).

To Aristotle, the psyche was responsible for human consciousness, perceptions, and emotions and for such processes as imagination, opinion, desire, pleasure, pain, memory, and reason. The nonmaterial psyche was an entity independent of the body. In formulating the concept of a soul, Christianity adopted Aristotle's view that a nonmaterial entity governs our behavior and that our essential consciousness survives our death.

Mind is an Anglo-Saxon word for *memory*, and when *psyche* was translated into English, it became *mind*. The philosophical position that a person's mind (psyche) is responsible for behavior is **mentalism**. Mentalism has influenced modern behavioral science, because many terms that originated with Aristotle—*consciousness, sensation, perception, attention, imagination, emotion, motivation, memory,* and *volition* among them—survive today as descriptions of behavior. Indeed, we use these terms in this book, and they frequently appear as chapter titles in contemporary psychology and neuroscience textbooks.

Descartes and Dualism

In the first book on brain and behavior, René Descartes (1664), a French philosopher, proposed a new explanation of behavior in which he retained the mind's prominence but gave the brain an important role. Descartes placed the seat of the mind in the brain and linked the mind to the body. He stated in the first sentence of *Treatise on Man* (1664) that mind and body "must be joined and united to constitute people."

Descartes's innovation was the insight into how body organs produce their actions. He realized that mechanical and physical principles could explain most activities of body and brain—motion, digestion, and breathing, for example. Descartes was influenced by complex machines, including gears, clocks, and waterwheels, being built in Paris at the time. He saw mechanical gadgets on public display. In the water gardens in Paris, one device caused a hidden statue to approach and spray water when an unsuspecting stroller walked past it. The statue's actions were triggered when the person stepped on a pedal hidden in the sidewalk. Influenced by these clever devices, Descartes developed mechanical principles to explain bodily functions.

But Descartes could not imagine how consciousness could be reduced to a mechanistic explanation. He thus retained the idea that a nonmaterial mind governs rational behavior. Descartes did, however, develop a mechanical explanation for how the mind interacts with the body to produce movement, working through a small structure at the brain's center, the pineal body (*pineal gland*). He concluded that the mind instructed the pineal body, which

François Gérard, *Psyche and Cupid* (1798)

psyche Synonym for *mind*, an entity once proposed to be the source of human behavior.

mind Proposed nonmaterial entity responsible for intelligence, attention, awareness, and consciousness.

mentalism Explanation of behavior as a function of the nonmaterial mind.

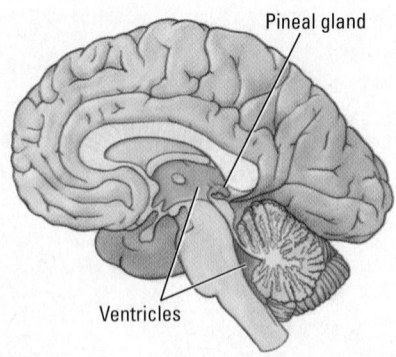

FIGURE 1-4 Dualist Hypothesis To explain how the mind controls the body, Descartes suggested that the mind resides in the pineal gland, where it directs the flow of fluid through the ventricles and into the muscles to move the body. The pineal gland actually influences daily and seasonal biorhythms; see Section 13-2.

A 2014 film, *The Imitation Game,* dramatizes Turing's efforts during World War II to crack the Nazi's Enigma code.

dualism Philosophical position that both a nonmaterial mind and a material body contribute to behavior.

mind–body problem Difficulty of explaining how a nonmaterial mind and a material body interact.

materialism Philosophical position that behavior can be explained as a function of the nervous system without recourse to the mind.

natural selection Darwin's theory for explaining how new species evolve and how existing species change over time. Differential success in the reproduction of different characteristics (phenotypes) results from the interaction of organisms with their environment.

species Group of organisms that can interbreed.

phenotype Set of individual characteristics that can be seen or measured.

lies beside fluid-filled brain cavities called *ventricles*, to direct fluid from them through nerves and into muscles (**Figure 1-4**). When the fluid expanded the muscles, the body would move.

Descartes's thesis that the mind directed the body was a serious attempt to give the brain an understandable role in controlling behavior. This idea that behavior is controlled by two entities, a mind and a body, is **dualism** (from Latin, meaning *two*). To Descartes, the mind received information from the body through the brain. The mind also directed the body through the brain. The rational mind, then, depended on the brain both for information and to control behavior.

Problems plague Descartes's dualistic theory. It quickly became apparent to scientists that people who have a damaged pineal body or even no pineal body still display typical intelligent behavior. Today, we understand that the pineal gland's role in behavior is relegated to biological rhythms; it does not govern human behavior. We now know that fluid is not pumped from the brain into muscles when they contract. Placing an arm in a bucket of water and contracting its muscles does not cause the water level in the bucket to rise, as it should if the volume of the muscle increased because fluid had been pumped into it. We now also know that there is no obvious way for a nonmaterial entity to influence the body: doing so requires the spontaneous generation of energy, which violates the physical law of conservation of matter and energy.

The difficulty in Descartes's theory of how a nonmaterial mind and a physical brain might interact has come to be called the **mind–body problem**. Nevertheless, Descartes proposed that his theory could be tested to determine whether an organism possessed a mind, Descartes proposed the language test and the action test. To pass the language test, an organism, or even an intelligent machine such as a robot, must use language to describe and reason about things that are not physically present. The action test requires behavior based on reasoning, not just an automatic response to a particular situation. Descartes proposed that nonhuman animals and machines would be unable to pass the tests because they lacked a mind.

The contemporary version of Descartes' language test, the Turing test, is named for Alan Turing, an English mathematician. In 1950, Turing proposed that a machine could be judged conscious if a questioner could not distinguish its answers from a human's. Machines are close to passing the Turing test; some might argue that it's happened. Experimental research also casts doubt on Descartes's view that nonhuman animals cannot pass the language and action tests. Studies of language in apes and other animals partly seek to discover whether other species can describe and reason about things that are not present. Comparative Focus 1-2, The Speaking Brain, summarizes a contemporary approach to studying language in animals.

Descartes's theory of mind led to bad results. Based on dualism, some people argued that young children and the insane must lack minds, because they often fail to reason appropriately. We still use the expression *he's lost his mind* to describe someone who is mentally ill. Some proponents of dualism also reasoned that, if someone lacked a mind, that person was simply a machine, not due respect or kindness. Cruel treatment of animals, children, and the mentally ill has for centuries been justified by Descartes's theory. It is unlikely that Descartes himself intended these interpretations. Reportedly he was very kind to his own dog, Monsieur Grat.

Darwin and Materialism

By the mid-nineteenth century, another brain–behavior theory emerged. **Materialism** advanced the idea that the workings of the brain and the rest of the nervous system alone fully explain rational behavior. The mind, literally, is immaterial. Materialism came to prominence when supported by the evolutionary theory of Alfred Russel Wallace and Charles Darwin.

COMPARATIVE FOCUS 1-2

The Speaking Brain

Language is such a striking characteristic of our species that it was once thought unique to humans. Yet evolutionary theory finds it unlikely that language appeared full-blown in modern humans. Language does have antecedents in other animals. Many species lacking a cerebral cortex, including fishes and frogs, are capable of elaborate vocalizations, and vocalization is still more elaborate in species having a cerebral cortex, such as birds, whales, and primates. But can nonhuman animals speak?

In language studies with chimpanzees, humans' closest living relatives, scientists have used two approaches: language training and analyzing spontaneous vocalizations and gestures (Gillespie-Lynch et al., 2014). To show that nonverbal forms of language might have preceded verbal language, Beatrice and Alan Gardner (1969) taught a version of American Sign Language (ASL) to a chimpanzee named Washoe. Sue Savage-Rumbaugh and her coworkers (1999) taught a pygmy chimpanzee named Malatta the symbolic language Yerkish. (The pygmy chimpanzee, or *bonobo,* is a species thought to be an even closer relative of humans than other chimps.)

Malatta's son Kanzi accompanied his mother to class and became an excellent Yerkish student. Kanzi also displayed clear evidence of understanding complex human speech. While recording his vocalizations when interacting with people and eating, Jared Taglialatela and coworkers found that Kanzi made many sounds associated with their meanings, or semantic context. For example, Kanzi associated various peeps with specific foods. The research group also found that chimps use a raspberry or extended grunt sound in a specific context to attract the attention of others, including people.

Imaging brain blood flow associated with the use of chimpanzeeish indicates that humans and chimpanzees activate the same brain regions when they speak (Taglialatela, 2011). Wild bonobos are found to use one distinct call to attract others to feeding locations and another to initiate a trip. The animals also use numerous gestures to signal intent to others.

Stewart Watson and colleagues (2015) report that in two chimpanzee colonies, the animals used different referential calls (names) for apples. When the groups were combined, both modified their calls and adopted a common call, an example of gestural drift analogous to people adopting the speech patterns of those around them. The study demonstrates that chimpanzees can learn and share referential calls.

Kanzi

Laurentiu Garofeanu/Barcroft USA/Barcroft Media via Getty Images

Evolution by Natural Selection

Wallace and Darwin independently arrived at the same conclusion—the idea that all living things are related. Both outlined this view in papers presented at the Linnaean Society of London in July 1858. Darwin further elaborated the topic in his book *On the Origin of Species by Means of Natural Selection*, published in 1859. *The Origin of Species* presented a wealth of supporting detail, which is why Darwin is regarded as the founder of modern evolutionary theory.

Both Darwin and Wallace had looked carefully at the anatomy of animals and at animal behavior. Both were struck by the myriad characteristics common to so many species despite their diversity. For example, the skeleton, muscles, and body parts of humans, monkeys, and other mammals are remarkably similar. So is their behavior: many animal species reach for food with their forelimbs.

Such observations led first to the idea that living organisms must be related, an idea widely held even before Wallace and Darwin. More important, these same observations led Darwin to explain how the great diversity in the biological world could have evolved from common ancestry. Darwin proposed that animals have traits in common because these traits are passed from parents to their offspring.

Natural selection is Darwin's theory for explaining how new species evolve and how existing species change over time. A **species** is a group of organisms that can breed among themselves. Individual organisms of any species vary extensively in their **phenotype**, the characteristics we can see or measure. No two individuals of any species are exactly alike. Some are big, some are small, some are fat, some are fast, some are light-colored, and some have large teeth.

Figure 2-1 illustrates this principle of *phenotypic plasticity.*

Individual organisms whose characteristics best help them to survive in their environment are likely to leave more offspring than are less-fit members. This unequal ability of individual members to survive and reproduce leads to a gradual change in a species' population over time, with characteristics favorable for survival in a particular habitat becoming more prevalent in succeeding generations. Natural selection is nature's blueprint for the methods of artificial selection practiced for centuries by plant and animal breeders to produce organisms with desirable traits.

Natural Selection and Heritable Factors

Neither Darwin nor Wallace understood the basis of the great variation in plant and animal species they observed. Another scientist, the monk Gregor Mendel, discovered one principle underlying phenotypic variation and how traits pass from parents to their offspring. Through experiments he conducted on pea plants in his monastery garden beginning about 1857, Mendel deduced that heritable factors, which we now call *genes*, govern various physical traits displayed by the species.

Members of a species that have a particular genetic makeup, or **genotype**, are likely to *express* (turn on) similar phenotypic traits, as posited in the Procedure section of **Experiment 1-1**. If the gene or combination of genes for a trait, say, flower color, is passed on

Section 3-3 explains what constitutes a gene, how genes function, and how genes can change, or *mutate*.

▶ EXPERIMENT **1-1**

Question: How do parents transmit heritable factors to offspring?

Procedure
Mendel crossbred pea plants, then observed which traits parent plants passed to their offspring in successive generations.

Results

White flower crosses produce white flowers in the first generation (F1).

Purple flower crosses produce purple flowers in the first generation.

First-generation white flower crossed with first-generation purple flower produces all purple flowers in the second generation (F2).

Second-generation purple flowers crossed with second-generation purple flower produces, on average, three purple flowers and one white flower in the third generation (F3).

Conclusion: An individual inherits two factors (genes) for each trait, but the effects of one gene may hide the other gene in the individual. The hidden gene can resurface after crossbreeding.

to offspring, the offspring will express the same trait, as illustrated at the top of the Results section in Experiment 1-1. Two white-flowered pea plants produce white-flowered offspring in the first generation, or F1, and purple-flowered parents produce purple-flowered offspring. Observing this result, Mendel reasoned that two alternative heritable elements govern the trait flower color.

Mendel then experimented with crossbreeding F_1 purple and white pea plant flowers. The illustration at the bottom of the Results section in Experiment 1-1 shows that second-generation (F2) offspring all express the purple phenotype. Had the element that expresses white flowers disappeared? To find out, Mendel crossbred the F2 purple flowers. The third generation, F3, produced flowers in the ratio of roughly 1 white to 3 purple blooms.

This result suggested to Mendel that the trait for white flowers had not disappeared but rather was hidden by the trait for purple flowers. He concluded that individuals inherit two factors, or genes, for each trait, but one may dominate and hide (suppress) the other in the individual's phenotype.

Thus, the unequal ability of individual organisms to survive and reproduce is related to the different genes they inherit from their parents and pass on to their offspring. By the same token, similar characteristics within or between species are usually due to similar genes. For instance, genes that produce the nervous system in different animal species tend to be very similar.

Interplay of Genes, Environment, and Experience

The principles of inheritance that Mendel demonstrated through his experiments have led to countless discoveries about genetics. We now know that new traits appear because new gene combinations are inherited from parents, existing genes change or mutate, suppressed genes are re-expressed, expressed genes are suppressed, or genes or parts of genes are deleted or duplicated.

But genes alone cannot explain most inherited traits. Mendel realized that environment participates in expression of traits: planting tall peas in poor soil reduces their height, for example. Experience likewise plays a part. The experience of children who attend a substandard school, for example, is far different from that of children who attend a model school.

Epigenetics is the study of differences in gene expression related to environment and experience. Epigenetic factors do not change your genes, but they do influence how your genes express the traits you've inherited from your parents. Epigenetic changes can persist throughout a lifetime, and their cumulative effects can make dramatic differences in how your genes work. Epigenetic factors described throughout this book are revolutionizing our understanding of gene–brain interactions in typical brain development and in brain function. They will also help investigators understand, and develop new treatments for, some neurological disorders.

Summarizing Materialism

Darwin's theory of natural selection, Mendel's discovery of genetic inheritance, and the reality of epigenetics have three important implications for studying the brain and behavior:

1. *Because all animal species are related, their brains must be related.* A large body of research confirms first that all animals' brain cells are so similar that these cells must be related and second that all animal brains are so similar that they must be related as well. Brain researchers study the nervous systems of animals as different as slugs, fruit flies, rats, and monkeys, knowing that they can extend their findings to the human nervous system.

2. *Because all animal species are related, their behavior must be related.* In his book *The Expression of the Emotions in Man and Animals*, Darwin (1872) argued that emotional

genotype Particular genetic makeup of an individual.

epigenetics Differences in gene expression related to environment and experience.

Consult Section 3-3 for details on genetic and epigenetic principles.

Section 3-1 describes the varieties of neurons and other brain cells.

More on emotions and their expression in Sections 12-2, 12-4, and 14-3.

FIGURE 1-5 An Inherited Behavior
People the world over display the same emotional expressions that they recognize in others—these smiles, for example. This evidence supports Darwin's suggestion that emotional expression is an inherited behavior.

expressions are similar in humans and other animals because we inherited them from a common ancestor. **Figure 1-5** offers evidence. That people the world over display the same behavior suggests that the trait is inherited rather than learned.

3. *Brain and behavior in complex animals such as humans evolved from simpler animals' brains and behaviors and also depend on learning.* Coming up in Section 1-3 we trace the evolution of nervous systems and their increasingly complex repertoires of actions, from a simple netlike arrangement to a multipart nervous system with a brain that controls behavior.

Contemporary Perspectives on Brain and Behavior

Where do modern students of the brain stand on the perspectives of mentalism, dualism, and materialism? In his influential 1949 book, *The Organization of Behavior*, psychologist Donald O. Hebb describes the scientific acceptance of materialism in a folksy manner:

> Modern psychology takes completely for granted that behavior and neural function are perfectly correlated, that one is completely caused by the other. There is no separate soul or life force to stick a finger into the brain now and then and make neural cells do what they would not otherwise. (Hebb, 1949, p. iii)

Hebb's claim dovetails with his theory of how the brain produces consciousness. He suggested that learning is enabled by neurons forming new connections with one another in the brain. He called the resulting neuronal network a *cell assembly*. As the neural substrate for the learned experience, cell assemblies interact: one cell assembly becomes connected to another. This linking of cell assemblies is thus the linking of memories, which to Hebb is what consciousness is.

Hebb's argument is materialistic. The contemporary philosophical school *eliminative materialism* takes the position that if behavior can be described adequately without recourse to the mind, then the mental explanation should be eliminated. Daniel Dennett (1978) and other philosophers, who have considered such mental attributes as consciousness, pain, and attention, argue that an understanding of brain function can replace mental explanations of these attributes. Mentalism, by contrast, defines consciousness as an entity, attribute, or thing. Let us use the concept of consciousness to illustrate the argument for eliminative materialism.

Recovering Consciousness: A Case Study

Darwin offered no suggestion about how the brain produces consciousness, although his theory predicted that it must. One patient's case study offers insight into how the study of brain and behavior begins to describe consciousness. The patient, a 38-year-old man, had lingered in a **minimally conscious state** (MCS) for more than 6 years after an assault. He was occasionally able to communicate with single words, occasionally able to follow simple commands. He was able to make a few movements but could not feed himself despite 2 years of inpatient rehabilitation and 4 years in a nursing home.

This patient is one of approximately 1.4 million people each year in the United States who, as described by Fred Linge in Clinical Focus 1-1, contend with TBI. Among them, as many as 100,000 may become comatose; as few as 20 percent recover consciousness. Among the remaining TBI patients, some are diagnosed as being in a **persistent vegetative state** (PVS), alive but unable to communicate or to function independently at even the most basic level. Their brain damage is so extensive that no recovery can be expected. Others, such as the MCS assault victim described earlier, are so diagnosed because behavioral observation and brain imaging studies suggest that they do have a great deal of functional brain tissue remaining.

Adrian Owen (2015) and his colleagues have found that by imaging the brain of comatose patients they can assess the extent to which the patients are conscious by the patterns of activity in their brain. Using an imaging system that measures brain function in terms of oxygen use, Owen's group discovered that some comatose patients are actually *locked in*, as was Martin Pistorius, whom you met in Section 1-1.

Furthermore, these investigators devised ways to communicate with conscious patients by teaching them a language that signals changes in their brains' activity patterns. For example, while imaging the brain of control subjects, Owen's group asks them to imagine hitting a tennis ball with a racket. The group identifies the active brain region associated with the imaginary act. They then ask patients to imagine hitting a tennis ball and so determine from their brain images whether they understand. If the patient understands the instruction and so demonstrates consciousness, procedures for further communication and rehabilitation can begin.

On the rehabilitation front, Nicholas Schiff and his colleagues (Schiff & Fins, 2007) reasoned that, if they could stimulate their MCS patient's brain by administering a small electrical current, they could improve his behavioral abilities. As part of a **clinical trial** (a consensual experiment directed toward developing a treatment), they implanted thin wire electrodes in his brainstem so they could administer a small electrical current.

Through these electrodes, which are visible in the X-ray image shown in **Figure 1-6**, the investigators applied the electrical stimulation for 12 hours each day. The procedure is called **deep brain stimulation** (DBS). The researchers found dramatic improvement in the patient's behavior and ability to follow commands. For the first time, he was able to feed himself and swallow food. He could even interact with his caregivers and watch television, and he showed further improvement in response to rehabilitation.

The experimenters' very practical measures of consciousness are formalized by the Glasgow Coma Scale (GCS), one indicator of the degree of unconsciousness and of recovery from unconsciousness. The GCS rates eye movement, body movement, and speech on a 15-point scale. A low score indicates coma and a high score indicates consciousness. Thus, the ability to follow commands, to eat, to speak, and even to watch TV provide quantifiable measures of consciousness contrasting sharply with the qualitative description that sees consciousness as a single entity. Eliminative materialists would argue, therefore, that the objective, measurably improved GCS score of behaviors in a

minimally conscious state (MCS)
Condition in which a person can display some rudimentary behaviors, such as smiling or uttering a few words, but is otherwise not conscious.

persistent vegetative state (PVS)
Condition in which a person is alive but unaware, unable to communicate or to function independently at even the most basic level.

clinical trial Consensual experiment directed toward developing a treatment.

deep brain stimulation (DBS)
Neurosurgery in which electrodes implanted in the brain stimulate a targeted area with a low-voltage electrical current to facilitate behavior.

FIGURE 1-6 Deep Brain Stimulation X-ray image showing electrodes implanted in the thalamus, a structure deep in the brain near the tip of the brainstem, for DBS. DBS can treat disorders such as Parkinson disease and depression (see Section 16-3) and aid recovery from TBI (see Section 14-5).

Zephyr/Science Source

brain-injured patient is more useful than a subjective mentalistic explanation that consciousness has "improved."

People under the age of 19 can be especially vulnerable to head trauma and concussion when they participate in recreational activities and sporting competitions. The Centers for Disease Control and Prevention has cited bicycling and football injuries as leading causes of TBI in this population. TBI can also lead to accelerated brain aging, an area of growing concern for participants in athletic competitions that lead to repeated concussion or other head trauma, and to military combatants.

The Separate Realms of Science and Belief

Contemporary brain theory is materialistic. Although materialists, your authors included, continue to use subjective mentalistic words such as *consciousness*, *pain*, and *attention* to describe more complex behaviors, at the same time they recognize that these words do not describe mental entities. Materialism argues for objective, *measurable* descriptions of behavior that can be referenced to brain activity.

Some people may question materialism's tenet that only the brain is responsible for behavior because they think it denies religion. But materialism is neutral with respect to religion. Many of the world's major religions accept both evolution and the brain's centrality in behavior as important scientific theories. Fred Linge, introduced in Clinical Focus 1-1, has strong religious beliefs, as do the other members of his family. They used their religious strength to aid in his recovery. Yet despite their religious beliefs, they realize that Linge's brain injury caused his changed behavior and that learning to compensate for his impairments caused his brain function to improve.

Indeed, many behavioral scientists hold religious beliefs and see no contradiction between them and their engagement with science. Science is not a belief system but rather a set of procedures designed to allow investigators to confirm answers to a question independently. As outlined in Experiment 1-1, this four-step procedure allows anyone to *replicate*, or repeat, their original conclusions—or find that they cannot.

More research on and treatments for MCS and TBI in Sections 7-3, 14-5, and 15-7. Concussion is the topic of Focus 16-3.

The four-step experimental procedure is (1) formulate a question (hypothesis), (2) design a procedure to test it, (3) evaluate the results, (4) confirm or modify the hypothesis.

(1-2) **REVIEW**

Perspectives on Brain and Behavior

Before you continue, check your understanding.

1. The view that behavior is the product of an intangible entity called the mind (psyche) is _____. The notion that the immaterial mind acts through the material brain to produce language and rational behavior is _____. _____, the view that brain function fully accounts for all behavior, guides contemporary research on the brain and behavior.

2. The implication that the brains and behaviors of complex animals such as humans evolved from the brains and behaviors of simpler animals draws on the theory of _____ advanced by _____.

3. The brain demonstrates a remarkable ability to recover, even after severe brain injury, but an injured person may linger in a _____, occasionally able to communicate or to follow simple commands but otherwise not conscious. Those who have such extensive brain damage that no recovery can be expected remain in a _____, alive but unable to communicate or to function independently at even the most basic level.

4. Darwin and Mendel were nineteenth-century contemporaries. Briefly contrast the methods they used to reach their scientific conclusions.

Answers appear at the back of the book.

For additional study tools, visit 🔲 LaunchPad:
www.macmillanhighered.com/launchpad/kolb5e

1-3 Evolution of Brains and of Behavior

Neither nervous system nor brain is common to all living organisms; rather, nervous systems and behavior have built up and changed bit by bit as animals have evolved. We trace the evolution of the human brain and behavior by describing (1) animals that first developed a nervous system and muscles with which to move, (2) how the nervous system grew more complex as the brain evolved to mediate complex behavior, and (3) how the human brain evolved its present complexity.

The popular interpretation of human evolution is that we are descended from apes. Actually, humans *are* apes. Other living apes are not our ancestors, although we are related to them through a **common ancestor**, a forebear from which two or more lineages or family groups arise. To demonstrate the difference, consider the following story.

Two people named Joan Campbell are introduced at a party, and their names provide a rich conversation starter. Although both belong to the Campbell lineage (family line), one Joan is not descended from the other. The two women live in different parts of North America, one in Texas and the other in Ontario, and both their families have been there for many generations.

Nevertheless, after comparing family histories, the two Joans discover that they have ancestors in common. The Texas Campbells are descended from Jeeves Campbell, brother of Matthew Campbell, from whom the Ontario Campbells are descended. Jeeves and Matthew both boarded the same fur-trading ship when it stopped for water in the Orkney Islands north of Scotland before sailing to North America in colonial times.

The Joan Campbells' common ancestors, then, were the mother and father of Jeeves and Matthew. Both the Texas and the Ontario Campbell family lines are descended from this man and woman. If the two Joan Campbells were to compare their genes, they would find similarities that correspond to their common lineage.

In much the same way, humans and other apes are descended from common ancestors. But unlike the Joan Campbells, we do not know exactly who those distant relatives were. By comparing the brain and behavioral characteristics of humans and related animals and by comparing their genes, however, scientists are tracing our lineage back farther and farther to piece together the origins of our brain and behavior.

Some living animal species display characteristics more similar to those of a common ancestor than do others. For example, in some ways chimpanzees are more similar to the common ancestor of humans and chimpanzees than are modern humans. In the following sections, we trace some major evolutionary events that led to human brains and human behavior by looking at the nervous systems of living animal species and the fossils of extinct animal species.

Origin of Brain Cells and Brains

Earth formed about 4.5 billion years ago, and the first life-forms arose about a billion years later. About 700 million years ago, animals evolved the first brain cells, and by 250 million years ago, the first brain had evolved. A humanlike brain first developed only about 6 million years ago, and our modern human brain has been around for only the past 200,000 years or so.

Although life arose very early in our planet's history, then, brain cells and brains evolved comparatively recently. Large, complex brains, such as ours, appeared only an eyeblink ago in evolutionary terms. If you are familiar with the principles of taxonomic classification, which names and orders living organisms according to their evolutionary relationships, read on. If you prefer a brief review before you continue, turn first to The Basics: Classification of Life on pages 16–17.

common ancestor Forebear of two or more lineages or family groups; ancestral to both groups.

THE BASICS

Classification of Life

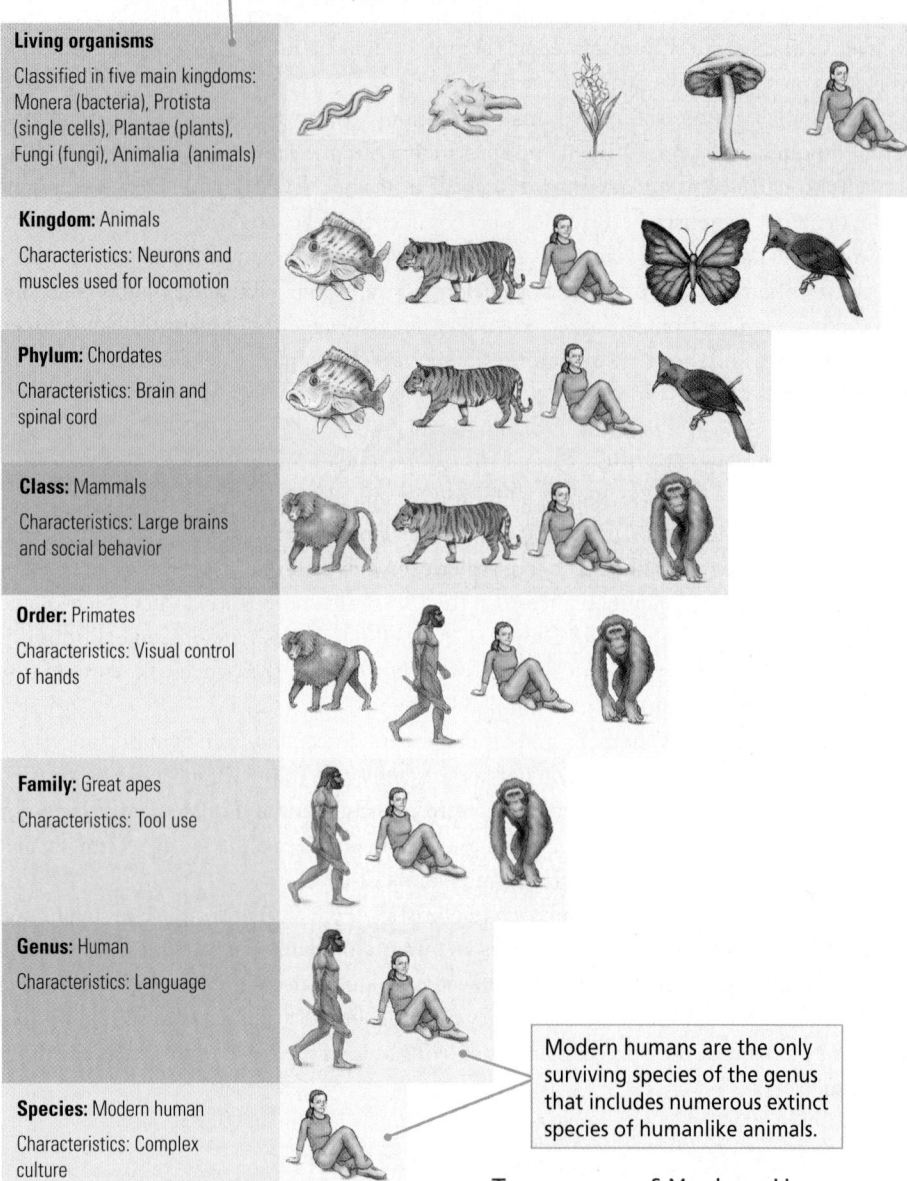

Taxonomy classifies groups of representative living organisms into increasingly specific, subordinate groups.

Living organisms
Classified in five main kingdoms: Monera (bacteria), Protista (single cells), Plantae (plants), Fungi (fungi), Animalia (animals)

Kingdom: Animals
Characteristics: Neurons and muscles used for locomotion

Phylum: Chordates
Characteristics: Brain and spinal cord

Class: Mammals
Characteristics: Large brains and social behavior

Order: Primates
Characteristics: Visual control of hands

Family: Great apes
Characteristics: Tool use

Genus: Human
Characteristics: Language

Species: Modern human
Characteristics: Complex culture

Modern humans are the only surviving species of the genus that includes numerous extinct species of humanlike animals.

Taxonomy of Modern Humans

Taxonomy is the branch of biology concerned with naming and classifying species by grouping representative organisms according to their common characteristics and their relationships to one another.

As shown in the left column of the figure Taxonomy of Modern Humans, which illustrates the human lineage, the broadest unit of classification is a kingdom, with more subordinate groups being phylum, class, order, family, genus, and species. This taxonomic hierarchy is useful in helping us trace the evolution of brain cells and the brain.

We humans belong to the animal kingdom, the chordate phylum, the mammalian class, the primate order, the great ape family, the genus *Homo*, and the species *sapiens*. Animals are usually identified by their genus and species names. So we humans are called *Homo sapiens sapiens*, meaning *wise, wise human*.

The branches in the figure Cladogram, which shows the taxonomy of the animal kingdom, represent the evolutionary sequence (phylogeny) that connects all living organisms. Cladograms are read from left to right: the most recently evolved organism (animal) or trait (muscles and neurons) is farthest to the right.

Of the five kingdoms of living organisms represented in the cladogram, only the one most recently evolved, Animalia, contains species with muscles and nervous systems. It is noteworthy that muscles and nervous systems evolved together to underlie the forms of movement (behavior) that distinguish members of the animal kingdom.

The figure Evolution of the Nervous System shows the taxonomy of the 15 groups, or *phyla*, of Animalia, classified according to increasing complexity of nervous systems and movement.

Evolution of the Nervous System on page 17 offers a visual recap.

Evolution of Nervous Systems in Animals

A nervous system is not essential for life. In fact, most organisms both in the past and at present have done without one. In animals that do have a nervous system, comparison of a wide variety of species broadly outlines how the nervous system has evolved. We summarize this evolution in the following general steps:

1. *Neurons and muscles.* Brain cells and muscles evolved first, allowing animals to move.

Brain cells, nervous systems, and muscles first evolved in animals.

Monera (bacteria) Protista (single cells) Plantae (plants) Fungi (fungi) Animalia (animals)

Muscles and neurons

Multicells

Common ancestor of animals

True cells (nuclei and organelles)

Cladogram

In proceeding to the right from the *nerve net*, we find that nervous systems in somewhat more recently evolved phyla, such as flatworms, have more complex structure. These organisms have heads and tails, and their bodies show both *bilateral symmetry* (one half of the body is the mirror image of the other) and *segmentation* (the body is composed of similarly organized parts). The structure of the human spinal cord resembles this segmented nervous system.

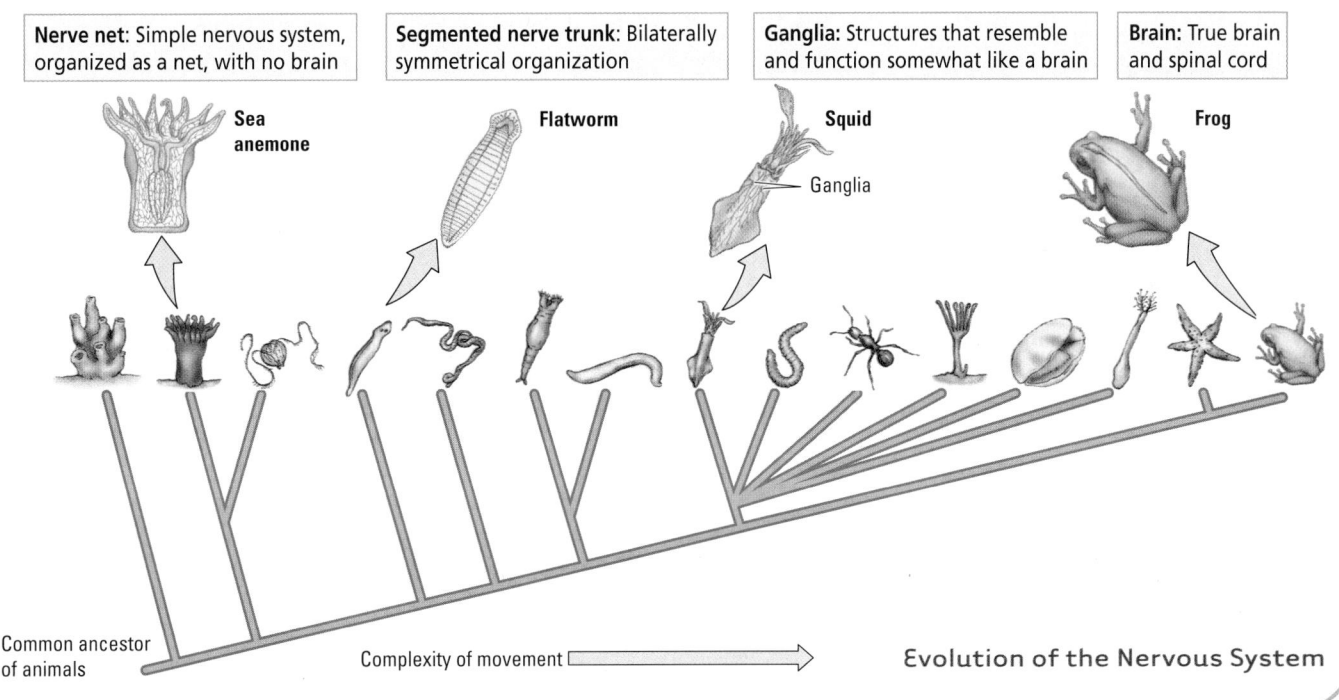

Nerve net: Simple nervous system, organized as a net, with no brain

Segmented nerve trunk: Bilaterally symmetrical organization

Ganglia: Structures that resemble and function somewhat like a brain

Brain: True brain and spinal cord

Sea anemone Flatworm Squid Frog

Ganglia

Common ancestor of animals

Complexity of movement

Evolution of the Nervous System

2. *Nerve net.* The nervous system representative of evolutionarily older phyla, such as jellyfishes and sea anemones, is extremely simple. It consists of a diffuse **nerve net**, which has no structure that resembles a brain or spinal cord but consists entirely of neurons that receive sensory information and connect directly to other neurons that move muscles. Look again at Figure 1-1 and imagine that the brain and spinal cord have been removed. The human PNS is reminiscent of the nerve net in phylogenetically simpler animals.

nerve net Simple nervous system that has no center but consists of neurons that receive sensory information and connect directly to other neurons that move muscles.

In the context of the brain's overall bilateral symmetry, Section 15-4 examines *asymmetries* between its cerebral hemispheres.

Figure 2-28 maps the human spinal cord's segments.

---

bilateral symmetry Body plan in which organs or parts present on both sides of the body are mirror images in appearance. For example, the hands are bilaterally symmetrical, whereas the heart is not.

segmentation Division into a number of parts that are similar; refers to the idea that many animals, including vertebrates, are composed of similarly organized body segments.

ganglia Collection of nerve cells that function somewhat like a brain.

chordate Animal that has both a brain and a spinal cord.

cladogram Phylogenetic tree that branches repeatedly, suggesting a taxonomy of organisms based on the time sequence in which evolutionary branches arise.

3. *Bilateral symmetry.* In more complex animals such as flatworms, the nervous system is more organized, and it features **bilateral symmetry**: the nervous system on one side of the animal mirrors that on the other side. The human nervous system is also bilaterally symmetrical (see Figure 1-1).

4. *Segmentation.* The body of animals such as earthworms consists of a series of similar muscular segments. Their nervous system has similar repeating segments. The human spinal cord and brain display such **segmentation**: the vertebrae contain the similar repeating nervous system segments of the spinal cord.

5. *Ganglia.* In still more recently evolved invertebrate phyla, including clams, snails, and octopuses, are clusters of neurons called **ganglia** that resemble primitive brains and function somewhat like them in that they are command centers. In some phyla, *encephalization*, having the ganglia in the head, is distinctive. For example, insects' ganglia are sufficiently large to merit the term *brain*.

6. *Spinal cord.* In relatively highly evolved **chordates**—animals that have both a brain and a spinal cord—a single nervous system pathway connects the brain with sensory receptors and muscles. Chordates get their name from the *notochord*, a flexible rod that runs the length of the back. In humans, the notochord is present only in the embryo; by birth, bony vertebrae encase the spinal cord.

7. *Brain.* The chordate phylum, of which amphibians, reptiles, birds, and mammals are class members, displays the greatest degree of encephalization: a true brain. Of all of the chordates, humans have the largest brain relative to body size, but many other chordates have large brains as well. Although built to a common plan, the brain of each chordate species displays specializations related to the distinctive behaviors of that species.

Chordate Nervous System

A chart called a **cladogram** (from the Greek word *clados*, meaning *branch*) displays groups of related organisms as branches on a tree. The cladogram in **Figure 1-7** represents seven of the nine classes to which the approximately 38,500 chordate species belong. Wide variation exists among the nervous systems of chordates, but common to all is the basic structural pattern of bilateral symmetry, segmentation, and a spinal cord and brain encased in cartilage or bone.

As chordates evolved limbs and new forms of locomotion, their brain became larger. For example, all chordates have a brainstem, but only the birds and mammals have a large forebrain. The evolution of more complex behavior in chordates is closely related to the evolution of the *cerebrum* and *cerebellum*. Their increasing size in various classes of chordates is illustrated in **Figure 1-8**. These increases accommodate new behaviors, including new forms of locomotion on land, complex movements of the mouth and hands for eating, improved learning ability, and highly organized social behavior.

FIGURE 1-7 Representative Classes of Chordates This cladogram illustrates evolutionary relationships among animals that have a brain and spinal cord. Brain size increased with the evolution of limbs in Amphibia. Birds and mammals are the most recently evolved chordates, and both classes have large brains relative to body size.

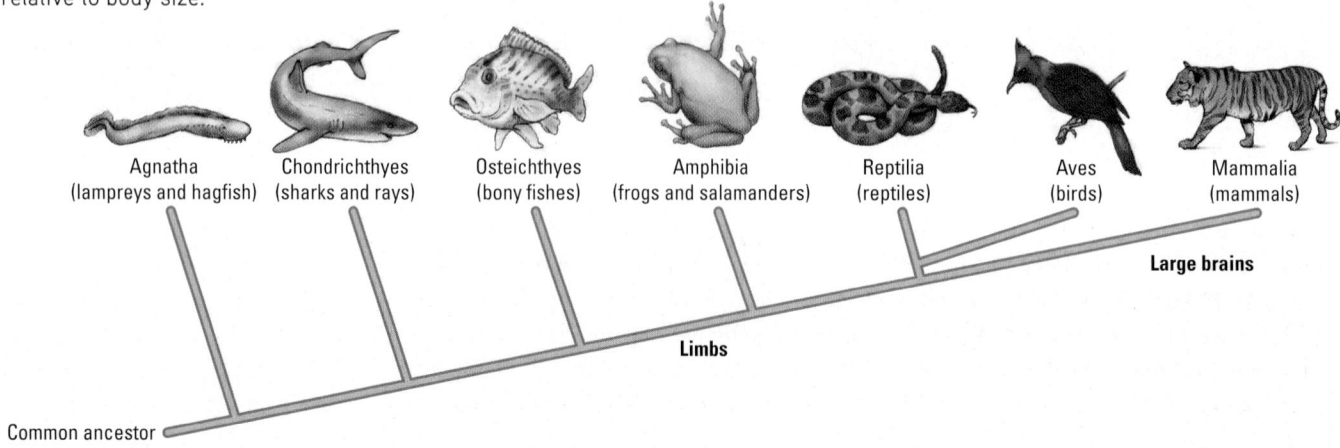

Agnatha (lampreys and hagfish)　Chondrichthyes (sharks and rays)　Osteichthyes (bony fishes)　Amphibia (frogs and salamanders)　Reptilia (reptiles)　Aves (birds)　Mammalia (mammals)

Large brains

Limbs

Common ancestor

Cerebrum Cerebellum

Fish

Cerebrum Cerebellum

Frog

Cerebrum Cerebellum

Bird

Cerebrum   Cerebellum

Human

FIGURE 1-8 Brain Evolution The brains of representative chordate species have many structures in common, illustrating a single basic brain plan.

The cerebrum and the cerebellum are proportionately small and smooth in the earliest evolved classes (e.g., fish, amphibians, and reptiles). In later-evolved chordates, especially the birds and mammals, these structures are much more prominent. In many large-brained mammals, both structures are extensively folded, which greatly increases their surface area while allowing them to fit into a small skull, just as folding a large piece of paper enables it to occupy a small envelope.

Increased size and folding are particularly pronounced in dolphins and primates, animals with large brains relative to their body size. Because relatively large brains with a complex cerebrum and cerebellum have evolved in a number of animal lineages, humans are neither unique nor special in these respects. We humans are distinguished, however, in belonging to the large-brained primate lineage and are unique in having the largest, most complex brain in this lineage.

1-3 REVIEW

Evolution of Brains and of Behavior

Before you continue, check your understanding.

1. Because brain cells and muscles evolved only once in the animal kingdom, a similar basic pattern exists in the _____ of all animals.

2. Evolutionary relationships among the nervous systems of animal lineages are classified by increasing complexity, progressing from the simplest _____ to a _____ segmented nervous system to nervous systems controlled by _____ to nervous systems in the phylum _____, which feature a brain and spinal cord.

3. A branching diagram that represents groups of related animals is called a _____.

4. Given that a relatively large brain with a complex cerebrum and cerebellum has evolved in a number of animal lineages, what if anything makes the human brain unique?

Answers appear at the back of the book.

For additional study tools, visit 🌀 **LaunchPad**:
www.macmillanhighered.com/launchpad/kolb5e

1-4 Evolution of the Human Brain and Behavior

Anyone can see similarities among humans, apes, and monkeys. Those similarities extend to the brain as well. In this section, we consider the brain and behaviors of some more prominent ancestors that link ancestral apes to our brain and our behaviors. Then we consider the relation between brain complexity and behavior across species. We conclude by surveying leading hypotheses about how the human brain evolved to become so large and the behavior that it mediates so complex. The evolutionary evidence shows that we humans are *specialized* in having an upright posture, making and using tools, and developing language but that we are not *special*, because our ancestors also shared these traits, at least to some degree.

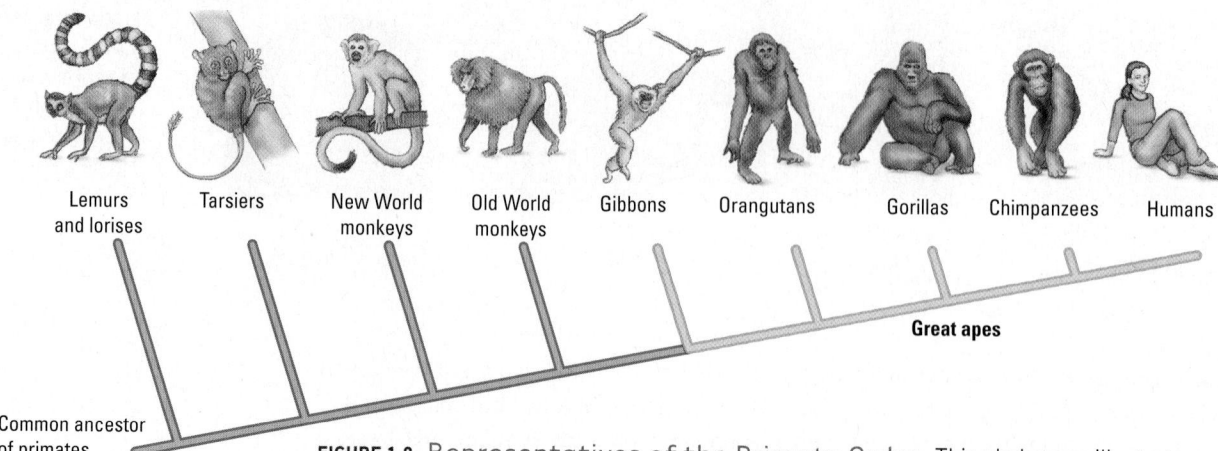

Lemurs and lorises   Tarsiers   New World monkeys   Old World monkeys   Gibbons   Orangutans   Gorillas   Chimpanzees   Humans

Great apes

Common ancestor of primates

FIGURE 1-9 Representatives of the Primate Order This cladogram illustrates hypothetical relationships among members of the primate order. Humans are members of the great ape family. In general, brain size increases across the groupings, with humans having the largest brain of all primates.

hominid General term referring to primates that walk upright, including all forms of humans, living and extinct.

FIGURE 1-10 *Australopithecus africanus* **(A)** The hominid *Australopithecus* walked upright with free hands, as do modern humans, but its brain was about one-third the size of ours. **(B)** Human and *Australopithecus* figures compared on the basis of the most complete *Australopithecus* skeleton yet found, a young female about 1 meter tall, popularly known as Lucy, who lived 3 million years ago.

(A)

Australopithecus

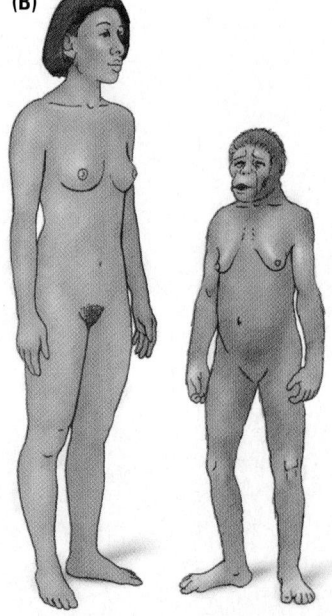

(B)

Homo sapiens   "Lucy"

Humans: Members of the Primate Order

Humans are members of the primate order, a subcategory of mammals that includes apes, Old World monkeys, New World monkeys, tarsiers, and lemurs as well (**Figure 1-9**). We humans are but one of about 275 primate species. Primates have excellent color vision, with the eyes positioned at the front of the face to enhance depth perception. They use their highly developed visual sense to deftly guide their hand movements.

Female primates usually have only one infant per pregnancy, and they spend a great deal more time caring for their young than most other animals do. Primate brains are on average larger than those of animals in other mammalian orders, such as rodents (mice, rats, beavers, squirrels) and carnivores (wolves, bears, cats, weasels).

Humans are members of the great ape family, which includes orangutans, gorillas, and chimpanzees. Apes are arboreal animals with limber shoulders that allow them to brachiate in trees (swing from one handhold to another), a trait retained by humans, who generally do not live in trees these days. Nevertheless, freeing the arms at the shoulder is handy for all sorts of human activities, from traversing monkey bars on the playground to competing in the Olympic hammer toss to raising a hand to ask a question in class. Apes are distinguished as well by their intelligence and large brain, traits that humans exemplify.

Among the apes, we are most closely related to the chimpanzee, having had a common ancestor between 5 million and 10 million years ago. Between that common ancestor and us over the past 5 million years, many **hominids**—primates that walk upright—in our lineage evolved. During most of this time, a number of hominid species coexisted. At present, however, we are the only surviving hominid species.

Australopithecus: Our Distant Ancestor

One of our hominid ancestors is probably an *Australopithecus* species (from the Latin *austral*, meaning *southern*, and the Greek *pithekos*, meaning *ape*.) **Figure 1-10** shows reconstructions of the face and body of one such animal, *Australopithecus africanus*. Many species of *Australopithecus* lived, some at the same time, so it is uncertain which is our common ancestor.

These early hominids were among the first primates to show distinctly human traits, including walking upright and using tools. Scientists have deduced their upright posture from the shape of their back, pelvic, knee, and foot bones and from a set of fossilized footprints that a family of australopiths left behind, walking through freshly fallen volcanic ash some 3.8 million years ago. These footprints feature impressions of a well-developed arch and an unrotated big toe—more like humans' than other apes'. (Nevertheless, australopiths retained the ability to skillfully climb trees.) The bone structure of their hands evinces tool use (Pickering et al., 2011).

The First Humans

One of the first finds to be designated as genus *Homo* (human) dates to about 2 million years ago. The remains were found by Mary and Louis Leakey in the Olduvai Gorge in Tanzania in 1964. The primates that left these skeletal remains had a strong resemblance to *Australopithecus* but more closely resembled modern humans in one important respect: they made simple stone tools. The Leakeys named the species *Homo habilis* (*handy human*) to signify that its members were toolmakers. To date, the earliest member of the genus *Homo*, found in Ethiopia, dates to about 2.8 million years ago. The fossils reveal a jaw and teeth much smaller than in any *Australopithecus* species but characteristic to humans (Villmoore et al., 2015).

The first humans who spread beyond Africa migrated into Europe and Asia. This species was *Homo erectus* (*upright human*), so named because of the mistaken notion that its predecessor, *H. habilis*, had a stooped posture. *Homo erectus* first shows up in the fossil record about 1.6 million years ago. As shown in **Figure 1-11**, its brain was bigger than that of any preceding hominid, overlapping in size the measurements of present-day human brains. The tools made by *H. erectus* were more sophisticated than those made by *H. habilis*. An especially small subspecies of *H. erectus*, about 3 feet tall, was found on the Indonesian island of Flores. Named *Homo floresiensis*, these hominids lived up to about 13,000 years ago (Gordon et al., 2008).

Australian Raymond Dart coined *Australopithecus* in naming the skull of a child he found among fossilized remains from a limestone quarry near Taung, South Africa, in 1924. Choosing so to represent his native land probably was no accident.

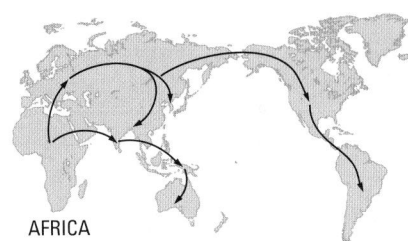

Early humans may have followed such proposed routes out of Africa, first to Asia and Europe, eventually to Australia, and finally to the Americas.

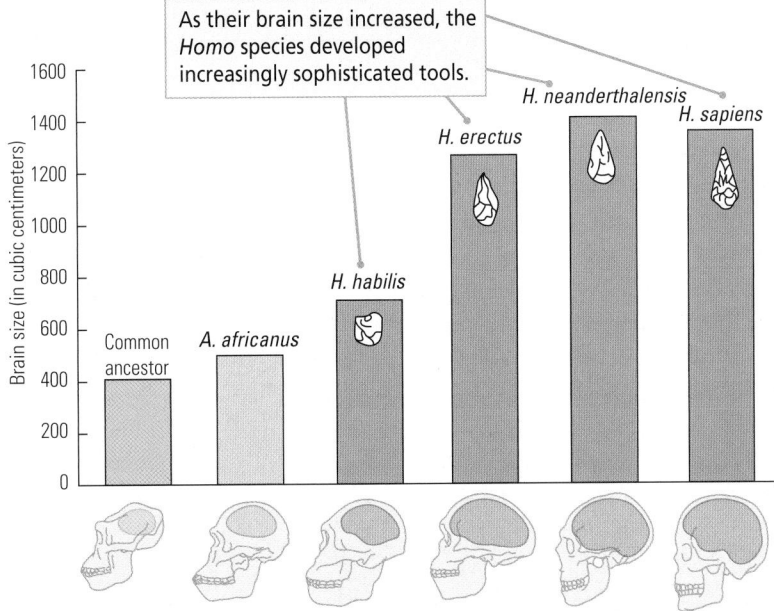

FIGURE 1-11 Increases in Hominid Brain Size The brain of *Australopithecus* was about the same size as that of living nonhuman apes, but succeeding members of the human lineage display increased brain size. Data from Johanson and Edey, 1981

FIGURE 1-12 Neanderthal Woman
A facial reconstruction by Elisabeth
Daynes made from a casting of the skull.
The female, whom the discoverers called
Pierrette, died a violent death between the
ages of 17 and 20. Her 36,000-year-old
remains were discovered in western
France in 1979, lying near tools from the
Neanderthal period. Focus 10-1 reports
on the discovery of a flute made by
Neanderthals.

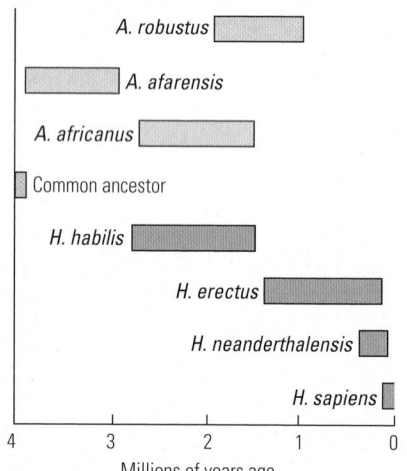

FIGURE 1-13 Human Origins The
human lineage and a lineage of extinct
Australopithecus probably arose from a
common ancestor about 4 million years
ago. The ancestor of the human lineage
Homo was probably an animal similar to
A. africanus.

---

encephalization quotient (EQ) Jerison's
quantitative measure of brain size obtained
from the ratio of actual brain size to expected
brain size, according to the principle of proper
mass, for an animal of a particular body size.

Modern humans, *Homo sapiens sapiens,* appeared within about the past 200,000 years. Most anthropologists think that they also migrated from Africa. Until about 30,000 years ago in Europe and 18,000 years ago in Asia, *H. sapiens sapiens* coexisted and interbred with other *H. sapiens* species, collectively called archaic humans. In Europe, for example, *H. sapiens sapiens* lived alongside another subspecies of modern humans, *H. neanderthalis,* named for the Neander Thal (Valley), Germany, where the first Neanderthal skulls were found. As the first fossil ancestral humans to be discovered, Neanderthals have maintained a preeminent place in the study of modern human ancestors.

Neanderthals had brains as large as or larger than those of modern humans, used similar tools, and wore jewelry and makeup. They lived in family groups similar to modern human ones, made music, cared for their elders, and buried their dead. From these archeological findings, we can infer that Neanderthals probably communicated using language and held religious beliefs.

We do not know how modern humans completely replaced archaic human species, but perhaps they had advantages in toolmaking, language use, or social organization. Contemporary genetic evidence shows that modern European humans who interbred with Neanderthals acquired genes that adapted them to the cold, to novel disease, and possibly to light skin that better absorbs vitamin D (Sankararaman et al., 2014). Reconstructions such as that in **Figure 1-12** show how similar to us Neanderthals really were.

One possible human lineage is shown in **Figure 1-13**. A common ancestor gave rise to the *Australopithecus* lineage, and one member of this group gave rise to the *Homo* lineage. The bars in Figure 1-13 are not connected because many more hominid species have been discovered than are shown, and exact direct ancestors are uncertain. The bars overlap because many hominid species coexisted until quite recently. The last of the australopith species disappeared from the fossil record about 1 million years ago.

Relating Brain Size and Behavior

Scientists who study brain evolution propose that increased brain size and complexity evolved in different species to enable more complex behavior. Having a large brain clearly has been adaptive for humans, but many animals have large brains. Whales' and elephants' brains are much larger than ours. Of course, whales and elephants are much larger than humans overall. How is relative brain size measured, and what does brain size signify? Two ways of estimating relative brain size are to compare brain size to body size and to count brain cells.

Estimating Relative Brain–Body Size

Harry Jerison (1973) developed an index that compares the ratio of brain size to body size across species. He calculated that as body size increases, brain size increases at about two-thirds the increase in body weight. Jerison's underlying assumption was that even if one knew very little about an animal's behavior, its brain size could provide some clues to its behavioral complexity. The idea is that species exhibiting more complex behaviors must possess more brain than species whose behaviors are fewer and less complex.

Using the ratio of actual brain size to expected size, Jerison developed a quantitative measure, the **encephalization quotient** (EQ). He defined an average animal (a domestic cat is Jerison's pick) as having an EQ of 1. The diagonal trend line in **Figure 1-14** plots the expected brain–body size ratio of animals with an EQ of 1. Some animals lie below the line: their brain size is smaller than would be expected for an animal of that size. Other animals lie above the line: their brain size is larger than would be expected for an animal of that size.

The lower an animal's brain falls below the trend line in Figure 1-14, the smaller its EQ. The higher an animal's brain lies above the trend line, the larger its EQ. Notice that the rat's brain is a little smaller (lower EQ) and the elephant's brain a little larger (higher EQ) than the ratio predicts. A modern human, farther above the line than any other animal, has the highest EQ.

FIGURE 1-14 Ratios of Brain to Body Size in Common Mammals As represented logarithmically on this graph, average brain size relative to body weight falls along a diagonal trend line, where you find the cat. Data from Jerison, 1973.

Jerison's EQ provides a rough estimate of comparative brain size, but body size and brain size can vary independently (**Figure 1-15**, top). To get around this problem, scientists have devised ways to count the cells in the brain.

Counting Brain Cells

Consider the roundworm *Caenorhabditis elegans*. *C. elegans* has 959 cells. Of these, 302 are neurons. In contrast, the blue whale—the largest animal that has ever lived, weighing as much as 200 tons—has a brain weighing 15,000 grams (33 lb). In cell number, 30 percent of *C. elegans* is nervous system, whereas in terms of body weight, less than 0.01 percent of the blue whale is nervous system.

Based on EQs, we would predict that *C. elegans* has a more complex behavioral repertoire than a blue whale. But it makes no sense to suggest that a worm's behavior is more complex than a whale's. Obviously a whale has a lot more neurons than a worm. Our estimate of brain size and behavioral complexity line up better if we simply compare cell counts.

Karina Fonseca-Azevedo and her colleagues (2012) have devised such a method, using a counting machine. Not only can they estimate the number of cells in a brain or a part of the brain but they also can estimate the brain cells' *packing density*. For example, two similar-sized brains could consist of either diffusely distributed large cells or closely packed small cells. It turns out that the packing density of cells differs by a lot among species and brain regions. Rodents have larger, more loosely packed cells, for example, and primates smaller and more densely packed cells.

Packing density is relatively constant in the primate lineage, and so EQ provides a good comparison of their brain sizes (Figure 1-15, bottom). Brain cell counts support the EQs Jerison calculated in the primate lineage: *Australopithecus* had about 50 billion to 60 billion neurons, *Homo habilis* about 60 billion, *Homo erectus* about 75 billion to 90 billion, and modern humans have about 86 billion neurons.

In terms of brain size and cell counts, then, what makes us humans unusual (along with archaic humans such as Neanderthals) are our large brain and many neurons. Although researchers have not made similar neuron counts in all other animal species with brains larger than the humans', if neurons are not densely packed, resembling the somewhat less-dense packing of a rodent, then they may well have far fewer neurons. For example, despite their large brains, dolphins' 30 billion neurons is similar to the number in chimpanzees, many fewer than in humans, because dolphin neurons are not densely packed. As detailed in Comparative Focus 1-3, The Elephant's Brain, on page 24, pachyderms have an enormous number of brain cells, but most are in the cerebellum, while the number in the elephant cerebrum is equivalent to that of dolphins and chimpanzees.

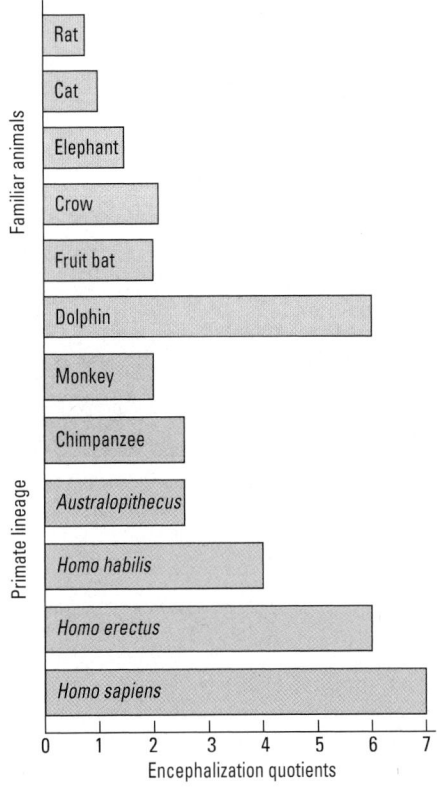

FIGURE 1-15 Comparing EQs The EQs of some familiar mammals are ranked at the top of the chart, and members of the primate lineage are ranked at the bottom. Clearly, intelligence is widespread among animals.

COMPARATIVE FOCUS 1-3

The Elephant's Brain

The cerebrum and cerebellum have evolved into the human brain's most distinct and largest structures, larger than in any other primate brain. Although the cerebellum appears smaller than the cerebrum physically, its small, tightly packed neurons are four times the number found in the cerebrum (about 68 billion vs. 16 billion), a 4:1 ratio that humans share with all other primates. Typically, the cerebrum is described as mediating cognitive functions, whereas the cerebellum mediates motor function. In fact, both structures contribute to both kinds of functions in different ways.

African elephants are enormous animals. It is not surprising that they have the largest brain of all terrestrial animals—three times the size of a human's. With such a large brain, why don't elephants share humans' intellectual abilities?

To investigate this question, Suzana Herculano-Houzel and her colleagues (2014) made a neuronal count of an African elephant. They found that its brain contains three times as many neurons as the human brain (257 billion vs. 86 billion neurons). But remarkably, 251 billion of those neurons (97.5 percent) reside in the elephant's cerebellum. In contrast, the elephant's cerebral cortex, with twice the mass of the human cortex, contains only 5.6 billion neurons, about one-third the number found in the human cerebrum. The elephant's cerebellum contains nearly 45 times as many neurons as its cerebrum.

What do these numbers tell us about the elephant's behavior? An elephant has almost infinite degrees of freedom in the use of its trunk: with it, it can bathe, lift a tree trunk, pick up a peanut, caress a baby, or paint a picture. The vast number of neurons in its cerebellum is probably requisite to controlling the trunk's sensory and motor abilities.

The elephant's cerebral cortex boasts more neurons than most animals can boast but somewhat fewer than chimpanzees' cerebrums. The elephant's cognitive ability also ranks slightly lower than a chimp's.

The Herculano-Houzel study offers a conclusion related to the function of the human cerebrum, as well. The remarkable cognitive abilities of humans, which exceed those of all other animal species, are best explained by the sheer number of cerebral neurons, which exceed the number found in all other animal species, even those with much larger brains, including elephants.

An African Elephant's Brain In this, the largest brain of all terrestrial animals, both the cerebrum (left) and the cerebellum (right) are gigantic compared to those of the human brain. But the cerebellum contains 97.5 percent of the neurons. Reproduced or adapted from our websites at http://www.brains.rad.msu.edu and http://brainmuseum.org, supported by the U. S. National Science Foundation.

FIGURE 1-16 The Course of Human Evolution The hominid brain has increased nearly threefold in relative size, illustrated here by the skulls of *Australopithecus afarensis* (left), *Homo erectus* (center), and modern *Homo sapiens* (right). Missing parts of the *Australopithecus* skull, shown in blue, have been reconstructed. *The Origin of Modern Humans* (p. 165), by R. Lewin, 1998, New York: Scientific American Library. Photo by Kevin O'Farrell/Concepts.

Why the Hominid Brain Enlarged

The evolution of modern humans—from when humanlike creatures first appeared until humans like us emerged—spans more than 4 million years. As the relative size differences of the hominid skulls pictured in **Figure 1-16** illustrate, much of this evolution was associated with increases in brain and body size and by changes in behavior. These changes were probably driven by many influences. Among the wide array of hypotheses that seek to explain why the modern human brain enlarged so much and so rapidly, we examine four ideas.

One hypothesis suggests that numerous drastic climate changes drove adaptation by hominids and led to more complex behavior. Another hypothesis contends that the primate lifestyle favors an increasingly complex nervous system that humans capitalize on. A third links brain growth to brain cooling. And a fourth proposes that a changed rate of maturation favors larger brains. Likely, a combination of all of these factors was influential.

Climate and the Evolving Hominid Brain

Climate changes have driven many physical changes in hominids, ranging from brain changes to the emergence of human culture. Evidence suggests that each new hominid species appeared after climate changes devastated old environments and led to new ones.

About 8 million years ago, a massive tectonic event (deformation of Earth's crust) produced the Great Rift Valley, which runs through the eastern part of Africa from south to north. The reshaped landmass left a wet jungle climate to the west and a much drier savannah climate to the east. To the west, the apes continued unchanged in their former habitat. But the fossil record shows that in the drier eastern region, apes evolved rapidly into upright hominids in response to the selective environmental pressures that formed their new home.

Thereafter, the climate in East Africa did not remain static. It underwent a number of alterations (Maslin et al., 2015). The appearance of *Homo habilis* 3 million years ago and that of *Homo erectus* 1 million years ago were associated with these climatic alterations. Climatic changes also track the disappearance of other members of the human family. The warming in Europe that ended the ice age as recently as 30,000 years ago contributed to modern humans migrating to the continent and to the Neanderthal and other archaic European and Asiatic human species disappearing.

What makes *Homo sapiens* the survivor? One suggestion is that we modern humans evolved to adapt to change itself and that this adaptability has allowed us to populate every region on Earth (Antón et al, 2014). The caution is that modern humans have been around only a short time relative to the millions of years that other hominid species survived: our adaptability has yet to be severely tested.

The Primate Lifestyle

British anthropologist Robin Dunbar (1998) argues that a primate's social group size, a cornerstone of its lifestyle, is correlated with brain size. His conclusion: the average group size of about 150 favored by modern humans explains their large brains. He cites as evidence that 150 is the estimated group size of hunter-gatherer groups and the average group size of many contemporary institutions—a company in the military, for instance—and coincidentally, the number of people that each of us can gossip about.

Consider how group size might affect how primates forage for food. Foraging is important for all animals, but while some foraging activities are simple, others are complex. Eating grass or vegetation is an individual pursuit: an animal need only munch and move on. Vegetation eaters such as gorillas do not have especially large brains relative to their body size. In contrast, apes that eat fruit, such as chimpanzees and humans, have relatively large brains.

Katharine Milton (2003) documented the relation between fruit foraging and larger brains by examining the feeding behavior and brain size of two South American (New World) monkeys of the same body size. As illustrated in **Figure 1-17**, spider monkeys obtain nearly three-quarters of their nutrients from fruit and have a brain twice as large as that of the howler monkey, which obtains less than half its nutrients from fruit.

What is so special about eating fruit? Good sensory skills such as color vision to see it, good motor skills to reach and manipulate it, good spatial skills to find it, good memory to return to it, and having friends to help find it and ward off competitors are all useful fruit-harvesting skills. Having a parent who can teach fruit-finding skills and being a good learner are also useful. The payoff in eating fruit is its nutritional value for nourishing a large, energy-dependent brain that uses more than 20 percent of the body's resources. These same skills are useful for obtaining other temporary and perishable types of food, such as those obtained by scavenging, hunting, and gathering.

A neuron's metabolic (energy) cost is estimated as relatively constant across different species but also high relative to that of other types of body cells. So any adaptive advantage to having more neurons must support that energy cost. Fonseca-Azevedo and Herculano-Houzel (2012) suggest that cooking food is a

Africa's Great Rift Valley cut off ape species living in a wetter climate to the west from species that evolved into hominids, adapted to a drier climate to the east.

FIGURE 1-17 Picky Eaters Katharine Milton examined the feeding behavior and brain size of two New World monkeys that have the same body size but different brain sizes and diets.

Paul A. Souders/Corbis

DC_Columbia/Getty Images

Spider monkey diet

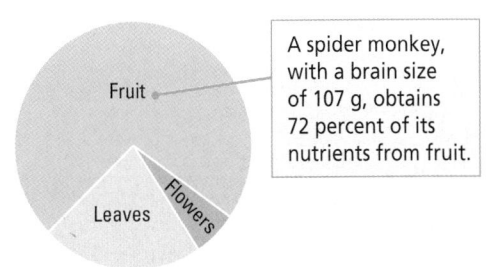

A spider monkey, with a brain size of 107 g, obtains 72 percent of its nutrients from fruit.

Howler monkey diet

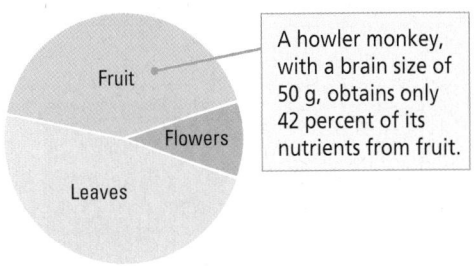

A howler monkey, with a brain size of 50 g, obtains only 42 percent of its nutrients from fruit.

unique contribution to hominid brain development. Gorillas must spend up to 8 hours of each day foraging for vegetation and eating it. Chimps and early hominids, with a more varied diet, could support more neurons provided that they also spent most of their waking time foraging.

The use of fire by *Homo erectus* and later hominids allowed for cooking, which predigests food and thus maximizes caloric gain to the point that much less time need be devoted to foraging. A high degree of male–male, female–female, and female–male cooperation in food gathering and cooking, characteristic of the hominid lifestyle, further supported the evolution of a larger brain.

Changes in Hominid Physiology

Cooking might foster genetic mutations associated with marked size reductions in individual muscle fibers in the face and entire masticatory muscles in hominids (Stedman et al., 2004). The Stedman team speculates that smaller masticatory muscles paved the way for smaller, more delicate bones in the head. Smaller bones in turn allowed for changes in diet and access to more energy-rich food.

Another physiological adaptation may have given a special boost to greater brain size in our human ancestors: changes in the morphology (form) of the skull. Dean Falk (Kunz and Iliadis, 2007) developed the radiator hypothesis from her car mechanic's remark that to increase the size of a car's engine, you also have to increase the size of the radiator that cools it. Falk reasoned that if the brain's radiator, the circulating blood, adapted into a more effective cooling system, brain size could increase.

Brain cooling is so important because the brain's metabolic activity generates a great deal of heat and is at risk for overheating under conditions of exercise or heat stress. Falk argued that, unlike australopith skulls, *Homo* skulls contain holes through which cranial blood vessels pass. These holes suggest that, compared to earlier hominids, *Homo* species had a much more widely dispersed blood flow from the brain, which would have greatly enhanced brain cooling.

Altered Maturation

All animal species' life history can be divided into stages. *Heterochrony* (from the Greek meaning *different times*) is the study of processes that regulate the onset and end of life stages and their developmental speed and duration. Several proposals suggest that altered heterochronicity accounts for the large human brain and other distinctive human features.

In **neoteny**, juvenile stages of predecessors become adult features of descendants. Neoteny is common in the animal world. Flightless birds are neotenic adult birds, domesticated dogs are neotenic wolves, and sheep are neotenic goats. Many anatomical features link us with the juvenile stages of other primates, including a small face, vaulted cranium, unrotated big toe, upright posture, and primary distribution of hair on the head, armpits, and pubic areas.

A small jaw distinguishes the earliest *Homo* fossils yet discovered.

Because a human infant's head is large relative to body size, neoteny has also led to adults with proportionally larger bodies and larger skulls to house larger brains. The shape of a baby chimpanzee's head is more similar to the shape of an adult human's head than to an adult chimpanzee's head (**Figure 1-18**). Along with this physical morphology, human adults also retain some behaviors of primate infants, including play, exploration, and intense interest in novelty and learning. The brain processes that support learning thus are retained in adulthood (Zollikofer, 2012).

Critics of neoteny offer an alternative view in which all of the stages of development still occur, but their onset and duration change (Workman et al., 2013). Evidence for this idea

FIGURE 1-18 Neoteny The shape of an adult human's head more closely resembles that of a juvenile chimpanzee's head (left) than an adult chimp's head (right). This observation leads to the hypothesis that we humans may be neotenic descendants of our more apelike common ancestors.

PHOTO24/Getty Images

FLPA/SuperStock

is that each stage of human development—gestation, infancy, childhood, adulthood—is prolonged relative to such ancestral species as macaques and chimpanzees. Prolonged infancy allows the birth and development of more neurons, more time for their growth to produce a bigger brain. Prolonged childhood enhances learning time; and prolonged adolescence allows for the growth of a bigger body.

neoteny Process in which juvenile stages of predecessors become adult features of descendants; idea derived from the observation that more recently evolved species resemble the young of their common ancestors.

(1-4) REVIEW

Evolution of the Human Brain and Behavior

Before you continue, check your understanding.

1. Modern humans share a _____ with the _____, our closest living relative.

2. Modern humans evolved from a _____ lineage that successfully featured _____, _____, and _____, groups in which more than one species existed concurrently.

3. The _____ describes brain size relative to body size, but a complete comparison of different species' brains requires _____.

4. The large human brain evolved in response to a number of pressures and opportunities, including _____, _____, _____, and _____.

5. One hypothesis proposes that *Homo sapiens* has evolved to adapt to change itself. Explain the reasoning behind this hypothesis in a brief paragraph.

Answers appear at the back of the book.

For additional study tools, visit 🎓 **LaunchPad**:
www.macmillanhighered.com/launchpad/kolb5e

(1-5) Modern Human Brain Size and Intelligence

In *The Descent of Man*, Charles Darwin detailed the following paradox:

> No one, I presume, doubts the large proportion which the size of man's brain bears to his body, compared to the same proportion in the gorilla or orang, is closely connected with his higher mental powers. . . . On the other hand, no one supposes that the intellect of any two animals or of any two men can be accurately gauged by the cubic contents of their skulls. (Darwin, 1871, p. 37)

Ignoring Darwin, many have tried to tie individual intelligence to gross brain size. If the functional unit of the brain is the brain cell and if larger human brains have more brain cells, does it not follow that brain size and intelligence are related? It depends.

The evolutionary approach that we have been using to explain how the large human brain evolved is based on comparisons *between* species. Special care attends the extension of evolutionary principles to physical comparisons *within* species, especially biological comparisons within or among groups of modern humans. We now illustrate the difficulty of within-species comparisons by considering the complexity of correlating human brain size with intelligence (Deary, 2000). Then we turn to another aspect of studying the brain and behavior in modern humans—the fact that unlike that of other animals, so much modern human behavior is culturally learned.

Meaning of Human Brain Size Comparisons

Over a century ago some investigators promoted a simple conclusion: people with the largest brains display the most intelligent behavior. The late Stephen Jay Gould, in his 1981 book *The Mismeasure of Man*, reviews much of this early literature and criticizes the research on three counts: brain measurement, correlating brain size and intelligence, and what intelligence is.

First, measuring a person's brain is difficult. If a tape measure is simply placed around a person's head, factoring out skull thickness is impossible. There is also no agreement about whether volume or weight is a better measure. And no matter which indicator we use, we must consider body size. The human brain varies in weight from about 1000 grams to more than 2000 grams, but people also vary in body mass. To what extent should we factor in body mass in deciding whether a particular brain is large or small? And how should we measure body mass, given that a person's total weight can fluctuate widely over time?

Large differences between the brains of individual people do exist, but the reasons for these differences are numerous and complex. Consider some examples. People may have larger or smaller brain cells. Larger people are likely to have a larger brain than smaller people. Men have a somewhat larger brain than women, but they are proportionately physically larger. Nevertheless, girls mature more quickly than boys, so in adolescence the brain and body size differences may be absent. As people age, they generally lose brain cells, so their brain shrinks.

Neurological diseases associated with aging accelerate the age-related decrease in brain size. Brain injury near the time of birth often results in a dramatic reduction in brain size, even in regions distant from the damage. Stress associated with physical or behavioral deprivation in infancy also reduces brain size (Herringa et al, 2013). Neurological disorders associated with a parent's abuse of alcohol or other drugs are associated with conditions such as *fetal alcohol spectrum disorder* (FASD), in which the brain can be greatly reduced in size. *Autism spectrum disorder* (ASD), a largely genetic condition affecting development, produces a wide variety of brain abnormalities, including either increases or decreases in brain size in different individuals.

Brain size may also increase in individuals. For example, just as good nutrition in the early years of life can be associated with larger body size, good nutrition can also be associated with an increase in brain size. The brain's **plasticity**—its ability to change—in response to an enriched environment is associated with growth of existing brain cells and thus an increase in brain size. Furthermore, one way in which the brain stores new skills and memories is to form new connections among brain cells, and these connections in turn contribute to increased brain size.

Finally, we must also consider what is meant by intelligence. When we compare behavior across species, we are comparing **species-typical behavior**—behavior displayed by all members of a species. For example, lamprey eels do not have limbs and cannot walk, whereas salamanders do have limbs and can walk: the difference in brain size *between* the two species can be correlated with this trait. When we compare behavior *within* a species, however, we are usually comparing how well one individual performs a certain task in relation to others—how well one salamander walks relative to how well another salamander walks, for example.

We can make intraspecies comparisons for humans, but this likewise presents problems. For one thing, individual performance on a task is influenced by many factors unrelated to inherent ability, among them opportunity, interest level, training, motivation, and health. For another, people vary enormously in their individual abilities, depending on the particular task. One person may have superior verbal skills but mediocre spatial abilities; another person may be adept at solving spatial puzzles but struggle with written work; still another may excel at mathematical reasoning and be average in everything else. Which of these people should we consider the most intelligent? Should certain skills carry greater weight as measures of intelligence? Clearly, it is difficult to say.

Early in the twentieth century, Charles Spearman carried out the first formal performance analysis among various tests used to rate intelligence. He found a positive correlation among tests and suggested that a single common factor explained them. Spearman named it *g* for *general intelligence factor*, but it turns out that *g* also varies. Many factors unrelated to inherent ability—among them opportunity, interest level, training, motivation, and health—influence individual performance on a task.

For example, when IQ tests that were given to young adults of one generation are given to the next generation, scores increase by as much as 25 points, a phenomenon called

To find information on specific conditions, consult the Index of Disorders inside the front cover of this book.

Sections 2-1 and 2-6 elaborate on plasticity, Focus 8-1 and Section 8-4 on environment and brain development, Section 11-3 on skilled movement, Section 14-1 on memory.

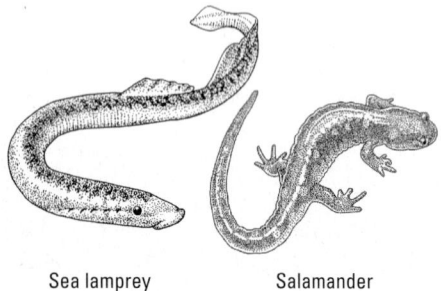

Sea lamprey   Salamander

plasticity The nervous system's potential for physical or chemical change; enhances its adaptability to environmental change and its ability to compensate for injury. (Also called neuroplasticity.)

species-typical behavior Behavior that is characteristic of all members of a species, such as walking in amphibians.

culture Learned behaviors that are passed on from one generation to the next through teaching and imitation.

meme An idea, behavior, or style that spreads from person to person within a culture.

the *Flynn effect* (Flynn, 2012). Taken at face value—though it shouldn't be—the increase suggests that human *g* has risen to such a degree in two generations that most young adults fall in the superior category relative to their grandparents. Obviously, the score change has not been accompanied by a similar increase in brain size. It is more likely that education and other life experiences explain the Flynn effect.

Howard Gardner (2006), furthermore, proposes that humans have a number of intelligences—verbal, musical, mathematical, social, and so on. Each type of intelligence is dependent on the function of a particular brain region or regions. Hampshire and colleagues (2012), who presented participants with a battery of typical intelligence assessment tests, support Gardner's idea. As participants took the tests, their brain activity was imaged and recorded. The study identified three separate abilities—reasoning, short-term memory, and verbal ability—each associated with a different brain network. The experimenters argue that this finding provides little support for Spearman's *g*. They further suggest that a wider array of assessments would reveal additional intelligence networks.

Given the difficulty in measuring brain size and in defining intelligence, it is not surprising that scant research appears in the contemporary literature on the problem of gross brain size and intelligence. If you are wondering whether having a larger brain might mean you could study a little less, consider this. The brains of people who are widely considered highly intelligent have been found to vary in size from the low end to the high end of the range for our species. The brain of the brilliant physicist Albert Einstein was average in size.

Figure 15-9 illustrates the profusion of brain networks; Section 15-6 relates network efficiency to intelligence.

Section 15-6 expands on theories of intelligence. Einstein's brain is pictured in Figure 15-20.

Acquisition of Culture

In evolutionary terms, the modern human brain developed rapidly. Many behavioral changes differentiate us from our primate ancestors, and these adaptations took place more rapidly still, long after the modern brain had evolved. The most remarkable thing that our brains have made possible is ever more complex **culture**—learned behaviors passed from generation to generation through teaching and experience.

Cultural growth and adaptation render many contemporary human behaviors distinctly different from those of *Homo sapiens* living 200,000 years ago. Only 30,000 years ago, modern humans made the first artistic relics: elaborate paintings on cave walls and carved ivory and stone figurines. Agriculture appears still more recently, about 15,000 years ago, and reading and writing were invented only about 7000 years ago.

Most forms of mathematics and many of our skills in using mechanical and digital devices have still more recent origins. Early *H. sapiens* brains certainly did not evolve to select smart phone apps or imagine traveling to distant planets. Apparently, the things that the human brain did evolve to do contained the elements necessary for adapting to more sophisticated skills.

Alex Mesoudi and his colleagues (2006) suggest that cultural elements, ideas, behaviors, or styles that spread from person to person—called **memes** (after genes, the elements of physical evolution)—can also be studied within an evolutionary framework. They propose that individual differences in brain structure may favor the development of certain memes. Once developed, memes would in turn exert selective pressure on further brain development. For example, chance variations in individuals' brain structure may have favored tool use in some individuals. Tool use proved so beneficial that toolmaking itself exerted selective pressure on a population to favor individuals well skilled in tool fabrication.

Similar arguments can be made with respect to other memes, from language to music, from mathematics to art. Mesoudi's reasoning supports neuroscience's ongoing expansion into seemingly disparate disciplines, including linguistics, the arts, business, and economics. Studying the human brain, far from examining a body organ's structure, means investigating how it acquires culture and fosters adaptation as the world changes and as the brain changes the world.

Saint Ambrose, who lived in the fourth century, is reportedly the first person who could read silently.

Section 15-3 explores some of psychology's expanding frontiers.

(1-5) REVIEW

Modern Human Brain Size and Intelligence

Before you continue, check your understanding.

1. Behavior that is displayed by all members of a species is called _____.

2. Some modern human behavior is inherent to our nervous system, but far more is learned—passed generation to generation by _____. Ideas, behaviors, or styles called _____ may spread from person to person and culture to culture.

3. Spearman proposed a common intelligence factor he called _____. Gardner supports the idea of _____.

4. Explain the reasoning behind the statement that what is true for evolutionary comparisons across different species may not be true for comparisons within a single species.

Answers appear at the back of the book.

For additional study tools, visit LaunchPad:
www.macmillanhighered.com/launchpad/kolb5e

■ SUMMARY

(1-1) Neuroscience in the Twenty-First Century

Studying the brain and behavior leads us to better understand our origins, our human nature, the causes of many behavioral disorders, and the rationale behind treatment for disorders.

The human nervous system is composed of the CNS, which includes the brain and the spinal cord, and the PNS, through which the brain and spinal cord communicate with sensory receptors, with muscles and other tissues, and with the internal organs. The cerebrum and the cerebellum have undergone the most growth in large-brained animal species.

We define behavior as any kind of movement, including mental processes such as thinking and imagining. In animals, behavior is caused by nervous system activity. Behavioral flexibility and complexity vary greatly across species, as does the nervous system.

For some species, including humans, the brain is the organ that exerts control over behavior. The brain seems to need ongoing sensory and motor stimulation to maintain its intelligent activity.

(1-2) Perspectives on Brain and Behavior

Mentalism views behavior as a product of an intangible entity called the mind (psyche); the brain has little importance. Dualism is the notion that the immaterial mind acts through the material brain to produce language and rational behavior, whereas the brain alone is responsible for the "lower" actions that we have in common with other animal species.

Materialism, the view that brain function fully accounts for all behavior, language and reasoning included, guides contemporary research on the brain and behavior. Support for the materialistic view comes from the study of natural selection—the evolutionary theory that behaviors such as human language evolved from the simpler language abilities of human ancestors—and from discoveries about how genes function. Experiments follow the process of science: first, formulate a question (hypothesis), then design a procedure to test it, evaluate the results, and confirm or modify the hypothesis.

After severe TBI, the brain demonstrates a remarkable ability to recover, but after either mild or severe injury, a person can be left with a permanent disability that prevents full recovery to former levels of function. Brain imaging techniques can confirm severe disabilities such as the MCS, locked-in syndrome, and PVS.

(1-3) Evolution of Brains and of Behavior

Behavioral neuroscientists subscribe to the evolutionary principle that all living organisms are descended from a common ancestor. Brain cells and muscles are quite recent developments in the evolution of life on Earth. Because they evolved only once, a similar basic pattern exists in the nervous systems of all animals.

The nervous systems of some animal lineages have become more complex, with evolution featuring first a nerve net, followed by a bilaterally symmetrical and segmented nervous system, a nervous system controlled by ganglia, and eventually, in chordates, a nervous system featuring a brain and spinal cord.

Mammals are a class of chordates characterized by a large brain relative to body size. Modern humans belong to the primate order, which is distinguished by especially large brains, and to the family of great apes, whose members' limber shoulders allow them to brachiate (hang and swing by the arms).

(1-4) Evolution of the Human Brain and Behavior

One of our early hominid ancestors was probably an *Australopithecus*, who lived in Africa several million years ago. It is from an australopith species that *Homo* evolved through species such as *Homo habilis* and *Homo erectus*. Modern humans, *Homo sapiens sapiens*, appeared about 200,000 years ago.

Since *Australopithecus*, the hominid brain has increased in size almost threefold, as has its number of brain cells. The EQ describes brain size relative to body size, but a complete comparison of different species' brains requires brain cell counts. Among the factors hypothesized to have stimulated brain evolution in human species are environmental challenges and opportunities, such as climate changes that favored the natural selection of adaptability and more complex behavior patterns. Also proposed are lifestyle changes such as social cooperation and cooking food, changes in physiology, and changed maturation rate.

1-5 Modern Human Brain Size and Intelligence

Evolutionary principles learned from studying the brain and behavior *across* species do not easily apply to the brain and behavior *within* a single species, such as *Homo sapiens*. As animals evolved, larger brains were associated with more complex behavior. Yet within our species, the complexity of different brain regions is related to behavioral abilities. People vary widely in body size and in brain size as well as in varying kinds of intelligence, making a simple comparison of brain size and general intelligence unwise.

Recognizing the great extent to which modern human behavior, rather than being inherent in our nervous systems, results from cultural learning and transmission is paramount to understanding how our brains function. Memes may spread from person to person and culture to culture.

KEY TERMS

bilateral symmetry, p. 18

brainstem, p. 5

central nervous system (CNS), p. 3

cerebellum, p. 5

cerebrum (forebrain), p. 5

chordate, p. 18

cladogram, p. 18

clinical trial, p. 13

common ancestor, p. 15

culture, p. 28

deep brain stimulation (DBS), p. 13

dualism, p. 8

embodied behavior, p. 5

encephalization quotient (EQ), p. 22

epigenetics, p. 11

genotype, p. 11

ganglia, p. 18

hemisphere, p. 5

hominid, p. 20

locked-in syndrome, p. 5

materialism, p. 8

meme, p. 28

mentalism, p. 7

mind, p. 7

mind–body problem, p. 8

minimally conscious state (MCS), p. 13

natural selection, p. 8

neoteny, p. 27

nerve net, p. 17

neuron, p. 3

peripheral nervous system (PNS), p. 3

persistent vegetative state (PVS), p. 13

phenotype, p. 8

plasticity, p. 28

psyche, p. 7

segmentation, p. 18

species, p. 8

species-typical behavior, p. 28

spinal cord, p. 3

traumatic brain injury (TBI), p. 3

⤷ Visit LaunchPad to access the e-Book, videos, LearningCurve adaptive quizzing, flashcards, and more.

www.macmillanhighered.com/launchpad/kolb5e

CHAPTER

2

What Is the Nervous System's Functional Anatomy?

Streeter

Katherine Streeter

Agenesis of the Cerebellum

When an adult's brain is damaged, as for example in *traumatic brain injury*, we see a pattern of behavioral changes that offer insight into brain functions, as described by Fred Linge in Clinical Focus 1-1, Living with Traumatic Brain Injury. Naturally occurring brain injuries rarely remove a single structure completely, leaving the rest of the brain intact. However, *agenesis*, the failure of brain regions to develop, offers researchers a unique window on the brain's organization and function, because in rare cases a complete structure is absent yet the rest of the brain appears normal.

Historically, the cerebellum was viewed as a motor structure, with the most obvious sign of damage being *ataxia*, a failure of muscular coordination and balance. But the cerebellum's functions are much more extensive than movement control (e.g., Schmahmann, 2010). Adult patients with damage to the cerebellum do have motor disturbances, but they also have cognitive deficits, for example, in abstract thinking and language and in emotional control.

The cerebellum contains the most neurons of any brain region, accounting for 80 percent of the neurons in humans and a whopping 97.5 percent of elephants' neurons—believed to be related to the dexterity of the elephant's trunk. What would happen if the cerebellum failed to develop but the rest of the brain developed apparently normally? We humans would be missing 80 percent of our neurons!

The accompanying images contrast the brain of a young man born with agenesis of the cerebellum (A and B) to the brain of a person whose brain developed normally (C and D). Even lacking 80 percent of his neurons, the young man's behavioral capacities are remarkable, but his behavior is not typical. Now in his thirties, he has an office job and lives alone. He has a distinctive speaking pattern, an awkward gait, and difficulties with balance, as well as deficits in planning and abstract thinking. His social skills and long-term memory are good, though, as is his mastery of routine activities.

Studies of other people with cerebellar agenesis reveal a heterogeneous set of symptoms, but neuropsychological assessments show behavioral deficits reminiscent of people with damage to frontal and parietal cortical regions (e.g., Baumann et al., 2015), even though these cerebral regions are intact. Although people with cerebellar agenesis develop slowly, they show remarkable improvement over time and seem able to compensate for many of their symptoms. The individual whose

MRI brain scans of a person with cerebellar agenesis (A, B) compared to a control person (C, D) of the same age. A and C are viewed in the coronal plane, B and D in the mid-sagittal plane. For more about this condition:
www.npr.org/blogs/health/2015/03/16/393351760

brain you see in images A and B had severe visuomotor spatial disabilities as a child and adolescent, but by age 30 he showed significant improvement (Chheda et al., 2002; Schmahmann et al., 2007; Jeremy D. Schmahmann and Janet C. Sherman, personal communication). Other patients' language develops slowly.

In people with absence of the cerebellum it is thought that brain plasticity in response to early perturbations emerge as regions of the cerebral cortex begin to function more efficiently. In fact, it has been reported that cerebellar agenesis patients appear to have some of the symptoms of *autism* early in life. This observation comports with evidence that dysfunction (rather than absence) of the cerebellum is related to autism (detailed in Clinical Focus 8-2, Autism Spectrum Disorder).

Massachusetts General Hospital; Credit: Courtesy of Jeremy Schmahmann

Throughout this book we examine the nervous system with a focus on function—on how our behavior and our brain interact. In this chapter, we consider the human nervous system's organization and how its basic components function in the context of plasticity, as illustrated in Research Focus 2-1, Agenesis of the Cerebellum. First, we emphasize the brain's biology. Then we elaborate on function—how the brain works in concert with the rest of the nervous system. This focus on nervous system function and plasticity suggests 10 principles of nervous system organization. We note each principle through the chapter and in detail at its end, in Section 2-6. These big ideas apply equally to the micro and macro views of the nervous system presented in this chapter and to the broader picture of behavior that emerges in later chapters.

2-1 Overview of Brain Function and Structure

The brain's primary function is to produce behavior, or *movement*. To produce behavior as we search, explore, and manipulate our environment, the brain must absorb information about the world—about the objects around us: their size, shape, and location. Without stimuli, the brain cannot orient the body and direct it to produce an appropriate response.

The nervous system's organs are designed to admit information from the world and to convert this information into biological activity that produces *perception*, subjective experiences of reality. The brain thus produces what we believe is reality so that we can move. This subjective reality is essential to carrying out any complex task.

When you answer the telephone, for example, your brain directs your body to reach for it as the nervous system responds to vibrating air molecules by producing the subjective experience of a ringtone. We perceive this stimulus as sound and react to it as if it actually exists, when in fact the sound is merely a fabrication of the brain. That fabrication is produced by a chain reaction that takes place when vibrating air molecules hit the eardrum. Without the nervous system, especially the brain, sound does not exist—only the movement of air molecules.

But there is more to hearing a phone's ringtone than vibrating air molecules. Our mental construct of reality is based not only on the sensory information we receive but also on the cognitive processes we might use to interact with that incoming information. Hearing a ringtone when we are expecting a call has a meaning vastly different from its ringing at three o'clock in the morning, when we are not expecting a call.

The subjective reality the brain constructs can be better understood by comparing the sensory realities of two different kinds of animals. You are probably aware that dogs perceive sounds that humans do not. This difference in perception does not mean that a dog's nervous system is better than ours or that our hearing is poorer. Rather, the perceptual world constructed by a dog brain simply differs from that of a human brain. Neither experience is "correct." The difference in subjective experience is due merely to two differently evolved systems for processing sensory stimuli.

When it comes to visual perception, our world is rich with color, whereas dogs see very little color. Human brains and dog brains construct different realities. Subjective differences in brains exist for good reason: they allow different animals to exploit different features in their environments. Dogs use their hearing to detect the movements of prey, such as mice in the grass; early humans probably used color vision for identifying ripe fruit in trees. Evolution, then, fosters *adaptability*, equipping each species with a view of the world that helps it survive.

> Principle 1: The nervous system produces movement in a perceptual world the brain constructs.

> Section 9-1 elaborates on the nature of sensation and perception.

Plastic Patterns of Neural Organization

The brain is *plastic*: neural tissue has the capacity to adapt to the world by changing how its functions are organized. Just as the brain of the young man profiled in Research Focus 2-1 adapted to cerebellar agenesis, a person blind from birth has enhanced auditory capacities because some of the brain's visual regions have been co-opted for hearing. The brain is also plastic in the sense that connections among neurons in a given functional system are constantly changing in response to experience.

For us to learn anything new, neural circuits must change to represent and store this knowledge. As we learn to play a musical instrument or speak a new language, the cortical regions taking part can actually increase in size to accommodate the learning. An important aspect of human learning and brain plasticity is related to the development of language and to the expansion of the brain regions related to language. We have learned to read, to calculate, to compose and play music, and to develop the sciences. Clearly, the human nervous system evolved long before we mastered these achievements.

Principle 2: Neuroplasticity is the hallmark of nervous system functioning.

Section 1-2 introduces the genotype, phenotype, and epigenetics in an evolutionary context.

Randy L. Jirtle, Adjunct Professor of Epigenetics, Department of Biological Sciences, NC State University, Raleigh, NC

FIGURE 2-1 Phenotypic Plasticity These two mice are genetically identical but express very different phenotypes because their mothers were fed different supplements when pregnant.

Figure 2-2A restates Figure 1-1, the gross anatomy of the human CNS and PNS.

FIGURE 2-2 Parsing the Nervous System The nervous system can be conceptualized **(A)** anatomically and **(B)** functionally. The functional approach employed in this book focuses on how the four parts of the nervous system interact.

In turn, culture now plays a dominant role in shaping our behavior. Because we drive cars and communicate electronically, we—and our nervous system—must differ from those of our ancestors who did not engage in these activities. The basis for change in the nervous system is **neuroplasticity**, the nervous system's fundamental potential for physical or chemical change that enhances its adaptability to environmental change and its ability to compensate for injury.

Although it is tempting to see neuroplasticity as a trait unique to animals' nervous systems, it is really part of a larger biological capacity called **phenotypic plasticity**, the individual's capacity to develop into more than one *phenotype*—the characteristics we can see or measure. (See Gilbert & Epel, 2009, for a wonderful discussion of biological plasticity.) Stated simply, an individual's *genotype* (genetic makeup) interacts with the environment to elicit a specific phenotype. This phenotype emerges from a large genetic repertoire of possibilities, a phenomenon that in turn results from *epigenetic* influences.

Epigenetic factors do not change genes but rather influence how genes inherited from parents express specific traits. The two mice pictured in **Figure 2-1** appear very different: one is fat, one thin; one has dark fur, the other is light-colored. Yet these mice essentially are clones, genetically identical. They appear so different because their mothers were fed different diets while pregnant. The diet supplements added chemical markers, or epigenetic tags, on specific genes. The tags determine whether the gene is available to influence cells, including neurons, leading to differences in body structure and eating behavior.

Functional Organization of the Nervous System

From an anatomical standpoint, the brain and spinal cord together make up the central nervous system. The nerve fibers radiating out beyond the brain and spinal cord, as well as all the neurons outside the brain and spinal cord, form the peripheral nervous system. **Figure 2-2**A charts this *anatomical* organization. PNS nerves carry sensory information into the CNS and carry motor instructions from the CNS to the body's muscles and tissues, including those that perform such functions as blood circulation and digestion.

In a *functional* organization, little changes, but the focus turns to how the parts of the system work together. Neurons in the somatic division of the PNS connect through the cranial and spinal nerves to receptors on the body's surface and on its muscles. Somatic neurons gather sensory information for the CNS and convey information from the CNS to move muscles of the face, body, and limbs. Similarly, the autonomic division of the PNS enables the CNS to govern the workings of your body's internal organs—your heartbeat, urination, pupillary response, and the diaphragm movements that inflate and deflate your lungs. The enteric nervous system, which is sometimes considered part of the ANS, controls digestion and stomach contractions.

And so, from a functional standpoint (Figure 2-2B), the major PNS divisions step up to constitute, along with the CNS, an interacting four-part system:

- The CNS includes the brain and the spinal cord—the nervous system core, which mediates behavior.

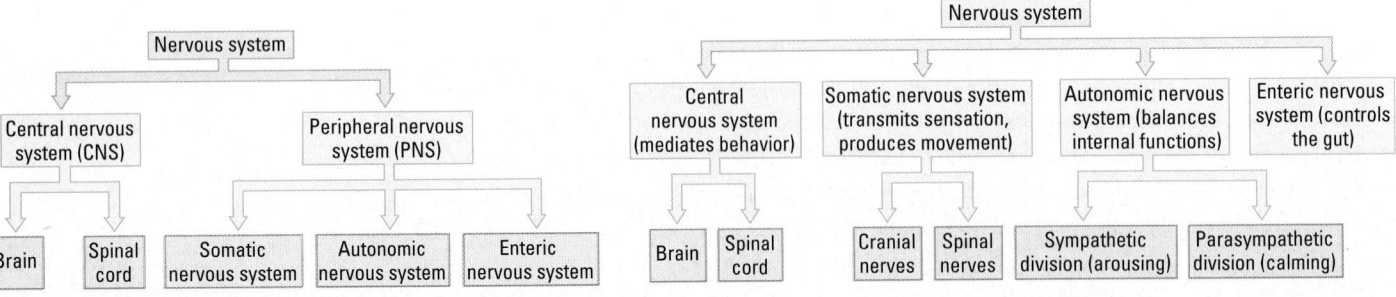

(A) Anatomic Organization

(B) Functional Organization

- The **somatic nervous system** (SNS) includes all the spinal and cranial nerves carrying sensory information to the CNS from the muscles, joints, and skin. It also transmits outgoing motor instructions that produce movement.

- The **autonomic nervous system** (ANS) balances the body's internal organs by producing the rest-and-digest response through the *parasympathetic* (calming) *nerves* or the fight-or-flight response or vigorous activity through the *sympathetic* (arousing) *nerves*.

- The **enteric nervous system** (ENS), formed by a mesh of neurons embedded in the lining of the gut, controls the gut. The ENS communicates with the CNS via the ANS but mostly operates autonomously.

The directional flow of neural information is important. **Afferent** (incoming) information is sensory, coming into the CNS or one of its parts, whereas **efferent** (outgoing) information is leaving the CNS or one of its parts. When you step on a tack, the afferent sensory signals are transmitted from the body into the brain and felt as pain. Efferent signals from the brain trigger a motor response: you lift your foot (**Figure 2-3**).

FIGURE 2-3 Neural Information Flow

The Brain's Surface Features

When buying a new car, people like to look under the hood and examine the engine, the part of the car responsible for most of its behavior—and misbehavior. All most of us can do is gaze at the maze of tubes, wires, boxes, and fluid reservoirs. What we see makes no sense except in the most general way. We know that the engine somehow generates power to make the car move and to run the sound system, lights, and wipers. But knowing this tells us nothing about what all the many engine parts do.

When it comes to our behavior, the brain is the engine. In many ways, examining a brain for the first time is similar to looking under the car hood. We have a vague sense of what the brain does, but most of us have no sense of how its parts accomplish these tasks. We may not even be able to identify those parts. If you are familiar with the anatomical terms and orientations used in drawings and images of brains, read on. If you prefer to review this terminology before you continue, consult The Basics: Finding Your Way Around the Brain on pages 38–39.

Protecting the Nervous System

We start our functional overview by opening the hood and observing the brain snug in its home in the skull. The first thing you encounter is not the brain but rather a tough triple-layered protective covering, the **meninges** (sing. *meninx*) (**Figure 2-4**). The outer *dura mater* (from Latin, meaning *hard mother*) is a tough double layer of fibrous tissue that encloses the brain and spinal cord in a kind of loose sac. In the middle is the *arachnoid layer* (from Greek, meaning *like a spider's web*), an ultrathin sheet of delicate connective tissue that follows the brain's contours. The inner layer, or *pia mater* (from Latin, meaning *soft mother*), is a moderately tough membrane of connective tissue fibers that cling to the brain's surface.

neuroplasticity The nervous system's potential for physical or chemical change to adapt to environmental change and to compensate for injury.

phenotypic plasticity An individual's capacity to develop into more than one phenotype.

somatic nervous system (SNS) Part of the PNS that includes the cranial and spinal nerves to and from the muscles, joints, and skin, which produce movement, transmit incoming sensory input, and inform the CNS about the position and movement of body parts.

autonomic nervous system (ANS) Part of the PNS that regulates the functioning of internal organs and glands.

enteric nervous system (ENS) Mesh of neurons embedded in the lining of the gut, running from the esophagus through the colon; controls the gut.

afferent Conducting toward a CNS structure.

efferent Conducting away from a CNS structure.

meninges Three layers of protective tissue—dura mater, arachnoid, and pia mater—that encase the brain and spinal cord.

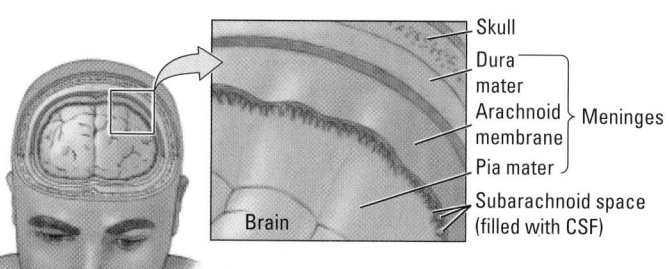

FIGURE 2-4 Cerebral Protection A triple-layered covering, the meninges, encases the brain and spinal cord, and cerebrospinal fluid (CSF) cushions them.

Finding Your Way Around the Brain

When the first anatomists began to examine the brain with the primitive tools of their time, the names they chose for brain regions often manifested their erroneous assumptions about how the brain works. They named one brain region the *gyrus fornicatus* because they thought that it had a role in sexual function, but most of this region actually has nothing to do with sexual activity.

A Wonderland of Nomenclature

As time went on, the assumptions and tools of brain research changed, but naming continued to be haphazard and inconsistent. Many brain structures have several names, and terms are often used interchangeably. This peculiar nomenclature arose because research on the brain and behavior spans several centuries and includes scientists of many nationalities and languages.

Early investigators named structures after themselves or objects or ideas. They used various languages, especially Latin, Greek, and English. More recently, investigators have often used numbers or letters, but even this system lacks coherence, because the numbers may be Arabic or Roman and are often used in combination with Greek or Latin letters.

Describing Locations in the Brain

Many names for nervous system structures reflect their anatomical locations with respect to other body parts of the animal, with respect to their relative spatial locations, and with respect to a viewer's perspective:

- Brain–Body Orientation illustrates brain structure location from the frame of reference of the human face.

- Spatial Orientation illustrates brain structure location in relation to other body parts and body orientation.

- Anatomical Orientation illustrates the direction of a cut, or section, through the human brain (part A) from the perspective of a viewer (part B).

Brain—Body Orientation

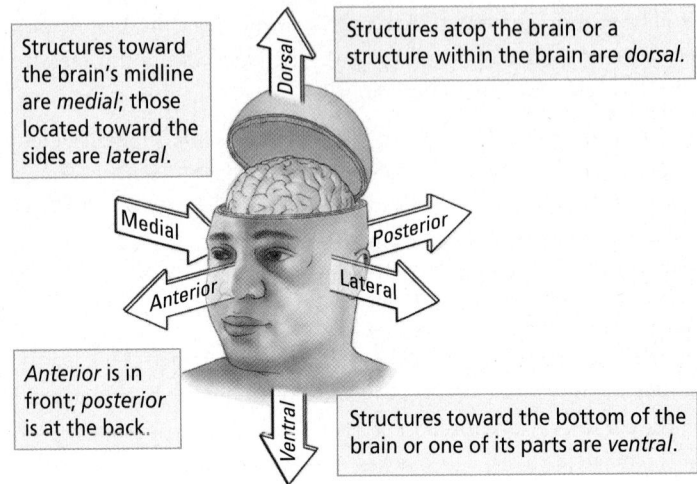

Structures toward the brain's midline are *medial*; those located toward the sides are *lateral*.

Structures atop the brain or a structure within the brain are *dorsal*.

Anterior is in front; *posterior* is at the back.

Structures toward the bottom of the brain or one of its parts are *ventral*.

Spatial Orientation

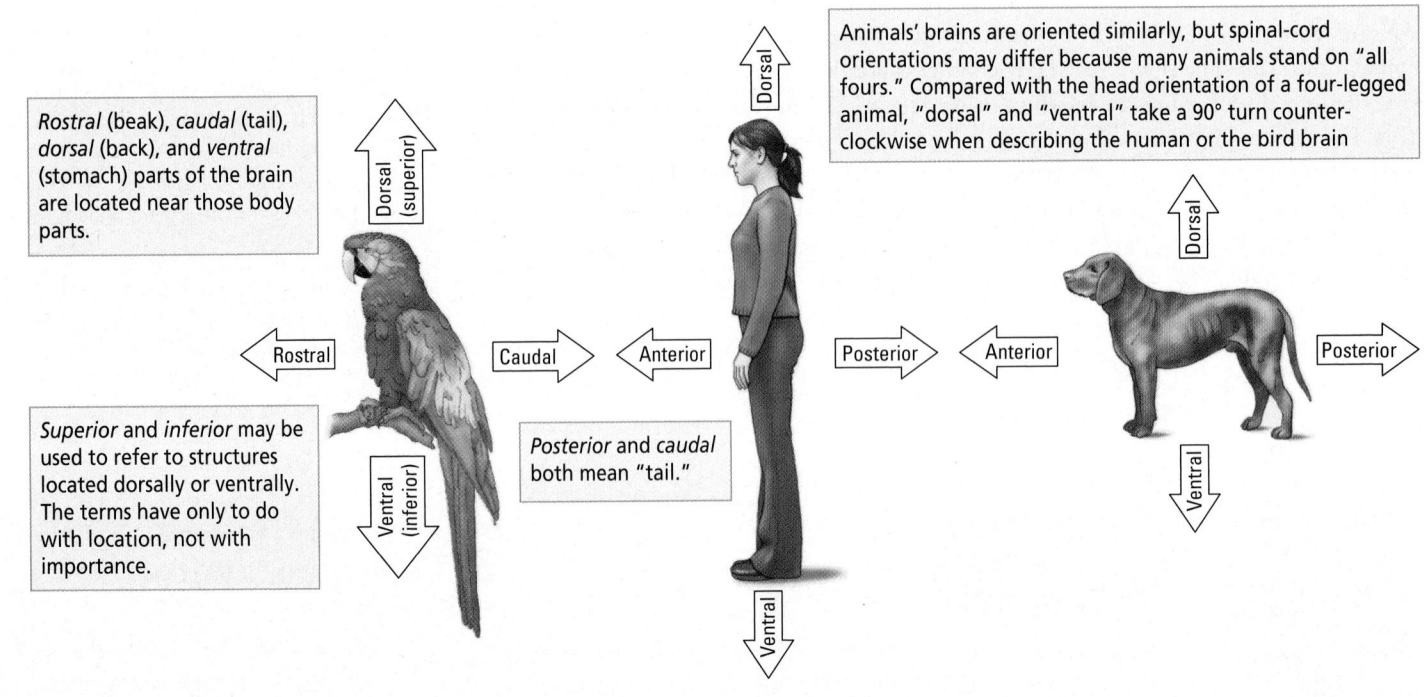

Rostral (beak), *caudal* (tail), *dorsal* (back), and *ventral* (stomach) parts of the brain are located near those body parts.

Superior and *inferior* may be used to refer to structures located dorsally or ventrally. The terms have only to do with location, not with importance.

Posterior and *caudal* both mean "tail."

Animals' brains are oriented similarly, but spinal-cord orientations may differ because many animals stand on "all fours." Compared with the head orientation of a four-legged animal, "dorsal" and "ventral" take a 90° turn counter-clockwise when describing the human or the bird brain

These orienting terms are derived from Latin. Consult the accompanying Glossary of Anatomical Location and Orientation for easy reference. It is common practice to combine orienting terms. A structure described as dorsolateral, for example, means that it lies up and to the side.

Finally, the nervous system, like the body, is bilaterally symmetrical: it has a left side and a right side. Structures that lie on the same side are *ipsilateral*; if they lie on opposite sides, they are *contralateral* to each other. Structures that occur in each hemisphere are *bilateral*. Structures that are close to one another are *proximal*; those far from one another are *distal*.

Anatomic Orientation

(A) Plane of section

(B) View of brain

Coronal section

Frontal view

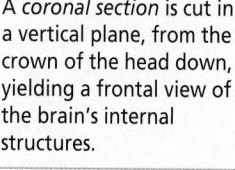

A *coronal section* is cut in a vertical plane, from the crown of the head down, yielding a frontal view of the brain's internal structures.

Horizontal section

Dorsal view

A *horizontal section*, so-called because the view or the cut falls along the horizon, is usually viewed looking down on the brain from above—a dorsal view.

Sagittal section

Medial view

A *sagittal section* is cut lengthways from front to back and viewed from the side. (Imagine the brain split by an arrow—in Latin, *sagitta*.) Here, a cut in the *midsagittal plane* divides the brain into symmetrical halves, a medial view.

Glossary of Anatomical Location and Orientation

Term	Meaning with respect to the nervous system	Term	Meaning with respect to the nervous system
Anterior	Near or toward the front of the animal or the front of the head (see also *frontal* and *rostral*)	Lateral	Toward the side of the body or brain
Caudal	Near or toward the tail of the animal (see also *posterior*)	Medial	Toward the middle, specifically the body's midline; in reference to brain sections, a side view of the central structures
Coronal	Cut vertically from the crown of the head down; used to reference the plane of a brain section that reveals a frontal view	Posterior	Near or toward the animal's tail (see also *caudal*); for human spinal cord, at the back
Dorsal	On or toward the back of a four-legged animal (equivalent to posterior for human spinal cord); in reference to human brain nuclei, above, and to brain sections, viewed from above	Rostral	Toward the beak (front) of the animal (see also *anterior* and *frontal*)
Frontal	Of the front (see also *anterior* and *rostral*); in reference to brain sections, a viewing orientation from the front	Sagittal	Cut lengthways from front to back of the skull to reveal a medial view into the brain from the side; a cut in the midsagittal plane divides the brain into symmetrical halves.
Horizontal	Cut along the horizon; used to reference the plane of a brain section that reveals a dorsal view	Superior	Above (see also *dorsal*)
Inferior	Below (see also *ventral*)	Ventral	On or toward the belly of four-legged animals (see also *inferior*); in reference to human brain nuclei, below.

The brain is made up of two hemispheres, left and right.

Frontal view

Cerebral cortex is the brain's thin, outer "bark" layer.

Your right hand, if made into a fist, represents the positions of the lobes of the left hemisphere of your brain.

Glauberman/ Science Source

Parietal lobe

Frontal lobe

Occipital lobe

Temporal lobe

Parietal lobe (knuckles)

Occipital lobe (wrist)

Frontal lobe (fingers)

Temporal lobe (thumb)

Bumps in the brain's folded surface are called gyri, and cracks are called sulci.

Lobes define broad divisions of the cerebral cortex.

FIGURE 2-5 The Cerebral Cortex Each cerebral hemisphere is divided into four lobes: frontal, parietal, temporal, and occipital, shown at left as oriented in the head. The brain surface, or cerebral cortex, shown in the frontal view, is a thin sheet of nerve tissue, heavily folded to fit inside the skull. Your right fist can map the orientation of the left hemisphere and its lobes.

Between the arachnoid layer and the pia mater flows **cerebrospinal fluid** (CSF), a colorless solution of sodium chloride and other salts. CSF cushions the brain so that it can move or expand slightly without pressing on the skull. The symptoms of meningitis, an infection of the meninges and CSF, are described in Clinical Focus 2-2, Meningitis and Encephalitis, on page 42.

Cerebral Geography

After removing the meninges, we can examine the brain's surface features, most prominently its two nearly symmetrical left and right hemispheres. **Figure 2-5** diagrams the left hemisphere of a typical human forebrain oriented in the upright human skull. The outer forebrain consists of a thin, folded film of nerve tissue, the **cerebral cortex**, detailed in the frontal view in Figure 2-5. The word *cortex*, Latin for *tree bark*, is apt, considering the cortex's heavily folded surface and its location, covering most of the rest of the brain. Unlike the bark on a tree, however, the brain's folds are not random but rather demarcate its functional cortical zones.

Make a fist with your right hand and hold it up, as shown on the right in Figure 2-5, to represent the positions of the forebrain's broad divisions, or *lobes*, in the skull. Each lobe is named for the skull bone it lies beneath.

- The forward-pointing **temporal lobe** lies at the side of the brain, in approximately the same place as the thumb on your upraised fist. The temporal lobe functions in connection with hearing and with language and musical abilities.

- Immediately above your thumbnail, your fingers correspond to the location of the **frontal lobe**, often characterized as performing the brain's executive functions, such as decision making.

- The **parietal lobe** is at the top of the skull, as represented by your knuckles, behind the frontal lobe and above the temporal lobe. Parietal functions include directing our movements toward a goal or to perform a task, such as grasping an object.

- The area at the back of each hemisphere, near your wrist, constitutes the **occipital lobe**, where visual processing begins.

Examining the Brain's Surface from All Angles

As we look at the dorsal view in **Figure 2-6A**, the brain's wrinkled left and right hemispheres resemble a walnut meat taken whole from its shell. These hemispheres constitute the cerebrum, the major forebrain structure and most recently evolved feature of the CNS. Visible from the opposite ventral view in Figure 2-6B are the brainstem, including the

cerebrospinal fluid (CSF) Clear solution of sodium chloride and other salts that fills the ventricles inside the brain and circulates around the brain and spinal cord beneath the arachnoid layer in the subarachnoid space.

cerebral cortex Thin, heavily folded film of nerve tissue composed of neurons that is the outer layer of the forebrain. Also called *neocortex*.

temporal lobe Part of the cerebral cortex that functions in connection with hearing, language, and musical abilities; lies below the lateral fissure, beneath the temporal bone at the side of the skull.

frontal lobe Part of the cerebral cortex often generally characterized as performing the brain's executive functions, such as decision making; lies anterior to the central sulcus and beneath the frontal bone of the skull.

parietal lobe Part of the cerebral cortex that directs movements toward a goal or to perform a task, such as grasping an object; lies posterior to the central sulcus and beneath the parietal bone at the top of the skull.

occipital lobe Part of the cerebral cortex where visual processing begins; lies at the back of the brain and beneath the occipital bone.

(A) Dorsal view

Frontal lobe — Central sulcus — Parietal lobe — Longitudinal fissure — Occipital lobe

Courtesy of Yakovlev Collection/National Museum of Health and Medicine.

(B) Ventral view

Temporal lobe — Cerebellum — Frontal lobe — Olfactory bulbs — Cranial nerves — Brainstem — Occipital lobe

Courtesy of Yakovlev Collection/National Museum of Health and Medicine.

(C) Lateral view

Central sulcus — Parietal lobe — Frontal lobe — Lateral fissure — Temporal lobe — Occipital lobe

Courtesy of Yakovlev Collection/National Museum of Health and Medicine.

(D) Medial view

Central sulcus — Parietal lobe — Frontal lobe — Occipital lobe — Temporal lobe — Brainstem — Cerebellum

Courtesy of Yakovlev Collection/National Museum of Health and Medicine.

FIGURE 2-6 Examining the Human Brain Locations of the lobes of the cerebral hemispheres, shown in dorsal, ventral, lateral, and medial (top, bottom, side, and midline) views, as are the cerebellum, longitudinal and lateral fissures, and the central sulcus.

Meningitis and Encephalitis

Harmful microorganisms can invade the layers of the meninges, particularly the pia mater and the arachnoid layer, as well as the CSF flowing between them, to cause a variety of infections that lead to *meningitis.* One symptom of this condition, inflammation, places pressure on the brain. Because the space between meninges and skull is slight, unrelieved pressure can lead to delirium and, if the infection progresses, to drowsiness, stupor, and even coma.

Usually the earliest symptom of meningitis is severe headache and a stiff neck (cervical rigidity). Head retraction (tilting the head backward) is an extreme form of cervical rigidity. Convulsions, a common symptom in children, indicate that the inflammation is affecting the brain.

Infection of the brain itself is called *encephalitis.* Some of its many forms have great historical significance. A century ago, during World War I, a form of encephalitis called sleeping sickness (*encephalitis lethargica*) reached epidemic proportions. Its first symptom is sleep disturbance. People sleep all day and become wakeful, even excited, at night. Subsequently they show symptoms of *Parkinson disease,* including severe tremors, muscular rigidity, and difficulty in controlling body movements. Many are completely unable to make voluntary movements, such as walking or even combing their hair. Survivors of sleeping sickness were immortalized by the neurologist Oliver Sacks in the book and movie *Awakenings.* Sacks died in 2015 at age 82.

Encephalitis symptoms are caused by the death of an area deep in the brain, the *substantia nigra (black substance),* which you will learn about in Section 2-3. Other forms of encephalitis may have different effects on the brain. For example, Rasmussen encephalitis attacks one cerebral hemisphere in children. In most cases, the only effective treatment is radical: *hemispherectomy,* surgical removal of the entire affected hemisphere.

CDC/Dr. Edwin P. Ewing, Jr.

Pus is visible over the surface of this brain infected with meningitis.

Surprisingly, some young children who lose a hemisphere adapt rather well. They may even complete college, literally with half a brain. But intellectual disabilities are a more common outcome of hemispherectomy as a result of encephalitis.

wrinkly hemispheres of the smaller *cerebellum* (Latin for *little brain*). Both the cerebrum and the brainstem are visible in the lateral and medial views in Figure 2-6C and D.

Much of the crinkled-up cerebral cortex is invisible from the brain's surface. All we can see are bumps, or **gyri** (sing. *gyrus*), and cracks, or **sulci** (sing. *sulcus*). Some sulci are so deep that they are called *fissures.* The longitudinal fissure runs between the cerebral hemispheres and the lateral fissure along the sides of the brain. Both are shown in various views in Figure 2-6, along with the central sulcus that runs from the lateral fissures across the top of the cerebrum.

Looking at the bottom of the brain, the ventral view in Figure 2-6B, we see in the midst of the wrinkled cerebrum and ventral to the cerebellum a smooth, whitish structure with little tubes attached. This central set of structures is the brainstem, the area responsible for most unconscious behavior. The tubes mark out the cranial nerves that run to and from the brain as part of the SNS.

Cerebral Circulation

The brain's surface appears to be covered with blood vessels. As with the rest of the body, the arteries feed blood to the brain and send it back through veins to the kidneys and lungs for cleaning and oxygenation. The cerebral arteries emerge from the neck to wrap around the

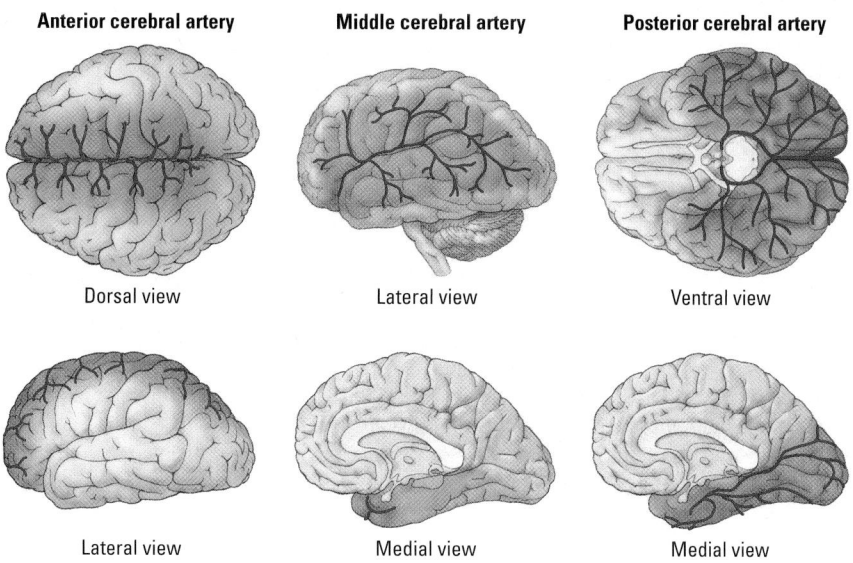

Anterior cerebral artery	Middle cerebral artery	Posterior cerebral artery
Dorsal view	Lateral view	Ventral view
Lateral view	Medial view	Medial view

FIGURE 2-7 Major Cerebral Arteries Each of the three major arteries that feed blood to the cerebral hemispheres branches extensively to supply the regions shaded in pink.

outside of the brainstem, cerebrum, and cerebellum, finally penetrating the brain's surface to nourish its inner regions.

Three major arteries send blood to the cerebrum—the anterior, middle, and posterior cerebral arteries, shown in **Figure 2-7**. Because the brain is highly sensitive to blood loss, a blockage or break in a cerebral artery is likely to lead to the death of the affected region. This condition, known as **stroke**, is the sudden appearance of neurological symptoms as a result of severely interrupted blood flow. Because the three cerebral arteries supply different parts of the brain, strokes disrupt different brain functions, depending on the artery affected.

Because the brain's connections are crossed, stroke in the left hemisphere affects sensation and movement on the right side of the body. The opposite is true for those with strokes in the right hemisphere. Clinical Focus 2-3, Stroke, on page 45, describes some disruptions that stroke causes, both to the person who has it and to those who care for stroke victims.

Section 16-3 elaborates on the effects of stroke and its treatment.

Principle 3: Many brain circuits are crossed.

The Brain's Internal Features

The simplest way to examine the inside of something is to cut it in half. Of course, the orientation of the cut affects what we see. Consider slicing through a pear. If we cut from side to side, we cut across the core, providing a dorsal view; if we cut from top to bottom, we cut parallel to the core, providing a medial view. Our impression of the inside of a pear is clearly influenced by how we slice it. The same is true of the brain.

Macro View

We can reveal the brain's inner features by slicing it parallel to the front of the body, downward through the middle in a coronal section (**Figure 2-8A**). The resulting frontal view, shown in Figure 2-8B, makes immediately apparent that the brain's interior is not homogeneous. Both dark and light regions of tissue are visible, and though these regions may not be as distinctive as car engine parts, they nevertheless represent different brain components.

The darker regions are **gray matter**, largely composed of cell bodies and capillary blood vessels. Gray matter neurons either collect and modify information or support this activity.

gyri (sing. gyrus) A small protrusion or bump formed by the folding of the cerebral cortex.

sulci (sing. sulcus) A groove in brain matter; most are in the neocortex or cerebellum.

stroke Sudden appearance of neurological symptoms as a result of severely interrupted blood flow.

gray matter Areas of the nervous system composed predominantly of cell bodies and capillary blood vessels that either collect and modify information or support this activity.

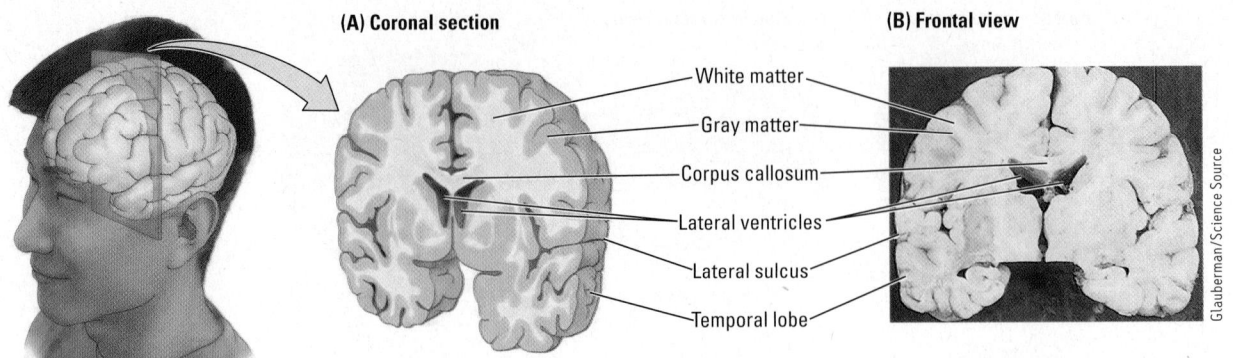

(A) Coronal section

(B) Frontal view

White matter

Gray matter

Corpus callosum

Lateral ventricles

Lateral sulcus

Temporal lobe

Glauberman/Science Source

FIGURE 2-8 Coronal Brain Section **(A)** The brain is cut down the middle parallel to the front of the body; then a coronal section is viewed at a slight angle. This frontal view **(B)** displays white matter, gray matter, and the lateral ventricles. Visible above the ventricles, a large bundle of fibers, the corpus callosum, joins the hemispheres.

white matter Areas of the nervous system rich in fat-sheathed neural axons that form the connections between brain cells.

ventricle One of four cavities in the brain that contain CSF to cushion the brain; may play a role in maintaining brain metabolism.

corpus callosum Band of white matter containing about 200 million nerve fibers that connects the two cerebral hemispheres to provide a route for direct communication between them.

The lighter regions are **white matter**, mostly nerve fibers with fatty coverings that produce the white appearance, much as fat droplets in milk make it appear white. White matter fibers form connections between and among the brain's cells.

A second feature, apparent at the center of our frontal view in Figure 2-8B, are the **ventricles**—two wing-shaped cavities that contain cerebrospinal fluid. The brain's four ventricles, shown in place in **Figure 2-9**, are filled with CSF made by the cells lining the ventricles. All four ventricles are connected, so CSF flows from the two lateral ventricles to the third and fourth ventricles, which lie on the brain's midline, and into the *cerebral aqueduct*, a canal that runs down the length of the spinal cord. CSF is also found in the space between the lower layers of the meninges that wrap around the brain and spinal cord (see Figure 2-4).

Although the ventricles' functions are not well understood, researchers think that they play an important role in maintaining brain metabolism. CSF may allow certain compounds access to the brain, and it probably helps the brain excrete metabolic wastes. In the event of trauma to the brain or spinal cord, CSF cushions the blow.

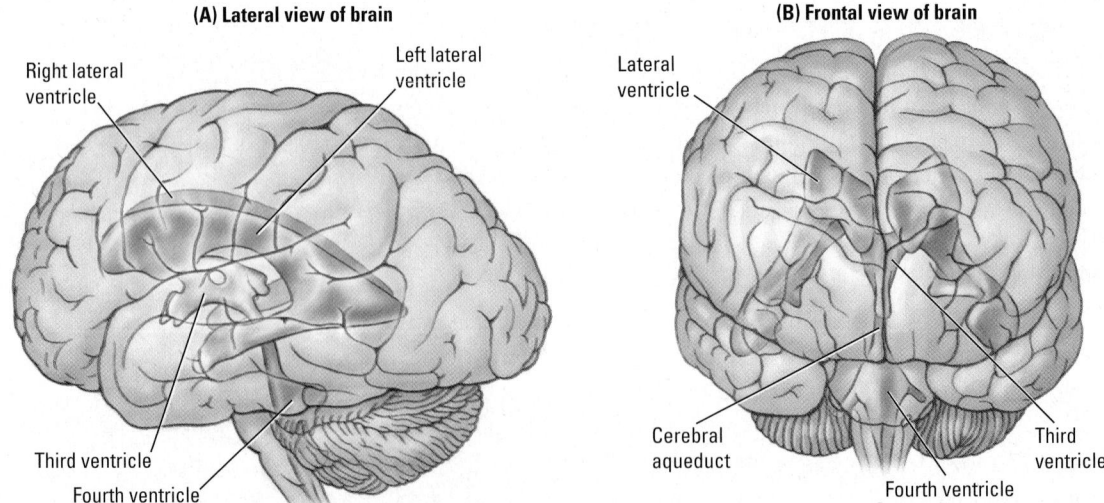

(A) Lateral view of brain

(B) Frontal view of brain

Right lateral ventricle

Left lateral ventricle

Lateral ventricle

Third ventricle

Fourth ventricle

Cerebral aqueduct

Third ventricle

Fourth ventricle

FIGURE 2-9 Interconnected Cerebral Ventricles The lateral ventricles are symmetrical, one in each hemisphere. The third and fourth ventricles lie in the brain's midline and drain into the cerebral aqueduct, which runs the length of the spinal cord.

Stroke

Approximately every minute in the United States, someone has a stroke with obvious visible symptoms—more than a half million every year. Worldwide, stroke is the second leading cause of death. Acute symptoms include facial droop, motor weakness in limbs, visual disturbance, speech difficulties, and sudden onset of severe headache.

In addition to visible strokes, at least twice as many silent strokes may occur each year. These ministrokes occur primarily in the white matter and do not produce obvious symptoms. (To view a brief video on silent stroke, go to https://www.youtube.com/watch?v=J3fb0CaDpEk).

Even with the best, fastest medical attention, most stroke patients have some residual motor, sensory, or cognitive deficit. According to the Canadian Stroke Network, for every 10 people who have a stroke, 2 die, 6 are disabled to varying degrees, and 2 recover to a degree but still have a diminished quality of life. Of those who survive, 1 in 10 risk further stroke.

The consequences of stroke are significant for those who have them, their family, and their lifestyle. Consider Mr. Anderson, a 45-year-old electrical engineer, who took his three children to the movies one Saturday afternoon in 1998 and collapsed. He had a massive stroke of the middle cerebral artery in his left hemisphere. The stroke has impaired Mr. Anderson's language ever since, and because the brain's connections are crossed, his right-side motor control as well.

Seven years after his stroke, Mr. Anderson remained unable to speak, but he understood simple conversations. Severe difficulties in moving his right leg required him to use a walker. He could not move the fingers of his right hand and so had difficulty feeding himself, among other tasks. Mr. Anderson will probably never return to his engineering career or drive or get around on his own.

Like him, most stroke survivors require help to perform everyday tasks. Caregivers are often female relatives who give up their own career and other pursuits. Half of the caregivers develop emotional illness, primarily depression or anxiety or both, in a year or so. Lost income and stroke-related medical bills significantly affect the family's living standard.

We tend to speak of stroke as a single disorder, but two major types of strokes have been identified. In the more common and often less severe *ischemic stroke*, a blood vessel is blocked, as by a clot. The more severe *hemorrhagic stroke* results from a burst vessel bleeding into the brain.

The hopeful news is that ischemic stroke can be treated acutely with a drug called *tissue plasminogen activator* (t-PA), which breaks up clots and allows normal blood flow to return to an affected region. Unfortunately, there is no treatment for hemorrhagic stroke, for which the use of clot-preventing t-PA would be disastrous.

Simon Fraser/Science Source

Dorsal view of a brain with a stroke, imaged by computed tomography (CT). The dark area in the right hemisphere has been damaged by the loss of blood flow.

When patients receive t-PA within 3 hours of an ischemic stroke, the number who make a nearly complete recovery increases by about 25 percent compared with those who receive a placebo (Hatcher and Starr, 2011). In addition, impairments are reduced in the remaining patients who survive the stroke. The risk of hemorrhage is about 6 percent in t-PA–treated patients relative to no risk in placebo-treated patients.

Many people are unable to reach a hospital soon enough for treatment with t-PA. Most stroke victims do not visit an emergency department until about 24 hours after symptoms appear, too late for the treatment. Apparently, most people fail to realize that stroke is an emergency.

By taking advantage of developments in neuroimaging, research has shown that it is possible to remove clots from cerebral vessels mechanically (Appireddy et al., 2015). Although quick treatment with t-PA is still preferred, these new procedures have expanded the window of benefit to as long as 8 hours post stroke. There is also intense interest in developing treatments that will stimulate the brain to initiate reparative processes during the postacute period. Such treatment will facilitate the patient's functional improvement (see a review by Langhorne et al., 2011).

Cutting through the brain vertically from front to back produces a sagittal section (**Figure 2-10**A). If we make our cut down the brain's midline, that is, in the midsagittal plane, we divide the cerebrum into its two hemispheres, revealing several distinctive structures in the resulting medial view (Figure 2-10B). One feature is a long band of white matter that runs much of the length of the cerebral hemispheres. This band, the **corpus callosum,** contains about 200 million nerve fibers that join the two hemispheres and allow them to communicate.

FIGURE 2-10 Sagittal Brain Section
(A) A section in the midsagittal plane
separates the hemispheres, allowing **(B)** a
medial view of the brain's midline structures,
including the subcortical structures that lie
ventral to the corpus callosum.

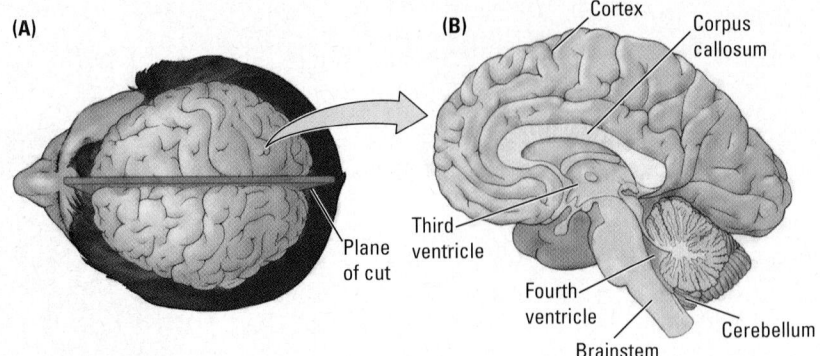

Principle 4: The CNS functions on multiple
levels.

Principle 5: The brain is symmetrical and
asymmetrical.

Human brains contain about 86 billion
neurons and 87 billion glia. Section 3-1
examines their structures and functions
in detail.

Figure 2-10B clearly shows that the cortex covers the cerebral hemispheres above the corpus callosum; below it are various internal *subcortical regions*. The brainstem is a subcortical structure that generally controls basic physiological functions. But many subcortical regions are forebrain structures intimately related to the cortical areas that process motor, sensory, perceptual, and cognitive functions. This relation between the cortex and the subcortex alerts us to the concept that redundant functions exist at many levels of nervous system organization.

If you were to compare medial views of the left and right hemispheres, you would be struck by their symmetry. The brain, in fact, has two of nearly every structure, one on each side. The few one-of-a-kind structures, such as the third and fourth ventricles, lie along the brain's midline (see Figure 2-9B). Another one-of-a-kind structure is the pineal gland, which Descartes declared the seat of the mind in his dualistic theory of how the brain works.

Microscopic Inspection: Cells and Fibers

The brain's fundamental units—its cells—are so small that they can be viewed only with the aid of a microscope. A microscope quickly reveals that the brain has two main types of cells, illustrated in **Figure 2-11**. *Neurons* carry out the brain's major functions, whereas *glial cells* aid and modulate the neurons' activities—for example, by insulating them. Both neurons and glia come in many forms, each marked by the work that they do.

We can see the brain's internal structures in even greater detail by dyeing their cells with special stains (**Figure 2-12**). For example, if we use a dye that selectively stains cell bodies, we can see that the neurons in the cortical gray matter lie in layers, revealed by the bands of

FIGURE 2-11 Brain Cells Branches
emanate from the cell bodies of a
prototypical neuron (left) and a glial
cell (right). This branching organization
increases the cell's surface area. This
type of neuron is called a pyramidal cell
because the cell body is shaped somewhat
like a pyramid; the glial cell is called an
astrocyte because of its star-shaped
appearance.

tissue in Figure 2-12A and C. Each layer contains cells that stain characteristically. Figure 2-12A and B shows that stained subcortical regions are composed of clusters, or **nuclei**, of similar cells.

Although layers and nuclei appear very different, both form functional units in the brain. Whether a particular brain region has layers or nuclei is largely an accident of evolution. By using a stain that selectively dyes neuronal fibers, as shown in Figure 2-12B and D, we can see the borders of the subcortical nuclei more clearly. In addition, we can see that the stained cell bodies lie in regions adjacent to those with most of the fibers.

A key feature of neurons is that they are connected to one another by fibers known as *axons*. When axons run along together, much like the wires that run from a car engine to the dashboard, they form a **nerve** or **tract** (**Figure 2-13**). By convention, a *tract* is a collection of nerve fibers in the brain and spinal cord, whereas bundles of fibers outside of the CNS are typically called nerves. Thus, the pathway from the eye to the brain is the optic nerve, whereas the pathway from the cerebral cortex to the spinal cord is the corticospinal tract.

(A) **(B)** Subcortical nuclei
(C) Gray-matter layers **(D)** White matter

Photos courtesy of Bryan Kolb

FIGURE 2-12 Cortical Layers and Glia Brain sections from the left hemisphere of a monkey (midline is to the left in each image), viewed through a microscope. Cells are stained with (**A** and **C**) a selective cell body stain for neurons (gray matter) and (**B** and **D**) a selective fiber stain for insulating glial cells, or *myelin* (white matter). The images reveal very different views of the brain at the macro (**A** and **B**) and microscopic (**C** and **D**) levels.

2-1 REVIEW

Overview of Brain Function and Structure

Before you continue, check your understanding.

1. The nervous system's function is to produce movement, or _____, in a perceptual world constructed by the _____.

2. The left and right cerebral hemispheres are each divided into four lobes: _____, _____, _____, and _____.

3. The human nervous system has evolved the potential to change, for example, to adapt to changes in the world or to compensate for injury. This attribute is called _____.

4. Neural tissue is of two main types: (1) _____ forms the connections among cells, and (2) _____ collects and processes incoming (afferent) sensory or outgoing (efferent) information.

5. The nerve fibers that lie in the brain form _____. Outside the brain they are called _____.

6. Chart the human nervous system's functional organization.

Answers appear at the back of the book.

For additional study tools, visit 🎧 **LaunchPad**:
www.macmillanhighered.com/launchpad/kolb5e

2-2 The Nervous System's Evolutionary Development

The developing brain, which is less complex than the mature adult brain, provides a clear picture of its basic structural plan. The striking biological similarity of embryos as diverse as amphibians and mammals is evident in the earliest stages of development. In the evolution of complex nervous systems in vertebrate species, simpler and evolutionarily more primitive forms have not been discarded and replaced but rather added to. As a result, all anatomical and functional features of simpler nervous systems are present in and form the base for the most complex nervous systems, including ours.

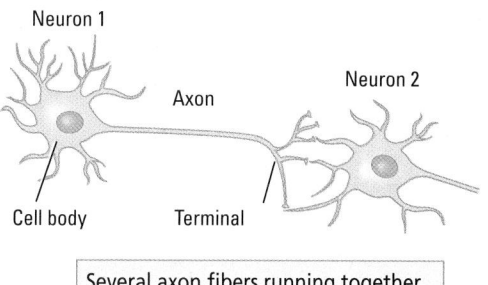

Neuron 1
Axon
Neuron 2
Cell body
Terminal

Several axon fibers running together form a *nerve* when outside the CNS or a *tract* within the CNS.

FIGURE 2-13 Neuronal Connections

nuclei (sing. nucleus) A group of cells forming a cluster that can be identified with special stains to form a functional grouping.

nerve Large collection of axons coursing together *outside* the CNS.

tract Large collection of axons coursing together *in* the CNS.

Section 1-3 outlines nervous system evolution and Section 8-1, developmental similarities among humans and other species.

The bilaterally symmetrical nervous system of simple worms, for example, is common to complex nervous systems. Indeed, we can recognize in humans the spinal cord that constitutes most of the simplest fishes' nervous system. The same is true of the brainstem of more complex fishes, amphibians, and reptiles. The neocortex, although particularly complex in humans, is clearly the same organ found in other mammals.

Stages in Brain Evolution

In a vertebrate embryo, the nervous system begins as a sheet of cells. This sheet folds into a hollow tube and develops into three regions, forebrain, midbrain, and hindbrain, recognizable as a series of three enlargements at the end of the embryonic spinal cord (**Figure 2-14**A). The adult brain of a fish, amphibian, or reptile is roughly equivalent to this three-part brain. The *prosencephalon* (front brain) is responsible for olfaction, the sense of smell; the *mesencephalon* (middle brain) is the seat of vision and hearing; and the *rhombencephalon* (hindbrain) controls movement and balance. The spinal cord is part of the hindbrain.

In mammals (Figure 2-14B), the prosencephalon develops further to form the subcortical structures known collectively as the *diencephalon* (between brain) and the cerebral hemispheres and cortex, or *telencephalon* (endbrain). The mammalian hindbrain develops further into the *metencephalon* (across brain), which includes the cerebellum, and the *myelencephalon* (spinal brain), including the spinal cord.

The human brain is particularly complex, possessing especially large cerebral hemispheres but retaining most other mammalian brain features (Figure 2-14C). Various human cerebral areas—regions in the frontal, temporal, and parietal lobes—are larger than those of other primates' brains—necessary to produce language. Language is thought to have fostered a novel worldview—in the way we think, reflect on our own thoughts, and imagine.

The Nervous System and Intelligent Behavior

Most behaviors are the product not of a single locus in the brain but rather of many interacting brain areas and levels. These several nervous system layers do not simply replicate function; rather, each region adds a different dimension to the behavior. This hierarchical organization affects virtually every human behavior. Abnormalities associated with brain injury and brain disease that seem bizarre in isolation are but the normal manifestation of parts of a hierarchically

FIGURE 2-14 Stages in Brain Evolution and Development Over the evolution of the mammalian brain, the forebrain has grown dramatically.

(A) Vertebrate embryo	(B) Mammalian embryo	(C) Fully developed human brain	
Prosencephalon (forebrain)	Telencephalon (endbrain)	Neocortex, basal ganglia, limbic system olfactory bulb, lateral ventricles	Forebrain
	Diencephalon (between brain)	Thalamus, hypothalamus, pituitary gland, pineal body, third ventricle	
Mesencephalon (midbrain)	Mesencephalon	Tectum, tegmentum, cerebral aqueduct	Brainstem
Rhombencephalon (hindbrain)	Metencephalon (across brain)	Cerebellum, pons, fourth ventricle	
	Myelencephalon (spinal brain)	Medulla oblongata, fourth ventricle	
Spinal cord	Spinal cord	Spinal cord	Spinal cord

organized brain. Our evolutionary history, our developmental history, and our own personal history are integrated at the various anatomical and functional levels of the nervous system.

Is the vertebrate nervous system the only path to evolving intelligent behavior? Invertebrate animals, such as the octopus, have traveled on an evolutionary pathway separate from that of vertebrates for over 700 million years. The octopus nervous system, while strikingly different from ours, is complex. Might the octopus learn much as vertebrate animals do?

Italian biologists Graziano Fiorito and Pietro Scotto (1992) placed individuals of *Octopus vulgaris* (the common octopus) in separate tanks, each with an independent water supply, and allowed them to interact visually for 2 hours. As shown in the Procedure section of **Experiment 2-1**, the observer octopus watched the demonstrator octopus from an adjacent tank through a transparent wall. The demonstrator was being conditioned to learn that a red ball was associated with a reward, whereas a white ball was associated with a weak electric shock.

As noted in the Results section, the demonstrator animals quickly learned to distinguish between the colored balls. The observers then were placed in isolation. When tested later, they selected the same object the demonstrators had, responded faster than the demonstrators did during their conditioning, and performed the task correctly for 5 days without significant error or further conditioning.

Principle 6: Brain systems are organized hierarchically and in parallel.

▶ EXPERIMENT **2-1**

Question: Does intelligent behavior require a vertebrate nervous system organization?

Procedure

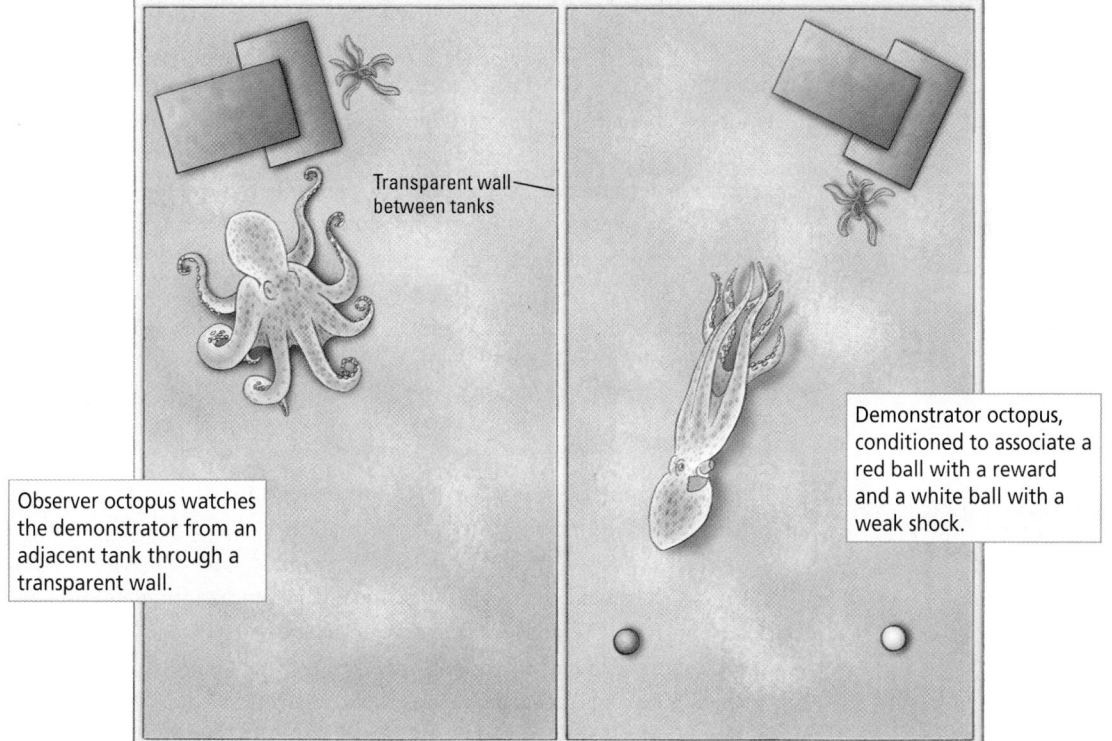

Transparent wall between tanks

Observer octopus watches the demonstrator from an adjacent tank through a transparent wall.

Demonstrator octopus, conditioned to associate a red ball with a reward and a white ball with a weak shock.

Results

1. The demonstrator animal quickly learns to distinguish between the colored balls.

2. When placed in isolation and tested later, the observer animals selected the same object as the demonstrators, responded faster, and performed the task correctly for 5 days without significant error.

Conclusion: Invertebrates display intelligent behavior, such as learning by observation.

Research from G. Fiorito and P. Scotto (1992). Observational learning in *Octopus vulgaris*. *Science, 256*, 545–547.

(2-3) The Central Nervous System: Mediating Behavior

When we look under the hood, we can make some pretty good guesses about what each part of a car engine does. The battery must provide electrical power to run the radio and lights, for example, and because batteries have to be charged, the engine must contain some mechanism for charging them. We can take the same approach to deduce how the parts of the brain function. The part connected to the optic nerve coming from each eye must have something to do with vision. Structures connected to the auditory nerve coming from each ear must have something to do with hearing.

From such simple observations, we can begin to understand how the brain is organized. The real test comes in analyzing actual brain function: how this seeming jumble of parts produces behaviors as complex as human thought. The place to start is the brain's functional anatomy: learning the name of a particular CNS structure is pointless without also learning something about what it does. We focus now on the names and functions of the three major CNS components: spinal cord, brainstem, and forebrain.

brainstem Central structure of the brain, including the hindbrain, midbrain, thalamus, and hypothalamus, that is responsible for most unconscious behavior.

Spinal Cord

Although producing movement is the brain's principal function, ultimately the spinal cord executes most body movements, usually following instructions from the brain but at times acting independently via the somatic nervous system. To understand how important the spinal cord is, think of the old saying "running around like a chicken with its head cut off." When a chicken's head is lopped off for the farmer's family dinner, the chicken is still capable of running around the barnyard until it collapses from loss of blood. The chicken accomplishes this feat because the spinal cord is acting independently of the brain.

Grasping the spinal cord's complexity is easier once you realize that it is not a single structure but rather a set of segmented switching stations. As detailed in Section 2-4, each spinal segment receives information from a discrete part of the body and sends out commands to that area. Spinal nerves, which are part of the SNS, carry sensory information to the cord from the skin, muscles, and related structures and in turn send motor instructions to control each muscle.

Patellar
tendon

You can demonstrate movement controlled by the spinal cord in your own body by tapping your patellar tendon, just below your kneecap (the patella). The sensory input causes your lower leg to kick out, and try as you might, it is very hard to prevent the movement. Your brain, in other words, has trouble inhibiting this *spinal reflex*: it is automatic.

We explain reflexes in Section 11-4.

Brainstem

The **brainstem** begins where the spinal cord enters the skull and extends upward into the lower areas of the forebrain. The brainstem receives afferent nerves coming in from all of the body's senses, and it sends efferent nerves out to the spinal cord to control virtually all of the body's movements except the most complex movements of the fingers and toes. The brainstem, then, both directs movements and creates a sensory world.

In some vertebrates, such as frogs, the entire brain is largely equivalent to the mammalian or avian brainstem. And frogs get along quite well, demonstrating that the brainstem is a fairly sophisticated piece of machinery. If we had only a brainstem, we would still be able to construct a world, but it would be a far simpler sensorimotor world, more like the world a frog experiences.

Alphabetically, *afferent* comes before *efferent*: sensory signals must enter the brain before an outgoing signal triggers a motor response.

The brainstem, which is responsible for most unconscious behavior, can be divided into three regions: hindbrain, midbrain, and diencephalon, meaning *between brain* because it borders the brain's upper and lower parts. In fact, the between-brain status of the diencephalon can be seen in a neuroanatomical inconsistency: some anatomists place it in the brainstem and others place it in the forebrain. **Figure 2-15**A illustrates the location of these three brainstem regions under the cerebral hemispheres. Figure 2-15B compares the shape of the brainstem regions to the lower part of your arm when held upright. The hindbrain is long and thick like your forearm, the midbrain is short and compact like your wrist, and the diencephalon at the end is bulbous like a fist.

The hindbrain and midbrain are essentially extensions of the spinal cord; they developed first as vertebrate animals evolved a brain at the anterior end of the body. It makes sense, therefore, that these lower brainstem regions should retain a division between structures having sensory functions and those having motor functions, with sensory structures lying dorsal and motor ones ventral, or in upright humans, posterior and anterior.

Principle 7: Sensory and motor divisions permeate the nervous system.

Each brainstem region performs more than a single task. Each contains various groupings of nuclei that serve various purposes. All three regions, in fact, have both sensory and motor functions. However, the hindbrain is especially important in motor functions, the midbrain in sensory functions, and the diencephalon in integrative sensorimotor tasks. Here we consider the central functions of these three regions; later chapters contain more detailed information about them.

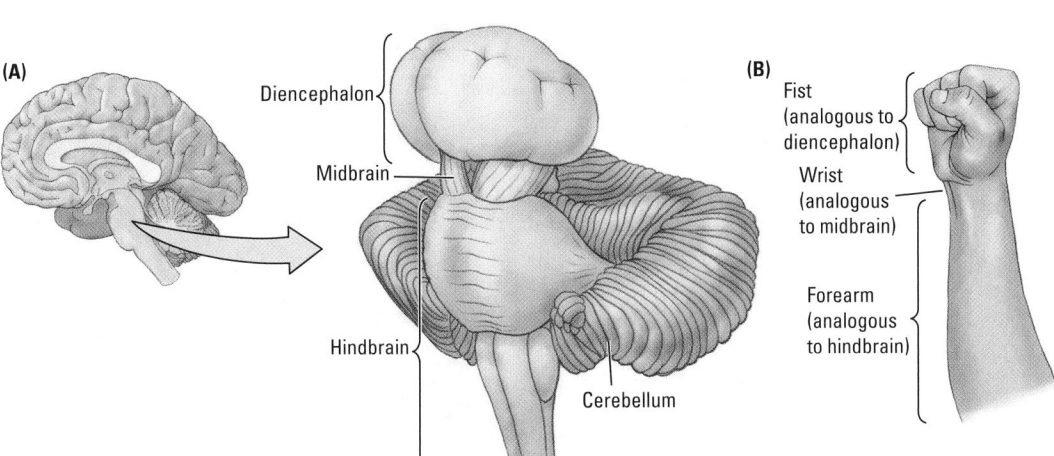

(A)
Diencephalon
Midbrain
Hindbrain
Cerebellum

(B)
Fist (analogous to diencephalon)
Wrist (analogous to midbrain)
Forearm (analogous to hindbrain)

FIGURE 2-15 Brainstem Structures **(A)** Medial view shows the relation of the brainstem to the cerebral hemispheres. **(B)** The shapes and relative sizes of the brainstem's three parts are analogous to your fist, wrist, and forearm.

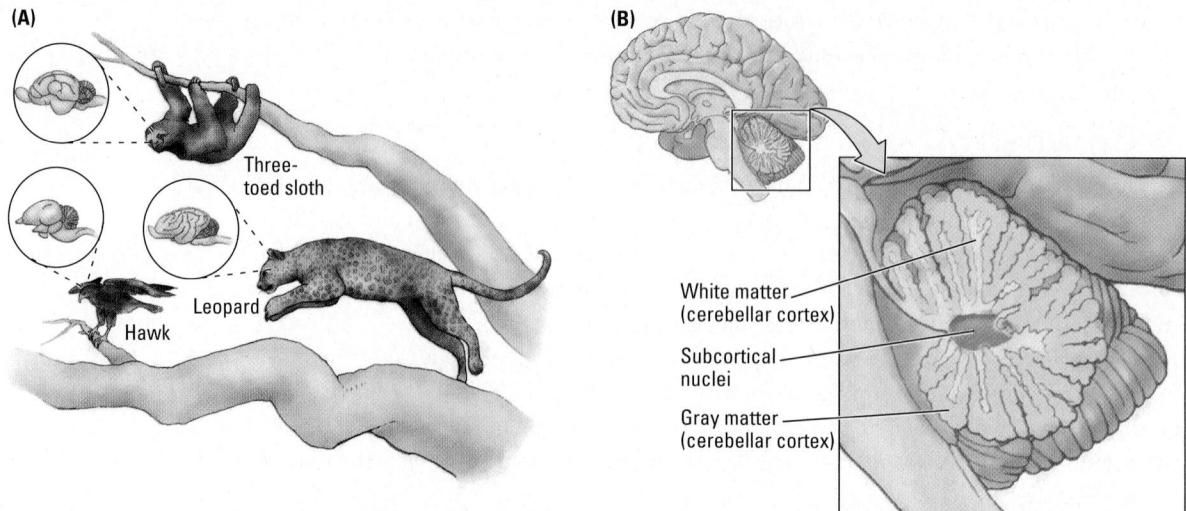

FIGURE 2-16 The Cerebellum and Movement **(A)** Their relatively large cerebellum enables finely coordinated movements such as flying and landing in birds and pouncing on prey in cats. Slow-moving animals such as the sloth have a smaller cerebellum relative to brain size. **(B)** Like the cerebrum, the human cerebellum has left and right hemispheres, an extensively folded cortex with gray and white matter, and subcortical nuclei.

hindbrain Evolutionarily the oldest part of the brain; contains the pons, medulla, reticular formation, and cerebellum, structures that coordinate and control most voluntary and involuntary movements.

reticular formation Midbrain area in which nuclei and fiber pathways are mixed, producing a netlike appearance; associated with sleep–wake behavior and behavioral arousal.

midbrain Central part of the brain; contains neural circuits for hearing and seeing as well as orienting movements.

tectum Roof (area above the ventricle) of the midbrain; its functions are sensory processing, particularly visual and auditory, and the production of orienting movements.

tegmentum Floor (area below the ventricle) of the midbrain; a collection of nuclei with movement-related, species-specific, and pain perception functions.

orienting movement Movement related to sensory inputs, such as turning the head to see the source of a sound.

diencephalon The between brain, which integrates sensory and motor information on its way to the cerebral cortex.

Hindbrain

The **hindbrain** controls motor functions ranging from breathing to balance to fine movements, such as those used in dancing. Its most distinctive structure, and one of the largest in the human brain, is the cerebellum. Its relative size increases with the physical speed and dexterity of a species, as shown in **Figure 2-16A**.

Animals that move relatively slowly (such as a sloth) have a relatively small cerebellum for their body size. Animals that can perform rapid acrobatic movements (such as a hawk or a cat) have a very large cerebellum relative to overall brain size. The human cerebellum, which resembles a cauliflower in the medial view in Figure 2-16B, likewise is important in controlling complex movements. But cerebellar size in humans is also related to cognitive capacity. Relative to other mammals, apes show an expansion of the cerebellum that correlates with increased capacity for planning and executing complex behavioral sequences, including tool use and language (see Barton, 2012).

As we look beyond the cerebellum at the rest of the hindbrain, shown in **Figure 2-17**, we find three subparts: the reticular formation, the pons, and the medulla. Extending the length of the entire brainstem at its core, the **reticular formation** is a netlike mixture of neurons (gray matter) and nerve fibers (white matter). This nerve net gives the structure the mottled appearance from which its name derives (from Latin *rete*, meaning *net*). The reticular formation's nuclei are localized into small patches along its length. Each has a special function in stimulating the forebrain, such as in waking from sleep.

FIGURE 2-17 Hindbrain The principal hindbrain structures integrate voluntary and involuntary body movements. The reticular formation is sometimes called the *reticular activating system.*

The *pons* and *medulla* contain substructures that control many vital body movements. Nuclei in the pons receive inputs from the cerebellum and actually form a bridge from it to the rest of the brain (in Latin, *pons* means *bridge*). At the rostral tip of the spinal cord, the medulla's nuclei regulate such vital functions as breathing and the cardiovascular system. For this reason, a blow to the back of the head can kill you: your breathing stops if the hindbrain control centers are injured.

Midbrain

In the **midbrain**, a sensory component, the **tectum** (roof), is dorsal (posterior in upright humans), whereas a motor structure, the **tegmentum** (floor), is ventral (anterior in humans; **Figure 2-18**A). The tectum receives a massive amount of sensory information from the eyes and ears. The optic nerve sends a large bundle of fibers to the *superior colliculus*, whereas the *inferior colliculus* receives much of its input from auditory pathways. The colliculi function not only to process sensory information but also to produce **orienting movements** related to sensory inputs, such as turning your head to see a sound's source.

This orienting behavior is not as simple as it may seem. To produce it, the auditory and visual systems must share a map of the external world so that the ears can tell the eyes where to look. If the auditory and visual maps differed, it would be impossible to use the two together. In fact, the colliculi also have a tactile map. After all, if you want to look at what's making your leg itch, your visual and tactile systems need a common representation of where that place is so you can scratch the itch by moving your arm and hand.

Lying ventral to the tectum, the tegmentum (shown in Figure 2-18B in cross section) is composed of many nuclei, largely with movement-related functions. Several tegmental nuclei control eye movements. The *red nucleus* controls limb movements, and the *substantia nigra* connects to the forebrain, a connection especially important in initiating movements. (Recall from Clinical Focus 2-2 that the symptoms of Parkinson disease are related to the destruction of the substantia nigra.) The *periaqueductal gray matter* (PAG), made up of cell bodies that surround the aqueduct joining the third and fourth ventricles, contains circuits controlling species-typical behaviors (e.g., female sexual behavior). These nuclei also play an important role in the modulation of pain by opioid drugs.

Diencephalon

The **diencephalon**, shown in sagittal section in the center of **Figure 2-19**, integrates sensory and motor information on its way to the cerebral cortex. Its two principal structures are the hypothalamus and the thalamus. The thalamus—one in each hemisphere—lies just to the left of the brainstem's tip, and the hypothalamus lies below the thalamus in each hemisphere.

FIGURE 2-18 Midbrain **(A)** Structures in the midbrain are critical for producing orienting movements, species-specific behaviors, and pain perception. **(B)** The tegmentum in cross section, revealing various nuclei. *Colliculus* comes from *collis*, Latin for *hill*. The colliculi resemble four little hills on the midbrain's posterior surface.

Principle 8: The brain divides sensory input for object recognition and motor control.

FIGURE 2-19 Diencephalon The diencephalon (center) is composed of the thalamus, shown at right, and the hypothalamus and other structures, shown at left. Thalamic regions connect to discrete cortical regions. Below the thalamus, at the base of the brain, the hypothalamus (*hypo-*, below) and pituitary lie above the roof of the mouth. The hypothalamus is composed of many nuclei, each with distinctly different functions.

hypothalamus Diencephalon structure that contains many nuclei associated with temperature regulation, eating, drinking, and sexual behavior.

thalamus Diencephalon structure through which information from all sensory systems is integrated and projected into the appropriate region of the neocortex.

forebrain Evolutionarily the newest part of the brain; coordinates advanced cognitive functions such as thinking, planning, and language; contains the limbic system, basal ganglia, and neocortex.

neocortex (cerebral cortex) Most recently evolved outer layer (*new bark*) of the forebrain, composed of about six layers of gray matter; constructs our reality.

We examine how thalamic sensory nuclei process incoming information in Sections 9-2, 10-2, 11-4, 12-2, and in Section 14-3, memory pathways.

FIGURE 2-20 Forebrain Structures The major internal and external forebrain structures integrate sensation, motivation and emotion, and memory to enable such advanced cognitive functions as thinking, planning, and using language.

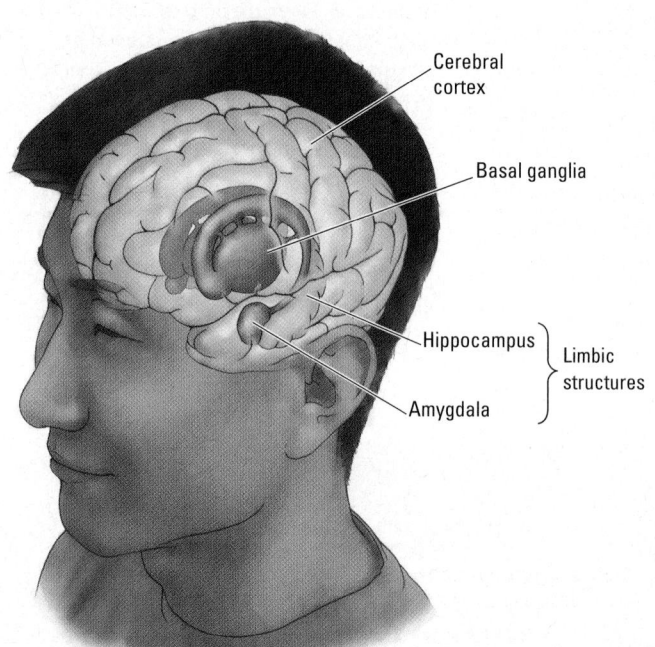

The **hypothalamus** in each hemisphere lies along the brain's midline; it is composed of about 22 small nuclei and the nerve fiber systems that pass through it. Its critical function is to control the body's production of hormones, accomplished via its interactions with the pituitary gland, shown at left in Figure 2-19. Although constituting only about 0.3 percent of the brain's weight, the hypothalamus takes part in nearly all aspects of behavior, including feeding, sleeping, temperature regulation, sexual and emotional behavior, hormone function, and movement. The hypothalamus is organized and functions more or less similarly across mammals. But sex differences have been found in the structures of some of its parts, owing probably to differences between males and females in activities such as sexual behavior and parenting.

The other principal structure of the diencephalon, the **thalamus**, is much larger than the hypothalamus, as are its 20-odd nuclei. Perhaps the most distinctive thalamic function, shown at the right in Figure 2-19, is its role as a gateway for channeling sensory information traveling to the cerebral cortex from all sensory systems. The thalamus integrates information from sensory inputs and relays it to the appropriate cortical area. The optic tract, for example, sends information through a large fiber bundle to a thalamic region called the *lateral geniculate nucleus* (LGN), shown at the right tip of the thalamus in Figure 2-19. In turn, the LGN processes some of this information, then sends it to the visual region of the cortex in each hemisphere.

The routes to the thalamus may be indirect. For example, the route for olfaction traverses several synapses before entering the *dorsomedial thalamic nucleus* on its way to the forebrain. Analogous sensory regions of the thalamus receive auditory and tactile information, which is subsequently relayed to the respective auditory and tactile cortical regions in each hemisphere. Some thalamic regions have motor functions or, like its dorsomedial nucleus, which connects to most of the frontal lobe, perform integrative tasks.

Forebrain

The largest and most recently evolved region of the mammalian brain is the **forebrain**. Its major internal and external structures are shown in **Figure 2-20**. Each of its three principal structures has multiple functions. To summarize briefly, the cerebral cortex regulates a host of mental activities ranging from perception to planning; the *basal ganglia* control voluntary movement; and the *limbic system* regulates emotions and behaviors that produce and require memory.

Extending our analogy between the brainstem and your forearm, imagine that the fist—the diencephalon—is thrust inside a watermelon—the forebrain, with the cortex as the rind and the subcortical limbic system and basal ganglia as the fruit inside. Just as watermelons come in sizes, so do brains, which in a sense is what evolution has done: the forebrain varies considerably in size across species.

Cerebral Cortex

The forebrain contains two types of cortex, three- or four-layered and six-layered. The six-layered **neocortex** (*new bark*) is the tissue visible when we view the brain from the outside, as in Figure 2-5. The more recently evolved neocortex is unique to mammals; its primary function is to construct a perceptual world and respond to that world. The older, more primitive three- or four-layered cortex, sometimes called *allocortex*, lies adjacent to the neocortex. Allocortex is found in the brains of other chordates in addition to mammals, especially in birds and reptiles.

The allocortex plays a role in controlling motivational and emotional states as well as in certain forms of memory. Although neocortex and allocortex have anatomical and functional differences, those distinctions are not critical for most discussions in this book. Therefore, we usually refer to both types of tissue simply as *cortex*.

Measured by volume, the cortex makes up most of the forebrain, constituting 80 percent of the human brain overall. It is the brain region that has expanded the most in the course of mammalian evolution. The human neocortex has a surface area as large as 2500 square centimeters but a thickness of only 1.5 to 3.0 millimeters, an area equivalent to about four pages of this book. By contrast, a chimpanzee has a cortical area equivalent to about one page.

The pattern of sulci and gyri formed by the folding of the cortex varies across species. Some, such as rats, have no sulci or gyri, whereas in carnivores, such as cats, the gyri form a longitudinal pattern. In primates, the sulci and gyri form a more diffuse pattern.

Cortical Lobes

To review, the human cortex consists of the nearly symmetrical left and right hemispheres, which are separated by the longitudinal fissure, shown at left in **Figure 2-21**. As shown at right, each hemisphere is subdivided into four lobes corresponding to the skull bones overlying them: frontal, temporal, parietal, and occipital. Unfortunately, bone location and brain function are unrelated. As a result, the cortical lobes are rather arbitrarily defined anatomical regions that include many functional zones.

Nevertheless, we can attach some gross functions to each lobe. The three posterior lobes have sensory functions: the occipital lobe is visual; the parietal lobe is tactile; and the temporal lobe is visual, auditory, and gustatory. In contrast, the frontal lobe is motor and is sometimes called the brain's executive because it integrates sensory and motor functions and formulates plans of action. We can also predict some effects of injuries to each lobe:

- People with an injured occipital lobe have deficits in processing visual information. Although they may perceive light versus dark, they may be unable to identify either the shape or the color of objects.

- Injuries to the parietal lobe make it difficult to identify or locate stimulation on the skin. Deficits in moving the arms and hands to points in space may occur.

- Temporal lobe injuries result in difficulty recognizing sounds, although unlike people with occipital injuries, those with temporal injury can still recognize that they are hearing something. Temporal lobe injuries can also produce difficulties in processing complex visual information, such as faces.

- Individuals with frontal lobe injuries may have difficulties organizing and evaluating their ongoing behavior as well as planning for the future.

Fissures and sulci often establish the boundaries of cortical lobes (Figure 2-21, right). For instance, in humans, the central sulcus and lateral fissure form the boundaries of each frontal lobe as well as the boundaries of each parietal lobe lying posterior to the central sulcus. The lateral fissure demarcates each temporal lobe, forming its dorsal boundary. The occipital lobes are not so clearly separated from the parietal and temporal lobes because no large fissure marks their boundaries.

Monkey   Chimpanzee   Human

The brains of a monkey, chimpanzee, and human, shown here to scale, differ dramatically in size and in surface appearance. With an encephalization quotient of 2.0, the monkey's brain is just over one-quarter the size of a human's (EQ 7.0). The chimp's brain, EQ 2.5, is a bit more than one-third as large (see Figure 1-15).

Principle 9: Brain functions are localized and distributed.

Anatomical features presented in Section 9-2 define occipital lobe boundaries.

Dorsal view of brain

Right hemisphere

Left hemisphere

Longitudinal fissure

Lateral view of brain

Frontal lobe (motor and executive functions)

Central sulcus

Parietal lobe (tactile functions)

Lateral fissure

Temporal lobe (visual, auditory, and gustatory functions)

Occipital lobe (visual functions)

FIGURE 2-21 Cortical Boundaries

cytoarchitectonic map Map of the neocortex based on the organization, structure, and distribution of the cells.

basal ganglia Subcortical forebrain nuclei that coordinate voluntary movements of the limbs and body; connected to the thalamus and to the midbrain.

Parkinson disease Disorder of the motor system correlated with a loss of dopamine from the substantia nigra and characterized by tremors, muscular rigidity, and a reduction in voluntary movement.

Tourette syndrome Disorder of the basal ganglia characterized by tics, involuntary vocalizations (including curse words and animal sounds), and odd, involuntary movements of the body, especially of the face and head.

limbic system Disparate forebrain structures lying between the neocortex and the brainstem that form a functional system controlling affective and motivated behaviors and certain forms of memory; includes cingulate cortex, amygdala, and hippocampus, among other structures.

FIGURE 2-22 Neocortical Layering Layer IV is relatively thick in the sensory cortex and relatively thin in the motor cortex. Afferents from the thalamus connect to layer IV and to layers II and III. Efferents in layers V and VI connect to other cortical areas and motor structures. Motor layers V and VI are thicker and denser than sensory layers V and VI.

Cortical Layers

In the neocortex, six layers of gray matter sit atop a layer of white matter. The allocortex, by contrast, has three or four layers of gray matter. The six layers of the neocortex have distinct characteristics:

- Different layers have different types of cells.
- The cell density varies from layer to layer, ranging from virtually no cells in layer I (the top layer) to very dense cell packing in layer IV of the neocortex (**Figure 2-22**).
- Other differences in appearance are both regional and functional.

These visible differences led neuroanatomists to map the cortex a century ago. Korbinian Brodmann developed the map in **Figure 2-23** around 1905. Because these maps are based on cell characteristics, the subject of cytology, they are called **cytoarchitectonic maps**. For example, viewed through a microscope, sensory cortex in the parietal lobe, shown in red in Figure 2-22, has a distinct layer IV. Motor cortex in the frontal lobe, shown in blue in Figure 2-22, has a distinctive layer V. Layer IV is afferent; layer V is efferent. It makes sense that a sensory region has a large input layer, whereas a motor region has a large output layer.

Staining cortical tissue can reveal chemical differences between cells and layers. Some regions are rich in one chemical, others rich in another. These differences presumably relate to functional specialization of cortical areas.

The one significant difference between the organization of the cortex and the organization of other brain parts is its range of connections. Unlike most structures, which connect only to certain brain regions, the cortex is connected to virtually all other parts of the brain. The cortex, in other words, is the ultimate meddler. It takes part in everything. This fact not only makes it difficult to identify specific cortical functions but also complicates our study of the rest of the brain, because we must always consider the cortex's role in other brain regions.

Consider your perception of clouds. You have no doubt gazed up at clouds on a summer day and imagined sailing ships, elephants, faces, and countless other objects. Although a cloud does not really look like an elephant, you can concoct an image of one if you impose your frontal cortex—that is, your imagination—on the sensory inputs. This kind of cortical activity is *top-down processing* because the top level of the nervous system, the cortex, is influencing how information is processed in lower regions of the hierarchy—in this case, the midbrain and hindbrain.

The cortex influences many behaviors besides object perception. It influences our cravings for foods, our lust for things (or people), and how we interpret the meaning of abstract concepts, words, and images. The cortex ultimately creates our reality, and one reason it serves this function is that it is so well-connected.

FIGURE 2-23 Early Brain Map In his cytoarchitectonic map of the cortex, Brodmann (1909) defined areas by the organization and characteristics of the cells he examined. The regions shown in color are associated with the simplest sensory perceptions of touch (red), vision (purple), and hearing (orange). As we shall see, the cortical areas that process sensory information are far more extensive than Brodmann's basic areas.

FIGURE 2-24 Basal Ganglia A coronal section through the cerebral hemispheres reveals a frontal view of the basal ganglia relative to surrounding forebrain structures. Two associated structures likewise instrumental in controlling and coordinating movement, the substantia nigra and subthalamic nucleus, also are shown.

Basal Ganglia

A collection of nuclei that lie in the forebrain just below the white matter of the cortex, the **basal ganglia** consist of three principal structures: the *caudate nucleus*, the *putamen*, and the *globus pallidus*, all shown in **Figure 2-24**. Together with the thalamus and two closely associated nuclei, the substantia nigra and subthalamic nucleus, the basal ganglia form a system that functions primarily to control voluntary movement.

We can observe the functions of the basal ganglia by analyzing the behavior resulting from the many diseases that interfere with their healthy functioning. **Parkinson disease**, a motor system disorder characterized by severe tremors, muscular rigidity, and a reduction in voluntary movement, is among the most common movement disorders among the elderly. People with Parkinsonism take short, shuffling steps; display bent posture; and may need a walker to get around. Many have almost continuous hand tremors and sometimes head tremors as well. Another disorder of the basal ganglia is **Tourette syndrome**, characterized by various motor tics; involuntary vocalizations (including curse words and animal sounds); and odd, involuntary body movements, especially of the face and head.

Neither Parkinsonism nor Tourette syndrome is a disorder of *producing* movements, as in paralysis. Rather, they are disorders of *controlling* movements. The basal ganglia, therefore, must play a critical role in controlling and coordinating movement patterns rather than in activating the muscles to move.

Details on Parkinson disease appear in Focus boxes 5-2, 5-3, and 5-4, Sections 11-3 and 16-3. Focus 11-4 details Tourette syndrome.

Limbic System

In the 1930s, psychiatry was dominated by the theories of Sigmund Freud, who emphasized the roles of sexuality and emotion in human behavior. At the time, the brain regions controlling these behaviors had not been identified, and coincidentally, a group of brain structures collectively called the limbic lobe had no known function. It was a simple step to thinking that perhaps the limbic structures played a central role in sexuality and emotion.

One sign that this hypothesis might be correct came from James Papez (1937), who discovered that people with rabies have infection in the limbic structures, and one symptom of rabies is heightened emotionality. We now know that such a simple view is inaccurate. In fact, the **limbic system** is not a unitary system at all. And although some limbic structures have roles in emotional and sexual behaviors, limbic structures serve other functions too, including contributing to memory and motivation.

Figure 2-25 diagrams the principal limbic structures Papez proposed. The *hippocampus*, *cingulate cortex* (a type of allocortex), and associated structures participate in certain memory functions as well as in controlling navigation in space. Many limbic structures, in particular the *amygdala*, are also believed to contribute to the

FIGURE 2-25 Limbic System This medial view of the right hemisphere illustrates the principal structures proposed by Papez to constitute the limbic system. This structure participates in emotional and sexual behaviors, motivation, and memory. For a contemporary view of limbic anatomy, see Figure 12-18.

All sorts of behaviors can prove addictive—eating, shopping, sex, video gaming, gambling, even Twitter! How else to explain these Canadian coeds tweeting all bundled up when they could be defrosting on the beach in the Florida sun? More on the limbic system and addiction in Section 6-3; motivation and emotion, Sections 12-3 and 12-4; memory, Section 14-3; and brain disorders, Focus 16-1 and Section 16-4.

rewarding properties of psychoactive drugs and other potentially addictive substances and behaviors. Repeated exposure to drugs such as amphetamine or nicotine produces both chemical and structural changes in the cingulate cortex and hippocampus, among other structures.

Removal of the amygdala produces truly startling changes in emotional behavior. A cat with the amygdala removed will wander through a colony of monkeys, completely undisturbed by their hooting and threats. No self-respecting cat would normally be caught anywhere near such bedlam.

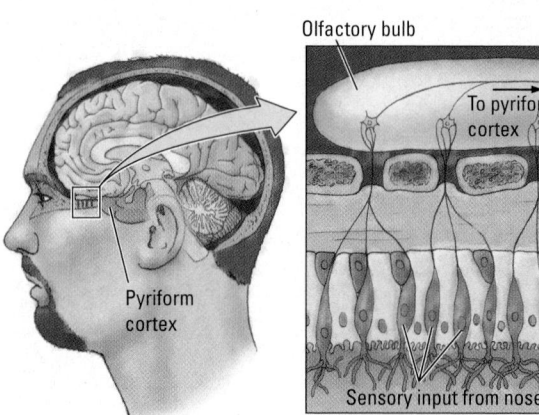

FIGURE 2-26 Sense of Smell Our small olfactory bulb lies at the base of the forebrain, connects to receptor cells that lie in the nasal cavity, and sends most of this input to the pyriform cortex en route to the amygdala and thalamus.

Section 12-2 considers the chemical senses smell and taste in the context of emotional and motivated behavior.

Olfactory System

At the very front of the brain lie the olfactory bulbs, the organs responsible for our sense of smell. The olfactory system is unique among human senses, as **Figure 2-26** shows, because it is almost entirely a forebrain structure. The other sensory systems project most of their inputs from the sensory receptors to the midbrain and thalamus. Olfactory input takes a less direct route: the olfactory bulb sends most of its inputs to a specialized region, the *pyriform cortex*, on the brain's ventral surface. From there, sensory input progresses to the amygdala and the dorsomedial thalamus (see Figure 2-19, right), which routes it to the frontal cortex.

Smell is one of the first senses to have evolved in animals, yet curiously, the olfactory system lies at the front of the human brain and is considered part of the forebrain (see the ventral view in Figure 2-6). This is partly an accident of evolution. The olfactory bulbs lie near the olfactory receptors in the nasal cavity. Although they send their inputs to the pyriform cortex in mammals, their input to the brainstem is more direct in simpler brains.

Compared with the olfactory bulbs of animals such as rats, cats, and dogs, which depend more heavily on smell than we do, the human olfactory bulb is relatively small. Nonetheless, it is very sensitive, allowing us to distinguish a surprisingly large number of odors. Smell plays important roles in various aspects of our feeding and sexual behavior.

(2-3) REVIEW

The Central Nervous System: Mediating Behavior

Before you continue, check your understanding.

1. The three functionally distinct sections of the CNS—spinal cord, brainstem, and forebrain—represent the evolution of multiple _____.

2. The _____ can perceive sensations from the skin and muscles and produce movements independent of the brain.

3. The brainstem includes three functional regions. The _____ is an extension of the spinal cord; the _____ is the first brain region to receive sensory inputs; and the _____ integrates sensory and motor information on its way to the cerebral cortex.

4. The _____ coordinates fine motor movements and various cognitive functions.

5. The forebrain's subcortical regions include the _____, which control voluntary movement, and the _____, which controls mood, motivation, and some forms of memory.

6. The two types of cerebral cortex are the older _____ and the _____, which features layers that vary in density to perform _____, _____, and _____ functions.

7. Briefly describe the functions performed by the forebrain.

Answers appear at the back of the book.

For additional study tools, visit **LaunchPad**:
www.macmillanhighered.com/launchpad/kolb5e

2-4 Somatic Nervous System: Transmitting Information

The SNS is monitored and controlled by the CNS—the cranial nerves by the brain and the spinal nerves by the spinal cord segments.

Cranial Nerves

The linkages provided by the **cranial nerves** between the brain and various parts of the head and neck as well as various internal organs are illustrated and tabulated in **Figure 2-27**. Cranial nerves can have afferent functions, such as sensory inputs to the brain from the eyes, ears, mouth, and nose, or they can have efferent functions, such as motor control of the facial muscles, tongue, and eyes. Some cranial nerves have both sensory and motor functions, such as modulation of both sensation and movement in the face.

The 12 pairs of cranial nerves are known both by their numbers and by their names, as listed in Figure 2-27. One set of 12 controls the left side of the head, whereas the other set controls the right side. This arrangement makes sense for innervating duplicated parts of the head (such as the eyes), but why separate nerves should control the right and left sides of a singular structure (such as the tongue) is not so clear. Yet that is how the cranial nerves work. If you have ever received lidocaine (often called Novocaine) for dental work, you know that usually just one side of your tongue becomes numb because the dentist injects the drug into only one side of your mouth. The rest of the skin and muscles on each side of the head are similarly controlled by cranial nerves located on the same side.

We consider many cranial nerves in detail in later chapters' discussions on topics such as vision, hearing, olfaction, taste, and stress responses. For now, you simply need to know that cranial nerves form part of the SNS, providing inputs to the brain from the head's sensory organs and muscles and controlling head and facial movements. Some cranial nerves also contribute to maintaining autonomic functions by connecting the brain and internal organs (the vagus, cranial nerve 10) and by influencing other autonomic responses, such as salivation.

Spinal Nerves

The spinal cord lies inside the bony spinal column, which is made up of a series of small bones called **vertebrae** (sing. *vertebra*), categorized into five anatomical regions from

cranial nerve One of a set of 12 nerve pairs that control sensory and motor functions of the head, neck, and internal organs.

vertebrae (sing. vertebra) The bones that form the spinal column.

Cranial nerve	Name	Function
1	Olfactory	Smell
2	Optic	Vision
3	Oculomotor	Eye movement
4	Trochlear	Eye movement
5	Trigeminal	Masticatory movements and facial sensation
6	Abducens	Eye movement
7	Facial	Facial movement and sensation
8	Auditory vestibular	Hearing and balance
9	Glossopharyngeal	Tongue and pharynx movement and sensation
10	Vagus	Heart, blood vessels, viscera, movement of larynx and pharynx
11	Spinal accessory	Neck movement
12	Hypoglossal	Tongue movement

FIGURE 2-27 Cranial Nerves Each of the 12 pairs of cranial nerves has a different function. A common mnemonic device for learning the order of the cranial nerves is "On old Olympus's towering top, a Finn and German view some hops." The first letter of each word is, in order, the first letter of the name of each nerve.

Sections 11-1 and 11-4 review the spinal cord's contributions to movement and to somatosensation.

dermatome Body segment corresponding to a segment of the spinal cord.

law of Bell and Magendie The principle that sensory fibers are dorsal and motor fibers are ventral.

top to bottom: cervical, thoracic, lumbar, sacral, and coccygeal, as diagrammed in **Figure 2-28A**. You can think of each vertebra in these five groups as a short segment of the spinal column. The corresponding spinal cord segment in each vertebral region functions as that segment's minibrain.

This arrangement may seem a bit odd, but it has a long evolutionary history. Think of a simpler animal, such as a snake, that evolved long before humans did. A snake's body is a segmented tube. In that tube is another tube, the spinal cord, which also is segmented. Each of the snake's nervous system segments receives nerve fibers from sensory receptors in the part of the body adjacent to it, and that nervous system segment sends fibers back to the muscles in that body part. Each segment, therefore, works independently.

A complication arises in animals such as humans, whose limbs may originate at one spinal segment level but extend past other segments of the spinal column. Your shoulders, for example, may begin at C5 (cervical segment 5), but your arms hang down well past the sacral segments. So unlike the snake, which has spinal cord segments that connect to body segments fairly directly adjacent to them, human body's segments fall schematically into more of a patchwork pattern, as shown in Figure 2-28B. This arrangement makes sense if the arms are extended as they are when we walk on all fours.

Regardless of their complex pattern, however, our body segments still correspond to the spinal cord segments. Each of these body segments is called a **dermatome** (meaning *skin cut*). A dermatome has both a sensory nerve to send information from the skin, joints, and muscles to the spinal cord and a motor nerve to control the muscle movements in that particular body segment.

These sensory and motor nerves, known as *spinal* (or *peripheral*) *nerves*, are functionally equivalent to the cranial nerves of the head. Whereas the cranial nerves receive information from sensory receptors in the eyes, ears, facial skin, and so forth, the spinal nerves receive information from sensory receptors in the rest of the body—that is, in the PNS. Similarly, whereas the cranial nerves move the muscles of the eyes, tongue, and face, the peripheral nerves move the muscles of the limbs and trunk.

Somatic Nervous System Connections

Like the CNS, the SNS is bilateral (two-sided). Just as the cranial nerves control functions on the side of the head where they are found, the spinal nerves on the left side of the spinal cord control the left side of the body, and those on the right side of the spinal cord control the body's right side.

Figure 2-29A on page 62 shows the spinal column in cross section. Look first at the nerve fibers entering its posterior side. These posterior fibers (dorsal in four-legged animals) are afferent: they carry in information from the body's sensory receptors. The fibers gather as they enter a spinal cord segment, and this collection of fibers is called a *posterior root* in humans (dorsal root in four-legged animals).

Fibers leaving the spinal cord's anterior side are efferent, carrying information out from the spinal cord to the muscles. They, too, bundle together as they exit the spinal cord and so form an *anterior root* (ventral root in four-legged animals). The outer part of the spinal cord, pictured in Figure 2-29B, consists of white matter, or CNS nerve tracts. These tracts are arranged so that with some exceptions posterior tracts are sensory and anterior tracts are motor. The inner part of the cord, which has a butterfly shape, is gray matter composed largely of cell bodies.

The observation that the dorsal spinal cord is sensory and the ventral side is motor in four-legged animals is one of the nervous system's very few established laws, the **law of Bell and Magendie**. Combined with an understanding of the spinal cord's segmental organization, this law enables neurologists to make accurate inferences about the location of spinal cord damage or disease on the basis of changes in sensation or movement. For instance, if a person has numbness in the fingers of the left hand but can still move the hand fairly normally, one or more of the posterior (dorsal) nerves in spinal cord segments C7 and C8 must be damaged. In contrast, if sensation in the hand is normal but the person cannot move the fingers, the anterior (ventral) roots of the same segments must be damaged. Clinical Focus 2-4, Magendie, Bell, and Bell Palsy, on page 62, further explores diagnosing spinal cord injury or disease.

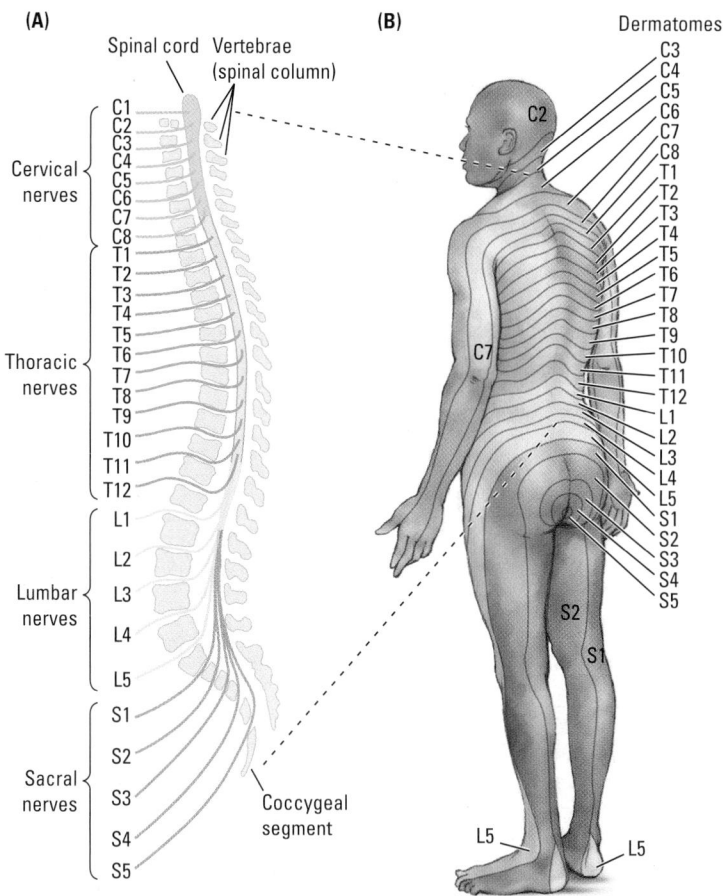

FIGURE 2-28 Spinal Segments and Dermatomes **(A)** Medial view showing the five spinal cord segments: cervical (C), thoracic (T), lumbar (L), sacral (S), and coccygeal. **(B)** Each segment corresponds to a region of body surface (a dermatome) identified by the segment number (e.g., C5 at the base of the neck and L2 in the lower back).

Sections 11-1 and 11-4 explore spinal cord injuries and treatments, and Section 12-3, the link between spinal injury and loss of emotion.

Integrating Spinal Functions

So far we have emphasized the spinal cord's segmental organization, but the spinal cord must also somehow coordinate inputs and outputs across different segments. For example, many body movements require coordinating muscles controlled by different segments, just as many sensory experiences require coordinating sensory inputs to different parts of the spinal cord. How is this coordination accomplished? The answer is that the spinal cord segments are interconnected in such a way that adjacent segments can operate together to direct rather complex coordinated movements.

Integrating spinal cord activities does not require the brain's participation, which is why the headless chicken can run around. Still, a close working relation must exist between the brain and the spinal cord. Otherwise, how could we consciously plan and execute our voluntary actions?

(A)

1 Fibers entering the posterior root bring sensory information from sensory receptors.

Posterior root (sensory)

Sensory neuron

Motor neuron

Anterior root (motor)

3 Collateral branches of sensory neurons may cross to the other side and influence motor neurons there.

Gray matter

White matter

2 Fibers leaving the anterior root carry motor information to the muscles.

4 White-matter fiber tracts carry information to and from the brain.

(B)

VideoSurgery/Getty Images

FIGURE 2-29 Spinal Nerve Connections **(A)** A cross section of the human spinal cord, viewed from the front. The butterfly-shaped inner regions consist of neural cell bodies (gray matter), and the outer regions consist of nerve tracts (white matter) traveling to and from the brain. **(B)** A posterior view shows the intact human spinal cord exposed.

Somehow information must be relayed back and forth, and examples of this information sharing are numerous. For instance, tactile information from sensory nerves in the skin travels not just to the spinal cord but also to the cerebral cortex through the thalamus. Similarly, the cerebral cortex and other brain structures can control movements through their connections to the spinal cord's anterior roots. So even though the brain and spinal cord can function independently, the two are intimately connected in their CNS functions.

CLINICAL F◎CUS 2.4

Magendie, Bell, and Bell Palsy

François Magendie, a volatile and committed French experimental physiologist, reported in a three-page paper in 1822 that he had succeeded in cutting the dorsal and ventral roots of puppies, animals in which the roots are sufficiently segregated to allow such surgery. Magendie found that cutting the dorsal roots caused loss of sensation, whereas cutting the ventral roots caused loss of movement.

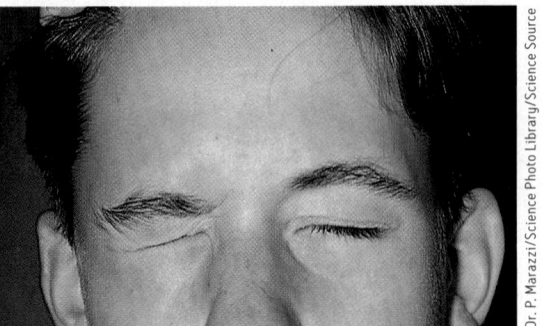

Dr. P. Marazzi/Science Photo Library/Science Source

A young man with Bell palsy, a paralysis of the facial nerve (cranial nerve 7) that causes weakness over one side of the face. He was photographed during an involuntary tic (a nervous reaction) that affects the right side of the face, causing his right eye to close tightly.

In 1811, a Scot named Charles Bell proposed functions for these nerve roots on the basis of anatomical information and the results of somewhat inconclusive experiments on rabbits. Although Bell's findings were not identical with those of Magendie, they were similar enough to ignite a controversy. Bell hotly disputed Magendie's claim to the discovery of dorsal and ventral root functions. As a result, the principle of sensory and motor segregation in the nervous system has been named after both researchers: the law of Bell and Magendie.

Magendie's conclusive experiment on puppies was considered extremely important because for the first time it enabled neurologists to localize nervous system damage from the symptoms that a patient displays. Bell went on to describe an example of such localized cranial motor nerve dysfunction, and it still bears his name—*Bell palsy*, a facial paralysis that develops when the motor part of the facial nerve on one side of the head becomes inflamed (see the accompanying photograph).

The onset of Bell palsy is typically sudden. Often the stricken person wakes up in the morning and is shocked to discover the face paralyzed on one side. He or she cannot open the mouth or completely close the eye on that side of the head. Most people fully recover from Bell palsy, although it may take several months. But in rare instances, such as that of Jean Chrétien, a former prime minister of Canada, partial paralysis of the mouth is permanent.

(2-4) **REVIEW**

Somatic Nervous System: Transmitting Information

Before you continue, check your understanding.

1. Two sets of SNS nerves, the _____ and the _____, receive sensory information or send motor signals to muscles or both.

2. Both sets of SNS nerves are symmetrically organized, and each set controls functions on the _____ side of the body.

3. The cranial nerves have both sensory and motor functions, receiving and sending information to the _____ and to the _____.

4. Define the law of Bell and Magendie and explain why it is important.

Answers appear at the back of the book.

For additional study tools, visit 🧠 **LaunchPad**:
www.macmillanhighered.com/launchpad/kolb5e

(2-5) Autonomic and Enteric Nervous Systems: Visceral Relations

Control of the viscera (internal organs), including the heart, gut, liver, and lungs, requires complex neural systems. Yet the ANS and ENS are hidden partners, functioning in the background as the CNS controls our perceptions and behaviors. If we had to focus consciously on visceral activities, we would do little else. The ANS and ENS interact with the CNS, but each has distinctive anatomy and functions.

ANS: Balancing Internal Functions

Without our conscious awareness, the ANS stays on the job to keep the heart beating, the liver releasing glucose, the pupils of the eyes adjusting to light, and so forth. Without the ANS, which regulates the internal organs and glands via connections through the SNS to the CNS, life would quickly cease. Although learning to exert some conscious control over some of these vegetative activities is possible, such conscious interference is normally unnecessary. An important reason is that the ANS must keep working during sleep, when conscious awareness is off duty. But gastrointestinal disorders are common, and stress is often a factor. Psychological therapies are often effective in treating such disorders.

It is tempting to think that the ANS's organization must be pretty simple because it functions outside our conscious awareness. Yet, like the SNS, we can think about the ANS as a collection of minibrains with a surprisingly complex organization. The two ANS divisions work in opposition. The **sympathetic division** arouses the body for action, for example, by stimulating the heart to beat faster and inhibiting digestion when we exert ourselves during exercise or times of stress—the familiar fight-or-flight response. The **parasympathetic division** calms the body down, for example, by slowing the heartbeat and stimulating digestion to allow us to rest and digest after exertion and during quiet times.

Like the SNS, the ANS interacts with the rest of the nervous system, and like the SNS, ANS connections are ipsilateral. Activation of the sympathetic division starts in the thoracic and lumbar spinal cord regions. But the spinal nerves do not directly control the target organs. Rather, the spinal cord is connected to autonomic control centers—collections of neural cells called *ganglia*. The ganglia control the internal organs, and each acts as a minibrain for specific organs.

The sympathetic ganglia are near the spinal cord on each side, forming chains that run parallel to the cord, as illustrated at left in **Figure 2-30** for one set of ganglia. The parasympathetic

sympathetic division Part of the autonomic nervous system; arouses the body for action, such as mediating the involuntary fight-or-flight response to alarm by increasing heart rate and blood pressure.

parasympathetic division Part of the autonomic nervous system; acts in opposition to the sympathetic division—for example, preparing the body to rest and digest by reversing the alarm response or stimulating digestion.

Section 5-3 explains CNS–ANS communication, Figure 6-22 diagrams the stress response, and Section 16-4 discusses how mood affects reactivity to stress.

Principle 10: The nervous system works by juxtaposing excitation (increased neural activity) and inhibition (decreased neural activity).

division also is connected to the spinal cord—specifically, to the sacral region—but the greater part of it derives from three cranial nerves: the vagus nerve, which calms most of the internal organs, and the facial and oculomotor nerves, which control salivation and pupil dilation, respectively (review Figure 2-27). In contrast with the sympathetic division, the parasympathetic division connects with ganglia that are near the target organs, as shown at right in Figure 2-30.

ENS: Controlling the Gut

The ENS is sometimes considered part of the ANS, but it functions largely independently. Digestion is complicated, and evolution has provided this dedicated nervous system to control it. Some scientists have even proposed that the CNS evolved from the gut of very simple organisms.

In fact, the ENS is sometimes called the second brain because, like the CNS, it contains a diversity of neuron types, the same chemical transmitters, a profusion of glial cells, and complex integrated neural circuits. Its estimated 200 million to 500 million neurons roughly equals the number in the spinal cord. The gut reacts to a range of hormones and other chemicals with exquisite neural responses. The ENS functions to control bowel motility, secretion, and blood flow to permit fluid and nutrient absorption and to support waste elimination (see Avetisyan et al., 2015). This is no simple task, given the number and balance of nutrients needed to support the body.

FIGURE 2-30 Autonomic Nervous System The two ANS pathways exert opposing effects. All fibers connect at "stops" formed by ganglia en route from the CNS to target ANS organs. *Left:* Arousing sympathetic fibers connect to a chain of ganglia near the spinal cord. *Right:* Calming parasympathetic fibers connect to individual ganglia near target organs.

ENS neurons are located in a sheet of tissue (*plexus*) lining the esophagus, stomach, small intestine, and colon. As shown in **Figure 2-31**, ENS neurons and glia form ganglia connected by nerve fibers found in two layers of gut tissue. The brain and ENS connect extensively through the ANS, especially via the vagus nerve. Although we are not conscious of our gut "thinking," the ENS sends information directly to the brain—information that affects our mental state—and the brain can modify gut function. Indeed, a growing body of evidence implicates the ENS in many behavioral disorders, and stress and anxiety commonly modify gut function, leading to such symptoms as nausea and diarrhea.

The ENS interacts with gut bacteria, known collectively as the *microbiome*. About 10^{14} microbiota populate the adult gut, outnumbering the host cells by a factor of 10 (Farmer et al., 2014). The microbiota influence nutrient absorption and are a source of neurochemicals that regulate an array of physiological and psychological processes. This relationship has inspired the development of a class of compounds known as *psychobiotics*, live microorganisms used to treat behavioral disorders. Thus, the microbiota can influence both the CNS and ENS, leading to changes in behavior.

Section 12-4 expands on how emotions and the ENS interact, Section 12-5 on the ENS and eating.

FIGURE 2-31 Enteric Nervous System The ENS is formed by a network of neurons embedded in the lining of the gastrointestinal tract. Congregations of neurons form ganglia that send projections to the ANS and CNS, in part through the vagus nerve (cranial nerve 10), to control gut function.

(2-5) **REVIEW**

Autonomic and Enteric Nervous Systems: Visceral Relations

Before you continue, check your understanding.

1. The ANS interacts with the CNS and SNS via sets of autonomic control centers called _____, which act as minibrains to control the internal organs.

2. The _____ division of the ANS arouses the body for action, and the _____ division calms the organs. The two divisions work _____ to allow for quick defensive responses (fight or flight) or to induce a calming (rest and digest) state.

3. Why is the ANS essential to life?

4. The ENS is often called a second brain because of the _____ it contains.

5. The ENS interacts with bacteria that form the _____, which absorbs _____ and produces _____ that can regulate CNS and ENS activity.

6. What are psychobiotics?

Answers appear at the back of the book.

For additional study tools, visit 🌎 **LaunchPad**:
www.macmillanhighered.com/launchpad/kolb5e

(2-6) Ten Principles of Nervous System Function

The balance of the whole nervous system, of the functioning brain, and of individual cells works in concert to produce behavior. Knowing the parts of the nervous system and some general notions about what they do is only the beginning. Learning how the parts work together allows us to proceed to a closer look, in the chapters that follow, at how the brain produces behavior.

Thus far, we have identified 10 principles related to the nervous system's functioning. Here we elaborate each one. As you progress through the book, review these ideas regularly with an eye toward understanding the concept rather than simply memorizing the principle. Soon you will find yourself applying the principles of function as you encounter new information about the brain and behavior.

Principle 1: The Nervous System Produces Movement in a Perceptual World the Brain Constructs

The nervous system's fundamental function is to produce behavior, or movement. Movements are not made in a vacuum but are related to objects, places, memories, and myriad other forces and factors. Your mental representation of the world depends on the information sent to your brain. People who are color-blind perceive the world very differently from those who perceive color. The perceptual world of people who have perfect pitch is different from that of those who do not.

Although we tend to think that the world we perceive is what is actually there, individual realities, both between and within species, clearly are just rough approximations of what is actually present. The brain of each animal species produces a reality that is adaptive for that species to survive. The behavior that the brain produces, in other words, is directly related to the world that the brain has constructed.

Principle 2: Neuroplasticity Is the Hallmark of Nervous System Functioning

Experience alters the brain's organization, and this neuroplasticity is requisite to learning and memory as well as to survival. In fact, the nervous system stores information *only* if neural connections change. Forgetting is presumably due to a loss of the connections that represented the memory.

As Experiment 2-1 on page 49 demonstrates, neuroplasticity is a characteristic not just of the mammalian brain; it is found in the nervous system of all animals, even the simplest worms. Nonetheless, larger brains have more capacity for change, and thus their neural organization is likely to show more plasticity.

Plasticity can be beneficial in recovering from disorders, such as brain injuries and diseases, as well as in coping with aging. Plasticity also allows the brain to compensate for developmental abnormalities, an extreme example being agenesis of brain structures, as discussed in Research Focus 2-1. Although beneficial in such circumstances, neuroplasticity has drawbacks. Brain analyses of animals given addicting doses of drugs such as cocaine or morphine reveal broad changes in neural connectivity suspected of underlying some maladaptive behaviors related to addiction. Among many other examples of pathological neuroplasticity are those associated with pain, epilepsy, and dementia.

Detail on plasticity and drug addiction in Section 14-4, on feeling and treating pain in Section 11-4, on epilepsy in Focus 4-1. Section 16-3 details diagnosis and treatment of epilepsy and dementias.

Principle 3: Many Brain Circuits Are Crossed

Most brain inputs and outputs are crossed, that is, serve the opposite side of the body. Each hemisphere receives sensory stimulation from the opposite (contralateral) side of the body and controls muscles on the contralateral side. Crossed organization explains why people who have a stroke or other damage to the left cerebral hemisphere may have difficulty in sensing stimulation to the right side of the body or in moving body parts on the right side. The opposite is true of people whose stroke occurs in the right cerebral hemisphere.

A crossed nervous system must somehow join both sides of the perceptual world together. To do so, innumerable neural connections link the brain's left and right sides. The most prominent connecting cable is the corpus callosum. Its roughly 200 million nerve fibers join the left and right cerebral hemispheres, allowing them to interact.

Four important exceptions to the crossed-circuit principle are olfactory sensation and the somatic, autonomic, and enteric PNS connections. Olfactory information does not cross but rather projects directly into the same (ipsilateral) side of the brain. The cranial and spinal nerves that constitute the SNS are connected ipsilaterally, as are the sympathetic and parasympathetic ANS division connections. Likewise, ipsilateral ENS connections link to the ANS on both sides.

Figure 9-10 illustrates how the human visual system represents the world seen through two eyes as a single perception: both eyes connect with both hemispheres.

Principle 4: The CNS Functions on Multiple Levels

In simple animals such as worms the spinal cord essentially constitutes the nervous system. More complex animals, such as fishes, have a brainstem as well, and yet more complex animals have also evolved a forebrain. Each new addition to the CNS has added a new level of behavioral complexity without discarding previous levels of control. As animals evolved legs, for example, brain structures evolved to move the legs. Later, the development of independent digit movements required even more brainpower. Thus, new brain areas add new levels of nervous system control. The new levels are not autonomous but rather must be integrated into existing neural systems as refinements and elaborations of the control earlier levels provided.

Multiple levels of function can be seen not only in the addition of forebrain areas to refine brainstem control but also in the forebrain itself. As mammals evolved, they developed an increased capacity to represent the world in the cortex, an ability related to the addition of more maps. The new maps must be related to the older ones, however, and again are simply an elaboration of the perceived sensory world that existed before.

Principle 5: The Brain Is Symmetrical and Asymmetrical

The left and the right hemispheres look like mirror images, but they have some dissimilar features. Cortical asymmetry is essential for integrative tasks, language and body control among them.

Consider speaking. If a language zone existed in both hemispheres, each connected to one side of the mouth, we would actually be able to talk out of both sides of our mouth at once. That would make talking awkward, to say the least. One solution is to locate language control of the mouth on one side of the brain. Organizing the brain in this way allows us to speak with a single voice.

A similar problem arises in controlling body movements in space. We would not want the left and the right hemispheres each trying to take us to a different place. Again, if a single brain area controls this sort of spatial processing, problem solved.

Language control is typically situated on the left side, and spatial functions are typically on the right. The brains of many species have such symmetrical and asymmetrical features. In the bird brain, the control of singing is in one hemisphere, usually on the left side, as is human language. It is likely that birds and humans evolved the same solution independently—namely, to assign the control to only one side of the brain.

Principle 6: Brain Systems Are Organized Hierarchically and in Parallel

When we consider the multiple levels of CNS function, it becomes apparent that these levels must be extensively interconnected to integrate their processing and produce unified perceptions or movements. The nature of neural connectivity leads to the principle that the brain has both serial (or hierarchical) and parallel circuitry.

A hierarchical circuit hooks up a linear series of all regions concerned with a particular function. Consider vision. In a serial system, the information from the eyes goes to regions that detect the simplest properties, such as color or brightness. This information is passed along to another region that determines shape, then to another that measures movement, and so on until at the most complex level the information is understood to be, say, your grandmother. Information therefore flows sequentially from simpler to more complex regions in the hierarchy, as illustrated in **Figure 2-32A**.

However, functionally related brain structures are not always linked linearly. Although the brain has many serial connections, many expected connections are missing. In the visual system, not all cortical regions are connected to one another. The simplest explanation is that the unconnected regions must have widely differing functions.

Parallel circuits operate on a different principle, also illustrated by the visual system. Imagine looking at a car. As we look at a car door, one set of visual pathways processes information about its nature, such as color and shape, whereas another set of pathways processes information about movements such as those necessary to open the door.

These two visual systems are independent of each other, yet they must interact somehow. When you pull the car door open, you do not perceive two different representations—the door's size, shape, and color on the one hand and the opening movements on the other. When you open the door, you have the impression of unity in your conscious experience.

Figure 2-32B illustrates the information flow in such a distributed hierarchy. If you trace the flow from the primary area to levels 2, 3, and 4, you follow the parallel pathways. And while these multiple parallel pathways are also connected to one another, those connections are more selective than connections in a purely serial circuit.

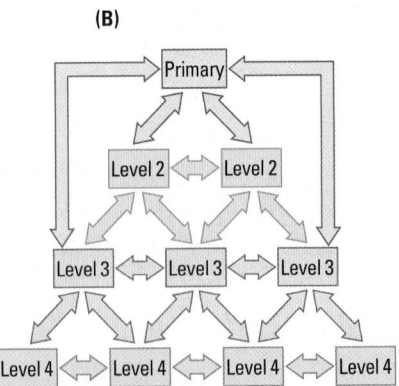

FIGURE 2-32 **Models of Neural Information Processing** **(A)** Simple hierarchical model of serial cortical processing. **(B)** In a distributed hierarchical processing model each of several processing streams has multiple levels. Areas at each level interconnect.

The brain's subsystems are organized into multiple parallel pathways, yet our conscious experiences are always unified. As we explore this conundrum throughout the book, keep in mind that your commonsense impressions of how the brain works may not always be correct.

Principle 7: Sensory and Motor Divisions Permeate the Nervous System

The segregation of SNS sensory and motor functions described by the Bell and Magendie law exists throughout the nervous system. Distinctions between motor and sensory functions become subtler in the forebrain.

Sensory and Motor Divisions in the SNS

Spinal nerves are either sensory or motor. Some cranial nerves are exclusively sensory; some are exclusively motor; and some have two parts, one sensory and one motor, much like spinal nerves serving the skin and muscles.

Review cranial nerve and spinal nerve connections in Figures 2-27 and 2-28.

Sensory and Motor Divisions in the CNS

The lower brainstem regions—hindbrain and midbrain—are essentially extensions of the spinal cord. They retain the spinal cord's division, with sensory structures posterior and motor structures anterior in humans. An important midbrain function is orienting the body to stimuli. Orienting movements require sensory input and motor output. The midbrain's colliculi, posterior in the human tectum, are the sensory component, whereas the tegmentum, which is anterior, is a motor structure that participates in controlling various movements, including orienting.

Figures 2-15 through 2-19 illustrate brainstem structures.

Distinct sensory nuclei are present in the thalamus, too, although their positions are not segregated, as they are in lower structures. Because all sensory information reaches the forebrain through the thalamus, to find separate nuclei associated with vision, hearing, and touch is not surprising. Separate thalamic nuclei also control movements. Other nuclei have neither sensory nor motor functions but rather connect to cortical areas, such as the frontal lobe, that perform more integrative tasks.

Finally, sensory and motor functions are divided in the cortex in two ways:

1. Separate sensory and motor cortical regions process a particular set of sensory inputs, such as vision, hearing, or touch. Others control fine movements of discrete body parts, such as the fingers.

2. The entire cortex is organized around the sensory and motor distinction. As diagrammed in Figure 2-22, layer IV of the cortex always receives sensory inputs, layers V and VI always send motor outputs, and layers I, II, and III integrate sensory and motor operations.

Principle 8: The Brain Divides Sensory Input for Object Recognition and Motor Control

Sensory systems evolved first for controlling motion, not for recognizing things. Simple organisms can detect stimulation such as light and move to or from it. It is not necessary to perceive an object to direct movements toward or away from it. Animals only began to evolve ways of representing their environment as their behaviors became more complex. Animals with a complex brain evolved separate systems for recognizing objects and for moving toward them. The human visual system exemplifies this separation.

Visual information travels from the eyes to the thalamus to visual regions of the occipital lobe. From the occipital cortex it follows one of two routes: the *ventral stream* leads to the temporal lobe for object identification, whereas the *dorsal stream* goes to the parietal lobe to guide movements relative to objects (**Figure 2-33**). People with ventral stream injuries are blind for object recognition. They cannot distinguish a cup from a spoon. Nevertheless, they shape their hands appropriately when asked to reach for objects that they cannot identify. In contrast, people with dorsal stream injuries can recognize objects, but they make clumsy

FIGURE 2-33 Neural Streams The dorsal and ventral streams mediate vision for action and recognition, respectively.

reaching movements because they do not form appropriate hand postures until they contact objects. Only then do they shape the hand on the basis of tactile information.

Recognizing that perception for movement and perception for object recognition are independent processes has three important implications for understanding brain organization:

1. The dorsal and ventral visual systems exemplify parallel information processing in the brain.

2. Although we may think we are aware of our entire sensory world, the sensory analysis required for some movements clearly is not conscious.

3. Unconscious and conscious brain processing underlies an important difference in our cognitive functions. The unconscious movement system is always acting in the present and in response to ongoing sensory input. In contrast, the conscious object recognition system allows us to escape the present and bring to bear information from the past, thus forming the neural basis of enduring memory.

Sections 9-2 and 9-3 review evidence that led to understanding the visual streams' functions and visual information processing.

Principle 9: Brain Functions Are Localized and Distributed

A great debate in the history of brain research has concerned what aspects of different functions are actually localized in specific brain regions. Perhaps the fundamental problem is defining a function. Language, for example, includes the comprehension of spoken words, written words, signed words (as in American Sign Language), and even touched words (as in Braille). Language also includes production of words orally, in writing, and by signing, as well as constructing whole linguistic compositions, such as stories, poems, songs, and essays.

Because the function that we call language has many aspects, it is not surprising that these aspects reside in widely separated areas of the brain. We see evidence of this widespread distribution in language-related brain injuries. People with injuries in different locations may selectively lose the abilities to produce words, to understand words, to read words, to write words, and so forth. Specific language-related abilities, therefore, reside in specific locations, but language as a whole is distributed throughout a wide brain region.

Figure 14-5 illustrates the extensive distribution of memory areas through the brain.

Memory provides another example of this same distributed pattern. Memories can be richly detailed and can include sensual feelings, words, images, and much more. Like language, then, aspects of memory are located in many brain regions distributed throughout a vast area of the brain.

Because many functions are both localized and distributed in the brain, damage to a small brain region produces only focal (specific) symptoms. Massive brain damage is required to obliterate some functions. A small injury could impair some aspect of language functioning, such as naming objects, but it would take widespread injury to remove all language abilities. In fact, one characteristic of dementing diseases is that people can endure widespread deterioration of the cortex yet maintain remarkably normal language functions until late stages of the disease. **Alzheimer disease** is a degenerative brain disorder related to aging that first appears as progressive memory loss and only much later develops into generalized dementia.

For Alzheimer neurochemistry, see Section 5-3; for incidence and possible causes, Section 14-3; for treatments, Section 16-4.

Alzheimer disease Degenerative brain disorder related to aging that first appears as progressive memory loss and later develops into generalized dementia.

excitation Increase in the activity of a neuron or brain area.

inhibition Decrease in the activity of a neuron or brain area.

Principle 10: The Nervous System Works by Juxtaposing Excitation and Inhibition

We have emphasized the brain's role in *making* movements, but we must also recognize that the brain *prevents* movements. To make a directed movement, such as picking up a glass of water, we must refrain from other movements, such as waving the hand back and forth. In producing movement, then, the brain uses both **excitation** (increased neural activity) to produce some action and **inhibition** (decreased neural activity) to prevent other actions.

Brain injury or disease can produce either a *loss* or a *release* of behavior by changing the balance between excitation and inhibition. A brain injury in a region that normally initiates speech may render a person unable to talk—a loss of behavior. A person with an abnormality in a region that inhibits inappropriate language (such as swearing) may be unable to inhibit this form of speech. Such a release of behavior can be seen in Tourette syndrome.

Patients with Parkinson disease may have uncontrollable shaking of the hands because the neural system that inhibits such movements has failed. Paradoxically, they often have difficulty initiating movements and appear frozen because they cannot generate the excitation needed to produce deliberate movements.

The juxtaposition of excitation and inhibition, central to the way the brain produces behavior, can be seen at the level of individual neurons. All neurons evince a spontaneous activity rate that can be either increased (excitation) or decreased (inhibition). Some neurons excite others; some inhibit. Both effects are produced by neuronal communication via specific neurochemicals.

Tourette syndrome and Parkinsonism are dysfunctions of the basal ganglia, which coordinates voluntary movement.

Chapter 3 details nervous system cell structure; Chapter 4, how neurons transmit and integrate information; and Chapter 5, neuronal communication and adaptation.

(2-6) REVIEW

Ten Principles of Nervous System Function

Before you continue, check your understanding.

1. Many of the brain's input and output circuits are crossed. In the nervous system, four exceptions to this principle are the _____, the _____, the _____, and the _____.

2. The vertebrate brain has evolved three regions—hindbrain, midbrain, and forebrain—leading to _____ and flexibility in controlling behavior.

3. One aspect of neural activity that resembles the on–off language of digital devices is the juxtaposition of _____ and _____.

4. Explain this statement: Perception is not reality.

Answers appear at the back of the book.

For additional study tools, visit 🐵 **LaunchPad:**
www.macmillanhighered.com/launchpad/kolb5e

■ SUMMARY

(2-1) Overview of Brain Function and Structure

The brain's primary function is to produce behavior, or movement, in a perceptual world the brain constructs. This perceptual world is ever-changing. To adapt, the brain must also change, a property referred to as neuroplasticity.

To study how the nervous system functions, we abandon the anatomical divisions between the central nervous system and the peripheral nervous system to focus instead on function—on how the CNS interacts with the divisions of the PNS: the somatic, autonomic, and enteric nervous systems.

(2-2) The Nervous System's Evolutionary Development

The vertebrate nervous system evolved from a relatively simple structure mediating reflexlike behaviors to the complex human brain mediating advanced cognitive processes. To allow for more complex behavior in an increasingly sophisticated perceptual world, primitive forms have not been replaced but rather have been adapted and modified as new structures have evolved.

The principles of nervous system organization and function generalize across the three vertebrate brain regions—hindbrain, midbrain, and forebrain—leading to multiple levels of functioning. The evolution of neural levels of control thus adds flexibility to behavioral control.

(2-3) Central Nervous System: Mediating Behavior

The CNS includes the brain and the spinal cord. The spinal cord can perceive sensations from the skin and muscles and produce movements independent of the brain. The brain can be divided into the brainstem and forebrain, each made up of hundreds of parts. The brainstem both directs movements and constructs a sensory world through its connections with the sensory systems, spinal cord, and forebrain. The forebrain modifies and elaborates basic sensory and motor functions; regulates cognitive activity, including thought and memory; and ultimately controls movement. The most elaborate parts of the brain, the cerebral cortex and cerebellum, grow disproportionately large in the human brain.

2-4 Somatic Nervous System: Transmitting Information

The SNS consists of two sets of spinal nerves that enter and leave the spinal column, connecting with muscles, skin, and joints in the body, and the cranial nerves that link the facial muscles and some internal organs to the brain. Both sets of SNS nerves are symmetrical: one set controls each side of the body. Some cranial nerves are sensory, some are motor, and some combine both functions. The spinal cord acts as a minibrain for the peripheral (spinal) nerves that enter and leave its five segments. Each spinal segment works independently, although CNS fibers interconnect them and coordinate their activities.

2-5 Autonomic and Enteric Nervous Systems: Visceral Functions

The ANS controls the body's glands and internal organs and operates largely outside conscious awareness. Its sympathetic (arousing) and parasympathetic (calming) divisions work in opposition. The parasympathetic division directs the organs to rest and digest, whereas the sympathetic division prepares for fight or flight.

The ENS controls the gut over its entire length, from the esophagus to the colon, interacting with the brain via the ANS. ENS activity can affect our behavior and mental state. In turn, the ENS is affected by the microbiome, the roughly 100 trillion bacteria that inhabit our gut.

2-6 Ten Principles of Nervous System Function

Ten principles listed in the right column below form the basis for discussions throughout this book. Understanding them fully will enhance your study of brain and behavior.

Ten Principles of Nervous System Function

1	The nervous system produces movement in a perceptual world the brain constructs.
2	Neuroplasticity is the hallmark of nervous system functioning.
3	Many brain circuits are crossed.
4	The CNS functions on multiple levels.
5	The brain is symmetrical and asymmetrical.
6	Brain systems are organized hierarchically and in parallel.
7	Sensory and motor divisions permeate the nervous system.
8	The brain divides sensory input for object recognition and motor control.
9	Brain functions are localized and distributed.
10	The nervous system works by juxtaposing excitation and inhibition.

■ KEY TERMS

afferent, p. 37
Alzheimer disease, p. 70
autonomic nervous system (ANS), p. 37
basal ganglia, p. 56
brainstem, p. 50
cerebral cortex, p. 41
cerebrospinal fluid (CSF), p. 41
corpus callosum, p. 44
cranial nerve, p. 59
cytoarchitectonic map, p. 56
dermatome, p. 60
diencephalon, p. 52
efferent, p. 37

enteric nervous system (ENS), p. 37
excitation, p. 70
forebrain, p. 54
frontal lobe, p. 41
gray matter, p. 43
gyri (sing. gyrus), p. 43
hindbrain, p. 52
hypothalamus, p. 54
inhibition, p. 70
law of Bell and Magendie, p. 60
limbic system, p. 56
meninges, p. 37
midbrain, p. 52

neocortex (cerebral cortex), p. 54
nerve, p. 47
neuroplasticity, p. 37
nuclei (sing. nucleus), p. 47
occipital lobe, p. 41
orienting movement, p. 52
parasympathetic division, p. 63
parietal lobe, p. 41
Parkinson disease, p. 56
phenotypic plasticity, p. 37
reticular formation, p. 52
somatic nervous system (SNS), p. 37

stroke, p. 43
sulci (sing. sulcus), p. 43
sympathetic division, p. 63
tectum, p. 52
tegmentum, p. 52
temporal lobe, p. 41
thalamus, p. 54
Tourette syndrome, p. 56
tract, p. 47
ventricle, p. 44
vertebrae (sing. vertebra), p. 59
white matter, p. 44

⟶ Visit ⬤ LaunchPad to access the e-Book, videos, ⬤ LearningCurve adaptive quizzing, flashcards, and more.

www.macmillanhighered.com/launchpad/kolb5e

CHAPTER 3

What Are the Nervous System's Functional Units?

Katherine Streeter

A Genetic Diagnosis

Fraternal twins Alexis and Noah Beery seemingly acquired cerebral palsy perinatally (at or near birth). They had poor muscle tone and could barely walk or sit. Noah drooled and vomited, and Alexis had tremors.

Typically, children with cerebral palsy, a condition featuring perinatal brainstem damage, do not get worse with age, but the twins' condition deteriorated. Their mother, Retta Beery, observed as well that Alexis's symptoms fluctuated: they improved after she slept or napped, for example.

Noah, Retta, Joe, and Alexis Beery at Baylor College with the Solid Sequencer, which decoded the genomes of twins Noah and Alexis.

In searching the literature for similar cases, Retta found a photocopy of a 1991 news report that described a child first diagnosed with cerebral palsy, then found to have a rare condition, dopa-responsive dystonia. (*Dystonia* means abnormal muscle tone.) It stems from a deficiency of a neurochemical, dopamine, produced by a relatively small cluster of cells in the midbrain.

When Alexis and Noah received a daily dose of l-dopa, a chemical that some brain cells convert to dopamine, they displayed remarkable improvement. "We knew that we were witnessing a miracle," Retta recalled.

A few years later, in 2005, Alexis began to have new symptoms marked by breathing difficulties. At this time the twins' father, Joe, worked for Life Technologies, a biotech company that makes equipment used for sequencing DNA, the genetic coding molecule found in the nucleus of every cell. Joe arranged for samples of the twins' blood to be sent to the Baylor College of Medicine's DNA sequencing center.

The twins' genome was sequenced and compared with that of their parents and close relatives. The analysis showed that the twins had an abnormality in a gene on chromosome 2 for an enzyme that enhances not only dopamine production but also the production of serotonin, another neurochemical made by brainstem cells (Bainbridge et al., 2011).

When the twins' doctors added tryptophan, the enzyme that is converted to serotonin, to the l-dopa, both twins showed remarkable improvement. Alexis competed in junior high school track, and Noah played volleyball in the Junior Olympics. This is the first diagnosis established through genome sequencing that led to a treatment success, a scientific miracle indeed.

The Beery twins' remarkable story highlights how neuroscientists are applying advances in genetics to treat brain disorders. Understanding genes, proteins, and cellular function allows us to understand healthy brain functioning as well.

We begin this chapter by describing nervous system cell structure and relating structure to functions. Brain cells not only give the nervous system its structure but also mediate its moment-to-moment activity, the activity that underlies our behavior. We conclude the chapter by elaborating on Mendelian genetics and how the science of epigenetics completes Mendel's theory.

⟨3-1⟩ Cells of the Nervous System

Cells have been likened to factories in that they make a product, proteins, the building blocks of our bodies. But cells are more than factories. Cells use the proteins they produce to participate in orchestrating our behavior.

Nervous system cells are small, are packed tightly together, and have the consistency of jelly. To see a brain cell, the observer must distinguish it from surrounding cells, magnified under a microscope. The first anatomists to study brain cells developed methods of highlighting individual cells in nervous system tissue. To make the tissue firm, they soaked it in formaldehyde to preserve and *fix* the tissue by binding together its constituent protein

RESEARCH FOCUS 3-2

Brainbow: Rainbow Neurons

Were it not for the discovery of stains that can highlight brain cell features, their complexity and connections would remain unknown. Jean Livet (2007) and his colleagues at Harvard University developed a transgenic technique that labels different neurons by highlighting them with distinct colors, a technique called *Brainbow*, a play on the word *rainbow*. (Transgenic techniques are a form of genetic engineering discussed in Section 3-3.)

In the same way a television monitor produces the full range of colors that the human eye can see by mixing only red, green, and blue, the Brainbow scientists introduced genes that produce cyan (blue), green, and red fluorescent proteins into mice cells. The red gene is obtained from coral, and the blue and green genes are obtained from jellyfish. (The 2008 Nobel Prize in chemistry was awarded to Roger Tsien, Osamu Shimomura, and Martin Chalfie for their discovery and development of fluorescent proteins in coral and jellyfish.)

The mice also received a bacterial gene called *Cre*. *Cre* activates the color genes inside each cell, but owing to chance factors, the extent to which each gene is activated varies. As the mice develop, the variable expression of the color-coding genes results in cells that fluoresce in at least a hundred hues. When viewed through a fluorescent microscope sensitive to these wavelengths, individual brain cells and their connections can be visualized because they have slightly different hues, as illustrated in the accompanying micrographs.

Because individual cells can be visualized, Brainbow offers a way to describe where each neuron sends its processes and how it interconnects with other neurons. You have probably seen an electrical power cord in which the different wires have different colors (black, white, red) that signify what they do and how they should be connected. By visualizing living brain tissue in a dish, Brainbow provides a method for examining changes in neural circuits with the passage of time.

In the future, Brainbow will prove useful for examining populations of cells and their connections—for example, cells implicated in specific brain diseases. In principle, Brainbow could be turned on at specific times, as an individual ages or solves problems, for example (Rojczyk-Gołębiewska et al., 2015). Despite Brainbow's promise, challenges remain. Even the simplest brain contains extraordinary numbers of neurons and fibers. Modifications in Brainbow that restrict visualization to only a few cells and fibers at a time are necessary for their connections to be understood.

Cell bodies

Axons

Terminal buttons

Livet, Draft, Sanes, and Lichtman, Harvard University

molecules. The fixed tissue was then sliced in thin sheets (sectioned), colored (stained) with various dyes, and placed under a microscope for viewing.

Scientists continue to fix, slice, and stain brain tissue and to improve on ways of visualizing cells to provide insights into what cells do. Visualization is aided not only by using dyes that either color an individual cell completely; color some cellular components. such as its proteins; or as described in Research Focus 3-2, Brainbow: Rainbow Neurons, color the cell only when it is engaged in a particular activity.

Scientists have developed other techniques of viewing living cells in the nervous system or viewing cells that are cultured in a dish with nurturing fluids. In doing so, they use staining techniques to produce an image of the cell and to allow its activity to be viewed and controlled. Investigators even implant tiny microscopes in the brain to view the activity of its neurons (Chen et al., 2013). There remains, however, the problem of making sense of what you see. Different brain samples can yield different images, and different people can interpret the images in different ways.

So began a controversy between two great scientists—the Italian Camillo Golgi and the Spaniard Santiago Ramón y Cajal—that resulted in defining neurons. Both men were awarded the Nobel Prize for medicine in 1906. Imagine that you are Camillo Golgi, hard at work in your laboratory staining and examining nervous system cells. You immerse a thin slice of brain tissue in a solution containing silver nitrate and other chemicals,

FIGURE 3-1 Two Views of a Cell
(A) Tissue preparation revealing human *pyramidal cells* stained using the Golgi technique. **(B)** Cajal's drawing of a single *Purkinje neuron* made from Golgi-stained tissue. (B) Drawing from *Histologie du système nerveux de l'homme et des vertèbres*, by S. Ramón y Cajal, 1909–1911, Paris: Maloine.

Golgi never revealed just how he came to develop his staining technique.

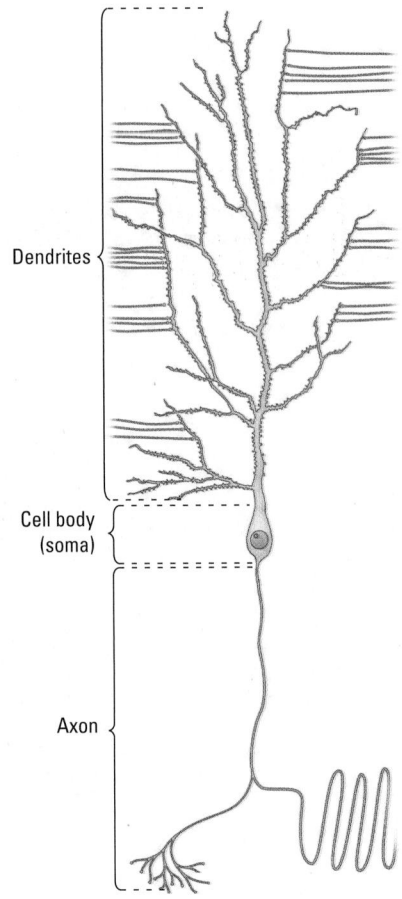

Dendrites

Cell body (soma)

Axon

FIGURE 3-2 Basic Structure of a Neuron Dendrites gather information from other neurons, the cell body (soma) integrates the information, and the axon sends the information to other cells. Although a neuron may have many dendrites, it has only one axon.

a technique used at the time to produce black-and-white photographs. A contemporary method, shown in **Figure 3-1**A, produces a color-enhanced microscopic image that resembles the images Golgi saw.

The image is beautiful and intriguing, but what do you make of it? To Golgi, this structure suggested that the nervous system is an interconnected network of fibers. He thought that information flowed around this "nerve net," like water running through pipes, and so produced behavior. His theory was reasonable, given what he saw.

But Santiago Ramón y Cajal came to a different conclusion. He used Golgi's stain to study chick embryos' brain tissue. He assumed that their developing nervous system would be simpler and easier to understand than an adult's. Figure 3-1B shows an image he rendered from the neural cells using the Golgi stain. Cajal concluded that the nervous system is made up of such discrete cells, which begin life as a rather simple structure that becomes more complex with age. When mature, each cell consists of a main body with many extensions projecting from it.

The structure looks something like a plant, with branches coming out of the top and roots coming out of the bottom. Cajal showed that neurons come in many shapes and sizes. Cajal's *neuron theory*—that neurons are the nervous system's functional units—is now universally accepted. The neuron theory includes the ideas that the interactions between these discrete cells enable behavior and that the more neurons an animal has, the more complex its behavior.

Figure 3-2 shows the three basic subdivisions of a neuron. The core region is called the **cell body**, or **soma** (Greek, meaning *body*; the root of words such as *somatic*). A neuron's branching extensions, or **dendrites** (from Greek for *tree*), collect information from other cells, and its main root is the single **axon** (Greek for *axle*), which carries messages to other neurons. A neuron has only one axon, but most have many dendrites. Some neurons have so many dendrites that they look like a garden hedge, as Cajal's drawing in Figure 3-1B illustrates.

The human nervous system contains 86 billion neurons (Herculano-Houzel et al., 2014). How can 86 billion cells cooperate, make connections, and produce behavior? Fortunately, neurons have a common plan: examining how one neuron works offers insights that we can generalize to other neuron types. As you learn to recognize different types of nervous system cells, you will begin to understand how their specialized structures contribute to their functions in your body.

Neurons: The Basis of Information Processing

As the information-processing units of the nervous system, neurons acquire information, interpret it, and pass the information along to other neurons that initiate a behavior. In engaging in this activity, neurons also encode memories and produce our thoughts and emotions. At the same time, they regulate body processes such as breathing, heartbeat, and body temperature, to which we seldom give a thought.

Some scientists think that a specific function can be assigned to an individual neuron. For example, many birds learn to sing during the breeding season, and this learning is associated with the seasonal development of new neurons (Bertram et al., 2014). To produce most behaviors in most species, however, scientists think that neurons work together in groups of many hundreds to many thousands. It is important, then, to understand not only how neurons function but also how they interconnect and influence one another.

Functional groups of neurons, or **neural networks**, connect wide areas of the brain and spinal cord. The loss of a neuron or two from a network is no more noticeable than the loss of one or two voices from a cheering crowd. It is the crowd that produces the overall sound, not each person. In much the same way, although neuroscientists call neurons the information-processing units of the brain, they really mean that neural networks serve this function. An ongoing effort aims to map the structural connectivity—the physical wiring, or **connectome**—of the entire human brain.

Scientists also speak informally about a particular neuron's structure as if that structure never changes. But neurons are the essence of plasticity. If you view fresh brain tissue through a microscope, the neurons reveal themselves to be surprisingly active, producing new branches, losing old ones, and making and losing connections with each other as you watch. This dynamic activity underlies both the constancies and the changes in our behavior.

Another important property of most neurons is their longevity. At a few locations in the human nervous system, ongoing production of new neurons does take place throughout life, and some behavior does depend on the production of new neurons. But most of our CNS neurons are with us for life. Although they change, they are not replaced when lost. For this reason, if the brain or spinal cord is damaged, functional recovery is often poor. In some nonhuman animal species, neurons can be replaced. The variability in neuronal longevity and replacement are important properties to scientists who study diseases of aging, disorders associated with age-related changes in the nervous system, and diseases or injuries that damage the nervous system.

Structure and Function of the Neuron

Figure 3-3 on page 78 details the external and internal features common to neurons. The cell's surface area is increased immensely by its extensions into dendrites and an axon (Figure 3-3A and B). The dendritic area is further increased by many small protrusions called **dendritic spines** (Figure 3-3C). A neuron may have up to 20 dendrites, each may have one to many branches, and the spines on the branches may number in the thousands. Dendrites collect information from other cells, and the spines are the points of contact with those neurons. The extent of a cell's branches and its spine number correspond to its information-processing capacity.

Each neuron has but a single axon to carry messages to other neurons. The axon begins at one end of the cell body at an expansion known as the **axon hillock** (little hill), shown in Figure 3-3D. The axon may branch out into one or many **axon collaterals**, which usually emerge from it at right angles, as shown at the bottom of Figure 3-3B.

The axon's lower tip may divide into multiple smaller branches (*telodendria*, or end branches). At the end of each telodendrion is a knob called an *end foot*, or **terminal button**. The terminal button sits very close to but usually does not touch a dendritic spine or some other part of another cell (Figure 3-3C). This near-connection, called a **synapse**, includes the surfaces of the end foot and the neighboring dendritic spine as well as the space between them. The synapse is the information transfer site between neurons.

cell body (soma) Core region of the cell containing the nucleus and other organelles for making proteins.

dendrite Branching extension of a neuron's cell membrane; greatly increases the cell's surface area; collects information from other cells.

axon Root, or single fiber, of a neuron that carries messages to other neurons.

neural network Functional group of neurons that connects wide areas of the brain and spinal cord.

connectome Comprehensive map of all structural connectivity (the physical wiring) in an organism's nervous system.

dendritic spine Protrusion that greatly increases the dendrite's surface area; typical point of dendritic contact with the axons of other cells.

axon hillock Juncture of soma and axon.

axon collateral Branch of an axon.

terminal button (end foot) Knob at the tip of an axon that conveys information to other neurons.

synapse Spatial junction between one neuron and another; forms the information transfer site between neurons.

FIGURE 3-3 Major Parts of a Neuron **(A)** Typical neuron Golgi-stained to reveal its dendrites and cell body. **(B)** The neuron's basic structures identified. **(C)** An electron micrograph captures the synapse between an axon from another neuron and a dendritic spine. **(D)** High-power light microscopic view inside the cell body. Note the axon hillock at the junction of the soma and axon.

(A)

Ian Whishaw

(B)

Axon from another neuron

Dendrites

Cell body (soma)

Nucleus

Axon

Teleodendria   Axon collateral

Terminal button (end foot)

Dendrites from neighboring neuron

(C)

End foot
Synapse
Dendritic spine

Ian Whishaw

(D)

Dendrite

Nucleus

Nucleolus

Cell body

Axon hillock

Axon

Ian Whishaw

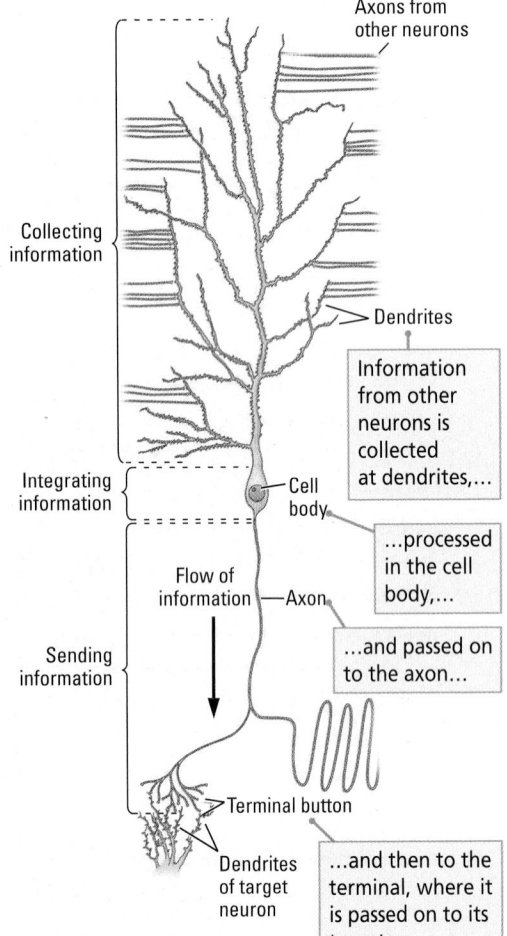

Axons from other neurons

Collecting information

Dendrites

Information from other neurons is collected at dendrites,...

Integrating information

Cell body

...processed in the cell body,...

Flow of information

Axon

...and passed on to the axon...

Sending information

Terminal button

Dendrites of target neuron

...and then to the terminal, where it is passed on to its target.

FIGURE 3-4 Information Flow Through a Neuron

Chapter 4 describes how neurons transmit information; here, we simply generalize about neuronal function by examining shape. Imagine looking down on a river system from an airplane. You see many small streams merging to make creeks, which join to form tributaries, which join to form the main river channel. As the river reaches its delta, it breaks up into many smaller channels again before discharging its contents into the sea.

The general shape of a neuron suggests that it works in a broadly similar way to a river. As illustrated in **Figure 3-4**, the neuron collects information from many sources on its dendrites. It channels the information to its axon, which can send out only a single message. The eventual branching of the axon then allows the message to be sent to many targets.

Three Functions of Neurons

Neurons of varying shapes and sizes are structured to perform specialized functions. **Sensory neurons** (**Figure 3-5A**) conduct information from the sensory receptors in or on the body into the spinal cord and brain. **Interneurons** (Figure 3-5B) associate sensory and motor activity in the CNS, and **motor neurons** (Figure 3-5C) carry information from the brain and spinal cord out to the body's muscles.

(A) Sensory neurons

Bring information to the central nervous system

(B) Interneurons

Associate sensory and motor activity in the central nervous system

(C) Motor neurons

Send signals from the brain and spinal cord to muscles

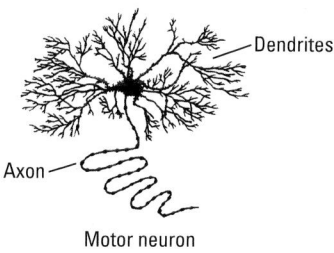

FIGURE 3-5 Neuron Shape and Function **(A)** Sensory neurons of many types detect stimulation or collect information and pass it on to **(B)** an interneuron. The multibranched interneuron dendrites collect information from varied sources and link to **(C)** motor neurons, which are distinctively large and which pass on commands to muscles to move. Cells are not drawn to scale.

SENSORY NEURONS Sensory neurons are the simplest structurally. A **bipolar neuron** found in the retina of the eye, for example, has a single short dendrite on one side of its cell body and a single short axon on the other side. Bipolar neurons transmit afferent (incoming) sensory information from the retina's light receptors to the neurons that carry information into the brain's visual centers.

A bit more structurally complicated is the **somatosensory neuron**, which brings sensory information from the body into the spinal cord, a long distance. Structurally, the somatosensory dendrite connects directly to its axon, so the cell body sits to one side of this long pathway.

INTERNEURONS Also called *association cells* because they link up sensory and motor neurons, interneurons branch extensively, the better to collect information from many sources. Animals with large brains have more interneurons, and their interneurons have more branches, than those of small-brained animals. A specific type of interneuron, the *stellate* (star-shaped) *cell*, is characteristically small, with many dendrites extending around the cell body. Its axon is difficult to see in the maze of dendrites.

A **pyramidal cell** has a long axon, a pyramid-shaped cell body, and two sets of dendrites. The apical set projects from the cell body apex, the basal set from the base of its cell body. Pyramidal interneurons carry information from the cortex to the rest of the brain and spinal cord. A **Purkinje cell** (named for its discoverer) is a distinctive interneuron with extremely branched dendrites that form a fan shape. It carries information from the cerebellum to the rest of the brain and spinal cord.

MOTOR NEURONS To collect information from many sources, motor neurons have extensive dendritic networks, large cell bodies, and long axons that connect to muscles. Motor neurons reside in the lower brainstem and spinal cord. All efferent (outgoing) neural information must pass through them to reach the muscles.

Neuronal Networks

Sensory neurons collect afferent (incoming) information from the body and connect to interneurons that process the information and pass it on to motor neurons. The motor neurons' efferent connections move muscles and so produce behavior. These three organizational aspects of neurons are thus features of neuronal networks: input, association, and output.

Neurons that project for long distances, such as somatosensory neurons, pyramidal neurons, and motor neurons, are relatively large. In general, neurons with a large cell body have long extensions, whereas neurons with a small cell body, such as stellate interneurons, have short extensions.

Long extensions carry information to distant parts of the nervous system; short extensions are engaged in local processing. For example, the dendrite tips of some somatosensory

sensory neuron Cell that detects or carries sensory information into the spinal cord and brain.

interneuron Association cell interposed between a sensory neuron and a motor neuron; in mammals, interneurons constitute most of the brain's neurons.

motor neuron Cell that carries efferent information from the brain and spinal cord to make muscles contract.

bipolar neuron Sensory neuron with one axon and one dendrite.

somatosensory neuron Brain cell that brings sensory information from the body into the spinal cord.

pyramidal cell Distinctively shaped interneuron found in the cerebral cortex.

Purkinje cell Distinctively shaped interneuron found in the cerebellum.

neurons are in your big toe, whereas the target of their axons is at the base of your brain. These sensory neurons send information over as much as 2 meters, even more in very large animals. The axons of some pyramidal neurons must reach from the cortex as far as the lower spinal cord, a distance that can be as long as a meter. The imposing size of this pyramidal cell body therefore accords with the work it must do in providing nutrients and other cellular supplies for its axons and dendrites.

The Language of Neurons: Excitation and Inhibition

Neurons are networkers with elaborate interconnections, but how do they communicate? Simply put, neurons either excite other neurons (turn them on) or inhibit other neurons (turn them off). Like digital computers, neurons send yes or no signals to one another; the yes signals are excitatory, and the no signals are inhibitory. Each neuron receives up to thousands of excitatory and inhibitory signals every second.

The neuron's response to all those inputs is reasonably democratic: it sums them. A neuron is spurred into action and sends messages to other neurons if its excitatory inputs exceed its inhibitory inputs. If the reverse occurs and inhibitory inputs exceed excitatory inputs, the neuron does not communicate.

By exciting or inhibiting one another, a neuronal network can detect sensory information and "decide" what kind of motor response to make to that information. To confirm whether they understand how an entire neural network produces behavior, scientists might make a model, such as a robot, intended to function in the same way. Robots, after all, engage in goal-oriented actions, just as animals do. A robot's computer must somehow sense the world, coordinate its actions in response, and perform much as an animal's nervous system performs.

Constructing humanlike machines is one scientific objective of *artificial intelligence* (AI) research. Barbara Webb's cricket robot, constructed from Lego blocks, wires, and a motor (**Figure 3-6**, left), is designed to mimic a female cricket, which listens for the source of a male's chirping song and travels to it (Reeve et al., 2007). This is the beginning step in constructing intelligent robots (Figure 3-6, right).

In approaching a male, a female cricket must avoid open, well-lit places where a predator could detect her. The female must often choose between competing males, preferring, for example, the male that makes the longest chirps. All of these behaviors must be wired into a successful cricket robot, making sure that one behavior does not interfere with another. In simulating cricket behavior in a robot, Webb is duplicating the rules of a cricket's nervous system, which are programmed by its genes.

The Procedure sections of **Experiment 3-1** illustrate some ways that neural inhibition and excitation might produce the cricket robot's behavior. The Results section confirms that this hypothetical arrangement mimics the functions of sensory and motor neurons and the principle of summating excitatory and inhibitory signals—but with only six neurons and each neuron connected to only one other neuron! Today, anthropomimetic robots, so-called because their parts are constructed to mimic the parts of a human body, including its billions of neurons, are being designed to model complex behavior (Wittmeier et al., 2013).

Five Types of Glial Cells

Another group of nervous system cell aids neurons in processing information. **Glial cells** (from the Greek for *glue*) are the nervous system's support cells. The

Principle 10: The nervous system works by juxtaposing excitatory and inhibitory signals. Section 4-3 explains how neurons summate excitatory and inhibitory signals.

glial cell Nervous system cell that provides insulation, nutrients, and support and that aids in repairing neurons and eliminating waste products.

FIGURE 3-6 Nervous System Mimics Left: Barbara Webb programmed rules she developed from studying cricket behavior into her Lego cricket robot. Right: Social roboticist Heather Knight conducts research on robot body language with her companion, Marilyn Monrobot.

James King-Holmes/Science Photo Library

Kike Calvo via AP Images

▶ EXPERIMENT **3-1**

Question: Can the principles of neural excitation and inhibition control the activity of a simple robot?

Procedure A

If we insert sensory neurons between the microphone for sound detection on each side of this hypothetical robot and the motor on the opposite side, we need only two rules to instruct the female robot to seek out a chirping male cricket.

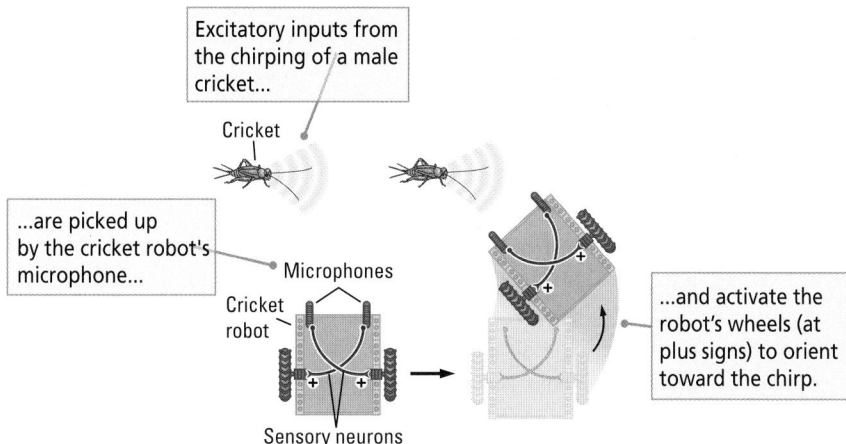

Rule 1 When a microphone detects a male cricket's song, an excitatory message is sent to the opposite wheel's motor, activating it so the robot turns toward the cricket.

Rule 2 If the chirp is coming from the robot's left side, it will be detected as being louder by the microphone on the left, which will make the right wheel turn a little faster, swinging the robot to the left.

Procedure B

We add two more sensory neurons, coming from photoreceptors on the robot. When activated, these light-detecting sensory neurons inhibit the motor neurons leading to the wheels and prevent the robot from moving toward a male cricket. Now the female cricket robot will move only when it is dark and "safe."

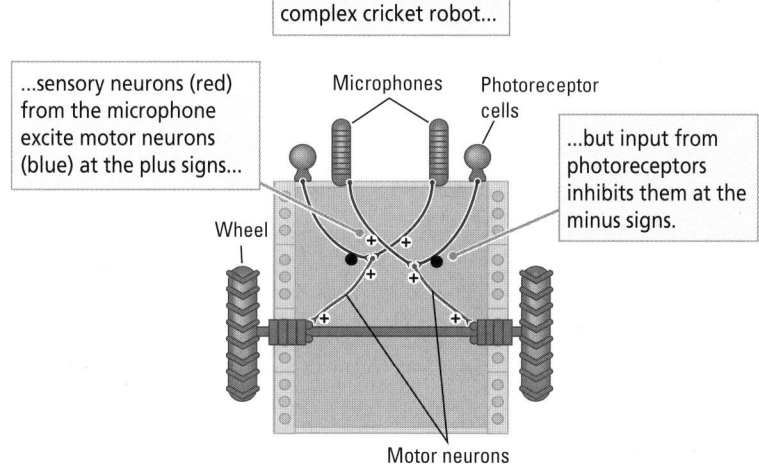

Result

This hypothetical arrangement illustrates the biological function of sensory and motor neurons and the neural principle of summating excitatory and inhibitory signals.

Conclusion: A simple robot will operate on the principles of neural excitation and inhibition. More neurons are necessary to make the robot more "intelligent."

Glia form the fatty coverings around neurons—the white matter in brain images such as Figure 2-12B and D.

human brain's estimated 87 billion glial cells reflect the typical nervous system ratio of roughly 1:1 between neurons and glial cells (Herculano-Houzel et al., 2014). Although they do not transmit information themselves, glial cells help neurons carry out this task, binding them together (some *do* act as glue) and providing support, nutrients, and protection, among other functions.

Table 3-1 lists the five major types of glia along with their characteristic structures and functions. Glial cells are different from neurons in that new glial cells are produced, and errors in replication can result in abnormal growths: brain tumors. Clinical Focus 3-3, Brain Tumors, describes the results of such uncontrolled glial cell growth.

Ependymal Cells

On the walls of the ventricles, the fluid-filled cavities inside your brain, are **ependymal cells**, which produce and secrete the cerebrospinal fluid that fills the ventricles. CSF is constantly being secreted, and it flows through the ventricles toward the base of the brain, where it is absorbed into the blood vessels. CSF serves several purposes. It acts as a shock absorber when the brain is jarred, carries away waste products, assists the brain in maintaining a constant temperature, and is a source of nutrients for parts of the brain adjacent to the ventricles.

Figure 2-9 shows the location of the cerebral aqueduct and the four ventricles.

As CSF flows through the ventricles, it passes through some narrow passages, especially from the cerebral aqueduct into the fourth ventricle, which runs through the brainstem. If these passages are fully or partly blocked, fluid flow is restricted. Because CSF is continuously being produced, this blockage causes a buildup of pressure that begins to expand the ventricles, which in turn push on the surrounding brain.

If such a blockage develops in a newborn infant, before the skull bones are fused, the pressure on the brain is conveyed to the skull, and the baby's head swells. This condition, called **hydrocephalus** (literally, *water brain*), can cause severe intellectual impairment, even death. To treat it, doctors insert one end of a tube, called a *shunt*, into the blocked ventricle and the other end into a vein, allowing excess CSF to drain into the bloodstream.

ependymal cell Glial cell that makes and secretes CSF; found on the walls of the brain's ventricles.

hydrocephalus Buildup of fluid pressure in the brain and, in infants, swelling of the head, if the flow of CSF is blocked; can result in intellectual impairment.

tumor Mass of new tissue that grows uncontrolled and independent of surrounding structures.

astrocyte Star-shaped glial cell that provides structural support to CNS neurons and transports substances between neurons and blood vessels.

blood–brain barrier Tight junctions between the cells that compose blood vessels in the brain, providing a barrier to the entry of an array of substances, including toxins, into the brain.

TABLE 3-1 Types and Functions of Glial Cells

Type	Appearance	Features and function
Ependymal cell		Small ovoid; secretes CSF
Astrocyte		Star shaped; contributes to neuronal nutrition, support, and repair; contributes to forming blood–brain barrier and to healing scarring after injury
Microglial cell		Small, derived from blood; defensive function to remove dead tissue
Oligodendroglial cell		Forms myelin around CNS axons in brain and spinal cord
Schwann cell		Wraps around peripheral nerves to form myelin

Brain Tumors

One day while watching a movie in a neuropsychology class, R. J., a 19-year-old college sophomore, collapsed on the floor, displaying symptoms of a seizure. The instructor helped her to the university clinic, where she recovered except for a severe headache. She reported that she had repeated severe headaches.

A few days later, a computed tomography (CT) scan showed a tumor over her left frontal lobe. The tumor was removed surgically, and R. J. returned to classes after an uneventful recovery. Her symptoms have not recurred.

A **tumor** is an uncontrolled growth of new tissue that is independent of surrounding structures. No region of the body is immune, but the brain is a site for the more than 120 kinds of tumors. They are a common cause of brain cancer in children.

The incidence of brain tumors in the United States is about 20 per 100,000, according to the Central Brain Tumor Registry of the United States (Quinn et al., 2014). In adults brain tumors grow from glia or other supporting cells rather than from neurons, but in infants, tumors may grow from developing neurons. Rate of tumor growth depends on the type of cell affected.

Some tumors are benign, as R. J.'s was, and not likely to recur after removal. Others are malignant, likely to progress, to invade other tissue, and apt to recur after removal. Both kinds can pose a risk to life if they develop in sites from which they are difficult to remove.

The earliest symptoms usually result from increased pressure on surrounding brain structures. They can include headaches, vomiting, mental dullness, changes in sensory and motor abilities, and seizures such as R. J. had. Many symptoms depend on the tumor's location. The three major types of brain tumors are classified according to how they originate:

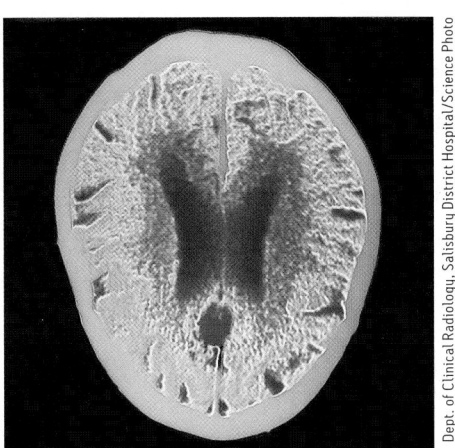

The red area in this false-color CT scan is a meningioma, a noncancerous tumor arising from the meninges, which cover the brain. Large meningiomas may compress the brain but usually do not invade brain tissue.

Dept. of Clinical Radiology, Salisbury District Hospital/Science Photo Library/Science Source

1. *Gliomas* arise from glial cells. They are slow growing, not often malignant, and relatively easy to treat if they arise from astrocytes. Gliomas that arise from the precursor *blast* or *germinal* cells that grow into glia are more often malignant, grow more quickly, and often recur after treatment. U.S. Senator Edward Kennedy was diagnosed with a malignant glioma in 2008 and died a year later. As with R. J., his first symptom was an epileptic seizure.

2. *Meningiomas*, such as R. J.'s, attach to the meninges and so grow entirely outside the brain, as shown in the accompanying CT scan. These tumors are usually encapsulated (contained), and if the tumor is accessible to surgery, chances of recovery are good.

3. *Metastatic tumors* become established when cells from one region of the body transfer to another area (which is what *metastasis* means). Typically, metastatic tumors are present in multiple locations, making treatment difficult. Symptoms of the underlying condition often first appear when the tumor cells reach the brain.

Treatment for brain tumors is usually surgical, and surgery also remains a main diagnostic tool. Chemotherapy is less successful in treating brain tumors than tumors elsewhere in the body, because the blood–brain barrier blocks the chemicals' entry. Radiation therapy (X-ray treatment) is more useful for destroying brain tumor cells. Nevertheless, radiation has negative effects especially on the developing brain and chemotherapy can affect brain function, a condition referred to as Chemo Brain.

Recent approaches to treating brain tumors exploit biochemical differences between tumors and healthy tissue, for example to visualize a tumor for surgical removal. Chlorotoxin, a scorpion venom that selectively binds to chloride channels in tumor cell membranes, combined with a fluorescent dye, forms a tumor paint (Butte et al., 2014). Injected into a vein, the paint crosses the blood–brain barrier and coats a tumor, which then glows when exposed to light in near-infrared wavelengths. Human trials began in 2015.

Nonsurgical tumor removal might also replace or aid chemotherapy and radiation therapy. It combines chlorotoxin with a poison to form a drug that kills tumor cells (Wang and Guo, 2015).

Astroglia

Astrocytes (star-shaped glia, shown in Table 3-1), also called astroglia, provide structural support to the CNS. Their extensions attach to blood vessels and to the brain's lining, forming a scaffolding that holds neurons in place. These same extensions provide pathways for certain nutrients to move between blood vessels and neurons. Astrocytes also secrete chemicals that keep neurons healthy and help them heal if injured.

At the same time, astrocytes contribute to the structure of a protective partition between blood vessels and the brain, the **blood–brain barrier**. As shown in **Figure 3-7**, the end feet of

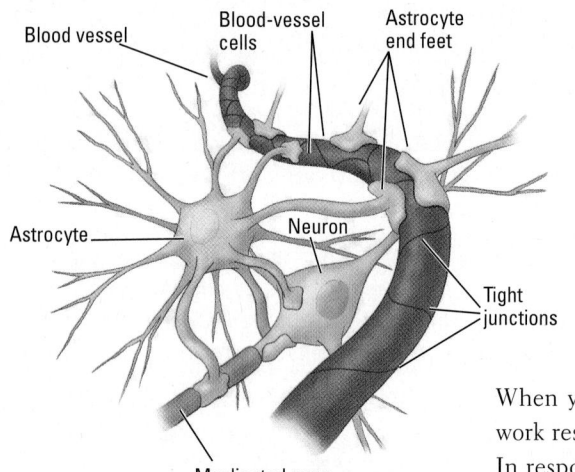

FIGURE 3-7 Blood—Brain Barrier
Astrocyte processes attach to neurons and to blood vessel cells to stimulate them to form tight junctions and so form the blood–brain barrier. Astrocytes also move nutrients and other chemicals between blood vessels and neurons, support brain structures, and stimulate repair of damaged brain tissue.

Growth factors, described Section 8-2, are chemicals that stimulate and support growth, survival, and perhaps even brain cell plasticity (see Section 14-4).

astrocytes attach to blood vessel cells, causing the vessels to bind tightly together. These tight junctions prevent an array of substances, including many toxins, from entering the brain through the blood vessel walls.

The molecules (smallest units) of these substances are too large to pass between the blood vessel cells unless the blood–brain barrier is somehow compromised. The downside is that many useful drugs, including antibiotics used to treat infections cannot pass through the blood–brain barrier to enter the brain. As a result, brain infections are very difficult to treat. Scientists can bypass the blood–brain barrier and introduce drugs into the brain by inserting small tubes that allow the delivery of a drug directly to a targeted brain region.

Yet another important function of astrocytes is to enhance brain activity. When you engage in any behavior, whether it's reading or running, the neuronal network responsible for that behavior requires more fuel in the form of oxygen and glucose. In response to neuron activity, the blood vessels that supply it expand, allowing greater oxygen- and glucose-carrying blood flow. What triggers the blood vessels to dilate? This is where astrocytes come in. They receive signals from the neurons, pass them on to the blood vessels, and so contribute to increased blood flow and fuel supply (Rosenegger and Gordon, 2015).

Astrocytes also contribute to healing damaged brain tissue. If the brain is injured by a blow to the head or penetrated by some object, astrocytes form a scar to seal off the damaged area. Although the scar tissue is beneficial in healing the injury, it can also act as a barrier to the regrowth of damaged neurons. One experimental approach to repairing brain tissue seeks to get the axons and dendrites of CNS neurons to grow around or through a glial scar.

Microglia

Unlike other glial cells, which originate in the brain, **microglia** originate in the blood as an offshoot of the immune system and migrate throughout the nervous system, where they make up about 20% of all glial cells. The brain is largely immune privileged, because the blood–brain barrier prevents most immune system cells from entering. Microglia monitor the health of brain tissue and play the role of its immune system. They identify and attack foreign tissue, as illustrated in **Figure 3-8**. When brain cells are damaged, microglia invade the area to provide *growth factors* that aid in repair.

There are several kinds of microglia, which take different shapes depending upon the role they are performing. Microglia engulf any foreign tissue and dead brain cells, an immune process called phagocytosis. When full they take on a distinctive appearance. The stuffed and no-longer-functioning microglia can be detected as small dark bodies, shown in Figure 3-8C, in and near damaged brain regions.

Because microglia are frontline players in protecting the nervous system and removing its waste, considerable research is directed toward the extent to which microglia are involved

FIGURE 3-8 Detecting Brain Damage **(A)** Arrows indicate the red nucleus in a rat brain. **(B)** Close-up of cresyl violet–stained neurons, the large dark bodies, in the healthy red nucleus. **(C)** After exposure to a neurotoxin, only microglia, the small dark objects in the micrograph, survive.

Ian Whishaw

in protecting the nervous system from disease. A characteristic of Alzheimer disease, the degenerative brain disorder commonly associated with aging, is the deposit of distinctive bodies called plaques in regions of damage. Microglia may also play a harmful role, consuming inflamed tissue rather than protecting it. They also interact with astrocytes in brain healing. Although small, as their name suggests, microglia play a mighty role in maintaining the brain's health (Casano & Peri, 2015).

Oligodendroglia and Schwann Cells

Two kinds of glial cells insulate neuronal axons. Like the plastic insulation on electrical wires, **myelin** prevents adjacent neurons from short-circuiting. Myelinated neurons send information much faster than neurons without myelin. Neurons that send messages over long distances quickly, including sensory and motor neurons, are heavily myelinated to increase their messaging speed.

Oligodendroglia myelinate axons in the brain and spinal cord by sending out large, flat branches that enclose and separate adjacent axons (the prefix *oligo-* means *few* and here refers to the fact that these glia have few branches in comparison with astrocytes; see Table 3-1). **Schwann cells** myelinate axons in the PNS. Each Schwann cell wraps itself repeatedly around a part of an axon, forming a structure somewhat like a bead on a string. In addition to myelination, Schwann cells and oligodendroglia contribute to a neuron's nutrition and functioning by absorbing chemicals that the neuron releases and releasing chemicals that the neuron absorbs.

Glial Cells and Neuron Repair

The multifaceted relations among neurons and glia provide insights into nervous system diseases and into brain injury and recovery from brain injury. Diseases that damage myelin impair a neuron's ability to send information. The consequences of damage to oligodendroglia and Schwann cells can be as debilitating as damage to neurons themselves. Damage to areas rich in neuron cell bodies can also be different from damage to fiber pathways, because pathway damage includes both neurons and myelin cells.

Glia can also aid in nervous system repair. A deep cut on your body—on your arm or leg for instance—may cut the axons connecting your spinal cord to muscles and to sensory receptors. Severing of motor neuron axons will render you unable to move the affected part of your body, whereas severing of sensory fibers will result in loss of sensation from that body part. Cessation of both movement and sensation is **paralysis**. Weeks to months after motor and sensory axons are severed, movement and sensation will return. What mediates this recovery?

Both microglia and Schwann cells participate in repairing damage to the peripheral nervous system. When a PNS axon is cut, it dies back to the cell body, as shown at the top of **Figure 3-9**. Microglia remove all of the debris left by the dying axon. Meanwhile, the Schwann cells that provided the axon's myelin shrink and divide to form numerous smaller glial cells along the path the axon formerly took. The cell body then sends out axon sprouts that search for and follow the path formed by the Schwann cells.

Eventually, one sprout reaches the intended target and becomes the new axon; all other sprouts retract. The Schwann cells envelop the new axon, forming new myelin and restoring function. In the PNS, then, Schwann cells serve as signposts to guide axons to their appropriate end points. Axons can get lost, however, as sometimes happens after surgeons reattach a

More on understanding and treating Alzheimer disease in Section 16-3.

Section 4-2, describes how myelin speeds up the neuron's information flow. Focus 4-2 describes effects of myelin damage.

microglia Glial cells that originate in the blood, aid in cell repair, and scavenge debris in the nervous system.

myelin Glial coating that surrounds axons in the central and peripheral nervous systems; prevents adjacent neurons from short-circuiting.

oligodendroglia Glial cells in the CNS that myelinate axons.

Schwann cell Glial cell in the PNS that myelinates sensory and motor axons.

paralysis Loss of sensation and movement due to nervous system injury.

FIGURE 3-9 Neuron Repair Schwann cells aid the regrowth of axons in the somatic nervous system.

1 When a peripheral axon is cut, the axon dies.

2 Schwann cells first shrink and then divide, forming glial cells along the axon's former path.

3 The neuron sends out axon sprouts, one of which finds the Schwann-cell path and becomes a new axon.

4 Schwann cells envelop the new axon, forming new myelin.

Sections 11-1 and 11-4 detail causes of and treatments for spinal cord injury.

severed limb. If axons destined to innervate one finger end up innervating another finger instead, the wrong finger will move when a message is sent along that axon.

When the CNS is damaged, as happens, for example, when the spinal cord is cut, regrowth and repair do not occur, even though the distance that damaged fibers must bridge is short. The oligodendrocytes that myelinate CNS cells do not behave like PNS Schwann cells to encourage brain repair. They may actually play a role in inhibiting neuron regrowth (Rusielewicz et al., 2014). That recovery should take place in the PNS but not in the CNS is puzzling. Regrowth in the CNS may not occur in part because as neuronal circuits mature, they become exquisitely tuned to mediate individualized behavior and so are protected from the proliferation of new cells or the regrowth of existing cells.

(3-1) REVIEW

Cells of the Nervous System

Before you continue, check your understanding.

1. The two classes of nervous system cells are _____, which in humans number around _____, and _____, which in humans number about _____, reflecting the typical ratio.

2. Neurons, the information-conducting units of the nervous system, act either by _____ or by _____ one another through their connecting synapses.

3. The three types of neurons and their characteristic functions are _____, which _____; _____, which _____; and _____, which _____.

4. The five types of glial cells are _____, _____, _____, _____, and _____. Their functions include _____, _____, _____, _____, and _____ neurons.

5. What is the main obstacle to producing a robot with all of the behavioral abilities displayed by a mammal?

Answers appear at the back of the book.

For additional study tools, visit 🔵 **LaunchPad**:
www.macmillanhighered.com/launchpad/kolb5e

(3-2) Internal Structure of a Cell

What is it about the structure of neurons that generates the remarkable ability to receive, process, store, and send a seemingly limitless amount of information? To answer this question, we must look inside a neuron to see what its components are and understand what they do. Although neurons are minuscule, when we view them with an electron microscope, we find packed inside hundreds of interrelated parts that do the cell's work.

To a large extent, a cell's proteins determine its characteristics and functions. Each cell can manufacture thousands of proteins, which variously take part in building the cell and in communicating with other cells. When a neuron malfunctions or contains errors, proteins are implicated and so are involved in many kinds of brain disease. In this section, we explain how the different parts of a cell contribute to protein manufacture, describe what a protein is, and detail some functions of proteins.

Water, salts, and ions play prominent parts in the cell's functions, as you will learn in this and the next few chapters. If you already understand the structure of water and you know what a salt is and what ions are, read on. If you prefer a brief chemistry review first, turn to The Basics: Chemistry Review, on pages 88–89.

The Cell as a Factory

We began Section 3-1 by comparing a cell to a miniature factory, with work centers that cooperate to make and ship the cell's products—proteins. To investigate the cell's internal parts—the organelles—and how they function, we begin with a quick overview of the cell's internal structure.

Figure 3-10 displays many external and internal cellular components. A factory's outer wall separates it from the rest of the world and affords some security. Likewise, a cell's double-layered outer wall, or *cell membrane*, separates the cell from its surroundings and allows it to regulate what enters and leaves its domain. The cell membrane envelopes the neuron's contents and contributes to forming its cell body, its dendrites and their spines, and its axon and terminals. It thus forms the boundary around a continuous intracellular compartment.

Very few substances can enter or leave a cell spontaneously, because the cell membrane is virtually *impermeable* (impenetrable). Some proteins made by the cell are embedded in the cell membrane, where they facilitate the transport of substances into and out of the cell. These proteins thus serve as the cellular factory's gates.

FIGURE 3-10 Typical Nerve Cell This view of the outside and inside of a neuron reveals its overall structure and internal organelles and other components.

Dendrite: Cell extension that collects information from other cells

Dendritic spine: Small protrusion on dendrites that increases surface area

Nucleus: Structure containing the chromosomes and genes

Nuclear membrane: Membrane surrounding the nucleus

Mitochondrion: Structure that gathers, stores, and releases energy

Endoplasmic reticulum: Folded layers of membrane where proteins are assembled

Intracellular fluid: Fluid in which the cell's internal structures are suspended

Golgi body: Membranous structure that packages protein molecules for transport

Lysosomes: Sacs containing enzymes that break down wastes

Microfilaments: Threadlike fibers making up much of the cell's "skeleton"

Tubule: Tiny tube that transports molecules and helps give the cell its shape

Cell membrane: Membrane surrounding the cell

Axon: Extension that transmits information from cell body to other cells

THE BASICS ■

Chemistry Review

The smallest unit of a protein or any other chemical substance is the molecule. Molecules and the even smaller atoms of elements that constitute them are the cellular factory's raw materials.

Elements, Atoms, and Ions

Chemists represent each element, a substance that cannot be broken down into another substance, by a symbol—for example, O for oxygen, C for carbon, and H for hydrogen. The 10 elements listed below in the table Chemical Composition of the Brain constitute virtually the entire makeup of an average living cell. Many other elements are vital to the cell but present only in minute quantities.

The smallest quantity of an element that retains the properties of that element is an atom. Ordinarily, as shown opposite in part A of the figure Ion Formation, atoms are electrically neutral: their total positive and negative charges are equal.

Atoms of chemically reactive elements such as sodium and chlorine can easily lose or gain negatively charged particles, or electrons. When an atom gives up electrons, it becomes positively charged; when it takes on extra electrons, it becomes negatively charged, as illustrated in part B of Ion Formation. Either way, the charged atom is now an ion. Ions' positive or negative charges allow them to interact. This property is central to cell function.

Chemical Composition of the Brain

Percentage of weight	Element name, symbol	Atomic structure (not to scale)	Percentage of weight	Element name, symbol	Atomic structure (not to scale)
65.0	Oxygen, O				
18.5	Carbon, C		0.4	Potassium, K	
9.5	Hydrogen, H				
3.5	Nitrogen, N		0.2	Sulfur, S	
1.5	Calcium, Ca		0.2	Sodium, Na	
1.0	Phosphorus, P		0.2	Chlorine, Cl	

Together, oxygen, carbon, and hydrogen account for more than 90 percent of a cell's makeup.

Some symbols derive from an element's Latin name—K for *kalium* (Latin for *potassium*) and Na for *natrium* (Latin for *sodium*), for example.

Ions Critical to Neuronal Communication

Na^+	Sodium
K^+	Potassium
Ca^{2+}	Calcium
Cl^-	Chloride

Ions formed by loss of electrons are represented by an element's symbol followed by one or more plus signs.

Ions formed by gain of electrons are represented by an element's symbol followed by a minus sign.

Ion Formation

(A) Atoms

Total positive (+) and negative (–) charges in atoms are equal. The nucleus contains *neutrons* (no charge) and *protons* (positive charge). Orbiting the nucleus are *electrons* (negative charge).

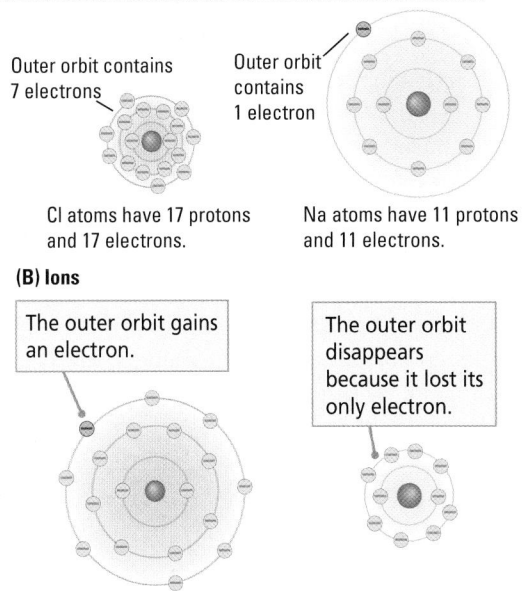

Outer orbit contains 7 electrons

Outer orbit contains 1 electron

Cl atoms have 17 protons and 17 electrons.

Na atoms have 11 protons and 11 electrons.

(B) Ions

The outer orbit gains an electron.

The outer orbit disappears because it lost its only electron.

Charged chloride ion (Cl⁻)

Charged sodium ion (Na⁺)

Chemistry of Water

(A) Water molecule

Two hydrogen atoms share electrons unequally with one oxygen atom, creating a polar water molecule positively charged on the hydrogen end and negatively charged on the oxygen end.

H H

O

O

H_2O

(B) Hydrogen bonds

Hydrogen bonds join water molecules to a maximum of four partners.

H^+ and O^{2-} ions in each water molecule are attracted to nearby water molecules.

Because water molecules are polar, they are attracted to other electrically charged substances and to one another. Part B of Chemistry of Water illustrates this attracting force, called a hydrogen bond. Hydrogen bonding enables water to dissolve electrically neutral salt crystals into their component ions. Salts thus cannot retain their shape in water: they dissolve. As illustrated in the figure Salty Water, the polar water molecules muscle their way into the Na^+ and Cl^- lattice, surrounding and separating the ions.

Essentially, it is salty water that bathes our brain cells, provides the medium for their activities, supports their communications, and constitutes the brain's CSF. Sodium chloride and many other dissolved salts, including KCl (potassium chloride) and $CaCl_2$ (calcium chloride) are among the constituents of the brain's salty water.

Molecules: Salts and Water

Salt crystals form bonds via the electrical attraction between ions. The formula for table salt, NaCl (sodium chloride), means that this molecule consists of one sodium ion and one chloride ion. KCl, the formula for the salt potassium chloride, is composed of one potassium ion (K^+) and one chloride ion (Cl^-).

Atoms bind together to form molecules, the smallest units of a substance that contain all of its properties. A water molecule (H_2O) is the smallest unit of water that retains the properties of water. Breaking down water any further would release its component elements, the gases hydrogen and oxygen. The symbol H_2O indicates that a water molecule is the union of two hydrogen atoms and one oxygen atom.

Ionic bonds hold salt molecules together, but the atoms of water molecules share electrons and electron sharing is not equal: H electrons spend more time orbiting the O atom than orbiting each H atom. As shown above in part A of Chemistry of Water, this structure gives the oxygen region of the water molecule a slight negative charge and leaves the hydrogen regions with a slight positive charge. Like atoms, most molecules are electrically neutral, but water is polar: it carries opposite charges on opposite ends, just as Earth does at the North and South Poles.

Salty Water

Negative Cl^- ions attract the positive poles of water molecules. Positive Na^+ ions attract the negative poles of water molecules.

Salt (NaCl)

Water (H_2O)

Polar water molecules surround Na^+ and Cl^- ions in a salt crystal, dissolving it.

In the CNS, the extracellular fluid is CSF.

Although neurons and glia appear to be packed tightly together, like all cells, they are separated by *extracellular fluid* composed mainly of water with dissolved salts and many other chemicals. A similar *intracellular fluid* is found inside a cell. What's important is the cell membrane's relative impermeability, which ensures that concentrations of substances inside and outside the cell are different.

Within the cell shown in Figure 3-10 are membranes that surround its *organelles*, similar to the work areas demarcated by a factory's interior walls. Each organelle membrane is also relatively impermeable and so concentrates needed chemicals while keeping out unneeded ones.

The prominent *nuclear membrane* surrounds the cell's *nucleus*. Within the nucleus the genetic blueprints for the cell's proteins are stored, copied, then sent to the "factory floor," the *endoplasmic reticulum*. The ER is an extension of the nuclear membrane, and here the cell's protein products are assembled in accordance with instructions from the nucleus. Once those proteins are assembled, many are packaged and sent throughout the cell. The *Golgi bodies* are "mailrooms," where proteins are wrapped, addressed, and shipped.

Other cell components are *tubules* of several kinds. Some (*microfilaments*) reinforce the cell's structure; others aid in the cell's movements. Still others (*microtubules*) form the transportation network that carries proteins to their destinations, much as roads allow a factory's trucks and forklifts to deliver goods to their destinations.

Two other important parts of the cellular factory shown in Figure 3-10 are the *mitochondria* (sing. *mitochondrion*), the cell's power plants, which supply its energy needs, and *lysosomes*, vesicles that transport incoming supplies and remove and store wastes. Interestingly, more lysosomes are found in old cells than in young ones. Cells apparently have trouble disposing of all of their garbage, just as societies do.

Cell Membrane: Barrier and Gatekeeper

The cell membrane separates the intracellular from the extracellular fluid, allowing the cell to function as an independent unit. The membrane's double-layered structure, shown in **Figure 3-11**A, regulates the movement of substances into and out of the cell.

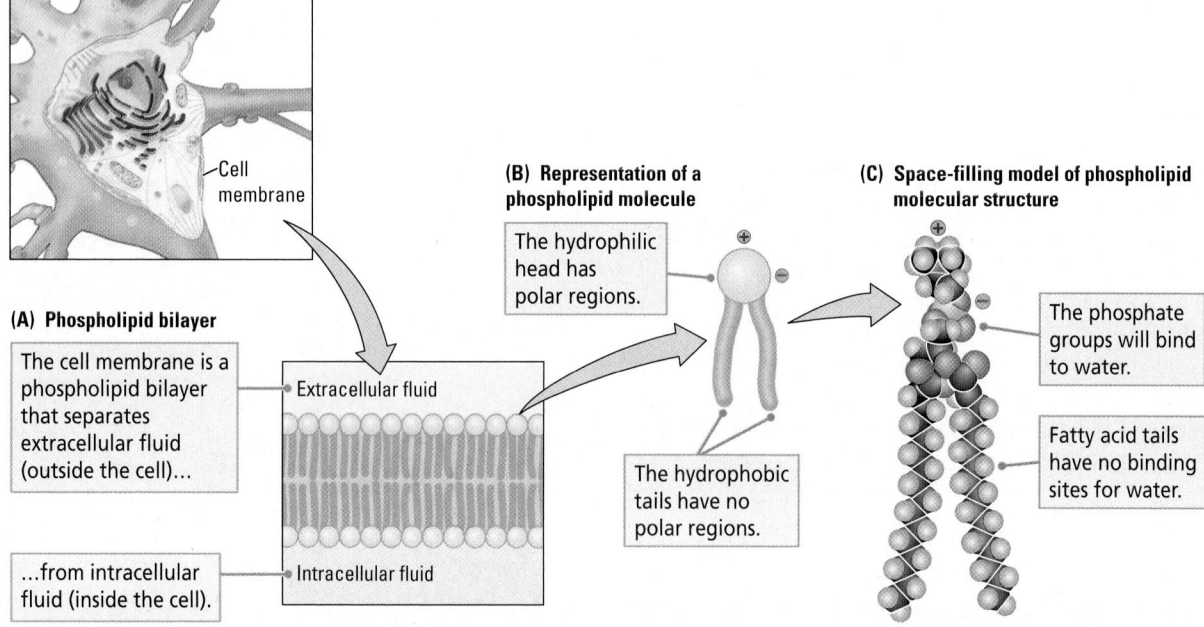

FIGURE 3-11 Bilayer Cell Membrane Structure **(A)** Double-layered cell membrane close up. **(B)** Detail of a phospholipid molecule's polar head and electrically neutral tails. **(C)** Space-filling model shows why the phosphate head's polar regions (positive and negative poles) are hydrophilic, whereas its nonpolar fatty acid tail is hydrophobic.

One regulated substance is water. If too much water enters a cell, it will burst; if too much water leaves a cell, it will shrivel. The cell membrane's structure helps ensure that neither happens.

The cell membrane also regulates the differing concentrations of salts and other chemicals on its inner and outer sides. This regulation is important because, if its concentrations of chemicals are unbalanced, the cell will not function normally. What properties of a cell membrane allow it to regulate water and salt concentrations? One property is its special molecular construction. These molecules, called *phospholipids*, are named for their structure, shown close up in Figure 3-11B.

Figure 3-11C shows a space-filling chemical model of the phospholipid molecule's structure. The molecule has a head containing the element phosphorus (P) bound to some other atoms, and it has two tails, which are lipids, or fat molecules. The head has a polar electrical charge, with a positive charge in one location and a negative charge in another, as do water molecules. The tails consist of hydrogen and carbon atoms that tightly bind to one another by their shared electrons; hence, the fatty tail has no polar regions.

The polar head and the nonpolar tails are the underlying reasons that a phospholipid molecule can form cell membranes. The heads are *hydrophilic* (Greek *hydro*, meaning *water*, and *philia*, meaning *love*) and so are attracted to one another and to polar water molecules. The nonpolar lipid tails have no such attraction for water. They are *hydrophobic*, or water hating (from the Greek word *phobia*, meaning *fear*).

Quite literally, then, the head of a phospholipid loves water and the tails hate it. To avoid water, the tails of phospholipid molecules point toward each other, and the hydrophilic heads align with one another and point outward to the watery intracellular and extracellular fluid. In this way, the cell membrane consists of a bilayer (two layers) of phospholipid molecules (see Figure 3-11A).

The bilayer cell membrane is flexible even as it forms a formidable barrier to a wide variety of substances. It is impenetrable to intracellular and extracellular water, because polar water molecules cannot pass through the hydrophobic tails on the membrane's interior. Ions in the extracellular and intracellular fluid also cannot penetrate this membrane, because they carry charges and thus cannot pass by the polar phospholipid heads. In fact, only a few small molecules, such as oxygen (O_2), carbon dioxide (CO_2), and the sugar glucose, can traverse a phospholipid bilayer.

The Nucleus and Protein Synthesis

In our factory analogy, the nucleus is the cell's executive office, where the blueprints for making proteins are stored, copied, and sent to the factory floor. These blueprints are called **genes**, segments of DNA that encode the synthesis of particular proteins. Genes are contained within the *chromosomes*, the double-helix structures that hold an organism's entire DNA library.

The chromosomes have been likened to a book of blueprints. Each chromosome contains thousands of genes. Each gene is the blueprint, or code, for making one protein. The location of the chromosomes in the cell nucleus, the appearance of a chromosome, and the structure of the DNA within a chromosome are shown in **Figure 3-12**.

This static picture of chromosomes does not represent the way they look in living cells. Videos of the cell nucleus show that chromosomes are constantly changing shape and moving in relation to one another, jockeying to occupy the best locations within the nucleus.

gene DNA segment that encodes the synthesis of a particular protein.

FIGURE 3-12 Chromosome The nerve cell's nucleus contains paired chromosomes of double-stranded DNA molecules bound together by a sequence of nucleotide bases.

Chromosome

Each chromosome is a double-stranded molecule of DNA.

DNA

Adenine (A) binds with thymine (T). Guanine (G) binds with cytosine (C).

Chromosome means *colored body*; they are so named because chromosomes can be readily stained with certain dyes.

By changing shape, chromosomes expose different genes to the surrounding fluid, thus allowing the gene to begin the process of making a protein.

A human somatic (body) cell has 23 pairs of chromosomes, or 46 chromosomes in all (in contrast, the 23 chromosomes within a reproductive cell are not paired). Each chromosome is a double-stranded molecule of *deoxyribonucleic acid* (DNA). The two strands of a DNA molecule coil around each other, as shown in Figure 3-12.

Each strand possesses a variable sequence of four *nucleotide bases*, the constituent molecules of the genetic code: *adenine* (A), *thymine* (T), *guanine* (G), and *cytosine* (C). Adenine on one strand always pairs with thymine on the other, whereas guanine on one strand always pairs with cytosine on the other. The two strands of the DNA helix are bound together by the attraction between the two bases in each pair, as illustrated in Figure 3-12. Sequences of hundreds of nucleotide bases within the chromosomes spell out the genetic code. Scientists represent this code by the letters of the nucleotide bases, for example ATGCCG and so forth.

A gene is a segment of a DNA strand. A gene's code is its sequence of thousands of nucleotide bases. Much as a sequence of letters spells out a word, the sequence of ACTG base pairs spells out the order in which *amino acids*, the constituent molecules of proteins, should be assembled to construct a certain protein. To begin to make a protein, the appropriate gene segment of the DNA strands first unwinds to expose its bases. The exposed sequence of nucleotide bases on one of the DNA strands then serves as a template to attract free-floating molecules called *nucleotides*. The nucleotides, once attached, form a complementary strand of *ribonucleic acid* (RNA), the single-stranded nucleic acid molecule required for protein synthesis. This process, called *transcription*, is shown in steps 1 and 2 of **Figure 3-13**. (To transcribe means *to copy*, as in copying part of a message you receive in a text.)

protein Folded-up polypeptide chain that serves a particular function in the body.

FIGURE 3-13 Protein Synthesis Information in a cell flows from DNA to mRNA to protein (peptide chain).

The Endoplasmic Reticulum and Protein Manufacture

RNA produced through transcription is much like a single strand of DNA except that the base *uracil* (U), which also is attracted to adenine, takes the place of thymine. The transcribed strand of RNA is called *messenger* RNA (mRNA) because it carries the protein code (the message) out of the nucleus to the endoplasmic reticulum, where proteins are manufactured.

Steps 3 and 4 in Figure 3-13 show that the ER consists of membranous sheets folded to form numerous channels. A distinguishing feature of the ER is that it may be studded with *ribosomes*, protein structures that act as catalysts to facilitate the building of proteins. When an mRNA molecule reaches the ER, it passes through a ribosome, where its genetic code is read. In this process of *translation*, a particular sequence of nucleotide bases in the mRNA is transformed into a particular sequence of amino acids. *Transfer* RNA (tRNA) assists in translating nucleotide bases into amino acids.

As shown in **Figure 3-14**, each group of three consecutive nucleotide bases along an mRNA molecule encodes one particular amino acid. These sequences of three bases are called *codons*. For example, the codon uracil, guanine, guanine (UGG) encodes the amino acid tryptophan (Trp), whereas the codon uracil, uracil, uracil (UUU) encodes the amino acid phenylalanine (Phe). The sequence of codons on the mRNA strand determines the sequence of the resulting amino acid chain.

Humans utilize 20 different amino acids, all structurally similar, as illustrated in **Figure 3-15A**. Each consists of a central carbon atom (C) bound to a hydrogen atom (H), an *amino group* (NH^{3+}), a *carboxyl group* (COO^-), and a *side chain* (represented by the letter R). The side chain varies in chemical composition from one amino acid to another. Each amino group (NH^{3+}) is bound to the carboxyl group (COO^-) of the adjacent amino acid by a *peptide bond*, which gives amino acid chains their alternative name, *polypeptide chain* (Figure 3-15B).

Just as a remarkable number of words can be made from the 26 letters of the English alphabet, a remarkable number of polypeptide (meaning *many peptides*) chains can be made from the 20 amino acids. These amino acids can form 400 (20 × 20) dipeptides (two-peptide combinations), 8000 (20 × 20 × 20) tripeptides (three-peptide combinations), and almost countless polypeptides.

In summary, the information flow driven by the genetic code is conceptually quite simple: a gene (portion of a DNA strand) is transcribed into a strand of mRNA, and ribosomes translate the mRNA into a molecular chain of amino acids, a polypeptide chain. Thus the sequence of events in building a protein:

$$DNA \rightarrow mRNA \rightarrow protein$$

Proteins: The Cell's Product

A polypeptide chain and a protein are related, but they are not the same. The relation is analogous to the relation between a length of ribbon and a bow that can be made from the ribbon. Long polypeptide chains have a strong tendency to twist into a helix (a spiral) or to form pleated sheets, which in turn have a strong tendency to fold together to form more complex shapes, as shown in **Figure 3-16**. A **protein** is a folded-up polypeptide chain that serves a particular function in the body.

Any one neuron contains as many as 20,000 genes, and it can, in principle, produce as many as 20,000 different protein molecules. The number of proteins that can ultimately be produced by a neuron is far larger than the number of its genes, however. Although each gene codes for one protein, a protein can be cleaved into pieces—by enzymes, for example—or combined with other proteins in a variety of cellular processes to form still other proteins.

FIGURE 3-14 Transcription and Translation In protein synthesis (see Figure 3-13), a particular sequence of nucleotide bases in a strand of DNA (top) is transcribed into mRNA (center). Each sequence of three nucleotide bases in the mRNA strand (a codon) encodes one amino acid. In translation, the amino acids, directed by the codons, link together to form a polypeptide chain (bottom). The amino acids are tryptophan (Trp), phenylalanine (Phe), glycine (Gly), and serine (Ser).

(A) Amino acid structure

(B) Polypeptide chain

FIGURE 3-15 Properties of Amino Acids **(A)** Each amino acid consists of a central carbon atom (C) attached to an amine group (NH^{3+}), a carboxyl group (COO^-), and a distinguishing side chain (R). **(B)** The amino acids are linked by peptide bonds to form a polypeptide chain.

Primary structure	Secondary structures	Tertiary structure	Quaternary structure
Amino acid chains...	...form pleated sheets or helices.	Sheets and helices fold to form a protein.	A number of proteins combine to form a more complex protein.

FIGURE 3-16 Four Levels of Protein Structure Whether a polypeptide chain forms a pleated sheet or a helix and what its three-dimensional shape ultimately will be are determined by the amino acid sequence in the primary structure. In rare circumstances, prion proteins can misfold and wreak havoc; see Section 16-3.

A protein's shape and its ability to change shape and to combine with other proteins are central to its function. Through their shapes and changes in shape, proteins can combine with other proteins in chemical reactions. They can modify the length and shape of other proteins and so act as enzymes. Proteins embedded in a cell membrane form passageways called channels, gates, and pumps that regulate the flow of substances through the membrane. And proteins can be exported through the axon terminal to travel to other cells and so act as messenger molecules.

Golgi Bodies and Microtubules: Protein Packaging and Shipment

Getting proteins to the right destination is the task of cellular components that package, label, and ship them. These components operate much like a postal or shipping service.

To reach their appropriate destinations, protein molecules that have been synthesized in the cell are wrapped in membranes and marked with addresses to indicate where they are to go. This wrapping and labeling take place in the organelles called Golgi bodies. The packaged proteins are then loaded onto motor molecules that move along the many microtubules radiating through the cell, carrying each protein to its destination. Protein export is illustrated in **Figure 3-17**.

If a protein is destined to remain within the cell, it is unloaded into the intracellular fluid. If it is to be incorporated into the cell membrane, it is carried to the membrane, where it inserts itself. Some proteins are expelled from the cell. In this process, called *exocytosis*, the membrane, or *vesicle*, in which the protein is wrapped fuses with the cell membrane, and the protein is excreted into the extracellular fluid. The roles proteins play when embedded

FIGURE 3-17 Protein Export Exporting a protein entails packaging, transport, and assigning its fate at the destination.

1 Proteins formed in the ER enter the Golgi bodies, where they are wrapped in a membrane and given a shipping address.

2 Each protein package is attached to a motor molecule and moves along a microtubule to its destination.

3 A protein may be incorporated into the membrane,...

4 ...remain within the cell to act as an enzyme,...

5 ...or be excreted from the cell by exocytosis.

in the cell membrane or exported from the cell are central to understanding how neurons process information and determine behavior.

Crossing the Cell Membrane: Channels, Gates, and Pumps

Proteins embedded in the cell membrane serve many functions. One is transporting substances across the membrane. We now consider how three such membrane proteins—channels, gates, and pumps—perform the transport function. In each case, the particular protein's function is an emergent property of its shape.

A protein's shape and its ability to change shape both derive from the precise amino acid sequence that composes the protein molecule. Some proteins change shape when other chemicals bind to them; others change shape as a function of temperature; and still others change shape in response to changes in electrical charge. The protein molecule's ability to change shape is analogous to a lock in a door. When a key of the appropriate size and shape is inserted into the lock and turned, the locking device activates and changes shape, allowing the door to be closed or opened.

Such a shape-changing protein is illustrated in **Figure 3-18**. The surface of this protein molecule has a groove, called a *receptor*, analogous to a keyhole. Small molecules, such as glucose, or other proteins can bind to a protein's receptors and cause the protein to change shape. Changes in shape allow the proteins to serve some new function.

Some membrane proteins form **channels** through which substances can pass. Different-sized channels regulate the passage of different-sized substances. **Figure 3-19**A illustrates a protein with a particular shape forming a channel large enough to pass potassium (K^+) but not other ions. Other protein channels allow sodium ions or chloride ions to pass into or out of the cell. Still others allow the passage of various other substances.

Figure 3-19B shows a protein molecule that acts as a **gate** to regulate the passage of substances. Like the protein in Figure 3-18, gates change their shape in response to some trigger. The protein allows substances to pass through when its shape forms a channel and prevents passage when its shape leaves the channel closed.

Changes in protein shape can also allow it to act as a **pump**. Figure 3-19C shows a protein that changes its shape to pump Na^+ and K^+ across the membrane, exchanging the Na^+ on one side for the K^+ on the other.

Channels, gates, and pumps play an important role in allowing substances to enter and leave a cell. This passage of substances is critical in explaining how neurons send messages. Chapter 4 explores how neurons use electrical activity to communicate.

Protein has a receptor site for glucose.

Glucose bound to receptor site

Protein changes shape when glucose docks with the receptor.

FIGURE 3-18 Receptor Binding When substances bind to a protein's receptors, the protein changes shape, which may change its function.

channel Opening in a protein embedded in the cell membrane that allows the passage of ions.

gate Protein embedded in a cell membrane that allows substances to pass through the membrane on some occasions but not on others.

pump Protein in the cell membrane that actively transports a substance across the membrane.

(A) Channel

K^+

Ions can cross a cell membrane through the appropriately shaped channel.

(B) Gated channel

Gates open Na^+ Gate closed

A gated channel changes shape to allow the passage of substances when gates are open...

...and to prevent passage when one or both gates are closed.

(C) Pump

Extracellular fluid K^+ Na^+

Na^+ Intracellular fluid K^+

A pump transporter changes shape...

...to carry substances across a cell membrane.

FIGURE 3-19 Transmembrane Proteins Channels, gates, and pumps are proteins embedded in the cell membrane.

(3-2) REVIEW

Internal Structure of a Cell

Before you continue, check your understanding.

1. The constituent parts of the cell include the _____, _____, _____, _____, _____, and _____.

2. The product of the cell is _____. They serve many functions, including acting at the cell membrane as _____, _____, and _____ to regulate movement of substances across the membrane.

3. The basic sequence of events in building a protein is that _____ makes _____ makes _____.

4. Once proteins are formed in the _____, they are wrapped in membranes by _____ and transported by _____ to their designated sites in the neuron or its membrane or exported from the cell by _____.

5. Why is a cell more than a protein factory?

Answers appear at the back of the book.

For additional study tools, visit 🌀 LaunchPad:
www.macmillanhighered.com/launchpad/kolb5e

(3-3) Genes, Cells, and Behavior

Your *genotype* (genetic makeup) influences your physical and behavioral traits, which combine to form your *phenotype* (individual characteristics). Genetic analysis conducted by the Human Genome Project has cataloged the human genome—all 20,000 or so genes in our species—and today individual genomes are routinely sequenced. (Recall the Beery twins in Research Focus 3-1.) James Watson, the codiscoverer of DNA, was the first to have his genome sequenced.

Researchers have succeeded in sequencing the long-extinct Neanderthal genome as well. The genomes of James Watson and the Neanderthal are surprisingly similar, as you'd expect for close hominid relatives. You can have your genome sequenced to reveal many aspects of its coding functions, including your relationship to Neanderthals. The cost is about $100. (Before you decide, you may want to check on any required information sharing with employers and insurers.)

Studying how genes influence our traits is the objective of Mendelian genetics, named for Gregor Mendel, whose research led to the concept of the gene. Studying how the environment influences gene expression is the objective of epigenetics. In this section we describe how both factors influence our phenotypes.

Mendelian Genetics and the Genetic Code

The nucleus of each human somatic cell contains 23 pairs of chromosomes, or 46 in all. One member of each pair comes from the mother, and the other member comes from the father. The chromosome pairs are numbered from 1 to 23, roughly according to size, with chromosome 1 being the largest (**Figure 3-20**).

Chromosome pairs 1 through 22 are called *autosomes*, and they contain the genes that contribute most to our physical appearance and behavior. The twenty-third pair are the *sex chromosomes*, which contribute to our physical and behavioral sexual characteristics. The two mammalian sex chromosomes are referred to as X and Y because of their appearance, shown at the right in Figure 3-20. Ordinarily, female mammals have two X chromosomes, whereas males have an X and a Y.

Because all but your sex chromosomes are matched pairs, each cell contains two copies of every gene, one inherited from your mother, the other from your father. These two copies

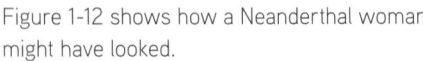

Figure 1-12 shows how a Neanderthal woman might have looked.

Nucleus

CNRI/Science Photo Library/Science Source

FIGURE 3-20 Human Chromosomes The nucleus of a human cell contains 23 chromosomes derived from the father and 23 from the mother. Sexual characteristics are determined by the twenty-third pair, the X and Y (sex) chromosomes.

of a gene are called **alleles**. The term *matched* here does not necessarily mean identical. The nucleotide sequences in a pair of alleles may be either identical or different. If they are identical, the two alleles are **homozygous** (*homo-* means *the same*). If they are different, the two alleles are **heterozygous** (*hetero-* means *different*).

The nucleotide sequence most common in a population is called the wild-type allele, whereas a less frequently occurring sequence is called a **mutation**. Any wild-type allele may have a number of mutations, some beneficial, some neutral and some harmful.

Dominant and Recessive Alleles

If both alleles in a gene pair are homozygous, the two encode the same protein, but if the two alleles in a pair are heterozygous, they encode somewhat different proteins. Three possible outcomes attend the heterozygous condition when these proteins express a physical or behavioral trait: (1) only the allele from the mother may be expressed, (2) only the allele from the father may be expressed, or (3) both alleles may be expressed simultaneously.

A member of a gene pair that is routinely expressed as a trait is called a *dominant* allele; a unexpressed allele is *recessive*. Alleles can vary considerably in their dominance. In complete dominance, only the allele's own trait is expressed in the phenotype. In incomplete dominance, the allele's own trait is expressed only partially. In *codominance*, both the allele's own trait and that of the other allele in the gene pair are expressed completely.

Each gene makes an independent contribution to the offspring's inheritance, even though the contribution may not always be visible in the offspring's phenotype. When paired with a dominant allele, a recessive allele is often not expressed. Still, it can be passed on to future generations and influence their phenotypes when not masked by the influence of some dominant trait.

Genetic Mutations

The mechanism described in Section 3-2 for reproducing genes and passing them on to offspring is fallible. Errors can arise in the nucleotide sequence when reproductive cells make gene copies. The altered alleles are mutations.

A mutation may be as small as a change in a single nucleotide base, or *single nucleotide polymorphism* (SNP, pronounced *snip*). This one base change results in a change in a codon and a resulting change in one amino acid in a protein. A single amino acid change is a mutation and is often sufficient to alter the protein's function.

Because the average gene has more than 1200 nucleotide bases, an enormous number of SNPs as well as more complex losses and changes in bases can occur on a single gene. For example, the *BRCA1* (breast cancer) gene, found on chromosome 17, is a caretaker gene that contributes to preventing breast cancer and other cancers in both men and women. More than 1000 mutations of this gene have already been found. Thus, in principle, there are more than 1000 ways in which to inherit a predisposition to a cancer just from this gene.

A mutation in a nucleotide or the addition of a nucleotide to a gene sequence can be beneficial or disruptive or both. For example, a SNP in which a T base is substituted for an A base

allele Alternative form of a gene; a gene pair contains two alleles.

homozygous Having two identical alleles for a trait.

heterozygous Having two different alleles for the same trait.

mutation Alteration of an allele that yields a different version of its protein.

In this micrograph a sickle cell is surrounded by healthy blood cells.

Experiment 1-1 describes one of Mendel's experiments.

Scientists Warren Tay and Bernard Sachs first described the disorder.

Tay-Sachs disease Inherited birth defect caused by the loss of genes that encode the enzyme necessary for breaking down certain fatty substances; appears 4 to 6 months after birth and results in intellectual disability, physical changes, and death by about age 5.

wild type Typical allele (most common in a population).

Huntington disease Hereditary disease characterized by chorea (ceaseless involuntary jerky movements) and progressive dementia, ending in death.

in the *HBB* (hemoglobin) gene on chromosome 11 causes sickle-cell anemia, a condition in which blood cells take on an abnormal sickle shape. The sickle shape offers some protection against malaria, but sickle cells also have poor oxygen-carrying capacity, which weakens the person who possesses them. Sickle-cell anemia is the most common genetic blood disease, affecting millions of people worldwide, including 80,000 people in the United States.

Each of us carries a surprisingly large number of genetic mutations. Because of cell division, different mutations may be localized in different parts of our body and brain and may contribute to individual variations in our organs, including the brain (Charney, 2012). While mutations may be beneficial or seemingly neutral to the functioning of the organism that carries them, most mutations have negative effects. If not lethal, they produce in their carrier debilitating physical and behavioral abnormalities.

Neuroscientists cannot yet explain human behavior in relation to genes and neurons, but we know the severe behavioral consequences of about 2000 genetic abnormalities that affect the nervous system. For example, an error in a gene could produce a protein that should be an ion channel but will not allow the appropriate substance to pass. It may produce a pump that will not pump or a protein that the cell's transportation system refuses to transport.

Applying Mendel's Principles

Gregor Mendel introduced the concept of dominant and recessive alleles in the nineteenth century, when he studied pea plants. Today, scientists study genetic variation to gain insight into how genes, neurons, and behaviors are linked. This knowledge is directed toward explaining healthy behavior and helping reduce the negative effects of genetic abnormalities, perhaps someday even eliminating them.

Allele Disorders That Affect the Brain

Some disorders caused by mutant genes illustrate Mendel's principles of dominant and recessive alleles. One is **Tay-Sachs disease**, caused by a dysfunctional protein that acts as the enzyme HexA (hexosaminidase A). The outcome is that it fails to break down a class of lipids (fats) in the brain.

Symptoms usually appear a few months after birth and rarely at later ages. The baby begins to have seizures, deteriorating eyesight, and degenerating motor and mental abilities. Inevitably, the child dies within a few years. Tay-Sachs mutations appear with high frequency among certain ethnic groups, including Jews of European origin and French Canadians, but the mutation in different populations can be different.

The dysfunctional Tay-Sachs HexA enzyme is caused by a recessive allele of the *HEXA* (hexosaminidase) gene on chromosome 15. Distinctive inheritance patterns result from recessive alleles, because two copies (one from the mother and one from the father) are needed for the disorder to develop. A baby can inherit Tay-Sachs disease only when both parents carry the recessive allele. However, a number of causative alleles exist, and even inheriting different mutant alleles, one from each parent, can cause Tay-Sachs disease.

Because both parents have survived to adulthood, both must also possess a corresponding dominant wild-type *HEXA* allele for that particular gene pair. The egg and sperm cells produced by this man and woman will therefore contain a copy of the **wild type** or the mutation of these two alleles. Which allele is passed on is determined completely by chance.

In any child born of two Tay-Sachs carriers, then, this situation gives rise to three possible gene combinations, as shown in **Figure 3-21**A. The child may have two wild-type alleles, in which case he or she will be spared the disorder and cannot pass it on. The child may have one normal and one Tay-Sachs allele, in which case he or she, like the parents, will be a carrier. Or the child may have two Tay-Sachs alleles, in which case he or she will develop the disease.

The chance of a child of two carriers being normal is 25 percent, the chance of being a carrier is 50 percent, and the chance of having Tay-Sachs disease is 25 percent. If one parent is a Tay-Sachs carrier and the other is normal, any child has a 50-50 chance being normal or a carrier. Such a couple has no chance of conceiving a baby with Tay-Sachs disease.

(A) Recessive gene carries Tay-Sachs allele

(B) Dominant gene carries Huntington's allele

Two copies required to exhibit trait

Only one copy required to exhibit trait

FIGURE 3-21 Inheritance Patterns **(A)** Recessive condition: If a parent has one mutant allele, the parent will not show symptoms of the disease but will be a carrier. If both parents carry a mutant allele, each of their offspring stands a 25 percent chance of developing the disease. **(B)** Dominant condition: A person with a single allele will develop the disease. If this person mates with a noncarrier, offspring have a 50-50 chance of developing the disease. If both parents are carriers, both will develop the disease, and offspring have a 75 percent chance of developing it.

The Tay-Sachs allele operates independently of the dominant allele. As a result, it still produces the defective HexA enzyme, so the person who carries it has a higher than normal lipid accumulation in the brain. Because this person also has a normal allele that produces a functional enzyme, the abnormal lipid accumulation is not enough to cause Tay-Sachs disease.

Fortunately, a blood test can detect whether a person carries the Tay-Sachs allele. People who find that they are carriers can make informed decisions about conceiving children. If they avoid having children with another Tay-Sachs carrier, none of their children will have the disorder, although some will probably be carriers. Where genetic counseling has been effective, the disease has been eliminated.

The normal dominant allele that a carrier of Tay-Sachs possesses produces enough functional enzyme to enable the brain to operate in a satisfactory way. That would not be the case if the normal allele were recessive, however, as happens with the genetic disorder **Huntington disease**. Here, the buildup of an abnormal version of the *huntingtin* protein kills brain cells, especially in the basal ganglia and the cortex.

Symptoms can begin at any time from infancy to old age, but they most often start in midlife and include abnormal involuntary movements, which is why the disorder was once called a *chorea* (from the Greek meaning *dance*). Other symptoms are memory loss and eventually a complete deterioration of behavior, followed by death. The abnormal *HTT* (huntingtin) allele is dominant, the recessive allele normal, so only one defective allele is needed to cause the disease.

Figure 3-21B illustrates the inheritance patterns associated with a dominant allele on chromosome 4 that produces Huntington disease. If one parent carries the defective allele, offspring have a 50 percent chance of inheriting the disorder. If both parents have the defective allele, the chance of inheritance increases to 75 percent. As discussed further in Clinical Focus 3-4, Huntington Disease, on page 100, because the abnormal *huntingtin* allele usually is not expressed until midlife, after the people who possess it have had children, it is passed down even though it is lethal.

As with the allele causing Tay-Sachs disease, a genetic test can determine whether a person carries the allele that causes Huntington disease. If so, the person can elect not to procreate. A decision not to have children in this case will reduce the incidence of the abnormal *huntingtin* allele in the human gene pool.

Huntington Disease

Woody Guthrie, whose protest songs made him a spokesman for farm workers during the Great Depression of the 1930s, is revered among the founders of American folk music. His best-known song is "This Land Is Your Land." Singer and songwriter Bob Dylan was instrumental in reviving Guthrie's popularity in the 1960s.

Guthrie died in 1967 after struggling with what was eventually diagnosed as Huntington disease. His mother had died of a similar condition, although her illness was never diagnosed. Two of Guthrie's five children from two marriages developed the disease, and his second wife, Marjorie, became active in promoting its study.

Huntington disease is devastating, characterized by memory impairment; choreas (abnormal, uncontrollable movements); and marked changes in personality, eventually leading to nearly total loss of healthy behavioral, emotional, and intellectual functioning. Even before the onset of motor symptoms, Huntington disease impairs *theory of mind*, a person's ability to assess the behavior of others (Eddy and Rickards, 2015).

The symptoms of Huntington disease result from neuronal degeneration in the basal ganglia and cortex. Symptoms can appear at any age but typically start in midlife. In 1983, the *HTT* (huntingtin) gene responsible for forming the abnormal huntingtin protein was found on chromosome 4.

The *HTT* gene has been a source of insights into the transmission of genetic disorders. Part of the gene contains repeats of the base sequence CAG. The CAG codon encodes the amino acid glutamine. If the number of CAG repeats exceeds about 40, then the carrier, with 40 or more glutamine amino acids in the huntingtin protein, has an increased likelihood of Huntington symptoms.

As the number of CAG repeats increases, the onset of symptoms occurs earlier in life, and the disease progresses more rapidly. Typically, non-Europeans have fewer repeats than do Europeans, among whom the disease is more common. The number of repeats can also increase with transmission from the father but not from the mother.

Investigations into why brain cells change in Huntington disease and into potential treatments use transgenic animal models. Mice, rats, and monkeys that have received the *HTT* gene feature the abnormal huntingtin protein and display symptoms of Huntington disease (Gu et al., 2015).

Woody Guthrie, whose unpublished lyrics and artwork are archived at woodyguthrie.org.

Chromosome Abnormalities

Genetic disorders are not caused solely by single defective alleles. Some nervous system disorders are caused by copy number variations, that is, aberrations in a part of a chromosome or even an entire chromosome. Copy number variations are related to a variety of disorders, including autism, schizophrenia, and learning disabilities. Often though, copy number variation has little obvious consequence or is beneficial. For example, humans average about 6 copies of the *AMY1* (amylase) gene but may have as many as 15 copies. The gene is an adaptation that improves the ability to digest starchy foods (Mimori et al., 2015).

One condition due to a change in chromosome number in humans is **Down syndrome**, which affects approximately 1 in 700 children. Down syndrome is usually the result of an extra copy of chromosome 21. One parent (usually the mother) passes on two copies of chromosome 21 to the child rather than the normal single chromosome. Combining these two with one chromosome from the other parent yields three chromosomes 21, an abnormal number called a *trisomy* (**Figure 3-22**).

Although chromosome 21 is the smallest human chromosome, its trisomy can dramatically alter a person's phenotype. People with Down syndrome have characteristic facial features and short stature. They are susceptible to heart defects, respiratory infections, and intellectual impairment. They are prone to developing leukemia and Alzheimer disease. Although people with Down syndrome usually have a much shorter than normal life span, some live to middle age or beyond. Improved educational opportunities for children with Down syndrome shows that they can learn to compensate greatly for their mental disabilities.

Down syndrome Chromosomal abnormality resulting in intellecutal impairment and other abnormalities, usually caused by an extra chromosome 21.

BSIP/Getty Images

© Everett Collection Inc/Alamy

FIGURE 3-22 Chromosome Aberration Left: Down syndrome, also known as trisomy 21, is caused by an extra chromosome 21 (colored red, bottom row at left). Right: Chris Burke, the first person with Down syndrome to play a leading role, on the television series *Life Goes On* in the 1990s, is now in his fifties. He performs as a lead singer in a band.

Genetic Engineering

Despite advances in understanding gene structure and function, the gap in understanding how genes produce behavior remains wide. To investigate gene structure and behavior relations, geneticists have invented methods to influence the traits genes express. This approach collectively defines the science of *genetic engineering*. In its simplest forms, genetic engineering entails manipulating a genome, removing a gene from a genome, or modifying or adding a gene to the genome. Its techniques include selective breeding, cloning, and transgenics.

Selective Breeding

The oldest means of influencing genetic traits is the selective breeding of animals and plants. Beginning with the domestication of wolves into dogs more than 30,000 years ago, humans have domesticated many animal species by selectively breeding males and females that display particular traits. The selective breeding of dogs, for example, has produced the species with the most diverse traits of all animal species: breeds that can run fast, haul heavy loads, retrieve prey, dig for burrowing animals, climb rocky cliffs in search of sea birds, herd sheep and cattle, or sit on an owner's lap and cuddle. Selective breeding especially influences dogs' sociability with humans (Persson et al., 2015).

Maintaining spontaneous mutations is one objective of selective breeding. Using this method, researchers produce whole populations of animals possessing some unusual trait that originally arose as an unexpected mutation in only one individual or in a few animals. In laboratory colonies of mice, for example, multiple spontaneous mutations have been discovered and maintained to produce over 450 different mouse strains.

Some strains of mice make abnormal movements, such as reeling, staggering, and jumping. Other strains have diseases of the immune system; others are blind or cannot hear. Some mice are smart; some mice are not; some have big brains;, some, small; and many display distinctive behavioral traits. Many such genetic variations can also be found in humans. As a result, the neural and genetic bases of the altered behavior in the mice can be studied systematically to understand and treat human disorders.

Cloning

More direct approaches to manipulating the expression of genetic traits include altering early embryonic development. One such method is *cloning*—producing an offspring that is genetically identical to another animal.

Unlike other animals, humans can consent to experimental procedures. Section 7-7 frames debates on the benefits and ethics of conducting research using nonhuman animals.

Sections 7-1 and 7-5 review genetic methods used in neuroscience research.

To clone an animal, scientists begin with a cell nucleus containing DNA, usually from a living animal donor, place it in an egg cell from which the nucleus has been removed, and after stimulating the egg to start dividing, implant the new embryo in the uterus of a female. Because each individual animal that develops from these cells is genetically identical to the donor, clones can be used to preserve valuable traits, to study the relative influences of heredity and environment, or to produce new tissue or organs for transplant to the donor. Dolly, a female sheep, was the first cloned mammal.

Cloning has matured from an experimental manipulation to a commercial enterprise. The first horse to be cloned was Charmayne James's horse Scamper, the mount she rode to 11 world championships in barrel racing. The first cat to be cloned, shown in **Figure 3-23**, was called Copycat. The first rare species cloned was an Asian gaur, an animal related to the cow. Investigators anticipate that cloning will be used to reanimate extinct animals, a process called *de-extinction*. They propose using preserved cells from the extinct passenger pigeon or from frozen carcasses of the mastodon (an enclosure to house a de-extinct mastodon has been prepared in Russia), an extinct elephant species, to clone those animals.

A team of researchers in Scotland cloned Dolly in 1996. As an adult, she mated and bore a lamb.

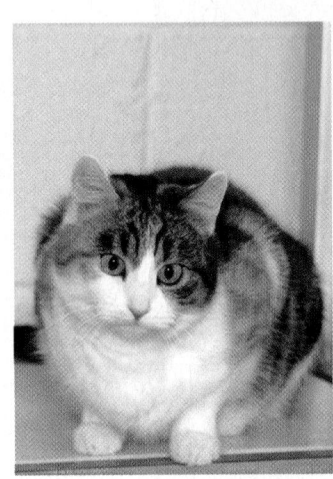

FIGURE 3-23 **A Clone and Her Mom** Copycat (left) and Rainbow (right), the cat that donated the cell nucleus for cloning. Although the cats' genomes are identical, their phenotypes, including fur color, differ. One copy of the X chromosome is randomly inactivated in each cell, which explains the color differences. Even clones are subject to phenotypic plasticity: they retain the capacity to develop into more than one phenotype.

Transgenic Techniques

Transgenic technology enables scientists to introduce genes into an embryo or remove genes from it. For example, introducing a new gene can enable cows or goats to produce medicines in their milk. The medicines can be extracted from the milk to treat human disease. Transgenic techniques used to take a mouse gene that affords resistance to tuberculosis and insert it into cows has increased their resistance to TB (Wu et al., 2015).

Chimeric animals are composites formed when an embryo of one species receives cells from a different species. The resulting animal has cells with genes from both parent species and behaviors that are a product of those gene combinations. The chimeric animal may display an interesting mix of the parent species' behaviors. For example, chickens that received Japanese quail cells in early embryogenesis display some aspects of quail crowing behavior rather than chicken crowing behavior—evidence for the genetic basis of the bird's vocalization (Balaban, 2005). The chimeric preparation provides an investigative tool for studying the neural basis of crowing, because quail neurons can be distinguished from chicken neurons when examined under a microscope.

Chimerism is common in humans (Giorgi, 2015). Twin zygotes (fertilized eggs) may fuse into a single individual, twins may exchange cells through placental circulation, and the fetus and the mother may exchange cells with one another. Even organ transplant or stem cell recipients may incorporate transplanted cells into other organs.

In *knock-in technology*, a number of genes or a single gene from one species is added to the genome of another species, passed along, and expressed in subsequent generations of **transgenic animals**. Brainbow technology, described in Research Focus 3-2, applies the knock-in technique. Another application is in the study and treatment of human genetic disorders. For instance, researchers have introduced into a line of mice and a line of Rhesus monkeys the human *HTT* gene that causes Huntington disease (Gill and Rego, 2009; see Focus 3-4). The mice express the abnormal allele and display humanlike Huntington symptoms. This mouse line is being used to study possible therapies for Huntington disease in humans.

Knockout technology is used to inactivate a gene, for example so that a line of mice fails to express it. The mouse line can then be examined to determine whether the targeted gene is responsible for a specific function or a human disorder and to examine possible therapies. It may be possible to knock out genes related to certain kinds of memory, such as emotional memory, social memory, or spatial memory. Knockout technology is a useful way of investigating the neural basis of memory as well as clinical conditions associated with learning impairments (Kusakari et al., 2015).

transgenic animal Product of technology in which one or more genes from one species is introduced into the genome of another species to be passed along and expressed in subsequent generations.

The neural basis of memory is the topic of Section 14-3.

Photos used with permission from Texas A&M College of Veterinary Medicine & Biomedical Sciences.

Phenotypic Plasticity and the Epigenetic Code

Our genotype is not sufficient to explain our phenotype. We all know that if we expose ourselves to the sun, our skin darkens; if we exercise, our muscles enlarge; if we study, we learn. Our phenotype also changes with our diet and as we age. In short, the extent of phenotypic variation, given the same genotype, is remarkable.

Every individual has a capacity to develop into more than one phenotype. This *phenotypic plasticity* is due in part to the genome's capacity to express a large number of phenotypes and in part to epigenetics, the influence of environment and experience in phenotypic expression.

Seemingly puzzling features in the expression of genomes in relation to phenotypes are illustrated in strains of genetically identical mice, some of which develop a brain with no corpus callosum (**Figure 3-24**). The absence of this hemispheric connector results from an epigenetic influence on whether the trait is expressed in a particular mouse. It occurs in the embryo at about the time the corpus callosum should form. This lack of concordance (incidence of similar behavioral traits) is also observed in patterns of disease incidence in human identical twins, who share the same genome.

The concordance rate between identical twins for a vast array of diseases—including schizophrenia, Alzheimer disease, multiple sclerosis, Crohn disease (a form of inflammatory bowel disease), asthma, diabetes, and prostate cancer—is between 30 and 60 percent. For cleft palate and breast cancer, identical twins' concordance rate is about 10 percent. The expectation from Mendelian genetics is 100 percent concordance. These less than perfect concordance rates point to other contributing factors.

Phenotypic plasticity is in evidence not only in adult organisms but also in cells. In Section 3-1, we described the variety of neurons and glia found in the nervous system. Each of these cells usually has the same genotype. So also do the 248 other cell types of our body. How then do they become so different?

Applying the Epigenetic Code

The genes expressed in a cell are influenced by factors within the cell and in the cell's environment. Once a fertilized egg begins to divide, each new cell finds itself in a somewhat different environment from that of its parent cell. The cell's environment will determine which genes are expressed and so what kind of tissue it becomes, including what kind of nervous system cell it becomes. Environmental influences do not end at birth, of course. Our environment changes daily throughout our lives, as does its influence on our genes.

Epigenetic mechanisms create phenotypic variation without altering the base pair nucleotide sequence of the genes. Through these mechanisms, experience and the environment can allow a gene to be expressed or prevent its expression. Epigenetics is viewed as a second code; the first code is the genome. Epigenetics describes how a single genetic code produces each somatic cell type, explains how a single genome can code for many phenotypes, and describes how cell functions go astray to produce diseases ranging from cancer to brain dysfunction.

Epigenetic mechanisms can influence protein production either by blocking a gene to prevent transcription or by unlocking a gene so that it can be transcribed. This is where experiential and environmental influences come into play. To review, each of your chromosomes consists of a long, double-stranded chain of nucleotide bases that forms your DNA. Each gene on a chromosome is a segment of DNA that encodes the synthesis of a particular protein (see Figure 3-13).

Chromosomes are wrapped around supporting molecules of a protein called histone. Histone wrapping allows the many yards of a chromosome to be packaged in a small space, as yards of thread are wrapped around a spool. For any gene to be transcribed into messenger RNA, its DNA must be unspooled from the histones. Once unspooled, each gene must be instructed to transcribe mRNA. Then the mRNA must be translated into an amino acid

FIGURE 3-24 Gene Expression Identical coronal sections through the brain of mice with identical genotypes reveal frontal views of distinctly different phenotypes. **(A)** This mouse had a corpus callosum. **(B)** This mouse did not.

Advances in Behavioral Biology Volume 42, 1994, pp. 125–133; Defects of the Fetal Forebrain in Acallosal Mice; Douglas Wahlsten, Hiroki S. Ozaki, © 1994 Plenum Press, New York, figure 1, with permission of Springer Science+Business Media

The cloned mice shown in Figure 2-1 exemplify phenotypic plasticity.

The International Human Epigenome Consortium (IHEC) mandate is to describe the epigenetic code, as the Human Genome Project has described the genetic code.

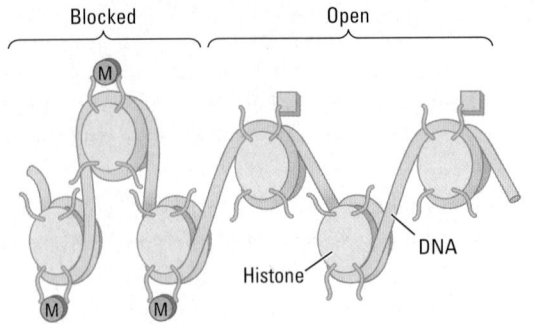

1 Histone modification
A methyl group (CH₃) or other molecules bind to the tails of histones, either blocking them from opening (orange circles) or allowing them to open for transcription (green squares).

2 Gene (DNA) methylation
Methyl groups (M) bind to CG base pairs to block transcription.

3 mRNA modification
ncRNA binds to mRNA, preventing translation.

FIGURE 3-25 Epigenetic Mechanisms

chain that forms the protein. **Figure 3-25** illustrates some ways that each step can be either enabled or blocked:

1. *Histone modification.* DNA may unwrap or be stopped from unwrapping from the histone. At the top of Figure 3-25, a methyl group (CH₃) or other molecule binds to the tails of histones to block DNA from unspooling. Its genes cannot be exposed for transcription with the block in place (left), but it can be opened for transcription (right) if the block is absent or removed.

2. *Gene (DNA) methylation.* Transcription of DNA into mRNA may be enabled or blocked. In Figure 3-25 at center, one or more methyl groups bind to CG base pairs to block transcription.

3. *mRNA modification.* mRNA translation may be enabled or blocked. In Figure 3-25, bottom, noncoding RNA (ncRNA) binds to mRNA, blocking translation.

An environmental influence can either induce or remove one or more blocks, thus allowing the environment to regulate gene expression (Charney, 2012). It is through these epigenetic mechanisms that cells are instructed to differentiate into various body tissues and that our unique environment and experience induce changes in our brain that make us a unique individual. Some experientially induced events can also be passed from one generation to the next, as the following case study illustrates.

Methylation dramatically alters gene expression during brain development (see Sections 8-2 and 12-5) and can affect memory and brain plasticity (see Section 14-4).

A Case of Inheriting Experience

The idea that traits are passed from parent to child through genes is a cornerstone of Mendelian genetics. Mendel's theory also predicts that individual life experience cannot be

gene (DNA) methylation Epigenetic process in which a methyl group attaches to the DNA sequence, suppressing or enabling gene expression.

inherited. Lars Olov Bygren and colleagues (Kaati et al., 2007) found, however, that individuals' nutritional experiences can affect their offspring's health.

The investigators focused on Norrbotten, a sparsely populated northern Swedish region. In the nineteenth century, Norrbotten was virtually isolated from the outside world. If the harvest there was bad, people starved. According to historical records, the years 1800, 1812, 1821, 1836, and 1856 saw total crop failure. The years 1801, 1822, 1828, 1844, and 1863 brought good harvests and abundance.

Bygren and colleagues identified at random individuals who had been subjected to famine or to plenty in the years just before they entered puberty. Then the researchers examined the health records and longevity of these people's children and grandchildren.

The findings seem to defy logic. The descendants of the plenty group had higher rates of cardiovascular disease and diabetes and had a life expectancy more than seven years shorter than that of the famine group! Notably, these effects were found only in male offspring of males and female offspring of females.

Bygren and colleagues propose that diet during a critical period can modify the genetic expression of sex chromosomes—the Y chromosome in males and the X chromosome in females. Further, this change can be passed on to subsequent generations. Dietary experience in the prepubertal period, just before the onset of sexual maturity, is important: this is the time at which gene expression on the sex chromosomes begins.

Many other studies support Bygren and coworkers' seminal findings. Together, this body of research makes a strong argument for epigenetics and for the idea that some epigenetic influences can be passed on for at least a few generations. Evidence that epigenetic influences play a demonstrable role in determining gene expression is disclosing how our experiences shape our brains to influence whom we become and how our current environment might influence our descendants' epigenetic inheritance (Guerrero-Bosagna and Jensen, 2015).

Section 8-4 examines critical periods, limited time spans during which events have long-lasting influences on development.

(3-3) REVIEW

Genes, Cells, and Behavior

Before you continue, check your understanding.

1. Each of our _____ chromosome pairs contains thousands of genes, and each gene contains the code for one _____.

2. The genes we receive from our parents may include slightly different _____ of particular genes, which will be expressed in slightly different _____.

3. Abnormalities in a gene, caused by a(n) _____, can result in an abnormally formed protein, hence in abnormal cell function. Chromosome abnormality can result in abnormal functioning of many genes. _____, for example, is caused by an extra copy of chromosome 21, a _____.

4. Tay-Sachs disease results from a(n) _____ allele being expressed; Huntington disease results from the expression of a(n) _____ allele.

5. _____ is the oldest form of genetic manipulation. Genetic engineering manipulates or alters the genome of an animal. _____ produces an animal that is genetically identical to a parent or sibling; _____ animals contain new, altered, or inactivated genes.

6. _____ is an epigenetic mechanism that either enables or blocks transcription.

7. What distinguishes Mendelian genetics from epigenetics?

Answers appear at the back of the book.

For additional study tools, visit 🔲 LaunchPad:
www.macmillanhighered.com/launchpad/kolb5e

■ SUMMARY

3-1 Cells of the Nervous System

The nervous system is composed of two kinds of cells: neurons, which transmit information, and glia, which support neuronal function. Sensory neurons may act as receptors to convey information from the body to the brain; motor neurons command muscles to move; and interneurons link up sensory and motor neuron activities.

Like neurons, glial cells can be grouped by structure and function. Ependymal cells produce CSF. Astrocytes structurally support neurons, help to form the blood–brain barrier, and seal off damaged brain tissue. Microglia aid in brain cell repair and waste removal. Oligodendroglia and Schwann cells myelinate axons in the CNS and in the somatic division of the PNS, respectively.

A neuron is composed of three parts: a cell body, or soma; multiple branching extensions called dendrites, designed to receive information; and a single axon that passes information along to other neurons. Numerous dendritic spines greatly increase a dendrite's surface area. An axon may have branches (axon collaterals), which further divide into telodendria, each ending at a terminal button (end foot). A synapse is the almost connection between a terminal button and another cell's membrane.

3-2 Internal Structure of a Cell

A surrounding cell membrane protects the cell and regulates what enters and leaves it. Within the cell are a number of organelles, also enclosed in membranes. These compartments include the nucleus (containing the cell's chromosomes and genes), the endoplasmic reticulum (where proteins are manufactured), the mitochondria (where energy is gathered and stored), the Golgi bodies (where protein molecules are packaged for transport), and lysosomes (which break down wastes). A cell also contains a system of tubules (microfilaments) that aid its movements, provide structural support, and act as highways for transporting substances.

To a large extent, the work of cells is carried out by proteins. The nucleus contains chromosomes—long chains of genes, each encoding a specific protein the cell needs. Proteins perform diverse tasks by virtue of their diverse shapes. Some act as enzymes to facilitate chemical reactions; others serve as membrane channels, gates, and pumps; still others are exported for use in other parts of the body.

A gene is a segment of a DNA molecule made up of a sequence of nucleotide bases. Through transcription, a copy of a gene is produced in a strand of messenger RNA. The mRNA travels to the endoplasmic reticulum, where a ribosome moves along the mRNA molecule, translating it into a sequence of amino acids. The resulting amino acid chain is a polypeptide. Polypeptides fold and combine to form protein molecules with distinctive shapes that serve specific purposes in the body.

3-3 Genes, Cells, and Behavior

From each parent, we inherit one of each chromosome in the 23 chromosome pairs that constitute the human genotype. Because all but the sex chromosomes are matched pairs, a cell contains two alleles of every gene. Sometimes the paired alleles are homozygous (the same), and sometimes they are heterozygous (different).

An allele may be dominant and expressed as a trait, recessive and not expressed, or codominant and expressed along with the other allele in the organism's phenotype. One allele of each gene is designated the wild type—the most common in a population—whereas the other alleles are called mutations. A person might inherit any of these alleles from a parent, depending on the parent's genotype.

Genes have the potential to undergo many mutations—of a single base pair, part of the chromosome, or the entire chromosome. Mutations can be beneficial, harmful, or neutral in their effects on nervous system structure and behavioral function. Genetic research seeks to prevent the expression of genetic and chromosomal abnormalities and to find cures for those that are expressed.

Selective breeding is the oldest form of genetic manipulation. In genetic engineering, an animal's genome is artificially altered. The genetic composition of a cloned animal is identical to that of a parent or sibling. In transgenic animals, a new or altered gene may be added or a gene removed.

The genome encodes a range of phenotypes. The phenotype eventually produced is determined by epigenetics and further influenced by experience and the environment. Epigenetic mechanisms such as DNA methylation can influence whether genes are transcribed or transcription is blocked without changing the genetic code itself.

■ KEY TERMS

➡ Visit 🔊 LaunchPad to access the e-Book, videos, 🔊 LearningCurve adaptive quizzing, flashcards, and more.

www.macmillanhighered.com/launchpad/kolb5e

CHAPTER 4

How Do Neurons Use Electrical Signals to Transmit Information?

Katherine Streeter

CLINICAL FOCUS 4-1

Epilepsy

J. D. worked as a disc jockey for a radio station and at parties in his off-hours. One evening, he set up on the back of a truck at a rugby field to emcee a jovial and raucous rugby party. Between musical sets, he made introductions, told jokes, and exchanged toasts.

About one o'clock in the morning, J. D. suddenly collapsed, making unusual jerky motions, then passed out. He was rushed to a hospital emergency room, where he gradually recovered. The attending physician noted that he was not intoxicated, released him to his friends, and recommended a series of neurological tests for the next day. Neuroimaging with state-of-the-art brain scans can usually reveal brain abnormalities (Bano et al., 2011), but it did not do so in J. D. 's case.

The EEG detects electrical signals given off by the brain in various states of consciousness, as explained in Sections 7-2 and 13-3. Section 16-3 details the diagnosis and treatment of epilepsy.

When the electrical activity in J. D.'s brain was recorded while a strobe light was flashed before his eyes, an *electroencephalogram*, or EEG, displayed a series of abnormal electrical patterns characteristic of epilepsy. The doctor prescribed Dilantin (diphenylhydantoin), an anti-seizure drug, and advised J. D. to refrain from drinking alcohol. He was required to give up his driver's license to prevent the possibility of an attack while driving. And he lost his job at the radio station.

After 3 uneventful months, medication was stopped and his driver's license was restored. J. D. convinced the radio station that he could resume work, and subsequently he has remained seizure free.

Epilepsy is a common neurological disease marked by periods of excessive neural synchrony called **electrographic seizures**. The disease is electrical in nature. Electrographic seizures often follow innocuous stimuli—events that would not typically cause seizures in people who do not have epilepsy. The core concept is that the brain of a person with epilepsy has a chronically low seizure threshold and so is subject to recurrent seizures. About 4 in 10 cases of epilepsy have been linked to specific neural causes, among them infections, trauma, tumors, structural abnormalities, or genetic mutations in the proteins that make up ion channels (Bhalla et al., 2011). But that leaves the remaining 60% without a clear cause.

If seizures occur repeatedly and cannot be controlled by drug treatment, as occurs in about 30% of people with epilepsy, other options may include the high-fat–low-carbohydrate ketogenic diet, deep brain stimulation, and surgical resection of the seizure focus (Duncan et al., 2006). Removing this small area of brain tissue may prevent seizures and keep them from spreading to other brain regions. The brain is normally electrically active. If this activity becomes abnormal, even infrequently, the consequences can be severe.

AJPhoto/Science Source

Descartes proposed the idea behind dualism—that the nonmaterial mind controls body mechanics; see Section 1-2.

The most reproduced drawing in behavioral neuroscience is nearly 350 years old, predating our understanding of the electrical basis of epilepsy by centuries. Taken from René Descartes's book *Treatise on Man* and reproduced in **Figure 4-1,** it illustrates the first serious attempt to explain how information travels through the nervous system. Descartes proposed that the carrier of information was cerebrospinal fluid flowing through nerve tubes.

Descartes reasoned that when the fire burns the man's toe, it stretches the skin, which tugs on a nerve tube leading to the brain. In response to the tug, a valve in a brain ventricle opens, and CSF flows down the tube, filling the leg muscles and causing them to contract and pull the toe back from the fire. The flow of fluid through other tubes to other muscles of the body (not shown in Figure 4-1) causes the head to turn toward the painful stimulus and the hand to rub the injured toe.

Descartes's theory was incorrect, yet it is remarkable because he isolated the three basic questions that underlie a behavioral response to stimulation:

1. How do our nerves detect a sensory stimulus and inform the brain about it?

2. How does the brain decide what response to make?

3. How does the brain command muscles to move?

Descartes was trying to explain the very same things that scientists have sought to explain in the intervening centuries. If not by stretched skin tugging on a nerve tube initiating the message, the message must still be initiated somehow. If not by opening valves to initiate the flow of CSF to convey information, the information must still be sent. If not by filling the muscles with fluid that produces movements, the muscles must contract by some other mechanism.

These mechanisms are the subject of this chapter. We examine how neurons convey information from the environment throughout the nervous system and ultimately activate muscles to produce movement. We begin by describing the clues and tools that explained the nervous system's electrical activity.

4-1 Searching for Electrical Activity in the Nervous System

FIGURE 4-1 Descartes's Theory of Information Flow

The first hints about how the nervous system conveys its messages came in the eighteenth century, following the discovery of electricity. Early discoveries about the nature of electricity quickly led to proposals that it plays a role in conducting information in the nervous system. We describe a few milestones that led from this idea to an understanding of how the nervous system really conveys information. If you have a basic understanding of how electricity works and how it is used to stimulate neural tissue, read on. If you prefer to brush up on electricity and electrical stimulation first, turn to The Basics: Electricity and Electrical Stimulation on page 110.

Early Clues That Linked Electricity and Neuronal Activity

In a dramatic demonstration in 1731, Stephen Gray, an amateur English scientist, rubbed a rod with a piece of cloth to accumulate electrons on the rod. Then he touched the charged rod to the feet of a boy suspended on a rope and brought a metal foil to the boy's nose. The foil was attracted to the boy's nose and bent on approaching it, and as foil and nose touched, electricity passed from the rod through the boy to the foil.

Yet the boy felt nothing. Therefore, Gray speculated that electricity might be the messenger that spreads information through the nervous system. Two other lines of evidence, drawn from electrical stimulation and electrical recording studies, implicated electrical activity in the nervous system's flow of information.

Gray's experiment resembles accumulating electrons by combing your hair. Hold a piece of paper near the comb, and the paper bends toward it. Negative charges on the comb push negative charges on the paper to its backside, leaving the front side positively charged. Because opposite charges attract, the paper bends toward the comb.

Electrical Stimulation Studies

When the Italian scientist Luigi Galvani, a contemporary of Gray, observed that frogs' legs hanging on a wire in a market twitched during a lightning storm, he surmised that sparks of electricity from the storm were activating the leg muscles. Investigating this possibility, he found that if an electrical current is applied to a dissected nerve, the muscle connected to that nerve contracts. While it was unclear how the process worked, Galvani had discovered **electrical stimulation:** passing an electrical current from the uninsulated tip of an electrode onto a nerve to produce behavior—a muscular contraction.

Among the many researchers who used Galvani's technique to produce muscle contraction, two mid-nineteenth-century Prussian scientists, Gustave Theodor Fritsch and Eduard Hitzig, demonstrated that electrical stimulation of the neocortex causes movement. They studied several animal species, including rabbits and dogs, and may even have stimulated the neocortex of a person whom they were treating for head injuries sustained on a Prussian battlefield. They observed their subjects' arm and leg movements in response to the stimulation of specific parts of the neocortex.

In 1874, Roberts Bartholow, a Cincinnati physician, first described the effects of human brain stimulation. His patient, Mary Rafferty, had a skull defect that exposed part of her

electrographic seizures Abnormal rhythmic neuronal discharges; may be recorded by an electroencephalogram.

electrical stimulation Passage of an electrical current from the uninsulated tip of an electrode through tissue, resulting in changes in the electrical activity of the tissue.

THE BASICS ■

Electricity and Electrical Stimulation

Electricity powers the lights in your home and the batteries that run so many electronic gadgets, from smartphones to electric cars. *Electricity* is the flow of electrons from a body that contains a higher charge (more electrons) to a body that contains a lower charge (fewer electrons). This electron flow can perform work—lighting an unlit bulb, for instance. When biological tissue contains an electrical charge, the charge can be recorded; if living tissue is sensitive to an electrical charge, the tissue can be stimulated.

How Electricity Works

In Power Source, negatively charged electrons are attracted to the positive pole because opposite charges attract. The electrons on the negative pole have the potential to flow to the positive pole. This *electrical potential*, or electrical charge, is the ability to do work using stored electrical energy.

Electrical potential is measured in *volts*, the difference in charge between the positive and the negative poles. These poles are separated by an insulator. Thus, when not connected, the positive and negative poles in a battery, like the poles in each wall socket in your home, hold voltage between the poles.

Electrical Activity in Cells

If the bare tip of an insulated wire, or *electrode*, from each pole of a battery comes into contact with biological tissue, current will flow from the electrode connected to the negative pole into the tissue and from the tissue into the electrode connected to the positive pole. The stimulation comes from the electrode's uninsulated tip. Microelectrodes can record from or stimulate tissue as small as parts of a single living cell.

Electrical stimulation, illustrated in part A of Studying Electrical Activity in Animal Tissue, is most effective when administered in brief pulses. A timer in the stimulator turns the current on and off to produce the pulses. In electrical recording, voltage can be displayed by the dial on a voltmeter, a recording device that measures the voltage of a battery or of biological tissue (part B).

Because electrons carry a negative charge, the negative pole has a higher electrical charge (more electrons) than the positive pole.

Positive pole

Negative pole

Battery

Uninsulated switch

Light bulb

1 The battery will light the bulb only when the switch is closed. A conducting medium, such as an uninsulated wire, connects the two poles...

2 ...and a flow, or current, of electrons streams through the bulb from the negative (–) to the positive (+) pole, lighting up the bulb.

Power Source

(A) Electrical stimulation

Current leaves the stimulator through a wire lead (red) that attaches to an electrode. From the uninsulated tip of the electrode, the current enters the tissue and stimulates it. The current flows back to the stimulator through a second lead (green) connected to a reference electrode.

1 A stimulating electrode delivers current (electrons) ranging from 2 to 10 millivolts, intensities sufficient to produce a response without damaging cells.

2 The reference electrode contacts a large surface area that spreads out the current and thus does not excite the tissue here.

Stimulator

Reference electrode

Stimulating electrode

Uninsulated tip

Nerve

Current flow

(B) Electrical recording

The difference in voltage between the tip of a recording electrode and a reference electrode deflects a needle that indicates the current's voltage.

Voltmeter

Reference electrode

Recording electrode

Current flow

Studying Electrical Activity in Animal Tissue

neocortex. Bartholow stimulated her exposed brain tissue to examine the effects. In one of his observations he wrote:

> Passed an insulated needle into the left posterior lobe so that the non-insulated portion rested entirely in the substance of the brain. The reference was placed in contact with the dura mater. When the circuit was closed, muscular contraction in the right upper and lower extremities ensued. Faint but visible contraction of the left eyelid, and dilation of the pupils, also ensued. Mary complained of a very strong and unpleasant feeling of tingling in both right extremities, especially in the right arm, which she seized with the opposite hand and rubbed vigorously. Notwithstanding the very evident pain from which she suffered, she smiled as if much amused. (Bartholow, 1874)

As you might imagine, Bartholow's report was not well received! The uproar after its publication forced him to leave Cincinnati. Despite the questionable ethics of his experiment, Bartholow had demonstrated that the brain of a conscious person could be stimulated electrically to produce movement of the body.

Electrical Recording Studies

A less invasive line of evidence that information flow in the brain is partly electrical came from the results of electrical recording experiments. Richard Caton, a Scottish physician who lived a century ago, was the first to measure the brain's electrical currents with a sensitive **voltmeter**, a device that measures the flow and the strength of electrical voltage by recording the difference in electrical potential between two bodies. When he placed electrodes on a human subject's skull, Caton reported fluctuations in his voltmeter recordings. Today, this type of brain recording, the **electroencephalogram** (EEG), is a standard tool used, among other things, to monitor sleep stages and to detect the excessive neural synchrony that characterizes electrographic seizures, as described in Clinical Focus 4-1, Epilepsy.

These pioneering studies provided evidence that neurons send electrical messages, but concluding that nerves and tracts carry the kind of electrical current that powers your phone would be incorrect. Hermann von Helmholtz, a nineteenth-century German scientist, stimulated a nerve leading to a muscle and measured the time the muscle took to contract. The nerve conducted information at only 30 to 40 meters per second, whereas electricity flows along a wire about a million times faster.

Information flow in the nervous system, then, is much too slow to be a flow of electricity (based on electrons). To explain the electrical signals of a neuron, Julius Bernstein suggested in 1886 that neuronal chemistry (based on ions) produces an electrical charge. He also proposed that the charge can change and so act as a signal. Bernstein's idea was that successive waves of electrical change constitute the message conveyed by the neuron.

Moreover, it is not the ions themselves that travel along the axon but rather a *wave* of charge. To understand the difference, consider other kinds of waves. If you drop a stone into a pool of still water, the contact produces a wave that travels away from the site of impact, as shown in **Figure 4-2**. The water itself does not travel. Only the change in pressure moves, shifting the height of the water surface and producing the wave effect.

Similarly, when you speak, you induce pressure waves in air, and these waves carry the sound of your voice to a listener. If you flick a towel, a wave travels to the other end of the towel. Just as waves through the air send a spoken message, Bernstein's idea was that waves of chemical change travel along an axon to deliver a neuron's message.

Tools for Measuring a Neuron's Electrical Activity

Waves that carry nervous system messages are minute and are restricted to the surfaces of neurons. Still, we can produce these waves using conventional electrical stimulation and measure them using electrical recording techniques to determine how they are produced. When a single axon is stimulated, it produces

voltmeter Device that measures the flow and the strength of electrical voltage by recording the difference in electrical potential between two bodies.

electroencephalogram (EEG) Graph that records electrical activity from the brain and mainly indicates graded potentials of many neurons.

By the 1960s, the scientific community had established ethical standards for research on human and nonhuman subjects (see Section 7-7). Today, brain stimulation is standard in many neurosurgical procedures (see Section 16-2).

Detail on these EEG applications appears in Sections 7-2, 13-3, and 16-3.

FIGURE 4-2 Wave Effect Waves formed by dropping stones into still water do not entail the water's forward movement but rather pressure differences that change the height of the water surface.

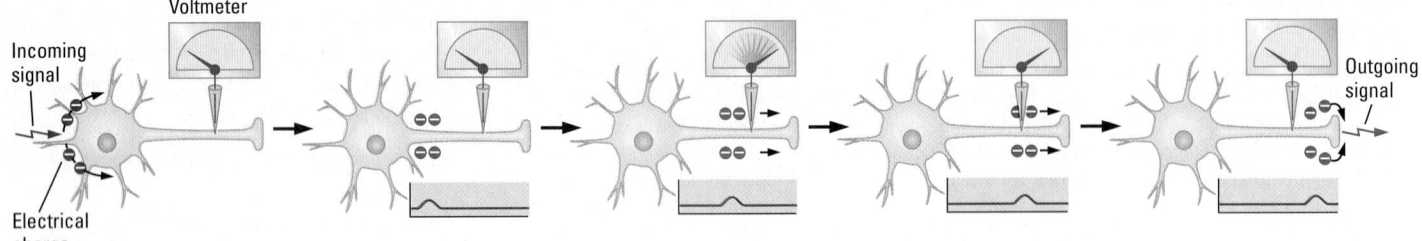

FIGURE 4-3 Wave of Information
Neurons can convey information as a wave induced by stimulation on the cell body traveling down the axon to its terminal. A voltmeter detects the wave's passage.

a wave of excitation. If an electrode connected to a voltmeter is placed on a single axon, as illustrated in **Figure 4-3**, the electrode can detect a change in electrical charge on that axon's membrane as the wave passes.

As simple as this process may seem, recording a wave and explaining how it is produced require a neuron large enough to record, a recording device sensitive enough to detect a tiny electrical impulse, and an electrode small enough to be placed on the surface of a single neuron. The fortuitous discovery of the giant axon of the squid, the invention of the oscilloscope, and the development of microelectrodes met all these requirements.

Giant Axon of the Squid

The neurons of most animals, including humans, are tiny, on the order of 1 to 20 micrometers (μm) in diameter, too small to be seen by the naked eye. The British zoologist J. Z. Young, when dissecting the North Atlantic squid, *Loligo vulgaris*, noticed that it has giant axons, as much as a millimeter (1000 μm, or about a twenty-fifth of an inch) in diameter. **Figure 4-4** illustrates *Loligo* and the giant axons leading to its body wall, or mantle, which contracts to propel the squid through the water.

1 micron (μm) = one-millionth of a meter or one-thousandth of a millimeter (mm).

Loligo is not a giant squid. It is only about a foot long. But its axons are giant, as axons go. Each is formed by the fusion of many smaller axons. Because larger axons send messages faster than smaller axons do, these giant axons allow the squid to jet-propel away from predators.

In 1936, Young suggested to Alan Hodgkin and Andrew Huxley, neuroscientists at Cambridge University in England, that *Loligo*'s axons were large enough to be used for electrical recording studies. A giant axon could be dissected out of the squid and kept functional in a bath of salty liquid that approximates body fluids. In this way, Hodgkin and Huxley (1939) described the neuron's electrical activity. In 1963 they received the Nobel Prize for their accomplishment.

(A)

(B)

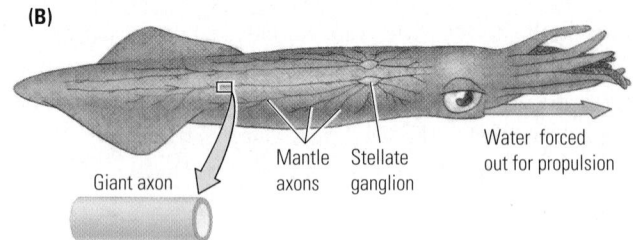

FIGURE 4-4 Laboratory Specimen **(A)** The North Atlantic squid propels itself both with fins and by contracting its mantle to force water out for propulsion. **(B)** The stellate ganglion projects giant axons to contract the squid's mantle.

(A)

(B)

Oscilloscope

Hodgkin and Huxley's experiments were made possible by the invention of the **oscilloscope,** a voltmeter with a screen sensitive enough to display the minuscule electrical signals emanating from a nerve or neuron over time (**Figure 4-5**A). As graphed in Figure 4-5B, the units used when recording the electrical charge from a nerve or neuron are millivolts (mV; 1 mV is one-thousandth of a volt) and milliseconds (ms; 1 ms is one-thousandth of a second).

Microelectrodes

The final device needed to measure a neuron's electrical activity is an electrode small enough to place on or in an axon—a **microelectrode.** Microelectrodes can deliver an electrical current to a single neuron or record from it. One way to make a microelectrode is to etch the tip of a piece of thin wire to a fine point about 1 μm in size and insulate the rest of the wire. The tip is placed on or in the neuron, as shown in the image at left in **Figure 4-6**A.

Microelectrodes can also be made from a thin glass tube tapered to a very fine tip (Figure 4-6A, right image). The tip of a hollow glass microelectrode can be as small as 1 μm. When the glass tube is filled with salty water, a conducting medium (through which an electrical current can travel), it acts as an electrode. A wire in the salt solution connects the electrode to either a stimulating or a recording device.

Microelectrodes can record from axons in many ways. The tip of a microelectrode placed on an axon provides an extracellular measure of the electrical current from a tiny part of the axon. The tip of one electrode can be placed on the surface of the axon and the tip of a second electrode can be inserted into the axon. This technique measures voltage across the cell membrane.

A still more refined use of a glass microelectrode is to place its tip on the neuron's membrane and apply a little suction until the tip is sealed to a patch of the membrane, as shown in Figure 4-6B. This technique, analogous to placing the end of a soda straw against a piece of plastic wrapping and sucking, allows a recording to be made from only the small patch of membrane sealed to the microelectrode tip.

Using the giant axon of the squid, an oscilloscope, and microelectrodes, Hodgkin and Huxley recorded the electrical voltage on an axon's membrane and explained the *nerve impulse* as changes in ion concentration across the cell membrane. The basis of electrical activity in nerves is the movement of intracellular

FIGURE 4-5 Oscilloscope Recording **(A)** Basic wave shapes are displayed on a digital oscilloscope, a versatile electronic instrument used to visualize and measure electrical signals as they change. **(B)** On the graph of a trace produced by an oscilloscope, S stands for stimulation. The horizontal axis measures time, and the vertical axis measures voltage. By convention, the axon voltage is represented as negative, in millivolts (mV). On the right, one trace of two action potentials from an individual neuron as displayed on a digital oscilloscope screen.

oscilloscope Device that serves as a sensitive voltmeter by registering changes in voltage over time.

microelectrode A microscopic insulated wire or a saltwater-filled glass tube whose uninsulated tip is used to stimulate or record from neurons.

(A)

FIGURE 4-6 Uses of Microelectrodes **(A)** A squid axon is larger than the tip of either a wire (left) or a glass (right) microelectrode. Both can be placed on an axon or in it. (Drawings are not to scale.) **(B)** A microelectrode can record from only a small area of an axon by suctioning the membrane up into the glass electrode.

and extracellular ions, which carry positive and negative charges across the cell membrane. To understand Hodgkin and Huxley's results, you first need to understand the principles underlying the movement of ions.

How Ion Movement Produces Electrical Charges

The intracellular fluid within a neuron and the extracellular fluid surrounding it contain various ions, including Na^+ (sodium) and K^+ (potassium)—positively charged, as the plus signs indicate—and negatively charged Cl^- (chloride). These fluids also contain numerous negatively charged protein molecules (A^-). Positively charged ions are *cations*, and negatively charged ions, including protein molecules, are *anions*. Three factors influence the movement of anions and cations into and out of cells: diffusion, concentration gradient, and charge.

Because molecules move constantly, they spontaneously spread out from a point of concentration. This spreading out is **diffusion.** Requiring no work, diffusion results from the random motion of molecules as they move and bounce off one another to gradually disperse in a solution. When diffusion is complete, a dynamic equilibrium, with an equal number of molecules everywhere, is the result.

Smoke from a fire gradually diffuses through the air in a room until every bit of air contains the same number of smoke molecules. Dye poured into water diffuses in the same way—from its point of contact to every part of the water in the container. Salts placed in water dissolve into ions surrounded by water molecules. Carried by the random motion of the water molecules, these ions diffuse throughout the solution to equilibrium, when every part of the container has the same salt concentration.

Concentration gradient describes the relative abundance of a substance in space or in a solution. As illustrated in **Figure 4-7A**, when you drop a little ink into a beaker of water, the dye starts out concentrated at the site of contact, then diffuses. The ink spreads out from a point of concentration until it is equally distributed and all the water in the beaker is the same color. A similar process takes place when a salt is put into water. The salt is initially concentrated where it enters the water, but it diffuses from that location until its ions are in equilibrium.

Because ions carry an electrical charge and because like charges repel one another, ion movement can be described either by a concentration gradient, the difference in the number of ions between two regions, or by a **voltage gradient,** the difference in charge between two regions. Ions will move down a voltage gradient from an area of higher charge to an area of lower charge, just as they move down a concentration gradient from an area of higher concentration to an area of lower concentration.

The Basics, pp. 88–89, covers ions. The illustration, Salty Water, shows how water molecules dissolve salt crystals.

diffusion Movement of ions from an area of higher concentration to an area of lower concentration through random motion.

concentration gradient Difference in the relative abundance of a substance among regions of a container; allows the substance to diffuse from an area of higher concentration to an area of lower concentration.

voltage gradient Difference in charge between two regions that allows a flow of current if the two regions are connected.

(A) Concentrating gradient

1 Ink dropped into water diffuses from the initial point of contact...

2 ...until it is equally distributed throughout the water.

Ink

Time

(B) Voltage gradient

3 If a salty solution is poured into water,...

4 ...the positive and negative ions will flow down their electrostatic gradients until positive and negative charges are everywhere equal.

Salt water

Time

FIGURE 4-7 Moving to Equilibrium

Figure 4-7B illustrates this process. When salt is dissolved in water, its diffusion can be described either as movement down a concentration gradient (for sodium and chloride ions) or movement down a voltage gradient (for the positive and negative charges). In a container that allows unimpeded movement of ions, the positive and negative charges eventually balance.

A thought experiment will illustrate how a cell membrane influences ion movement. **Figure 4-8A** shows a container of water divided in half by a solid, impermeable membrane. If we place a few grains of table salt (NaCl) in the left half of the container, the salt dissolves. The ions diffuse down their concentration and voltage gradients until the water in the left compartment is in equilibrium.

In the left side of the container, there is no longer a gradient for either sodium or chloride ions because the water everywhere is equally salty. There are no gradients for these ions on the other side of the container either, because the solid membrane prevents the ions from entering that side. But there are concentration and voltage gradients for both sodium and chloride ions *across* the membrane—that is, from the salty side to the freshwater side.

Transmembrane protein molecules embedded in a cell membrane form channels, some with gates, and pumps that allow certain kinds of ions to pass through the membrane. Returning to our thought experiment, we place a few chloride channels in the membrane that divides the container of water, making the membrane semipermeable, as illustrated at the left in Figure 4-8B. Chloride ions will now diffuse across the membrane and move down their concentration gradient on the side of the container that previously had no chloride ions, shown in the middle of Figure 4-8B. The sodium ions, in contrast, cannot cross through the chloride channels or the cell membrane.

If the only factor affecting the movement of chloride ions were the chloride concentration gradient, the efflux (outflow) of chloride from the salty to the freshwater side of the container would continue until chloride ions were in equilibrium on both sides. But this is not what happens. Because opposite charges attract, the chloride ions, which carry a negative charge, are attracted to the positively charged sodium ions they left behind. Because they are pulled back toward the sodium ions, the chloride ions cannot diffuse completely. Consequently, the concentration of chloride ions remains higher in the left side of the container than in the right, as illustrated at the right in Figure 4-8B.

In other words, the efflux of chloride ions down the chloride concentration gradient is counteracted by the influx (inflow) of chloride ions down the chloride voltage gradient. At some point, equilibrium is reached: the chloride concentration gradient on the right side of the beaker is balanced by the chloride voltage gradient on the left. In brief:

$$\text{concentration gradient} = \text{voltage gradient}$$

The cell membrane is an insulator impermeable to salty solutions: salt ions, surrounded by water molecules, will not pass through the membrane's hydrophobic tails (review Figure 3-11).

Dissolved sodium ions are smaller than chloride ions but more likely to stick to water molecules and so are bulkier and will not pass through a small chloride channel.

(A) Impermeable membrane

1 Salt placed in one side of a beaker of water that is divided by a barrier dissolves.

2 Positive and negative ions distribute themselves evenly throughout half of the container but cannot cross the barrier.

Salt (NaCl)

Cell membrane

Time

(B) Semipermeable membrane

3 If the barrier has a channel through which Cl⁻ can pass but Na⁺ cannot, Cl⁻ will diffuse from the side of high concentration through the hole in the barrier.

4 Cl⁻ will not be equally distributed on the two sides, because of the voltage gradient pulling them back toward the positve sodium ions.

Time   Time

FIGURE 4-8 Modeling the Cell Membrane

5 At equilibrium, one half of the container will be positively charged,...

6 ...the other half will be negatively charged, and the voltage difference will be greatest close to the membrane.

At this equilibrium, the differential concentration of the chloride ions on the two sides of the membrane produces a difference in charge—voltage. The left side of the container is positively charged because some chloride ions have migrated, leaving a preponderance of positive (Na⁺) charges. The right side of the container is negatively charged because some chloride ions have entered that chamber, where none were before. The charge is highest on the surface of the semipermeable membrane, the area at which positive and negative ions accumulate. Much the same process happens in a real cell.

(4-1) REVIEW

Searching for Electrical Activity in the Nervous System

Before you continue, check your understanding.

1. Although he was incorrect, _____ was the first to seriously attempt to explain how information travels through the nervous system.

2. Experimental results obtained over hundreds of years from electrical _____ and more recently from electrical _____ implicated electrical activity in the nervous system's flow of information.

3. By the mid-twentieth century, scientists had solved three technical problems in measuring the changes in electrical charge that travel like a wave along an axon's membrane: _____, _____, and _____.

4. The electrical activity of neuronal axons entails the diffusion of ions. Ions may move down a(n) _____ and down a(n) _____.

5. In what three ways does the semipermeable cell membrane affect the movement of ions in the nervous system?

Answers appear at the back of the book.

For additional study tools, visit 🧠 LaunchPad:
www.macmillanhighered.com/launchpad/kolb5e

(4-2) Electrical Activity of a Membrane

Specific aspects of the cell membrane's electrical activity interact to convey information throughout the nervous system. The movement of ions across neuronal membranes produces the electrical activity that enables this information flow.

Resting Potential

Figure 4-9 shows how the voltage difference is recorded when one microelectrode is placed on the outer surface of an axon's membrane and another is placed on its inner surface. In the absence of stimulation, the difference is about 70 mV. Although the charge on the outside of the membrane is actually positive, by convention it is given a charge of zero. Therefore, the inside of the membrane at rest is −70 mV *relative to* the extracellular side.

If we were to continue to record for a long time, the charge across the unstimulated membrane would remain much the same. The charge can change, given certain changes in the membrane, but at rest the difference in charge on the inside and outside of the membrane produces an electrical *potential*—the ability to use its stored power, analogous to a charged battery. The charge is thus a store of potential energy called the membrane's **resting potential.**

resting potential Electrical charge across the insulating cell membrane in the absence of stimulation; a store of potential energy produced by a greater negative charge on the intracellular side relative to the extracellular side.

...while another records the inner surface.

Axon

One electrode records the outer surface of an axon...

By convention, the extracellular side of the membrane is given a charge of 0 mV;...

...therefore the intracellular side of the membrane is –70 mV relative to the extracellular side. This measurement is the membrane's resting potential.

FIGURE 4-9 Resting Potential The electrical charge across a resting cell membrane stores potential energy.

We might use the term *potential* in the same way to talk about the financial potential of someone who has money in the bank—the person can spend the money at some future time. The resting potential, then, is a store of energy that can be used later. Most of your body's cells have a resting potential, but it is not identical on every axon. Resting potentials vary from −40 to −90 mV, depending on neuronal type and animal species.

Four charged particles take part in producing the resting potential: ions of sodium (Na^+), potassium (K^+), chloride (Cl^-), and large protein molecules (A^-). These are the cations and anions, respectively, defined in Section 4-1. As **Figure 4-10** shows, these charged particles are distributed unequally across the axon's membrane, with more protein anions and potassium ions in the intracellular fluid and more chloride and sodium ions in the extracellular fluid. How do the unequal concentrations arise, and how does each contribute to the resting potential?

A^- ions and K^+ ions have higher concentration inside the axon relative to the outside,...

...whereas Cl^- ions and Na^+ ions are more concentrated outside the axon.

Axon

A^- K^+ Na^+ Cl^-

Intracellular

Extracellular

FIGURE 4-10 Ion Distribution Across the Resting Membrane The number of ions distributed across the resting cell membrane is unequal. Protein ions are represented by the label, A^-.

Maintaining the Resting Potential

The cell membrane's channels, gates, and pumps maintain the resting potential. **Figure 4-11**, which shows the resting membrane close up, details how these three features contribute to the cell membrane's resting charge:

1. Because the membrane is relatively impermeable to large molecules, the negatively charged proteins remain inside the cell.

2. Ungated potassium and chloride channels allow potassium and chloride ions to pass more freely, but gates on sodium channels keep out positively charged sodium ions.

3. Na^+–K^+ pumps extrude Na^+ from the intracellular fluid and inject K^+.

Inside the Cell

Large protein anions are manufactured inside cells. No membrane channels are large enough to allow these proteins to leave the cell, and their negative charge alone is sufficient to produce transmembrane voltage, or a resting potential. Because most cells in the body manufacture these large, negatively charged protein molecules, most cells have a charge across the cell membrane.

To balance the negative charge produced by large protein anions in the intracellular fluid, cells accumulate positively charged potassium ions to the extent that about 20 times as

K^+ is free to enter and leave the cell.

Na^+ channels are ordinarily closed to prevent entry of Na^+.

Na^+–K^+ pumps out three Na^+ for two K^+.

Extracellular fluid

K^+

Na^+

$2 K^+$

K^+

A^-

$3 Na^+$

Intracellular fluid

FIGURE 4-11 Maintaining the Resting Potential Channels, gates, and pumps in the cell membrane contribute to the transmembrane charge.

many potassium ions cluster inside the cell as outside it. Potassium ions cross the cell membrane through open potassium channels, as shown in Figure 4-11. With this high concentration of potassium ions inside the cell, however, the potassium concentration gradient across the membrane limits the number of potassium ions entering the cell. In other words, not all the potassium ions that could enter do enter. Because the internal concentration of potassium ions is much higher than the external potassium concentration, potassium ions are drawn out of the cell by the potassium concentration gradient.

A few residual potassium ions on the outside of the membrane are enough to contribute to the charge across the membrane. They add to the negative charge on the intracellular side of the membrane relative to the extracellular side. You may be wondering whether you read the last sentence correctly. If there are 20 times as many potassium ions inside the cell as there are outside, why should the inside of the membrane have a negative charge? Should not all those potassium ions in the intracellular fluid give the inside of the cell a positive charge instead? No, because not quite enough potassium ions are able to enter the cell to balance the negative charge of the protein anions.

Think of it this way: if the number of potassium ions that could accumulate on the intracellular side of the membrane were unrestricted, the positively charged potassium ions inside would exactly match the negative charges on the intracellular protein anions. There would be no charge across the membrane at all. But the number of potassium ions that accumulate inside the cell is limited, because when the intracellular K^+ concentration becomes higher than the extracellular concentration, further potassium ion influx is opposed by its concentration gradient.

Outside the Cell

The equilibrium of the potassium voltage and concentration gradients results in some potassium ions remaining outside the cell. It is necessary to have only a few potassium ions outside the cell to maintain a negative charge inside the cell. As a result, potassium ions contribute to the charge across the membrane.

Sodium (Na^+) and chloride (Cl^-) ions also take part in producing the resting potential. If positively charged sodium ions were free to move across the membrane, they would diffuse into the cell and eliminate the transmembrane charge produced by the unequal distribution of potassium ions inside and outside the cell. This diffusion does not happen, because a gate on the sodium ion channels in the cell membrane is ordinarily closed (see Figure 4-11), blocking the entry of most sodium ions. Still, given enough time, sufficient sodium ions could leak into the cell to neutralize its membrane potential. The cell membrane has a different mechanism to prevent this neutralization.

When sodium ions do leak into the neuron, they are immediately escorted out again by the action of a *sodium–potassium pump*, a protein molecule embedded in the cell membrane. A membrane's many thousands of pumps continually exchange three intracellular sodium ions for two potassium ions, as shown in Figure 4-11. The potassium ions are free to leave the cell through open potassium channels, but closed sodium channels slow the reentry of the sodium ions. In this way, sodium ions are kept out to the extent that about 10 times as many sodium ions reside on the outside of the axon membrane as on its inside. The difference in sodium concentrations also contributes to the membrane's resting potential.

Now consider the chloride ions. Unlike sodium ions, chloride ions move in and out of the cell through open channels in the membrane. The equilibrium point, at which the chloride's concentration gradient equals its voltage gradient, is approximately the same as the membrane's resting potential, and so chloride ions ordinarily contribute little to the resting potential. At this equilibrium point, there are about 12 times as many chloride ions outside the cell as inside it.

The cell membrane's semipermeability and the actions of its channels, gates, and pumps thus produce voltage across the cell membrane: its resting potential (**Figure 4-12**).

Graded Potentials

The resting potential provides an energy store that can be used somewhat like the water in a dam: small amounts can be released by opening gates for irrigation or to generate electricity. If the concentration of any of the ions across the unstimulated cell membrane changes, the membrane voltage changes. These **graded potentials** are small voltage fluctuations across the cell membrane.

Stimulating a membrane electrically through a microelectrode mimics the way the membrane's voltage changes to produce a graded potential in the living cell. If the voltage applied to the inside of the membrane is negative, the membrane potential increases in negative charge by a few millivolts. As illustrated in **Figure 4-13**A, it may change from a resting potential of −70 mV to a slightly greater potential of −73 mV.

This change is a **hyperpolarization** because the charge (polarity) of the membrane increases. Conversely, if positive voltage is applied inside the membrane, its potential decreases by a few millivolts. As illustrated in Figure 4-13B, it may change from, say, a resting potential of −70 mV to a slightly lower potential of −65 mV. This change is a **depolarization** because the membrane charge decreases. Graded potentials usually last only milliseconds.

Hyperpolarization and depolarization typically take place on the soma (cell body) membrane and on neuronal dendrites. These areas contain gated channels that can open and

Unequal distribution of different ions causes the inside of the axon to be relatively negatively charged.

FIGURE 4-12 Resting Transmembrane Charge

FIGURE 4-13 Graded Potentials **(A)** Stimulation (S) that increases relative membrane voltage produces a hyperpolarizing graded potential. **(B)** Stimulation that decreases relative membrane voltage produces a depolarizing graded potential.

graded potential Small voltage fluctuation across the cell membrane.

hyperpolarization Increase in electrical charge across a membrane, usually due to the inward flow of chloride or sodium ions or the outward flow of potassium ions.

depolarization Decrease in electrical charge across a membrane, usually due to the inward flow of sodium ions.

close, changing the membrane potential as illustrated in Figure 4-13. Three channels—for potassium, chloride, and sodium ions—underlie graded potentials:

1. *Potassium channels* For the membrane to become hyperpolarized, its extracellular side must become more positive, which can be accomplished with an efflux of potassium ions. But if potassium channels are ordinarily open, how can the efflux of potassium ions increase? Apparently, even though potassium channels are open, some resistance to the outward flow of potassium ions remains. Reducing this resistance enables hyperpolarization.

2. *Chloride channels* The membrane can also become hyperpolarized if an influx of chloride ions occurs. Even though chloride ions can pass through the membrane, more ions remain on the outside than on the inside, so a decreased resistance to Cl⁻ flow can result in brief increases of Cl⁻ inside the cell.

3. *Sodium channels* Depolarization can be produced if normally closed sodium channel gates open to allow an influx of sodium ions.

Evidence that potassium channels have a role in hyperpolarization comes from the fact that the chemical tetraethylammonium (TEA), which blocks potassium channels, also blocks hyperpolarization. The involvement of sodium channels in depolarization is indicated by the fact that the chemical tetrodotoxin (TTX), which blocks sodium channels, also blocks depolarization. The puffer fish, considered a delicacy in some countries, especially Japan, secretes this potentially deadly poison to fend off potential predators. Skill is required to prepare this fish for dinner. It can be lethal to the guests of careless cooks because its toxin impedes the electrical activity of neurons.

Action Potential

Electrical stimulation of the cell membrane at resting potential produces local graded potentials. An **action potential** is a brief but large reversal in an axon membrane's polarity (**Figure 4-14A**). It lasts about 1 ms. The voltage across the membrane suddenly reverses, making the intracellular side positive relative to the extracellular side, then abruptly reverses again to restore the resting potential. Because the action potential is brief, many action potentials can occur within a second, as illustrated in Figure 4-14B and C, where the time scales are compressed.

An action potential occurs when a large concentration of first Na⁺ and then K⁺ crosses the membrane rapidly. The depolarizing phase of the action potential is due to Na⁺ influx, and the hyperpolarizing phase, to K⁺ efflux. Sodium rushes in, then potassium rushes out. As shown in **Figure 4-15,** the *combined* flow of sodium and potassium ions underlies the action potential.

An action potential is triggered when the cell membrane is depolarized to about −50 mV. At this **threshold potential,** the membrane charge undergoes a remarkable further change

Puffer Fish

action potential Large, brief reversal in the polarity of an axon membrane.

threshold potential Voltage on a neural membrane at which an action potential is triggered by the opening of sodium and potassium voltage-sensitive channels; about −50 mV relative to extracellular surround. Also called *threshold limit*.

FIGURE 4-14 Measuring Action Potentials (A) Phases of a single action potential. The time scales on the horizontal axes are compressed to chart (B) each action potential as a discrete event and (C) the ability of a membrane to produce many action potentials in a short time.

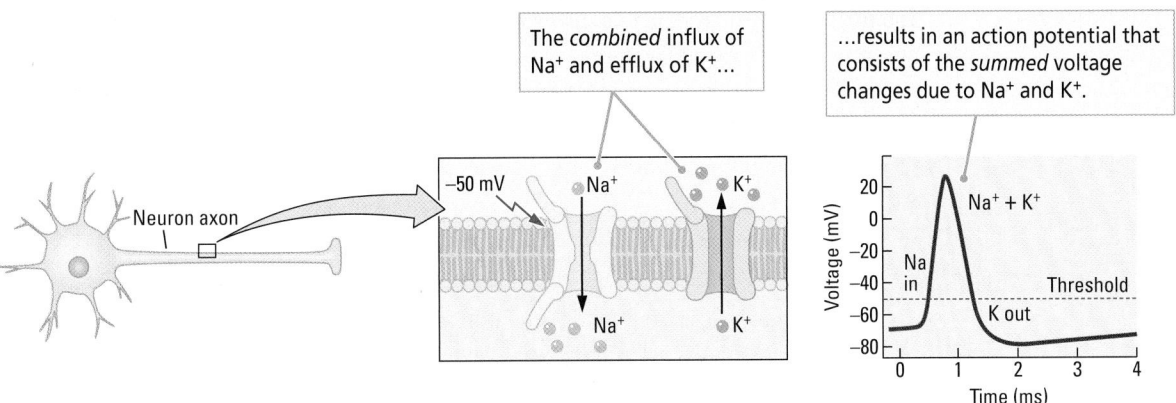

FIGURE 4-15 Triggering an Action Potential

with no additional stimulation. The relative voltage of the membrane drops to zero and continues to depolarize until the charge on the inside of the membrane is as great as +30 mV—a total voltage change of 100 mV. Then the membrane potential reverses again, becoming slightly hyperpolarized—a reversal of a little more than 100 mV. After this second reversal, the membrane slowly returns to its resting potential at −70 mV.

The action potential normally consists of the summed current changes caused first by the inflow of sodium and then by the outflow of potassium on an axon. Experimental results reveal that if an axon membrane is stimulated electrically while the solution surrounding the axon contains the chemical TEA (to block potassium channels), the result is a smaller-than-normal ion flow due entirely to an Na^+ influx. Similarly, if an axon's membrane is stimulated electrically while the solution surrounding the axon contains TTX (to block sodium channels), a slightly different ion flow due entirely to the efflux of K^+ is recorded. **Figure 4-16** illustrates these experimental results. The graphs in Figure 4-16 represent *ion flow* rather than voltage change.

Role of Voltage-Sensitive Ion Channels

What cellular mechanisms underlie the movement of sodium and potassium ions to produce an action potential? The answer is the behavior of a class of gated sodium and potassium

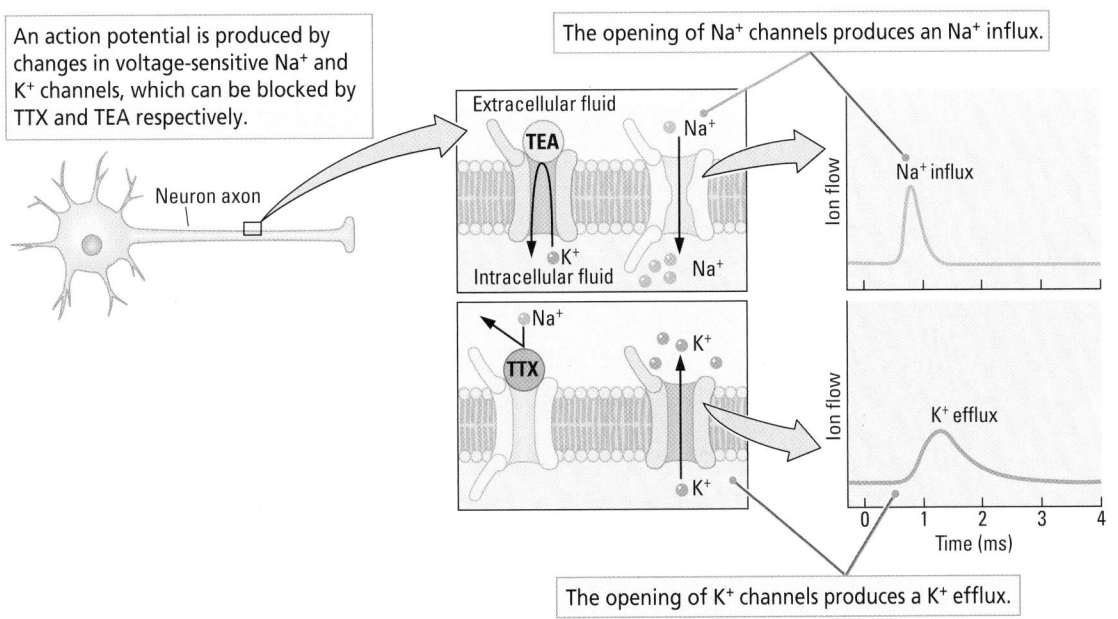

FIGURE 4-16 Blocking an Action Potential

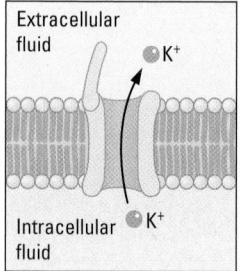

FIGURE 4-17 Voltage-Sensitive Potassium Channel

Exceptions do exist: some CNS neurons discharge during the repolarizing phase.

voltage-sensitive channel Gated protein channel that opens or closes only at specific membrane voltages.

absolutely refractory The state of an axon in the repolarizing period, during which a new action potential cannot be elicited (with some exceptions), because gate 2 of sodium channels, which are not voltage sensitive, are closed.

relatively refractory The state of an axon in the later phase of an action potential during which increased electrical current is required to produce another action potential; a phase during which potassium channels are still open.

nerve impulse Propagation of an action potential on the membrane of an axon.

FIGURE 4-18 Phases of an Action Potential Initiated by changes in voltage-sensitive sodium and potassium channels, an action potential begins with a depolarization: gate 1 of the sodium channel opens and then gate 2 closes. The slower-opening potassium channel gate contributes to repolarization and hyperpolarization until the resting membrane potential is restored.

channels sensitive to the membrane's voltage (**Figure 4-17**). These **voltage-sensitive channels** are closed when an axon's membrane is at its resting potential: ions cannot pass through them. When the membrane reaches threshold voltage, the configuration of the voltage-sensitive channels alters: they open briefly, enabling ions to pass through, then close again to restrict ion flow. The sequence of actions:

1. Both sodium and potassium voltage-sensitive channels are attuned to the threshold voltage of about −50 mV. If the cell membrane changes to reach this voltage, both types of channels open to allow ion flow across the membrane.

2. The voltage-sensitive sodium channels are more sensitive than the potassium channels and so open first. As a result, the voltage change due to Na^+ influx takes place slightly before the voltage change due to K^+ efflux can begin.

3. Sodium channels have two gates. Once the membrane depolarizes to about +30 mV, one of the gates closes. Thus, Na^+ influx begins quickly and ends quickly.

4. The potassium channels open more slowly than the sodium channels, and they remain open longer. Thus, the efflux of K^+ reverses the depolarization produced by Na^+ influx and even hyperpolarizes the membrane.

Action Potentials and Refractory Periods

There is an upper limit to how frequently action potentials occur, and sodium and potassium channels are responsible for it. Stimulation of the axon membrane during the depolarizing phase of the action potential will not produce another action potential. Nor is the axon able to produce another action potential when it is repolarizing. During these times, the membrane is described as being **absolutely refractory.**

If on the other hand the axon membrane is stimulated during hyperpolarization, another action potential can be induced, but the second stimulation must be more intense than the first. During this phase, the membrane is **relatively refractory.**

Refractory periods result from the way gates of the voltage-sensitive sodium and potassium channels open and close. Sodium channels have two gates, and potassium channels have one gate. **Figure 4-18** illustrates the position of these gates before, during, and after the phases of the action potential. We describe changes first in the sodium channels and then in the potassium channels.

During the resting potential, gate 1 of the sodium channel depicted in Figure 4-18 is closed; only gate 2 is open. At the threshold level of stimulation, gate 1 also opens. Gate 2, however, closes very quickly after gate 1 opens. This sequence produces a brief period during which both sodium gates are open. When both gates are open and when gate 2 is closed, the membrane is absolutely refractory.

The opening of the potassium channels repolarizes and eventually hyperpolarizes the cell membrane. The potassium channels open and close more slowly than the sodium channels do. The hyperpolarization produced by a continuing efflux of potassium ions makes it more difficult to depolarize the membrane to the threshold that reopens the gates underlying an action potential. While the membrane is hyperpolarizing, it is relatively refractory.

The action of a lever-activated toilet is analogous to some of the changes in polarity that take place during an action potential. Pushing the lever slightly produces a slight water flow that stops when the lever is released. This activity is analogous to a graded potential. A harder lever press brings the toilet to threshold and initiates flushing, a response that is out of all proportion to the lever press. This activity is analogous to the action potential.

During the flush, the toilet is absolutely refractory: another flush cannot be induced at this time. During the refilling of the bowl, in contrast, the toilet is relatively refractory, meaning that flushing again is possible but harder. Only after the cycle is over and the toilet is once again at rest can a full flush be produced again.

Nerve Impulse

Suppose you place two recording electrodes at a distance from one another on an axon membrane, then electrically stimulate an area adjacent to one electrode. That electrode would immediately record an action potential. A similar recording would register on the second electrode in a flash. An action potential has arisen near this second electrode also, even though it is some distance from the original point of stimulation.

Is this second action potential simply an echo of the first that passes down the axon? No, it cannot be, because the action potential's size and shape are exactly the same at the two electrodes. The second is not just a faint, degraded version of the first but is equal in magnitude. Somehow the full action potential has moved along the axon. This propagation of an action potential along an axon is called a **nerve impulse.**

Why does an action potential move? Remember that the total voltage change during an action potential is 100 mV, far beyond the 20-mV change needed to bring the membrane from its resting state of −70 mV to the action potential threshold level of −50 mV. Consequently, the voltage change on the part of the membrane where an action potential first occurs is large enough to bring adjacent parts of the membrane to a threshold of −50 mV.

When the membrane at an adjacent part of the axon reaches −50 mV, the voltage-sensitive channels at that location pop open to produce an action potential there as well. This second occurrence in turn induces a change in the membrane voltage still farther along the axon, and so on and on, down the axon's length. **Figure 4-19** illustrates this process. The nerve impulse occurs because each action potential propagates another action potential on an adjacent part of the axon membrane. The word *propagate* means *to give birth*, and that is exactly what happens. Each successive action potential gives birth to another down the length of the axon.

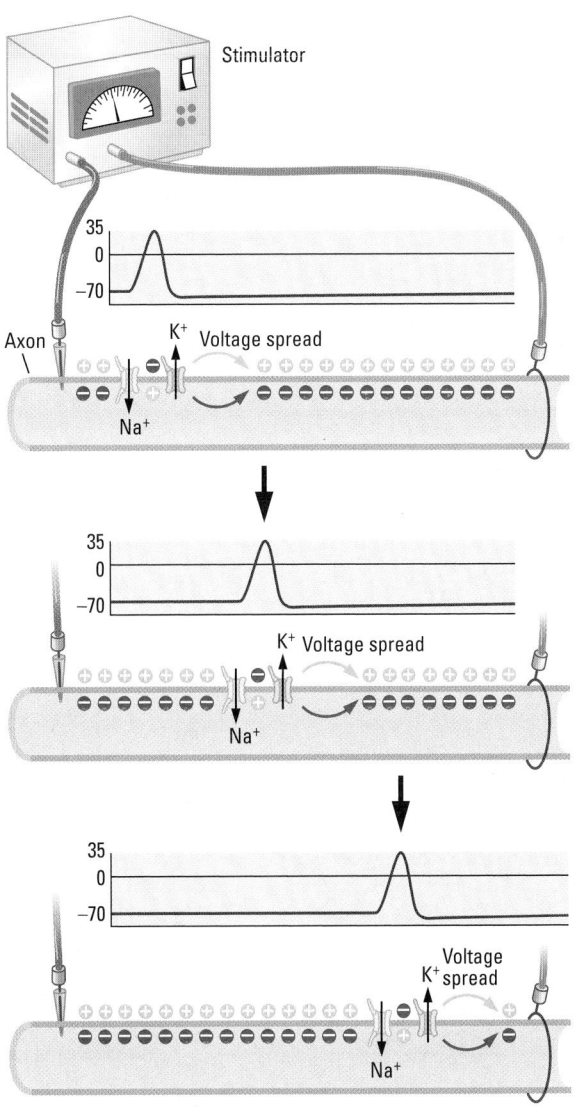

FIGURE 4-19 Propagating an Action Potential Voltage sufficient to open Na⁺ and K⁺ channels spreads to adjacent sites of the axon membrane, inducing voltage-sensitive gates to open. Here, voltage changes are shown on only one side of the membrane.

Because they are propagated by gated ion channels acting on the membrane in their own vicinity, action potentials on a nerve or tract are the same magnitude wherever they occur. An action potential depends on energy expended where it occurs, and the same amount of energy is expended at every site along the membrane as a nerve impulse is propagated.

As a result, action potentials do not dissipate: an action potential is either generated completely or not generated at all. Action potentials are all-or-none events. As the nerve's impulse, or message, the action potential maintains a constant size and arrives unchanged to every terminal on the nerve that receives it.

Think of the voltage-sensitive channels along the axon as a series of dominoes. When one falls, it knocks over its neighbor, and so on down the line. There is no decrement in the size of the fall. The last domino travels exactly the same distance and falls just as hard as the first one did.

Essentially, the domino effect happens when voltage-sensitive channels open. The opening of one channel produces a voltage change that triggers its neighbor to open, just as one domino knocks over the next. The channel-opening response does not grow any weaker as it moves along the axon, and the last channel opens exactly like the first, just as the domino action stays constant to the end of the line.

The domino effect

Refractory Periods and Nerve Action

Refractory periods are determined by the position of the gates that mediate ion flow in the voltage-sensitive channels. This limits the frequency of action potentials to about 5 ms. The action potential's refractory phase thus has two practical uses for nerves that are conducting information.

First, the maximum rate at which action potentials can occur is about 200 per second (1 s or 1000 ms/5 ms limit = 200 action potentials in 1 s). The sensitivity of voltage-sensitive channels, which varies among kinds of neurons, likewise affects firing frequency.

Second, although an action potential can travel in either direction on an axon, refractory periods prevent it from reversing direction and returning to its point of origin. Refractory periods thus produce a single, discrete impulse that travels away from the initial point of stimulation. When an action potential begins near the cell body, it usually travels down the axon to the terminals.

To return to our domino analogy, once a domino falls, setting it back up takes time. This is its refractory period. Because each domino falls as it knocks down its neighbor, the sequence cannot reverse until the domino is set upright again: the dominos can fall in only one direction. The same principle determines the action potential's direction.

Saltatory Conduction and the Myelin Sheath

Because the giant axons of squid are so large, they can transmit nerve impulses very quickly, much as a large-diameter pipe can rapidly deliver a lot of water. But large axons take up substantial space: a squid cannot accommodate many of them or its body would be too bulky. For us mammals, with our many axons producing repertoires of complex behaviors, giant axons are out of the question. Our axons must be extremely slender because our complex behaviors require a great many of them.

Our largest axons are only about 30 μm wide, so the speed with which they convey information should not be especially fast. And yet, like most vertebrate species, we humans are hardly sluggish creatures. We process information and generate responses with impressive speed. How do we manage to do so if our axons are so thin? The vertebrate nervous system has evolved a solution that has nothing to do with axon size.

Glial cells play a role in speeding nerve impulses in the vertebrate nervous system. Schwann cells in the human peripheral nervous system and oligodendroglia in the central nervous system wrap around each axon, forming the myelin sheath that insulates it (**Figure 4-20**). Action

FIGURE 4-20 Myelination An axon is insulated by **(A)** oligodendroglia in the CNS and **(B)** Schwann cells in the PNS. Each glial cell is separated by a gap, or node of Ranvier.

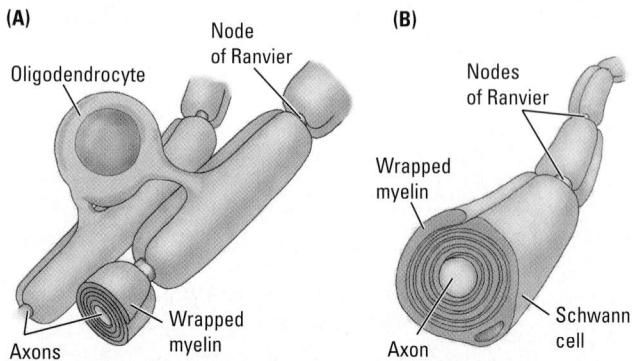

(A)

Oligodendrocyte

Node of Ranvier

Axons

Wrapped myelin

(B)

Nodes of Ranvier

Wrapped myelin

Axon

Schwann cell

potentials cannot occur where myelin is wrapped around an axon. For one thing, the myelin is an insulating barrier to ionic current flow. For another, axonal regions that lie under myelin have few channels through which ions can flow, and ion channels are essential to generating an action potential.

But axons are not totally encased in myelin. Unmyelinated gaps between successive glial cells are richly endowed with voltage-sensitive channels. These tiny gaps in the myelin sheath, the **nodes of Ranvier,** are sufficiently close to one another that an action potential at one node can open voltage-sensitive gates at an adjacent node. In this way, a relatively slow action potential jumps quickly from node to node, as shown in **Figure 4-21.** This flow of energy is called **saltatory conduction** (from the Latin verb *saltare,* meaning *to leap*).

Myelin has two important consequences for propagating action potentials. First, propagation becomes energetically cheaper, since action potentials regenerate only at the nodes of Ranvier, not along the axon's entire length. Action potential conduction in unmyelinated axons, by contrast, has a significant metabolic energy cost (Crotty et al., 2006). The second consequence is that myelin improves the action potential's conduction speed.

Jumping from node to node speeds the rate at which an action potential can travel along an axon, because the current flowing within the axon beneath the myelin sheath travels very fast. While the current moves speedily, the voltage drops quickly over distance. But the nodes of Ranvier are spaced ideally to ensure sufficient voltage at the next node to regenerate the action potential. On larger, myelinated mammalian axons, nerve impulses can travel at a rate as high as 120 meters per second. On smaller, uninsulated axons they travel only about 30 meters per second.

Spectators at sporting events sometimes initiate a wave that travels around a stadium. Just as one person rises, the next person begins to rise, producing the wave effect. This human wave is like conduction along an unmyelinated axon. Now think of how much faster the wave would complete its circuit around the field if only spectators in the corners rose to produce it. This is analogous to a nerve impulse that travels by jumping from one node of Ranvier to the next. The quick reactions that humans and other mammals are capable of are due in part to this saltatory conduction in their nervous system.

Neurons that send messages over long distances quickly, including sensory and motor neurons, are heavily myelinated. If myelin is damaged, a neuron may be unable to send any messages over its axons. In **multiple sclerosis (MS),** the myelin formed by oligodendroglia is damaged, which disrupts the functioning of neurons whose axons it encases. Clinical Focus 4-2, Multiple Sclerosis on page 126, describes the course of the disease.

To review glial cell types, appearance, and functions, see Table 3-1.

node of Ranvier The part of an axon that is not covered by myelin.

saltatory conduction Fast propagation of an action potential at successive nodes of Ranvier; *saltatory* means *leaping.*

multiple sclerosis (MS) Nervous system disorder resulting from the loss of myelin around axons in the CNS.

FIGURE 4-21 Saltatory Conduction Myelinated stretches of axons are interrupted by nodes of Ranvier, rich in voltage-sensitive channels. In saltatory conduction, the action potential jumps rapidly from node to node.

Multiple Sclerosis

One day J. O., who had just finished university requirements to begin work as an accountant, noticed a slight cloudiness in her right eye. It did not go away when she wiped her eye. Rather, the area grew over the next few days. Her optometrist suggested that she see a neurologist, who diagnosed optic neuritis, an indication that can be a flag for multiple sclerosis (MS).

MS is caused by a loss of myelin produced by oligodendroglia cells in the CNS (see illustration). It disrupts the affected neurons' ability to propagate action potentials via saltatory conduction. This loss of myelin occurs in patches, and scarring frequently results in the affected areas.

Eventually, a hard scar, or *plaque,* forms at the site of myelin loss. (MS is called a *sclerosis* from the Greek word meaning *hardness.*) Associated with the loss of myelin is impairment of neuron function, causing characteristic MS symptoms of sensory loss and difficulty in moving.

Fatigue, pain, and depression are commonly associated with MS. Bladder dysfunction, constipation, and sexual dysfunction all complicate it. MS, about twice as common in women as in men, greatly affects a person's emotional, social, and vocational functioning.

Multiple sclerosis is the most common of nearly 80 **autoimmune diseases,** conditions in which the immune system makes antibodies to a person's own body (Rezania et al., 2012). Although MS patients are treated with anti-inflammatory agents, it has no cure as yet.

J. O.'s eye cleared over the next few months, and she had no further symptoms until after the birth of her first child 3 years later, when she felt a tingling in her right hand. The tingling spread up her arm, until gradually she lost movement in the arm for 5 months. Then J. O.'s arm movement returned. But 5 years later, after her second child was born, she felt a tingling in her left big toe that spread along the sole of her foot and then up her leg, eventually leading again to loss of movement.

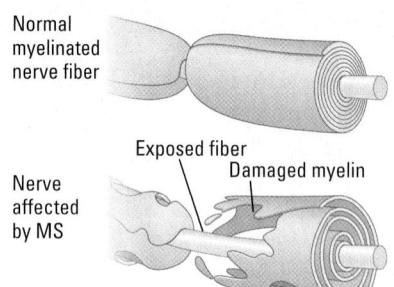

Normal myelinated nerve fiber

Exposed fiber Damaged myelin

Nerve affected by MS

J. O. received corticosteroid treatment, which helped, but the condition rebounded when she stopped treatment. Then it subsided and eventually disappeared.

Since then, J. O. has had no major outbreaks of motor impairment, but she reports enormous fatigue, takes long naps daily, and is ready for bed early in the evening. Her sister and a female cousin have experienced similar symptoms, and recently a third sister began to display similar symptoms in middle age. One of J. O.'s grandmothers was confined to a wheelchair, although the source of her problem was never diagnosed.

MS is difficult to diagnose. Symptoms usually appear in adulthood, their onset is quite sudden and their effects can be swift. Initial symptoms may be loss of sensation in the face, limbs, or body or loss of control over movements or loss of both sensation and control. Motor symptoms usually appear first in the hands or feet.

Early symptoms often go into remission and do not appear again for years. In some forms, however, MS progresses rapidly over just a few years until the person is bedridden.

MS is common in the most northern and most southern latitudes, so it may be related to a lack of vitamin D, which is produced by the action of sunlight on the skin. The disease may also be related to genetic susceptibility, as is likely in J. O.'s case. Many MS patients take vitamin D_3 and vitamin B_{12}.

It has been suggested that blood flow from the brain is reduced in MS, allowing a buildup of toxic iron. Widening veins that drain blood from the brain is suggested as a treatment. Clinical trials have been initiated on the basis of reports from media and in response to patient groups rather than on established scientific evidence. It has been argued that methodological flaws and lack of evidence disqualify both the venous cause of MS and venous widening as an appropriate treatment (Valdueza et al., 2013).

4-2 REVIEW

Electrical Activity of a Membrane

Before you continue, check your understanding.

1. The _____ results from the unequal distribution of _____ inside and outside the cell membrane.

2. Because it is _____, the cell membrane prevents the efflux of large protein anions and pumps sodium ions out of the cell to maintain a slightly _____ charge in the intracellular fluid relative to the extracellular fluid.

3. For a graded potential to arise, a membrane must be stimulated to the point that the transmembrane charge increases slightly to cause a(n) _____ or decreases slightly to cause a(n) _____.

4. The voltage change associated with a(n) _____ is sufficiently large to stimulate adjacent parts of the axon membrane to the threshold for propagating it along the length of an axon as a(n) _____ .

5. Briefly explain why nerve impulses travel faster on myelinated than on unmyelinated axons.

Answers appear at the back of the book.

For additional study tools, visit 🌐 LaunchPad:
www.macmillanhighered.com/launchpad/kolb5e

4-3 How Neurons Integrate Information

A neuron's extensive dendritic tree is covered with spines, and through them it can establish more than 50,000 connections from other neurons. Lying between its dendritic tree and axon, a neuron's cell body, too, can receive multiple connections. Nerve impulses traveling from other neurons to each of these synaptic locations bombard the receiving neuron with excitatory and inhibitory inputs.

In the 1960s, John C. Eccles (1965) and his students performed experiments that helped to answer the question, how does the neuron integrate such an enormous array of inputs into a nerve impulse? Rather than recording from the giant axon of a squid, Eccles recorded from the cell bodies of large motor neurons in the vertebrate spinal cord. In doing so, he refined the electrical stimulating and recording techniques first developed for studying squid axons (see Section 4-1). Eccles received the Nobel Prize in Physiology or Medicine in 1963.

Motor neurons, for example, receive input from multiple sources. A spinal cord motor neuron has an extensive dendritic tree with as many as 20 main branches that subdivide numerous times and are covered with dendritic spines. Input from the skin, joints, muscles, spinal cord, and brain make motor cells ideal for studying how a neuron responds to diverse inputs. Each motor neuron sends its axon directly to a muscle. The motor neuron is the final common pathway the nervous system takes to produce behavior.

Excitatory and Inhibitory Postsynaptic Potentials

To study motor neuron activity, Eccles inserted a microelectrode into a vertebrate's spinal cord until the tip was in or right beside a motor neuron's cell body. He then placed stimulating electrodes on sensory nerve fiber axons entering the spinal cord. By teasing apart the incoming sensory fibers, he was able to stimulate one nerve fiber at a time.

Experiment 4-1 diagrams the experimental setup Eccles used. As shown at the left in the Procedures section, stimulating some incoming sensory fibers produced a depolarizing graded potential (reduced the charge) on the membrane of the motor neuron to which these fibers were connected. Eccles called these graded potentials **excitatory postsynaptic potentials** (EPSPs). As graphed at left in the Results section, EPSPs reduce the charge on the membrane toward the threshold level and increase the likelihood that an action potential will result.

At the right in the Procedures section, when Eccles stimulated other incoming sensory fibers, he produced a hyperpolarizing graded potential (increased the charge) on the receiving motor neuron membrane. Eccles called these graded potentials **inhibitory postsynaptic potentials** (IPSPs). As graphed at the right in the Results section, IPSPs increase the charge on the membrane away from the threshold level and decrease the likelihood that an action potential will result.

Neurons that receive more than one kind of input sum up the information they get.

Figure 2-29A diagrams the human spinal cord in cross section.

autoimmune disease Illness resulting from an abnormal immune response by the body against substances and tissues normally present in the body.

excitatory postsynaptic potential (EPSP) Brief depolarization of a neuron membrane in response to stimulation, making the neuron more likely to produce an action potential.

inhibitory postsynaptic potential (IPSP) Brief hyperpolarization of a neuron membrane in response to stimulation, making the neuron less likely to produce an action potential.

▶ EXPERIMENT **4-1**

Question: How does stimulating a neuron influence its excitability?

Procedure

Using an oscilloscope, Eccles recorded from the cell body of a motor neuron while stimulating...

Oscilloscope

Stimulate

Stimulate

...an excitatory sensory pathway or...

Excitatory pathway

Inhibitory pathway

...an inhibitory sensory pathway.

Motor neuron

Results

EPSP

IPSP

Stimulating the excitatory pathway produced a membrane depolarization, or excitatory postsynaptic potential (EPSP).

Voltage (mv)

Stimulating the inhibitory pathway produced a membrane hyperpolarization, or inhibitory postsynaptic potential (IPSP).

Time (ms)

S

S

Conclusion: EPSPs increase the likelihood that an action potential will result. IPSPs decrease the likelihood that an action potential will result.

Both EPSPs and IPSPs last only a few milliseconds before they decay and the neuron's resting potential is restored. EPSPs are associated with the opening of sodium channels, which allows an influx of sodium ions. IPSPs are associated with the opening of potassium channels, which allows an efflux of potassium ions (or with the opening of chloride channels, which allows an influx of chloride ions).

Although the size of a graded potential is proportional to the intensity of the stimulation, an action potential is not produced on the motor neuron's cell body membrane even when an EPSP is strongly excitatory. The reason is simple: the cell body membrane of most neurons does not contain voltage-sensitive channels. The stimulation must reach the **initial segment**, the area near or overlapping the axon hillock, where the action potential begins. The initial segment is rich in voltage-sensitive channels (Bender & Trussel, 2012).

A brief video at www.youtube.com/ watch?v=-qdH3WGL99Q describes how the initial segment initiates an action potential.

Summation of Inputs

A motor neuron's myriad dendritic spines can each contribute to membrane voltage, via either an EPSP or an IPSP. How do these incoming graded potentials interact at its membrane? What happens if two EPSPs occur in succession? Does it matter if the time between them increases or decreases? What happens when an EPSP and an IPSP arrive together?

initial segment Area near or overlapping the axon hillock where the action potential begins.

temporal summation Addition of one graded potential to another that occur close in time.

spatial summation Addition of one graded potential to another that occur close in space.

FIGURE 4-22 Temporal Summation **(A)** Two depolarizing pulses stimulation (S_1 and S_2) separated in time produce two EPSPs similar in size. Pulses close together in time partly sum. Simultaneous EPSPs sum as one large EPSP. **(B)** Two hyperpolarizing pulses (S_1 and S_2) widely separated in time produce two IPSPs similar in size. Pulses coming fast partly sum. Simultaneous IPSPs sum as one large IPSP.

Temporal Summation

If one excitatory pulse is followed some time later by a second excitatory pulse, one EPSP is recorded and after a delay, a second identical EPSP is recorded, as shown at the top left in **Figure 4-22.** These two widely spaced EPSPs are independent and do not interact. If the delay between them is shortened so that the two occur in rapid succession, however, a single large EPSP is produced, as shown in the left-center panel of Figure 4-22.

Here, the two excitatory pulses are summed—added together to produce a larger depolarization of the membrane than either would induce alone. This relation between two EPSPs occurring close together or even at the same time (bottom left panel) is called **temporal summation.** The right side of Figure 4-22 illustrates that equivalent results are obtained with IPSPs. Therefore, temporal summation is a property of both EPSPs and IPSPs.

Spatial Summation

How does spacing affect inputs to the cell body membrane? By using two recording electrodes (R_1 and R_2) we can see the effects of spatial relations on the summation of inputs.

If two EPSPs are recorded at the same time but on widely separated parts of the membrane (**Figure 4-23A**), they do not influence one another. If two EPSPs occurring close together in time are also close together on the membrane, however, they sum to form a larger EPSP (Figure 4-23B). This **spatial summation** occurs when two separate inputs are very close to one another both on the cell membrane and in time. Similarly, two IPSPs produced at the same time sum if they occur at approximately the same place and time on the cell body membrane but not if they are widely separated.

Role of Ions in Summation

Summation is a property of both EPSPs and IPSPs in any combination. These interactions make sense when you

FIGURE 4-23 Spatial Summation The process for EPSPs. The process for IPSPs is equivalent.

(A)

EPSPs produced at the same time, but on separate parts of the membrane, do not influence each other.

(B)

EPSPs produced at the same time, and close together, sum to form a larger EPSP.

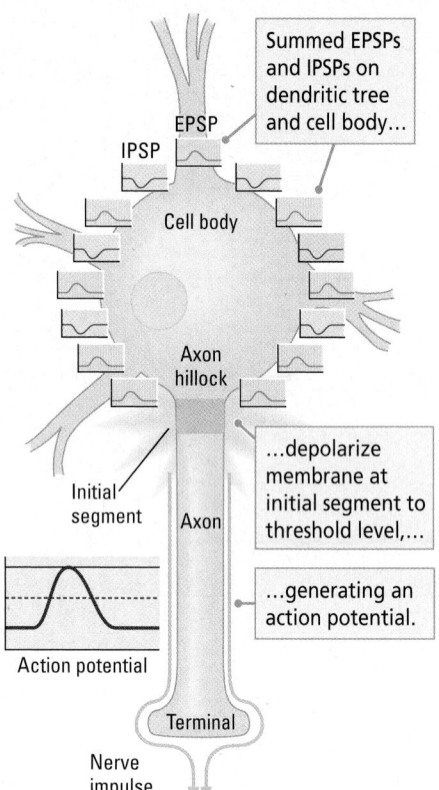

FIGURE 4-24 Triggering an Action Potential If the summated graded potentials—the EPSPs and IPSPs—on the dendritic tree and cell body of a neuron charge the membrane to threshold level at the initial segment, an action potential is initiated, and it travels down the axon membrane.

back propagation Reverse movement of an action potential into the soma and dendritic field of a neuron; postulated to play a role in plastic changes that underlie learning.

optogenetics Transgenic technique that combines genetics and light to excite or inhibit targeted cells in living tissue.

The hippocampus (from the Greek meaning *seahorse* because its shape is similar) participates in aspects of memory and is vulnerable to stress (see Section 6-5).

consider that ion influx and efflux are being summed. The influx of sodium ions accompanying one EPSP is added to the influx of sodium ions accompanying a second EPSP if the two occur close together in time and space. If the two influxes are remote in time or in space or in both, no summation is possible.

The same is true regarding effluxes of potassium ions. When they occur close together in time and space, they sum; when they are far apart in either or both ways, there is no summation. The patterns are identical for an EPSP and an IPSP. The influx of sodium ions associated with the EPSP is added to the efflux of potassium ions associated with the IPSP, and the difference between them is recorded as long as they are spatially and temporally close together. If, on the other hand, they are widely separated in time or in space or in both, they do not interact and there is no summation.

A neuron with thousands of inputs responds no differently from one with only a few inputs. It democratically sums all inputs that are close together in time and space. The cell body membrane, therefore, always indicates the summed influences of multiple temporal and spatial inputs. And so a neuron can be said to analyze its inputs before deciding what to do. The ultimate decision is made at the initial segment, the region on the axon that initiates the action potential.

Voltage-Sensitive Channels and the Action Potential

Unlike the cell body membrane, the axon is rich in voltage-sensitive channels, beginning at the initial segment (**Figure 4-24**). These channels, like those on the squid axon, open at a particular membrane voltage. The actual threshold voltage varies with the type of neuron, but to keep things simple, we will stay with a threshold level of −50 mV.

To produce an action potential, the summed graded potentials—the IPSPs and EPSPs—on the cell body membrane must depolarize the membrane at the initial segment to −50 mV. If that threshold voltage is obtained only briefly, voltage-sensitive channels open, and just one or a few action potentials may occur. If the threshold level is maintained for a longer period, however, action potentials will follow one another in rapid succession, just as quickly as the gates on the voltage-sensitive channels can reset. Each action potential is then repeatedly propagated to produce a nerve impulse that travels from the initial segment down the length of the axon.

Many neurons have extensive dendritic trees, but dendrites and dendritic branches do not have many voltage-sensitive channels and ordinarily do not produce action potentials. And distant branches of dendrites may have less influence in producing action potentials initiated at the initial segment than do the more proximal branches of the dendrites. Consequently, inputs close to the initial segment are usually much more influential than those occurring some distance away. Those distant inputs usually have a modulating effect. As in all governments, some inputs have more say than others (Debanne, 2011).

The Versatile Neuron

Dendrites collect information as graded potentials (EPSPs and IPSPs), and the initial segment initiates discrete action potentials delivered to other target cells via the axon. Exceptions to this picture of how a neuron works do exist. For example, some cells in the developing hippocampus can produce additional action potentials, called *giant depolarizing potentials*, when the cell would ordinarily be refractory. It is thought that giant depolarizing potentials aid in developing the brain's neural circuitry (Mohajerani & Cherubini, 2006).

Because the cell body membrane does not contain voltage-sensitive channels, a typical neuron does not initiate action potentials on its dendrites. In some neurons, however, voltage-sensitive channels on dendrites do enable action potentials. The reverse movement of an action potential from the initial segment into the dendritic field of a neuron is called **back propagation.** Back propagation, which signals the dendritic field that the neuron is sending an action potential over its axon, may play a role in plastic changes in the neuron that underlie learning. For example, back propagation may make the dendritic field refractory to incoming inputs, set the dendritic field to an electrically neutral baseline, or reinforce signals coming in to certain dendrites (Legenstein and Maass, 2011).

We explore the neuronal basis of learning in Sections 5-4 and 14-4.

The neurons of some nonmammalian species have no dendritic branches. And some ion channels, rather than responding to voltage, respond to light by opening and allowing ions to pass. The many differences among neurons suggest that the nervous system capitalizes on structural and functional modifications to produce adaptive behavior in each species. In research to determine the neuron's specific functions, neuroscientists have incorporated into certain types of neurons ion channels that respond to light, as described in Research Focus 4-3, Optogenetics and Light-Sensitive Channels.

Section 7-1 describes the promise of optogenetics for neuroscience research and for clinical applications.

RESEARCH FOCUS 4.3

Optogenetics and Light-Sensitive Ion Channels

Membrane channels that are responsive to light have been discovered in nonmammalian animal species. Using the transgenic technique of **optogenetics,** researchers have successfully introduced light-sensitive channels into worms, fruit flies, and mice.

Optogenetics combines genetics and light to control targeted cells in living tissue. Here we examine how introducing different light-sensitive channels into a species excites the organism's movements with one wavelength and inhibits them with another wavelength.

One class of light-activated ion channels in the green alga *Chlamydomonas reinhardtii* is channelrhodopsin-2. The ChR2 channel absorbs blue light and in doing so opens briefly to allow the passage of cations, including sodium and potassium. These light-sensitive channels allow the passage of Na^+ and K^+ when a cell is illuminated with blue light. The resulting depolarization excites the cell to generate action potentials.

Halorhodopsin (NpHR) is a light-driven ion pump, specific for chloride ions and found in phylogenetically ancient bacteria (archaea) known as halobacteria. When illuminated with green-yellow light, the halorhodopsin pumps chloride anions into the cell, hyperpolarizing it and so inhibiting its activity.

The movements of worms, fruit flies, and mice with genetically introduced light-sensitive channels have been controlled when their nervous system cells were illuminated with appropriate wavelengths of light. One such species, *Caenorhabditis elegans*, is a roundworm about 1 millimeter long that lives in soil.

C. elegans is popular in neuroscience experiments because it is transparent and has a simple nervous system. It is also the first species to have all its neurons, synapses, and genome completely described. The illustration shows **(A)** the normal movements of *C. elegans* and the light-sensitive membrane channel responses that **(B)** excite or **(C)** inhibit its movement.

Using optogenetic techniques, light-sensitive channels can be incorporated into specific neural circuits so that light stimulation controls only a subset of neurons. The promise is that investigating specific neuron populations can provide insight into brain disease, including conditions such as addiction (Cao et al., 2011).

Also encouraging are the results of a study suggesting that impaired vision due to the loss of the light-sensitive retina of the eye could be restored with light-sensitive channels (Fenno et al., 2011).

(A) *C. elegans*

Sinclair Stammers/Science Source

(B) Excitation

Extracellular fluid

Blue light

Na^+

ChR2

Intracellular fluid

K^+

(C) Inhibition

Extracellular fluid

Green-yellow light

Cl^-

NpHR

Intracellular fluid

Light-Sensitive Channels

(A) Normal movements of *C. elegans*. **(B)** When light-sensitive channelrhodopsin-2 ion channels are introduced into its neurons, *C. elegans* becomes active and coils when exposed to blue light. Information from Zhang et al., 2007. **(C)** With light-sensitive halorhodopsin ion pumps introduced into its muscles, *C. elegans* elongates and becomes immobile when exposed to green-yellow light. Information from Liewald et al., 2008.

(4-3) **REVIEW**

How Neurons Integrate Information

Before you continue, check your understanding.

1. Graded potentials that decrease the charge on the cell membrane, moving it toward the threshold level, are called _____ because they increase the likelihood that an action potential will occur. Graded potentials that increase the charge on the cell membrane, moving it away from the threshold level, are called _____ because they decrease the likelihood that an action potential will result.

2. EPSPs and IPSPs that occur close together in both _____ and _____ are summed. This is how a neuron _____ the information it receives from other neurons.

3. The membrane of the _____ does not contain voltage-sensitive ion channels, but if summed inputs excite the _____ to a threshold level, action potentials are triggered and then propagated as they travel along the cell's _____ as a nerve impulse.

4. Explain what happens during back propagation.

Answers appear at the back of the book.

For additional study tools, visit 🌀 **LaunchPad**:
www.macmillanhighered.com/launchpad/kolb5e

(4-4) # Into the Nervous System and Back Out

stretch-sensitive channel Ion channel on a tactile sensory neuron that activates in response to stretching of the membrane, initiating a nerve impulse.

end plate On a muscle, the receptor–ion complex that is activated by the release of the neurotransmitter acetylcholine from the terminal of a motor neuron.

transmitter-sensitive channel Receptor complex that has both a receptor site for a chemical and a pore through which ions can flow.

The nervous system allows us to respond to afferent sensory stimuli by detecting them and sending messages about them to the brain. The brain interprets the information, triggering efferent responses that contract muscles and produce behavior. Until now, we have been dealing only with the middle of this process—how neurons convey information to one another, integrate the information, and generate action potentials. Now we explore the beginning and end of the journey.

To fill in the missing pieces, we explain how a sensory stimulus initiates a nerve impulse and how a nerve impulse produces a muscular contraction. Once again, ion channels are vitally important, but in muscles, the channels are different from those described so far.

How Sensory Stimuli Produce Action Potentials

We receive information about the world through bodily sensations (touch and balance), auditory sensations (hearing), visual sensations (sight), and chemical sensations (taste and olfaction). Each sensory modality has one or more separate functions. In addition to touch, for example, the body senses include pressure, joint sense, pain, temperature, and itch. Receptors for audition and balance are modified touch receptors. The visual system has receptors for light and for colors. And taste and olfactory senses respond to a plethora of chemical compounds.

For detail on how sensory receptors transduce external energy into action potentials:

Hearing, Section 10-1
Sensation and perception, Section 9-1
Smell and taste, Section 12-2
Touch, pain, and balance, Section 11-4
Vision, Section 9-2

To process all these varied sensory inputs requires a remarkable array of sensory receptors. But in all our sensory systems, the neurons related to these diverse receptors have one thing in common: conduction of information begins at ion channels. They initiate the chain of events that produces a nerve impulse.

An example is touch. Each hair on the human body allows us to detect even a very slight displacement. You can demonstrate this sensitivity to yourself by selecting a single hair on your arm and bending it. If you are patient and precise in your experimentation, you will discover that some hairs are sensitive to displacement in one direction only, whereas others respond to displacement in any direction. What enables this finely tuned sensitivity?

The base of each hair is wrapped in a dendrite of a touch neuron. When you bend a hair or otherwise mechanically displace it, the encircling dendrite is stretched (**Figure 4-25**). The displacement opens **stretch-sensitive channels** in the dendrite's membrane. When open, these channels allow an influx of sodium ions sufficient to depolarize the dendrite to threshold. At threshold, the voltage-sensitive sodium and potassium channels initiate a nerve impulse that conveys touch information to your brain.

Other kinds of sensory receptors have similar mechanisms for *transducing* (transforming) the energy of a sensory stimulus into nervous system activity. When displaced, the *hair receptors* that provide information about hearing and balance likewise activate stretch-sensitive channels. In the visual system, photons (light particles) strike opsin proteins in receptors within specialized cells in the eye. The resulting chemical change activates ion channels in *relay neuron* membranes. An odorous molecule in the air that lands on an olfactory receptor and fits itself into a specially shaped compartment opens chemical-sensitive ion channels. When tissue is damaged, injured cells release chemicals that activate channels on a pain nerve. The point here is that ion channels originate conduction of information in all our sensory systems.

FIGURE 4-25 Tactile Stimulation A hair's touch receptor activated by a feather results in a nerve impulse heading to the brain.

Feather

Displacement of hair...

Hair

Dendrite of sensory neuron wrapped around hair

...causes stretch-sensitive channels on dendrite to open, allowing an influx of Na+.

This Na+ influx causes voltage-sensitive Na+ and K+ channels to open, producing a nerve impulse.

Extracellular fluid

Na^+ Current flow

Nerve impulse

Na^+

K^+

Stretch-sensitive channel

Voltage-sensitive channels

Intracellular fluid

How Nerve Impulses Produce Movement

What happens at the end of the neural journey? After sensory information has traveled to the brain and been interpreted, how does the brain generate output—a behavioral response that includes muscle contractions? Behavior, after all, is movement, and for movement to take place, muscles must contract. Motor neurons in the spinal cord are responsible for activating muscles. Without them movement becomes impossible and muscles atrophy, as described in Clinical Focus 4-4, ALS: Lou Gehrig's Disease.

Motor neurons send nerve impulses to synapses on muscle cells. These synapses are instrumental in making the muscle contract. Each motor neuron axon makes one or a few synapses with its target muscle, synapses similar to those neurons make with one another **Figure 4-26**A). The axon terminal contacts a specialized area of the muscle membrane called an **end plate.** Onto the muscle's end plate the axon terminal releases the chemical transmitter *acetylcholine.*

Acetylcholine does not enter the muscle but rather attaches to **transmitter-sensitive channels** on the end plate (Figure 4-26B). When these channels open in response, they allow a flow of Na+ and K+ across the muscle membrane sufficient to depolarize the muscle to the threshold for its action potential. Yes, to contract, muscles generate action potentials. At this threshold, adjacent voltage-sensitive channels open. They in turn produce an action potential on the muscle fiber, as they do in a neuron.

The transmitter-sensitive channels on muscle end plates are somewhat different from the channels on axons and dendrites. A single end plate channel is larger than two sodium and two potassium channels on a neuron, combined. So when its transmitter-sensitive channels open, they allow both Na+ influx and K+ efflux through the same pore. Generating a sufficient depolarization on the end plate to activate neighboring

FIGURE 4-26 Muscle Contraction **(A)** When a motor neuron's axon collaterals contact a muscle fiber end plate, **(B)** acetylcholine attaches to receptor sites on the end plate's transmitter-sensitive channels, opening them. These large membrane channels allow simultaneous influx of Na+ and efflux of K+, generating current sufficient to activate voltage-sensitive channels, triggering action potentials, and causing the muscle to contract.

(A)

Motor nerve

Axon

End plate

Axon terminal

Muscle fiber

(B)

Acetylcholine

Receptor site

Na^+ Current flow

Na^+

K^+

Transmitter-sensitive channel

Voltage-sensitive channel

ALS: Lou Gehrig's Disease

In 1869, French physician Jean-Martin Charcot first described ALS, amyotrophic lateral sclerosis. In North America, ALS is also known as Lou Gehrig's disease. Gehrig, a baseball legend who played for the New York Yankees from 1923 until 1939, set a host of individual records. He was an outstanding hitter, and his incredible durability earned him the nickname the Iron Horse.

Gehrig played on many World Series championship teams, but ALS sapped his strength, forcing him to retire from baseball at age 36. *Amyotrophic* means *muscle weakness*; *lateral sclerosis* means *hardening of the lateral spinal cord.* Gehrig's condition deteriorated rapidly. He died 2 years later. ALS strikes most commonly at age 50 to 75, although its onset can be as early as the teenage years.

While death often occurs within 5 years of diagnosis, internationally renowned theoretical physicist and cosmologist Stephen Hawking is a notable exception. Diagnosed at age 21, Hawking has a rare early-onset and slowly progressing form of ALS. As a doctoral student at Oxford, he grew increasingly clumsy, and his speech was slightly slurred. In his late twenties he began to use crutches. In his thirties his speech deteriorated until and only his family and close friends understood him. Now in his seventies, and confined to a wheelchair, Hawking, pictured at right, communicates by using a single cheek muscle attached to a speech-generating device.

Roughly 10 percent of people with ALS have a family history of the disorder. About 5000 new cases are reported in the United States each year. ALS is due primarily to the death of spinal motor neurons but can affect brain neurons as well in some cases.

ALS typically begins with general weakness, at first in the throat or upper chest and in the arms and legs. Gradually, walking becomes difficult and falling common. ALS does not usually affect any sensory systems, cognitive functions, bowel or bladder control, or even sexual function. Even as his motor neurons continue to die, Stephen Hawking's mind-blowing advancements continue to enrich our understanding of the universe.

At present, no cure for ALS exists, although some newly developed drugs appear to slow its progression and offer some hope for future treatments. In 2014 the ALS Ice Bucket Challenge appeared on YouTube to promote awareness of ALS and encourage donations to research. The Challenge went viral.

Rex Features via AP Images

Sections 5-2 and 5-3 describe the varieties of chemical transmitters and how they function.

FIGURE 4-27 Myasthenia Gravis
Asked to look up **(1)**, this patient's eyelids quickly become fatigued and droop **(2, 3)**. After a few minutes of rest her eyelids open normally **(4)**.

voltage-sensitive channels on the muscle membrane requires the release of an appropriate amount of acetylcholine.

Should the acetylcholine receptors on muscle end plates be blocked, acetylcholine released from the motor neuron cannot properly exert its depolarizing effect. This prevents muscular contraction in conditions such as the autoimmune disease *myasthenia gravis*. In affected individuals the thymus, an immune system gland that normally produces antibodies to foreign material like viruses, makes antibodies to the acetylcholine receptors on muscles, causing weakness and fatigue (**Figure 4-27**).

Unlike MS, another autoimmune disease, myasthenia gravis is usually well controlled by treatments including drugs that suppress the immune system or inhibit acetylcholine breakdown, extending the time it can act, and by removal of the thymus gland (thymectomy).

The actions of membrane channels can explain a wide range of neural events. Some channels generate the transmembrane charge. Others mediate graded potentials. Still others trigger the action potential. Sensory stimuli activate channels on neurons to initiate a nerve impulse, and the nerve impulse eventually activates channels on motor neurons to produce muscle contractions.

These various channels and their different functions evolved over a long time in the same way that new species of animals and their behaviors evolve. We have not described all the different ion channels that neural membranes possess, but you will learn about some additional ones in subsequent chapters.

(4-4) REVIEW

Into the Nervous System and Back Out

Before you continue, check your understanding.

1. Different sensory stimuli initiate nerve impulses for each _____ in a similar way.

2. A(n) _____ membrane contains a mechanism for transducing sensory energy into changes in ion channels. In turn, the channels allow ion flow to alter the membrane voltage to the point that _____ channels open, initiating a nerve impulse.

3. Sensory stimuli activate ion channels to initiate a nerve impulse that activates channels on _____ neurons, which in turn contract _____.

4. In myasthenia gravis, a(n)_____ disease, the thymus gland produces antibodies to _____ receptors on muscles, causing weakness and fatigue.

5. Why have so many kinds of ion channels evolved on cell membranes?

Answers appear at the back of the book.

For additional study tools, visit **LaunchPad:**
www.macmillanhighered.com/launchpad/kolb5e

SUMMARY

(4-1) Searching for Electrical Activity in the Nervous System

Electrical stimulation studies dating as far back as the eighteenth century show that stimulating a nerve with electrical current induces a muscle contraction. In more recent recording studies, the brain's electrical current, measured using an oscilloscope, shows that electrical activity in the nervous system is continuous.

In the twentieth century, researchers used giant axons of the squid to measure the electrical activity of a single neuron. Using microelectrodes that they could place on or in the cell, they recorded small, rapid electrical changes with an oscilloscope. Today, digital oscilloscopes and computers record these measurements.

A neuron's electrical activity is generated by ions flowing across the cell membrane. Ions flow both down a concentration gradient (from an area of relatively high concentration to an area of lower concentration) and down a voltage gradient (from an area of relatively high voltage to an area of lower voltage). The opening, closing, and pumping of ion channels in neural cell membranes also affect ion distribution.

(4-2) Electrical Activity of a Membrane

Unequal ion distribution on a cell membrane's two sides generates the neuron's resting potential. At rest, the intracellular membrane registers about −70 mV relative to the extracellular side. Negatively charged protein anions are too large to leave the neuron, and the cell membrane actively pumps out positively charged sodium ions. Unequal distributions of potassium cations and chloride anions contribute to the resting potential as well.

Graded potentials, short-lived small increases or decreases in transmembrane voltage, result when the neuron is stimulated. Voltage changes affect the membrane's ion channels and in turn change the cross-membrane ion distribution. An increase in transmembrane voltage causes hyperpolarization; a decrease causes depolarization.

An action potential is a brief but large change in axon membrane polarity triggered when the transmembrane voltage drops to a threshold level of about −50 mV. During an action potential, transmembrane voltage suddenly reverses—the intracellular side becomes positive relative to the extracellular side—and abruptly reverses again. Gradually, the resting potential is restored. These membrane changes result from voltage-sensitive channels—sodium and potassium channels sensitive to the membrane's voltage.

When an action potential is triggered at the initial segment, it can propagate along the axon as a nerve impulse. Nerve impulses travel more rapidly on myelinated axons because of saltatory conduction: the action potentials leap between the nodes separating the glial cells that form the axon's myelin sheath.

(4-3) How Neurons Integrate Information

Inputs to neurons from other cells can produce both excitatory postsynaptic potentials and inhibitory postsynaptic potentials. The membrane sums their voltages both temporally and spatially to integrate the incoming information. If the summed EPSPs and IPSPs move the membrane voltage at the initial segment to threshold, the axon generates an action potential.

The neuron is a versatile kind of cell. Some species' ion channels respond to light rather than to voltage changes, an attribute that genetic engineers are exploiting. Most of our neurons do not initiate action potentials on dendrites, because the cell body membrane does not contain voltage-sensitive channels. But some voltage-sensitive channels on dendrites do enable action potentials. Back propagation, the reverse movement of an action potential from the initial segment into the dendritic field of a neuron, may play a role in plastic changes that underlie learning.

(4-4) Into the Nervous System and Back Out

Sensory receptor cells convert sensory energy to graded potentials. These changes, in turn, alter transmembrane voltage to trigger an action potential and propagate a nerve impulse that transmits sensory information to relevant parts of the nervous system.

Ion channels come into play to activate muscles as well, because the chemical transmitter acetylcholine, released at the axon terminal of a motor neuron, activates channels on the end plate of a muscle cell membrane. The subsequent ion flow depolarizes the muscle cell membrane to the threshold for its action potential. In turn, this depolarization activates voltage-sensitive channels, producing an action potential on the muscle fiber, hence the muscle contractions that enable movement. In myasthenia gravis, antibodies to the acetylcholine receptor prevent muscle depolarization, which is the basis of weakness and fatigue.

▮KEY TERMS

absolutely refractory, p. 122

action potential, p. 120

autoimmune disease, p. 127

back propagation, p. 130

concentration gradient, p. 114

depolarization, p. 119

diffusion, p. 114

electrical stimulation, p. 109

electroencephalogram (EEG), p. 111

electrographic seizures, p. 109

end plate, p. 132

excitatory postsynaptic potential (EPSP), p. 127

graded potential, p. 119

hyperpolarization, p. 119

inhibitory postsynaptic potential (IPSP), p. 127

initial segment, p. 128

microelectrode, p. 113

multiple sclerosis (MS), p. 125

nerve impulse, p. 122

node of Ranvier, p. 125

optogenetics, p. 130

oscilloscope, p. 113

relatively refractory, p. 122

resting potential, p. 116

saltatory conduction, p. 125

spatial summation, p. 128

stretch-sensitive channel, p. 132

temporal summation, p. 128

threshold potential, p. 120

transmitter-sensitive channel, p. 132

voltage gradient, p. 114

voltage-sensitive channel, p. 122

voltmeter, p. 111

➥ Visit 🐢 **LaunchPad** to access the e-Book, videos, 🐢 **LearningCurve** adaptive quizzing, flashcards, and more.

www.macmillanhighered.com/launchpad/kolb5e

How Do Neurons Communicate and Adapt?

Katherine Streeter

Streeter

137

The Basis of Neural Communication in a Heartbeat

Discoveries about how neurons communicate stem from experiments designed to study what controls an animal's heart rate. As with any animal, your heartbeat quickens if you are excited or exercising; if you are resting, it slows. Heart rate changes to match energy expenditure—that is, to meet the body's nutrient and oxygen needs.

Heartbeat undergoes a most dramatic change when you dive beneath water: it slows almost to stopping. This drastic slowing, called diving *bradycardia*, conserves the body's oxygen when you are not breathing. Bradycardia (*brady-*, meaning *slow*, and *-cardia*, meaning *heart*) is a useful survival strategy. This energy-conserving response under water is common to many animals. But what controls your heartbeat?

Otto Loewi, a great storyteller, recounted that his classic experiment, which earned him a Nobel Prize in 1936, came to him in a dream. As shown in the Procedure section of Experiment 5-1. Loewi first maintained a frog's heart in a salt bath, then electrically stimulated the vagus nerve—the cranial nerve that leads from the brain to the heart. At the same time, he channeled some of the fluid bath from the vessel containing the stimulated heart through a tube to another vessel in which a second heart was immersed but not electrically stimulated.

Loewi recorded both heart rates. His findings are represented in the Results section of Experiment 5-1. The electrical stimulation decreased the rate of the first heart, but more important, the second heartbeat also slowed. This result indicated that the fluid transferred from the first to the second container carried instructions to slow down.

Where did the message come from originally? Loewi reasoned that a chemical released from the stimulated vagus nerve must have diffused into the fluid bath to influence the second heart. His experiment therefore demonstrated that the vagus nerve contains a chemical that tells the heart to slow its rate.

Loewi subsequently identified the messenger chemical. Later, he also identified a chemical that tells the heart to speed up. The heart adjusts its rate in response to at least two different messages: an excitatory message that says speed up and an inhibitory message that says slow down.

Helgiskulason/Getty Images

Puffins fish by diving underwater, propelling themselves by flapping their short, stubby wings as if flying. During these dives, their heart displays the diving bradycardia response, just as our heart does. Here, a puffin emerges from a dive, fish in beak.

In this chapter, first we explain how neurons communicate with one another using excitatory and inhibitory signals. Next we describe how chemicals carried by one neuron signal receptors on receiving neurons to produce a response. We conclude the chapter by exploring the neural bases of *learning*—that is, how neural synapses adapt physically as a result of an organism's experience.

Acetylcholine (ACh)

Epinephrine (EP)   Norepinephrine (NE)

Three-dimensional space-filling models contrast the molecular structure of ACh, which inhibits heartbeat, to EP and NE, which excite the heart in frogs and humans, respectively.

5-1 A Chemical Message

Loewi's successful heartbeat experiment, diagrammed in **Experiment 5-1,** marked the beginning of research into how chemicals carry information from one neuron to another in the nervous system. Loewi was the first to isolate a chemical messenger. We now know that chemical as **acetylcholine** (ACh), the same transmitter that activates skeletal muscles, as described in Section 4-4. Yet here, ACh acts to inhibit heartbeat, to slow it down. It turns out that ACh activates skeletal muscles in the somatic nervous system and may either excite or inhibit various internal organs in the autonomic system. And, yes, acetylcholine is the chemical messenger that slows the heart in diving bradycardia.

In further experiments modeled on his procedure in Experiment 5-1, Loewi stimulated another nerve to the heart, the accelerator nerve, and heart rate increased. The fluid that bathed the accelerated heart also speeded the beat of a second heart that was not electrically stimulated. Loewi identified the chemical that carries the message to speed up heart rate in frogs as **epinephrine** (EP; *epi-*, *above*; *nephron*, *kidney*), also known as *adrenaline*. Adrenaline (Latin) and epinephrine (Greek) are the same substance, produced by the adrenal

► EXPERIMENT 5-1

Question: How does a neuron pass on a message?

Procedure

Stimulating device

Recording device

1 Vagus nerve of frog heart 1 is stimulated.

2 Fluid is transferred from first to second container.

Vagus nerve

Fluid transfer

Results

Frog heart 1

Frog heart 2

Rate of heartbeats

Stimulation

3 Recording from frog heart 1 shows decreased rate of beating after stimulation,…

4 …as does the recording from frog heart 2 after the fluid transfer.

Conclusion: The message is a chemical released by the nerve.

acetylcholine (ACh) First neurotransmitter discovered in the PNS and CNS; activates skeletal muscles in the SNS; may either excite or inhibit internal organs in the ANS.

epinephrine (EP, *or* adrenaline) Chemical messenger that acts as a neurotransmitter in the CNS and as a hormone to mobilize the body for fight or flight during times of stress.

norepinephrine (NE, *or* noradrenaline) Neurotransmitter that accelerates heart rate in mammals; found in the brain and in the sympathetic division of the ANS.

neurotransmitter Chemical with an excitatory or inhibitory effect when released by a neuron onto a target.

glands located atop the kidneys. Adrenaline is the name more people know, in part because a drug company used it as a trade name, but epinephrine is common parlance in the science community.

Further experimentation eventually demonstrated that in mammals, the chemical that accelerates heart rate is **norepinephrine** (NE; also *noradrenaline*), a chemical closely related to EP. The results of Loewi's complementary experiments showed that acetylcholine from the vagus nerve inhibits heartbeat, and epinephrine from the accelerator nerve excites it.

Chemical messengers released by a neuron onto a target to cause an excitatory or inhibitory effect are **neurotransmitters**. Outside the central nervous system, many of the same chemicals, epinephrine among them, circulate in the bloodstream as *hormones*. Under control of the hypothalamus, the pituitary gland releases hormones into the bloodstream to excite or inhibit targets such as the organs and glands in the autonomic and enteric nervous systems. In part because hormones travel throughout the body to distant targets, their action is slower than that of CNS neurotransmitters prodded by the lightning-quick nerve impulse. But the real difference between neurotransmitters and hormones is the distances they travel before they encounter their receptors.

Loewi's discoveries led to the search for more neurotransmitters and their functions. The actual number of transmitters is an open question, with 100 posited as the maximum. The confirmed number is 60. Whether a chemical is accepted as a neurotransmitter depends on the extent to which it meets certain criteria. As this chapter unfolds, you will learn those criteria along with the names and functions of many neurotransmitters. You will also learn how groups of neurons form neurotransmitter systems throughout the brain

The vagus nerve influences the heart and other internal body processes; see Figure 2-29.

Section 6-5 explains how hormones influence the brain and behavior.

Parkinson Disease

Case VI: The gentleman . . . is seventy-two years of age. . . . About eleven or twelve, or perhaps more, years ago, he first perceived weakness in the left hand and arm, and soon after found the trembling to commence. In about three years afterwards the right arm became affected in a similar manner: and soon afterwards the convulsive motions affected the whole body and began to interrupt speech. In about three years from that time the legs became affected. (James Parkinson, 1817/1989)

In the 1817 essay from which this case study is taken, British physician James Parkinson reported similar symptoms in six patients, some of whom he had observed only in the streets near his clinic. Shaking was usually the first symptom, and it typically began in a hand. Over a span of years, the shaking spread to include the arm and then other parts of the body.

As the disease progressed, patients had a propensity to lean forward and walk on the balls of their feet. They also tended to run forward to prevent themselves from falling. In the later stages, patients had difficulty eating and swallowing. They drooled, and their bowel movements slowed. Eventually, the patients lost all muscular control and were unable to sleep because of the disruptive tremors.

More than 50 years after James Parkinson's descriptions, French neurologist Jean-Martin Charcot named the condition Parkinson's disease, known today as **Parkinson disease**. Three findings have helped researchers understand its neural basis:

1. In 1919, Constantin Tréatikoff (1974) studied the brains of nine Parkinson patients on autopsy and found that the substantia nigra, a small midbrain nucleus, had degenerated. In the brain of one patient who had parkinsonian symptoms only on one side of the body, the substantia nigra had degenerated on the side opposite that of the symptoms.

2. Chemical examination of the brains of Parkinson patients showed that disease symptoms appear when the level of **dopamine**, then a proposed neurotransmitter, was reduced to less than 10 percent of normal in the basal ganglia (Ehringer & Hornykiewicz, 1960/1974).

3. Confirming the role of dopamine in a neural pathway connecting the substantia nigra to the basal ganglia, Urban Ungerstedt found in 1971 that injecting a neurotoxin called 6-hydroxydopamine into rats selectively destroyed these dopamine-containing neurons and produced symptoms of Parkinson disease.

Researchers have now linked the loss of dopamine-containing substantia nigra neurons to an array of causes, including genetic predisposition, the flu, pollution, insecticides, herbicides, and toxic drugs. Dopamine itself in other brain areas has been linked not only to motor behavior but also to some forms of learning and to neural structures that mediate reward and addiction. This remarkable series of discoveries, initiated by James Parkinson, has yielded tremendous insight into brain function.

 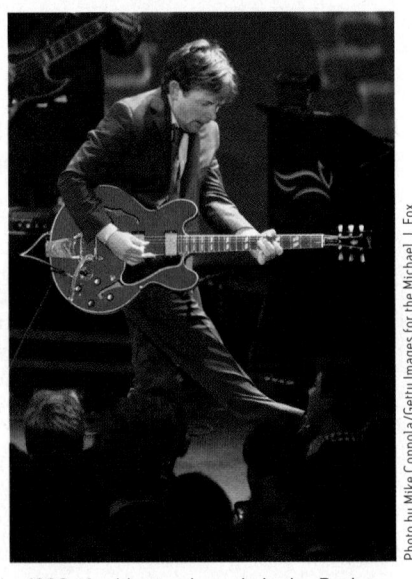

Universal Pictures/Photofest

Photo by Mike Coppola/Getty Images for the Michael J. Fox Foundation for Parkinson's Research

Actor Michael J. Fox gained wide fame in the 1980s for his starring role in the *Back to the Future* film series, which included his rendition of Chuck Berry's pop classic, "Johnny B. Goode" (left). In 1991, at age 30, Fox was diagnosed with young-onset Parkinson disease. When he performed the song 20 years later to benefit the Michael J. Fox Foundation for Parkinson's Research, he labored but still had the moves (right).

to modulate, or temper, aspects of behavior. The three Clinical Focus boxes in this chapter tell the fascinating story of how one such neurotransmitter system has yielded deep insight into brain function. When depleted in a particular brain area, this neurotransmitter is associated with a specific neurological disorder. The story begins with Clinical Focus 5-2, Parkinson Disease.

Structure of Synapses

Loewi's discovery about the chemical messengers that regulate heart rate was the first of two seminal findings that form the foundation for current understanding of how neurons communicate. The second had to wait nearly 30 years, for the invention of the electron microscope. Shown at the right in **Figure 5-1**, it enables scientists to see the structure of a synapse.

Light microscope

Electron microscope

Electron gun

Specimen

Specimen

Light

Image

Biophoto Associates/Science Source

Joseph F. Gennaro Jr./Science Source, *Colorization by:* Mary Martin

FIGURE 5-1 Microscopic Advance Whereas an observer can use a light microscope (left) to see the general features of a cell, an electron microscope (right) allows the observer to examine the cell's organelles in detail.

The electron microscope uses some principles of a light microscope, shown at the left in Figure 5-1, and an oscilloscope. The light microscope illuminates the tissue and magnifies the image. The electron microscope projects a beam of electrons through a very thin slice of tissue. The tissue's varying structures scatter the electron beam onto a reflective surface, where they leave an image, or shadow, of the tissue. Electron waves are smaller than light waves and scatter much less when the beam strikes tissue, allowing for much higher resolution.

To see how much finer an electron microscope's resolution is relative to that of a light microscope, compare the images at the bottom of Figure 5-1. An electron microscope's resolution can be much higher than a light microscope because electron waves are smaller than light waves, so much less scatter attends the beam striking the tissue. When tissue is stained with a substance that reflects electrons, vanishingly fine structural details emerge.

Chemical Synapses

The first good electron micrographs, made in the 1950s, revealed synaptic structure for the first time. In the center of the micrograph in **Figure 5-2A**, the upper part of the synapse is the axon terminal, or end foot; the lower part is the receiving dendrite. The round granular substances in the terminal are the **synaptic vesicles**, containing neurotransmitter.

Dark patches on the axon terminal membrane are proteins that serve largely as ion channels to signal the release of the transmitters or as pumps to recapture the transmitter after its release. The dark patches on the dendrite consist mainly of receptor molecules also made up of proteins that receive chemical messages. The terminal and the dendrite are separated by a small space, the **synaptic cleft**. The synaptic cleft is central to synapse function, because neurotransmitter chemicals must bridge this gap to carry a message from one neuron to the next.

You can also see in the micrograph that the synapse is sandwiched by many surrounding structures, including glial cells, other axons and dendritic processes, and other synapses. The surrounding glia contribute to chemical neurotransmission in several ways—by supplying the building blocks for neurotransmitter synthesis, by confining the movement of neurotransmitters to the synapse, and by mopping up excess neurotransmitter molecules, for example.

Figure 4-5 describes how a digital oscilloscope measures voltage in biological tissue.

Parkinson disease Motor system disorder correlated with dopamine loss in the substantia nigra; characterized by tremors, muscular rigidity, and reduction in voluntary movement.

dopamine (DA) Amine neurotransmitter involved in coordinating movement, attention, learning, and in reinforcing behaviors.

synaptic vesicle Membranous compartment that encloses a quantum of neurotransmitter.

synaptic cleft Gap separating the neuronal presynaptic membrane from the postsynaptic membrane.

(A)

Axon
Presynaptic terminal
Presynaptic membrane
Synaptic vesicles
Synaptic cleft
Postsynaptic membrane
Dendritic spine
Glial cell

Joseph F. Gennaro Jr./Science Source, *Colorization by:* Mary Martin

FIGURE 5-2 Chemical Synapse
(A) Surrounding the central synapse in this electron micrograph are glial cells, axons, dendrites, other synapses, and a synaptic cleft. **(B)** Within a chemical synapse, storage granules hold vesicles containing neurotransmitter that travel to the presynaptic membrane in preparation for release. Neurotransmitter is expelled into the synaptic cleft by exocytosis, crosses the cleft, and binds to receptor proteins on the postsynaptic membrane.

(B)

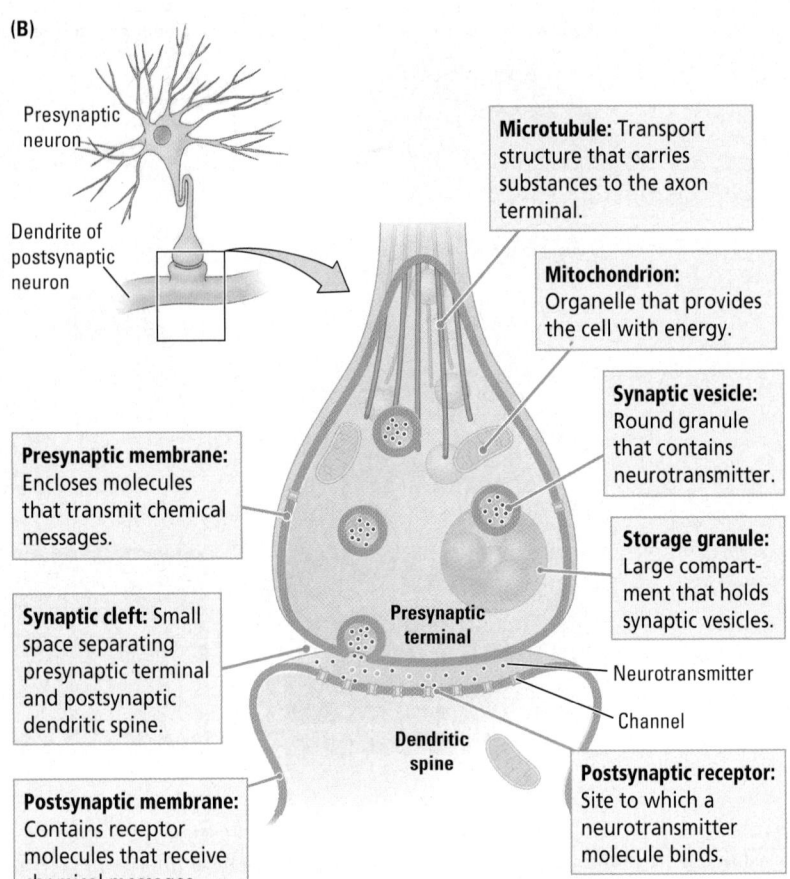

Presynaptic neuron

Dendrite of postsynaptic neuron

Microtubule: Transport structure that carries substances to the axon terminal.

Mitochondrion: Organelle that provides the cell with energy.

Synaptic vesicle: Round granule that contains neurotransmitter.

Storage granule: Large compartment that holds synaptic vesicles.

Presynaptic membrane: Encloses molecules that transmit chemical messages.

Synaptic cleft: Small space separating presynaptic terminal and postsynaptic dendritic spine.

Postsynaptic membrane: Contains receptor molecules that receive chemical messages.

Presynaptic terminal

Dendritic spine

Neurotransmitter

Channel

Postsynaptic receptor: Site to which a neurotransmitter molecule binds.

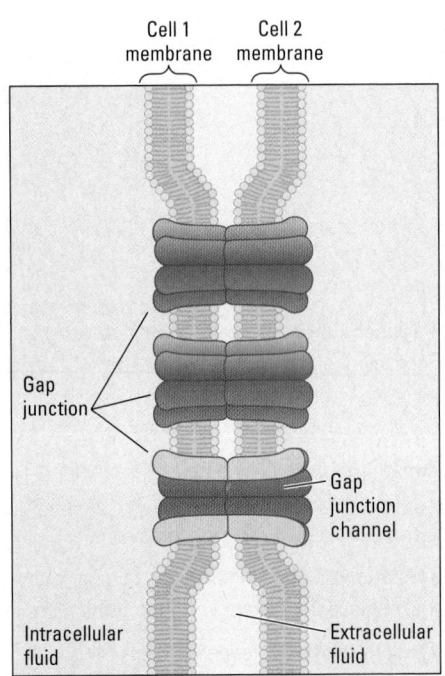

Cell 1 membrane   Cell 2 membrane

Gap junction

Gap junction channel

Intracellular fluid

Extracellular fluid

FIGURE 5-3 Gap Junction

Figure 5-2B details the process of neurotransmission at a **chemical synapse**, the junction where messenger molecules are released from one neuron to interact with the next neuron. Here the **presynaptic membrane** forms the axon terminal, the **postsynaptic membrane** forms the dendritic spine, and the space between the two is the synaptic cleft. Within the axon terminal are specialized structures, including mitochondria, the organelles that supply the cell's energy needs; **storage granules**, large compartments that hold several synaptic vesicles; and microtubules, which transport substances, including neurotransmitter, to the terminal.

Electrical Synapses

Chemical synapses are the rule in mammalian nervous systems, but they are not the only kind of synapse. Some neurons influence each other electrically through a **gap junction**, or *electrical synapse*, where the cell membranes of two neurons come into direct contact (**Figure 5-3**). Ion channels in one cell membrane connect to ion channels in the other membrane, forming a pore that allows ions to pass from one neuron to the other in both directions.

This fusion eliminates the brief delay in information flow—about 5 milliseconds per synapse—of chemical transmission (compare Figure 5-3 with Figure 5-2B). For example, the crayfish's gap junctions activate its tail flick, a response that provides quick escape from a predator. Gap junctions are found in the mammalian brain, where in some regions they allow groups of interneurons to synchronize their firing rhythmically. Gap junctions also allow glial cells and neurons to exchange substances (Dere & Zlomuzica, 2012).

Why, if chemical synapses transmit messages more slowly, do mammals rely on them more than on gap junctions? The answer is that chemical synapses flexibly control whether a message is passed from one neuron to the next; they can amplify or diminish a signal sent from one neuron to the next; and they can change with experience to alter their signals and so mediate learning.

Neurotransmission in Four Steps

The four-step process of transmitting information across a chemical synapse is illustrated in **Figure 5-4**. In brief, the neurotransmitter must be

1. synthesized somewhere inside the neuron and stored at the axon terminal.

2. transported to the presynaptic membrane and released into the cleft in response to an action potential.

3. able to bind to and activate receptors on the postsynaptic membrane.

4. inactivated, so it will not continue to work indefinitely.

Step 1: Neurotransmitter Synthesis and Storage

Neurotransmitters are derived in two general ways, and these origins define two broad classes of neurotransmitters. Some are synthesized in the cell body according to instructions in the neuron's DNA, packaged in membranes on the Golgi bodies, and transported on microtubules to the axon terminal. Cell-derived neurotransmitters may also be manufactured within the presynaptic terminal from mRNA transported to the terminal.

Other neurotransmitters are synthesized in the axon terminal from building blocks derived from food. **Transporters**, protein molecules that pump substances across the cell membrane, absorb the required precursor chemicals from the blood supply. (Sometimes transporter proteins absorb the neurotransmitter ready-made.) Mitochondria in the axon terminal provide the energy needed both to synthesize precursor chemicals into the neurotransmitter and to wrap them in membranous vesicles.

Regardless of their origin, neurotransmitters in the axon terminal can usually be found in three locations, depending on their type. Some vesicles are warehoused in granules, some are attached to microfilaments (a type of microtubule; see Figure 5-2B) in the terminal, and still others are attached to the presynaptic membrane. These sites are the steps by which a transmitter is transported from a granule to the membrane, ready to be released into the synaptic cleft.

Step 2: Neurotransmitter Release

Synaptic vesicles loaded with neurotransmitters must dock near release sites on the presynaptic membrane. Then the vesicles are primed to prepare them to fuse rapidly in response to calcium (Ca^{2+}) influx. When an action potential reaches the presynaptic membrane, voltage changes on the membrane set the release process in motion. Calcium cations play a critical role. The presynaptic membrane is rich in voltage-sensitive calcium channels, and the surrounding extracellular fluid is rich in Ca^{2+}. As illustrated in **Figure 5-5**, the action potential's arrival opens these calcium channels, allowing an influx of calcium ions into the axon terminal.

Primed vesicles fuse with the presynaptic membrane quickly in response to the calcium influx and empty their contents into the synaptic cleft by exocytosis. The vesicles from storage granules and on filaments then move up to replace the vesicles that just emptied their contents.

Step 3: Receptor–Site Activation

After its release from vesicles on the presynaptic membrane, the neurotransmitter diffuses across the synaptic cleft and binds to specialized protein molecules embedded in the postsynaptic membrane. These **transmitter-activated receptors** have binding sites for the transmitter, which we elaborate on in Section 5-3. Depending on the properties of receptors on the postsynaptic membrane, the postsynaptic cell may be affected in one of

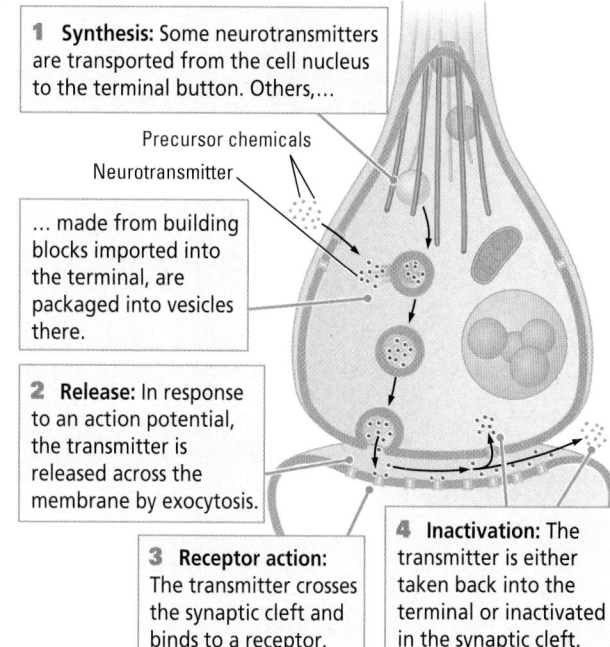

1 **Synthesis:** Some neurotransmitters are transported from the cell nucleus to the terminal button. Others,...

Precursor chemicals

Neurotransmitter

... made from building blocks imported into the terminal, are packaged into vesicles there.

2 **Release:** In response to an action potential, the transmitter is released across the membrane by exocytosis.

3 **Receptor action:** The transmitter crosses the synaptic cleft and binds to a receptor.

4 **Inactivation:** The transmitter is either taken back into the terminal or inactivated in the synaptic cleft.

FIGURE 5-4 Synaptic Transmission

For a refresher on protein export, review Figure 3-17.

chemical synapse Junction at which messenger molecules are released when stimulated by an action potential.

presynaptic membrane Axon terminal membrane on the transmitter, or output, side of a synapse.

postsynaptic membrane Membrane on the transmitter, or input, side of a synapse.

storage granule Membranous compartment that holds several vesicles containing a neurotransmitter.

gap junction (electrical synapse) Area of contact between adjacent cells in which ion channels form a pore that allows ions to pass directly from one cell to the next.

transporter Protein molecule that pumps substances across a membrane.

transmitter-activated receptor Protein that has a binding site for a specific neurotransmitter and is embedded in the membrane of a cell.

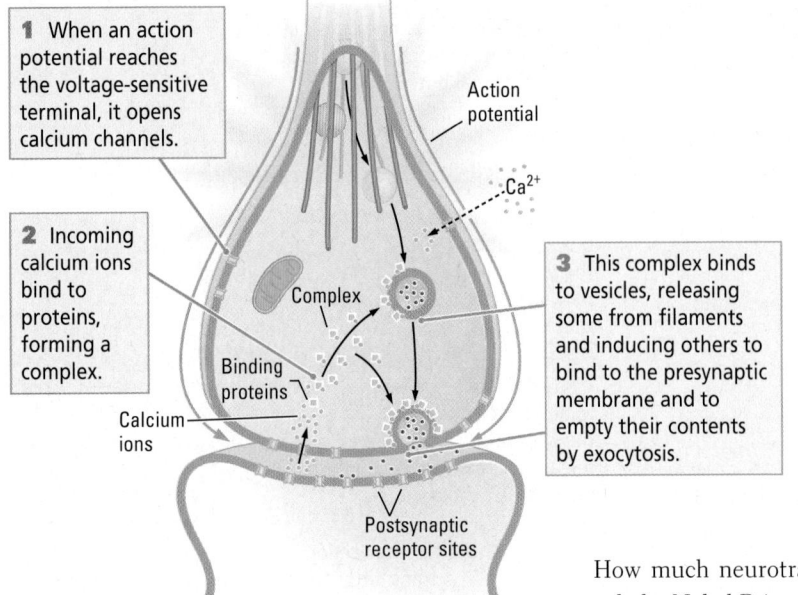

1 When an action potential reaches the voltage-sensitive terminal, it opens calcium channels.

2 Incoming calcium ions bind to proteins, forming a complex.

Action potential

Ca²⁺

Complex

Binding proteins

Calcium ions

3 This complex binds to vesicles, releasing some from filaments and inducing others to bind to the presynaptic membrane and to empty their contents by exocytosis.

Postsynaptic receptor sites

FIGURE 5-5 Neurotransmitter Release

three ways. The receptor and its associated ion channel or intracellular messenger system may

1. depolarize the postsynaptic membrane and so have an excitatory action on the postsynaptic neuron.

2. hyperpolarize the postsynaptic membrane and so have an inhibitory action on the postsynaptic neuron.

3. initiate other chemical reactions that modulate either effect, inhibitory or excitatory, or that influence other functions of the receiving neuron.

In addition to interacting with the postsynaptic membrane's receptors, a neurotransmitter may interact with receptors on the presynaptic membrane: it may influence the cell that just released it. That is, a neurotransmitter may activate presynaptic receptors called **autoreceptors** (self-receptors) to receive messages from their own axon terminals.

How much neurotransmitter is needed to send a message? Bernard Katz was awarded a Nobel Prize in 1970 for providing an answer. Recording electrical activity from the postsynaptic membranes of muscles, he detected small, spontaneous depolarizations now called *miniature postsynaptic potentials*. The potentials varied in size, but each size appeared to be a multiple of the smallest potential.

Katz concluded that the smallest postsynaptic potential is produced by the release of the contents of just one synaptic vesicle. This amount of neurotransmitter is called a **quantum**. To produce a postsynaptic potential large enough to initiate a postsynaptic action potential requires the simultaneous release of many quanta from the presynaptic cell.

The results of subsequent experiments show that the number of quanta released from the presynaptic membrane in response to a single action potential depends on two factors: (1) the amount of Ca^{2+} that enters the axon terminal in response to the action potential and (2) the number of vesicles docked at the membrane, waiting to be released. Both factors are relevant to synaptic activity during learning, which we consider in Section 5-4.

Step 4: Neurotransmitter Deactivation

Chemical transmission would not be an effective messenger system if a neurotransmitter lingered within the synaptic cleft, continuing to occupy and stimulate receptors. If this happened, the postsynaptic cell could not respond to other messages sent by the presynaptic neuron. Thus, after a neurotransmitter has done its work, it is quickly removed from receptor sites and from the synaptic cleft. Deactivation is accomplished in at least four ways:

1. *Diffusion.* Some of the neurotransmitter simply diffuses away from the synaptic cleft and is no longer available to bind to receptors.

2. *Degradation.* Enzymes in the synaptic cleft break down the transmitter.

3. *Reuptake.* Membrane transporters specific to that transmitter may bring it back into the presynaptic axon terminal for reuse. The by-products of degradation by enzymes also may be taken back into the terminal to be used again in the cell.

4. *Astrocyte uptake.* Some neurotransmitters are taken up by neighboring astrocytes. Potentially, the astrocytes can also store transmitters for re-export to the axon terminal.

Highlighting the flexibility of synaptic function, an axon terminal has chemical mechanisms that enable it to respond to the frequency of its own use. If the terminal is very active, the amount of neurotransmitter made and stored there increases. If the terminal is not often used, however, enzymes within the terminal buttons may break down excess transmitter. The by-products are then reused or excreted from the neuron. Axon terminals may even send messages to the neuron's cell body requesting increased supplies of the neurotransmitter or the molecules with which to make it.

autoreceptor Self-receptor in a neuronal membrane; that is, it responds to the same transmitter released by the neuron.

quantum (pl. quanta) Amount of neurotransmitter, equivalent to the content of a single synaptic vesicle, that produces a just-observable change in postsynaptic electric potential.

reuptake Deactivation of a neurotransmitter when membrane transporter proteins bring the transmitter back into the presynaptic axon terminal for reuse.

Table 3-1 describes astrocytes and other types of glial cells and their functions.

Varieties of Synapses

So far we have considered a generic chemical synapse, with features possessed by most synapses. Synapses vary widely in the nervous system. Each type is specialized in location, structure, function, and target. **Figure 5-6** illustrates this diversity on a single hypothetical neuron.

You have already encountered two kinds of synapses. One is the *axomuscular synapse*, in which an axon synapses with a muscle end plate, releasing acetylcholine. The other synapse familiar to you is the *axodendritic synapse*, detailed in Figure 5-2B, in which the axon terminal of a neuron synapses with a dendrite or dendritic spine of another neuron.

Figure 5-6 diagrams axon terminals at the axodendritic synapse as well as the *axosomatic synapse*, at a cell body; the *axoaxonic synapse*, on another axon; and the *axosynaptic synapse*, on another presynaptic terminal—that is, at the synapse between some other axon and its target. *Axoextracellular synapses* have no specific targets but instead secrete their transmitter chemicals into the extracellular fluid. In the *axosecretory synapse*, a terminal synapses with a tiny blood vessel, a capillary, and secretes its transmitter directly into the blood. Finally, synapses are not limited to axon terminals. Dendrites also may send messages to other dendrites through *dendrodendritic synapses*.

This wide variety of connections makes the synapse a versatile chemical delivery system. Synapses can deliver transmitters to highly specific sites or diffuse locales. Through connections to the dendrites, cell body, or axon of a neuron, transmitters can control the neuron's actions in different ways.

Through *axosynaptic connections*, they can also exert exquisite control over another neuron's input to a cell. By excreting transmitters into extracellular fluid or into the blood, axoextracellular and axosecretory synapses can modulate the function of large areas of tissue or even the entire body. Many transmitters secreted by neurons act as hormones circulating in your blood, with widespread influences on your body.

Gap junctions, shown in Figure 5-3, further increase the signaling diversity between neurons. Such interneuronal communication may occur via dendrodendritic and axoaxonic gap

Figure 4-26 shows both microscopic and schematic views of an axomuscular synapse

More about hormones in Section 6-5.

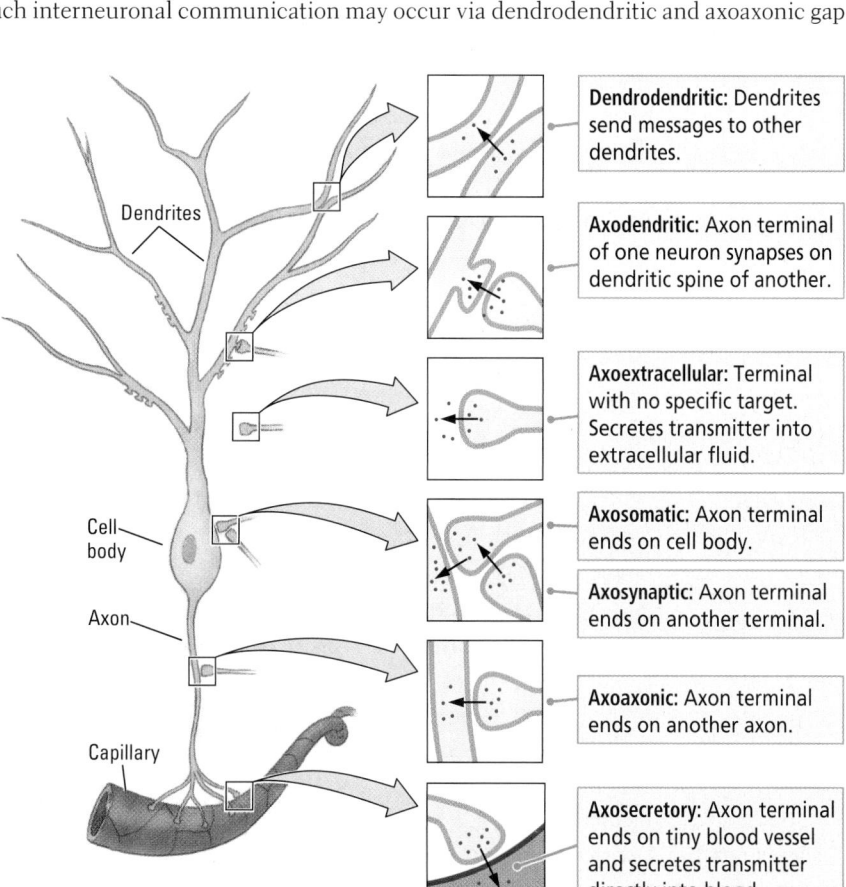

Dendrodendritic: Dendrites send messages to other dendrites.

Axodendritic: Axon terminal of one neuron synapses on dendritic spine of another.

Axoextracellular: Terminal with no specific target. Secretes transmitter into extracellular fluid.

Axosomatic: Axon terminal ends on cell body.

Axosynaptic: Axon terminal ends on another terminal.

Axoaxonic: Axon terminal ends on another axon.

Axosecretory: Axon terminal ends on tiny blood vessel and secretes transmitter directly into blood.

FIGURE 5-6 The Versatile Synapse

junctions. Gap junctions also allow neighboring neurons to synchronize their signals through *somatosomatic* (cell body to cell body) connections, and they allow glial cells, especially astrocytes, to pass nutrient chemicals to neurons and to receive waste products from them.

Excitatory and Inhibitory Messages

A neurotransmitter can influence a neuron's functioning through a remarkable variety of mechanisms. In its direct actions in influencing a neuron's electrical activity, however, a neurotransmitter acting through its receptors has only one of two effects. It influences transmembrane ion flow either to increase or to decrease the likelihood that the cell with which it comes in contact will produce an action potential. Thus, despite the wide variety of synapses, they all convey messages of only these two types, excitatory or inhibitory. To be precise, neurotransmitters themselves do not determine excitation or inhibition. The receptor makes the call.

Excitatory and inhibitory synapses differ in their appearance and are generally located on different parts of the neuron. As shown in **Figure 5-7**, excitatory synapses are typically on the shafts or spines of dendrites, whereas inhibitory synapses are typically on the cell body. Excitatory synapses have round synaptic vesicles; the vesicles in inhibitory synapses are flattened. The material on the presynaptic and postsynaptic membranes is denser in an excitatory synapse than it is in an inhibitory synapse, and the excitatory synaptic cleft is wider. Finally, the active zone on an excitatory synapse is larger than that on an inhibitory synapse.

The differing locations of excitatory and inhibitory synapses divide a neuron into two zones: an excitatory dendritic tree and an inhibitory cell body. Think of excitatory and inhibitory messages as interacting from these two different perspectives. Viewed from an inhibitory perspective, you can picture excitation coming in over the dendrites and spreading past the axon hillock to trigger an action potential at the initial segment. If the message is to be stopped, it is best stopped by inhibiting the cell body close to the initial segment. In this model of excitatory–inhibitory interaction, inhibition blocks excitation by a "cut 'em off at the pass" strategy.

Another way to conceptualize excitatory–inhibitory interaction is to picture excitation overcoming inhibition. In fact, excitatory synaptic inputs that are farther away from the soma are larger, to counteract the loss of signal that occurs over distance (Magee & Cook, 2000). If the cell body is typically in an inhibited state, the only way to generate an action potential is to reduce cell body inhibition. In this "open the gates" strategy, the excitatory message is like a racehorse ready to run down the track, but first the inhibitory starting gate must be removed.

Evolution of Complex Neurotransmission Systems

Considering all the biochemical steps required for getting a message across a synapse and the variety of synapses, you might well wonder why—and how—such a complex communication system ever evolved. How did chemical transmitters originate?

To make the origin of chemical secretions for neuronal communication easier to imagine, think about the feeding behaviors of simple single-celled creatures. The earliest unicellular creatures secreted juices onto bacteria to immobilize and prepare them for ingestion. These digestive juices were probably expelled from the cell body by exocytosis: a vacuole or vesicle attaches itself to the cell membrane then opens into the extracellular fluid to discharge its contents. The prey thus immobilized is captured through the reverse process of endocytosis.

The exocytosis mechanism for digestion in a single-celled organism parallels its use to release a neurotransmitter for communication in more complex creatures. Quite possibly, evolution long ago adapted these primordial digestive processes into processes of neural communication in more complex organisms.

Each neuron receives thousands of excitatory and inhibitory signals every second. The nervous system works by juxtaposing these signals.

Behaviors are lost when a disorder prevents excitatory instructions and released when a disorder prevents inhibitory instructions.

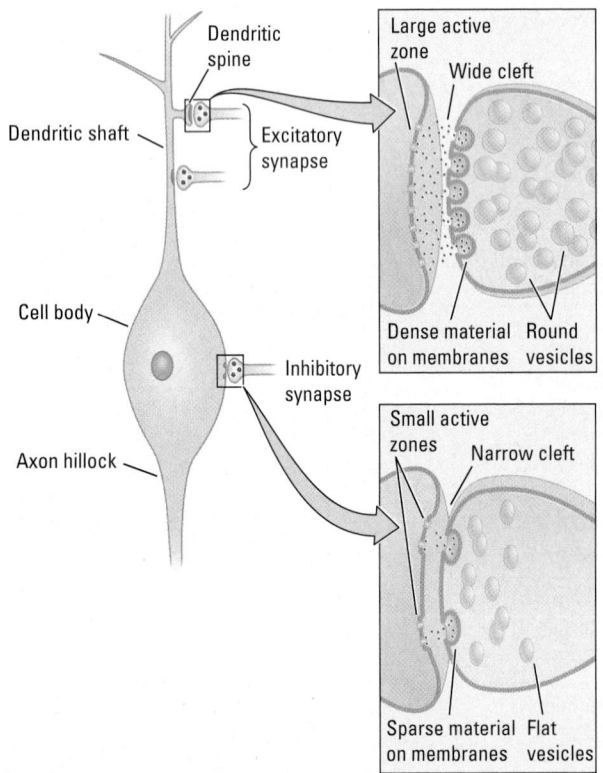

FIGURE 5-7 Excitatory and Inhibitory Zones Excitatory synapses typically occupy spines and dendritic shafts on a neuron. Inhibitory synapses are typically found on the cell body.

A Chemical Message

Before you continue, check your understanding.

1. In mammals, the principal form of communication between neurons occurs via _____, even though this structure is slower and more complex than the fused _____.

2. The principal benefit of chemical synapses over electrical synapses is that they can change with _____ to alter their signals and so mediate _____.

3. The nervous system has evolved a variety of synapses:
   _____ between axon terminals and dendrites,
   _____ between axon terminals and cell bodies,
   _____ between axon terminals and muscles,
   _____ between axon terminals and other axons,
   _____ between axon terminals and other synapses.
   A(n) _____ synapse releases chemical transmitters into extracellular fluid, a(n) _____ synapse releases transmitter into the bloodstream as hormones, and still another, the _____ synapse, connects dendrites to other dendrites.

4. Excitatory synapses are usually located on a(n) _____, whereas inhibitory synapses are usually located on a(n) _____.

5. Describe the four steps in chemical neurotransmission.

Answers appear at the back of the book.

For additional study tools, visit 🌀 LaunchPad:
www.macmillanhighered.com/launchpad/kolb5e

5-2 Varieties of Neurotransmitters and Receptors

Subsequent to Otto Loewi's 1921 discovery that excitatory and inhibitory chemicals control heart rate, many researchers thought that the brain must work under much the same type of dual control. They reasoned that norepinephrine and acetylcholine were the transmitters through which excitatory and inhibitory brain cells worked. They did not imagine what we know today: the human brain employs a dazzling variety of neurotransmitters and receptors. The neurotransmitters operate in even more versatile ways: some may be excitatory at one location and inhibitory at another, for example, and two or more may team up in a single synapse so that one makes the other more potent. Moreover, each neurotransmitter may interact with several varieties of receptors, each with a somewhat different function.

In this section, you will learn how neurotransmitters are identified and how they fit within four broad categories on the basis of their chemical structure. The functional aspects of neurotransmitters interrelate and are intricate, with no simple one-to-one relation between a single neurotransmitter and a single behavior. Furthermore, receptor variety is achieved by the unique combination of protein molecules that come together to form a functional receptor.

Four Criteria for Identifying Neurotransmitters

Among the many thousands of chemicals in the nervous system, which are neurotransmitters? **Figure** 5-8 presents four identifying criteria:

1. The chemical must be synthesized in the neuron or otherwise be present in it.

2. When the neuron is active, the chemical must be released and produce a response in some target.

1 Chemical must be *synthesized* or present in neuron.

2 When *released,* chemical must produce a *response* in target cell.

Chemical

3 Same *receptor action* must be obtained when chemical is experimentally placed on the receptor.

4 There must be a mechanism for *removal* after the chemical's work is done.

FIGURE 5-8 Criteria for Identifying Neurotransmitters

small-molecule transmitter Quick-acting neurotransmitter synthesized in the axon terminal from products derived from the diet.

histamine (H) Neurotransmitter that controls arousal and waking; can cause the constriction of smooth muscles; when activated in allergic reactions, constricts airway and contributes to asthma.

Figure 4-6 illustrates the use of a glass microelectrode.

3. The same response must be obtained when the chemical is experimentally placed on the target.

4. A mechanism must exist for removing the chemical from its site of action after its work is done.

These identifying criteria are fairly easy to apply for examining the somatic nervous system, especially at an accessible nerve–muscle junction with only one main neurotransmitter, acetylcholine. But identifying chemical transmitters in the CNS is not so easy. In the brain and spinal cord, thousands of synapses are packed around every neuron, preventing easy access to any single synapse and its activities. Consequently, multiple techniques, including staining, stimulating, and collecting, are used to identify substances thought to be CNS neurotransmitters. A suspect chemical that has not yet been shown to meet all the criteria is called a *putative* (supposed) *transmitter*.

Researchers trying to identify new CNS neurotransmitters can use microelectrodes to stimulate and record from single neurons. A glass microelectrode is small enough to be placed on specific neuronal targets. It can be filled with a chemical of interest, and when a current is passed through the electrode, the chemical can be ejected into or onto the neuron to mimic neurotransmitter release onto the cell.

Many staining techniques can identify specific chemicals inside the cell. Methods have also been developed for preserving nervous system tissue in a saline bath while experimenters determine how the neurons in the tissue communicate. The use of such tissue slices simplifies the investigation by allowing the researcher to view a single neuron through a microscope while stimulating it or recording from it.

Acetylcholine was not only the first substance identified as a neurotransmitter but also the first substance identified as a CNS neurotransmitter. A logical argument that predicted its presence even before experimental proof was gathered greatly facilitated the process. All motor neuron axons leaving the spinal cord use acetylcholine as a transmitter. Each axon has an axon collateral within the spinal cord that synapses on a nearby CNS interneuron. The interneuron, in turn, synapses on the motor neuron's cell body. This circular set of connections, called a *Renshaw loop* after the researcher who first described it, is shown in **Figure 5-9**.

Because the main axon to the muscle releases acetylcholine, investigators suspected that its axon collateral also might release acetylcholine. For two terminals of the same axon to use different transmitters seemed unlikely. Knowing what chemical to look for made it easier to find and obtain the required evidence that ACh is in fact a neurotransmitter in both locations.

The loop made by the axon collateral and the interneuron in the spinal cord forms a feedback circuit that enables the motor neuron to inhibit itself from overexcitation, should it receive a great many excitatory inputs from other parts of the CNS. Follow the positive and negative signs in Figure 5-9 to see how the Renshaw loop works. If the loop is blocked, as can be done with the toxin strychnine, motor neurons become overactive, producing convulsions that can choke off respiration and so cause death.

The term *neurotransmitter* is used more broadly now than it was when researchers began to identify these chemicals. Today, the term applies to chemicals that

- carry a message from the presynaptic membrane of one neuron to another by influencing postsynaptic membrane voltage.

- change the structure of a synapse.

- communicate by sending messages in the opposite direction. These *retrograde* (reverse-direction) *messages* influence the release or reuptake of transmitters on the presynaptic side.

Four Classes of Neurotransmitters

We can impose some order on the diversity of neurotransmitters by classifying them into four groups based on their chemical composition: (1) small-molecule transmitters, (2) peptide transmitters, (3) lipid transmitters, and (4) gaseous transmitters.

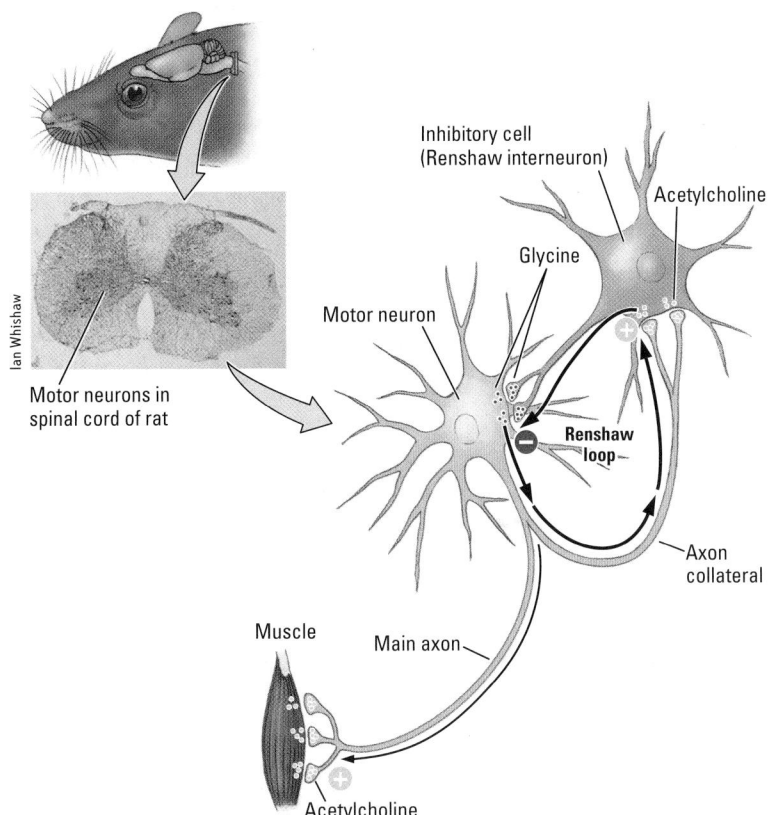

FIGURE 5-9 Renshaw Loop Left: Some spinal cord motor neurons project to the rat's forelimb muscles. Right: In a Renshaw loop the main motor axon (green) projects to a muscle, and its axon collateral remains in the spinal cord to synapse with a Renshaw interneuron (red). The Renshaw interneuron contains the inhibitory transmitter glycine, which acts to prevent motor neuron overexcitation. Both the main motor axon and its collateral terminals contain acetylcholine. When the motor neuron is highly excited, it can modulate its activity level through the Renshaw loop (plus and minus signs).

Small-Molecule Transmitters

The first neurotransmitters identified are the quick-acting **small-molecule transmitters,** such as acetylcholine. Typically, they are synthesized from dietary nutrients and packaged ready for use in axon terminals. When a small-molecule transmitter has been released from a terminal button, it can quickly be replaced at the presynaptic membrane.

Because small-molecule transmitters or their main components are derived from the food we eat, diet can influence their abundance and activity in our bodies. This fact is important in the design of drugs that act on the nervous system. Many neuroactive drugs are designed to reach the brain by the same route that small-molecule transmitters or their precursor chemicals follow: the digestive tract.

Table 5-1 lists some of the best-known and most extensively studied small-molecule transmitters. In addition to acetylcholine, four amines (related by a chemical structure that contains an NH group, or *amine*) and three amino acids are included in this list. A few other substances, including histamine, also are classified as small-molecule transmitters.

Among its many functions, which include control of arousal and of waking, the transmitter **histamine** (H) can cause the constriction of smooth muscles. When activated in allergic reactions, histamine contributes to asthma, a constriction of the airways. You are probably familiar with antihistamine drugs used to treat allergies.

ACETYLCHOLINE SYNTHESIS Acetylcholine is present at the junction of neurons and muscles, including the heart, as well as in the CNS. **Figure 5-10** illustrates how ACh molecules are synthesized from choline and acetate by two enzymes, then broken down. Choline is among the breakdown products of fats in foods such as egg yolk, avocado, salmon, and olive oil; acetate is a compound found in acidic foods, such as vinegar and lemon juice.

As depicted in Figure 5-10, inside the cell, acetyl coenzyme A (acetyl CoA) carries acetate to the synthesis site, and a second enzyme, choline acetyltransferase (ChAT), transfers the acetate to choline to synthesize acetylcholine. After ACh has been released into the synaptic cleft and diffuses to receptor sites on the postsynaptic membrane, a third enzyme,

Taking drugs orally is easy and comparatively safe, but not all drugs can traverse the digestive tract. Section 6-1 explains.

TABLE 5-1 Small-Molecule Neurotransmitters

Acetylcholine (ACh)
Histamine (H)
Amines
Dopamine (DA)
Norepinephrine (NE, *or* noradrenaline, NA)
Epinephrine (EP, *or* adrenaline)
Serotonin (5-HT)
Amino acids
Glutamate (Glu)
Gamma-aminobutyric acid (GABA)
Glycine (Gly)

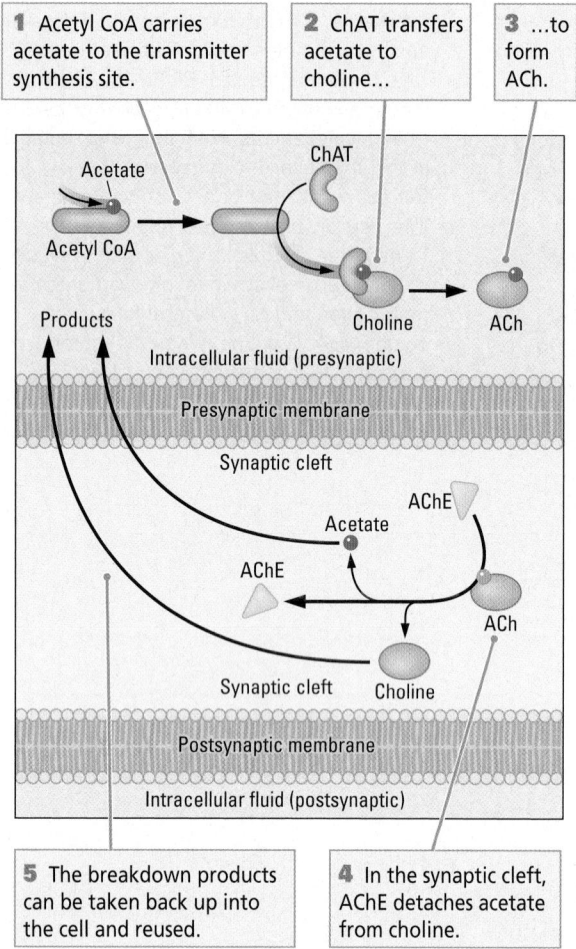

1 Acetyl CoA carries acetate to the transmitter synthesis site.

2 ChAT transfers acetate to choline...

3 ...to form ACh.

5 The breakdown products can be taken back up into the cell and reused.

4 In the synaptic cleft, AChE detaches acetate from choline.

FIGURE 5-10 Chemistry of Acetylcholine Two enzymes combine the dietary precursors of ACh within the cell, and a third breaks them down in the synapse for reuptake.

FIGURE 5-11 Sequential Synthesis of Three Amines A different enzyme is responsible for each successive molecular modification in this biochemical sequence of amine neurotransmitters. The twins featured in Focus 3-1 lack an enzyme that enhances DA production.

Figure 3-15 diagrams peptide bonding and Figure 3-17, protein export.

acetylcholinesterase (AChE), reverses the process, breaking down the transmitter by detaching acetate from choline. The breakdown products can then be taken back into the presynaptic terminal for reuse.

AMINE SYNTHESIS Some transmitters grouped together in Table 5-1 have common biochemical pathways to synthesis and so are related. You are familiar with the amines dopamine (DA), norepinephrine (NE), and epinephrine (EP). To review, DA loss figures in Parkinson disease, EP is the excitatory transmitter at the amphibian heart, and NE is the excitatory transmitter at the mammalian heart.

Figure 5-11 charts the biochemical sequence that synthesizes these amines in succession. The precursor chemical is tyrosine, an amino acid abundant in food. (Hard cheese and bananas are good sources.) The enzyme tyrosine hydroxylase (enzyme 1 in Figure 5-11) changes tyrosine into L-dopa, which other enzymes convert into dopamine, then norepinephrine, and, finally, epinephrine.

Interestingly, the supply of the enzyme tyrosine hydroxylase is limited. Consequently, so is the rate at which dopamine, norepinephrine, and epinephrine can be produced, regardless of how much tyrosine is present or ingested. This **rate-limiting factor** can be bypassed by the oral administration of L-dopa, which is why L-dopa is a medication used in treating Parkinson disease, as described in Clinical Focus 5-3, Awakening with L-Dopa, on page 152.

SEROTONIN SYNTHESIS The amine transmitter **serotonin** (5-HT, for 5-hydroxy-tryptamine) is synthesized from the amino acid L-tryptophan. Tryptophan is abundant in pork, turkey, milk, and bananas, among other foods. Serotonin plays a role in regulating mood and aggression, appetite and arousal, respiration, and pain perception.

AMINO ACID SYNTHESIS Two amino acid transmitters, **glutamate** (Glu) and **gamma-aminobutyric acid** (GABA), are closely related. GABA is formed by a simple modification of the glutamate molecule, as shown in **Figure 5-12**. These two transmitters are the workhorses of the brain because so many synapses use them.

In the forebrain and cerebellum, glutamate is the main excitatory transmitter and GABA is the main inhibitory transmitter. Thus, glutamate is a neurotransmitter in excitatory synapses, and GABA is a neurotransmitter in inhibitory synapses. So a synapse's appearance provides information about the neurotransmitter and its function (review Figure 5-7). Interestingly, glutamate is widely distributed in CNS neurons, but it becomes a neurotransmitter only if it is appropriately packaged in vesicles in the axon terminal. The amino acid transmitter glycine (Gly) is a much more common inhibitory transmitter in the brainstem and spinal cord, where it acts within the Renshaw loop, for example (review Figure 5-9).

Peptide Transmitters

More than 50 short amino acid chains of various lengths (fewer than 100) form the families of peptide transmitters, or **neuropeptides**, listed in **Table 5-2**. Synthesized through the translation of mRNA from instructions contained in the neuron's DNA, neuropeptides are multifunctional chains of amino acids that act as neurotransmitters.

In some neurons, peptide transmitters are made in the axon terminal, but most are assembled on the neuron's ribosomes, packaged in a membrane by Golgi bodies, and transported by the microtubules to the axon terminals. The entire process of neuropeptide synthesis and transport is relatively slow compared with the nearly ready-made small-molecule neurotransmitters. Consequently, peptide transmitters act slowly and are not replaced quickly.

Neuropeptides, however, perform an enormous range of functions in the nervous system, as might be expected from their large numbers. They act as hormones that respond to stress, enable a mother to bond with her infant, regulate eating and drinking and pleasure and pain, and probably contribute to learning.

Opium and related synthetic chemicals such as morphine, long known both to produce euphoria and to reduce pain, appear to mimic the actions of endogenous brain opioid neuropeptides: enkephalins, dynorphins, and endorphins. (The term *enkephalin* derives from the phrase *in the cephalon*, meaning *in the brain or head*, whereas the term *endorphin* is a shortened form of *endogenous morphine*.)

A part of the amino acid chain in each of these naturally occurring opioid peptides is structurally similar to the others, as illustrated for two of them in **Figure 5-13**. Presumably, opium mimics this part of the chain. The discovery of naturally occurring opium-like neuropeptides suggested that one or more of them might have analgesic properties and take part in pain perception. It turns out that beta-endorphin, released in response to exercise and thought responsible for runner's high, has many times the analgesic potency of morphine.

Some CNS peptides take part in specific periodic behaviors, each month or each year perhaps. For instance, in female deer, neuropeptide transmitters act as hormones (luteinizing hormone) that prepare her for the fall mating season. Come winter, a different set of biochemicals facilitates the developing deer fetus. When the mother gives birth in the spring, yet another set of highly specific neuropeptide hormones—such as oxytocin, which enables her to bond to her fawn, and prolactin, which enables her to nurse—takes control.

The same neuropeptides serve similar specific hormonal functions in humans. Others, such as neuropeptide growth hormones, perform far more general functions in regulating growth. Unlike small-molecule transmitters that bind to ion channels, neuropeptides have no direct effects on postsynaptic membrane voltage. Instead, peptide transmitters activate synaptic receptors that indirectly influence cell structure and function. Digestive processes degrade neuropeptide amino acid chains, so they generally cannot be taken orally as drugs, as small-molecule transmitters can.

FIGURE 5-12 Amino Acid Transmitters Top: Removal of a carboxyl (COOH) group from the bottom of the glutamate molecule produces GABA. Bottom: Their different shapes, illustrated by three-dimensional space-filling models, thus allow these amino acid transmitters to bind to different receptors.

Met-enkephalin

(Tyr)(Gly)(Gly)(Phe)(Met)

Leu-enkephalin

(Tyr)(Gly)(Gly)(Phe)(Leu)

FIGURE 5-13 Opioid Peptides Parts of the amino acid chains of some neuropeptides that act on brain centers for pleasure and pain are structurally similar and also share similarities to drugs such as opium and morphine, which mimic their functions (see Section 6-2).

Sections 12-4 and 12-5 explain hormonal influence over human emotional and motivated behavior.

TABLE 5-2 Peptide Neurotransmitters

Family	Examples
Opioids	Met-enkephalin, dynorphin, beta-endorphin
Neurohypophyseals	Vasopressin, oxytocin
Secretins	Secretin, motilin, glucagon, growth hormone–releasing factor
Insulins	Insulin, insulin growth factors
Gastrins	Gastrin, cholecystokinin
Somatostatins	Somatostatin
Tachykinins	Neurokinin A, neurokinin B, substance P

Lipid Transmitters

Predominant among the lipid neurotransmitters are the **endocannabinoids** (endogenous cannabinoids), a class of lipid neurotransmitters synthesized at the postsynaptic membrane to act on receptors at the presynaptic membrane. The endocannabinoids include anandamide and 2-AG (2-arachidonoylglycerol), both derived from arachidonic acid, an unsaturated fatty acid. Poultry and eggs are especially good sources. Endocannabinoids participate

rate-limiting factor Any chemical in limited supply that restricts the pace at which another chemical can be synthesized.

serotonin (5-HT) Amine neurotransmitter; helps to regulate mood and aggression, appetite and arousal, perception of pain, and respiration.

glutamate (Glu) Amino acid neurotransmitter; typically excites neurons.

gamma-aminobutyric acid (GABA) Amino acid neurotransmitter; typically inhibits neurons.

neuropeptide Short (fewer than 100), multifunctional amino acid chain; acts as a neurotransmitter and can act as a hormone; may contribute to learning.

endocannabinoid Class of lipid neurotransmitters, including anandamide and 2-AG, synthesized at the postsynaptic membrane to act on receptors at the presynaptic membrane; affects appetite, pain, sleep, mood, memory, anxiety, and the stress response.

Awakening with L-Dopa

He was started on L-dopa in March 1969. The dose was slowly raised to 4.0 mg a day over a period of three weeks without apparently producing any effect. I first discovered that Mr. E. was responding to L-dopa by accident, chancing to go past his room at an unaccustomed time and hearing regular footsteps inside the room. I went in and found Mr. E., who had been chair bound since 1966, walking up and down his room, swinging his arms with considerable vigor, and showing erectness of posture and a brightness of expression completely new to him. When I asked him about the effect, he said with some embarrassment: "Yes! I felt the L-dopa beginning to work three days ago—it was like a wave of energy and strength sweeping through me. I found I could stand and walk by myself, and that I could do everything I needed for myself—but I was afraid that you would see how well I was and discharge me from the hospital." (Sacks, 1976)

In this case history, neurologist Oliver Sacks describes administering L-dopa to a patient who had acquired parkinsonism as an aftereffect of severe influenza in the 1920s. The relation between the influenza and the parkinsonian symptoms suggests that the flu virus had entered the brain and selectively attacked dopamine neurons in the substantia nigra. By increasing the amount of DA in remaining synapses, L-dopa relieved the patient's symptoms.

Two separate groups of investigators independently gave L-dopa to Parkinson patients beginning in 1961 (Birkmayer & Hornykiewicz, 1961; Barbeau et al., 1961). Both research teams knew that the chemical is catalyzed into dopamine at DA synapses (see Figure 5-11). The L-dopa turned out to reduce the patients' muscular rigidity.

This work was the first demonstration that a neurological condition can be relieved by a drug that aids in increasing the amount of a neurotransmitter. L-Dopa has since become a standard treatment for Parkinson disease. Its effects have been improved by the administration of drugs that prevent L-dopa from being converted to dopamine in the body before it passes through the blood–brain barrier and gets to dopamine neurons in the brain.

L-Dopa is not a cure. Parkinson disease still progresses during treatment, and as more and more dopamine synapses are lost, the treatment becomes less and less effective. Eventually, L-dopa begins to produce *dyskinesias*—involuntary, unwanted movements, such as ballistic (throwinglike) or choreic (dancelike) movements. When these side effects eventually become severe, the treatment must be discontinued.

Everett Collection

The movie *Awakenings* recounts the L-dopa trials conducted by Oliver Sacks and described in his book of the same title.

---

in a diverse set of physiological and psychological processes that affect appetite, pain, sleep, mood, memory, anxiety, and the stress response. Their scientific history is brief but illustrates how science can progress, punctuated by short steps.

Because endocannabinoids are lipophilic (fat-loving) molecules, they are not soluble in water and are not stored in vesicles. Rather, investigators hypothesize that endocannabinoids are synthesized on demand after a neuron has depolarized and calcium has entered. Calcium activates the enzyme transacylase, the first step in producing anandamide. Once anandamide or 2-AG is synthesized, it diffuses across the synaptic cleft and interacts with its receptor on the presynaptic membrane. Thus, both molecules act as retrograde neurotransmitters, for a time reducing the amount of small-molecule transmitter being released. In this way, the postsynaptic neuron has some control over the amount of incoming neural signal.

The CB_1 receptor is the target of all cannabinoids, whether generated by the body (endocannabinoids), from plants (phytocannabinoids), or synthetically. CB_1 receptors are found at both glutamate and GABA synapses, and so cannabinoids act as neuromodulators to inhibit release of glutamate and GABA. Cannabinoids thus dampen both neuronal excitation and inhibition.

Phytocannabinoids are obtained from the hemp plants *Cannabis sativa* and *Cannabis indica*. These plants have been used medically and recreationally for thousands of years, but only recently was an extract from cannabis synthesized. Early in the last century, many constituents of cannabis, including cannabidiol and tetrahydrocannabinol (THC), were isolated

Fatty acid molecules that contribute to forming the cell membrane likewise are hydrophobic. See Figure 3-11.

Cannabis is among the psychotropic drugs discussed in Section 6-2.

and their chemical structure determined. In 1964, Yehiel Gaoni and Raphael Mechoulam reported the structure of the THC molecule, the main psychoactive constituent in cannabis. Next, investigators determined how THC is metabolized. (The process is quite slow, which explains why THC can be detected in urine for weeks after cannabis use.)

Research on the physiological and psychological effects of THC in animals and people, which began after its isolation and purification, is ongoing. Twenty-four years after the structure of the THC molecule was determined, the first cannabinoid receptor (CB₁) was found. Typically, receptors are activated by endogenous molecules, which motivated researchers to look for endogenous cannabinoids. Four years later, in 1992, anandamide was isolated and its structure determined, but it took another couple of decades to figure out that endocannabinoids act as retrograde transmitters (Mechoulam et al., 2014).

Gaseous Transmitters

The gases **nitric oxide (NO)**, **carbon monoxide (CO)**, and **hydrogen sulfide** (H_2S) further expand the biochemical strategies that transmitter substances display. As water-soluble gases, they are neither stored in synaptic vesicles nor released from them; instead, the cell synthesizes them on demand. After synthesis, each gas diffuses away, easily crossing the cell membrane and immediately becoming active. Both NO and CO activate metabolic (energy-expending) processes in cells, including processes modulating the production of other neurotransmitters. H_2S prevents oxygen from binding in the mitochondria and thus functions to slow down metabolism.

All three gaseous transmitters serve as chemical messengers in many parts of the body. NO and H_2S control intestinal wall muscles and dilate blood vessels in active brain regions, allowing these regions to receive more blood. Because NO and H_2S also dilate blood vessels in the sexual organs, both are active in producing penile erections. Drugs used to treat erectile dysfunction in men, such as Viagra and Cialis, act by enhancing the chemical pathways influenced by NO. NO does not of itself produce sexual arousal.

Varieties of Receptors

Each of the two general classes of receptor proteins produces a different effect: one directly changes the postsynaptic membrane's electrical potential, and the other induces cellular change indirectly. A dazzling array of receptor subtypes allows for subtle differences in receptor function.

Two Classes of Receptors

When a neurotransmitter is released from any of the wide varieties of synapses onto a wide variety of targets, as illustrated in Figure 5-6, it crosses the synaptic cleft and binds to a receptor. What happens next depends on the receptor type.

Ionotropic receptors allow the ions, such as Na⁺, K⁺, and Ca²⁺, to move across a membrane (the suffix *-tropic* means *moving toward*). As **Figure 5-14** illustrates, an ionotropic receptor has two parts: (1) a binding site for a neurotransmitter and (2) a pore, or channel. When the neurotransmitter attaches to the binding site, the receptor quickly changes shape, either opening the pore and allowing ions to flow through it or closing the pore and blocking the ion flow. Thus, ionotropic receptors bring about rapid changes in membrane voltage and are usually excitatory: they trigger an action potential.

In contrast, a **metabotropic receptor** has a binding site for a neurotransmitter but lacks its own pore through which

nitric oxide (NO) Gaseous neurotransmitter; acts, for example, to dilate blood vessels, aid digestion, and activate cellular metabolism.

carbon monoxide (CO) Gaseous neurotransmitter; activates cellular metabolism.

hydrogen sulfide (H_2S) Gaseous neurotransmitter; slows cellular metabolism.

ionotropic receptor Embedded membrane protein; acts as (1) a binding site for a neurotransmitter and (2) a pore that regulates ion flow to directly and rapidly change membrane voltage.

metabotropic receptor Embedded membrane protein with a binding site for a neurotransmitter linked to a G protein; can affect other receptors or act with second messengers to affect other cellular processes, including opening a pore.

Structurally, ionotropic receptors resemble voltage-sensitive channels, which propagate the action potential. See Figure 4-17.

| Transmitter binds to the binding site. | The pore opens, allowing the influx or efflux of ions. |

Extracellular fluid — Ion
— Transmitter
— Binding site

Intracellular fluid — Pore closed — Pore open

FIGURE 5-14 Ionotropic Receptor When activated, embedded transmitter proteins bring about direct, rapid changes in membrane voltage.

ions can flow. Through a series of steps, activated metabotropic receptors indirectly produce changes in nearby membrane-bound ion channels or in the cell's metabolic activity. **Figure 5-15**A shows the first of these two indirect effects. The metabotropic receptor consists of a single protein that spans the cell membrane, its binding site facing the synaptic cleft. Each receptor is coupled to one of a family of guanyl nucleotide–binding proteins, **G proteins** for short, shown on the inner side of the cell membrane in Figure 5-15A. When activated, a G protein binds to other proteins.

A G protein consists of three subunits: alpha, beta, and gamma. (A **subunit** is a protein that assembles with other proteins.) The alpha subunit detaches when a neurotransmitter binds to the G protein's associated metabotropic receptor. The detached alpha subunit can then bind to other proteins within the cell's membrane or its intracellular fluid. If the alpha subunit binds to a nearby ion channel in the membrane, as shown at the bottom of Figure 5-15A, the channel structure changes, modifying the flow of ions through it. If the channel is open, the alpha subunit may close it or, if closed, it may open. Changes in the channel and the ion flow across the membrane influence the membrane's electrical potential.

The binding of a neurotransmitter to a metabotropic receptor can also trigger more complicated cellular reactions, summarized in Figure 5-15B. All these reactions begin when the detached alpha subunit binds to an enzyme. The enzyme in turn activates a **second**

FIGURE 5-15 Metabotropic Receptors When activated by a neurotransmitter, embedded membrane receptor proteins trigger associated G proteins, exerting indirect effects **(A)** on nearby ion channels or **(B)** in the cell's metabolic activity.

messenger (the neurotransmitter being the first messenger) that carries instructions to other cellular structures. As illustrated at the bottom of Figure 5-15B, the second messenger can

- bind to a membrane-bound channel, causing the channel to change its structure and thus alter ion flow through the membrane.

- initiate a reaction that incorporates intracellular (within the cell) protein molecules into the cell membrane, resulting, for example, in the formation of new ion channels.

- bind to sites on the cell's DNA to initiate or cease the production of specific proteins.

Metabotropic receptors also allow for the possibility that a single neurotransmitter's binding to a receptor can activate an escalating sequence of events called an *amplification cascade*. The cascade effect is that many downstream proteins (second messengers or channels or both) are activated or deactivated. Ionotropic receptors do not have such a widespread amplifying effect.

Recall that acetylcholine has an excitatory effect on skeletal muscles. Here it activates an ionotropic receptor. Conversely, acetylcholine has an inhibitory effect on the heart rate. Here it activates a metabotropic receptor. Further, each transmitter may bind with several different kinds of ionotropic or metabotropic receptors. Elsewhere in the nervous system, for example, ACh may activate a wide variety of either receptor type.

Receptor Subtypes

While there are two general classes of receptors, ionotropic and metabotropic, each neurotransmitter may interact with a number of receptor subtypes specific to that neurotransmitter. Serotonin (5-HT), for instance, has one ionotropic receptor subtype (5-HT$_3$) and 12 subtypes of metabotropic receptors. **Table 5-3** lists the variety of small-molecule neurotransmitter receptor subtypes.

How is this variety achieved? Alternative forms of each subunit can assemble in unique combinations to make a functional receptor. For instance, the functional NMDA receptor, an ionotropic receptor for glutamate, is always composed of 4 subunits, but a total of 12 distinct subunits are available to come together in various combinations to form the functional receptor.

Why does the brain contain so many receptor subtypes for each neurotransmitter? The answer seems to be that each subtype has slightly different properties, which confer different activities. These activities can include the presence or absence of binding sites for other molecules, how long a channel remains open or closed, and the ability to interact with intracellular signaling molecules.

G protein Guanyl nucleotide–binding protein coupled to a metabotropic receptor; when activated, binds to other proteins.

subunit Protein molecule that assembles with other protein molecules.

second messenger Chemical that initiates a biochemical process when activated by a neurotransmitter (the first messenger).

Figure 14-18 diagrams how glutamate and the NMDA receptor function in associative learning.

TABLE 5-3 Small-Molecule Transmitter Receptors*

Neurotransmitter	Ionotropic Receptors	Metabotropic Receptors
Acetylcholine (ACh)	Nicotinic	Muscarinic† M1, M2, M3, M4, M5
Dopamine (DA)	—	D$_1$, D$_2$, D$_3$, D$_4$, D$_5$
GABA	GABA$_A$	GABA$_B$
Glutamate (Glu)	NMDA, AMPA, kainate	mGluR$_1$, mGluR$_2$, mGluR$_3$, mGluR$_4$, mGluR$_5$, mGluR$_6$, mGluR$_7$
Glycine (Gly)	Glycine, NMDA	—
Histamine (H)	—	H$_1$, H$_2$, H$_3$
Norepinephrine (NE)	—	α_{1a}, α_{1b}, α_{1c}, α_{1d}, α_{2a}, α_{2b}, α_{2c}, α_{2d}, β_1, β_2, β_3
Serotonin (5-HT)	5-HT$_3$	5-HT$_{1A}$, 5-HT$_{1B}$, 5-HT$_{1D}$, 5-HT$_{1E}$, 5-HT$_{1F}$, 5-HT$_{2A}$, 5-HT$_{2B}$, 5-HT$_{2C}$, 5-HT$_4$, 5-HT$_5$, 5-HT$_6$, 5-HT$_7$

*Peptide neurotransmitters and the lipid neurotransmitters anandamide and 2-AG have specific metabotropic-class receptors. Gaseous neurotransmitters do not have a specific receptor.
†All metabotropic cholinergic receptors are muscarinic.

It should not be surprising that a brain such as ours, with its incredible complexity, is built upon a vast array of units, including copious neurotransmitter types and even more copious receptor types. All this, and more, allows the human brain to function successfully.

5-2 REVIEW

Varieties of Neurotransmitters and Receptors

Before you continue, check your understanding.

1. Neurotransmitters are identified using four experimental criteria: _____, _____, _____, and _____.

2. The four broad classes of chemically related neurotransmitters are _____, _____, _____, and _____.

3. Acetylcholine is composed of _____ and _____. After release into the synaptic cleft, ACh is broken down by _____, and the products can be recycled.

4. Endocannabinoids are _____ neurotransmitters, made on demand and released from the _____ membrane.

5. Contrast the major characteristics of ionotropic and metabotropic receptors.

Answers appear at the back of the book.

For additional study tools, visit 🌑 LaunchPad:
www.macmillanhighered.com/launchpad/kolb5e

5-3 Neurotransmitter Systems and Behavior

When researchers began to study neurotransmission, they reasoned that any given neuron would contain only one transmitter at all its axon terminals. Newer methods of analysis revealed that this hypothesis isn't strictly accurate. A single neuron may use one transmitter at one synapse and a different transmitter at another synapse. Moreover, different transmitters may coexist in the same terminal or synapse. Neuropeptides have been found to coexist in terminals with small-molecule transmitters, and more than one small-molecule transmitter may be found in a single synapse. In some cases, more than one transmitter may even be packaged within a single vesicle.

All these findings allow for multiple combinations of neurotransmitters and receptors for them. They caution as well against assuming a simple cause-and-effect relation between a neurotransmitter and a behavior. What are the functions of so many combinations? The answer will likely vary, depending on the behavior that is controlled. Generally, neurotransmission is simplified by concentrating on the dominant transmitter within any given axon terminal. The neuron and its dominant transmitter can then be associated with a function or behavior.

We now consider some links between neurotransmitters and behavior. We begin by exploring the three peripheral nervous system divisions: SNS, ANS, and ENS. Then we investigate neurotransmission in the central nervous system.

Neurotransmission in the Somatic Nervous System

Motor neurons in the brain and spinal cord send their axons to the body's skeletal muscles, including the muscles of the eyes and face, trunk, limbs, fingers, and toes. Without these SNS neurons, movement would not be possible. Motor neurons are also called **cholinergic neurons**

cholinergic neuron Neuron that uses acetylcholine as its main neurotransmitter; *cholinergic* applies to any neuron that uses ACh as its main transmitter.

because acetylcholine is their main neurotransmitter. At a skeletal muscle, cholinergic neurons are excitatory, producing muscular contractions.

Just as a single main neurotransmitter serves the SNS, so does a single main receptor, a transmitter-activated ionotropic channel called a *nicotinic acetylcholine receptor* (nAChr). When ACh binds to this receptor, its pore opens to permit ion flow, thus depolarizing the muscle fiber. The nicotinic receptor pore is large enough to permit the simultaneous efflux of K^+ and influx of Na^+. The molecular structure of nicotine, a chemical found in tobacco, activates the nAChr in the same way that acetylcholine does, which is how this receptor got its name. The molecular structure of nicotine is sufficiently similar to that of ACh that nicotine acts as a mimic, fitting into acetylcholine receptor binding sites.

Acetylcholine is the primary neurotransmitter at skeletal muscles, but other neurotransmitters also occupy these cholinergic axon terminals and are released onto the muscle along with ACh. One is a neuropeptide called calcitonin gene–related peptide (CGRP), which acts through CGRP metabotropic receptors to increase the force with which a muscle contracts.

Dual Activating Systems of the Autonomic Nervous System

The complementary ANS divisions, sympathetic and parasympathetic, regulate the body's internal environment. The sympathetic division rouses the body for action, producing the fight-or-flight response. Heart rate ramps up and digestive functions ramp down. The parasympathetic division calms the body down, producing an essentially opposite rest-and-digest response. Digestive functions ramp up, heart rate ramps down, and the body is ready to relax.

Figure 5-16 shows the neurochemical organization of the ANS. Both divisions are controlled by acetylcholine neurons that emanate from the CNS at two levels of the spinal cord. The CNS neurons synapse with parasympathetic neurons that also contain acetylcholine and with sympathetic neurons that contain norepinephrine. In other words, cholinergic

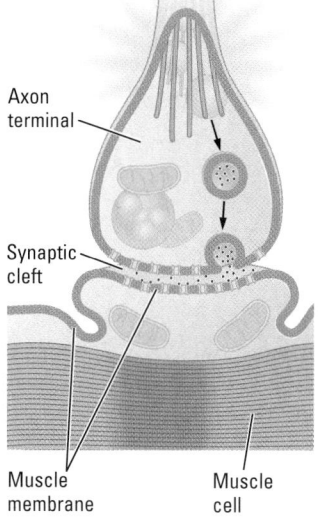

Nicotinic ACh Receptor Research from J. E. Heuser and T. Reese, 1977, in E. R. Kandel, ed, The Nervous System, vol. 1, *Handbook of Physiology*. Oxford University Press, p. 266.

FIGURE 5-16 Controlling Biological Functions in the Autonomic Nervous System The neurotransmitter in all the neurons leaving the spinal cord is acetylcholine. Left: In the sympathetic division, ACh neurons activate autonomic norepinephrine neurons in the sympathetic ganglia. NE stimulates organs required for fight or flight and suppresses activity in organs used to rest and digest. Right: In the parasympathetic division, ACh neurons from the spinal cord activate ACh neurons in the parasympathetic ganglia near their target organs to suppress activity in organs used for fight or flight and to stimulate organs used to rest and digest. To review the ANS divisions and connections in detail, see Figure 2-30.

neurons in the CNS synapse with sympathetic NE neurons to prepare the body's organs for fight or flight. Cholinergic neurons in the CNS synapse with autonomic ACh neurons in the parasympathetic division to prepare the body's organs to rest and digest.

Which type of synapse is excitatory and which inhibitory depends on the particular body organ's receptors. During sympathetic arousal, norepinephrine turns up heart rate and turns down digestive functions, because NE receptors on the heart are excitatory, whereas NE receptors on the gut are inhibitory. Similarly, acetylcholine turns down heart rate and turns up digestive functions because its receptors on these organs are reversed: on the heart, inhibitory; on the gut, excitatory. Neurotransmitter activity, excitatory in one location and inhibitory in another, mediates the sympathetic and parasympathetic divisions, forming a complementary autonomic regulating system that maintains the body's internal environment under varying circumstances.

Enteric Nervous System Autonomy

The ENS can act without input from the CNS, which is why it has been called the second brain. It uses all four classes of neurotransmitters, more than 30 transmitters in total. Most are identical to those employed by the CNS. Chief among the small-molecule neurotransmitters used by the enteric nervous system are serotonin and dopamine.

Sensory ENS neurons detect mechanical and chemical conditions in the system. Via intestinal muscles, motor neurons in the ENS control the mixing of intestinal contents. Secretion of digestive enzymes is also under ENS control.

Four Activating Systems in the Central Nervous System

Just as there is an organization to the neurochemical systems of the PNS, there is an organization of neurochemical systems in the CNS. These systems are remarkably similar across a wide range of animal species, which allowed for their identification, first in the rat brain and then in the human brain (Hamilton et al., 2010).

For each of the four **activating systems** that we describe here, a relatively small number of neurons grouped together in one or a few brainstem nuclei send axons to widespread CNS regions, suggesting that these nuclei and their terminals help to synchronize activity throughout the brain and spinal cord. You can envision an activating system as analogous to the power supply in a house. The fuse or breaker box is the source of the power, and from it transmission lines go to each room.

Just as in the ANS, the precise action of the CNS transmitter depends on the brain region that is innervated and on the types of receptors the transmitter acts on at that region. To continue our analogy, precisely what the activating effect of the power is in each room depends on the electrical devices in that room.

Each of four small-molecule transmitters participates in its own neural activating system—the cholinergic, dopaminergic, noradrenergic, and serotonergic systems. **Figure 5-17** locates each system's nuclei, with arrow shafts mapping the axon pathways and arrowheads indicating axon terminal locales.

As summarized on the right in Figure 5-17, each CNS activating system is associated with numerous behaviors. Associations among activating systems, behavior, and brain disorders are far less certain. All these relations are subjects of ongoing research. Making definitive correlations between activating systems and behavior or activating systems and a disorder is difficult, because the axons of these systems connect to almost every part of the brain and spinal cord. They likely have both specific functions and modulatory roles. We detail some of the documented relations between the systems and behavior and disorders here and in many subsequent chapters.

activating system Neural pathways that coordinate brain activity through a single neurotransmitter; its cell bodies lie in a brainstem nucleus; axons are distributed through a wide CNS region.

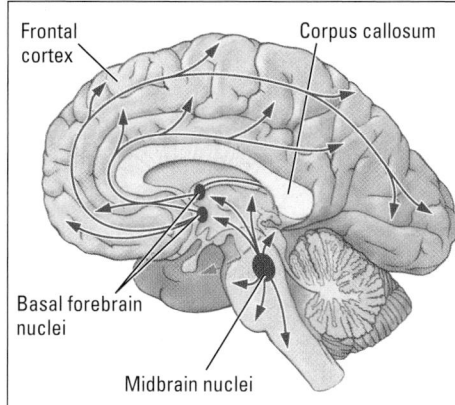

Cholinergic system (acetylcholine)
- Active in maintaining attention and waking EEG pattern.
- Thought to play a role in memory by maintaining neuron excitability.
- Death of cholinergic neurons and decrease in ACh in the neocortex are thought to be related to Alzheimer disease.

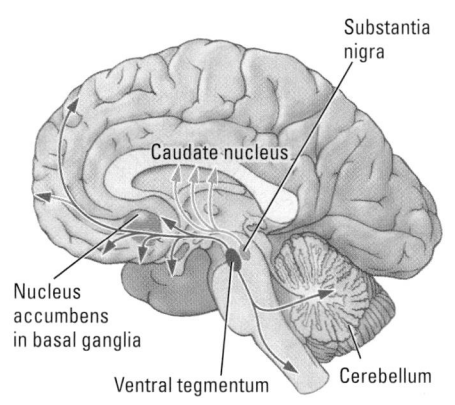

Dopaminergic system (dopamine)
Nigrostriatal pathways (orange projections)
- Active in maintaining normal motor behavior.
- Loss of DA is related to muscle rigidity and dyskinesia in Parkinson disease.

Mesolimbic pathways (purple projections)
- Dopamine release causes feelings of reward and pleasure.
- Thought to be the neurotransmitter system most affected by addictive drugs and behavioral addictions.
- Increases in DA activity may be related to schizophrenia.
- Decreases in DA activity may be related to deficits of attention.

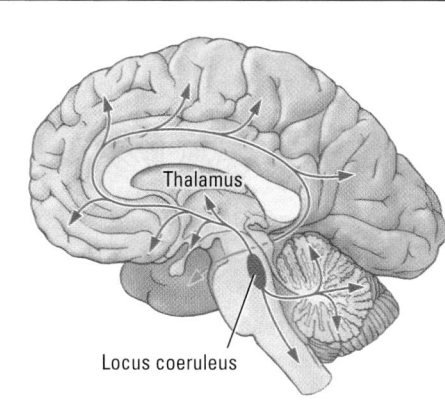

Noradrenergic system (norepinephrine)
- Active in maintaining emotional tone.
- Decreases in NE activity are thought to be related to depression.
- Increases in NE are thought to be related to mania (overexcited behavior).
- Decreased NE activity is associated with hyperactivity and attention-deficit/hyperactivity disorder.

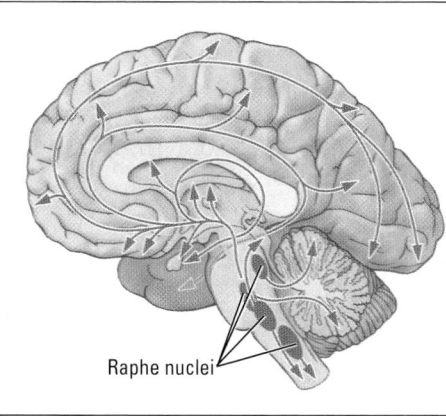

Serotonergic system (serotonin)
- Active in maintaining waking EEG pattern.
- Changes in serotonin activity are related to obsessive-compulsive disorder, tics, and schizophrenia.
- Decreases in serotonin activity are related to depression.
- Abnormalities in brainstem 5-HT neurons are linked to disorders such as sleep apnea and SIDS.

FIGURE 5-17 Major Activating Systems Each system's cell bodies are gathered into nuclei (shown as ovals) in the brainstem. Their axons project diffusely through the CNS and synapse on target structures. Each activating system is associated with one or more behaviors or diseases.

FIGURE 5-18 Cholinergic Activation
Drawing at left shows the cortical location of the micrograph at right, stained to reveal AChE. Cholinergic neurons in the rat's basal forebrain project to the neocortex, and the darkly stained bands in the cortex show areas rich in cholinergic synapses. The darker central parts of the section, also rich in cholinergic neurons, are the basal ganglia.

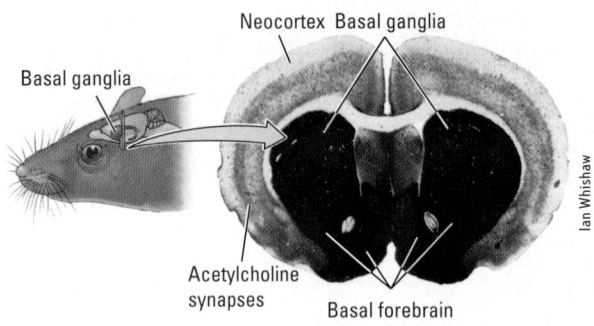

Neocortex   Basal ganglia
Basal ganglia
Acetylcholine synapses
Basal forebrain cholinergic neurons

Ian Whishaw

The EEG detects electrical signals the brain emits during various conscious states; see Sections 7-2 and 13-3.

Focus 14-3 details research on Alzheimer disease. Section 16-3 reviews dementias' causes and treatments.

Cholinergic System

Figure 5-18 shows in cross section a rat brain stained for the enzyme acetylcholinesterase (AChE), which breaks down ACh in synapses, as diagrammed earlier in Figure 5-10. The darkly stained areas have high AChE concentrations, indicating the presence of cholinergic terminals. AChE permeates the cortex and is especially dense in the basal ganglia. Many of these cholinergic synapses are connections from ACh nuclei in the brainstem, as illustrated in the top panel of Figure 5-17.

The cholinergic system participates in typical waking behavior, attention, and memory. For example, cholinergic neurons take part in producing one form of waking EEG activity. People affected by the degenerative **Alzheimer disease**, which begins with minor forgetfulness, progresses to major memory dysfunction, and later develops into generalized dementia, show a profound loss of cholinergic neurons at autopsy. One treatment strategy for Alzheimer disease is drugs that stimulate the cholinergic system to enhance alertness. But the beneficial effects of these drugs are minor at best (Herrmann et al., 2011). Recall that ACh is synthesized from nutrients in food; thus, the role of diet in maintaining acetylcholine levels also is being investigated.

The brain abnormalities associated with Alzheimer disease are not limited to the cholinergic neurons, however. Autopsies reveal extensive damage to the neocortex and other brain regions. As a result, what role, if any, the cholinergic neurons play in the progress of the disorder is not yet clear. Perhaps their destruction causes degeneration in the cortex or perhaps the cause-and-effect relation is the other way around, with cortical degeneration causing cholinergic cell death. Then too, the loss of cholinergic neurons may be just one of many neural symptoms of Alzheimer disease.

Copyright Katsuyoshi Tanaka, courtesy of the Mark Morris Dance Group

Rhythmic movement helps Parkinson patients restore the balance between neural excitation and inhibition—between the loss and the release of behavior. Some patients participate in a specially designed Dance for PD (http://danceforparkinsons.org/) class for people with Parkinson's (PwP). Participants at the Mark Morris Dance Center, pictured here, report that moving to music helps them regain muscle control.

Dopaminergic System

Figure 5-17 maps the dopaminergic activating system's two distinct pathways. The *nigrostriatal dopaminergic system* plays a major role in coordinating movement. As described throughout this chapter in relation to parkinsonism, when dopamine neurons in the substantia nigra are lost, the result is a condition of extreme muscular rigidity. Opposing muscles contract at the same time, making it difficult for an affected person to move.

Parkinson patients also exhibit rhythmic tremors, especially of the limbs, which signals a release of formerly inhibited movement. Although the causes of Parkinson disease are not fully known, it can actually be triggered by the ingestion of certain toxic drugs, as described in Clinical Focus 5-4, The Case of the Frozen Addict. Those drugs may act as selective neurotoxins that specifically kill dopamine neurons in the substantia nigra.

Dopamine in the *mesolimbic dopaminergic system* may be the neurotransmitter most affected in addiction—to food, to drugs, and to other behaviors that involve a loss of impulse control. A common feature of addictive behaviors is that stimulating the mesolimbic dopaminergic system enhances responses to environmental stimuli, thus making

The Case of the Frozen Addict

Patient 1: During the first 4 days of July 1982, a 42-year-old man used 4½ grams of a "new synthetic heroin." The substance was injected intravenously three or four times daily and caused a burning sensation at the site of injection. The immediate effects were different from heroin, producing an unusual "spacey" high as well as transient visual distortions and hallucinations. Two days after the final injection, he awoke to find that he was "frozen" and could move only in "slow motion." He had to "think through each movement" to carry it out. He was described as stiff, slow, nearly mute, and catatonic during repeated emergency room visits from July 9 to July 11. (Ballard et al., 1985, p. 949)

Patient 1 was one of seven young adults hospitalized at about the same time in California. All showed symptoms of severe Parkinson disease that appeared very suddenly after drug injection. These symptoms are extremely unusual in this age group. All who were affected reportedly injected a synthetic heroin that was being sold on the streets in the summer of 1982.

J. William Langston (2008) and his colleagues found that the synthetic heroin contained a contaminant called MPTP (1-methyl-4-phenyl-1,2,3,6-tetrahydropyridine) resulting from poor technique during its synthesis. The results of experimental studies in rodents showed that MPTP was not itself responsible for the patients' symptoms but was metabolized into MPP^+ (1-methyl-4-phenylpyridinium), a neurotoxin.

The autopsy of one individual who was suspected of having died of MPTP poisoning showed that the brain had selectively lost dopamine neurons in the substantia nigra. The rest of the brain appeared healthy. Injecting MPTP into monkeys, rats, and mice produced similar symptoms and a similar selective loss of dopaminergic neurons in the substantia nigra. Thus, the combined clinical and experimental evidence indicates that a toxin can selectively kill dopamine neurons and that the die-off can induce Parkinson disease.

In 1988, Patient 1 received an experimental treatment at University Hospital in Lund, Sweden. Living dopamine neurons taken from human fetal brains at autopsy were implanted into the caudate nucleus and putamen (Widner et al., 1992). Extensive work with rodents and nonhuman primates in a number of laboratories had demonstrated that fetal neurons, before they develop dendrites and axons, can survive transplantation, mature, and secrete neurotransmitters.

Patient 1 had no serious postoperative complications and was much improved 24 months after the surgery. He could dress and feed himself, visit the bathroom with help, and make trips outside his home. He also responded much better to medication. The accompanying diagrams contrast DA levels in the brain of a Parkinson patient before (left) and 2 years, 4 months after implantation (right).

Transplantation of fetal neurons to treat Parkinson disease typically does not work. Unlike the case of the frozen addict, Parkinson disease is associated with a continuing, active process that destroys dopaminergic neurons, including transplanted neurons, in the substantia nigra. Because Parkinson disease can affect as many as 20 people per 100,000, scientists continue to experiment with new approaches to transplantation and with genetic approaches for modifying remaining dopamine neurons (Lane et al., 2010).

DA levels before fetal DA cell implantation   DA production at 2 years, 4 months after implantation

These diagrams represent PET scans that contrast DA levels in a Parkinson patient's brain before, and 28 months after, implantation. Research from "Bilateral Fetal Mesencephalic Grafting in Two Patients with Parkinsonism Induced by 1-Methyl-4-phenyl-1,2,3,6-tetrahydropyradine (MPTP)," by H. Widner, J. Tetrud, S. Rehngrona, B. Snow, P. Brundin, B. Gustavii, A. Bjorklund, O. Lindvall, and J. W. Langston, 1992, *New England Journal of Medicine, 327,* p. 151.

those stimuli attractive and rewarding. Indeed, some Parkinson patients who take dopamine receptor agonists as medications show a loss of impulse control that manifests in such behaviors as pathological gambling, hypersexuality, and compulsive shopping (Moore et al., 2014).

Excessive mesolimbic dopaminergic activity is proposed as well to play a role in **schizophrenia,** a behavioral disorder characterized by delusions, hallucinations, disorganized speech, blunted emotion, agitation or immobility, and a host of associated symptoms. Schizophrenia is one of the most common and most debilitating psychiatric disorders, affecting about 1 in 100 people.

Noradrenergic System

Norepinephrine (noradrenaline) may participate in learning by stimulating neurons to change their structure. Norepinephrine may also facilitate healthy brain development and contribute to organizing movements. A neuron that uses norepinephrine as its

Sections 6-3, 6-4, and 12-3 describe drug effects on the mesolimbic DA system. Sections 6-2 and 7-4 discuss schizophrenia's possible causes and Section 16-4, its neurobiology.

Alzheimer disease Degenerative brain disorder related to aging; first appears as progressive memory loss and later develops into generalized dementia.

schizophrenia Behavioral disorder characterized by delusions, hallucinations, disorganized speech, blunted emotion, agitation or immobility, and a host of associated symptoms.

transmitter is termed a **noradrenergic neuron** (derived from *adrenaline*, the Latin name for *epinephrine*).

In the main, behaviors and disorders related to the noradrenergic system concern the emotions. Some symptoms of **major depression**—a mood disorder characterized by prolonged feelings of worthlessness and guilt, the disruption of typical eating habits, sleep disturbances, a general slowing of behavior, and frequent thoughts of suicide—may be related to decreased activity of noradrenergic neurons. Conversely, some symptoms of **mania** (excessive excitability) may be related to increased activity in these same neurons. Decreased NE activity has also been associated both with hyperactivity and attention-deficit/hyperactivity disorder (ADHD).

Serotonergic System

The serotonergic activating system maintains a waking EEG in the forebrain when we move and thus participates in wakefulness, as does the cholinergic system. Like norepinephrine, serotonin plays a role in learning, as described next in Section 5-4. Some symptoms of depression may be related to decreased activity in serotonin neurons, and drugs commonly used to treat depression act on 5-HT neurons. Consequently, two forms of depression may exist, one related to norepinephrine and another related to serotonin.

Likewise, some research results suggest that various symptoms of schizophrenia also may be related to increases in serotonin activity, which implies that different forms of schizophrenia may exist. Decreased serotonergic activity is related to symptoms observed in **obsessive-compulsive disorder** (OCD), in which a person compulsively repeats acts (such as hand washing) and has repetitive and often unpleasant thoughts (obsessions). Evidence also points to a link between abnormalities in serotonergic nuclei and conditions such as *sleep apnea* and *sudden infant death syndrome* (SIDS).

Consult the Index of Disorders inside the book's front cover for more information on major depression, mania, ADHD, OCD, sleep apnea, and SIDS.

(5-3) REVIEW

Neurotransmitter Systems and Behavior

Before you continue, check your understanding.

1. Although neurons can synthesize more than one _____, they are usually identified by the principal _____ in their axon terminals.

2. In the peripheral nervous system, the neurotransmitter at somatic muscles is _____; in the autonomic nervous system, _____ neurons from the spinal cord connect with _____ neurons for parasympathetic activity and with _____ neurons for sympathetic activity.

3. The two principal small-molecule transmitters used by the enteric nervous system are _____ and _____.

4. The four main activating systems of the CNS are _____, _____, _____, and _____.

5. How would you respond to the comment that a behavior is caused solely by a chemical imbalance in the brain?

Answers appear at the back of the book.

For additional study tools, visit **LaunchPad**:
www.macmillanhighered.com/launchpad/kolb5e

(5-4) Adaptive Role of Synapses in Learning and Memory

Among our most cherished abilities are learning and remembering. Neuroplasticity is a requirement for learning and memory and a characteristic of the mammalian brain. In fact, it is a trait of the nervous systems of all animals, even the simplest worms. Larger brains with more connections are more plastic, however, and thus likely to show more adaptability in neural organization.

Greater adaptability happens because experience can alter the synapse. Not only are synapses versatile in structure and function, they are plastic: they can change. The synapse, therefore, is the site for the neural basis of **learning**, a relatively permanent change in behavior that results from experience.

Donald O. Hebb (1949) was not the first to suggest that learning is mediated by structural changes in synapses. But the change that he envisioned in his book *The Organization of Behavior* was novel 65 years ago. Hebb theorized, "When an axon of cell A is near enough to excite a cell B and repeatedly or persistently takes part in firing it, some growth process or metabolic change takes place in one or both cells such that A's efficiency, as one of the cells firing B, is increased" (Hebb, 1949, p. 62). Simply put, cells that fire together wire together. A synapse that physically adapts in this way is called a *Hebb synapse* today.

Eric Kandel was awarded a Nobel Prize in 2000 for his descriptions of the synaptic basis of learning in a way that Hebb envisaged: learning in which the conjoint activity of nerve cells serves to link them. Kandel's subject, the marine slug *Aplysia californica*, is an ideal subject for learning experiments. Slightly larger than a softball and lacking a shell, *Aplysia* has roughly 20,000 neurons. Some are quite accessible to researchers, who can isolate and study circuits having few synapses.

When threatened, *Aplysia* defensively withdraws its more vulnerable body parts—the gill (through which it extracts oxygen from the water to breathe) and the siphon (a spout above the gill that excretes seawater and waste). By stroking or shocking the slug's appendages, Kandel and his coworkers (Bailey et al., 2015) produced enduring changes in its defensive behaviors. They used these behavioral responses to study underlying changes in *Aplysia*'s nervous system.

We illustrate the role of synapses in two kinds of learning that Kandel has studied: habituation and sensitization. For humans, both are called *unconscious* because they do not depend on a person's knowing precisely when and how they occur.

Habituation Response

In **habituation**, the response to a stimulus weakens with repeated stimulus presentations. If you are accustomed to living in the country, then move to a city, you might at first find the sounds of traffic and people extremely loud and annoying. With time, however, you stop noticing most of the noise most of the time. You have habituated to it.

Habituation develops with all our senses. When you first put on a shoe, you feel it on your foot, but very soon it is as if the shoe were not there. You have not become insensitive to sensations, however. When people talk to you, you still hear them; when someone steps on your foot, you still feel the pressure. Your brain simply has habituated to the customary background sensation of a shoe on your foot.

Aplysia habituates to waves in the shallow tidal zone where it lives. These slugs are constantly buffeted by the flow of waves against their body, and they learn that waves are just the background noise of daily life. They do not flinch and withdraw every time a wave passes over them. They habituate to this stimulus.

A sea slug that is habituated to waves remains sensitive to other touch sensations. Prodded with a novel object, it responds by withdrawing its siphon and gill. The animal's reaction to repeated presentations of the same novel stimulus forms the basis for **Experiment 5-2**, studying its habituation response.

Neural Basis of Habituation

The Procedure section of Experiment 5-2 shows the setup for studying what happens to the withdrawal response of *Aplysia*'s gill after repeated stimulation. A gentle jet of water is sprayed on the siphon while gill movement is recorded. If the water jet is presented to *Aplysia*'s siphon as many as 10 times, the gill withdrawal response is weaker some minutes

Experiment 2-1 demonstrates observational learning in the octopus and the ubiquity of neuroplasticity.

Hebb's "cell-assembly" diagram appears at the end of Section 15-1.

Aplysia californica

Section 14-4 investigates the neural bases of brain plasticity in conscious learning and in memory.

noradrenergic neuron From *adrenaline*, Latin for *epinephrine*; a neuron containing norepinephrine.

major depression Mood disorder characterized by prolonged feelings of worthlessness and guilt, the disruption of normal eating habits, sleep disturbances, a general slowing of behavior, and frequent thoughts of suicide.

mania Disordered mental state of extreme excitement.

obsessive-compulsive disorder (OCD) Behavior characterized by compulsively repeated acts (such as hand washing) and repetitive, often unpleasant, thoughts (obsessions).

learning Relatively permanent change in behavior that results from experience.

habituation Learned behavior in which the response to a stimulus weakens with repeated presentations.

Question: What happens to the gill response after repeated stimulation?

Procedure

Siphon

1 Gill withdraws from water jet.

After repeated stimulation

2 Gill no longer withdraws from water jet, demonstrating habituation.

Water jet

Result

The sensory neuron stimulates the motor neuron to produce gill withdrawal before habituation.

Sensory neuron

Skin of siphon

Motor neuron

Gill muscle

Ca^{2+}

1 With habituation, the influx of calcium ions in response to an action potential decreases,...

Presynaptic membrane

2 ...resulting in less neurotransmitter released at the presynaptic membrane...

Postsynaptic membrane

Ca^{2+}

3 ...and less depolarization of the postsynaptic membrane.

Conclusion: The withdrawal response weakens with repeated presentation of water jet (habituation) owing to decreased Ca^{2+} influx and subsequently less neurotransmitter release from the presynaptic axon terminal.

sensitization Learned behavior in which the response to a stimulus strengthens with repeated presentations.

posttraumatic stress disorder (PTSD) Syndrome characterized by physiological arousal associated with recurrent memories and dreams arising from a traumatic event that occurred months or years earlier.

later, when the animal is again tested. The decrement in the strength of the withdrawal is habituation, which can last as long as 30 minutes.

The Results section of Experiment 5-2 starts by showing a simple representation of the pathway that mediates *Aplysia*'s gill withdrawal response. For purposes of illustration, only one sensory neuron, one motor neuron, and one synapse are shown; in actuality, about 300 neurons may take part in this response. The water jet stimulates the sensory neuron, which in turn stimulates the motor neuron responsible for the gill withdrawal. But exactly where do the changes associated with habituation take place? In the sensory neuron? In the motor neuron? In the synapse between the two?

Habituation does not result from an inability of either the sensory or the motor neuron to produce action potentials. In response to direct electrical stimulation, both the sensory neuron and the motor neuron retain the ability to generate action potentials even after habituation. Electrical recordings from the motor neuron show that as habituation develops, the excitatory postsynaptic potentials (EPSPs) in the motor neuron become smaller.

The most likely way in which these EPSPs decrease in size is that the motor neuron is receiving less neurotransmitter from the sensory neuron across the synapse. And if less neurotransmitter is being received, then the changes accompanying habituation must be taking place in the presynaptic axon terminal of the sensory neuron.

Reduced Sensitivity of Calcium Channels Underlies Habituation

Kandel and his coworkers measured neurotransmitter output from a sensory neuron and verified that less neurotransmitter is in fact released from a habituated neuron than from a nonhabituated one. Recall from Figure 5-5 that neurotransmitter release in response to an action potential requires an influx of calcium ions across the presynaptic membrane. As habituation takes place, that Ca^{2+} influx decreases in response to the voltage changes associated with an action potential. Presumably, with repeated use, voltage-sensitive calcium channels become less responsive to voltage changes and more resistant to the passage of calcium ions.

The neural basis of habituation lies in the change in presynaptic calcium channels. Its mechanism, which is summarized close up in the Results section of Experiment 5-2, is a reduced sensitivity of calcium channels and a consequent decrease in neurotransmitter release. Thus, habituation can be linked to a specific molecular change, as summarized in the experiment's Conclusion.

Sensitization Response

A sprinter crouched in her starting blocks is often hyperresponsive to the starter's gun: its firing triggers in her a rapid reaction. The stressful, competitive context of the race helps to sensitize the sprinter to this sound. **Sensitization**, an enhanced response to some stimulus, is the opposite of habituation. The organism becomes hyperresponsive to a stimulus rather than accustomed to it.

Sensitization occurs within a context. Sudden, novel stimulation heightens our general awareness and often results in larger-than-typical responses to all kinds of stimulation. If a loud noise startles you suddenly, you become much more responsive to other stimuli in your surroundings, including some to which you previously were habituated. In **posttraumatic stress disorder** (PTSD), physiological arousal related to recurring memories and dreams surrounding a traumatic event persist for months or years after the event. One characteristic of PTSD is a heightened response to stimuli, suggesting that the disorder is in part related to sensitization.

Stress can foster and prolong PTSD effects. See Sections 6-5 and 12-4. Section 16-4 covers treatment strategies.

The same thing happens to *Aplysia*. Sudden, novel stimuli can heighten a slug's responsiveness to familiar stimulation. When attacked by a predator, for example, the slug displays heightened responses to many other stimuli in its environment. In the laboratory, a small electric shock to *Aplysia*'s tail mimics a predatory attack and effects sensitization, as illustrated in the Procedure section of **Experiment 5-3**. A single electric shock to the slug's tail enhances its gill withdrawal response for a period that lasts for minutes to hours.

Neural Basis of Sensitization

The neural circuits participating in sensitization differ from those that take part in a habituation response. The Results section of Experiment 5-3 shows the sensory and motor neurons that produce the gill withdrawal response and adds an interneuron that is responsible for sensitization.

An interneuron that receives input from a sensory neuron in *Aplysia*'s tail (and so carries information about the shock) makes an axoaxonic synapse with a sensory neuron in the siphon. The interneuron's axon terminal contains serotonin. Consequently, in response to a tail shock, the tail sensory neuron activates the interneuron, which in turn releases 5-HT onto the axon of the siphon sensory neuron. Information from the siphon still comes through the sensory neuron to activate the motor neuron leading to the gill muscle, but the interneuron's action in releasing 5-HT onto the sensory neuron's presynaptic membrane amplifies the gill withdrawal response.

At the molecular level, shown close up in Experiment 5-3 Results, the serotonin released from the interneuron binds to a metabotropic serotonin receptor on the siphon's sensory neuron axon. This binding activates second messengers in the sensory neuron. Specifically, the serotonin receptor is coupled through its G protein to the enzyme adenyl cyclase. This enzyme increases the concentration of second messenger cyclic adenosine monophosphate (cAMP) in the presynaptic membrane of the siphon's sensory neuron.

Through several chemical reactions, cAMP attaches a phosphate molecule (PO_4) to potassium channels, rendering them less responsive. The close-up in Experiment 5-3 sums it up. In response to an action potential traveling down the axon of the siphon's sensory neuron (such as one generated by a touch to the siphon), the potassium channels on that neuron are slower to open. Consequently, K^+ ions cannot repolarize the membrane as quickly as normal, so the action potential lasts longer than it usually would.

Less–Responsive Potassium Channels Underlie Sensitization

The longer-lasting action potential that occurs because potassium channels are slower to open prolongs Ca^{2+} inflow. Ca^{2+} influx is necessary for neurotransmitter release. Thus, greater Ca^{2+} influx results in more neurotransmitter being released from the sensory synapse onto the motor neuron.

This increased neurotransmitter release produces greater activation of the motor neuron and thus a larger-than-normal gill withdrawal

▶ EXPERIMENT 5-3

Question: What happens to the gill response in sensitization?

Procedure

Gill withdrawal

A single shock to the tail enhances the gill withdrawal response (sensitization).

Water jet   Shock

Results

An interneuron receives input from a shocked sensory neuron in the tail and releases serotonin onto the axon of a siphon sensory neuron.

Interneuron

Sensory neuron   Motor neuron   Gill muscle

Skin of siphon

1 Serotonin reduces K^+ efflux through potassium channels, prolonging an action potential on the siphon sensory neuron.

Interneuron

Serotonin K^+ Motor neuron

Sensory neuron   Second messenger

2 The prolonged action potential results in more Ca^{2+} influx and increased transmitter release,...

3 ...causing greater depolarization of the postsynaptic membrane after sensitization.

Ca^{2+}

Conclusion: Enhancement of the withdrawal response after a shock is due to increased Ca^{2+} influx and subsequently more neurotransmitter release from the presynaptic axon terminal.

response. If the second messenger cAMP mobilizes more synaptic vesicles, making more neurotransmitter ready for release into the sensory–motor synapse, gill withdrawal may also be enhanced.

Sensitization, then, is the opposite of habituation at the molecular level as well as at the behavioral level. In sensitization, more Ca^{2+} influx results in more transmitter being released, whereas in habituation, less Ca^{2+} influx results in less neurotransmitter being released. The structural basis of cellular memory in these two forms of learning is different, however. In sensitization, the change takes place in potassium channels, whereas in habituation, the change takes place in calcium channels.

Learning as a Change in Synapse Number

Neural changes associated with learning must last long enough to account for a relatively permanent change in an organism's behavior. The changes at synapses described in the preceding sections develop quite quickly, but they do not last indefinitely, as memories often do. How then, can synapses be responsible for the long-term changes associated with learning and memory?

Repeated stimulation produces habituation and sensitization that can persist for months. Brief training produces short-term learning; longer training periods produce more enduring learning. If you cram for an exam the night before you take it, you might forget the material quickly, but if you study a little each day for a week, your learning may tend to endure. What underlies this more persistent form of learning?

Researchers working with Eric Kandel (Bailey et al., 2015) found that the number and size of sensory synapses change in well-trained, habituated, and sensitized *Aplysia*. Relative to a control neuron, the number and size of synapses decrease in habituated animals and increase in sensitized animals, as represented in **Figure 5-19**. Apparently, synaptic events associated with habituation and sensitization can also trigger processes in the sensory cell that result in the loss or formation of new synapses.

A mechanism through which these processes can take place begins with calcium ions that mobilize second messengers to send instructions to nuclear DNA. The transcription and translation of nuclear DNA in turn initiate structural changes at synapses, including the formation of new synapses and new dendritic spines. Research Focus 5-5, Dendritic Spines: Small but Mighty, summarizes experimental evidence about structural changes in dendritic spines.

The second messenger cAMP plays an important role in carrying instructions regarding these structural changes to nuclear DNA. The evidence for cAMP's involvement comes from studies of the fruit fly *Drosophila*. Two genetic mutations in the fruit fly can produce similar learning deficiencies. Both render the second messenger cAMP inoperative, but in opposite ways. One mutation, called *dunce*, lacks the enzymes necessary to degrade cAMP, so the fruit fly has abnormally high cAMP levels. The other mutation, called *rutabaga*, reduces levels of cAMP below the normal range for *Drosophila* neurons.

Significantly, fruit flies with either mutation are impaired in acquiring habituated and sensitized responses because their levels of cAMP cannot be regulated. New synapses seem

FIGURE 5-19 Physical Basis of Memory Relative to a control neuronal connection (left), the number of synapses between *Aplysia*'s sensory neuron and a motor neuron decline as a result of habituation (center) and increase as a result of sensitization (right). Such structural changes may underlie enduring memories.

Motor neuron

Sensory neuron

Control　　　　**Habituated**　　　　**Sensitized**

Dendritic Spines: Small but Mighty

Dendritic spines, which protrude from the dendrite's shaft, measure about 1 to 3 micrometers (μm, one-millionth of a meter) long and less than 1 μm in diameter. Each neuron can have many thousands of spines. The number of dendritic spines in the human cerebral cortex is estimated at 10^{14}.

Dendritic spines originate in filopodia (from the Latin *file*, for *thread*, and the Greek *podium*, for *foot*) that bud out of neurons, especially at dendrites. Microscopic observation of dendrites shows that filopodia are constantly emerging and retracting over times on the order of seconds.

This budding of filopodia is much more pronounced in developing neurons and in the developing brain (see Figure 8-13). Because filopodia can grow into dendritic spines, their budding suggests that they are searching for contacts from axon terminals to form synapses. When contact is made, some new synapses may have only a short life; others will endure.

A permanent dendritic spine tends to have a large, mushroom-shaped head, giving it a large contact area with a terminal button, and a long stem, giving it an identity apart from that of its dendrite. The heads of spines and the terminals of presynaptic connections form functional compartments that can generate huge electrical potentials and so influence the neuron's electrical messages.

Dendritic spines mediate learning that lasts, including habituation and sensitization. To mediate learning, each spine must be able to act independently, undergoing changes that its neighbors do not undergo.

Examination of dendritic spines in the nervous system shows that some are simple and others complex. The cellular mechanisms that allow synapses to appear on spines and to change shape include microfilaments linked to the membrane receptors, protein transport from the cell body, and the incorporation of nutrients from the extracellular space.

The variety suggests that all this activity changes the appearance of both presynaptic and postsynaptic structures. The illustration summarizes synaptic structures that can be measured and related to learning and behavior and to structural changes that may subserve learning.

Dendritic spines provide the structural basis for our behavior, our individual skills, and our memories (Bosch & Hayashi, 2012). Impairments in forming spines characterize some kinds of mental disability, and the loss of spines is associated with the dementia of Alzheimer disease.

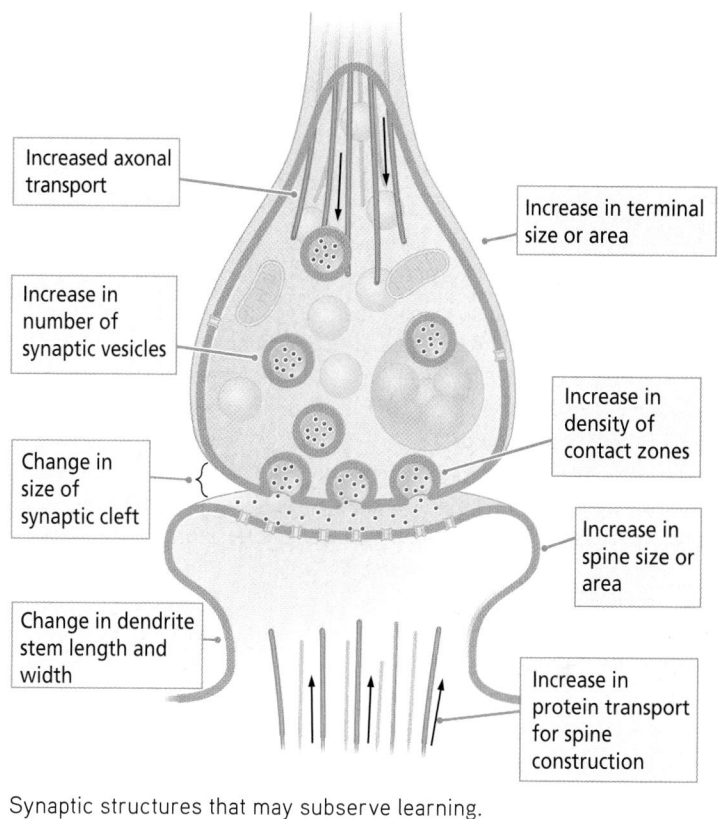

Synaptic structures that may subserve learning.

to be required for learning to take place, and the second messenger cAMP seems to carry instructions to form them. **Figure 5-20** summarizes these research findings.

More lasting habituation and sensitization are mediated by relatively permanent changes in neuronal structure—by fewer or more synaptic connections—and the effects can be difficult to alter. As a result of sensitization, for example, symptoms of PTSD can persist indefinitely.

5-4 REVIEW

Adaptive Role of Synapses in Learning and Memory

Before you continue, check your understanding.

1. Experience alters the _____, the site of the neural basis of _____, a relatively permanent change in behavior that results from experience.

2. *Aplysia's* synaptic function mediates two basic forms of learning: _____ and _____.

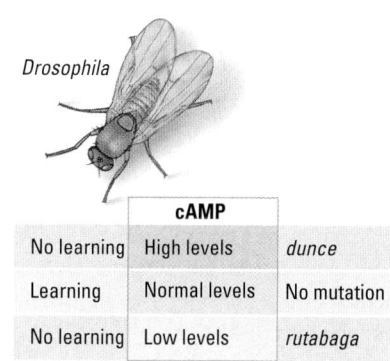

Drosophila

	cAMP	
No learning	High levels	*dunce*
Learning	Normal levels	No mutation
No learning	Low levels	*rutabaga*

FIGURE 5-20 Genetic Disruption of Learning Either of two mutations in the fruit fly *Drosophila* inactivates the second messenger cAMP by moving its level either above or below the concentration range the cell can regulate, thus disrupting learning.

3. Changes that accompany habituation take place within the _____ of the _____ neuron, mediated by _____ channels that grow _____ sensitive with use.

4. The sensitization response is amplified by _____ that release serotonin onto the presynaptic membrane of the sensory neuron, changing the sensitivity of presynaptic _____ channels and increasing the influx of _____.

5. One characteristic of _____, defined as physiological arousal related to recurring memories and dreams surrounding a traumatic event that persist for months or years after the event, is a heightened response to stimuli. This suggests that the disorder is in part related to _____.

6. Describe the benefits and/or drawbacks of permanent habituation and sensitization.

Answers appear at the back of the book.

For additional study tools, visit 🎓 LaunchPad:
www.macmillanhighered.com/launchpad/kolb5e

SUMMARY

5-1 A Chemical Message

In the 1920s, Otto Loewi suspected that nerves to the heart secrete a chemical that regulates its beat rate. His subsequent experiments with frogs showed that acetylcholine slows heart rate, whereas epinephrine increases it. This observation proved key to understanding the basis of chemical neurotransmission.

The systems for chemically synthesizing an excitatory or inhibitory neurotransmitter are in the presynaptic neuron's axon terminal or its soma, whereas the systems for neurotransmitter storage are in its axon terminal. The receptor systems on which that neurotransmitter acts typically are on the postsynaptic membrane. Such chemical neurotransmission is dominant in the human nervous system. Nevertheless, neurons also make direct connections with each other through gap junctions, channel-forming proteins that allow direct sharing of ions or nutrients.

The four major stages in the life of a neurotransmitter are (1) synthesis and storage, (2) release from the axon terminal, (3) action on postsynaptic receptors, and (4) inactivation. After synthesis, the neurotransmitter is wrapped in a membrane to form synaptic vesicles in the axon terminal. When an action potential is propagated on the presynaptic membrane, voltage changes set in motion the vesicles' attachment to the presynaptic membrane and neurotransmitter release by exocytosis.

One synaptic vesicle releases a quantum of neurotransmitter into the synaptic cleft, producing a miniature potential on the postsynaptic membrane. To generate an action potential on the postsynaptic cell requires simultaneous release of many quanta of transmitter. After a transmitter has done its work, it is inactivated by such processes as diffusion out of the synaptic cleft, breakdown by enzymes, and reuptake of the transmitter or its components into the axon terminal (or sometimes uptake into glial cells).

5-2 Varieties of Neurotransmitters and Receptors

Small-molecule transmitters, peptide transmitters, lipid transmitters, and gaseous transmitters are broad classes for ordering the roughly 100 neurotransmitters that investigators propose might exist. Neurons containing these transmitters make a variety of connections with other neurons as well as with muscles, blood vessels, and extracellular fluid.

Functionally, neurons can be both excitatory and inhibitory, and they can participate in local circuits or in general brain networks. Excitatory synapses are usually on a dendritic tree, whereas inhibitory synapses are usually on a cell body.

Some neurotransmitters are associated with both ionotropic and metabotropic receptors. An ionotropic receptor quickly and directly induces voltage changes on the postsynaptic cell membrane. Slower-acting metabotropic receptors activate second messengers to indirectly produce changes in the cell's function and structure. A plethora of receptors, formed from combinations of multiple types of proteins called subunits, exist for most transmitters.

5-3 Neurotransmitter Systems and Behavior

Because neurotransmitters are multifunctional, scientists find it impossible to isolate relations between a single neurotransmitter and a single behavior. Rather, activating systems of neurons that employ the same principal neurotransmitter influence various general aspects of behavior. For instance, acetylcholine, the main neurotransmitter in the SNS, controls movement of the skeletal muscles, whereas acetylcholine and norepinephrine, the main neurotransmitters in the ANS, control the body's internal organs. In the ENS, dopamine and serotonin serve as the main neurotransmitters regulating the gut's functioning.

The CNS contains not only widely dispersed glutamate and GABA neurons—its main neurotransmitters—but also neural activating systems that employ acetylcholine, norepinephrine, dopamine, or serotonin. All these systems ensure that wide areas of the brain act in concert, and each is associated with various classes of behaviors and disorders.

5-4 Adaptive Role of Synapses in Learning and Memory

Changes in synapses underlie the neural basis of learning and memory. In habituation, a form of learning in which a response weakens as a result of repeated stimulation, calcium channels become less responsive to an action potential. Consequently, less neurotransmitter is released when an action potential is propagated.

In sensitization, a form of learning in which a response strengthens as a result of stimulation, changes in potassium channels prolong the action potential's duration, resulting in an increased influx of calcium ions and consequently, release of more neurotransmitter. With repeated training, new synapses can develop, and both forms of learning can become relatively permanent.

In *Aplysia*, the number of synapses connecting sensory neurons and motor neurons decreases in response to repeated sessions of habituation. Conversely, the number of synapses connecting sensory and motor neurons increases in response to repeated sensitization sessions. These changes in the numbers of synapses and dendritic spines are related to long-term learning.

■ KEY TERMS

acetylcholine (ACh), p. 139

activating system, p. 158

Alzheimer disease, p. 161

autoreceptor, p. 144

carbon monoxide (CO), p. 153

chemical synapse, p. 143

cholinergic neuron, p. 156

dopamine (DA), p. 141

endocannabinoid, p. 151

epinephrine (EP), p. 139

G protein, p. 155

gamma-aminobutyric acid (GABA), p. 151

gap junction (electrical synapse), p. 143

glutamate (Glu), p. 151

habituation, p. 163

histamine (H), p. 148

hydrogen sulfide (H_2S), p. 153

ionotropic receptor, p. 153

learning, p. 163

major depression, p. 163

mania, p. 163

metabotropic receptor, p. 153

neuropeptide, p. 151

neurotransmitter, p. 139

nitric oxide (NO), p. 153

noradrenergic neuron, p. 163

norepinephrine (NE), p. 139

obsessive-compulsive disorder (OCD), p. 163

Parkinson disease, p. 141

postsynaptic membrane, p. 143

posttraumatic stress disorder (PTSD), p. 164

presynaptic membrane, p. 143

quantum (pl. quanta), p. 144

rate-limiting factor, p. 151

reuptake, p. 144

schizophrenia, p. 161

second messenger, p. 155

sensitization, p. 164

serotonin (5-HT), p. 151

small-molecule transmitter, p. 148

storage granule, p. 143

subunit, p. 155

synaptic cleft, p. 141

synaptic vesicle, p. 141

transmitter-activated receptor, p. 143

transporter, p. 143

→ Visit 🔵 LaunchPad to access the e-Book, videos, 🔵 LearningCurve adaptive quizzing, flashcards, and more.

www.macmillanhighered.com/launchpad/kolb5e

How Do Drugs and Hormones Influence the Brain and Behavior?

Katherine Streeter

Cognitive Enhancement

A new name for an old game? An article in the preeminent science publication *Nature* floated the idea that certain "cognitive-enhancing" drugs improve school and work performance in otherwise healthy individuals by improving brain function (Greely et al., 2008). The article was instigated in part by reports that up to 20 percent—and in some schools up to 80 percent—of high school and university students were using the combination of Adderall (mainly dextroamphetamine) and methylphenidate (Ritalin) as a study aid to help meet deadlines and to cram for examinations.

Both drugs are prescribed as a treatment for **attention-deficit/hyperactivity disorder** (ADHD), a developmental disorder characterized by core behaviors: impulsivity, hyperactivity, and/or inattention. Methylphenidate and dextroamphetamine are Schedule II drugs, signifying that they carry the potential for abuse and require a prescription when used medically. Their main illicit source is through falsified prescriptions or purchase from someone who has a prescription. Both drugs share the pharmacological properties of cocaine: stimulating dopamine release and blocking its reuptake (see Section 6-2).

The use of cognitive enhancers is not new. In his classic paper on cocaine, Viennese psychoanalyst Sigmund Freud stated in 1884, "The main use of coca [cocaine] will undoubtedly remain that which the Indians [of Peru] have made of it for centuries . . . to increase the physical capacity of the body." Freud later withdrew his endorsement when he realized that cocaine is addictive.

In 1937, an article in the *Journal of the American Medical Association* reported that a form of amphetamine, Benzedrine, improved performance on mental efficiency tests. This information was quickly disseminated among students, who began using the drug as a study aid for examinations. In the 1950s, dextroamphetamine, marketed as Dexedrine, was similarly prescribed for narcolepsy, a sleep disorder, and used illicitly by students as a study aid.

The complex neural effects of amphetamine stimulants center on learning at the synapse by means of habituation and sensitization. With repeated use for nonmedicinal purposes, the drugs can also begin to produce side effects, including sleep disruption, loss of appetite, and headaches. Some people develop cardiovascular abnormalities and/or become addicted to amphetamine.

Treating ADHD with prescription drugs is itself controversial, despite their widespread use for this purpose. According to Aagaard and Hansen (2011), assessing the adverse effects of cognitive enhancement medication is hampered because many participants drop out of studies and the duration of the studies is short.

Despite the contention that stimulant drugs can improve school and work performance by improving brain function in otherwise healthy individuals, evidence for their effectiveness, other than a transient improvement in motivation, is weak.

Robert Stolarik/The New York Times

Psychopharmacology, the study of how drugs affect the nervous system and behavior, is the subject of this chapter. We begin by looking at the major ways drugs are administered, the routes they take to reach the central nervous system, and how they are eliminated from the body. We then group psychoactive drugs based on their major behavioral effects and on how they act on neurons. Next we consider why different people may respond differently to the same dose of a drug and why people may become addicted to drugs. Many principles related to drugs also apply to the action of hormones, the chapter's final topic, which includes a discussion of synthetic steroids that act as hormones.

Before we examine how drugs produce their effects on the brain for good or for ill, we must raise a caution: the sheer number of neurotransmitters, receptors, and possible sites of drug action is astounding. Most drugs act at many sites in the body and brain and affect more than one neurotransmitter system, and most receptors on which drugs act display many variations. Individual differences—sex, genetic makeup, age, height, and weight—all influence how drugs affect people. Considering all the variables, psychopharmacological research has made important advances in understanding drug action. Yet it remains safe to say that neuroscientists do not know everything there is to know about any drug.

6-1 Principles of Psychopharmacology

Drugs are chemical compounds administered to bring about some desired change in the body and brain. Drugs are usually used to diagnose, treat, or prevent illness; to relieve pain and suffering; or to improve some adverse physiological condition. In this chapter, we focus on **psychoactive drugs**—substances that alter mood, thought, or behavior; are used to manage neuropsychological illness; and may be abused. We also consider psychoactive drugs that can act as toxins, producing sickness, brain damage, or death.

Drug Routes into the Nervous System

To be effective, a psychoactive drug has to reach its target in the nervous system. The way a drug enters and passes through the body to reach its target is called its *route of administration*. Drugs can be administered orally, inhaled into the lungs, administered rectally in a suppository, absorbed from patches applied to the skin or mucous membranes, or injected into the bloodstream, into a muscle, or even into the brain. **Figure 6-1** illustrates some of these routes of drug administration and summarizes the characteristics of drugs that allow them to pass through various barriers to reach their targets.

Oral administration is easy and convenient but is nonetheless a complex route. To reach the bloodstream, an ingested drug must first be absorbed through the lining of the stomach or small intestine. Drugs in liquid form are absorbed more readily. Drugs taken in solid form are not absorbed unless the stomach's gastric juices can dissolve them. Some drugs may be destroyed or altered by enzymes in the gastrointestinal tract's microbiome. Whether a drug is an acid or a base influences its absorption.

Once absorbed by the stomach or intestine, the drug must enter the bloodstream. This leg of the journey requires that the drug have additional properties. Because blood has a high water concentration, the drug must be water-soluble. It is then diluted by the approximately 6 liters of blood that circulates through an adult body. When the drug leaves the bloodstream, the body's roughly 35 liters of extracellular fluid further dilute it.

Drugs administered as gases or aerosols penetrate the cell linings of the respiratory tract easily and are absorbed across these membranes into the bloodstream nearly as quickly as they are inhaled. Thus, they reach the bloodstream by circumventing the barriers in the digestive system. When administered as a gas or in smoke, drugs of abuse, including nicotine, cocaine, and marijuana, are similarly absorbed.

Our largest organ, the skin, has three cell layers designed to be a protective body coat. Some small-molecule drugs (e.g., nicotine in a patch) penetrate the skin barrier almost as easily as they penetrate the lungs. Still fewer obstacles confront a drug destined for the brain if that drug is injected directly into the bloodstream. The fewest obstacles are encountered if a psychoactive drug is injected directly into the brain.

With each obstacle eliminated en route to the brain, a drug's dosage can be reduced by a factor of 10. For example, 1000 micrograms (μg; 1 μg is equal to one-millionth of a gram) of amphetamine, a psychomotor stimulant and major component of the drugs described in Clinical Focus 6-1, Cognitive Enhancement, produces a noticeable behavioral change when ingested orally. If inhaled into the lungs or injected into the blood, circumventing the

attention-deficit/hyperactivity disorder (ADHD) Developmental disorder characterized by core behavioral symptoms, including impulsivity, hyperactivity, and/or inattention.

psychopharmacology Study of how drugs affect the nervous system and behavior.

psychoactive drug Substance that acts to alter mood, thought, or behavior; is used to manage neuropsychological illness; or is abused.

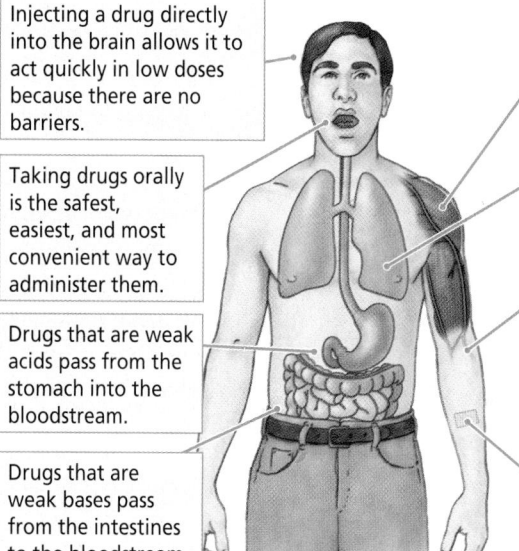

Injecting a drug directly into the brain allows it to act quickly in low doses because there are no barriers.

Taking drugs orally is the safest, easiest, and most convenient way to administer them.

Drugs that are weak acids pass from the stomach into the bloodstream.

Drugs that are weak bases pass from the intestines to the bloodstream.

Drugs injected into muscle encounter more barriers than do drugs inhaled.

Drugs inhaled into the lungs encounter few barriers en route to the brain.

Drugs injected into the bloodstream encounter the fewest barriers to the brain but must be hydrophilic.

Drugs contained in adhesive patches are absorbed through the skin and into the bloodstream.

FIGURE 6-1 Routes of Drug Administration

1000 μg = 1 mg (milligram)

174

stomach, a dose of just 100 μg produces the same results. If amphetamine is injected into the cerebrospinal fluid, bypassing both the stomach and the blood, 10 μg is enough to produce an identical outcome, as is merely 1 μg if dilution in the cerebrospinal fluid also is skirted and the drug is applied directly to target neurons.

This math is well known to sellers and users of illicit drugs. Drugs prepared for inhalation or intravenous injection are much cheaper per dose, because the amount required is so much smaller than that needed for an effective oral dose.

Revisiting the Blood—Brain Barrier

The body presents barriers to the internal movement of drugs: cell membranes, capillary walls, and the placenta. The passage of drugs across capillaries in the brain is made difficult by the *blood–brain barrier*, the tight junctions between the cells of blood vessels in the brain that block passage of most substances. The blood–brain barrier protects the brain's ionic balance and denies neurochemicals from the rest of the body passage into the brain, where they can disrupt communication between neurons. It protects the brain from the effects of many circulating hormones and from toxic and infectious substances. Injury or disease can sometimes rupture the blood–brain barrier, letting pathogens through. For the most part, however, the brain is well protected from harmful substances.

The brain has a rich capillary network. None of its neurons is farther than about 50 micrometers (μm; 1 μm is equal to one-millionth of a meter) from a capillary. As shown at the left in **Figure 6-2**, like all capillaries, brain capillaries are composed of a single layer of endothelial cells. In most parts of the body, endothelial cells in capillary walls are not fused, so substances can pass through the clefts between the cells. In most parts of the brain, by contrast, endothelial cell walls are fused to form tight junctions, so molecules of most substances cannot squeeze between them.

Figure 6-2 also shows that brain capillaries' endothelial cells are surrounded by the end feet of astrocytes attached to the capillary wall, covering about 80 percent of it. The glial cells provide a route for the exchange of food and waste between capillaries and the brain's extracellular fluid and from there to other cells, shown at the right in Figure 6-2.

The cells of capillary walls in the three brain regions shown in **Figure 6-3** lack a blood–brain barrier. The pituitary is a source of many hormones secreted into the blood, and their release is triggered in part by other hormones carried to the pituitary by the blood. The absence of a blood–brain barrier in the lower brainstem's area postrema allows toxic substances in the blood to trigger vomiting. The pineal gland also lacks a blood–brain barrier, enabling hormones to reach it and modulate the day–night cycles it controls.

Figures 4-7 and 4-8 illustrate ion diffusion and concentration and voltage gradients.

Section 13-2 details the pineal gland's pacemaking function.

Capillaries in the brain form tight junctions and are covered with astrocyte feet. These properties prevent materials from moving in and out easily.

Small, uncharged molecules are able to pass through the endothelial membrane.

Certain other molecules are carried across the membrane by active transport.

Amino acids Glucose Fats

CO_2 O_2

CO_2 O_2

Transporter

Astrocyte feet

Capillaries in the body have few tight junctions. Materials can move in and out quite easily.

Capillary

Astrocyte feet

Tight junction

Large and electrically charged molecules are unable to pass out of the capillary.

Endothelial cells

FIGURE 6-2 Blood—Brain Barrier Capillaries in most of the body allow for substances to pass between capillary cell membranes, but those in the brain, stimulated by the actions of astrocytes, form the tight junctions of the blood–brain barrier.

To carry out its work, the brain needs, among other substances, oxygen and glucose for fuel and amino acids to build proteins. Fuel molecules reach brain cells from the blood, just as carbon dioxide and other waste products are excreted from brain cells into the blood. Molecules of these vital substances cross the blood–brain barrier in two ways:

1. Small molecules such as oxygen and carbon dioxide can pass through the endothelial membrane.

2. Complex molecules of glucose, amino acids, and other food components are carried across the membrane by active transport systems or ion pumps—transporter proteins specialized to convey a particular substance.

Few psychoactive drug molecules are sufficiently small or have the correct chemical structure to gain access to the CNS. An important property possessed by those few drugs that have CNS effects, then, is an ability to cross the blood–brain barrier.

How the Body Eliminates Drugs

After a drug is administered, the body soon begins to break it down (*catabolize*) and remove it. Drugs are diluted throughout the body and are sequestered in many regions, including fat cells. They are also catabolized throughout the body, including in the kidneys and liver, and in the intestine by bile. They are excreted in urine, feces, sweat, breast milk, and exhaled air. Drugs developed for therapeutic purposes are usually designed not only to increase their chances of reaching their targets but also to enhance their survival time in the body.

The liver is especially active in catabolizing drugs. Owing to a family of enzymes involved in drug catabolism, the *cytochrome P450 enzyme family* (some are also present in the gastro-intestinal tract microbiome), the liver is capable of breaking down many different drugs into forms more easily excreted from the body. Substances that cannot be catabolized or excreted can build up in the body and become toxic. The metal mercury, for instance, is not easily eliminated and can produce severe neurological effects.

Drugs eliminated from the body and discharged into the environment are extensive and problematic. They may be reingested, via food and water, by many animal species, including humans (Brown et al., 2015). Some may affect fertility, embryonic development, even the physiology and behavior of adult organisms. The solution is redesigning waste management systems to remove by-products eliminated by humans as well as by other animals (Berninger et al., 2015).

Drug Action at Synapses: Agonists and Antagonists

Most drugs that produce psychoactive effects work by influencing chemical reactions at synapses. So to understand how drugs work, we must explore the ways they modify synaptic actions. **Figure 6-4** summarizes seven major steps in neurotransmission at a synapse—each a site of drug action:

1. *Synthesis* of the neurotransmitter can take place in the cell body, the axon, or the terminal.

2. *Storage* of the neurotransmitter is in granules or in vesicles or in both.

3. *Release* of the transmitter is from the terminal's presynaptic membrane into the synapse.

4. *Receptor interaction* takes place in the postsynaptic membrane, as the transmitter acts on an embedded receptor.

5. *Inactivation* of excess neurotransmitter occurs at the synapse.

6. *Reuptake* into the presynaptic terminal for reuse is one outcome.

7. *Degradation* of excess neurotransmitter by synaptic mechanisms and removal of unneeded by-products from the synapse is the other outcome.

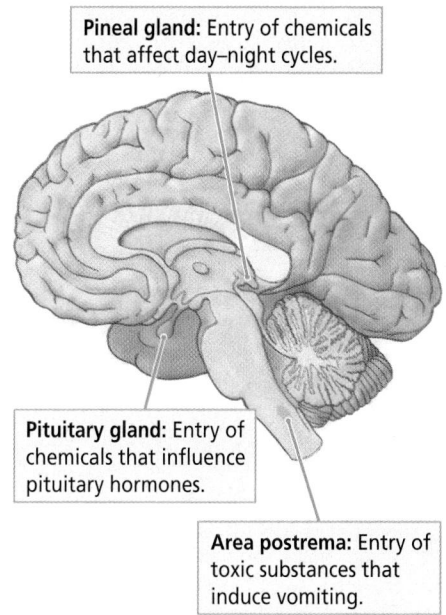

Pineal gland: Entry of chemicals that affect day–night cycles.

Pituitary gland: Entry of chemicals that influence pituitary hormones.

Area postrema: Entry of toxic substances that induce vomiting.

FIGURE 6-3 Barrier-Free Brain Sites The pituitary gland is a target for many blood-borne hormones; the pineal gland, for hormones that affect circadian rhythms. The area postrema initiates vomiting of noxious substances.

Catabolic processes break down; metabolic processes build up.

FIGURE 6-4 Points of Influence In principle, a drug can modify seven major chemical processes, any of which results in enhanced or reduced synaptic transmission, depending on the drug's action as an agonist or antagonist.

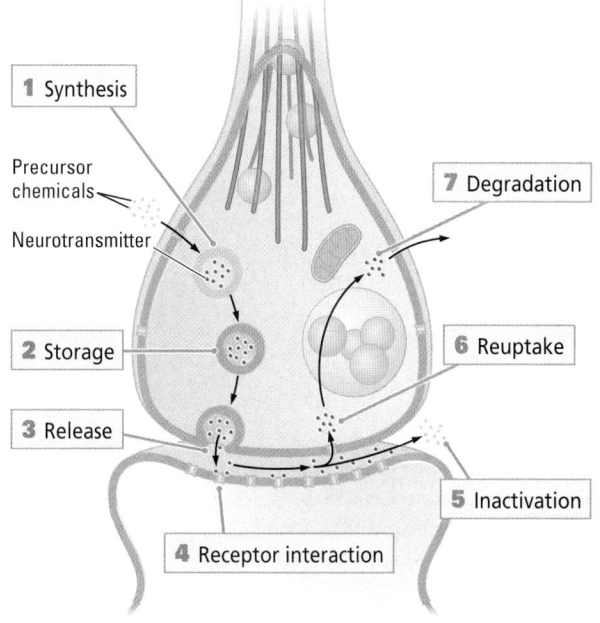

1 Synthesis

Precursor chemicals

Neurotransmitter

7 Degradation

2 Storage

6 Reuptake

3 Release

5 Inactivation

4 Receptor interaction

CHAPTER 6 • HOW DO DRUGS AND HORMONES INFLUENCE THE BRAIN AND BEHAVIOR?

176

Ultimately, a drug that affects any of these synaptic functions either increases or diminishes neurotransmission. Drugs that increase neurotransmission are classified as **agonists**; drugs that decrease neurotransmission are classified as **antagonists**. To illustrate, consider a typical synapse: the acetylcholine synapse between motor neurons and muscles.

An Acetylcholine Synapse: Examples of Drug Action

Figure 6-5 shows how some drugs and toxins act as agonists or antagonists at the ACh synapse on skeletal muscles. ACh agonists excite muscles, increasing muscle tone, whereas ACh antagonists inhibit muscles, decreasing muscle tone. Some of these substances may be new to you, but you have probably heard of others. If you know their effects at the ACh synapse, you can understand the relationships between these substances' neurochemical actions and their behavioral effects.

Figure 6-5 includes two toxins that influence ACh release from the axon terminal. Black widow spider venom acts as an agonist by promoting ACh release to excess. A black widow spider bite does not inject enough drug to paralyze a person, though a victim may feel some muscle weakness.

Botulinum toxin, or botulin, is the poisonous agent in improperly processed canned goods. An antagonist, it blocks ACh release, an effect that can last for weeks to months. Severe poisoning can paralyze both movement and breathing and so cause death.

Botulin has medical uses. Injected into a muscle, it can selectively paralyze the muscle. This action makes it useful for blocking excessive and enduring muscular twitches or contractions, including the spasms that make movement difficult, for example in people with cerebral palsy. Under the trade name Botox, botulin is also used cosmetically to paralyze facial muscles that cause wrinkling.

Figure 6-5 also shows two drugs that act on ACh receptors. Nicotine's molecular structure is similar enough to that of ACh to allow nicotine to fit into ACh receptors' binding sites, where it acts as an agonist. Curare acts as an ACh antagonist by occupying cholinergic receptors and so preventing ACh from binding to them. Once introduced into the body, curare acts quickly and is cleared from the body in a few minutes. Large doses, however, arrest movement and breathing for a period sufficient to result in death.

Figure 4-26 details the structure and action of ACh at a neuromuscular synapse.

Focus 11-2 describes the causes and range of outcomes for cerebral palsy.

As illustrated in Section 5-3, a single main receptor serves the sympathetic nervous system: the nicotinic ACh receptor (nAChR).

FIGURE 6-5 Acetylcholine Agonists and Antagonists Drugs and nutrients can affect ACh transmission by altering its synthesis or release or by binding to the postsynaptic receptor and affecting its breakdown or inactivation.

Agonist
Choline-rich diet increases acetylcholine (ACh).

Agonist
Black widow spider venom promotes release.

Antagonist
Botulin toxin blocks release.

Agonist
Nicotine stimulates receptors.

Acetylcholine terminal

Acetylcholine

Antagonist
Curare blocks receptors.

Agonist
Physostigmine and organophosphates block inactivation.

Early European explorers of South America discovered that the indigenous peoples living along the Amazon River in South America killed small animals using arrowheads coated with curare prepared from the seeds of a plant. The hunters did not poison themselves when eating the animals, because ingested curare cannot pass from the gut into the body. Many curarelike drugs have been synthesized. Some are used to briefly paralyze large animals for examination or tagging for identification. You have probably seen this use of these drugs in wildlife videos. Skeletal muscles are more sensitive to curarelike drugs than are respiratory muscles; an appropriate dose paralyzes an animal's movement temporarily but allows it to breathe.

The final drug action shown in Figure 6-5 is that of physostigmine, an agonist that inhibits acetylcholinesterase (AChE), the enzyme that breaks down ACh, thus increasing the amount available in the synapse. Physostigmine, obtained from an African bean, is used as a poison by hunters.

Large doses of physostigmine can be toxic because they produce excessive excitation of the neuromuscular synapse, disrupting movement and breathing. In small doses, however, physostigmine is used to treat myasthenia gravis, a condition of muscular weakness in which muscle receptors are less than normally responsive to ACh. Physostigmine's action is short lived, lasting only a few minutes or at most a half hour.

Organophosphate compounds bind irreversibly to AChE and consequently allow a toxic buildup of ACh in the synaptic space. Many insecticides and chemical weapons are organophosphates. Insects use glutamate as a neurotransmitter at the nerve–muscle junction, but elsewhere in their nervous system, they have nicotinic receptors. Thus, organophosphates poison insects by acting centrally, but they poison chordates by acting peripherally as well. The Chemical Weapons Convention of 1993 banned one potent organophosphate agent, the lethal nerve gas Sarin. That international ban did not restrain the governments of Iraq, in 1999, and Syria, in 2013, from using Sarin against their own citizens.

Does a drug or toxin that affects neuromuscular synapses also affect ACh synapses in the brain? That depends on whether the substance can cross the blood–brain barrier. Physostigmine and nicotine readily pass the barrier; curare cannot. Nicotine is the psychoactive ingredient in cigarette smoke, and its actions on the brain account for its addictive properties (see Section 6-4). Physostigminelike drugs reportedly have some beneficial effects for memory disorders.

Tolerance

Tolerance is a decreased response to a drug with repeated exposure. Harris Isbell and coworkers (1955) conducted an experiment that, while questionable by today's ethical standards, did suggest how tolerance comes about. The researchers gave volunteers in a prison enough alcohol daily in a 13-week period to keep them in a constant state of intoxication. Yet they found that the participants did not remain drunk for 3 months straight.

When the experiment began, the participants showed rapidly rising blood alcohol levels and behavioral signs of intoxication, as shown in the Results section of **Experiment 6-1, on page 178.** Between the twelfth and twentieth days of alcohol consumption, however, blood alcohol and the signs of intoxication fell, even though the participants maintained their alcohol intake. Thereafter, blood alcohol levels and signs of intoxication fluctuated; one did not always correspond to the other. A relatively high blood alcohol level was sometimes associated with a low outward appearance of intoxication. Why?

The three results were the products of three kinds of tolerance, each much more likely to develop with repeated drug use:

1. In *metabolic tolerance,* the number of enzymes needed to break down alcohol in the liver, blood, and brain increases. As a result, any alcohol consumed is metabolized more quickly, so blood alcohol levels fall.

Figure 5-10 illustrates ACh synthesis and how AChE breaks it down.

In myasthenia gravis, muscle receptors lose their sensitivity to motor neuron messages, as illustrated in Section 4-4.

The Basics, Section 1-3, charts nervous system evolution in the animal kingdom.

In tolerance, as in habituation, learning takes place when the response to a stimulus weakens with repeated presentations (see Experiment 5-2).

agonist Substance that enhances synapse function.

antagonist Substance that blocks synapse function.

tolerance Decrease in response to a drug with the passage of time.

▶ **EXPERIMENT** 6-1

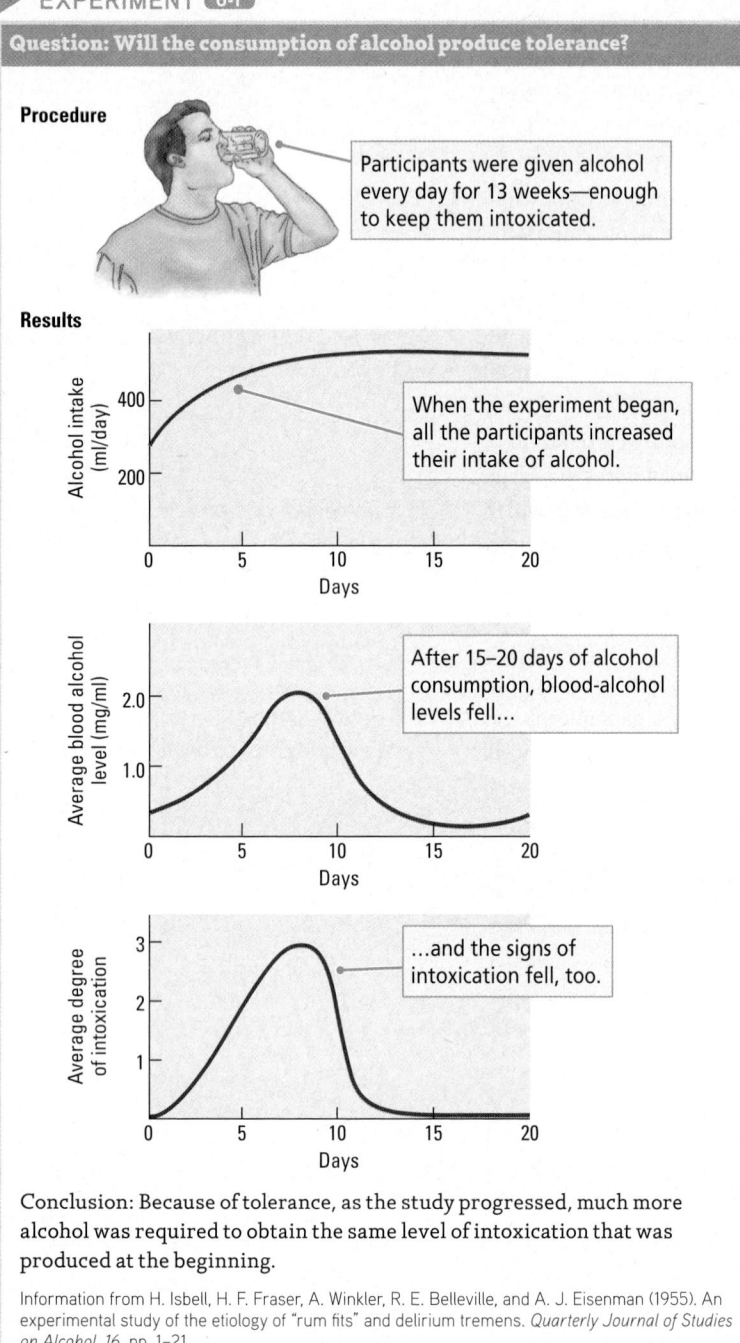

Question: Will the consumption of alcohol produce tolerance?

Procedure

Participants were given alcohol every day for 13 weeks—enough to keep them intoxicated.

Results

When the experiment began, all the participants increased their intake of alcohol.

After 15–20 days of alcohol consumption, blood-alcohol levels fell...

...and the signs of intoxication fell, too.

Conclusion: Because of tolerance, as the study progressed, much more alcohol was required to obtain the same level of intoxication that was produced at the beginning.

Information from H. Isbell, H. F. Fraser, A. Winkler, R. E. Belleville, and A. J. Eisenman (1955). An experimental study of the etiology of "rum fits" and delirium tremens. *Quarterly Journal of Studies on Alcohol, 16*, pp. 1–21.

Experiment 5-3 describes sensitization at the level of neurons and synapses. Section 14-4 relates sensitization to neuroplasticity and learned addictions.

2. In *cellular tolerance*, brain cell activities adjust to minimize the effects of alcohol in the blood. Cellular tolerance can help explain why the behavioral signs of intoxication may be so low despite a relatively high blood alcohol level.

3. *Learned tolerance* explains a drop in outward signs of intoxication. As people learn to cope with the demands of living under the influence of alcohol, they may no longer appear intoxicated.

Does it surprise you that learning plays a role in alcohol tolerance? It has been confirmed in many studies, including a description of the effect first reported by John Wenger and his coworkers (1981). They trained rats to prevent electric foot shocks as they walked on a narrow conveyor belt sliding over an electrified grid. One group of rats received alcohol after training in walking the belt; another group received alcohol before training. A third group received training only, and a fourth group received alcohol only.

After several days' exposure to their respective conditions, all groups received alcohol before a walking test. The rats that had received alcohol before training performed well, whereas those that had received training and alcohol separately performed just as poorly as those that had never had alcohol or those that had not been trained. Despite alcohol intoxication, then, animals can acquire the motor skills needed to balance on a narrow belt. With motor experience, they can learn to compensate for being intoxicated.

Sensitization

Drug tolerance is much more likely to develop with repeated use than with periodic use, but tolerance does not always follow repeated exposure to a drug. Tolerance resembles habituation in that the response to the drug weakens with repeated presentations. The drug user may have the opposite reaction, sensitization—increased responsiveness to successive equal doses. Whereas tolerance generally develops with repeated drug use, sensitization is much more likely to develop with periodic use.

To demonstrate drug sensitization, Terry Robinson and Jill Becker (1986) isolated rats in observation boxes and recorded their reactions to an injection of amphetamine, which stimulates dopamine receptors. Every 3 or 4 days, the investigators injected the rats and found their motor activities—sniffing, rearing, and walking—more vigorous with each administration of the same drug dose, as graphed in Results 1 of **Experiment 6-2**.

The increased motor activity on successive tests was not due to the animals becoming comfortable with the test situation. Control animals that received no drug failed to display a similar escalation. Administering the drug to rats in their home cages did not affect activity in subsequent tests, either. Moreover, the sensitization to amphetamine was enduring. Even when two injections were separated by months, the animals still showed an escalation of motor behavior. Even a single exposure to amphetamine produced sensitization.

▶ EXPERIMENT 6-2

Question: Does the injection of a drug always produce the same behavior?

Procedure 1

In the Robinson and Becker study, animals were given periodic injections of the same dose of amphetamine. Then the researchers measured the number of times each rat reared in its cage.

Procedure 2

In the Whishaw study, animals were given different numbers of swims after being injected with Flupentixol. Then the researchers measured their speed to escape to a platform in a swimming pool.

Agonist
Amphetamine

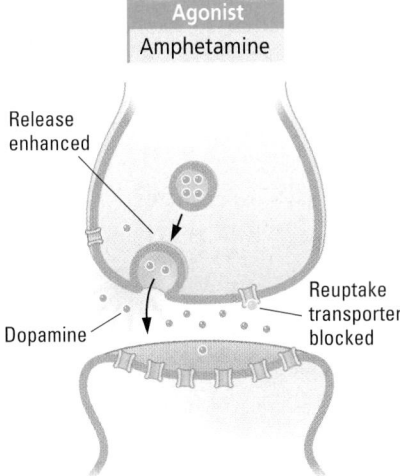

Release enhanced

Dopamine

Reuptake transporter blocked

Antagonist
Flupentixol

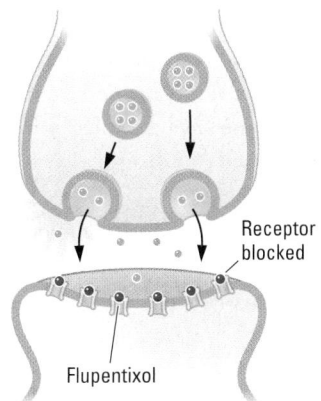

Receptor blocked

Flupentixol

Results 1

Number of incidents of rearing

24

12

1   3   5   9
Number of injections

Results 2

Time to platform(s)

60

3

1   4   8   12
Number of trials

Conclusion 1: Sensitization indicated by increased rearing, develops with periodic repeated injections.

Conclusion 2: Sensitization depends on the occurrence of a behavior: the number of swims increases the time that it takes the rat to reach the platform.

Left: Information from T. E. Robinson and J. B. Becker (1986). Enduring changes in brain and behavior produced by chronic amphetamine administration: A review and evaluation of animal models of amphetamine psychosis. *Brain Research Reviews, 397,* pp. 157–198. Right: Information from I. Q. Whishaw, G. Mittleman, and J. L. Evenden (1989). Training-dependent decay in performance produced by the narcoleptic cist(Z)-flupentixol on spatial navigation by rats in a swimming pool. *Pharmacology, Biochemistry, and Behavior, 32,* pp. 211–220.

Sensitization is not always characterized by an increase in an elicited behavior but may also manifest as a progressive decrease in behavior. Ian Whishaw and his colleagues (1989) administered flupentixol, a drug that blocks dopamine receptors, to rats that had been well trained in a swimming task. As illustrated in Results 2 of Experiment 6-2, the rats displayed such a marked trial-dependent slowing in swimming speed when escaping from the water that they completely stopped swimming over successive trials. The trial-dependent decrease in swimming was similar whether the trials were massed on the same day or spaced over days or weeks.

The neural basis of sensitization lies in part in changes at the synapse. Studies on the dopamine synapse after sensitization to amphetamine show more dopamine released from the presynaptic terminal in sensitized animals. Sensitization can also be associated with changes in receptor numbers on the postsynaptic membrane, in the rate of transmitter metabolism in the synaptic space, in transmitter reuptake by the presynaptic membrane, and in the number and size of synapses.

Another basis of sensitization is learned. Animals show a change in learned responses to environmental cues as sensitization progresses. Consequently, sensitization is difficult to achieve in an animal tested in its home cage. In the Whishaw group's experiment, administering flupentixol to rats left in their home environment did not influence their performance in subsequent swim tests.

Sabina Fraioli and her coworkers (1999) gave amphetamine to two groups of rats and recorded the behavioral responses to successive injections. One group of rats lived in the test apparatus, so for that group, home was the test box. The other group was taken out of their home cage and placed in the test box for each day's experimentation. The home group showed no sensitization to amphetamine, whereas the out group displayed robust sensitization.

At least part of the explanation of the home–out effect is that the animals are accustomed to engaging in a certain behavioral repertoire in their home environment, so it is difficult to get them to change their response to home cues even when influenced by a drug. When subjects are away from home, they receive novel out cues, which favor conditioning of new responses.

Sensitization is relevant to understanding some psychopharmacological effects of drugs:

1. Many drug therapies, including those for the psychiatric disorder schizophrenia, must be taken for several weeks before they produce beneficial effects. Possibly sensitization underlies the development of these beneficial effects.

2. Sensitization is related to drug dependence. Before a person becomes dependent on or addicted to a drug, he or she must be sensitized by numerous experiences with the drug away from the home environment.

3. Life experiences, especially stressful ones, can produce effects resembling sensitization that prime the nervous system for addiction (Roberts et al., 2015).

Focus 8-5 relates the possible origin of schizophrenia and its progress.

(6-1) **REVIEW**

Principles of Psychopharmacology

Before you continue, check your understanding.

1. _____, substances that produce changes in behavior by acting on the nervous system, are one subject of _____, the study of how drugs affect the nervous system and behavior.

2. Perhaps the most important obstacle on a psychoactive drug's journey between its entry into the body and its action at a target is the _____, which generally allows only substances needed for nourishment to pass from the capillaries into the

_____.

3. Most drugs that have psychoactive effects influence chemical reactions at neuronal _____. Drugs that influence communication between neurons do so by acting either as _____ (increasing the effectiveness of neurotransmission) or as _____ (decreasing the effectiveness of neurotransmission).

4. Behavior may change with the repeated use of a psychoactive drug. These changes include _____ and _____, in which the effect of the drug decreases or increases, respectively, with repeated use.

5. The body eliminates drugs through _____, _____, _____, _____, and _____.

6. Describe briefly how tolerance and sensitization might affect someone who uses cognitive enhancers occasionally (a) at home or (b) at work.

Answers appear at the back of the book.

For additional study tools, visit 🅜 **LaunchPad**:
www.macmillanhighered.com/launchpad/kolb5e

6-2 Grouping Psychoactive Drugs

Did you know that most psychoactive drugs and their effects were discovered by accident? Scientists and pharmaceutical companies have experimented ever since, to explain drug action, to synthesize alternative forms for therapeutic treatments, and to modify drugs to reduce side effects. But the process is complex. Drugs with similar chemical structure can have different effects, and drugs with different structure can have similar effects. And a single drug usually acts on many neurochemical systems and has many effects.

A full appreciation of any drug's action requires a multifaceted description, such as can be found in compendiums of drug action. Unambiguously grouping psychoactive drugs is virtually impossible, because most drugs influence many behaviors. Behavioral descriptions undergo constant review, as illustrated by continuing revisions of the *Diagnostic and Statistical Manual of Mental Disorders* (DSM-5). Published by the American Psychiatric Association and now in its fifth edition, the DSM offers a classification system for diagnosing neurological and behavioral disorders.

Table 6-1 groups psychoactive drugs based on their most pronounced behavioral or psychoactive effects (Advokat et al., 2014). Each of the five groups may contain a few to thousands of chemicals in its subcategories. In the following sections we highlight drug actions, both on neurochemical systems in the brain and on synaptic function.

Most psychoactive drugs have three names: chemical, generic, and branded. The chemical name describes a drug's structure; the generic name is nonproprietary and is spelled lowercase; and the proprietary, or brand, name, given by the pharmaceutical company that sells it, is capitalized. Some psychoactive drugs also sport street names or are known as club drugs.

Group I: Antianxiety Agents and Sedative-Hypnotics

At low doses, antianxiety drugs and sedative-hypnotics reduce anxiety; at medium doses, they sedate; at high doses, they anesthetize or induce coma.

TABLE 6-1 Grouping Psychoactive Drugs

Group I: Antianxiety agents and sedative-hypnotics
Benzodiazepines: diazepam (Valium), alprazolam (Xanax), clonazepam (Klonopin)
Barbiturates (anesthetic agents); alcohol
Other anesthetics: gamma-hydroxybutyrate (GHB), ketamine (Special K), phencyclidine (PCP, angel dust)
Group II: Antipsychotic agents
First generation: phenothiazines: chlorpromazine (Thorazine); butyrophenones: haloperidol (Haldol)
Second generation: clozapine (Clozaril), aripiprazole (Abilify, Aripiprex)
Group III: Antidepressants and mood stabilizers

Antidepressants
    MAO inhibitors
    Tricyclic antidepressants: imipramine (Tofranil)
    SSRIs (atypical antidepressants): fluoxetine (Prozac); sertraline (Zoloft); paroxetine (Paxil, Seroxat)
 	
Mood stabilizers
    Lithium, sodium valproate, carbamazepine (Tegretol)

Group IV: Opioid analgesics
Opium derivatives: morphine, codeine, heroin
Endogenous opioid neuropeptides: enkephalins, dynorphins, endorphins
Group V: Psychotropics
Behavioral stimulants: amphetamine, cocaine

Psychedelic and hallucinogenic stimulants (listed by neurotransmitter)
    Acetylcholine psychedelics: atropine, nicotine
    Anandamide psychedelics: tetrahydrocannabinol (THC)
    Glutamate psychedelics: phencyclidine (PCP, angel dust), ketamine (Special K)
    Norepinephrine psychedelics: mescaline
    Serotonin psychedelics: Lysergic acid diethylamide (LSD), psilocybin, MDMA (Ecstasy)

General stimulants: caffeine

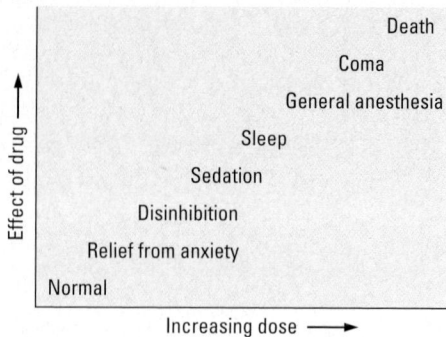

FIGURE 6-6 Behavioral Continuum of Sedation Increasing doses of sedative-hypnotic and antianxiety drugs affect behavior: low doses reduce anxiety and very high doses result in death.

GABA is an amino acid. Figure 5-12 shows its chemical structure.

antianxiety agent Drug that reduces anxiety, including minor tranquilizers such as benzodiazepines and sedative-hypnotic agents.

barbiturate Drug that produces sedation and sleep.

cross-tolerance Reduction of response to a novel drug because of tolerance to a chemically related drug.

fetal alcohol spectrum disorder (FASD) Range of physical and intellectual impairments observed in some children born to alcoholic parents.

At very high doses, they can kill (**Figure 6-6**). Even so, antianxiety drugs are safer at high doses than sedative-hypnotics are. Indeed, the prescribing of sedative-hypnotics for all purposes is decreasing.

Many psychoactive drugs have sedative-hypnotic and antianxiety actions. They include phencyclidine (PCP, angel dust) and two drugs—gamma-hydroxybutyric acid (GHB) and ketamine (Special K)—that gained notoriety as date rape drugs. Both are soluble in alcohol, act quickly, and, like other sedative-hypnotics, impair memory of recent events. Because they can be dissolved in a drink, partygoers and clubbers should never accept drinks from anyone, drink from punch bowls, or leave drinks unattended.

Drug Action in the Brain

The best-known **antianxiety agents**, or minor tranquilizers, are the benzodiazepines. One, diazepam, is marketed as the widely prescribed brand-name drug Valium. Others are alprazolam (Xanax) and clonazepam (Klonopin). Benzodiazepines are often used by people who are having trouble coping with a major life stress, such as a traumatic accident or a death in the family. They aid sleep and also are used as presurgical relaxation agents.

Sedative-hypnotics include alcohol and **barbiturates**. Both induce sleep, anesthesia, and coma at doses only slightly higher than those that sedate. Alcohol is well known to most people and widely consumed. While sometimes prescribed as a sleeping medication, today barbiturates are mainly used to induce anesthesia before surgery.

A characteristic feature of sedative-hypnotics is that the user who takes repeated doses develops a tolerance for them. A larger dose is then required to maintain the drug's initial effect. **Cross-tolerance** results when the tolerance for one drug is carried over to a different member of the drug group.

Drug Action at the Synapse

Cross-tolerance suggests that antianxiety and sedative-hypnotic drugs act on the nervous system in similar ways. One target common to both alcohol and barbiturate drugs is a receptor for gamma-aminobutyric acid (GABA), the inhibitory neurotransmitter that is widely distributed in the CNS. The GABA$_A$ receptor, illustrated in **Figure 6-7**, contains a chloride ion channel.

Excitation of the GABA$_A$ receptor produces an influx of Cl$^-$ through its pore. An influx of Cl$^-$ increases the concentration of negative charges inside the cell membrane, hyperpolarizing it and making it less likely to propagate an action potential. GABA therefore has its inhibitory effect by decreasing a neuron's firing rate. Widespread reduction of neuronal firing underlies the behavioral effects of drugs that affect the GABA$_A$ synapse.

The GABA$_A$ receptor illustrated in Figure 6-7 has different binding sites for GABA, barbiturates, and benzodiazepines. Activation of each site promotes an influx of Cl$^-$, but in different ways. Because the effects of actions at these three sites summate, sedative-hypnotics, including alcohol and antianxiety drugs, should not be consumed together. Combined doses of drugs reportedly contribute to as many deaths as occur annually from automobile accidents in the United States. Such was the case in 2012, when singer Whitney Houston drowned.

The GABA$_A$ receptor also has binding sites that block the ion pore when active, reducing the flow of Cl$^-$ and increasing the target neuron's excitability. Picrotoxin, a compound that blocks the pore, produces epileptic discharges in postsynaptic neurons. Administering GABA$_A$ agonists can block picrotoxin's action. Sedative-hypnotic and antianxiety drugs are thus useful in treating epileptic discharges.

Drugs that act on GABA receptors may affect brain development, because GABA is one of the substances that regulate brain development. Clinical Focus 6-2, Fetal Alcohol Spectrum Disorder, explores alcohol's potentially devastating effects on developing fetuses.

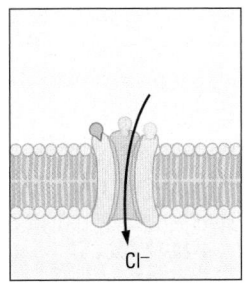

Sedative-hypnotic drugs (alcohol or barbiturates) increase GABA binding, thereby maximizing the time the pore is open.

Antianxiety drugs (benzodiazepines) influence the frequency of pore opening.

Because their different actions summate, these drugs should not be taken together.

FIGURE 6-7 Drug Effects at the GABA$_A$ Receptor Sedative-hypnotics act at the barbiturate site (left), and antianxiety agents act at the benzodiazepine site (center). Taken together (right), these two types of drugs can be lethal.

CLINICAL FOCUS 6-2

Fetal Alcohol Spectrum Disorder

The term *fetal alcohol syndrome* (FAS) was coined in 1973 to describe a pattern of physical malformation and intellectual disability observed in some children born to alcoholic mothers. It is now called **fetal alcohol spectrum disorder** (FASD) to acknowledge the range of its effects. Children with FASD may have abnormal facial features, such as unusually wide spacing between the eyes. Their brains display a range of abnormalities, from small size with abnormal gyri to abnormal clusters of cells and misaligned cells in the cortex.

Related to these brain abnormalities are certain behavioral symptoms that children with FASD tend to have in common. They display varying degrees of learning disabilities and low intelligence test scores as well as hyperactivity and other social problems. Individuals with FASD are 19 times as likely to be incarcerated as those without it (Popova et al., 2011).

The offspring of approximately 6 percent of alcoholic mothers have pronounced FASD. In major cities, its incidence is about 1 in 700 births and is especially high among Native Americans on reservations in Canada, some other minority groups, and single mothers (Mead & Sarkar, 2014).

A major problem is that women who are most at risk for bearing FASD babies are poor and not well educated, their alcohol consumption problems predate pregnancy, and they have little access to prenatal care. It is often difficult to inform these women about the dangers that alcohol poses to a fetus and to encourage them to abstain from drinking before and while they are pregnant.

Alcohol-induced abnormalities can vary from hardly noticeable physical and psychological effects to full-blown FASD. The severity of effects is related to when, how much, and how frequently alcohol is consumed over the course of pregnancy. The effects are worse if alcohol is consumed in the first trimester, a time when many women do not yet realize that they are pregnant.

Severe FASD is also more likely to coincide with binge drinking, which produces high blood alcohol levels. Other factors related to a severe outcome are poor nutritional health of the mother and the mother's use of other drugs, including nicotine. In addition, alcohol use by mothers and fathers *before* conception can change the methylation status of some genes that contribute to disabilities found on the spectrum (Lee et al., 2015).

A major question raised by FASD is how much alcohol is too much to drink during pregnancy. To be completely safe, it is best not to drink at all in the months preceding as well as during pregnancy. This conclusion is supported by findings that as little as a single drink of alcohol per day during pregnancy can lead to a decrease in children's intelligence test scores.

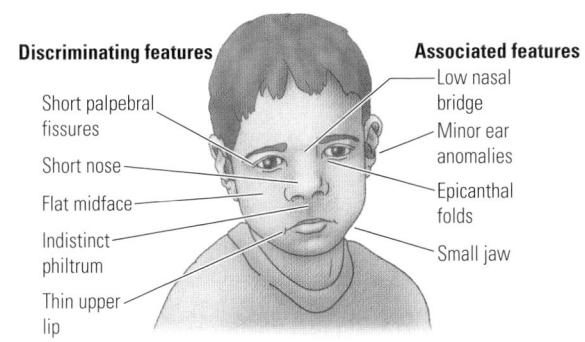

Discriminating features
- Short palpebral fissures
- Short nose
- Flat midface
- Indistinct philtrum
- Thin upper lip

Associated features
- Low nasal bridge
- Minor ear anomalies
- Epicanthal folds
- Small jaw

Courtesy of Sterling K. Clarren, M.D., Professor of Pediatrics, University of British Columbia Faculty of Medicine.

(Top) Characteristic facial features that indicate FASD. Effects are not merely physical; many children endure severe intellectual disabilities. (Bottom) The convolutions characteristic of the brain of a healthy child at age 6 weeks (left) are grossly underdeveloped in the brain of a child with FASD (right).

dopamine hypothesis of schizophrenia
Idea that excess dopamine activity causes symptoms of schizophrenia.

major depression Mood disorder characterized by prolonged feelings of worthlessness and guilt, disruption of normal eating habits, sleep disturbances, a general slowing of behavior, and frequent thoughts of suicide.

monoamine oxidase (MAO) inhibitor Antidepressant drug that blocks the enzyme monoamine oxidase from degrading such neurotransmitters as DA, NE, and 5-HT.

tricyclic antidepressant First-generation antidepressant; its chemical structure, characterized by three rings, blocks 5-HT reuptake transporter proteins.

second-generation antidepressant Drug that acts similarly to tricyclics (first-generation antidepressants) but more selectively on 5-HT reuptake transporter proteins; also called atypical antidepressant.

selective serotonin reuptake inhibitor (SSRI) Tricyclic antidepressant drug that blocks 5-HT reuptake into the presynaptic terminal.

FIGURE 6-8 Drug Effects at D_2 Receptors The antipsychotic agent chlorpromazine can lessen schizophrenia symptoms, and amphetamine or cocaine abuse can produce them. This suggests that schizophrenia is related to excessive activity at the D_2 receptor.

Group II: Antipsychotic Agents

The term *psychosis* is applied to behavioral disorders such as *schizophrenia*, which is characterized by hallucinations (false sensory perceptions) and delusions (false beliefs), among a host of symptoms. The use of antipsychotic drugs has improved the functioning of schizophrenia patients. Since 1955, when psychoactive drugs were introduced into widespread therapeutic use, resident patient populations in state and municipal mental hospitals in the United States have decreased dramatically.

The success of antipsychotic agents is an important therapeutic achievement, because the incidence of schizophrenia is high—about 1 in every 100 people. Although antipsychotic agents make mental disorders manageable, they do not constitute cures. In fact, according to the National Institute on Disability and Rehabilitation Research, although the number of people in mental institutions remains relatively low, as many as 75% of the homeless and 50% of incarcerated people have mental health issues. According to Human Rights Watch, in 2015, 10 times as many mentally ill people were incarcerated as resided in mental institutions.

Antipsychotic agents have been widely used since the mid-1950s, beginning with the development of what are now called first-generation antipsychotics (FGAs). They include the drug classes phenothiazines (e.g., chlorpromazine, Thorazine) and butyrophenones (e.g., haloperidol, Haldol). FGAs act mainly by blocking the dopamine D_2 receptor. Beginning in the 1980s, newer drugs such as clozapine (Clozaril) and several other compounds emerged as the second-generation antipsychotics (SGAs). SGAs weakly block dopamine D_2 receptors but also block serotonin 5-HT$_2$ receptors. Antipsychotic drugs now in development will likely form a third generation.

Antipsychotic agents' therapeutic actions are not understood fully, and these drugs can produce many unwanted side effects. Joint experimentation by patients and physicians with different drugs and doses is common (Pouget et al., 2014). The **dopamine hypothesis of schizophrenia** holds that some forms of the disease may be related to excessive dopamine activity—especially in the frontal lobes. Other support for the dopamine hypothesis comes from the schizophrenialike symptoms of chronic users of amphetamine, a stimulant.

As **Figure 6-8** shows, amphetamine is a dopamine agonist. It fosters dopamine release from the presynaptic membrane of D_2 synapses and blocks dopamine reuptake from the synaptic cleft. The logic is that if amphetamine causes schizophrenialike symptoms by increasing dopamine activity, perhaps naturally occurring schizophrenia is related to excessive dopamine action too. Both FGAs and SGAs block the D_2 receptor, which immediately reduces motor activity and alleviates the excessive agitation of some schizophrenia patients. Because schizophrenia involves more than just D_2 receptors, changes in dopamine synapses do not completely explain the disorder or the effects of antipsychotic agents.

Group III: Antidepressants and Mood Stabilizers

Major depression—a mood disorder characterized by prolonged feelings of worthlessness and guilt, disruption of normal eating habits, sleep disturbances, a general slowing of behavior, and frequent thoughts of suicide—is rather common. At any given time, about 6 percent of the U.S. adult population has major depression, and in the course of a lifetime, 30 percent may have at least one episode that lasts for months or longer. Depression is diagnosed in twice as many women as men.

Inadequate nutrition, stress from difficult life conditions, acute changes in neuronal function, and damage to brain neurons are among the factors implicated in depression.

These factors may be related: nutritional deficiencies may increase vulnerability to stress; stress may change neuronal function; and if unrelieved, altered neuronal function may lead to neuron damage. Section 6-5 offers more information on stress.

Among the nutrient deficiencies that may be related to depression (Smith et al., 2010) are folic acid and other B vitamins and omega-3 fatty acids, a rich source of vitamin D obtained from fish. Our skin synthesizes vitamin D on exposure to sunlight, but our body cannot store it. Vitamin D deficiency is reportedly widespread in people living in northern climates because they don't eat enough fish and they lack exposure to sunlight in winter. Although vitamin D deficiency is associated with depressive symptoms, little is known about the relations among long-term deficiencies in nutrients, depression and associated brain changes, and the effectiveness of dietary supplements (Kerr et al., 2015).

Not surprisingly, alongside improved nutrition, a number of pharmacological approaches to depression are available. They include normalizing stress hormones, modifying neuronal responses, and stimulating neuronal repair.

Antidepressant Medications

Three types of drugs have antidepressant effects: the **monoamine oxidase** (MAO) **inhibitors**; the **tricyclic antidepressants**, so called because of their three-ring chemical structure; and the **second-generation antidepressants**, sometimes called *atypical antidepressants* (see Table 6-1). Second-generation antidepressants lack a three-ring structure but do share some similarities to the tricyclics in their actions.

Antidepressants are thought to act by improving chemical neurotransmission at serotonin, noradrenaline (norepinephrine), histamine, and acetylcholine synapses, and perhaps at dopamine synapses as well. **Figure 6-9** shows the actions of MAO inhibitors and second-generation antidepressants at a 5-HT synapse, on which most research is focused. MAO inhibitors and the tricyclic and second-generation antidepressants all act as agonists but have different mechanisms for increasing serotonin availability.

MAO inhibitors provide for more serotonin release with each action potential by inhibiting monoamine oxidase, an enzyme that breaks down serotonin in the axon terminal. In contrast, the tricyclics and second-generation antidepressants block the reuptake transporter that takes serotonin back into the axon terminal. The second-generation antidepressants are thought to be especially selective in blocking serotonin reuptake; consequently, some are also called **selective serotonin reuptake inhibitors** (SSRIs). Because the transporter is blocked, serotonin remains in the synaptic cleft, prolonging its action on postsynaptic receptors.

Although these drugs begin to affect synapses very quickly, their antidepressant actions take weeks to develop. One explanation is that antidepressants, especially SSRIs, stimulate second messengers in neurons to activate the repair of neurons damaged by stress. Of interest in this respect, one SSRI, fluoxetine (Prozac), increases the production of new neurons in the hippocampus, a limbic structure in the temporal lobes. As detailed in Section 6-5, the hippocampus is vulnerable to stress-induced damage, and its restoration by fluoxetine is proposed to underlie one of the drug's antidepressant effects (Hill et al., 2015).

Most people recover from depression within a year of its onset. If left untreated, however, depression's incidence of suicide is high, as described in Clinical Focus 6-3, Major Depression, on page 186. Of all psychological disorders, major depression is one of the most treatable, and cognitive and intrapersonal therapies are as effective as drug therapies (Comer, 2011).

Even so, about 20 percent of patients with depression fail to respond to antidepressant drugs. Accordingly, depression likely can have many other causes, including dysfunction in other transmitter systems and even

Section 12-4 explores the neuroanatomy of emotional disorders such as depression and Section 16-4 its neurobiology and treatments for it.

Reuptake is part of transmitter deactivation, the last of the four steps of neurotransmission (see Figure 5-4).

FIGURE 6-9 Drug Effects at 5–HT Receptors Different antidepressant drugs act on the serotonin synapse in different ways to increase its availability.

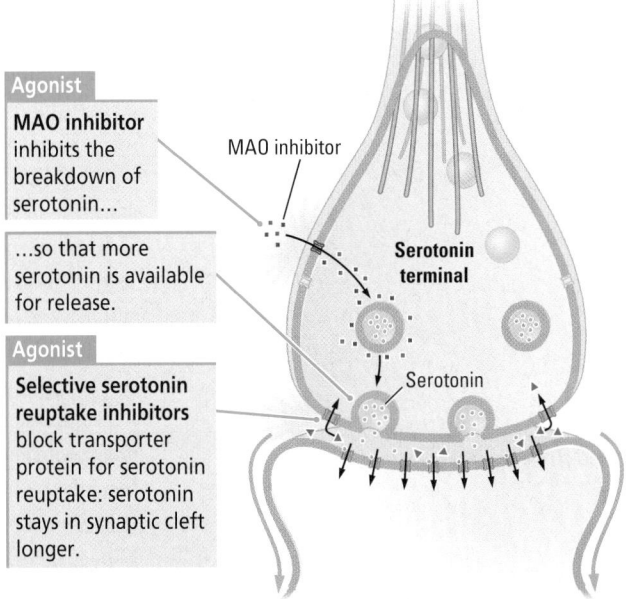

Agonist

MAO inhibitor inhibits the breakdown of serotonin...

...so that more serotonin is available for release.

Agonist

Selective serotonin reuptake inhibitors block transporter protein for serotonin reuptake: serotonin stays in synaptic cleft longer.

MAO inhibitor

Serotonin terminal

Serotonin

Major Depression

P. H. was a 53-year-old high school teacher who, although popular with his students, was deriving less and less satisfaction from his work. His marriage was foundering because he was growing apathetic and no longer wanted to socialize or go on vacations. He was having difficulty getting up in the morning and arriving at school on time.

P. H. eventually consulted a physician, complaining of severe chest pains, which he feared signaled an impending heart attack. He informed his doctor that a heart attack would be a welcome relief because it would end his problems. The physician concluded that P. H. had depression and referred him to a psychiatrist.

Since the 1950s, depression has been treated with antidepressant drugs, a variety of *cognitive-behavioral therapies* (CBTs), and electro-convulsive therapy (ECT), in which electrical current is passed briefly through one hemisphere of the brain. Of the drug treatments available, tricyclic antidepressants and SSRIs are favored.

The risk of suicide and self-injurious behaviors is high in major depression, especially among depressive adolescents who are resistant to treatment with SSRIs (Asarnow et al., 2011). Even for patients who do respond positively to SSRI treatment, the benefits may not occur for weeks.

The glutamate antagonist ketamine, when given in smaller than anes-thetic doses, can produce rapid beneficial effects that last for weeks, even in patients who are resistant to SSRI medication (Reinstatler and Youssef, 2015). Ketamine is thus proposed to be useful as an acute treat-ment for patients with major depression who are at risk for suicide and even for patients with bipolar depression who are at risk for suicide.

Prompted by complaints from family members that antidepressant drug treatments have caused suicide, especially in children, the U.S. Food and Drug Administration has advised physicians to monitor the side effects of SSRIs, including fluoxetine (Prozac), sertraline (Zoloft), and paroxetine (Paxil, Seroxat). Findings from several studies show no difference in the suicide rate between children and adolescents who receive SSRIs and a placebo, and the incidence of suicide after prescrip-tions were curtailed subsequent to the FDA warning actually increased (Isacsson and Rich, 2014).

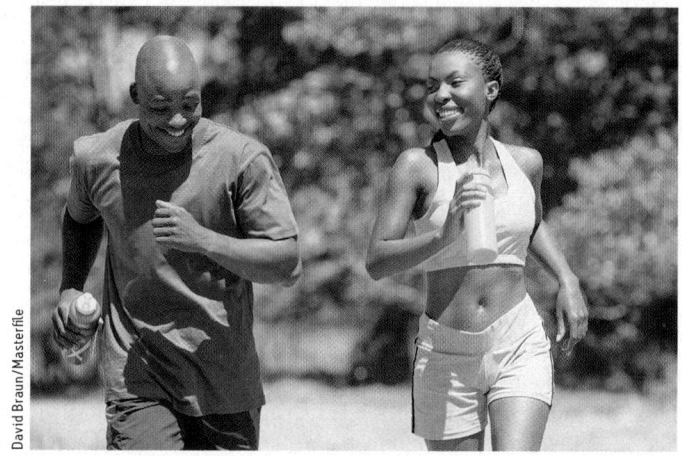

Depressed? Virtually everyone who exercises will tell you that it can work wonders to brighten your mood.

brain damage, including frontal lobe damage. Some people have difficulty tolerating the side effects of antidepressants—increased anxiety, sexual dysfunction, sedation, dry mouth, blurred vision, and memory impairment among them.

Mood Stabilizers

Bipolar disorder, once referred to as manic-depressive psychosis, is characterized by periods of depression alternating with normal periods and periods of intense excitation, or *mania*. According to the National Institute of Mental Health, bipolar disorder may affect as much as 2.6% of the adult population of the United States.

The difficulty in treating bipolar disorder with drugs relates to the difficulty in under-standing how a disease produces symptoms that appear to be opposites: mania and depres-sion. Consequently, bipolar disorder often is treated with numerous drugs, each directed toward a different symptom. **Mood stabilizers,** which include the salt lithium, mute the intensity of one pole of the disorder, thus making the other less likely to occur. Lithium does not directly affect mood and so may act by stimulating mechanisms of neuronal repair, such as the production of neuron growth factors.

A variety of drugs for epilepsy (carbamazepine, valproate) have positive effects; perhaps they mute the excitability of neurons during the mania phase. And antipsychotic drugs that block D_2 receptors effectively control the hallucinations and delusions associated with mania. It is important to remember, though, that all these treatments have side effects: enhancing beneficial effects while minimizing side effects is a major focus of new drug development (Grande and Vieta, 2015).

Group IV: Opioid Analgesics

An *opioid* is any compound that binds to a group of morphine-sensitive brain receptors. The term *narcotic analgesic* was first used to describe these drugs because **opioid analgesics** have sleep-inducing (narcotic) and pain-relieving (analgesic) properties. There are two natural sources of opioids.

One source is *opium*, an extract of the seeds of the opium poppy, *Papaver somniferum*, shown at left in **Figure 6-10**. Opium has been used for thousands of years to produce euphoria, analgesia, sleep, and relief from diarrhea and coughing. In 1805, German chemist Friedrich Sertürner synthesized two chemicals from opium: codeine and morphine. Codeine is often an ingredient in prescription cough medicine and pain relievers. The liver converts it to morphine. Morphine, shown at center in Figure 6-10 and named for Morpheus, the Greek god of dreams, is a powerful pain reliever. Despite decades of research, no other drug has been found that exceeds morphine's effectiveness as an analgesic.

The second natural source of opioids is the brain. In the 1970s, several groups of scientists injected radioactive opioids into the brain of experimental animals and identified receptors there to which opioids bind. At roughly the same time, other groups of investigators identified several brain peptides as the neurotransmitters that naturally affect these receptors. The peptides in the body that have opioidlike effects are collectively called **endorphins** (endogenous morphines).

Research has identified four classes of opioid peptides: endorphins, enkephalins, dynorphins, and endomorphins. The three receptors on which each endorphin is relatively specific are, respectively, *mu*, *kappa*, and *delta*. All endorphins and their receptors occur in many CNS regions as well as in other areas of the body, including the enteric nervous system. Morphine most closely mimics the endomorphins and binds most selectively to the *mu* receptors.

In addition to the natural opioids, synthetic opioids such as heroin affect *mu* receptors. Heroin, shown at right in Figure 6-10, is synthesized from morphine. It is more fat-soluble than morphine and penetrates the blood–brain barrier more quickly, allowing it to produce very rapid but shorter-acting pain relief. Heroin is a legal drug in some countries but is illegal in others, including the United States. Notwithstanding, in some parts of the country, heroin use is on the rise.

Among the synthetic opioids prescribed for clinical use in pain management are hydromorphone, levorphanol, oxymorphone, methadone, meperidine, oxycodone, and fentanyl. All opioids are potently addictive, and abuse of prescription opioids is growing more common. Opioids are also illegally modified, manufactured, and distributed. People who use opioids for relief of chronic pain and take them when they are not in pain can become addicted; some obtain multiple prescriptions and sell them illicitly.

Many drugs, including *nalorphine* (Lethidrone, Nalline) and *naloxone* (Narcan, Nalone), act as antagonists at opioid receptors. These drugs are **competitive inhibitors**: they compete with opioids for neuronal receptors. Because they can enter the brain quickly, they rapidly block the actions of morphine and so are essential aids in treating morphine overdoses.

Peptides, including the endorphins illustrated in Figure 5-13, are molecular amino acid chains connected by peptide bonds. Table 5-2 lists the families of peptide neurotransmitters.

bipolar disorder Mood disorder characterized by periods of depression alternating with normal periods and periods of intense excitation, or mania.

mood stabilizer Drug for treating bipolar disorder; mutes the intensity of one pole of the disorder, thus making the other pole less likely to recur.

opioid analgesic Drug such as morphine, with sleep-inducing (narcotic) and pain-relieving (analgesic) properties; originally called narcotic analgesic.

endorphin Opioid peptide that acts as a neurotransmitter and may be associated with feelings of pain or pleasure; mimicked by opioid drugs such as morphine, heroin, opium, and codeine.

competitive inhibitor Drug, such as nalorphine and naloxone, that acts quickly to block opioid action by competing with the opioid for binding sites; used to treat opioid addiction.

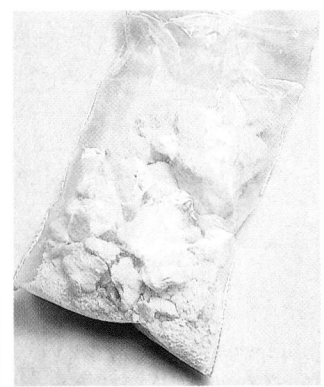

Eye Ubiquitous/Corbis

Science Source

Bonnie Kamin/PhotoEdit

FIGURE 6-10 Potent Poppy Opium is obtained from the seeds of the opium poppy (left). Morphine (center) is extracted from opium, and heroin (right) is in turn synthesized from morphine.

Feeling and treating pain are topics in Section 11-4. Focus 12-1 reports that emotional pain activates the same neural areas as physical pain.

Many people addicted to opioids carry a competitive inhibitor as a treatment for overdosing. Because they can also be long-acting, competitive inhibitors can be used to treat opioid addiction after the addicted person has recovered from withdrawal symptoms.

Researchers have extensively studied whether opioid peptides produced in the brain can be used as drugs to relieve pain without morphine's addictive effects. The answer so far is mixed, and one of the objectives of pain research, producing an analgesic that does not produce addiction, may be difficult to realize.

Opioid drugs, such as heroin, are addictive and are abused worldwide. The hypodermic needle was developed in 1853 and used in the American Civil War for the intravenous injection of morphine for pain treatment. This practice is said to have produced 400,000 cases of the "Soldier's Disease," morphine addiction. Morphine has many routes of administration, but intravenous injection is preferred because it produces a euphoria described as a rush. Morphine does not readily cross the blood–brain barrier, but heroin does and is even more likely to produce a rush.

If opioids are used repeatedly, they produce tolerance such that within a few weeks the effective dose may increase tenfold. Thereafter, many desired effects with respect to both pain and addiction no longer occur. An addicted person cannot simply stop using the drug: a severe sickness called withdrawal results if drug use is abruptly stopped.

Because morphine results in both tolerance and sensitization, the morphine user is always flirting with the possibility of overdosing. The unreliability of appropriate information on the purity of street forms of morphine contributes to the risk. A lack of sterile needles for injections also leaves the morphine user at risk for many other diseases, including AIDS (acquired immunodeficiency syndrome) and hepatitis.

Opioid ingestion produces wide-ranging physiological changes in addition to pain relief, including relaxation and sleep, euphoria, and constipation. Other effects include respiratory depression, decreased blood pressure, pupil constriction, hypothermia, drying of secretions (e.g., dry mouth), reduced sex drive, and flushed, warm skin. Withdrawal is characterized by symptoms that are physiologically and behaviorally opposite those produced by the drug. A major part of the addiction syndrome, then, is the drive to prevent withdrawal symptoms.

Group V: Psychotropics

Psychotropic drugs are stimulants that mainly affect mental activity, motor activity, arousal, perception, and mood. Behavioral stimulants affect motor activity and mood. Psychedelic and hallucinogenic stimulants affect perception and produce hallucinations. General stimulants mainly affect mood.

Behavioral Stimulants

Behavioral stimulants increase motor behavior as well as elevating mood and alertness. Rapid administration of behavioral stimulants is most likely to be associated with addiction. As shown in Figure 6-1, the quicker a drug reaches its target—in this case, the brain—the quicker it takes effect. Further, with each obstacle eliminated en route to the brain, drug dosage can be reduced by a factor of 10, making it cheaper per dose. Two behavioral stimulants are amphetamine and cocaine.

Section 5-1 describes experiments Otto Loewi performed to identify epinephrine, or adrenaline. Section 7-7 details symptoms and outcomes of ADHD and the search for an animal model of the disease.

Amphetamine is a synthetic compound. It was discovered in attempts to synthesize the CNS neurotransmitter epinephrine, which also acts as a hormone to mobilize the body for fight or flight in times of stress (see Figure 6-20). Both amphetamine and cocaine are dopamine agonists that act first by blocking the dopamine reuptake transporter. Interfering with the reuptake mechanism leaves more dopamine available in the synaptic cleft. Amphetamine also stimulates dopamine release from presynaptic membranes. Both mechanisms increase the amount of dopamine available in synapses to stimulate dopamine receptors. As noted in Focus 6-1, amphetamine-based drugs are widely prescribed to treat ADHD.

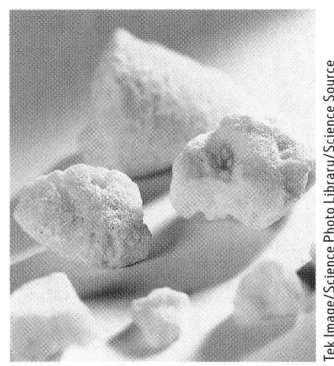

FIGURE 6-11 Behavioral Stimulant Cocaine (left) is obtained from the leaves of the coca plant (center). Crack cocaine (right) is chemically altered to form rocks that vaporize when heated at low temperatures.

One form of amphetamine was first used as an asthma treatment: Benzedrine was sold in inhalers as a nonprescription drug through the 1940s. Soon people discovered that they could open the container and ingest its contents to obtain an energizing effect. Amphetamine was widely used in World War II—and is still used today to help troops and pilots stay alert, increase confidence and aggression, and boost morale—and also was used then to improve wartime workers' productivity. Today, amphetamine is also used as a weight loss aid. Many over-the-counter compounds marketed as stimulants or weight loss aids have amphetaminelike pharmacological actions.

An illegal amphetamine derivative, methamphetamine (also known as meth, speed, crank, smoke, or crystal ice) continues in widespread use. Lifetime prevalence of methamphetamine use in the U.S. population, once estimated to be as high as 8 percent (Durell et al., 2008), is related to its ease of manufacture in illicit laboratories and to its potency, thus making it a relatively inexpensive, yet potentially devastating, drug.

Cocaine is a powder extracted from the Peruvian coca shrub, both shown in **Figure 6-11**. The indigenous people of Peru have chewed coca leaves through the generations to increase their stamina in the harsh environment and high elevations where they live. Refined cocaine powder can either be sniffed (snorted) or injected. Cocaine users who do not like to inject cocaine intravenously or cannot afford it in powdered form sniff or smoke rocks, or crack, a potent, highly concentrated form shown at right in Figure 6-11. Crack is chemically altered so that it vaporizes at low temperatures, and the vapors are inhaled.

Sigmund Freud (1974) popularized cocaine in the late 1800s as an antidepressant. It was once widely used in soft drinks and wine mixtures promoted as invigorating tonics. It is the origin of the trade name of Coca-Cola, which once contained cocaine (**Figure 6-12**). Its addictive properties soon became apparent, however.

Freud also recommended that cocaine be used as a local anesthetic. Cocaine did prove valuable for this purpose, and many derivatives, such as xylocaine (often called Novocain), are used today. These local anesthetic agents reduce a cell's permeability to sodium ions and so reduce nerve conduction.

Psychedelic and Hallucinogenic Stimulants

Psychedelic drugs alter sensory perception and cognitive processes and can produce hallucinations. We categorize the major groups of psychedelics by their actions on specific neurotransmitters, here and in Table 6-1 on page 181.

ACETYLCHOLINE PSYCHEDELICS These drugs either block (atropine) or facilitate (nicotine) transmission at ACh synapses.

ANANDAMIDE PSYCHEDELICS Results from numerous lines of research suggest that the endogenous neurotransmitter anandamide enhances forgetting. Anandamide prevents the brain's memory systems from being overwhelmed by all the information to which we are exposed each day. Tetrahydrocannabinol (THC) is one of 84 cannabinoids and the main psychoactive constituent in marijuana, obtained from the hemp plant *Cannabis sativa*, shown

FIGURE 6-12 Warning Label Cocaine was once an ingredient in such invigorating beverages as Coca-Cola.

amphetamine Drug that releases the neurotransmitter dopamine into its synapse and like cocaine, blocks dopamine reuptake.

psychedelic drug Drug that can alter sensation and perception; examples are lysergic acid diethylamide (LSD), mescaline, and psilocybin.

Anandamide (from Sanskrit, meaning *joy* or *bliss*) acts on a receptor that naturally inhibits adenyl cyclase, part of a second messenger system active in sensitization (see Section 5-4).

FIGURE 6-13 *Cannabis sativa* The hemp plant, an annual herb, grows over a wide range of altitudes, climates, and soils. Hemp has myriad uses, including in manufacturing rope, cloth, and paper.

Glutamate is the main excitatory neurotransmitter in the forebrain and cerebellum. Section 14-4 describes how Glu and NMDA receptors affect long-term learning.

in **Figure 6-13.** THC alters mood primarily by interacting with the anandamide CB1 receptor found on neurons, and it also binds with the anandamide CB2 receptors found on glial cells and in other body tissues. THC has low toxicity but may have a detrimental effect on memory as well as a positive effect on mental overload.

Evidence points to the usefulness of THC, or other cannabinoids, as a therapeutic agent for a number of disorders. It relieves nausea and emesis (vomiting) in patients undergoing cancer chemotherapy who are not helped by other treatments and stimulates the appetite in AIDS patients with anorexia–cachexia (wasting) syndrome. THC has been found helpful for treating chronic pain through mechanisms that appear to be different from those of the opioids. It has also proved useful for treating glaucoma (increased pressure in the eye), for spastic disorders such as multiple sclerosis, for disorders associated with spinal cord injury, and for epilepsy. THC may also have some neuroprotective properties (see Section 6-4). Many people self-prescribe THC for a wide range of ailments, including PTSD (Roitman et al., 2014).

Synthetic and derived forms of THC have been developed in part to circumvent legal restrictions on its use. Nevertheless, legal restrictions against THC use hamper investigations into its useful medicinal effects.

GLUTAMATE PSYCHEDELICS PCP (angel dust) and ketamine (Special K) can produce hallucinations and out-of-body experiences. Both drugs, formerly used as anesthetics (see Table 6-1, Group I), exert part of their action by blocking glutamate NMDA receptors involved in learning. Other NMDA receptor antagonists include dextromethorphan and nitrous oxide (NO).

Although PCP's primary psychoactive effects last for a few hours, its total elimination rate from the body can extend its action for 8 days or longer. That psychotropic drugs, including PCP and ketamine, can produce schizophrenialike symptoms, including hallucinations and out-of -body experiences, suggests the involvement of excitatory glutamate synapses in schizophrenia.

NOREPINEPHRINE PSYCHEDELICS Mescaline, obtained from the peyote cactus, is legal in the United States for use by Native Americans for religious practices. Mescaline produces pronounced psychic alterations, including a sense of spatial boundlessness and visual hallucinations. The effects of a single dose last up to 10 hours.

SEROTONIN PSYCHEDELICS The synthetic drug lysergic acid diethylamide (LSD) and naturally occurring psilocybin (obtained from various mushrooms) stimulate some 5-HT receptors and block the activity of other serotonergic neurons through 5-HT autoreceptors.

Serotonin psychedelics may stimulate other transmitter systems, including norepinephrine receptors. MDMA (Ecstasy), one of several synthetic amphetamine derivatives, induces a sense of well-being and disembodiment as well as visual distortions. Repeated MDMA use is associated with sleep, mood, and anxiety disorders and may also be associated with memory and attention deficits. Drug models of schizophrenia include LSD, which produces hallucinations and is a serotonin agonist that acts at the 5-HT_2 receptor. Again, that hallucinations are a symptom of schizophrenia suggests that excess 5-HT action can be involved.

General Stimulants

General stimulants cause an overall increase in cells' metabolic activity. Caffeine, a widely used stimulant, inhibits an enzyme that ordinarily breaks down the second messenger cyclic adenosine monophosphate (cAMP). The resulting increase in cAMP leads to increased glucose production, making more energy available and allowing higher rates of cellular activity.

Caffeine boosts cAMP concentrations, action potentials last longer than usual, and we get the coffee jitters.

A cup of coffee contains about 100 mg of caffeine; many common soft drinks contain almost as much; and some energy drinks pack as much as 500 mg. You may be using more caffeine than you realize. Excessive levels can lead to the jitters. Regular caffeine users who quit may have headaches, irritability, and other withdrawal symptoms.

6-2 REVIEW

Grouping Psychoactive Drugs

Before you continue, check your understanding.

1. Because of their diverse actions, it is useful to group drugs in terms of their most pronounced _____ or _____ effects.

2. Antianxiety and sedative-hypnotic drugs affect the _____ receptor, which through _____ influx hyperpolarizes neurons.

3. Among the antidepressant drug types, _____ increase the amount of 5-HT available in the presynaptic terminal, while _____ block 5-HT reuptake at the synapse.

4. Opioids mimic the action of _____ by binding to the same receptors.

5. Amphetamine stimulates _____ and cocaine blocks _____ at the _____ synapse.

6. On which neurotransmitters do drugs that produce psychotropic effects act?

Answers appear at the back of the book.

For additional study tools, visit 🧠 **LaunchPad:**
www.macmillanhighered.com/launchpad/kolb5e

6-3 Factors Influencing Individual Responses to Drugs

Many behaviors trigger predictable results. You strike the same piano key repeatedly and hear the same note each time. You flick a light switch today, and the bulb glows exactly as it did yesterday. This cause-and-effect consistency does not extend to the effects of psychoactive drugs. Individuals respond to drugs in remarkably different ways at different times.

Behavior on Drugs

Ellen is a healthy, attractive, intelligent 19-year-old university freshman who knows the risks of unprotected sexual intercourse. She learned about HIV and other sexually transmitted diseases (STDs) in her high school health class. A seminar about the dangers of unprotected sexual intercourse was part of her college orientation: seniors provided the freshmen in her residence free condoms and safe sex literature. Ellen and her former boyfriend were always careful to use latex condoms during intercourse.

At a homecoming party in her residence hall, Ellen has a great time, drinking and dancing with her friends and meeting new people. She is particularly taken with Brad, a sophomore at her college, and the two of them decide to go back to her room to order a pizza. One thing leads to another, and Ellen and Brad have sexual intercourse without using a condom. The next morning, Ellen wakes up, dismayed and surprised at her behavior and concerned that she may be pregnant or may have contracted an STD. She is terrified that she may have AIDS (MacDonald et al., 2000).

What happened to Ellen? What is it about drugs, especially alcohol, that make people sometimes do things they would not ordinarily do? Alcohol links to many harmful behaviors that are costly both to individuals and to society. These harmful behaviors include not only unprotected sexual activity but also driving while intoxicated, date rape, spousal or child abuse and other aggressive behaviors, and crime. Among the explanations for alcohol's effects are disinhibition, learning, and behavioral myopia.

Disinhibition and Impulse Control

An early and still widely held explanation of alcohol's effects is **disinhibition theory**. It holds that alcohol has a selective depressant effect on the cortical brain region that controls

disinhibition theory Explanation holding that alcohol has a selective depressant effect on the brain's frontal cortex, which controls judgment, while sparing subcortical structures responsible for more instinctual behaviors, such as desire.

judgment while sparing subcortical structures, those responsible for more instinctual behaviors, such as desire. Stated differently, alcohol depresses learned inhibitions based on reasoning and judgment while releasing the "beast" within.

A variation of disinhibition theory argues that the frontal lobes check impulsive behavior. According to this idea, impulse control is impaired after drinking alcohol because of a higher relative sensitivity of the frontal lobes to alcohol. A person may then engage in risky behavior (Hardee et al., 2014).

Proponents of these theories often excuse alcohol-related behavior, saying for example, "She was too drunk to know better" or "The boys had a few too many and got carried away." Do disinhibition and impulse control explain Ellen's behavior? Not entirely. Ellen had used alcohol in the past and managed to practice safe sex despite its effects. Neither theory explains why her behavior was different on this occasion. If alcohol is a disinhibitor, why is it not always so?

Learning

Craig MacAndrew and Robert Edgerton (1969) questioned disinhibition theory along just these lines in their book *Drunken Comportment*. They cite many instances in which behavior under the influence of alcohol changes from one context to another. People who engage in polite social activity at home when consuming alcohol may become unruly and aggressive when drinking in a bar.

Even behavior at the bar may be inconsistent. Take Joe, for example. While drinking one night at a bar, he acts obnoxious and gets into a fight. On another occasion, he is charming and witty, even preventing a fight between two friends; on a third occasion, he becomes depressed and worries about his problems. MacAndrew and Edgerton also cite examples of cultures in which people are disinhibited when sober only to become inhibited after consuming alcohol and cultures in which people are inhibited when sober and become more inhibited when drinking. What explains all these differences in alcohol's effects?

MacAndrew and Edgerton suggested that behavior under the effects of alcohol is learned. Learned behavior is specific to culture, group, and setting and can in part explain Ellen's decision to sleep with Brad. Where alcohol is used to facilitate social interactions, behavior while intoxicated is a time-out from more conservative rules regarding dating.

Behavioral Myopia

But Ellen's lapse in judgment regarding safe sex is more difficult to explain by learning theory. Ellen had never practiced unsafe sex before and had never made it a part of her time-out social activities. So why did she engage in it with Brad?

A different explanation for alcohol-related lapses in judgment, **behavioral myopia** (nearsightedness), is the tendency for people under the influence of (in this case) alcohol to respond to a restricted set of immediate and prominent cues while ignoring more remote cues and possible consequences. Immediate and prominent cues are very strong and obvious and close at hand (Griffin et al., 2010).

In an altercation, the person with behavioral myopia will be quicker than usual to throw a punch, because the fight cue is so strong and immediate. At a raucous party, the myopic drinker will be more eager than usual to join in, because the immediate cue of boisterous fun dominates his or her view. Once Ellen and Brad arrived at Ellen's room, the sexual cues at the moment were far more immediate than concerns about long-term safety. As a result, Ellen responded to those immediate cues and behaved atypically.

Oliver Furrer/Brand X/Corbis

People who enjoy high-risk adventure may be genetically predisposed to experiment with drugs, but people with no interest in risk taking are just as likely to use drugs. Section 6-4 discusses genetic influences on drug taking.

Behavioral myopia can explain many lapses in judgment that lead to risky behavior—aggression, date rape, and reckless driving while intoxicated. Individuals who have been drinking may also have poor insight into their level of intoxication: they may assume that they are less impaired than they actually are (Sevincer and Oettingen, 2014).

Addiction and Dependence

B. G. started smoking when she was 13 years old. She has quit many times without success. After successfully abstaining from cigarettes by using a nicotine patch for more than 6 months, B. G. began smoking again. Because the university where she works has a no smoking policy, she has to leave campus and stand across the street to smoke. Her voice has developed a rasping sound, and she has an almost chronic "cold." She says that she used to enjoy smoking but does not any more. Concern about quitting dominates her thoughts.

B. G. has a drug problem. She is one of the 25 percent or so of North Americans who smoke. Like B. G., most smokers realize that it is a health hazard, have experienced unpleasant side effects from it, and have attempted to quit but cannot. B. G. is exceptional only in her white-collar occupation. Today, most smokers are found in blue-collar occupations rather than among professional workers. And the use of electronic cigarettes (e-cigarettes) by young people is on the rise (Czoli et al., 2015). The health hazards posed by nicotine delivery via e-cigarettes are unknown.

Substance abuse is a pattern of drug use in which people rely on a drug chronically and excessively, allowing it to occupy a central place in their life. In a more advanced state of *substance dependence*, popularly known as **addiction**, people are physically dependent on a drug in addition to abusing it. They have developed tolerance for the drug and so require increased doses to obtain the desired effect.

Drug addicts may also experience unpleasant, sometimes dangerous physical **withdrawal symptoms** if they suddenly stop taking the abused drug. Symptoms can include muscle aches and cramps, anxiety attacks, sweating, nausea, and even, for some drugs, convulsions and death. Symptoms of alcohol or morphine withdrawal can begin within hours of the last dose and tend to intensify over several days before they subside.

Although B. G. abuses nicotine, she is not physically dependent on it. She smokes approximately the same number of cigarettes each day (she has not developed tolerance to nicotine), and she does not get sick if she is deprived of cigarettes (does not have severe withdrawal symptoms but does display irritability, anxiety, increased appetite, and insomnia). B. G. illustrates that the power of psychological dependence can be as influential as the power of physical dependence.

Many abused or addictive drugs—including sedative-hypnotics, antianxiety agents, opioids, and stimulants—have a common property: they produce **psychomotor activation** in some part of their dose range. That is, at certain levels of consumption, these drugs make the user feel energetic and in control. This common effect has led to the hypothesis that all abused drugs may act on the same target in the brain: dopamine in the mesolimbic pathways of the dopaminergic activating system. Drugs of abuse increase mesolimbic dopamine activity, either directly or indirectly, and drugs that blunt abuse and addiction decrease mesolimbic dopamine activity.

Sex Differences in Addiction

Vast differences in individual responses to drugs are due to differences in age, body size, metabolism, and sensitivity to a particular substance. Larger people, for instance, are generally less sensitive to a drug than smaller people are: their greater volume of body fluids dilutes drugs more. Old people may be twice as sensitive to drugs as young people are. The elderly often have less effective barriers to drug absorption as well as less effective processes for metabolizing and eliminating drugs from their body. Individuals also respond to drugs in different ways at different times.

behavioral myopia "Nearsighted" behavior displayed under the influence of alcohol: local and immediate cues become prominent; remote cues and consequences are ignored.

substance abuse is a pattern of drug use in which people rely on a drug chronically and excessively, allowing it to occupy a central place in their life.

addiction Desire for a drug; manifested by frequent use, leading to physical dependence in addition to abuse; often associated with tolerance and unpleasant, sometimes dangerous, withdrawal symptoms on cessation. Per the DSM-5, called substance use disorder.

withdrawal symptom Physical and psychological behavior displayed by an addict when drug use ends.

psychomotor activation Increased behavioral and cognitive activity: at certain levels of consumption, the drug user feels energetic and in control.

To view the brain areas nicotine affects most, see Figure 12-30.

Females are about twice as sensitive to drugs as are males, on average, owing in part to their smaller size but also to hormonal differences. The long-held general assumption that human males are more likely to abuse drugs than are human females led investigators to neglect researching drug use and abuse in human females. But the results of recent research support quite the opposite view: females are less likely to become addicted to some drugs than are males, but females are catching up and for some drugs are surpassing males in the incidence of addiction.

Although the general pattern of drug use is similar in males and females, the sex differences are striking (Becker and Hu, 2008). Females are more likely than males to abuse nicotine, alcohol, cocaine, amphetamine, opioids, cannabinoids, caffeine, and PCP. Females begin to regularly self-administer licit and illicit drugs of abuse at lower doses than do males; females' use escalates more rapidly to addiction; and females are at greater risk for relapse after abstinence.

(6-3) **REVIEW**

Factors Influencing Individual Responses to Drugs

Before you continue, check your understanding.

1. Of the three explanations for alcohol's effects on behavior, _____ and _____ are less explicative than _____.

2. _____ is a condition in which people rely on drugs chronically and to excess, whereas _____ is a condition in which people are physically dependent on a drug as well.

3. The evidence that many abused or addictive drugs produce _____, which makes the user feel energetic and in control, suggests that activation in the _____ plays a role in drug abuse and addiction.

4. Common wisdom is incorrect in suggesting that _____ are less likely to abuse drugs than _____ are.

5. Why can alcohol-related behavior vary widely in a single individual from time to time?

Answers appear at the back of the book.

For additional study tools, visit 🔊 LaunchPad:
www.macmillanhighered.com/launchpad/kolb5e

(6-4) Explaining and Treating Drug Abuse

Why do people become addicted to drugs? Early explanations centered on pleasure and dependence: habitual drug users initially feel pleasure but then endure psychological and physiological withdrawal symptoms as the drug wears off. They feel anxious, insecure, or just plain sick without the drug, so they take it again to alleviate those symptoms. In this way, they get hooked on the drug.

Although this dependency hypothesis may account for part of drug-taking behavior, it has shortcomings as a general explanation. For example, an addict may abstain from a drug for months, long after any withdrawal symptoms have abated, yet still be drawn back to using it. In addition, some psychoactive drugs, such as the tricyclic antidepressants, produce withdrawal symptoms when discontinued, but these drugs are not abused.

Wanting-and-Liking Theory

To account for all the facts about drug abuse and addiction, Terry Robinson and Kent Berridge (2008) proposed the incentive sensitization theory, also called the **wanting-and-liking theory** because wanting and liking are produced by different brain systems.

---

wanting-and-liking theory Explanation holding that when a drug is associated with certain cues, the cues themselves elicit desire for the drug; also called incentive sensitization theory.

Their wanting is craving, whereas liking is the pleasure the drug produces. With repeated use, tolerance for liking develops, and the expression of liking (pleasure) decreases as a consequence (**Figure 6-14**). In contrast, the system that mediates wanting sensitizes, and craving increases.

The first step on the proposed road to drug dependence is the initial experience, when the drug affects a neural system associated with pleasure. At this stage, the user may like the substance—including liking to take it within a given social context. With repeated use, liking the drug may decline from its initial level. At this stage, the user may also begin to show tolerance to the drug's effects and so may begin to increase the dosage to increase liking.

With each use, the drug taker increasingly associates the cues related to drug use—be it a hypodermic needle, the room in which the drug is taken, or the people with whom the drug is taken—with the drug-taking experience. The user makes this association because the drug enhances classically conditioned cues associated with drug taking. Eventually, these cues come to possess incentive salience: they induce wanting, or craving, the drug-taking experience.

The neural basis of addiction is proposed to involve multiple brain systems. The decision to take a drug is made in the prefrontal cortex, an area that participates in most daily decisions. When a drug is taken, it activates opioid systems in the brainstem that are generally related to pleasurable experiences. And wanting drugs may spring from activity in the mesolimbic pathways of the dopaminergic activating system.

In these mesolimbic pathways, diagrammed in **Figure 6-15**, the axons of dopamine neurons in the midbrain project to structures in the basal ganglia, to the frontal cortex, and to the limbic system. When drug takers encounter cues associated with drug taking, the mesolimbic system becomes active, releasing dopamine. Dopamine release is the neural correlate of wanting.

Another brain system may be responsible for conditioning drug-related cues to drug taking. Barry Everitt (2014) proposes that the repeated pairing of drug-related cues to drug taking forms neural associations, or learning, in the dorsal striatum, a region in the basal ganglia consisting of the caudate nucleus and putamen. As the user repeatedly takes the drug, voluntary control gives way to unconscious processes—a habit. The result: drug users lose control of decisions related to drug taking, and the wanting—the voluntary control over drug taking—gives way to the craving of addiction.

Multiple findings align with the wanting-and-liking explanation of drug addiction. Ample evidence confirms that abused drugs and the context in which they are taken initially has a pleasurable effect and that habitual users continue using their drug of choice, even when taking it no longer produces any pleasure. Heroin addicts sometimes report that they are miserable: their lives are in ruins, and the drug is not even pleasurable anymore. But they still want it. What's more, desire for the drug often is greatest just when the addicted person is maximally high, not during withdrawal. Finally, cues associated with drug taking—the social situation, the sight of the drug, and drug paraphernalia—strongly influence decisions to take, or continue taking, a drug.

Notwithstanding support for a dopamine basis for addiction, recent research suggests more than one type of addiction. Some rats become readily conditioned to cues associated with reinforcement, for example a bar that delivers a reward when pressed. Other animals ignore the bar's incentive salience but are attracted to the location where they receive reinforcement. Animals that display the former behavior are termed sign trackers and the other group, goal trackers. Sign trackers exposed to addictive drugs appear to attribute incentive salience to drug-associated cues. Their drug wanting is dependent upon the brain's dopamine systems.

Peter Dokus/Stone

FIGURE 6-14 Wanting-and-Liking Theory With repeated drug use, wanting a drug and liking the drug progress in opposite directions. Wanting (craving) is associated with drug cues.

In classical (Pavlovian) conditioning, learning to associate a formerly neutral stimulus (the sound of a bell) with a stimulus (food) elicits an involuntary response (salivation).

When a rat is placed in an environment where it anticipates a favored food or sex, investigators record dopamine increases in the striatum (see Section 7-5).

FIGURE 6-15 Mesolimbic Dopamine Pathways Axons of neurons in the midbrain ventral tegmentum project to the basal ganglia, prefrontal cortex, and hippocampus.

Prefrontal cortex

Basal ganglia

Hippocampus (part of limbic system)

Ventral tegmental area of midbrain

196

Goal trackers may also become addicted, possibly via different neural systems. Such findings imply at least two types of addiction (Yager et al., 2015).

We can extend wanting-and-liking theory to many life situations. Cues related to sexual activity, food, and even sports can induce wanting, sometimes in the absence of liking. We frequently eat when prompted by the cue of other people eating, even though we may not be hungry and derive little pleasure from eating at that time. The similarities between exaggerating normal behaviors and drug addiction suggest that they depend on the same learning and brain mechanisms. For this reason, any addiction is extremely difficult to treat.

Why Doesn't Everyone Abuse Drugs?

Observing that some people are more prone than others to drug abuse and dependence, scientists have investigated and found three lines of evidence suggesting a genetic contribution to differences in drug use. First, if one identical twin (same genotype) abuses alcohol, the other twin is more likely to abuse it than if the twins are fraternal (have only some genes in common). Second, people adopted shortly after birth are more likely to abuse alcohol if their biological parents were alcoholic, even though they have had almost no contact with those parents. Third, although most animals do not care for alcohol, selective breeding of mice, rats, and monkeys can produce strains that consume large quantities of it.

Each line of evidence presents problems, however. Perhaps identical twins show greater concordance rates (incidence of similar behavioral traits) for alcohol abuse because their environments are more similar than those of fraternal twins. And perhaps the link between alcoholism in adoptees and their biological parents has to do with nervous system changes due to prenatal exposure to the drug. Finally, the fact that animals can be selectively bred for alcohol consumption does not mean that all human alcoholics have a similar genetic makeup. The evidence for a genetic basis of alcohol abuse will become compelling only when a gene or set of genes related to alcoholism is found.

Epigenetics offers another explanation of susceptibility to addiction (Hillemacher et al., 2015). Addictive drugs may reduce the transcriptional ability of genes related to voluntary control and increase the transcriptional ability of other genes related to behaviors susceptible to addiction. Epigenetic changes in an individual's gene expression may be relatively permanent and can be passed along, perhaps through the next few generations. For these reasons, epigenetics can account both for the enduring behaviors that support addiction and for the tendency of drug addiction to be inherited.

Less-than-perfect concordance rates between identical twins for diseases ranging from schizophrenia to asthma point to epigenetic inheritance of behaviors by the next generation (see Section 3-3).

Treating Drug Abuse

Figure 6-16 charts the relative incidence of drug use in the United States—people aged 12 and older who reported using at least one psychoactive drug during the year preceding in a national survey conducted by the U.S. Department of Health and Human Services in 2013. The two most-used drugs, alcohol and tobacco, are legal. The drugs that carry the harshest penalties, cocaine and heroin, are used by far fewer people. But criminalizing drugs clearly is not a solution to drug use or abuse, as illustrated by the widespread use of marijuana, the third most used drug on the chart. In response to its widespread use, several states have legalized marijuana to some degree, but it remains illegal under federal law.

Treating drug abuse is difficult in part because legal proscriptions are irrational. In the United States, the Harrison Narcotics Act of 1914 made heroin and a variety of other drugs illegal and made the treatment of addicted people by physicians in their private offices illegal. The Drug Addiction Treatment Act of 2000 partly reversed this prohibition, allowing the treatment of patients but with a number of restrictions. In addition, legal consequences attending drug use vary greatly with the drug and the jurisdiction.

From a health standpoint, tobacco has much higher proven health risks than does marijuana. Moderate use of alcohol is likely benign. Moderate use of opioids is likely impossible. Social coercion is useful in reducing tobacco use: witness the marked decline in smoking as a result of prohibitions against smoking in public places. Medical intervention is necessary to provide methadone and other drug treatment of opioid abusers.

The numerous approaches to treating drug abuse vary, depending on the drug. Many online sites support self-help groups and professional groups that address the treatment of various drug addictions. Importantly, because addiction is influenced by unconscious conditioning to drug-related cues and by a variety of brain changes, relapse remains an enduring risk for people who have apparently kicked their habit.

Neuroscience research will continue to lead to a better understanding of the neural basis of drug use and to better treatment. The best approach to any drug treatment likely recognizes that addiction is a lifelong problem for most people. Thus, drug addiction must be treated in the same way as chronic behavioral addictions and medical problems—analogous to recognizing that controlling weight with appropriate diet and exercise is a lifelong struggle for many people.

Can Drugs Cause Brain Damage?

Many natural substances can act as neurotoxins; **Table 6-2** lists some of them. Ongoing investigations of the neurotoxicity of these substances and other drugs in animal models show that many cause brain damage. Whether drugs of abuse cause brain damage in humans—especially whether they can do so at the doses that humans take—is more difficult to determine. It is difficult to sort out other life experiences from drug taking. It is also difficult to obtain the brains of drug users for examination at autopsy. Nevertheless, there is evidence that the developing brain can be particularly sensitive to drug effects, especially in adolescence, a time when drug experimentation is common (Teixeira-Gomes, 2015).

In the late 1960s, many reports linked monosodium glutamate, MSG, a salty-tasting, flavor-enhancing food additive, to headaches in some people. In investigating this effect, scientists placed large doses of MSG on cultured neurons, which died. Subsequently, they injected MSG into the brains of experimental animals, where it also killed neurons.

This line of research led to the discovery that many glutamatelike substances, including domoic acid and kainic acid, both toxins in seaweed, and ibotenic acid, which is found in some poisonous mushrooms, similarly kill neurons (**Figure 6-17**). Some drugs, such as PCP and ketamine, also act as glutamate agonists, leaving open the possibility that at high doses they too can cause neuronal death.

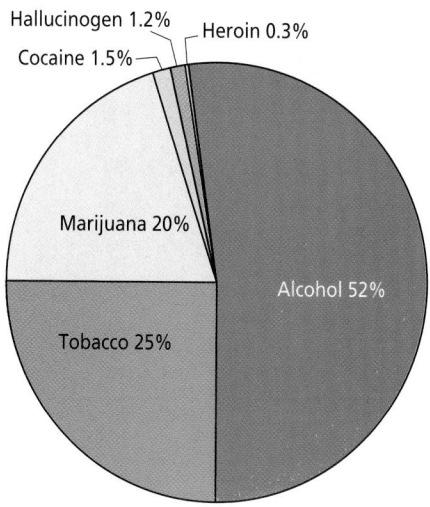

FIGURE 6-16 Drug Use in the United States, 2013 Results from an annual national survey of Americans aged 12 and older who reported using at least one psychoactive drug during the past year. Percentages for alcohol, tobacco, and marijuana are rounded to the nearest whole number. Data from the *2013 National Survey on Drug Use and Health: Summary of National Findings*, U.S. Department of Health and Human Services, Substance Abuse and Mental Health Services Administration, Center for Behavioral Health Statistics and Quality. Available for download at www.hhs.gov.

FIGURE 6-17 Neurotoxicity Domoic acid damage in this rat's hippocampus and to a lesser extent in many other brain regions, indicated by the darkest coloring. Domoic acid, a Glu antagonist, is the causative agent in amnesic shellfish poisoning, which can result in permanent short-term memory loss, brain damage, and in severe cases, death.

TABLE 6-2 Some Neurotoxins, Their Sources, and Their Actions

Substance	Origin	Action
Tetrodotoxin	Puffer fish	Blocks membrane permeability to Na⁺
Magnesium	Natural element	Blocks Ca^{2+} channels
Reserpine	Tree	Destroys storage granules
Colchicine	Crocus plant	Blocks microtubules
Caffeine	Coffee bean	Blocks adenosine receptors, blocks Ca^{2+} channels
Spider venom	Black widow spider	Stimulates ACh release
Botulin	Spoiled food	Blocks ACh release
Curare	Berry	Blocks ACh receptors
Rabies virus	Infected animal	Blocks ACh receptors
Ibotenic acid	Mushroom	Similar to domoic acid, mimics glutamate
Strychnine	Plant	Blocks glycine
Apamin	Bees and wasps	Blocks Ca^{2+} channels

Domoic acid produces hippocampal damage, as shown by a dark silver stain that highlights degeneration.

Hippocampus

Micrograph from NeuroScience Associates

Monosodium glutamate   Glutamate
(MSG)

Focus 5-4 reports the chilling case of heroin addicts who developed Parkinson disease after using synthetic heroin, owing to a contaminant (MPTP) in the drug.

Focus 7-3 explores the hypothesis that genetic vulnerability predisposes some adolescents to develop a psychosis when exposed to cannabis.

Glutamatelike drugs are toxic because they act on glutamate receptors. Glutamate receptor activation results in an influx of Ca^{2+} into the cell, which through second messengers activates a suicide gene leading to apoptosis (cell death). This discovery shows that a drug might be toxic not only because of its general effect on cell function but also as an agent that activates normal cell processes related to apoptosis.

We must add that there is no evidence that moderate consumption of MSG is harmful.

What about the many recreational drugs that affect the nervous system? Are any neurotoxic? Sorting out the effects of the drug itself from the effects of other factors related to taking the drug is a major problem. Chronic alcohol use, for instance, can be associated with damage to the thalamus and limbic system, producing severe memory disorders. Alcohol, however, does not directly cause this damage. Alcoholics typically obtain low amounts of thiamine (vitamin B_1) in their diet, and alcohol interferes with the intestine's absorption of thiamine. Thiamine plays a vital role in maintaining cell membrane structure.

Similarly, among the many reports of people who have a severe psychiatric disorder subsequent to abusing certain recreational drugs, in most cases determining whether the drug initiated the condition or aggravated an existing problem is difficult. Exactly determining whether the drug itself or some contaminant in it caused a harmful outcome also is difficult. With the increasing sensitivity of brain imaging studies, however, evidence is increasing that many drugs used recreationally can cause brain damage and cognitive impairments.

The strongest evidence comes from the study of the synthetic amphetaminelike drug MDMA, also called Ecstasy, and in pure powdered form, Molly (Büttner, 2011). Although MDMA is structurally related to amphetamine, it produces hallucinogenic effects and is called a hallucinogenic amphetamine. Findings from animal studies show that doses of MDMA approximating those taken by human users result in the degeneration of very fine serotonergic nerve terminals. In monkeys, significant terminal loss may be permanent, as shown in **Figure 6-18**.

Memory impairments and damage in MDMA users revealed by brain imaging may be a result of similar neuronal damage (Cowan et al., 2008). MDMA may also contain a contaminant, paramethoxymethamphetamine (PMMA). This notoriously toxic amphetamine is often called Dr. Death because the difference between a dose that causes behavioral effects and a dose that causes death is minuscule (Vevelstad et al., 2012). Contamination by unknown compounds can occur in any drug purchased on the street.

The psychoactive properties of cocaine are similar to those of amphetamine, and so cocaine also is suspect with respect to brain damage. Cocaine use is related to the blockage of cerebral blood flow and other changes in blood circulation. Brain imaging studies suggest that cocaine use can be toxic to neurons, because several brain regions are reduced in size in cocaine users (Liu et al., 2011).

Chronic marijuana use has been associated with psychotic attacks. Clinical Focus 6-4, Drug-Induced Psychosis, describes one. The marijuana plant contains at least 400 chemicals, 60 or more of which are structurally related to its active ingredient, tetrahydrocannabinol. Determining whether a psychotic attack is related to THC or to some other chemical in marijuana is almost impossible.

Whether or not THC can cause psychosis, there is no evidence that the disease is a result of brain damage. Indeed, beyond the therapeutic applications of TCH cited in Section 6-2, recent studies suggest that THC may have neuroprotective properties. It can aid brain healing after traumatic brain injury and slow the progression of diseases associated with brain degeneration, including Alzheimer disease and Huntington disease (Nguyen et al., 2014).

Drug-Induced Psychosis

At age 29, R. B. S. smoked marijuana chronically. For years, he had been selectively breeding a potent strain of marijuana in anticipation of the day when it would be legalized. R. B. S. made his living as a pilot, flying small freight aircraft into coastal communities in the Pacific Northwest.

One evening, R. B. S. had a sudden revelation: he was no longer in control of his life. Convinced that a small computer had been implanted in his brain when he was 7 years old and was manipulating his behavior, he confided in a close friend, who urged him to consult a doctor. R. B. S. insisted that he had undergone the surgery when he participated in an experiment at a local university. He also claimed that all the other children who participated in the experiment had been murdered.

The doctor told R. B. S. that the computer implantation was unlikely but called the psychology department at the university and got confirmation that children had in fact taken part in an experiment conducted years before. The records of the study had long since been destroyed. R. B. S. believed that this information completely vindicated his story. His delusional behavior persisted and eventually cost him his pilot's license.

R. B. S. seemed to compartmentalize the delusion. When asked why he could no longer fly, he intently recounted the story of the implant and the murders, asserting that its truth had cost him the medical certification needed for a license. Then he happily and appropriately discussed other topics.

R. B. S. had a mild focal psychosis: he was losing contact with reality. In some cases, this break is so severe and the capacity to respond to the environment so impaired and distorted that the person can no longer function. People in a state of psychosis may hallucinate, may have delusions, or may withdraw into a private world isolated from people and events around them.

A variety of drugs can produce psychosis, including LSD, amphetamine, cocaine, and, as shown by this case, marijuana. At low doses THC, the active ingredient in marijuana, has mild sedative-hypnotic effects similar to those of alcohol. At the high doses that R. B. S. used, THC can produce euphoria and hallucinations.

Marijuana comes from the leaves of the hemp plant, *Cannabis sativa*. Humans have used hemp for thousands of years to make rope, paper, cloth, and a host of other products. And marijuana has a number of beneficial medical effects. In the Pacific Northwest, marijuana is the largest agricultural crop and makes a larger contribution to the economy than does forestry. In some states marijuana can legally be purchased for personal use, and in many states its medical use is legal. Under federal law, however, it remains illegal everywhere in the United States.

R. B. S.'s heavy marijuana use certainly raises the suspicion that the drug had some influence on his delusional condition (Wilkinson et al., 2014). *Cannabis* use has been reported to moderately increase the risk of psychotic symptoms in young people and has a much stronger effect in those with a predisposition for psychosis, especially if potent strains are used (Di Forti et al., 2015). Although there is evidence that heavy marijuana use may be associated with alterations in brain development, it is unclear whether brain abnormalities are a result of marijuana use or a causal factor in its use (Lubman et al., 2015).

Employees fill prescriptions at a medical marijuana clinic in San Francisco. At this writing California is one of more than 20 states that have decriminalized the use of medical marijuana.

Jim Wilson/The New York Times/Redux

6-4 REVIEW

Explaining and Treating Drug Abuse

Before you continue, check your understanding.

1. The wanting-and-liking theory of addiction suggests that with repeated use, _____ of the drug decreases as a result of _____, while _____ increases as a result of _____.

2. At the neural level, the decision to take a drug is made in the brain's _____. Once taken, the drug activates opioid systems related to pleasurable experiences in the _____. Drug cravings may originate in the _____, and the repeated pairing of drug-related cues and drug taking forms neural associations in the _____ that loosen voluntary control over drug taking.

3. As an alternative to explanations of susceptibility to addiction based on genetic _____, _____ can account both for the enduring behaviors that support addiction and for the tendency of drug addiction to be inherited.

4. It is hard to determine whether recreational drugs cause brain damage in humans because it is difficult to distinguish the effects of _____ from the effects of _____.

5. Briefly describe the basis for a reasonable approach to treating drug addiction.

Answers appear at the back of the book.

For additional study tools, visit 🌀 **LaunchPad**:
www.macmillanhighered.com/launchpad/kolb5e

⬡6-5 Hormones

Berthold's experiment demonstrated that *hormones*—chemicals released by *endocrine glands* into the bloodstream—circulate to a body target and affect it. The endocrine glands operate under CNS and ANS influence (see Figure 2-30).

Intact rooster

Capon (rooster with gonads removed)

In 1849, European scientist A. A. Berthold removed a rooster's testes and found that it no longer crowed, nor did it engage in sexual or aggressive behavior. Berthold then reimplanted one testis in the rooster's body cavity. The rooster began crowing and displaying normal sexual and aggressive behavior again. The reimplanted testis did not establish any nerve connections, so Berthold concluded that it must release a chemical into the rooster's circulatory system that influenced the animal's behavior.

That chemical, we now know, is **testosterone,** the sex hormone secreted by the testes and responsible for the distinguishing characteristics of the male. The effect Berthold produced by reimplanting the rooster's testis mimics the effect of administering testosterone to a castrated rooster, or capon. The hormone is sufficient to make the capon behave like a rooster.

We now know that many hormones affect the sexual characteristics and reproductive behavior of animals, including us humans. Hormonal effects are not limited to sexual behavior but also influence eating and drinking, growth, stress responses, and other bodily functions. Hormones are secreted by glands in the body and by the brain. Interacting brain and body hormones form feedback loops that regulate their activity. Hormonal influences change across the life-span, influencing development and body and brain function (Nugent et al., 2012). In many respects, hormone systems are like neurotransmitter-activating systems except that hormones use the bloodstream as a conveyance. Indeed, many hormones act as neurotransmitters, and many neurotransmitters act as hormones.

Hierarchical Control of Hormones

Many hormones operate in a feedback system that includes the brain and the body. **Figure 6-18** shows how the hypothalamus produces neurohormones that stimulate the pituitary gland to secrete releasing hormones into the circulatory system. The pituitary hormones in turn influence the remaining endocrine glands to release appropriate hormones into the bloodstream to act on various targets in the body and send feedback to the brain about the need for more or less hormone release.

Hormones not only affect body organs but also target virtually all aspects of brain function. Almost every neuron in the brain contains receptors on which various hormones can act. In addition to influencing sex organs and physical appearance, hormones affect neurotransmitter function, especially in neurons that influence sexual development and behavior (Barth et al., 2015). Hormones can influence gene expression by binding to special receptors on or in the cell, then being transported to the nucleus to influence gene transcription. Transcription in turn influences the synthesis of proteins needed for a variety of cellular processes. Thus, hormones influence brain and body structure and behavior.

1 In response to sensory stimuli and cognitive activity, the hypothalamus produces neurohormones that enter the anterior pituitary through veins and the posterior pituitary through axons.

Hypothalamus

Sensory stimuli

Pituitary gland

Target organs and tissues

2 On instructions from these releasing hormones, the pituitary sends hormones into the bloodstream to target endocrine glands.

Endocrine hormones

3 Endocrine glands release their own hormones that stimulate target organs, including the brain.

Target endocrine gland

FIGURE 6-18 Hormonal Hierarchy

testosterone Sex hormone secreted by the testes that produces the distinguishing characteristics of the male.

steroid hormone Fat-soluble chemical messenger synthesized from cholesterol.

peptide hormone Chemical messenger synthesized by cellular DNA that acts to affect the target cell's physiology.

homeostatic hormone One of a group of hormones that maintain internal metabolic balance and regulate physiological systems in an organism.

Although many questions remain about how hormones produce or contribute to complex behavior, the diversity of their functions clarifies why the body uses hormones as messengers: their targets are so widespread that the best possible way of reaching all of them is to travel in the bloodstream, which goes everywhere in the body.

Consult the entry Hormonal Disorders inside the book's front cover for more information.

Classes and Functions of Hormones

Hormones can be used as drugs to treat or prevent disease. People take synthetic hormones as replacement therapy if the glands that produce the hormones are removed or malfunction. People also take hormones, especially sex hormones, to counteract the effects of aging, to increase physical strength and endurance, and to gain an advantage in sports. In the human body, as many as 100 hormones are classified chemically as either steroids or peptides.

Steroid hormones, such as testosterone and cortisol, are synthesized from cholesterol and are lipid (fat) soluble. Steroids diffuse away from their site of synthesis in glands, including the gonads, adrenal cortex, and thyroid. They bind to steroid receptors on the cell membrane or in the cell and frequently act on cellular DNA to influence gene transcription.

Peptide hormones, such as insulin, growth hormone, and the endorphins, are made by cellular DNA in the same way other proteins are made. They influence their target cell's activity by binding to metabotropic receptors on the cell membrane, generating a second messenger that affects the cell's physiology or gene transcription.

Steroid and peptide hormones fall into one of three main functional groups with respect to behavior, and they may function in more than one group:

To refresh your understanding of metabotropic receptors, review Figure 5-15.

1. **Homeostatic hormones** maintain a state of internal metabolic balance and regulate physiological systems. Mineralocorticoids (e.g., aldosterone) control both the concentration of water in blood and cells and the levels of sodium, potassium, and calcium in the body, and they promote digestive functions.

2. **Gonadal (sex) hormones** control reproductive functions. They instruct the body to develop as male (testosterone) or female (estrogen); influence sexual behavior and conception; and in women, control the menstrual cycle (estrogen and progesterone), birthing of babies, and release of breast milk (prolactin, oxytocin). These hormones, especially oxytocin, influence mother–infant bonding, and in some species, including sheep, are essential for bonding to occur.

3. **Glucocorticoids** (e.g., cortisol and corticosterone), a group of steroid hormones secreted in times of stress, are important in protein and carbohydrate metabolism and in controlling blood sugar levels and cellular absorption of sugar. Hormones activated in psychologically challenging events or emergencies prepare the body to cope by fighting or fleeing.

Homeostatic Hormones

Homeostasis comes from the Greek words *stasis* (*standing*) and *homeo* (*in the same place*).

Homeostatic hormones are essential to life. The body's internal environment must remain within relatively constant parameters for us to function. An appropriate balance of sugars, proteins, carbohydrates, salts, and water is necessary in the blood, in the extracellular compartments of muscles, in the brain and other body structures, and in all cells. The internal environment must be maintained regardless of a person's age, activities, or conscious state. As children or adults, at rest or in strenuous work, when we have overeaten or when we are hungry, to survive we need a relatively constant internal environment.

A typical homeostatic function is controlling blood sugar level. After a meal, digestive processes result in increased glucose in the blood. One group of cells in the pancreas releases insulin, a homeostatic hormone that instructs the enzyme glycogen synthase in liver and muscle cells to start storing glucose in the form of glycogen. The resulting decrease in glucose decreases the stimulation of pancreatic cells so that they stop producing insulin, and glycogen storage stops. When the body needs glucose for energy, another hormone in the liver, glucagon, acts as a countersignal to insulin. Glucagon stimulates another enzyme, glycogen phosphorylase, to initiate glucose release from its glycogen storage site.

Normal glucose concentration in the bloodstream varies between 80 and 130 mg per 100 milliliters (about 3.3 oz) of blood.

Diabetes mellitus is caused by a failure of the pancreatic cells to secrete enough insulin, or any at all. As a result, blood sugar levels can fall (hypoglycemia) or rise (hyperglycemia). In hyperglycemia, blood glucose levels rise because insulin does not instruct body cells to take up glucose. Consequently, cell function, including neuronal function, can fail through glucose starvation, even in the presence of high glucose levels in the blood. Chronic high blood glucose levels cause damage to the eyes, kidneys, nerves, heart, and blood vessels.

In hypoglycemia, inappropriate diet can lead to low blood sugar severe enough to cause fainting. Eric Steen and his coworkers (2005) propose that insulin resistance in brain cells may be related to Alzheimer disease. They raise the possibility that Alzheimer disease may be a third type of diabetes.

Hunger and eating are influenced by a number of homeostatic hormones, including leptin and ghrelin. Leptin (from the Greek for *thin*), secreted by adipose (animal fat) tissue, inhibits hunger and so is called the satiety hormone. Ghrelin (from the Indio-European *gher*, meaning *to grow*), secreted by the gastrointestinal tract, regulates growth hormones and energy use. Ghrelin also induces hunger. It is secreted when the stomach is empty; secretion stops when the stomach is full. Leptin and ghrelin act on receptors on the same neurons of the arcuate nucleus of the hypothalamus and so contribute to energy homeostasis by managing eating.

Gonadal Hormones

We are prepared for our adult reproductive roles by the gonadal hormones that give us our sexual appearance, mold our identity on the continuum of male to female, and allow us to engage in sex-related behaviors. Sex hormones begin to act on us even before we are born and continue their actions throughout our lives.

The male Y chromosome contains a gene called the sex-determining region Y, or SRY, gene. If cells in the undifferentiated gonads of the early embryo contain an SRY gene, they develop into a testis, and if they do not, they develop into an ovary. In the male, the testes produce testosterone, which masculinizes the body and the brain.

The **organizational hypothesis** proposes that hormone action in the course of development alters tissue differentiation. Thus, testosterone masculinizes the brain early in life, having been taken up in brain cells, where it is converted into estrogen by the enzyme aromatase. Estrogen then acts on estrogen receptors to initiate a chain of events that includes activating certain genes in the cell nucleus. These genes contribute to the masculinization of brain cells and their interactions with other brain cells.

That estrogen, a hormone usually associated with the female, masculinizes the male brain may seem surprising. Estrogen does not have the same effect on the female brain, because females have a blood enzyme that binds to estrogen and prevents its entry into the brain. Hormones play a somewhat lesser role in producing the female body and brain, but they control the mental and physical aspects of menstrual cycles, regulate many facets of pregnancy and birth, and stimulate milk production for breastfeeding. In males, gonadal hormones demethylate, and so release, genes in the preoptic area of the hypothalamus to become active. The expression of these genes influences male sexual characteristics and behavior. Thus, active methylation of male sex–related genes maintains the female phenotype (Nugent et al., 2015).

Gonadal hormones contribute to surprising differences in the brain and in cognitive behavior and play a role in male–female differences in drug dependence and addiction (see Section 6-3). The male brain is slightly larger than the female brain after corrections are made for body size, and the right hemisphere is somewhat larger than the left in males. The female brain has a higher rate both of cerebral blood flow and of glucose utilization. Differences in size appear in different brain regions, including nuclei in the hypothalamus related to sexual function, parts of the corpus callosum that are larger in females, and a somewhat larger language region in the female brain.

Three lines of evidence, summarized by Elizabeth Hampson and Doreen Kimura (2005), support the conclusion that sex-related cognitive differences result from these anatomical brain differences and that these cognitive differences also depend in part on the continuing circulation of the sex hormones. The evidence:

1. Spatial and verbal tests given to females and males in many different settings and cultures show that males tend to excel in spatial tasks and females in verbal tasks.

2. Results of similar tests given to female participants in the course of the menstrual cycle show fluctuations in these test scores with phases of the cycle. During the phase in which the female sex hormones estradiol (metabolized from estrogen) and progesterone are at their lowest levels, women perform comparatively better on spatial tasks; during the phase in which levels of these hormones are high, women do comparatively better on verbal tasks.

3. Tests comparing premenopausal and postmenopausal women, women in various stages of pregnancy, and females and males with varying levels of circulating sex hormones all provide some evidence that hormones affect cognitive function.

Sex hormone–related differences in cognitive function are not huge. Performance scores between males and females overlap broadly. Yet statistically, the differences are reliable. Similar influences of sex hormones on behavior are found in other species. Berthold's rooster experiment described earlier shows the behavioral effects of testosterone. Findings from many studies demonstrate that motor skills in female humans and other animals improve at estrus, a time when progesterone levels are high.

Section 8-4 explains how gonadal hormones participate in brain development.

Section 12-5 describes gonadal hormones' effects on sexual behavior. Section 15-5 recounts sex differences in thinking patterns.

gonadal (sex) hormone One of a group of hormones, such as testosterone, that control reproductive functions and bestow sexual appearance and identity as male or female.

glucocorticoid One of a group of steroid hormones, such as cortisol, secreted in times of stress; important in protein and carbohydrate metabolism.

organizational hypothesis Proposal that hormonal action during development alters tissue differentiation; for example, testosterone masculinizes the brain.

Anabolic—Androgenic Steroids

A class of synthetic hormones related to testosterone has both muscle-building (anabolic) and masculinizing (androgenic) effects. Commonly known simply as **anabolic steroids**, they were synthesized originally to build body mass and enhance endurance. Russian weight lifters were the first to use them, in 1952, to enhance performance and win international competitions.

Synthetic steroid use rapidly spread to other countries and sports, eventually leading to a ban from track and field and then from many other sports, enforced by drug testing. Testing policy has led to a cat-and-mouse game in which new anabolic steroids and new ways of taking them and masking them are devised to evade detection.

Today, the use of anabolic steroids is about equal among athletes and nonathletes. More than 1 million people in the United States have used anabolic steroids not only to enhance athletic performance but also to enhance physique and appearance. Anabolic steroid use in high schools may be as high as 7 percent for males and 3 percent for females.

The use of anabolic steroids carries health risks. Their administration results in the body reducing its manufacture of testosterone, which in turn reduces male fertility and spermatogenesis. Muscle bulk is increased and so is aggression. Cardiovascular effects include increased risk of heart attack and stroke. Liver and kidney function may be compromised, and the risk of tumors may increase. Male-pattern baldness may be enhanced. Females may have an enlarged clitoris, acne, increased body hair, and a deepened voice.

Anabolic steroids have approved clinical uses. Testosterone replacement is a treatment for hypogonadal males. It is also useful for treating muscle loss subsequent to trauma and for the recovery of muscle mass in malnourished people. In females, anabolic steroids are used to treat endometriosis and fibrocystic disease of the breast.

Glucocorticoids and Stress

Stress is a term borrowed from engineering to describe a process in which an agent exerts a force on an object. Applied to humans and other animals, a stressor is a stimulus that challenges the body's homeostasis and triggers arousal. Stress responses, behavioral as well as physiological, include both arousal and attempts to reduce stress. A stress response can outlast a stress-inducing incident and may even occur in the absence of an obvious stressor. Living with constant stress can be debilitating.

Activating a Stress Response

Surprisingly, the body's response is the same whether the stressor is exciting, sad, or frightening. Robert Sapolsky (2004) uses the vivid image of a hungry lion chasing down a zebra to illustrate the stress response. The chase elicits divergent behavior in the two animals, but their physiological responses are identical. The stress response begins when the body is subjected to a stressor and especially when the brain perceives a stressor and responds with arousal, directed from the brain by the hypothalamus. The response consists of two separate sequences, one fast and the other slow.

THE FAST RESPONSE Shown at left in **Figure 6-19**, the sympathetic division of the ANS is activated to prepare the body and its organs for fight or flight. The parasympathetic division for rest and digest is turned off. The sympathetic division stimulates the medulla on the interior of the adrenal gland to release epinephrine. The epinephrine surge (often called the adrenaline surge after epinephrine's original name) prepares the body for a sudden burst of activity. Among its many functions, epinephrine stimulates cell metabolism, readying the body's cells for action.

THE SLOW RESPONSE As shown at right in Figure 6-19, the slow response is controlled by the steroid cortisol, a glucocorticoid released from the outer layer (cortex) of the

anabolic steroid Class of synthetic hormones related to testosterone that have both muscle-building (anabolic) and masculinizing (androgenic) effects; also called *anabolic–androgenic steroid*.

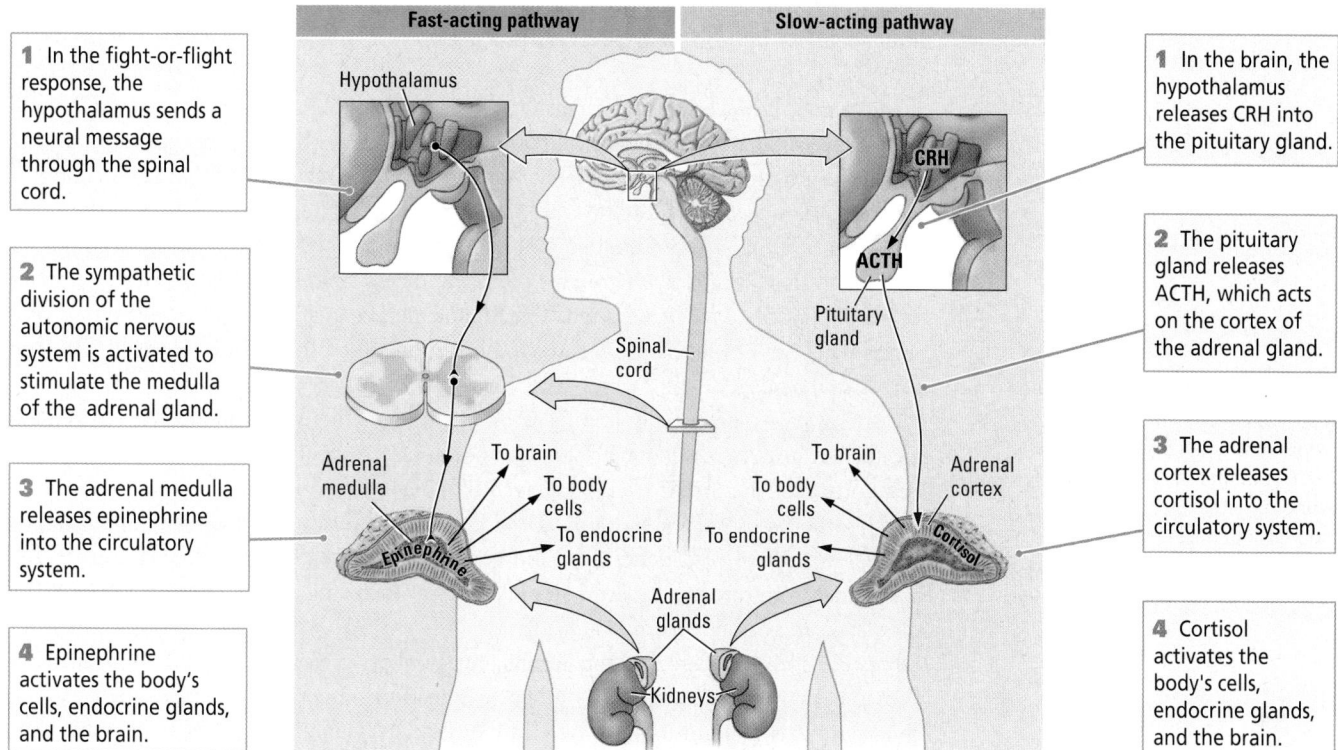

1 In the fight-or-flight response, the hypothalamus sends a neural message through the spinal cord.

2 The sympathetic division of the autonomic nervous system is activated to stimulate the medulla of the adrenal gland.

3 The adrenal medulla releases epinephrine into the circulatory system.

4 Epinephrine activates the body's cells, endocrine glands, and the brain.

1 In the brain, the hypothalamus releases CRH into the pituitary gland.

2 The pituitary gland releases ACTH, which acts on the cortex of the adrenal gland.

3 The adrenal cortex releases cortisol into the circulatory system.

4 Cortisol activates the body's cells, endocrine glands, and the brain.

FIGURE 6-19 Activating a Stress Response Two pathways to the adrenal gland control the body's stress response. The fast-acting pathway primes the body immediately for fight or flight. The slow-acting pathway both mobilizes the body's resources to confront a stressor and repairs stress-related damage. CRH, corticotropin-releasing hormone; ACTH, adrenocorticotropic hormone.

adrenal gland. Activating the cortisol pathway takes anywhere from minutes to hours. Cortisol has wide-ranging functions, which include turning off all bodily systems not immediately required to deal with a stressor. For example, cortisol turns off insulin so that the liver starts releasing glucose, thus temporarily increasing the body's energy supply. It also shuts down reproductive functions and inhibits the production of growth hormone. In this way, it concentrates the body's energy on dealing with the stress.

Ending a Stress Response

Normally, stress responses are brief. The body mobilizes its resources, deals with the challenge physiologically and behaviorally, and shuts down the stress response. Just as the brain is responsible for turning on the stress reaction, it is also responsible for turning it off. Consider what can happen if the stress response is not shut down:

- The body continues to mobilize energy at the cost of energy storage.

- Proteins are used up, resulting in muscle wasting and fatigue.

- Growth hormone is inhibited, so the body cannot grow.

- The gastrointestinal system remains shut down, reducing the intake and processing of nutrients to replace used resources.

- Reproductive functions are inhibited.

- The immune system is suppressed, contributing to the possibility of infection or disease.

Sapolsky (2005) argues that the hippocampus plays an important role in turning off the stress response. The hippocampus contains a high density of cortisol receptors, and

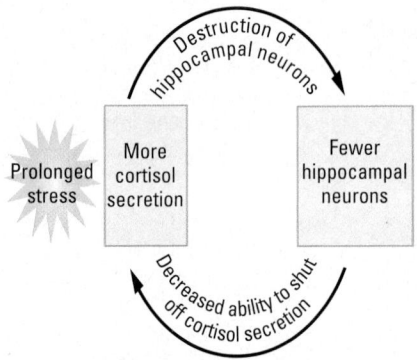

FIGURE 6-20 Vicious Circle Unrelieved stress promotes excessive release of cortisol, which damages hippocampal neurons. The damaged neurons cannot detect cortisol and therefore cannot signal the adrenal gland to stop producing it. The resulting feedback loop enhances cortisol secretion, further damaging hippocampal neurons.

PTSD, introduced in Section 5-4 in relation to sensitization, is among the anxiety disorders detailed in Section 12-4. Focus 16-1 and Section 16-4 consider treatments.

it has axons that project to the hypothalamus. Consequently, the hippocampus is well suited to detecting cortisol in the blood and instructing the hypothalamus to reduce blood cortisol levels.

There may, however, be a more insidious relation between the hippocampus and blood cortisol levels. Sapolsky observed wild-born vervet monkeys that had become agricultural pests in Kenya and had therefore been trapped and caged. He found that some monkeys sickened and died of a syndrome that appeared to be related to stress. Those that died seemed to have been subordinate animals housed with particularly aggressive dominant monkeys. Autopsies showed high rates of gastric ulcers, enlarged adrenal glands, and pronounced hippocampal degeneration. The hippocampal damage may have been due to prolonged high cortisol levels produced by the unremitting stress of being caged with the aggressive monkeys.

Cortisol levels are usually regulated by the hippocampus, but if these levels remain elevated because a stress-inducing situation continues, cortisol eventually damages the hippocampus, reducing its size. The damaged hippocampus is then unable to do its work of reducing the level of cortisol. Thus, a vicious circle is set up in which the hippocampus undergoes progressive degeneration and cortisol levels are not controlled (**Figure 6-20**). Interestingly, other research with rats suggests that following similar stress, the size of the amygdala is increased (Bourgin et al., 2015).

Because stress response circuits in rats and monkeys are similar to those in humans, it is possible that excessive stress in humans can lead to similar brain changes. Because the hippocampus is thought to play a role in memory, stress-induced hippocampal damage is postulated to result in impaired memory. Because the amygdala is thought to play a role in emotion, stress-induced changes are postulated to result in increased emotional responses. This pattern of behavioral changes resembles posttraumatic stress disorder. People with PTSD feel as if they are reliving the trauma, and the accompanying physiological arousal enhances their belief that danger is imminent.

Research has not yet determined whether the cumulative effects of stress damage the human hippocampus. For example, research on women who were sexually abused in childhood and were diagnosed with PTSD yields some reports of changes in memory or in hippocampal volume, as measured with brain imaging techniques. Other studies report no differences in abused and nonabused subjects (Landré et al., 2010). The fact that such apparently similar studies can obtain different results can be explained in several ways.

First, the amount of damage to the hippocampus that must occur to produce a stress syndrome is not certain. Second, brain imaging techniques may not be sensitive to subtle changes in hippocampal cell function or to moderate cell loss. Third, wide individual and environmental differences influence how people respond to stress. Fourth, neonatal stress can influence hippocampal neurogenesis (Lajud and Torner, 2015). The long-term consequence is a smaller hippocampus and increased susceptibility to stress.

Finally, humans are long-lived and gather many life experiences that complicate simple extrapolations from a single stressful event. Nevertheless, Patrick McGowan and his coworkers (2009) report that the density of glucocorticoid receptors in the hippocampus of people who committed suicide after sexual abuse in childhood was lower than that of both controls and suicide victims who had not been abused.

The decrease in receptors and in glucocorticoid mRNA suggests that childhood abuse induces epigenetic changes in the expression of glucocorticoid genes. The decrease in glucocorticoid receptors presumably renders the hippocampus less able to depress stress responses. The importance of the McGowan study is its suggestion of a mechanism through which stress can influence hippocampal function without necessarily being associated with a decrease in hippocampal volume. This study further underscores the point that stress likely produces many changes in many brain regions. It is unlikely that all have been described or are understood (Clauss et al., 2015).

(6-5) REVIEW

Hormones

Before you continue, check your understanding.

1. The hypothalamus produces _____ that stimulate the _____ to secrete _____ into the circulatory system. Hormone levels circulating in the bloodstream send feedback to the _____.

2. Hormones are classified chemically as _____ or _____.

3. Broadly speaking, _____ hormones regulate metabolic balance; _____ hormones regulate reproduction; and _____ regulate stress.

4. One class of synthetic hormones is _____, which increase _____ and have _____ effects.

5. The stress response has a fast-acting pathway mediated by the release of _____ and a slow-acting pathway mediated by the release of _____.

6. Describe the proposed relationship among stress, cortisol, and the hippocampus.

Answers appear at the back of the book.

For additional study tools, visit 🧠 LaunchPad:
www.macmillanhighered.com/launchpad/kolb5e

■ SUMMARY

(6-1) Principles of Psychopharmacology

Psychoactive drugs—substances that alter mood, thought, or behavior—produce their effects by acting on neuronal receptors or on chemical processes in the nervous system, especially on neurotransmission at synapses. Drugs act either as agonists to stimulate neuronal activity or as antagonists to depress it. Psychopharmacology is the study of drug effects on the brain and behavior.

Drugs are administered by mouth, by inhalation, by absorption through the skin, rectally by suppository, and by injection. To reach a nervous system target, a psychoactive drug must pass through numerous barriers posed by digestion and dilution, the blood–brain barrier, and cell membranes. Drugs are diluted by body fluids as they pass through successive barriers, are metabolized in the body, and are excreted through sweat glands and in feces, urine, breath, and breast milk.

A common misperception about psychoactive drugs is that they act specifically and consistently, but learning also affects individual responses to drugs. The body and brain may rapidly become tolerant of (habituated to) many drugs, so the dose must increase to produce a constant effect. Alternatively, people may become sensitized to a drug: the same dose produces increasingly strong effects. These forms of unconscious learning also contribute to a person's behavior under a drug's influence.

(6-2) Grouping Psychoactive Drugs

Psychoactive drugs can be organized according to their major behavioral effects into five groups: antianxiety agents and sedative-hypnotics, antipsychotic agents, antidepressants and mood stabilizers, opioid analgesics, and psychotropics. Each group, summarized in Table 6-1 on page 181, contains natural or synthetic drugs or both, and they may produce their actions in different ways.

(6-3) Factors Influencing Individual Responses to Drugs

A drug does not have a uniform action on every person. Physical differences—in body weight, sex, age, or genetic background—influence a given drug's effects on a given person, as do behaviors, such as learning, and cultural and environmental contexts.

The influence of drugs on behavior varies widely with the situation and as a person learns drug-related behaviors. Behavioral myopia, for example, can influence a person to focus primarily on prominent environmental cues. These cues may encourage the person to act in uncharacteristic ways.

Females are more sensitive to drugs than males are and may become addicted more quickly than males to lower doses of drugs. The incidence of female abuse of many kinds of drugs equals or exceeds male abuse of those drugs.

(6-4) Explaining and Treating Drug Abuse

The neural mechanisms implicated in addiction are the same neural systems responsible for wanting and liking more generally. So anyone is likely to be a potential drug abuser. Addiction develops in a number of stages as a result of repeated drug taking.

Initially, drug taking produces pleasure (liking), but with repeated use the behavior becomes conditioned to associated objects, events, and places. Eventually, the conditioned cues motivate the drug user to seek them out (wanting), which leads to more drug taking. These subjective experiences become associated with prominent cues, and drug seeking promotes craving for the drug. As addiction proceeds, the subjective experience of liking decreases while wanting increases.

Treatment varies with the drug. Whatever the treatment approach, success likely depends on permanent lifestyle changes. Considering how many people use tobacco, drink alcohol, use recreational drugs, or abuse prescription drugs, to find someone who has not used a drug when it was available is probably rare. But because of either genetic or epigenetic influences, some people do seem particularly vulnerable to drug abuse and addiction.

Excessive alcohol use can be associated with damage to the thalamus and hypothalamus, but the damage is caused by poor nutrition rather than the direct actions of alcohol. Cocaine can produce brain damage by reducing blood flow or by bleeding into neural tissue. MDMA (Ecstasy) use can result in the loss of fine axon collaterals of serotonergic neurons and associated impairments in cognitive function.

Psychedelic drugs, such as marijuana and LSD, can be associated with psychotic behavior. Whether this behavior is due to the drugs' direct effects or to the aggravation of preexisting conditions is not clear.

6-5 Hormones

Steroid and peptide hormones produced by endocrine glands circulate in the bloodstream to affect a wide variety of targets. Interacting to regulate hormone levels is a hierarchy of sensory stimuli and cognitive activity in the brain that stimulates the pituitary gland through the hypothalamus. The pituitary stimulates or inhibits the endocrine glands, which send feedback to the brain via other hormones.

Homeostatic hormones regulate the balance of sugars, proteins, carbohydrates, salts, and other substances in the body. Gonadal hormones regulate the physical features and behaviors associated with sex characteristics and behaviors, reproduction, and parenting. Glucocorticoids are steroid hormones that regulate the body's ability to cope with stress—with arousing and challenging situations.

The hippocampus plays an important role in ending the stress response. Failure to turn stress responses off after a stressor has passed can contribute to susceptibility to PTSD and other psychological and physical diseases. Stress may activate epigenetic changes that modify the expression of genes regulating hormonal responses to stress and may produce brain changes persisting long after the stress-provoking incident has passed.

Synthetic anabolic steroids, used by athletes and others alike, mimic the effects of testosterone and so increase muscle bulk, stamina, and aggression but can have deleterious side effects.

■ KEY TERMS

addiction, p. 193

agonist, p. 177

amphetamine, p. 189

anabolic steroid, p. 204

antagonist, p. 177

antianxiety agent, p. 182

attention-deficit/hyperactivity disorder (ADHD), p. 173

barbiturate, p. 182

behavioral myopia , p. 193

bipolar disorder, p. 187

competitive inhibitor, p. 187

cross-tolerance, p. 182

disinhibition theory, p. 191

dopamine hypothesis of schizophrenia, p. 184

endorphin, p. 187

fetal alcohol spectrum disorder (FASD), p. 182

glucocorticoid, p. 203

gonadal (sex) hormone, p. 203

homeostatic hormone, p. 201

major depression, p. 184

monoamine oxidase (MAO) inhibitor, p. 184

mood stabilizer, p. 187

opioid analgesic, p. 187

organizational hypothesis, p. 203

peptide hormone, p. 201

psychedelic drug, p. 189

psychoactive drug, p. 173

psychomotor activation, p. 193

psychopharmacology, p. 173

second-generation antidepressant, p. 184

selective serotonin reuptake inhibitor (SSRI), p. 184

steroid hormone, p. 201

substance abuse, p. 193

testosterone, p. 201

tolerance, p. 177

tricyclic antidepressant, p. 184

wanting-and-liking theory, p. 194

withdrawal symptom, p. 193

➩ Visit 🔗 **LaunchPad** to access the e-Book, videos, 🔗 **LearningCurve** adaptive quizzing, flashcards, and more.

www.macmillanhighered.com/launchpad/kolb5e

CHAPTER 7

How Do We Study the Brain's Structures and Functions?

RESEARCH FOCUS 7-1 TUNING IN TO LANGUAGE

7-1 MEASURING AND MANIPULATING BRAIN AND BEHAVIOR

LINKING NEUROANATOMY AND BEHAVIOR

EXPERIMENT 7-1 QUESTION: DO HIPPOCAMPAL NEURONS CONTRIBUTE TO MEMORY FORMATION?

METHODS OF BEHAVIORAL NEUROSCIENCE

MANIPULATING BRAIN–BEHAVIOR INTERACTIONS

7-2 MEASURING THE BRAIN'S ELECTRICAL ACTIVITY

RECORDING ACTION POTENTIALS FROM SINGLE CELLS

EEG: RECORDING GRADED POTENTIALS FROM THOUSANDS OF CELLS

MAPPING BRAIN FUNCTION WITH EVENT-RELATED POTENTIALS

CLINICAL FOCUS 7-2 MILD HEAD INJURY AND DEPRESSION

MAGNETOENCEPHALOGRAPHY

7-3 ANATOMICAL IMAGING TECHNIQUES: CT AND MRI

7-4 FUNCTIONAL BRAIN IMAGING

FUNCTIONAL MAGNETIC RESONANCE IMAGING

OPTICAL TOMOGRAPHY

POSITRON EMISSION TOMOGRAPHY

7-5 CHEMICAL AND GENETIC MEASURES OF BRAIN AND BEHAVIOR

MEASURING BRAIN CHEMISTRY

MEASURING GENES IN BRAIN AND BEHAVIOR

CLINICAL FOCUS 7-3 CANNABIS USE, PSYCHOSIS, AND GENETICS

EPIGENETICS: MEASURING GENE EXPRESSION

7-6 COMPARING NEUROSCIENCE RESEARCH METHODS

7-7 USING ANIMALS IN BRAIN–BEHAVIOR RESEARCH

BENEFITS OF ANIMAL MODELS OF DISEASE

ANIMAL WELFARE AND SCIENTIFIC EXPERIMENTATION

RESEARCH FOCUS 7-4 ATTENTION-DEFICIT/HYPERACTIVITY DISORDER

Katherine Streeter

Streeter

209

Tuning In to Language

The continuing search to understand the organization and operation of the human brain is driven largely by emerging technologies. Over the past decade, neuroscience researchers have developed dramatic new noninvasive ways to image the brain's activity in people who are awake. One technique, **functional near-infrared spectroscopy** (fNIRS), gathers light transmitted through cortical tissue to image oxygen consumption in the brain. NIRS, a form of *optical tomography*, is detailed in Section 7-4.

fNIRS allows investigators to measure oxygen consumption as a surrogate marker of neuronal activity in relatively select cortical regions, even in newborn infants. In one study (May et al., 2011), newborns (0–3 days old) wore a mesh cap containing the NIRS apparatus, made up of optical fibers, as they listened to a familiar or unfamiliar language.

When newborns listened to a familiar language, their brain showed a general increase in oxygenated hemoglobin; when they heard an unfamiliar language, oxygenated hemoglobin decreased overall. But when the babies heard the same sentences played backward, there was no difference in brain response to either language.

The opposing responses to familiar and unfamiliar languages mean that prenatal language experience shapes how the newborn brain responds to familiar and unfamiliar tongues. This finding leads to many questions. Among them: How does prenatal exposure to language influence later language learning? Do children who are exposed to multiple languages prenatally show better language acquisition than those exposed to just one? How much prenatal language exposure is necessary, and do premature infants show the same results as full-term babies?

Whatever the answers, this study shows that the prenatal brain is tuned in to the language environment into which it will be born.

"Language and the newborn brain: does prenatal language experience shape the neonate neural response to speech?" by L. May, K. Byers-Heinlein, J. Gervain, and J.F. Werker, 2011. *Frontiers in Psychology*, 2, 1–9. Photo by Krista Byers-Heinlein

Newborn with probes placed on the head.

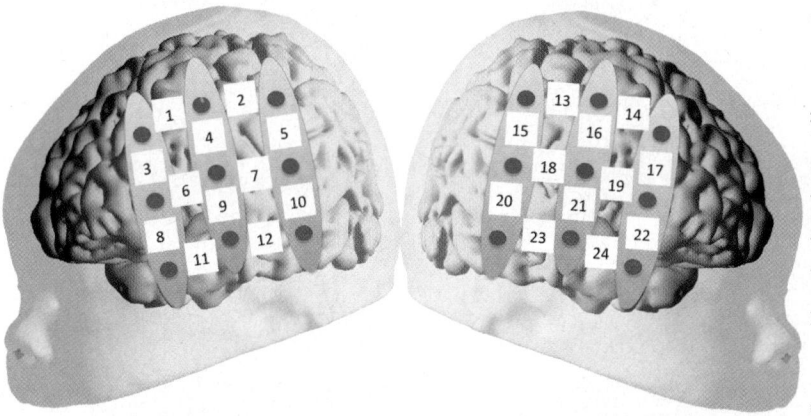

"Language and the newborn brain: does prenatal language experience shape the neonate neural response to speech?" by L. May, K. Byers-Heinlein, J. Gervain, and J.F. Werker, 2011. *Frontiers in Psychology*, 2, 1–9. Image by Judit Gervain.

Probe configurations overlaid on schematics of an infant's left and right hemispheres. Red dots indicate light-emitting fibers; blue dots indicate light detectors. The light detectors in the outer strips in both hemispheres sit over regions specialized for language in adults.

The simple, noninvasive nature of fNIRS likely will yield new insights not only into brain development but also into adult brain function. Over the coming decades, our understanding of the brain–behavior relationship will continue to be driven in large part by new and better technologies and by cleverly exploiting existing ones.

To understand how far neuroscience research methods have progressed, imagine that it is the year 1800. You are a neurologist interested in studying how the brain works. The challenge is how to begin. The two most obvious choices are to dissect the brains of dead people and other animals or to study people who have sustained a brain injury. Indeed, this was how the relationship between brain and behavior was studied well into the twentieth century.

Techniques for studying the brain's physiological processes emerged in the years between World War I and World War II. One breakthrough was the *electroencephalograph* (EEG), developed for humans by Hans Berger in the 1930s. Advances in understanding genetics and the analysis of behavior in the early 1950s set the stage for phenomenal advances

Section 4-1 reviews how the EEG enabled investigators to explain electrical activity in the nervous system.

in neuroscience knowledge. Scientists recognize that new technologies allow for novel insights, lead to more questions, and can dramatically advance their discipline. A large number of Nobel Prizes have been awarded for the development and implementation of new technologies.

Today, brain–behavior analyses combine the efforts of anatomists and geneticists, psychologists and physiologists, chemists and physicists, endocrinologists and neurologists, pharmacologists and psychiatrists, engineers and biologists. For the aspiring brain researcher in the twenty-first century, the range of available research methods is breathtaking.

We begin this chapter by reviewing how investigators measure behavior in both human and nonhuman subjects and how neuroscientists can manipulate behavior by perturbing the brain. We then consider electrical techniques, including the EEG, for recording brain activity; noninvasive procedures, such as fNIRS, that image the brain; and chemical and genetic methods for measuring brain and behavior. After comparing these methods at the chapter's end, we review some issues surrounding the use of nonhuman animals in research.

(7-1) Measuring and Manipulating Brain and Behavior

During a lecture at a meeting of the Anthropological Society of Paris in 1861, Ernest Auburtin, a French physician, argued that language functions are located in the brain's frontal lobes. Five days later a fellow French physician, Paul Broca, observed a brain-injured patient who had lost his speech and was able to say only "tan" and utter a swear word. The patient soon died. Broca and Auburtin examined the man's brain and found the focus of his injury in the left frontal lobe.

By 1863 Broca had collected eight similar cases and concluded that speech is located in the third frontal convolution of the left frontal lobe—a region now called *Broca's area*. Broca's findings attracted others to study brain–behavior relationships in patients. The field that developed is what we now call **neuropsychology**, the study of the relations between brain function and behavior with a particular emphasis on humans. Today, measuring brain and behavior increasingly includes noninvasive imaging, complex neuroanatomical measurement, and sophisticated behavioral analyses.

Linking Neuroanatomy and Behavior

At the beginning of the twentieth century, neuroanatomy's primary tools were *histological*: brains were sectioned postmortem and the tissue (*histo-* in Greek) stained with various dyes. As shown in **Figure 7-1**, staining sections of brain tissue can identify cell bodies in the brain viewed with a light microscope (A), and selectively staining individual neurons reveals their complete structure (B). An electron microscope (C) makes it possible to view synapses in detail.

By 1905, light microscopic techniques allowed researchers such as Korbinian Brodmann to divide the cerebral cortex into many distinct zones based on the characteristics of neurons in those zones. Investigators presumed that cortical zones had specific functions. By the dawn of the twenty-first century, dozens of techniques had developed for labeling neurons and their connections, as well as glial cells. Contemporary techniques allow researchers to identify molecular, neurochemical, and morphological (structural) differences among neuronal types and ultimately to relate these characteristics to behavior. One fast-developing technique, shown in Figure 7-1D, uses a multiphoton microscope that makes it possible to image living brain tissue in three dimensions.

Connections between anatomy and behavior can be seen in studies of animals trained on various types of learning tasks, such as spatial mazes. Such learning can be correlated with a variety of neuronanatomical changes, such as modifications in the synaptic organization of cells in specific cortical regions—the visual cortex in animals trained in visually guided

---

functional near-infrared spectroscopy (fNIRS) Noninvasive technique that gathers light transmitted through cortical tissue to image oxygen consumption; form of optical tomography.

neuropsychology Study of the relations between brain function and behavior, especially in humans.

Section 10-4 explores the anatomy of language and music and describes Broca's contributions.

Compare Brodmann's map of the cortex, based on staining, shown in Figure 2-23.

FIGURE 7-1 Staining Cerebral Neurons Viewed through a light microscope, **(A)** Nissl-stained section of parietal cortex shows all cell bodies but no cell processes (axons and dendrites). **(B)** At higher magnification, an individual Golgi-stained pyramidal cell from the parietal cortex is visible. The cell body (dark triangular shape at center) and spiny dendrites (A and B) are visible in detail at right. **(C)** The view through an electron microscope shows neuronal synapses in detail. **(D)** Multiple images from a multiphoton microscope, merged to generate a three-dimensional image of living tissue.

(A) Light microscope, low magnification

Bryan Kolb

(B) Light microscope, high magnification

Bryan Kolb

(C) Electron microscope

Douglas Bray, University of Lethbridge

(D) Multiphoton microscope

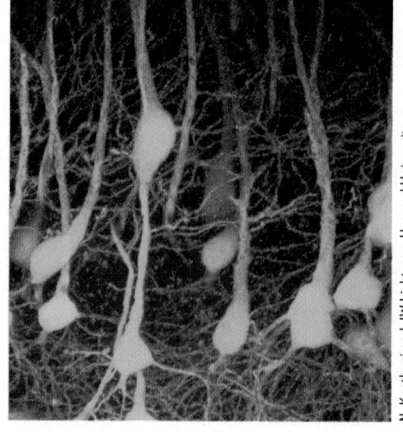

N. Kasthuri and JW Lichtman, Harvard University

Corticosterone, a steroid hormone secreted in times of stress, is important in protein and carbohydrate metabolism (see Section 6-5).

mazes is one example—or in the number of newly generated cells that survive in the hippocampus. The hippocampus is necessary, in mammals, for remembering the context in which we encounter information.

Although changes in synaptic organization or cell survival have not yet been proved to be the basis of the new learning, experimental evidence reveals that preventing the growth of new hippocampal neurons leads to memory deficits. To test the idea that hippocampal neurons contribute to memory formation, researchers tested healthy rats and ADX rats—rats with adrenal glands removed, which eliminates the hormone corticosterone. Without corticosterone, neurons in the hippocampus die.

Procedure 1 in **Experiment 7-1** contrasts the appearance of a healthy rat hippocampus (left) and neuronal degeneration in an ADX rat after surgery (right). The behavior of healthy and ADX rats was studied in the object–context mismatch task diagrammed in Procedure 2. During the training phase, the rats were placed in two distinct contexts, A and B, for 10 minutes on each of 2 days. Each context contained a different type of object. On the test day, the rats were placed in either context A or context B but with two different objects, one from that context and a second from the other context.

As noted in the Results section of the experiment, when healthy rats encounter objects in the correct context, they spend little time investigating because the objects are familiar. If, however, they encounter an object in the wrong context, they are curious and spend about three-quarters of their time investigating, essentially treating the mismatched object as new. But the ADX rats with hippocampal cell loss treated the mismatched and in-context objects the same, spending about half of their investigation time with each object.

▶ EXPERIMENT 7-1

Question: Do hippocampal neurons contribute to memory formation?

Procedure 1

Rat hippocampus before (left) and after (right) surgical removal of the adrenal glands.
Arrows point to neuronal degeneration resulting from a lack of corticosterone.

Healthy rat hippocampus

Hippocampus

ADX-induced hippocampal degeneration

Spanswick S.C., Sutherland R.J. (2010). Object-context specific memory deficits associated with loss of hippocampal granule cells after adrenalectomy in rats. *Learning and Memory*, 17:241–245.

Procedure 2

The behavior of healthy and ADX rats was studied in an object–context mismatch task in which two distinct contexts each contained a different type of object.

Training phase

During the training phase, each rat was placed in contexts A and B, each for 10 minutes on each of 2 days. Each context contained one type of object.

Context A   Context B

Testing phase

Contexts A and B with mismatched objects

OR

During the testing phase, each rat was placed either in context A or in context B, but with two *different* objects, one from that context and a second from the other context.

Results

Healthy rats investigate the mismatch object more than the object that is in context, but the ADX rats performed at chance. The rats in another ADX group were given treatments known to increase neuron generation in the hippocampus (enriched housing and exercise in running wheels). The rats with hippocampal regeneration were not impaired at the mismatch task.

The confocal photo at right shows a rat hippocampus. A specific stain was used to identify new neurons, which appear yellow.

Courtesy Bryan Kolb

Conclusion: Hippocampal neurons are necessary for the contextual learning.

Information from S. Spanswick & R. J. Sutherland (2010). Object/context-specific memory deficits associated with loss of hippocampal granule cells after adrenalectomy in rats. *Learning and Memory*, 17, 241–245. Information from S. Spanswick, H. Lethman, & R. J. Sutherland (2011). A novel animal model of hippocampal cognitive deficits, slow neurodegeneration, and neuroregeneration. *Journal of Biomedicine and Biotechnology*. Article ID 527201.

behavioral neuroscience Study of the biological bases of behavior in humans and other animals.

Another group of ADX rats given treatment known to increase neuron generation in the hippocampus—enriched housing and exercise in running wheels—was unimpaired at the context mismatch task. Experiment 7-1 concludes that cellular changes in the hippocampus and behavioral changes are closely linked: hippocampal neurons are necessary for contextual learning.

Methods of Behavioral Neuroscience

The brain's ultimate function is to produce behavior (movement). It follows that brain dysfunction should alter behavior in some way. The study of brain–behavior relationships in both humans and laboratory animals is **behavioral neuroscience,** the study of the biological bases of behavior.

A major challenge to behavioral neuroscientists is developing methods for studying both typical and atypical behavior. Measuring behavior in humans and laboratory animals differs in large part because humans speak: investigators can ask them about their symptoms. It is also possible to use both paper-and-pencil and computer-based tests to identify specific symptoms in people.

Measuring behavior in laboratory animals is more complex. Researchers must learn to speak "ratese" with rat subjects or "monkeyese" with monkeys. In short, researchers must develop ways to enable the animals to reveal their symptoms. The development of the fields of animal learning and *ethology,* the objective study of animal behavior, especially under natural conditions, provided the basis for modern behavioral neuroscience (see Whishaw & Kolb, 2005). To illustrate the logic of behavioral neuroscience, we describe some measurement tools used with humans and some used with rats.

Table 7-2 on page 239 summarizes selected brain measurement techniques, their goals, and examples.

Neuropsychological Testing of Humans

The brain has exquisite control of an amazing array of functions ranging from movement control and sensory perception to memory, emotion, and language. As a consequence, any analysis of behavior must be tailored to the particular function(s) under investigation. Consider the analysis of memory.

People with damage to the temporal lobes often complain of memory disturbance. But memory is not a single function; rather, multiple as well as independent memory systems exist. We have memory for events, colors, names, places, and motor skills, among other categories, and each must be measured separately. It would be rare indeed for someone to be impaired in *all* forms of memory. Neuropsychological tests of three distinct forms of memory are illustrated in **Figure 7-2**.

Sections 14-1 through 14-3 analyze the varied categories of memory.

(A) Corsi block-tapping test

The examiner taps out a sequence of blocks.

Examiner's view

The block numbers are visible on the examiner's side of the board but not on the participant's side.

(B) Mirror-drawing task

Participants' task is to trace between the two outlines of the star while looking only at their hand in a mirror.

Crossing a line constitutes an error.

(C) Test of recent memory

Participants' task is to identify which picture they saw most recently.

FIGURE 7-2 Neuropsychological Tests of Memory

The Corsi block-tapping test shown in Figure 7-2A requires participants to observe an experimenter tap a sequence of blocks—blocks 4, 6, 1, 8, 3, for instance. The task is to repeat the sequence correctly. The subject does not see numbers on the blocks but rather must remember the location of the tapped blocks.

The Corsi test provides a measure of short-term recall of spatial position, an ability we can call *block span*. The test can be made more difficult by determining the maximum block span of an individual (say, 6 blocks) and then adding one (*span + 1*). By definition, the participant will fail on the first presentation, but given the span + 1 repeatedly, will eventually learn it.

Span + 1 identifies a different form of memory from block span. Different types of neurological dysfunction interfere differentially with tasks that superficially appear quite similar. Block span measures the short-term recall of information, whereas the span + 1 task reflects the learning and longer-term memory storage of information.

The *mirror-drawing task* (Figure 7-2B) requires a person to trace a pathway, such as a star, by looking in a mirror. This motor task initially proves difficult because our movements appear backward in the mirror. With practice, participants learn how to accomplish the task accurately, and they show considerable recall of the skill when retested days later. Curiously, patients and subjects with certain types of memory problems have no recollection of learning the task on the previous day but nevertheless perform it flawlessly.

In the *recency memory task* (Figure 7-2C), participants are shown a long series of cards, each bearing two stimulus items that are words or pictures. On some trials a question mark appears between the items. The subjects' task is to indicate whether they have seen the items before and if so, which item they saw most recently. People may be able to recall that they have seen items before but be unable to recall which was most recent. Conversely, they may not be able to identify the items as being familiar, but when forced to choose the most recent one, they can identify it correctly.

The latter, counterintuitive result reflects the need for behavioral researchers to develop ingenious ways of identifying memory abilities. It is not enough simply to ask people to recall information verbally, although this too measures a form of memory.

In this book, we refer to healthy human volunteers in research studies as *participants* and to people or animals that have a brain or behavioral impairment as *patients* or *subjects*.

Focus 15-4 compares effects of injuries to particular brain regions on performance of particular neuropsychological tasks.

Behavioral Analysis of Rats

Over the past century, psychologists interested in the neural basis of memory have devised a vast array of mazes and other tests and tasks to investigate different forms of memory in laboratory animals. **Figure 7-3** illustrates three tests based on a task devised by Richard Morris in 1980. Researchers place rats in a large swimming pool where an escape platform lies just below the water surface, invisible to the rats.

In one version of the task, *place learning*, the rat must find the platform from any starting location in the pool (Figure 7-3A). The only cues available are outside the pool, so the rat must learn the relation between several cues in the room and the platform's location. In a second version of the task, *matching-to-place learning*, the rat has already learned that a platform always lies somewhere in the pool but is moved to a different location every day. The rat is released and searches for the platform (Figure 7-3B). Once the rat finds the platform, the animal is removed from the pool and after a brief delay (such as 10 seconds) is released again. The rat's task is to swim directly to the platform.

The challenge for the rat in the matching-to-place test is to develop a strategy for finding the platform consistently: it is always in the same location on each trial each day, but each new day brings a new location. In the *landmark* version of the task, the platform's location is identified by a cue on the pool wall (Figure 7-3C). The platform moves on every trial, but the relation to the cue is constant. In this task the brain is learning that the distant cues outside the pool are irrelevant; only the local cue is relevant. Rats with different neurological perturbations are selectively impaired in the three versions of the swimming pool task.

Another type of behavioral analysis in rats is related to movement. A major problem facing people with stroke is a deficit in controlling hand and limb movements. The prevalence of stroke has prompted considerable interest in devising ways to analyze such motor behaviors

FIGURE 7-3 Swimming Pool Tasks General arrangement of the swimming pool used in three visuospatial learning tasks for rats. Red lines in parts A, B, and C mark the rat's swimming path on each trial (T).
(A) Information from R. G. M. Morris (1981). Spatial localization does not require the presence of local cues. *Learning and Motivation, 12,* 239–260.
(B) Information from I. Q. Whishaw (1989). Dissociating performance and learning deficits in spatial navigation tasks in rats subjected to cholinergic muscarinic blockade. *Brain Research Bulletin, 23,* 347–358. **(C)** Information from Kolb, B., and Walkey, J. (1987). Behavioural and anatomical studies of the posterior parietal cortex of the rat. *Behavioural Brain Research, 23,* 127–145.

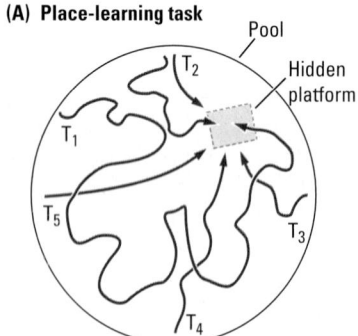

(A) Place-learning task

A rat placed in the pool at various starting locations must learn to find a hidden platform. The rat can do this only by considering the configuration of visual cues in the room—windows, wall decorations, potted plants, and the like.

(B) Matching-to-place task

The rat is again put into the pool at random locations, but the hidden platform is in a new location on each test day. The animal must learn that the location where it finds the platform on the first trial each day is its location for all trials on that day.

(C) Landmark-learning task

The rat must ignore the room cues and learn that only the cue on the wall of the pool signals the location of the platform. The platform and cue are moved on each trial, so the animal is penalized for using room cues to try to solve the problem.

for the purpose of testing new therapies for facilitating recovery. Ian Whishaw (Whishaw & Kolb, 2005) has devised both novel tasks and novel scoring methods to measure the fine details of skilled reaching movements in rats.

In one test, rats are trained to reach through a slot to obtain a piece of sweet food. The movements, which are remarkably similar to the movements people make in a similar task, can be broken down into segments. Investigators can score the segments separately, as they are differentially affected by different types of neurological perturbation.

The photo series in **Figure 7-4** details how a rat orients its body to the slot (A), puts its hand through the slot (B), rotates the hand horizontally to grasp the food (C), then rotates the hand vertically and withdraws it to obtain the food (D). Contrary to reports common in neurology textbooks, primates are not the only animals to make fine digit movements, but because the rat's hand is small and moves so quickly, digit dexterity can be seen in rodents only with use of high-speed videography.

Experiments in Chapter 14 demonstrate fear conditioning in rats, plasticity in the monkey's motor cortex, and neuronal effects of amphetamine sensitization in rats.

(A) (B) (C) (D)

Bryan Kolb

FIGURE 7-4 Skilled Reaching in Rats Movement series displayed by rats trained to reach through a narrow vertical slot to obtain sweet food: **(A)** aim the hand, **(B)** reach over the food, **(C)** grasp the food, **(D)** withdraw and move food to the mouth.

Manipulating Brain—Behavior Interactions

One strategy for studying brain–behavior relationships is to manipulate some aspect of brain function and see how behavior changes. Investigators do so to develop hypotheses about how the brain affects behavior, then to test those hypotheses.

Neuroscientists hypothesize about the functions of brain regions by studying how removing or inhibiting them affects behavior. Broca studied patients with naturally occurring injuries and made inferences about language organization. Similarly, Parkinson patients have motor disturbances and associated cell death in the substantia nigra (**Figure 7-5**). It is a small step experimentally to injure specific brain regions in laboratory animals, then study their behavior. Such studies tell investigators not only about the injured region's function but also what the remaining brain can do in the absence of the injured region. Neuroscientists also study brain region functions to form hypotheses, for example, on how exciting a region affects behavior. Certain drugs and stimulation techniques that increase brain region activity result in behavioral change.

A second reason to manipulate the brain is to develop animal models of neurological and psychiatric disorders. The general presumption in neurology and psychiatry is that it ought to be possible to restore at least some healthy functioning by pharmacological, behavioral, or other interventions. A major hurdle for developing such treatments is that, like most new medical treatments, they must be tested in nonhuman subjects first. (In Section 7-7, we take up scientific and ethical issues surrounding the use of animals in research.)

For brain disorders, researchers must develop models of diseases before they can be treated. Consider dementia, a progressive memory impairment that appears to be related to neuronal death in specific brain regions. The goal for treatment is to reverse or prevent cell death, but developing effective treatments requires an animal model that mimics dementia.

Brains can be manipulated in various ways, the precise manner depending on the specific research question being asked. Researchers can manipulate the whole animal by exposing it to differing diets, social interactions, exercise, sensory stimulation, and a host of other experiences. For brain manipulation, the principal direct techniques are to inactivate the brain via lesion or with drugs or to activate it with electrical stimulation, drugs, or light.

Focus features 5-2, 5-3, and 5-4 detail many aspects of Parkinson disease.

Table 7-1 on page 238 summarizes selected brain manipulation techniques, their goals, and examples.

FIGURE 7-5 Pathology in Parkinson Disease A variety of motor disturbances appear when enough dopamine-producing cells in the substantia nigra die. Information from healthguide.howstuffworks.com/substantia-nigra-and-parkinsons-disease-picture.htm

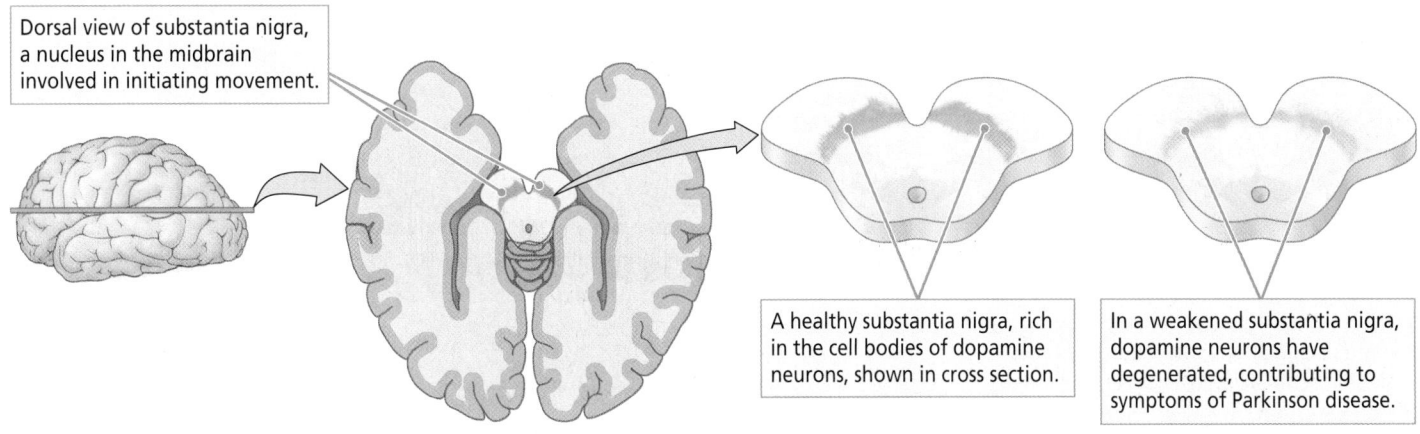

Dorsal view of substantia nigra, a nucleus in the midbrain involved in initiating movement.

A healthy substantia nigra, rich in the cell bodies of dopamine neurons, shown in cross section.

In a weakened substantia nigra, dopamine neurons have degenerated, contributing to symptoms of Parkinson disease.

Brain Lesions

The first—and the simplest—technique used was to ablate (remove or destroy) tissue. Beginning in the 1920s, Karl Lashley, a pioneer of neuroscience research, used *ablation,* and for the next 30 years he tried to find the site of memory in the brain. He trained monkeys and rats on various mazes and motor tasks, then removed bits of cerebral cortex with the goal of producing amnesia for specific memories.

To his chagrin, Lashley failed in his quest. He observed instead that memory loss was related to the amount of tissue he removed. The only conclusion Lashley could reach was that memory is distributed throughout the brain and not located in any single place. Subsequent research strongly indicates that specific brain functions and associated memories are indeed localized to specific brain regions. Ironically, just as Lashley was retiring, William Scoville and Brenda Milner (1957) described a patient from whose brain Scoville had removed both hippocampi as a treatment for epilepsy. The surgery rendered this patient amnesic. During his ablation research, Lashley had never removed the hippocampi because he had no reason to believe the structures had any role in memory. And because the hippocampus is not accessible on the brain's surface, other techniques had to be developed before subcortical lesions could be used.

The solution to accessing subcortical regions is to use a **stereotaxic apparatus**, a device that permits a researcher or a neurosurgeon to target a specific part of the brain for ablation, as shown in **Figure 7-6**. The head is held in a fixed position, and because the location of brain structures is fixed in relation to the junction of the skull bones, it is possible to visualize a three-dimensional brain map.

Rostral–caudal (front to back) measurements, corresponding to the *x*-axis in Figure 7-6, are made relative to the junction of the frontal and parietal bones (the *bregma*). Dorsal–ventral (top to bottom) measurements, the *y*-axis, are made relative to the surface of the brain. Medial–lateral measurements, the *z*-axis, are made relative to the midline junction of the cranial bones. Atlases of the brains of humans and laboratory animals have been constructed from postmortem tissue so that the precise location of any structure can be specified in three-dimensional space.

Consider the substantia nigra. To ablate this region to induce a rat to display symptoms of Parkinson disease, the structure and its three-dimensional location in the brain atlas is located. A small hole is then drilled in the skull, as shown in Figure 7-6, and an electrode lowered to the substantia nigra. If a current is passed through the electrode, the tissue in the region of the electrode tip is killed, producing an *electrolytic lesion.*

Scoville's patient, H. M., profiled in Section 14-2, became the most-studied case in neuroscience.

Review the brain's anatomical locations and orientations in The Basics, in Section 2-1. The brain atlas in Figure 8-14 tracks cortical thickness over time.

stereotaxic apparatus Surgical instrument that permits the researcher to target a specific part of the brain.

hypokinesia Slowness or absence of movement.

compensation Following brain damage, neuroplastic ability to modify behavior from that used prior to the damage.

deep-brain stimulation (DBS) Neurosurgical technique: electrodes implanted in the brain stimulate a targeted area with a low-voltage electrical current to produce or facilitate behavior.

FIGURE 7-6 Stereotaxic Apparatus This instrument allows the precise positioning of electrodes for lesioning or for stimulating brain regions.

A problem with electrolytic lesions: not only are the neurons of the targeted tissue killed but so are any nerve fibers passing through the region (in this case, substantia nigra). One solution is to lower a narrow metal tube (a cannula) instead of an electrode, infuse a neuron-killing chemical, and thus produce a *neurotoxic lesion*. (Figure 7-22 diagrams this procedure.) A selective toxin can be injected that kills only neurons, sometimes only certain types of neurons, and spares the fibers.

To make a rat parkinsonian, a toxin can be injected that is selectively taken up by dopaminergic neurons; this leads to a condition that mimics human Parkinson pathology. Animals with such neurotoxic lesions have a variety of motor symptoms including **hypokinesia** (slowness or absence of movement), short footsteps, and tremor. Drugs such as L-dopa, an agonist that enhances dopamine production, and atropine, an antagonist that blocks acetylcholine production, relieve these symptoms in Parkinson patients. Ian Whishaw and his colleagues (Schallert et al., 1978) thus were able to selectively lesion the substantia nigra in rats to produce a behavioral model of Parkinson disease.

The invasive techniques described so far result in permanent brain damage. With time, the research subject will show **compensation**, the neuroplastic ability to modify behavior from that used prior to the damage. To avoid compensation following permanent lesions, researchers have also developed temporary and reversible lesion techniques such as *regional cooling*, which prevents synaptic transmission. A hollow metal coil is placed next to a neural structure; then chilled fluid is passed through the coil, cooling the brain structure to about 18°C (Lomber & Payne, 1996). When the chilled fluid is removed from the coil, the brain structure quickly warms, and synaptic transmission is restored. Another technique involves local administration of a GABA agonist, which increases local inhibition and in turn prevents the brain structure from communicating with other structures. Degradation of the GABA agonist reverses the local inhibition and restores function.

Brain Stimulation

The brain operates on both electrical and chemical energy, so it is possible to selectively turn brain regions on or off by using electrical or chemical stimulation. Wilder Penfield, in the mid-twentieth century, was the first to use electrical stimulation directly on the human cerebral cortex during neurosurgery. Later researchers used stereotaxic instruments to place an electrode or a cannula in specific brain locations. The objective: enhancing or blocking neuronal activity and observing the behavioral effects.

Perhaps the most dramatic research example comes from stimulating specific regions of the hypothalamus. Rats with electrodes placed in the lateral hypothalamus will eat whenever the stimulation is turned on. If the animals have the opportunity to press a bar that briefly turns on the current, they quickly learn to press the bar to obtain the current, a behavior known as *electrical self-stimulation*. It appears that the stimulation is affecting a neural circuit that involves both eating and pleasure.

Brain stimulation can also be used as a therapy. When the intact cortex adjacent to cortex injured by a stroke is stimulated electrically, for example, it leads to improvement in motor behaviors such as those illustrated in Figure 7-4. Cam Teskey and his colleagues (Brown et al., 2011) successfully restored motor deficits in a rat model of Parkinson disease by electrically stimulating a specific brain nucleus.

Deep-brain stimulation (DBS) is a neurosurgical technique. Electrodes implanted in the brain stimulate a targeted area with a low-voltage electrical current to facilitate behavior. DBS to subcortical structures—for example, the globus pallidus in the basal ganglia of Parkinson patients—makes movements smoother. Medications can often be reduced dramatically. DBS using several neural targets is an approved treatment for obsessive-compulsive disorder. Experimental trials are underway to identify the brain regions optimal for DBS to be used as a treatment for intractable psychiatric disorders such as major depression (Schlaepfer et al., 2013), schizophrenia, and possibly for epilepsy; also for stimulating recovery from TBI.

Ian Whishaw

Shuffling gait of a parkinsonian rat, captured in prints left by its ink-stained hind feet.

Read more about Penfield's dramatic discoveries in Sections 10-4 and 11-2.

Figure 12-12 diagrams hypothalamus anatomy. Section 12-3 details its role in motivated and emotional behavior.

View DBS in place in Figure 1-6.

(A)

(B)

The TMS coil, shown here in a composite MRI and PET scan photograph, interferes with brain function in the adjacent area.

TMS COIL

L   R

Marcello Massimini/University of Milan.

Composite MRI and PET scan from Dr. Tomáš Paus, Rotman Research Institute, Baycrest Centre for Geriatric Care

FIGURE 7-7 Transcranial Magnetic Stimulation **(A)** In clinical therapy for depression, TMS influences neural activity in a localized region. **(B)** Composite photo shows how TMS works.

Electrical stimulation of the brain is invasive: holes must be drilled in the skull and an electrode lowered into the brain. Researchers have taken advantage of the relation between magnetism and electricity to develop a noninvasive technique, **transcranial magnetic stimulation** (TMS). A small wire coil is placed adjacent to the skull, as illustrated in **Figure 7-7**A. A high-voltage current pulsed through the coil produces a rapid increase and subsequent decrease in the magnetic field around the coil. The magnetic field easily passes through the skull and causes a population of neurons in the cerebral cortex to depolarize and fire (Figure 7-7B).

If the motor cortex is stimulated, movement is evoked, or if a movement is in progress, it is disrupted. Similarly, if the visual cortex is stimulated, the participant sees dots of light (*phosphenes*). The effects of brief pulses of TMS do not outlive the stimulation, but *repetitive TMS* (rTMS), or continuous stimulation for up to several minutes, produces more long-lasting effects. TMS and rTMS can be used to study brain–behavior relationships in healthy participants, and rTMS has been tested as a potential treatment for a variety of behavioral disorders. A growing body of research also supports its antidepressant actions.

Research Focus 16-2 describes use of rTMS to treat depression and other behaviorral disorders.

Drug Manipulations

Brain activity can also be stimulated by administration of drugs that pass into the blood-stream and eventually enter the brain or, through an indwelling cannula (illustrated in Figure 7-22), that allows direct application of them to specific brain structures. Drugs can influence the activity of specific neurons in specific brain regions. For example, the drug haloperidol, used to treat schizophrenia, reduces dopaminergic neuron function and makes healthy rats dopey and inactive (*hypokinetic*).

In contrast, drugs that increase dopaminergic activity, such as amphetamine, produce *hyperkinetic rats*—rats that are hyperactive. The advantage of administering drugs is that their effects wear off in time as the drugs are metabolized. It thus is possible to study drug effects on learned behaviors, such as skilled reaching (see Figure 7-4), and then to reexamine the behavior after the drug effect wears off.

Claudia Gonzalez and her colleagues (2006) administered nicotine to rats as they learned a skilled reaching task, then studied their later acquisition of a new skilled reaching task. The researchers found that the earlier nicotine-enhanced motor learning impaired the later motor learning. This finding surprised the investigators, but it now appears that repeated exposure to psychomotor stimulants such as amphetamine, cocaine, and nicotine can produce long-term effects on the brain's later plasticity, its ability to change in response to experience, including learning specific tasks.

transcranial magnetic stimulation (TMS) Procedure in which a magnetic coil is placed over the skull to stimulate the underlying brain; used either to induce behavior or to disrupt ongoing behavior.

synthetic biology Design and construction of biological devices, systems, and machines not found in nature.

optogenetics Transgenic technique that combines genetics and light to control targeted cells in living tissue.

chemogenetics Transgenic technique that combines genetics and synthetic drugs to activate targeted cells in living tissue.

Optogenetics and Chemogenetics

Within the span of a decade, **synthetic biology**, the design and construction of biological devices, systems, and machines not found in nature, has transformed how neuroscientists manipulate brain cells. Techniques include inserting a genetic sequence into the genome of a living organism. The transgenic technique of **optogenetics**, for example, combines genetics and light to control targeted cells in living tissue. A sequence that codes for a light-sensitive protein associated with an ion channel enables investigators to use light to change the shape (conformation) of the channel.

Optogenetics is based on the discovery that light can activate certain proteins that occur naturally and have been inserted into cells of model organisms. For example, opsins, proteins derived from microorganisms, combine a light-sensitive domain with an ion channel. The first opsin used for the optogenetic technique was channelrhodopsin-2 (ChR2). When ChR2 is expressed in neurons and exposed to blue light, the ion channel opens and immediately depolarizes the neuron, causing excitation. In contrast, stimulation of halorhodopsin (NpHR) with a green-yellow light activates a chloride pump, hyperpolarizing the neuron and causing inhibition. A fiber-optic light can be delivered to selective brain regions such that all genetically modified neurons exposed to the light respond immediately (Haubensak et al., 2010).

Optogenetics has tremendous potential as a research tool. Investigators can insert light-sensitive proteins into specific neuron types, such as pyramidal cells, and use light to selectively activate a single cell type. Researchers hail optogenetics for its high spatial and temporal (time) resolution. Ion channels can be placed into specific cell lines and turned on and off on millisecond time scales. Optogenetics also finds application in behavioral studies. Within the limbic system, for example, the amygdala is a key structure in generating fear in animals. If it is targeted with opsins then exposed to an inhibitory light, rats immediately show no fear and wander about in a novel open space. As soon as the light is turned off, they scamper back to a safe hiding place.

In the transgenic technique, **chemogenetics**, the inserted synthetic genetic sequence codes for a G protein–coupled receptor engineered to respond exclusively to a synthetic small-molecule "designer drug." Chemogenetics is best known by the acronym *DREADD* (designer receptor exclusively activated by designer drugs). Its principle advantage is that the drug will activate only the genetically modified receptors, and the receptors will be activated only by the designer drug, not by endogenous molecules (Wess et al., 2013). Thus, specificity is high, but temporal resolution is much lower than with optogenetics because receptors are activated by drugs rather than by light.

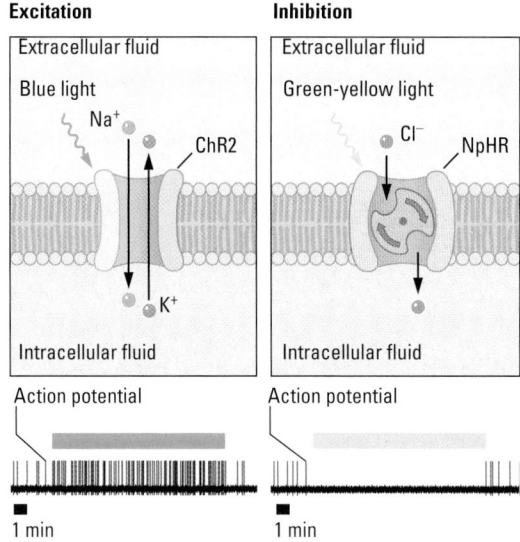

Lighting Up Neurons Optogenetics allows precise temporal control of cell firing and is rapidly reversible. Specific wavelengths activate light-sensitive proteins expressed in neurons. At bottom left, when blue light illuminates a cell in which ChR2 has been incorporated, its firing rate increases dramatically. At right, when green-yellow light illuminates a cell in which NpHR is incorporated, its firing rate decreases dramatically. See more at https://www.youtube.com/watch?v=I64X7vHSHOE.

Figure 2-25 diagrams the limbic structures.

DREADD does not employ the sort of designer drug that may come to mind. Rather than synthetic versions of controlled substances (e.g., heroin), these synthetic drugs interact with a synthetic receptor.

7-1 REVIEW

Measuring and Manipulating Brain and Behavior

Before you continue, check your understanding.

1. Behavioral neuroscience, the study of relations between _____ and _____, employs memory tests such as _____ in nonhuman animals such as rats.

2. Anatomical studies rely on techniques such as _____ tissue postmortem or visualizing living tissue using a _____.

3. Methods developed to manipulate the brain include _____, _____, _____, and _____.

4. Outline the various brain stimulation methods that either activate or inhibit neural activity.

Answers appear at the back of the book.

For additional study tools, visit **LaunchPad**:
www.macmillanhighered.com/launchpad/kolb5e

7-2 Measuring the Brain's Electrical Activity

The brain is always electrically active, even when we sleep. Electrical measures of brain activity are important for studying brain function, for medical diagnosis, and for monitoring the effectiveness of therapies used to treat brain disorders. The four major techniques for tracking the brain's electrical activity are single-cell recording, electroencephalography (EEG), event-related potentials (ERPs), and magnetoencephalography (MEG).

In part, these techniques are used to record electrical activity from different parts of neurons. The electrical behavior of cell bodies and dendrites, which give rise to graded potentials, tends to be much more varied and slower than that of axons, which conduct action potentials.

Figure 4-11 diagrams a cell membrane at rest, Figure 4-13 during graded potentials, and Figure 4-15 generating the action potential.

Recording Action Potentials from Single Cells

By the early 1950s it was becoming possible to record the activity of individual cells by measuring a single neuron's action potentials with fine electrodes inserted into the brain. These microelectrodes can be placed next to cells (*extracellular recording*) or inside cells (*intracellular recording*). Modern extracellular recording techniques make it possible to distinguish the activity of as many as 40 neurons at once. Intracellular recording allows direct study and recording of a single neuron's electrical activity. The two disadvantages of inserting an electrode into a cell are (1) it can kill the cell, and (2) it cannot be done in awake, freely moving animals. Single-cell recording is therefore confined to neurons grown in a dish or, for short periods (hours), from neurons in living brain slices.

Figure 4-6 illustrates the structure and use of microelectrodes.

We now know that cells recorded extracellularly in the brain's sensory regions are highly specific to what excites them. Some cells in the visual system fire vigorously to specific wavelengths of light (a color) or to specific orientations of bars of light (vertical, for example). Other cells respond to more complex patterns, such as faces or hands. Similarly, cells in the auditory system respond to specific sound frequencies (a low or high pitch) or to more complex sound combinations, such as speech (the syllable *ba*, for example).

See, for example, Seeing Shape and Seeing Color in Section 9-4 and Processing Language in Section 10-4.

But certain cells have a far more complex nature that reveals much about brain–behavior relationships. John O'Keefe and his colleagues (O'Keefe & Dostrovsky, 1971) showed that neurons in the rat and mouse hippocampus vigorously fire when an animal is in a specific place in the environment. These **place cells**, illustrated in **Figure 7-8**, code the spatial location of the animal and contribute to a spatial map of the world in the brain. The Nobel Prize in Physiology or Medicine 2014 was awarded to John O'Keefe, May-Britt Moser, and

Section 13-4 discusses how place cells help to store memories.

FIGURE 7-8 Classes of Spatially Related Cells in the Hippocampal Formation
(A and B) Place cells discharge when a rat is at a spatial location, irrespective of its orientation. **(C)** Head-direction cells discharge to indicate where the rat's head points, irrespective of its location.
(D) Grid cells discharge at many locations, forming a virtual grid that is invariant in the face of changes in the rat's direction, movement, or speed. At right in each part, *xy* coordinates indicate the directional selectivity of the cell recorded at left.
Courtesy of John O'Keefe.

(A) Place cell

(B) Place-by-direction cell

(C) Head-direction cell

(D) Grid cell

Courtesy of John O'Keefe.

Edvard I. Moser "for their discoveries of cells that constitute a positioning system in the brain."

O'Keefe's group (Cacucci et al., 2008) also demonstrated that, in mice with a genetically engineered mutation that produces deficits in spatial memory, place cells lack specificity: the cells fire to a very broad region of their world. As a result, these mice have difficulty finding their way around, much as human patients with dementia tend to get lost. One reason may be that a change, similar to the engineered mutation in mice, takes place in human brain cells.

place cells Neurons maximally responsive to specific locations in the world.

electrocorticography (ECoG) Graded potentials recorded with electrodes placed directly on the brain's surface.

EEG: Recording Graded Potentials from Thousands of Cells

In the early 1930s, Hans Berger discovered that the brain's electrical activity could be recorded simply by placing electrodes on the scalp. In Berger's words, recording these "brain waves" produces an "electrical record from the head"—an electroencephalogram. The EEG measures the summed graded potentials from many thousands of neurons. EEG waves, shown in **Figure 7-9**, are recorded by computer. In **electrocorticography**, or ECoG, a method used during neurosurgery, electrodes are placed directly on the cerebral cortex.

EEGs reveal some remarkable features of the brain's electrical activity. The EEG recordings in **Figure 7-10** illustrate three:

1. EEG changes as behavior changes.

2. An EEG recorded from the cortex displays an array of patterns, some rhythmical.

3. The living brain's electrical activity is never silent, even when a person is asleep or comatose.

When a person is aroused, excited, or even just alert, the EEG pattern has a low amplitude and a fast frequency, as shown in Figure 7-10A. This pattern is typical of an EEG taken from anywhere on the skull of an alert subject, not only humans but other animals too. In contrast,

1 Electrodes attached to the scalp correspond to specific brain areas...

2 ...to record their electrical activity. This EEG indicates a relaxed person.

FIGURE 7-9 Recording EEG Waves A simple, noninvasive method for recording the brain's electrical activity, EEG waves recorded via computer (see Figure 4-5) can match wave activity to specific brain regions.

(A) Awake or excited

(B) Relaxed, eyes closed, alpha rhythms generated

(C) Drowsy—slowed frequency, increased-amplitude waves

(D) Asleep—slower, higher-amplitude waves

(E) Deep sleep—even slower and higher-amplitude waves
Time (s)

(F) Coma—further slowing
Time (s)

FIGURE 7-10 Characteristic EEG Recordings Brain wave patterns reflect different states of consciousness in humans. Data from W. Penfield & H. H. Jasper (1954). *Epilepsy and the functional anatomy of the human brain* (p. 12). Boston: Little, Brown.

Amplitude is a recorded brain wave's height. *Frequency* is the number of brain waves recorded per second.

alpha rhythm Regular wave pattern in an electroencephalogram; found in most people when they are relaxed with eyes closed.

event-related potential (ERP) Complex electroencephalographic waveform related in time to a specific sensory event.

Section 13 3 describes how EEG measures sleep and dreaming. Focus features 4-1 and 10-3 detail epilepsy diagnoses and Section 16-3, treatments.

FIGURE 7-11 Detecting ERPs In the averaging process for an auditory ERP, a tone is presented at time 0, and EEG activity in response is recorded. After many successive presentations of the tone, the EEG wave sequence develops a distinctive shape that becomes extremely clear after 100 responses are averaged (bottom panel). Positive and negative waves that appear at different times after the stimulus presentation are used for analysis.

when a participant is calm and quietly relaxed, especially with eyes closed, the rhythmical brain waves shown in Figure 7-10B often emerge. These **alpha rhythms** are extremely regular, with a frequency of approximately 11 cycles per second and amplitudes that wax and wane as the pattern is recorded. In humans, alpha rhythms are generated in the region of the visual cortex at the back of the brain. If a relaxed person is disturbed, performs mental arithmetic, or opens his or her eyes, the alpha rhythms abruptly stop.

EEG is a sensitive indicator of behaviors beyond simple arousal and relaxation. Parts C, D, and E of Figure 7-10 illustrate EEG changes as a person moves from drowsiness to sleep and finally into deep sleep. EEG rhythms become progressively slower and larger in amplitude. Still slower waves appear during anesthesia, after brain trauma, or when a person is in a coma (shown in Figure 7-10F). Only in brain death does the EEG permanently become a flat line.

These distinctive brain wave patterns make EEG a reliable tool for monitoring sleep stages, estimating the depth of anesthesia, evaluating the severity of head injury, and searching for brain abnormalities. In epilepsy, for example, brief periods of impaired awareness or responsiveness and involuntary movements associated with spiking patterns in the EEG characterize electrographic seizures.

The important point here is that EEG recording provides a useful tool both for research and for diagnosing brain dysfunction. EEG can also be used in combination with the brain-imaging techniques described in Sections 7-3 and 7-4 to provide more accurate identification of the source of the large and highly synchronized EEG waves in epilepsy.

Mapping Brain Function with Event-Related Potentials

Brief changes in an EEG signal in response to a discrete sensory stimulus produce complex electroencephalographic waveforms called **event-related potentials** (ERPs). ERPs are largely the graded potentials on dendrites that a sensory stimulus triggers. You might think that they should be easy to detect, but they are not.

ERPs are mixed in with so many other electrical signals in the brain that they are difficult to spot just by visually inspecting an EEG record. One way to detect ERPs is to produce the stimulus repeatedly and average the recorded responses. Averaging tends to cancel out any irregular and unrelated electrical activity, leaving in the EEG record only the potentials the stimulus generated.

To clarify this procedure, imagine throwing a small stone into a lake of choppy water. Although the stone produces a splash, the splash is hard to see among all the ripples and waves. Like the splash surrounded by choppy water, the ERP caused by a sensory stimulus is hard to discern from all the other electrical activity around it.

A solution is to throw a number of stones exactly the same size, always hitting the same spot in the water, and producing the same splash over and over. If a computer then calculates an average of the water's activity, random wave movements will tend to average one another out, and you will see the splashes produced by the stones as clearly as a single stone thrown into a pool of calm water.

Figure 7-11 shows an ERP record (top) that results when a person hears a tone. The EEG record is highly irregular when the tone is first presented. But after averaging over 100 stimulus presentations, a distinctive wave pattern appears, as shown in the bottom panel of Figure 7-11. This ERP pattern consists of a number of negative (N) and positive (P) waves that occur within a few hundred milliseconds after the stimulus.

The waves are numbered in time sequence. For instance, in Figure 7-11, N_1 is a negative wave occurring about 100 milliseconds after the stimulus, whereas P_2 is a positive wave occurring about 200 milliseconds after the stimulus. (The waves may also be labeled as N100 and P200.) Not all these waves are unique to this particular stimulus. Some are common to any auditory stimulus. Other waves, however, correspond to important differences in specific tone. ERPs to spoken words even contain distinctive peaks and patterns that differentiate such similar-sounding words as *cat* and *rat*.

Mild Head Injury and Depression

When a pallet of boxed tools tipped and part of the load struck his head, B. D., an industrial tool salesman, did not lose consciousness. He did sustain a serious cut to his scalp and damage to two spinal vertebrae. The attending physician at the hospital emergency room suspected mild concussion but ordered no further neurological workup at the time.

B. D.'s spinal symptoms gradually cleared, but irritability, anxiety, and depression persisted even 2 years later. B. D. was unable to work, and his behavioral change placed a major strain on his family. His emotional problems led him to withdraw from the world, only worsening his predicament.

A neuropsychological exam administered to B. D. about 2 years after the injury found his general cognitive ability to be well above average, with an IQ score of 115. But B. D. also had significant attentional and short-term memory deficits. A subsequent magnetic resonance image of his brain failed to find any injury that could explain his symptoms. In fact, B. D.'s serious emotional symptoms are common following mild head injury, even when no other neurological or radiological signs of brain injury present themselves.

One tool for investigating brain functioning in such cases is ERP. Reza and colleagues (2007) compared healthy controls to groups of subjects with mild head injuries, with or without depression. The investigators found that all subjects with head injury displayed a delayed P_3 wave, but only those who were depressed as well also had a delayed N_2 wave. These findings demonstrate that ERP can identify cerebral processing abnormalities in people with depression after mild head injury, even when MRI scans are negative. Such evidence can be critical for people like B. D., who are seeking long-term disability support following what appears to be a mild head injury.

Among the many practical reasons for using ERPs to study the brain is the advantage that this EEG technique is noninvasive. Electrodes are placed on the scalp, not in the brain. Therefore, ERPs can be used to study humans, including those most frequently used participants: college students.

Another advantage is cost. Compared to other techniques, such as brain imaging, EEG and ERP are inexpensive and can be recorded from many brain areas simultaneously by pasting an array of electrodes (sometimes more than 200) to different parts of the scalp. Because certain brain areas respond only to certain sensory stimuli (e.g., auditory areas respond to sounds and visual areas to sights), relative responses at different locations can be used to map brain function.

Figure 7-12 shows a multiple-recording method that uses 128 electrodes simultaneously to detect ERPs at many cortical sites. Computed averaging techniques reduce the masses of information obtained to simpler comparisons between electrode sites. For example, if the focus of interest is P_3, a positive wave occurring about 300 milliseconds after the stimulus, the computer can display a graph of the skull showing only the amplitude of P_3. A computer can also convert the averages at different sites into a color code, graphically representing the brain regions most responsive to the signal.

ERPs not only can detect which brain areas are processing particular stimuli but also can be used to study the order in which different regions participate. This second use of ERPs is important because we want to know the route that information takes as it travels through the brain. In Figure 7-12, the participant is viewing a picture of a rat that appears repeatedly in the same place on a computer screen. The P_3 recorded from the posterior right side of the head is larger than any other P_3 occurring elsewhere, meaning that this region is a hot spot for processing the visual stimulus. Presumably, this particular participant's right posterior brain is central in decoding the picture of the rat 300 milliseconds after it is presented.

Many other interesting research areas benefit from using ERPs, as described in Clinical Focus 7-2, Mild Head Injury and Depression. ERPs also can be used to study how children learn and process information differently as they mature. ERPs can examine how a person with a brain injury compensates for the impairment by using undamaged brain regions. ERPs can even help reveal which brain areas are most sensitive to aging and therefore contribute most to declining behavioral functions among the elderly. This simple, inexpensive research tool can address all these areas.

Electrodes attached to the scalp of a research subject are connected to...

Electrodes in geodesic sensor net

...a computer display of electrical activity, showing a large positive (P_3) wave at the posterior right side of the head.

P_3

This electrical activity can be converted into a color representation showing the hot spot for the visual stimulus.

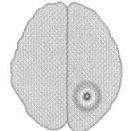

Resting   300 ms after viewing

FIGURE 7-12 Using ERPs to Image Brain Activity

magnetoencephalogram (MEG) Magnetic potentials recorded from detectors placed outside the skull.

computed tomography (CT) X-ray technique that produces a static three-dimensional image of the brain in cross section—a *CT scan*.

magnetic resonance imaging (MRI) Technique that produces a static three-dimensional brain image by passing a strong magnetic field through the brain, followed by a radio wave, then measuring a radio frequency signal emitted from hydrogen atoms.

Magnetoencephalography

Passing a magnetic field across a wire induces an electrical current in the wire. Conversely, current flowing along a wire induces a magnetic field around the wire. The same is true in the brain. Neural activity, by generating an electrical field, also produces a magnetic field. Although the magnetic field produced by a single neuron is vanishingly small, the field produced by many neurons is sufficiently strong to be recorded on the scalp. The record of this phenomenon, a **magnetoencephalogram** (MEG), is the magnetic counterpart of the EEG or ERP.

Calculations based on MEG measurements not only describe neuronal groups' electrical activity but also localize the cell groups generating the measured field in three dimensions. Magnetic waves conducted through living tissue undergo less distortion than electrical signals do, so an MEG can yield a higher resolution than an ERP. A major advantage of the MEG over the EEG and ERP, then, is MEG's ability to more precisely identify the source of the activity being recorded. For example, MEG has proved useful in locating the source of epileptic discharges. MEG's disadvantage is its high cost in comparison with the apparatus used to produce EEGs and ERPs.

7-2 **REVIEW**

Measuring the Brain's Electrical Activity

Before you continue, check your understanding.

1. The four major techniques for tracking the brain's electrical activity are _____, _____, _____, and _____.

2. Single-cell recording measures _____ from a single neuron.

3. EEG measures _____ on the cell membrane.

4. Magnetoencephalography measures the _____ and also provides a _____.

5. What is the advantage of EEG techniques over MEG?

Answers appear at the back of the book.

For additional study tools, visit 🌀 **LaunchPad:**
www.macmillanhighered.com/launchpad/kolb5e

7-3 Anatomical Imaging Techniques: CT and MRI

Tomo- comes from the Greek word for *section*, indicating that tomography yields a picture through a single brain slice.

Until the early 1970s, the only way to actually image the living brain was by using X-rays that produce static images of brain anatomy from one angle. The modern era of brain imaging began in the early 1970s, when Allan Cormack and Godfrey Hounsfield independently developed an X-ray approach now called **computed tomography**: the *CT scan*. Cormack and Hounsfield both recognized that a narrow X-ray beam could be passed through the same object at many angles, creating many images; the images could be combined with the use of computing and mathematical techniques to produce a three-dimensional image of the brain.

The CT method resembles the way in which our two eyes (and our brain) work in concert to perceive depth and distance to locate an object in space. The CT scan, however, coordinates many more than two images, roughly analogous to our walking to several vantage points to obtain multiple views. X-ray absorption varies with tissue density. High-density tissue, such as bone, absorbs a lot of radiation. Low-density material, such as ventricular fluid or blood, absorbs little. Neural tissue absorption lies between these extremes. CT scanning

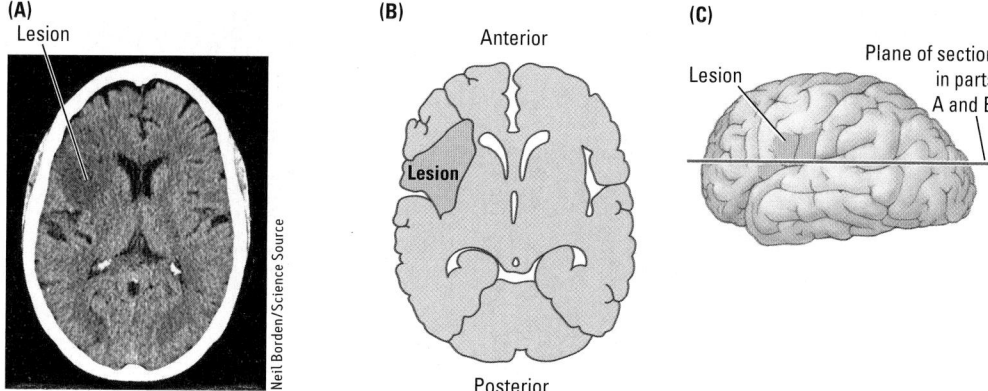

FIGURE 7-13 CT Scan and Brain Reconstruction **(A)** Dorsal view of a horizontal CT scan of a subject with Broca's aphasia. The dark region at the left anterior is the area of the lesion. **(B)** A schematic representation of the horizontal section, with the area of the lesion shown in blue. **(C)** A reconstruction of the brain, showing a lateral view of the left hemisphere with the lesion shown in blue. Research from Damasio, H., & Damasio, A. R. (1989). *Lesion analysis in neuropsychology* (p. 56). New York: Oxford University Press.

software translates these differences in absorption into a brain image in which dark colors indicate low-density regions and light colors indicate high-density regions.

Figure 7-13A shows a typical CT scan. The dense skull forms a white border. The brain's gray matter density does not differ sufficiently from that of white matter for a CT scan to distinguish between the two clearly, so the cortex and its underlying white matter show up as a more or less homogeneous gray. Ventricles can be visualized, however, because the fluid in them is far less dense: they, as well as some major fissures in the cortex, are rendered darker in the CT scan. Each point on the image in Figure 7-13A represents about a 1-millimeter-diameter circle of tissue, a resolution sufficient to distinguish two objects about 5 millimeters apart and appropriate for localizing brain tumors and lesions.

The lesion revealed in Figure 7-13A is a damaged region where the presence of fewer neurons and more fluid produces a contrast that appears as a dark area in the CT scan. This subject presented with symptoms of *Broca's aphasia*, the inability to speak fluently despite having average comprehension and intact vocal mechanisms. The location of the lesion, in the left frontal cortex (adjacent to the butterfly-shaped lateral ventricles), confirms this diagnosis. Figure 7-13B, a drawing of the same horizontal section, uses color to portray the lesion. Figure 7-13C is a lateral view of the left hemisphere reconstructed from a series of horizontal CT scans and showing the lesion's extent.

An anatomical alternative to the CT scan, **magnetic resonance imaging** (MRI), is based on the principle that hydrogen atoms behave like spinning bar magnets in the presence of a magnetic field. The MRI procedure is illustrated in **Figure 7-14**. The dorsal view of the brain portrays density differences among the hydrogen atoms in different neural regions as colors on the horizontal slice through the head.

Normally, hydrogen atoms point randomly in different directions, but when placed in a large, static magnetic field, they line up in parallel as they orient themselves with respect to the static field's lines of force. In an MRI scanner, radio pulses are applied to a brain whose atoms have been aligned in this manner, and each radio pulse forms a second magnetic field. The second field causes the spinning atoms to deviate from the parallel orientation caused by the static magnetic field to a new orientation.

As each radio pulse ends and the hydrogen atoms realign with the static field, they emit a tiny amount of energy, and a coil detects this realignment. Based on the signals from the coil, a computer re-creates the position of the hydrogen nuclei, producing a magnetic resonance image. MRI images may be based on the density of the hydrogen atoms in different brain

Section 10-4 delves into aphasias that result from damaged speech areas.

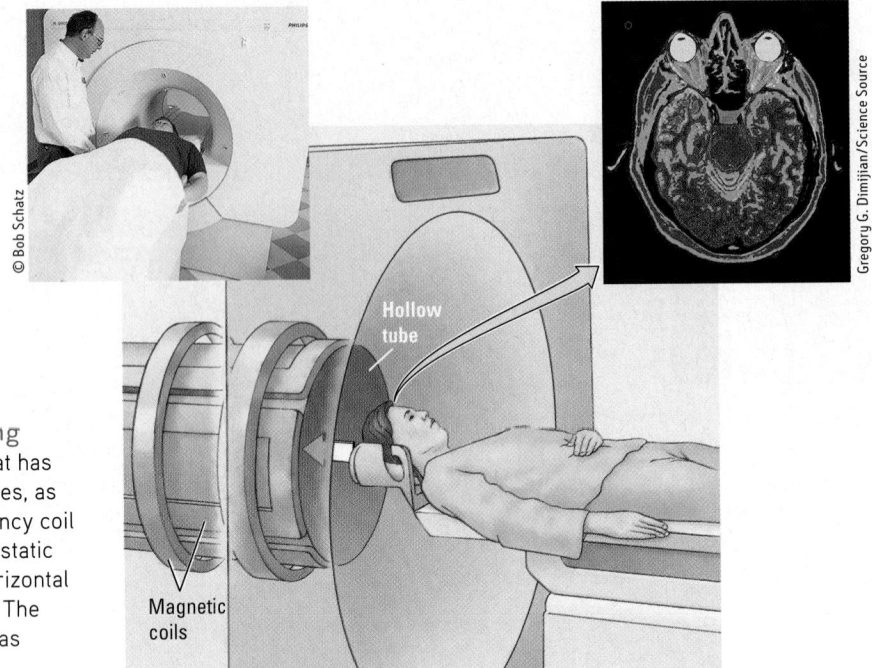

FIGURE 7-14 Magnetic Resonance Imaging The subject is placed in a long metal cylinder that has two sets of magnetic coils arranged at right angles, as shown in the drawing. An additional radiofrequency coil (not shown) surrounds the head, perturbing the static magnetic fields to produce an MRI image of a horizontal section through the head, shown in dorsal view. The density differences in hydrogen atoms show up as colors in the image.

FIGURE 7-15 Magnetic Resonance Image Electrical currents emitted by wobbling atoms are recorded by MRI to represent different types of tissue—cerebrospinal fluid, brain matter, and bone, for example—as lighter or darker depending on the density of hydrogen atoms in the tissue.

diffusion tensor imaging (DTI) Magnetic resonance imaging method that can image fiber pathways in the brain by detecting the directional movements of water molecules.

magnetic resonance spectroscopy (MRS) Magnetic resonance imaging method that uses the hydrogen proton signal to determine the concentration of brain metabolites.

Clinical Focus 4-2 describes how myelin loss in MS disrupts neuronal function.

Focus 16-3 explores the relationship between concussion and degenerative brain disease.

regions. Areas with high water (H_2O) content (cell body–rich areas), for example, stand out from areas with lower water content (axon-rich areas). **Figure 7-15** shows such a magnetic resonance image.

Diffusion tensor imaging (DTI) is an MRI method that detects the directional movements of water molecules to image nerve fiber pathways in the brain. Water can move relatively freely along the axon but less freely across cell membranes. The direction of this water movement is detected by a coil and interpreted by a computer. DTIs can delineate abnormalities in neural pathways. They are also used to identify changes in fiber myelination, such as the damage that leads to myelin loss in multiple sclerosis.

Each scan in the series of DTIs shown in **Figure 7-16** represents a dorsal view at increasing depths through the brain. Although the images appear to show real fibers, DTIs are virtual and based on computer reconstructions of water movement along axons, which should correspond to actual fibers. Nonetheless, DTI easily detects abnormalities, such as those that occur in multiple sclerosis, stroke, or concussion, in the imaged fiber pathways and in their myelin sheaths.

Zephyr/Science Source

FIGURE 7-16 Diffusion Tensor Imaging MRI can measure the diffusion of water molecules in white matter, allowing the visualization of nerve fiber tracts. The front of the brain is at the top in these scans of sections through a healthy brain. The axons are colored according to orientation: fibers running left–right are red, front–back are blue, and up–down are green. Section 15-3 outlines how DTI is helping researchers develop a *brain connectome* to map functional connections in the living brain.

Magnetic resonance spectroscopy (MRS) is an MRI method that uses the hydrogen proton signal to determine the concentration of brain metabolites such as N-acetylaspartate (NAA) in brain tissue. This measurement is especially useful for detecting persisting abnormalities in brain metabolism in disorders such as concussion.

7-3 REVIEW

Anatomical Imaging Techniques: CT and MRI

Before you continue, check your understanding.

1. The principal anatomical brain imaging methods are _____ and _____.

2. Diffusion tensor imaging identifies _____, whereas magnetic resonance spectroscopy determines _____.

3. In addition to imaging the density of different brain regions, CT and MRI can be used to assess _____.

4. Explain briefly how the development of the CT scan ushered in the brain-imaging techniques used today in neuroscience research.

Answers appear at the back of the book.

For additional study tools, visit 🧠 **LaunchPad**:
www.macmillanhighered.com/launchpad/kolb5e

7-4 Functional Brain Imaging

Advances in MRI and computing technologies led from anatomical to functional brain-imaging techniques, which allow investigators to measure the amount of blood, oxygen, and glucose the brain uses as subjects or participants solve cognitive problems. When a brain region is active, the amount of blood, oxygen, and glucose flowing to the region increases. It therefore is possible to infer changes in brain activity by measuring either blood flow or levels of the blood's constituents, such as oxygen, glucose, and iron. Three techniques developed from this logic are functional MRI, optical tomography, and positron emission tomography.

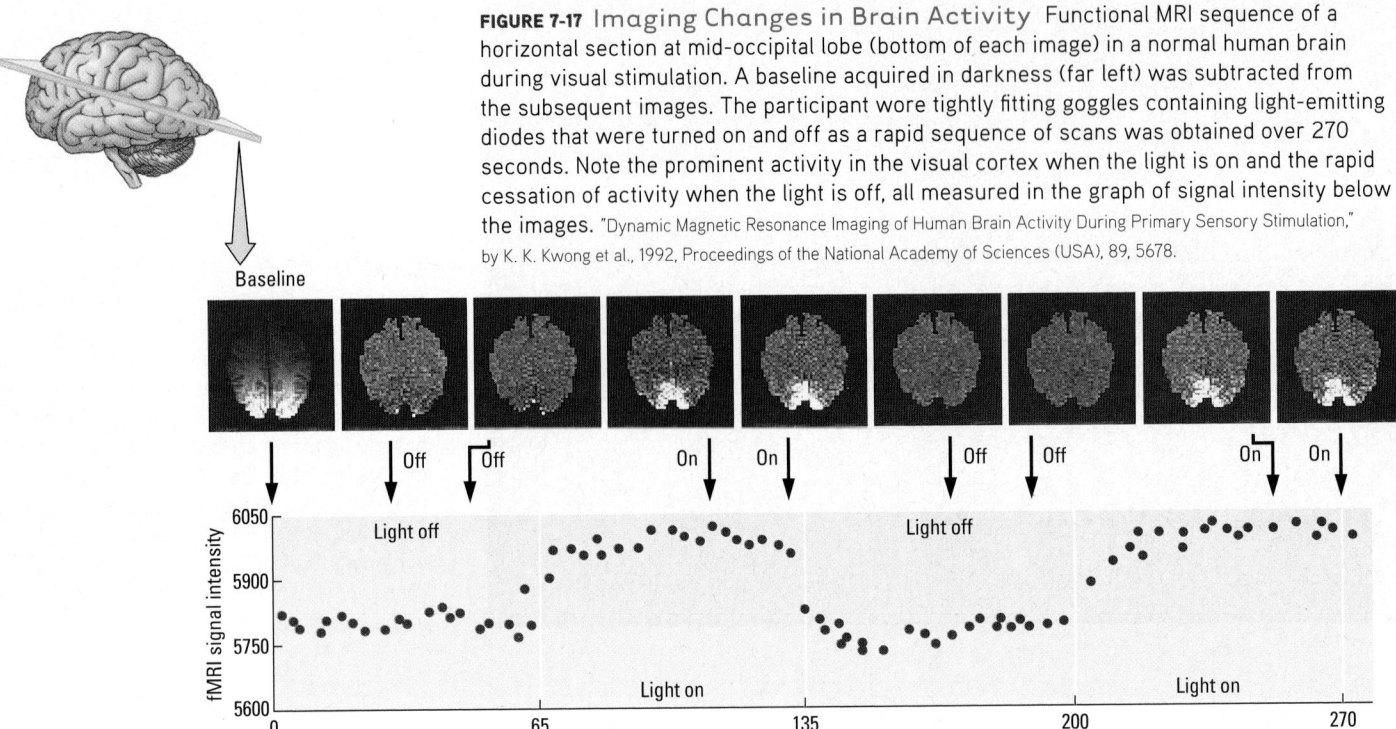

FIGURE 7-17 Imaging Changes in Brain Activity Functional MRI sequence of a horizontal section at mid-occipital lobe (bottom of each image) in a normal human brain during visual stimulation. A baseline acquired in darkness (far left) was subtracted from the subsequent images. The participant wore tightly fitting goggles containing light-emitting diodes that were turned on and off as a rapid sequence of scans was obtained over 270 seconds. Note the prominent activity in the visual cortex when the light is on and the rapid cessation of activity when the light is off, all measured in the graph of signal intensity below the images. "Dynamic Magnetic Resonance Imaging of Human Brain Activity During Primary Sensory Stimulation," by K. K. Kwong et al., 1992, Proceedings of the National Academy of Sciences (USA), 89, 5678.

functional magnetic resonance imaging (fMRI) Magnetic resonance imaging in which changes in elements such as iron or oxygen are measured during the performance of a specific behavior; used to measure cerebral blood flow during behavior or resting.

resting-state fMRI (rs-fMRI) Magnetic resonance imaging method that measures changes in elements such as iron or oxygen when the individual is resting (not engaged in a specific task).

Figure 2-7 diagrams the extent of the major cerebral arteries.

Functional Magnetic Resonance Imaging

As neurons become active, they use more oxygen, resulting in a temporary dip in the blood oxygen level. At the same time, active neurons signal blood vessels to dilate to increase blood flow and bring more oxygen to the area. Peter Fox and colleagues (1986) discovered that when human brain activity increases, the extra oxygen produced by increased blood flow actually exceeds the tissue's needs. As a result, the amount of oxygen in an activated brain area increases.

Oxygen is carried on the hemoglobin molecule in red blood cells. Changes in the ratio of oxygen-rich hemoglobin to oxygen-poor hemoglobin alters the blood's magnetic properties, because oxygen-rich hemoglobin is less magnetic than oxygen-poor hemoglobin. In 1990, Segi Ogawa and his colleagues showed that MRI could accurately match these changes in magnetic properties to specific brain locations (Ogawa et al., 1990). This process, **functional magnetic resonance imaging** (fMRI), signals which areas are displaying changes in activity.

Figure 7-17 shows changes in the fMRI signal in the visual cortex of a person who is being stimulated with light. When the light is turned on, the visual cortex (bottom of the brain images) becomes more active than during baseline (no light). In other words, functional changes in the brain are inferred from increases and decreases in the MRI signal produced by changes in oxygen levels.

When superimposed on MRI-produced anatomical brain images, fMRI changes in activity can be attributed to particular structures. The dense blood vessel supply to the cerebral cortex allows for a spatial resolution of fMRI on the order of 1 millimeter, affording good spatial resolution of the brain activity's source. On the other hand, because changes in blood flow take as long as a third of a second, the temporal resolution of fMRI is not as precise as that obtained with EEG recordings and ERPs.

fMRI also has the disadvantage that subjects must lie motionless in a long, noisy tube, an experience that can prove claustrophobic. The confined space and lack of mobility also restrict the types of behavioral experiments that can be performed. Nonetheless, fMRI is a major tool in cognitive neuroscience.

The living brain is always active, and researchers have succeeded in inferring brain function and connectivity by studying fMRI signals when participants are resting, that is, not engaged in any specific task. This signal, **resting-state fMRI** (rs-fMRI), is collected when participants are asked to look at a fixation cross and to keep their eyes open.

The scanner collects brain activity, typically for at least 4-minute blocks. Researchers are attempting to shorten the period by increasing the strength of the static magnetic field and developing more sensitive coils. Statistical analysis of the data entails correlating activity in different brain regions over time. Although rs-fMRI is still in its growth phase, investigators already have identified many consistent networks of brain activity and abnormalities in disease states such as dementia and schizophrenia (Van den Heuvel & Hulshoff Pol, 2010).

Optical Tomography

Research Focus 7-1, Tuning into Language, describes a brain-imaging study that used functional near-infrared spectroscopy (fNIRS) to investigate newborn infants' responses to language. fNIRS is a form of *optical tomography*, a functional imaging technique that operates on the principle that an object can be reconstructed by gathering light transmitted through it. One requirement is that the object at least partially transmit light. Thus, optical tomography can image soft body tissue, such as that in the breast or the brain.

In fNIRS, reflected infrared light is used to determine blood flow because oxygen-rich hemoglobin and oxygen-poor hemoglobin differ in their absorption spectra. By measuring the blood's light absorption it is possible to measure the brain's average oxygen consumption. So fNIRS and fMRI measure essentially the same thing but with different tools. In fNIRS, an array of optical transmitter and receiver pairs are fitted across the scalp, as illustrated in **Figure 7-18A**.

The obvious advantage of fNIRS is that it is relatively easy to hook subjects up repeatedly and record from them for short periods, from infancy to senescence. The disadvantage is that the light does not penetrate far into the brain, so researchers are restricted to measuring cortical activity (Figure 7-18B). The spatial resolution is also not as good as with other noninvasive methods, although NIRS equipment now uses over 100 light detectors on the scalp,

FIGURE 7-18 How NIRS Works **(A)** Light injectors (red) and detectors (blue) are distributed in an array across the head. **(B)** Light injected through the scalp and skull penetrates the brain to a depth of about 2 centimeters. A small fraction of the light is reflected and captured by a detector on the scalp surface. Light is reflected from as deep as 2 centimeters but also from the tissue above it, as illustrated by the banana shape of the curves. Information from L. Spinney (2005). Optical topography and the color of blood, *The Scientist, 19*, 25–27.

(A)

Hitachi, Ltd. Research & Development Group. Photo by Atsushi Maki

(B)

Light injector

Light detector

2 cm

Scalp

Skull

Dura mater

Arachnoid layer and cerebral spinal fluid

Cerebral cortex (gray matter)

White matter

positron emission tomography (PET)
Imaging technique that detects changes in blood flow by measuring changes in the uptake of compounds such as oxygen or glucose; used to analyze the metabolic activity of neurons.

Tagged to a glucose molecule, fluorine-18 (^{18}F) acts as a marker for metabolism and is used far more in PET than is ^{15}O. The methods are essentially the same.

which allows acceptable spatial resolution in the image. NIRS has been used to differentiate cancerous from noncancerous brain tissue. This advance should lead to safe, extensive surgical removal of brain cancers and improved outcomes (Kut et al., 2015).

Positron Emission Tomography

Researchers use **positron emission tomography** (PET) to study the metabolic activity of brain cells engaged in processing brain functions such as language. PET imaging detects changes in the brain's blood flow by measuring changes in the uptake of compounds such as oxygen and glucose (Posner & Raichle, 1997). A PET camera, like the one shown in **Figure 7-19**, is a doughnut-shaped array of radiation detectors that encircles a person's head. A small amount of water, labeled with radioactive molecules, is injected into the bloodstream. The person injected with these molecules is in no danger because those used, including the radioactive isotope oxygen-15 (^{15}O), are very unstable. They break down in just a few minutes and are quickly eliminated from the body. (Most of the oxygen in air we breathe is the stable ^{16}O molecule.)

Radioactive ^{15}O molecules release tiny, positively charged subatomic particles known as positrons (electrons with a positive charge). Positrons are emitted from an unstable atom because it is deficient in neutrons. The positrons are attracted to the negatively charged electrons in the brain, and the collision of the two particles leads to annihilation of both, which produces energy.

This energy, in the form of two photons (a unit of light energy), leaves the head at the speed of light and is detected by the PET camera. The photons leave the head in exactly opposite directions from the site of positron–electron annihilation, so annihilation photon detectors can detect their source, as illustrated in Figure 7-19. A computer identifies the coincident photons and locates the annihilation source to generate the PET image.

The PET system enables blood flow measurement in the brain because the unstable radioactive molecules accumulate there in direct proportion to the rate of local blood flow. Local blood flow in turn is related to neural activity because potassium ions released from stimulated neurons dilate adjacent blood vessels. The more the blood flow, the higher the radiation counts recorded by the PET camera.

Sophisticated computer imaging can map blood flow in the brain when a person is at rest with closed eyes (**Figure 7-20**). The resting-state map shows, in a series of frames, where blood flow is highest. Even though the distribution of blood is not uniform, it is still difficult

FIGURE 7-19 PET Scanner and Image Subject lying in a PET scanner, whose design is illustrated in the drawing. In the scan, the bright red and yellow areas are regions of high blood flow.

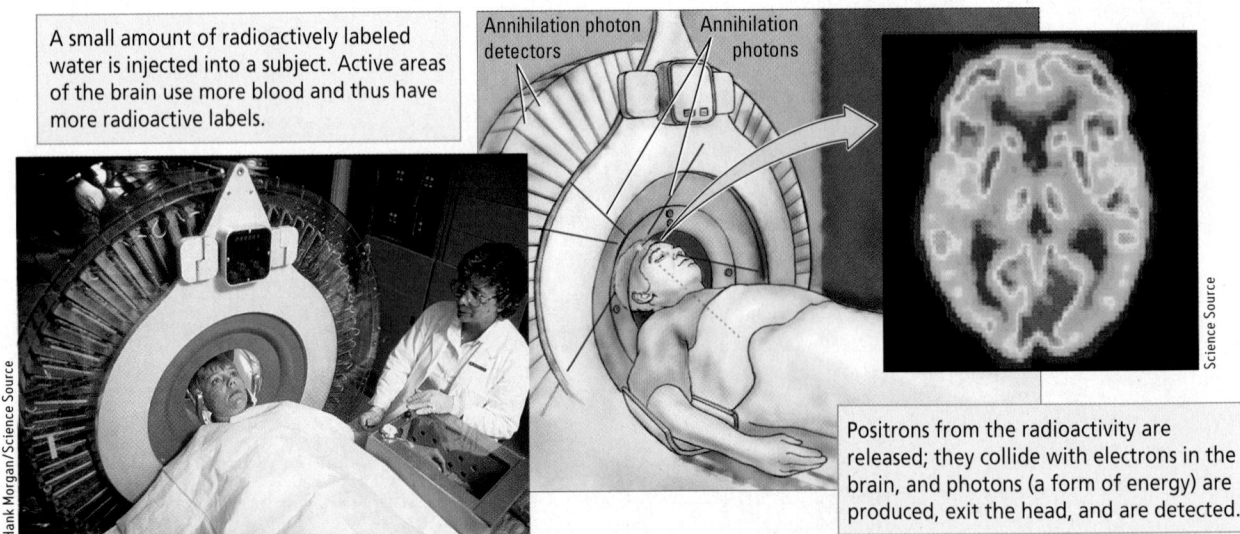

A small amount of radioactively labeled water is injected into a subject. Active areas of the brain use more blood and thus have more radioactive labels.

Annihilation photon detectors

Annihilation photons

Positrons from the radioactivity are released; they collide with electrons in the brain, and photons (a form of energy) are produced, exit the head, and are detected.

Hank Morgan/Science Source

Science Source

FIGURE 7-20 Resting State PET images of blood flow obtained while a single subject rested quietly with eyes closed. Each scan represents a horizontal brain section, from the dorsal surface (1) to the ventral surface (31). Development of rs-fMRI suggests that resting-state PET analysis may emerge.

to conclude much from such a map because the entire brain is receiving oxygen and glucose.

But PET researchers who are studying the link between blood flow and mental activity use a *subtraction procedure*. They subtract the blood flow pattern when the brain is in a carefully selected control state from the pattern of blood flow imaged when the subject is engaged in the task under study, as illustrated in the top row of **Figure 7-21**. This subtraction process images the change in blood flow between the two states. The change can be averaged across subjects (middle row) to yield a representative average image difference that reveals which brain areas are selectively active during the task (bottom). PET does not measure local neural activity directly; rather, it infers activity on the assumption that blood flow increases where neuron activity increases.

A significant limitation of PET is that radiochemicals, including so-called radiopharmaceuticals used in diagnosing human patients, must be prepared in a cyclotron quite close to the scanner because their half-lives are so short that transportation time is a severely limiting factor. Generating these materials is very expensive. But in spite of the expense, PET has important advantages over other imaging methods:

- PET can detect the decay of literally hundreds of radiochemicals, which allows the mapping of a wide range of brain changes and conditions, including changes in pH, glucose, oxygen, amino acids, neurotransmitters, and proteins.

- PET can detect relative amounts of a given neurotransmitter, the density of neurotransmitter receptors, and metabolic activities associated with learning, brain poisoning, and degenerative processes that might be related to aging.

FIGURE 7-21 The Procedure of Subtraction In the upper row of scans, the control condition, resting while looking at a static fixation point (control), is subtracted from the experimental condition, looking at a flickering checkerboard (stimulation). The subtraction produces a different scan for each of five experimental subjects, shown in the middle row, but all show increased blood flow in the occipital region. The difference scans are averaged to produce the representative image at the bottom.

- PET is widely used to study cognitive function with great success. For example, PET confirms that various brain regions perform differing functions.

- There are now hybrid scanners for diagnostic imaging and they come in different combinations in which the imaging modalities combines PET with CT, PET with MRI and also PET with MRI and EEG. The advantage of these hybrid scanners is that they can acquire high-quality anatomical images and then overlay the functional/metabolic image information, allowing for precise localization that was not available before, and all within a single examination.

(7-4) **REVIEW**

Functional Brain Imaging

Before you continue, check your understanding.

1. The principal methods of functional brain imaging are _____, _____, and _____.

2. PET uses _____ to measure brain processes and to identify _____ changes in the brain.

3. fMRI and optical imaging measure changes in _____.

4. Why are resting-state measurements useful to researchers?

   Answers appear at the back of the book.

For additional study tools, visit 🎧 **LaunchPad**:
www.macmillanhighered.com/launchpad/kolb5e

(7-5) Chemical and Genetic Measures of Brain and Behavior

Our focus so far has been on how neuroscientists study the individual and collective activity of neurons and how neuronal activity relates to behavior. Neurons are regulated by *genes*, DNA segments that encode the synthesis of particular proteins within cells. Genes control the cell's production of chemicals, so it is possible to relate behavior to genes and to chemicals inside and outside the cell. Chemical and genetic approaches require sophisticated technologies that have seen major advances in the past decade.

Section 3-2 investigates how neurons function. Section 3-3 relates genes to cell function, genetic engineering, and epigenetic mechanisms.

Measuring Brain Chemistry

The brain contains a wide mixture of chemicals ranging from neurotransmitters and hormones to glucose and gases, among many others. Abnormalities in amounts of these chemicals can cause serious disruptions in behavior. Prime examples are Parkinson disease, characterized by low dopamine levels in the substantia nigra, and depression, correlated with low serotonin and/or noradrenaline production. The simplest way to measure brain chemistry in such diseases is to extract tissue postmortem from affected humans or laboratory animals and undertake traditional biochemical techniques, such as high-performance liquid chromatography (HPLC), to measure specific chemical levels.

microdialysis Technique used to determine the chemical constituents of extracellular fluid in freely moving animals.

striatum Caudate nucleus and putamen of the basal ganglia.

cerebral voltammetry Technique used to identify the concentration of specific chemicals in the brain as animals behave freely.

Fluctuations in brain chemistry are associated not only with behavioral dysfunction but also with ongoing healthy behavior. For example, research over at least the past 30 years shows that dopamine levels fluctuate in the nucleus accumbens (a structure in the subcortical basal ganglia) in association with stimuli related to rewarding behaviors such as food and sex. Changes in brain chemistry can be measured in freely moving animals using two methods, cerebral microdialysis and cerebral voltammetry.

Section 12-6 explores neural effects of rewarding events.

Microdialysis, which can determine the chemical constituents of extracellular fluid, is widely used in the laboratory. The technique has found clinical application over the past decade. A catheter with a semipermeable membrane at its tip is placed in the brain, as illustrated in **Figure 7-22**. A fluid flows through the cannula and passes along the cell membrane. Simple diffusion drives extracellular molecules across the membrane along their concentration gradient.

Fluid containing the molecules from the brain exits through tubing to be collected for analysis. The fluid is removed at a constant rate so that changes in brain chemistry can be correlated with behavior. For example, if a rat is placed in an environment in which it anticipates sex or a favored food, microdialysis will record an increase in dopamine within the basal ganglia regions of the caudate nucleus and putamen, known as the **striatum**.

Microdialysis is used in some medical centers to monitor chemistry in the injured brain. The effects of TBI or stroke can be worsened by secondary events such as a drastic increase in the neurotransmitter glutamate. Such biochemical changes can lead to irreversible cell damage or death. Physicians are beginning to use microdialysis to monitor such changes, which can then be treated.

Cerebral voltammetry works on a different principle. A small carbon fiber electrode and a metal electrode are implanted in the brain, and a weak current is passed through the metal electrode. The current causes electrons to be added to or removed from the surrounding chemicals. Changes in extracellular levels of specific neurotransmitters can be measured as they occur.

Because different currents lead to changes in different compounds, it is possible to identify levels of different transmitters, such as serotonin or dopamine, and related chemicals. Voltammetry has the advantage of not requiring the chemical analysis of fluid removed from the brain, as microdialysis does, but it has the disadvantage of being destructive. That is, the chemical measurements require the degradation of one chemical into another. Thus this technique is not well suited to clinical uses.

Section 4-1 explains diffusion and concentration gradients in detail.

This result mirrors wanting-and-liking theory described in Section 6-4.

Section 6-4 investigates why glutamate and similar chemicals can act as neurotoxins.

FIGURE 7-22 Microdialysis
Information from M. M. Tisdall & M. Smith (2006). Cerebral microdialysis: Research technique or clinical tool. *British Journal of Anaesthesia, 97,* 18–25.

Measuring Genes in Brain and Behavior

Most human behaviors cannot be explained by genetic inheritance alone, but variations in gene sequences do contribute significantly to brain organization. About 1 in 250 live births are identical twins, people who share an identical genome. Identical twins often have remarkably similar behavioral traits. Twin studies show strong concordance rates that support genetic contributions to drug addiction and other psychiatric disorders. But twin studies also show that environmental factors and life experience must be involved: concordance for most behavioral disorders, such as schizophrenia and depression, is far less than 100 percent. Life experiences are acting epigenetically to alter gene expression.

Genetic factors can also be studied by comparing people who were adopted early in life and usually would not have a close genetic relationship to their adoptive parents. Here, a high concordance rate for behavioral traits would imply a strong environmental influence on behavior. Ideally, an investigator would be able to study both the adoptive and biological parents to tease out the relative heritability of behavioral traits.

Cannabis Use, Psychosis, and Genetics

Cannabis is the most widely used illicit drug in the world. Because it is nearly impossible to overdose, cannabis is usually considered safe, but it is not completely free of side effects. A relationship has been established between cannabis use and the emergence of psychosis, especially with use in adolescence: earlier use is associated with both an earlier onset and worse long-term prognosis of disease.

Given that most adolescents who use cannabis do not develop psychosis, however, some genetic vulnerability likely predisposes certain individuals to develop a psychotic condition when exposed to it. Cannabis use thus may act more as a trigger for the onset of schizophrenia than as the primary cause of the disease.

A working hypothesis contends that one culprit may be the *COMT* gene, because *COMT* has been associated with schizophrenia. The *COMT* gene product is an enzyme involved in metabolizing dopamine in the synapse, and abnormalities in dopaminergic activity are associated with psychosis. The hypothesis predicts that adolescents who develop psychosis after cannabis use have an abnormality in the *COMT* gene.

Avshalom Caspi and colleagues (2005) analyzed the *COMT* gene in nearly a thousand 26-year-old adults who had participated in a long-term health study in New Zealand. As shown in the nearby figure, although no genotype was more likely to use cannabis in adolescence, carriers of the *Val* allele were far more likely to develop psychotic symptoms if they did use cannabis in adolescence (graph on the left) but not if they used it in adulthood (graph on the right). The *Met/Met* genotype showed no adverse effect of cannabis use in adolescence.

These results show that genetic variations can predispose people to show adverse effects of environmental experiences and that the experiences may have age-related effects. Presumably these effects relate to the significant development the brain undergoes during adolescence.

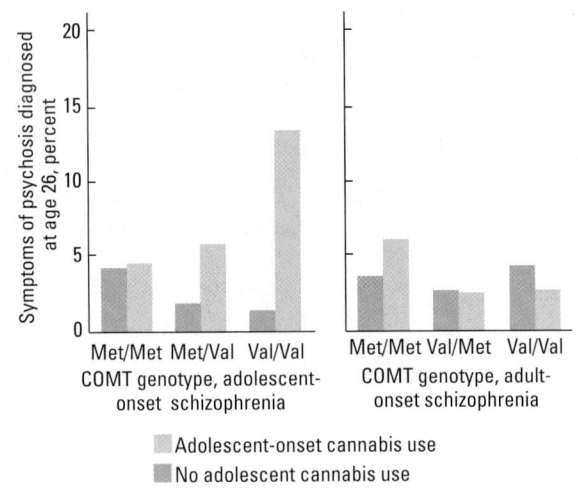

Information from A. Caspi, T. E. Moffitt, M. Cannon, J. McClay, R. Murray, et al. (2005). Moderation of the effect of adolescent-onset cannabis use on adult psychosis by a functional polymorphism in the catechol-O-methyltransferase gene: Longitudinal evidence of a gene X environment interaction. *Biological Psychiatry, 57,* 1117–1122.

Section 8-2 explains how neurotrophic factors, nourishing chemical compounds, support growth and differentiation in developing neurons.

Sections 2-6 and 5-3 introduce factors that contribute to dementias. Focus 14-3 describes research and Section 16-3, treatments.

Focus 6-4 relates a case in which chronic cannabis use may have led to psychosis.

See A Case of Inheriting Experience in Section 3-3.

With the development of relatively inexpensive methods of identifying specific genes in people, it is now possible to relate the *alleles* (different forms) of specific genes to behaviors. A gene related to the production of a compound called brain-derived neurotrophic factor (BDNF) is representative. BDNF plays an important role in stimulating neural plasticity, and low levels of BDNF have been revealed in mood disorders such as depression. The two alleles of this gene are *BDNF Val 66Met* and *BDNF Val 66Val*.

Joshua Bueller and his colleagues (2006) showed that the *Met* allele is associated with an 11 percent reduction in hippocampal volume in healthy participants. Other studies have associated the *Met* allele with poor memory for specific events (*episodic memory*) and a high incidence of dementia later in life. However, the *Val* allele is by no means the better variant: although *Val* carriers have better episodic memory, they also have a higher incidence of neuroticism and anxiety disorders, as illustrated in Clinical Focus 7-3, Cannabis Use, Psychosis, and Genetics. The two alleles produce different phenotypes because they influence brain structure and functions differently. Other genes that were not measured also differed among Bueller's participants and may have contributed to the observed difference.

Epigenetics: Measuring Gene Expression

An individual's genotype exists in an environmental context fundamental to *gene expression,* the way genes become active or not. While epigenetic factors do not change the DNA sequence, the genes that are expressed can change dramatically in response to environment and experience. Epigenetic changes can persist throughout a lifetime and even across multiple generations.

Changes in gene expression can result from widely ranging experiences, including chronic stress, traumatic events, drugs, culture, and disease. A study by Mario Fraga and his colleagues (2005) stands as a powerful example of gene–experience interactions. The investigators examined epigenetic patterns in 40 pairs of identical twins by measuring two molecular markers related to gene expression.

Although twins' patterns of gene expression were virtually identical when measured in childhood, 50-year-old twins exhibited differences so remarkable as to make them as different epigenetically as young non-twin siblings! The specific cause or causes of such differences are unknown but thought to be related to lifestyle factors, such as smoking and exercise habits, diet, stressors, drug use, and education, and to social experiences, such as marriage and child rearing, among others. The epigenetic drift in the twins supports the findings of less than 100 percent concordance for diseases in identical twins.

The role of epigenetic differences can also be seen across populations. Moshe Szyf, Michael Meaney, and their colleagues (e.g., 2008) have shown, for example, that the amount of maternal attention mother rats give to their newborn pups alters the expression of certain genes in the adult hippocampus. These genes are related to the infants' stress response when they are adults. (Maternal attention is measured as the amount and type of mother–infant contact; a difference of up to 6 hours per day can exist between attentive and inattentive mothers.)

A subsequent study by the same group (McGowan et al., 2009) examined epigenetic differences in hippocampal tissue obtained from two groups of humans: (1) suicides with histories of childhood abuse and (2) either suicides with no childhood abuse or controls who died of other causes. The epigenetic changes found in the abused suicide victims parallel those found in the rats with inattentive mothers, again suggesting that early experiences can alter hippocampal organization and function via changes in gene expression.

Experience-dependent changes in gene expression are probably found not only in the hippocampus but throughout the brain as well. For example, Richelle Mychasiuk and colleagues (2011) found that stressing pregnant rat dams led to wide changes in gene expression in their offspring, in both the frontal cortex and the hippocampus. However, the investigators found virtually no overlap in the altered genes in the two brain regions: the same experience changed different brain regions differently.

Epigenetic studies promise to revolutionize our understanding of gene–brain interactions in healthy brain development and brain function. They will also help researchers develop new treatments for neurological disorders. For example, specific epigenetic changes appear to be related to the ability to make a functional recovery after stroke.

Consult the Index entry *epigenetics* to locate coverage throughout the book.

7-5 REVIEW

Chemical and Genetic Measures of Brain and Behavior

Before you continue, check your understanding.

1. Concentrations of different chemicals in the brain can be measured in postmortem tissue using a(n) _____ assay or in vivo using _____ or _____.

2. Gene–environment interactions can be investigated in human populations by comparing _____ of behavioral traits in identical twins and adopted children.

3. The study of genes and behavior focuses on individual differences in _____, whereas the study of epigenetics and behavior examines differences in _____.

4. Describe briefly how epigenetic studies have led to the recognition that life experience and the environment can alter brain function.

Answers appear at the back of the book.

For additional study tools, visit LaunchPad:
www.macmillanhighered.com/launchpad/kolb5e

[7-6] Comparing Neuroscience Research Methods

We have considered a wide range of research methods for manipulating and measuring brain–behavior interactions. **Tables 7-1** and **7-2** summarize these methods, including goals and examples of each method. How do researchers choose among them all? Their main consideration is their research question. Ultimately, that question is behavioral, but many steps lie along the route to understanding behavior.

Some researchers focus on morphology (structure) in postmortem tissue. This approach allows detailed analysis of both macro and micro structure, depending on the method chosen. Identifying brain pathology, as in Parkinson disease, can lead to insights about the causes and nature of a disorder.

Other investigators focus more on the ways neurons generate electrical activity in relation to behavior or on functional changes in brain activity during specific types of cognitive processing. Both approaches are legitimate: the goal is gaining an understanding of brain–behavior relationships.

But investigators must consider practical issues, too. Temporal resolution (how quickly the measurement or image is obtained); spatial resolution (how accurate localization is in the brain); and the degree of invasiveness all are pertinent. It is impractical to consider MRI-based methods for studies of very young children, for example, because although the images are highly accurate, the participants must remain absolutely still for long periods.

Similarly, studies of brain-injured patients must take into account factors such as the subject's ability to maintain attention for long periods—during neuropsychological testing or imaging studies, for example. And practical problems such as motor or language impairment may limit the types of methods that researchers can use.

Of course, cost is an ever-present practical consideration. Studying brain and behavior linkages by perturbing the brain are generally less costly than some imaging methods, many of which require expensive machinery. EEG, ERP, and fNIRS are noninvasive and relatively inexpensive to set up (less than $100,000). MRI-based methods, MEG, and PET are very

TABLE 7-1 Manipulating Brain and Behavior

Method	Goal	Examples
Whole-animal manipulations (Section 7-1)	Determine how an environmental condition affects brain and behavior	Diet, exercise, social interactions, sensory stimulation, drug usage
Brain lesions, permanent (Section 7-1)	Remove or destroy neural tissue to observe behavioral changes	Knife cuts or aspirations Electrolytic lesions Neurotoxic lesions
Brain lesions, temporary and reversible (Section 7-1)	Short-term silencing of neural tissue to observe behavioral changes	Regional cooling to arrest synaptic transmission Delivery of an agonist for GABA through a cannula to increase local inhibition
Genetic lesions (Section 3-3)	Remove genetic material	Knockout technology
Genetic stimulation (Section 3-3)	Add genetic material	Knock-in technology
Drug manipulations (Section 7-1)	Determine receptor system's role in the CNS	Use drugs to activate (agonists) or inactivate (antagonists) a receptor system
Electrical and magnetic stimulation (Section 7-1)	Excite tissue activity	DBS TMS
Optogenetics (Section 7-1)	Use light to activate specific ion channels and relate to behavior	Insertion of specific light-sensitive proteins
Chemogenetics (Section 7-1)	Use specific synthetic drugs to activate designer receptors	Insertion of specific G protein–coupled receptors

TABLE 7-2 Measuring Brain and Behavior

Method	Goal	Examples
Behavioral analysis (Section 7-1)	Observe behavior; generate tests to allow people and lab animals to demonstrate behavioral capacities	Naturalistic observation; tests, mazes
Tissue analysis (Section 7-1)	Identify cell types and connections; identify disease states	Stains
Record electrical and magnetic activity (Section 7-2)	Measure action potentials from individual neurons; measure graded potentials to assess coordinated activity of thousands of neurons; measure magnetic fields	Single cell recording; EEG, ERP; MEG
Anatomical brain imaging (Section 7-3)	Noninvasive examination of brain structures	Miniature microscopes; X-ray; CT; MRI; DTI
Functional brain imaging (Section 7-4)	Measure brain activity as specific behaviors are performed	fMRI; fNIRS; MRS; PET
In vivo chemistry (Section 7-5)	Relate fluctuations in transmitter release to behavior	HPLC; microdialysis, voltammetry
Genetics (Section 7-5)	Determine presence of a gene and its products	DNA, RNA, protein analysis
Epigenetics (Section 7-5)	Discover effect of experience on gene expression, brain, and behavior	Gene expression analysis

expensive (more than $2 million) and therefore typically found only in large research centers or hospitals. Similarly, epigenetic studies can be very expensive if investigators consider the entire genome in a large number of biological samples.

7-6 REVIEW

Comparing Neuroscience Research Methods

Before you continue, check your understanding.

1. Neuroscience measurements and imaging vary along the dimensions of _____, _____, and _____.

2. Relative to the expense of fMRI and PET imaging, noninvasively perturbing the brain using methods such as _____ or administering neuropsychological testing is _____.

3. The main consideration for choosing a research method is the question being asked. What is the fundamental goal of neuroscience research?

Answers appear at the back of the book.

For additional study tools, visit 🌐 LaunchPad:
www.macmillanhighered.com/launchpad/kolb5e

7-7 Using Animals in Brain–Behavior Research

A complete understanding of brain–behavior relationships is limited in part by the voluntary ethical constraints investigators place upon experimentation on humans and nonhuman species. Most individual countries decide independently which experimental practices are acceptable for humans, for other vertebrates, and for invertebrate species. In general, the experimental methods acceptable for use on our species are fewer than those employed on our most closely related primate relatives. Thus, like most new treatments in medicine, a wide variety of nonhuman species have been used to develop and test treatments for human neurological or psychiatric disorders before they are tested on humans.

Although the human and the nonhuman brain have obvious differences with respect to language, the general brain organization across mammalian species is remarkably similar, and the functioning of basic neural circuits in nonhuman mammals appears to generalize to humans. Thus, neuroscientists use widely varying animal species to model human brain diseases as well as to infer typical human brain functioning.

Two important issues surface in use of animal models to develop treatments for brain and behavioral disorders. The first is whether animals actually display neurological diseases in ways similar to humans. The second surrounds the ethics of using animals in research. We consider each separately.

Benefits of Animal Models of Disease

Some disorders—stroke, for example—seem relatively easy to model in laboratory animals because it is possible to interrupt blood supply to a brain area and induce injury and consequent behavioral change. However, it is far more difficult to determine whether human behavioral disorders can actually be induced in laboratory animals. Consider *attention-deficit/hyperactivity disorder* (ADHD), a developmental disorder characterized by core behavioral symptoms: impulsivity, hyperactivity, and/or inattention. The most common issue for children with ADHD is problems at school. Lab animals such as rats and mice do not go to school, so how does one model ADHD in rodents?

ADHD has proved difficult to treat in children, and interest in developing an animal model is high. One way to proceed is to take advantage of the normal variance in the performance of rats on a variety of tests of working memory and cognitive functioning—tests that require attentional processes. The idea is that we can think of ADHD in people or in rats as one extreme on a spectrum of behaviors that are part of a normal distribution in the general population. Many studies show that treating rats with the dopaminergic agonist methylphenidate (Ritalin), a common treatment for children diagnosed with ADHD, actually improves the performance of rats that do poorly on tests requiring attentional processes.

One rat strain, the Kyoto SHR rat, has proved an especially good model for ADHD and is widely used in the lab. The strain presents known abnormalities in prefrontal dopaminergic innervation that correlate with behavioral abnormalities such as hyperactivity. Dopaminergic abnormalities are believed to be one underlying symptom of ADHD in children, as explained in Research Focus 7-4, Attention-Deficit/Hyperactivity Disorder. Methylphenidate can reverse behavioral abnormalities, both in children with ADHD and in the SHR rats.

Animal Welfare and Scientific Experimentation

Using nonhuman animals in scientific research has a long history, but only in the past half-century have ethical issues surrounding animal research gained considerable attention and laws been instituted. Just as the scientific community has established ethical standards for research on humans, it has also developed regulations governing experimentation on animals. The governments of most developed nations regulate the use of animals in research; most states and provinces have additional legislation. Universities and other organizations engaged in research have their own rules governing animal use, as do professional societies of scientists and the journals in which they publish.

Here are four principles, used as guidelines in Canada, for reviewing experimental and teaching protocols that will use animals:

1. The use of animals in research, teaching, and testing is acceptable only if it promises to contribute to the understanding of environmental principles or issues, fundamental biological principles, or development of knowledge that can reasonably be expected to benefit humans, animals, or the environment.

2. Optimal standards for animal health and care result in enhanced credibility and reproducibility of experimental results.

Focus 6-1 reports on illicit use of prescription ADHD medications to boost performance at school and at work. Section 15-4 explores the nature of attention and disorders that result in deficits of attention.

We present experiments that predate current ethical standards. Bartholow's brain stimulation (Section 4-1), the inmate volunteers in Experiment 6-1, and Magendie's studies with puppies (Focus 2-4) are examples.

RESEARCH FOCUS 7.4

Attention-Deficit/Hyperactivity Disorder

Together, attention-deficit/hyperactivity disorder (ADHD) and attention-deficit disorder (ADD) are probably the most common disorders of brain and behavior in children, with an incidence of 4 percent to 10 percent of school-aged children. Although it often goes unrecognized, an estimated 50 percent of children with ADHD still show symptoms in adulthood, where its behaviors are associated with family breakups, substance abuse, and driving accidents.

The neurobiological basis of ADHD and ADD is generally believed to be a dysfunction in the noradrenergic or dopaminergic activating system, especially in the frontal basal ganglia circuitry. Psychomotor stimulants such as methylphenidate (Ritalin) and Adderall (mainly

In this mainstreamed first-grade classroom, a special education student with ADHD uses the *turtle technique* to cope with frustration and stress.

dextroamphetamine) act to increase brain levels of noradrenaline and dopamine and are widely used for treating ADHD. About 70 percent of children show improvement of attention and hyperactivity symptoms with treatment, but there is little evidence that drugs directly improve academic achievement. This is important because about 40 percent of children with ADHD fail to get a high-school diploma, even though many receive special education for their condition.

Stephen Faraone and coworkers (Lecendreux et al., 2015) have challenged a common view, that ADHD is a cultural phenomenon reflecting parents' and teachers' tolerance of children's behavior. These investigators conclude that the prevalence of ADHD worldwide is remarkably similar when the same rating criteria are used. Little is known about incidence in developing countries, however. It is entirely possible that the incidence may actually be higher in developing countries, given that the learning environment for children is likely to be less structured than it is in developed nations.

The cause of ADHD is unknown but probably involves dopamine receptors in the forebrain. The most likely areas are the frontal lobe and subcortical basal ganglia. Evidence of reduced brain volumes in these regions in ADHD patients is growing, as is evidence of an increase in the dopamine transporter protein. The dopamine transporter increase would mean that dopamine reuptake into the presynaptic neuron occurs faster than it does in the brain of people without ADHD. The result is a relative decrease in dopamine. Ritalin works by blocking dopamine reuptake.

ADHD is believed to be highly heritable, a conclusion supported by twin studies showing a concordance of about 75 percent in identical twins. Molecular genetic studies have identified at least seven candidate genes, and several of them are related to the dopamine synapse, in particular to the D_4 receptor gene.

3. Acceptance of animal use in science critically depends on maintaining public confidence in the mechanisms and processes used to ensure necessary, humane, and justified animal use.

4. Animals are used only if the researcher's best efforts to find an alternative have failed. Researchers who use animals employ the most humane methods on the smallest number of appropriate animals required to obtain valid information.

Legislation concerning the care and use of laboratory animals in the United States is set forth in the Animal Welfare Act, which includes laws passed by Congress in 1966, 1970, 1976, and 1985. Legislation in other countries is similar and in some European countries much stricter. The U.S. act covers mammals, including rats, mice, cats, dogs, primates, and birds, but it excludes farm animals that are not used in research. The U.S. Department of Agriculture (USDA) administers the Act through inspectors in the Animal Care section of the Animal and Plant Health Inspection Service.

In addition, the Office of Human Research Protections of the National Institutes of Health (NIH) administers the Health Research Extension Act (passed in 1986). The act covers all animal uses conducted or supported by the U.S. Public Health Service and applies to any live vertebrate animal used in research, training, or testing. The Act requires that each institution provide acceptable assurance that it meets all minimum regulations and conforms with *The Guide for the Care and Use of Laboratory Animals* (National Research Council, 2011) before conducting any activity that includes animals. The typical method for demonstrating conformance with the Guide is to seek voluntary accreditation from the Association for Assessment and Accreditation of Laboratory Animal Care International.

All accredited U.S. and Canadian universities that receive government grant support are required to provide adequate treatment for all vertebrate animals. Reviews and specific protocols for vertebrates, including fish, amphibians, reptiles, birds, and mammals, to be used in research, teaching, or testing are administered through the same process. Anyone using animals in a U.S. or Canadian university submits a protocol to the university's institutional animal care and use committee, composed of researchers, veterinarians, people who have some knowledge of science, and laypeople from the university and the community.

Companies that use animals for research are not required to follow this process. In effect, however, if they do not, they will be unable to publish the results of their research, because journals require that research conform to national guidelines on animal care. In addition, discoveries made using animals are not recognized by government agencies that approve drugs for clinical trials with humans if they do not follow the prescribed process. Companies therefore use Good Laboratory Practice (GLP) standards, which are as rigorous as those used by government agencies.

Regulations specify that researchers consider alternatives to procedures that may cause more than momentary or slight pain or distress to animals. Most of the attention on alternatives has focused on the use of animals in testing and stems from high public awareness of some tests for pharmacological compounds, especially toxic compounds. In the United States, the National Institute of Environmental Health Sciences now regulates testing of such compounds.

In spite of the legislation related to animal use, considerable controversy remains over using animals in scientific research. At the extremes, people on one side approve any usage and people on the other side disapprove of using animals for any form of research. Most fall somewhere in between. The debate centers on issues of philosophy, law, morals, custom, and biology.

Because researchers in many branches of science experiment with animals to understand the functions of the human and nonhuman body, brain, and behavior, the issues in this debate are important to them. Because human and veterinary medicine benefit from this research, as well as do people and other animals with diseases or damage of the nervous system, this debate is important. Because many people are philosophically opposed to using animals for work or food, this debate is important to them. And because you, as a student, encounter many experiments on animals in this book, these issues are important to you as well.

7-7 REVIEW

Using Animals in Brain—Behavior Research

Before you continue, check your understanding.

1. Laboratory animals can model such human dysfunctions as _____ and _____.

2. One difficulty in using lab animals as models of human disease is determining _____.

3. Animal models provide a way to investigate both proposed _____ and _____ for behavioral disorders.

4. Outline the controversies that surround the use of animals in scientific research on brain and behavioral relationships.

Answers appear at the back of the book.

SUMMARY

7-1 Measuring and Manipulating Brain and Behavior

The brain's primary function is to produce behavior, so the fundamental research technique in behavioral neuroscience is to study the direct relationship between brain and behavior. Investigators study healthy humans and other animals as well as human patients and laboratory animals with neurological problems.

Initially, scientists simply observed behavior, but they later developed neuropsychological testing measures designed to study specific functions such as fine movements, memory, and emotion. Today, researchers correlate these behavioral outcomes with anatomical, physiological, chemical, genetic, and other molecular measures of brain organization.

Brain and behavioral relations can be manipulated by altering brain function, either permanently or temporarily. Permanent changes involve damaging the brain directly by ablation or neurotoxins that remove or destroy brain tissue. Transient changes in brain activity can be induced either by use of a mild electrical or magnetic current, as in DBS or TMS, or by administration of drugs. Optogenetics, a transgenic technique, employs light-activated ion channels to excite or inhibit targeted cells in living tissue. Chemogenetic stimulation combines designer receptors and synthetic drugs to excite targeted cells in living tissue.

7-2 Measuring the Brain's Electrical Activity

Recording from single or multiple cells shows that neurons employ a code and that cortical neurons are organized into functional groups that work as coordinated networks. Neurons in sensory areas respond to specific characteristics of stimuli, such as color or pitch. Other neurons, such as place cells in the hippocampal formation, can code for more complex information, such as an object's location in space.

Electroencephalographic or magnetoencephalographic recordings measure electrical or magnetic activity from thousands of neurons at once. EEG can reveal a gross relationship between brain and behavior, as when a person is alert and displays the beta wave pattern versus when the person is resting or sleeping, indicated by the slower alpha wave patterns. Event-related potentials tell us, on the other hand, that even though the entire brain is active during waking, certain parts are momentarily much more active than others. ERP records how the location of increased activity changes as information moves from one brain area to another.

EEG and ERP are noninvasive methods that record from electrodes on the scalp; in the case of MEG, from magnetic detectors above the head. Electrocorticography, by contrast, records via electrodes attached directly to the cortex. ECoG and single-cell recording techniques are invasive.

7-3 Anatomical Imaging Techniques: CT and MRI

Computed tomography and magnetic resonance imaging are sensitive to the density of brain structures, ventricles, nuclei, and pathways. CT is a form of three-dimensional X-ray, whereas MRI works on the principle that hydrogen atoms behave like spinning bar magnets in the presence of a magnetic field.

Although CT scans are quicker and less expensive, MRI provides exceptionally clear images, both of nuclei and of fiber pathways in the brain. MRI also indicates that people's brain structure varies widely. Both CT and MRI can be used to assess brain damage from neurological disease or injury, but MRI is more useful as a research tool.

Diffusion tensor imaging is a form of MRI that makes it possible to identify normal or abnormal fiber tracts and myelin in the brain. Magnetic resonance spectroscopy, another form of MRI, permits practitioners to detect brain metabolites, such as those produced following concussion.

7-4 Functional Brain Imaging

Metabolic imaging shows that any behavior requires the collaboration of widespread neural circuits. Positron emission tomography records blood flow and other metabolic changes in periods measured in minutes, and requires complex subtraction procedures and the averaging of responses across multiple subjects. Records of blood flow obtained using functional magnetic resonance imaging can be combined with anatomical MRI images to locate changes in the individual brain and to complement ERP results. Resting-state fMRI allows investigators to measure connectivity across brain regions.

Functional near-infrared spectroscopy is the form of optical tomography usually used for functional brain imaging studies. It works on the principle that an object, including brain tissue, can be reconstructed by gathering light transmitted through the object. fNIRS is much simpler to use than PET or fMRI, but because light does not penetrate very far into the brain, it can be used only to study cortical function.

7-5 Chemical and Genetic Measures of Brain and Behavior

Analysis of changes in both genes and neurochemicals provides insight into the molecular correlates of behavior. Although genes code all the information needed to construct and regulate cells, epigenetic research reveals that the environment and life experience can modify gene expression. Even identical twins, who have an identical genome at birth, in adulthood have widely differing patterns of gene expression and very different brains.

7-6 Comparing Neuroscience Research Methods

The main consideration in neuroscience research is the question. Whatever the approach, the goal is to understand brain–behavior relationships. Tables 7-1 and 7-2 on pages 238 and 239 summarize the manipulations and measurements used in behavioral neuroscience. Among all the practical issues of measurement resolution and invasiveness, cost may prove the ultimate consideration.

7-7 Using Animals in Brain—Behavior Research

Understanding brain function, in both the healthy and the disordered brain, often benefits from animal models. Investigators develop animal models to manipulate the brain—to determine how experiential factors and neurological treatments affect brain function.

Because animal subjects cannot protect themselves from abuse, governments and researchers have cooperated to develop ethical guidelines for the use of laboratory animals. These guidelines are designed to ensure that discomfort is minimized, as is the number of animals used for invasive procedures.

KEY TERMS

alpha rhythm, p. 224

behavioral neuroscience, p. 214

cerebral voltammetry, p. 234

chemogenetics, p. 220

compensation, p. 218

computed tomography (CT), p. 226

deep-brain stimulation (DBS), p. 218

diffusion tensor imaging (DTI), p. 228

electrocorticography (ECoG), p. 223

event-related potential (ERP), p. 224

functional magnetic resonance imaging (fMRI), p. 230

functional near-infrared spectroscopy (fNIRS), p. 211

hypokinesia, p. 218

magnetic resonance imaging (MRI), p. 226

magnetic resonance spectroscopy (MRS), p. 228

magnetoencephalogram (MEG), p. 226

microdialysis, p. 234

neuropsychology, p. 211

optogenetics, p. 220

place cells, p. 223

positron emission tomography (PET), p. 232

resting-state fMRI (rs-fMRI), p. 230

stereotaxic apparatus, p. 218

striatum, p. 234

synthetic biology, p. 220

transcranial magnetic stimulation (TMS), p. 220

➦ Visit 🐾 LaunchPad to access the e-Book, videos, 🐾 LearningCurve adaptive quizzing, flashcards, and more.

www.macmillanhighered.com/launchpad/kolb5e

How Does the Nervous System Develop and Adapt?

Streeter

Katherine Streeter

Linking Socioeconomic Status to Cortical Development

Nobel Prize–winning American economist James Heckman has argued passionately about one effective strategy for economic growth: investing as early as possible in disadvantaged families promotes optimal development of young children at risk. Heckman notes that children from lower SES families typically develop gaps in knowledge and ability relative to their more advantaged peers.

These gaps influence health and prosperity, and they persist throughout life. Childhood SES correlates with cognitive development, language, memory, social and emotional processing, and ultimately with income and health in adulthood. One reason: early experiences related to SES influence children's cerebral development.

To examine cerebral development, neuroimaging studies (as shown in Figure 8-14) visualize differences in brain development that relate to growing up in under-resourced environments. As the brain grows throughout childhood and adolescence, the cortical surface area expands before declining in adulthood (Schnack et al., 2014). Cortical surface area reflects the amount of neural tissue available for different behaviors and correlates positively with cognitive ability. It should be possible to estimate the effect of early experiences on brain and behavioral development by comparing the cortical surface area and cognitive abilities of people raised in lower or higher SES families.

Kimberly Noble and her colleagues (2015) used neuroimaging to investigate the relationship between SES and cortical surface area in more than 1000 participants aged 3 to 20. As shown in the illustration, lower family income, independent of race or sex, was associated with decreased cortical surface area in widespread regions of frontal, temporal, and parietal lobes, the regions shown in red.

The investigators also measured participants' cognitive performance on tests of attention, memory, vocabulary, and reading. The larger the cortical surface area, the better the test outcomes. The negative effects of low SES were especially dramatic at the lower end of the family income spectrum, especially in families with annual incomes less than $30,000.

Low SES is associated with poor nutrition, high stress, and insufficient prenatal and infant care. Following on Heckman's thesis, investing in children from low-income families will increase societal health and prosperity, because these children can optimize their brain development and realize their developmental potential. Policies aimed toward decreasing poverty can lead to clear improvements in children's cognitive and brain development.

Research from "Family income, parental education, and brain structure in children and adolescents" by K. G. Noble et al., 2015, NatureNeuroscience, online doi: 10.1038/nn.3983, Figure 2C, p. 4.

Left hemisphere   Right hemisphere

After adjusting for age, sex, race, and parental education, Noble and colleagues associated family income with cortical surface area. Areal brain regions shown in red were significantly smaller in children from low-SES families.

To see how scientists go about studying the interconnected processes of brain and behavioral development, think about all the architectural parallels between how the brain is constructed and how a house is built. House plans are drawn as blueprints; the plans for a brain are encoded in genes. Architects do not specify every detail in a blueprint, nor do genes include every instruction for brain assembly and wiring.

The brain is too complex to be encoded entirely and precisely in genes. This leaves the fate of billions of brain cells partly undecided, especially in regard to the massive undertaking of forming appropriate connections between cells.

If the structure and fate of each brain cell are not specified in advance, what controls brain development? Many factors are at work, and as with house building, brain development is influenced by the environment in the course of the construction phase and by the quality of the materials. As we saw in Research Focus 8-1, Linking Socioeconomic Status to Cortical Development, living in poverty can compromise children's brain development.

We can shed light on nervous system development by viewing its architecture from different vantage points—structural, functional, and environmental. In this chapter, we consider the neurobiology of development first, explore behavioral correlates of developing brain functions next, then explore how experiences and environments influence neuroplasticity over the life-span.

8-1 Three Perspectives on Brain Development

Brain and behavior develop apace, and scientists thus reason that the two are closely linked. Events that alter behavioral development should similarly alter the brain's structural development and vice versa. As the brain develops, neurons become more and more intricately connected, and these increasingly complex interconnections underlie increasingly complex behaviors. These observations enable neuroscientists to study the relation between brain and behavioral development from three perspectives:

1. Structural development can be correlated with emerging behaviors.

2. Behavioral development can be predicted by the underlying circuitry that must be emerging.

3. Research can focus on factors such as language, injury, or socioeconomic status (SES) that influence both brain structure and behavioral development.

Correlating Emerging Brain Structures with Emerging Behaviors

We can look at the nervous system's structural development and correlate it with the emergence of specific behaviors. For example, the development of certain brain structures links to the motor development of, say, grasping or crawling in infants. As brain structures mature, their functions emerge and develop, as manifested in behaviors we can observe.

Neural structures that develop quickly—the visual system, for instance—exhibit their functions sooner than do structures that develop more slowly, such as those used for speech. Because the human brain continues to develop well into adulthood, some abilities emerge or mature rather late. Some cognitive behaviors controlled by the frontal lobes are among the last to develop. One such behavior, the ability to plan efficiently, is a skill vital to many complexities of life, including organizing daily activities or making travel plans.

The Tower of Hanoi test, illustrated in **Figure 8-1**, shows how planning skills can be measured in the laboratory. The task is to plan how to move colored discs one by one, in the minimum number of moves, from one configuration to another. Most 10-year-olds can solve simple configurations, but more difficult versions of the task, such as shown in Figure 8-1, cannot be performed efficiently until about age 15 to 17. No surprise then that adolescents often appear disorganized: their ability to plan has yet to mature.

Mature adults with acquired frontal lobe injuries also fail to perform well on the Tower of Hanoi test. Such evidence reinforces the idea that children are not miniature adults who simply need to learn the "rules" of adult behavior. A child's brain is vastly different from an adult's, and the brains of children at different ages are not really comparable either.

Correlating Emerging Behaviors with Neural Maturation

We can turn our observational sequence around and scrutinize behavior for the emergence of new abilities, then, inferring underlying neural maturation. For example, as language emerges in the young child, we expect to find corresponding changes in neural structures that control language. In fact, neuroscientists do find such changes.

At birth, children do not speak, and even extensive training would not enable them to do so. The neural structures that control speech are not yet ready. Thus, as language emerges, the speech-related structures in the brain are undergoing the necessary maturation.

The same reasoning can be applied to frontal lobe development. As frontal lobe structures mature through adolescence and into early adulthood, we look for related changes

GOAL

Move discs on towers below one by one to match goal above.

FIGURE 8-1 Testing Cognitive Development The Tower of Hanoi is a mathematical puzzle consisting of three rods and several different-sized discs. The task is to match the goal in as few moves as possible, obeying two rules: (1) only one disc may be moved at a time; (2) no disc may be placed on top of a smaller disc.

in behavior. We can also do the reverse: because we observe new abilities emerging in the teenage years and even later, we infer that they must be controlled by late-maturing neural structures and connections.

Identifying Influences on Brain and Behavior

The third approach to developmental interrelations between brain and behavior is to identify and study factors that influence both. From this perspective, the mere emergence of a fully developed brain structure is not enough. We must also know the events that shape how that structure functions and produces behaviors. Some events that influence brain function are sensory experience, injuries, and the actions of hormones and genes.

Logically, if one factor influences behavior, then the brain structures changed by that factor are those responsible for the behavioral outcomes. For example, we might study how the abnormal secretion of a hormone affects both a certain brain structure and a certain behavior. We can then infer that because the observed behavioral abnormality results from the abnormally functioning brain structure, the structure must typically play some role in controlling the behavior.

(8-1) REVIEW

Three Perspectives on Brain Development

Before you continue, check your understanding.

1. Structural brain development is correlated with the emergence of _____.

2. Behavioral development predicts the maturation of _____.

3. Three factors that influence brain function are _____, _____, and _____.

4. What important constraint determines when behaviors emerge?

Answers appear at the back of the book.

For additional study tools, visit 🅜 LaunchPad:
www.macmillanhighered.com/launchpad/kolb5e

(8-2) Neurobiology of Development

Some 2000 years ago, the Roman philosopher Seneca the Younger proposed that a human embryo is an adult in miniature, and thus the task of development is simply to grow bigger. This idea of *preformation* was so appealing that it was widely believed for centuries. Even with the development of the microscope, the appeal of preformation proved so strong that biologists claimed to see microscopic horses in horse semen.

By the mid-1800s, preformation began to lose ground as people realized that embryos look nothing like the adults they become. In fact, it was obvious that embryos of different species more closely resemble one another than their respective parents. The top row of **Figure 8-2** shows the striking similarity among embryos of species as diverse as salamanders, chickens, and humans, each shown in fetal form in the bottom row.

As embryos, all vertebrate species have a similar-looking primitive head, a region with bumps or folds, and a tail. Only as an embryo develops does it acquire the distinctive characteristics of its species. The similarity of young embryos is so great that many nineteenth-century biologists saw it as evidence for Darwin's view that all vertebrates arose from a common ancestor millions of years ago.

Salamander   Chick   Human

FIGURE 8-2 Embryos and Evolution The physical similarity of embryos of different species is striking in the earliest stages of development, as the salamander, chick, and human embryos in the top row show. This similarity led to the conclusion that embryos are not simply miniature versions of adults.

The embryonic nervous systems of vertebrates are as similar structurally as their bodies are. **Figure 8-3** details the three-chambered brain of a young vertebrate embryo: forebrain, midbrain, and hindbrain. The remaining neural tube forms the spinal cord. How do these three regions develop? We can trace the events as the embryo matures.

Gross Development of the Human Nervous System

When a sperm fertilizes an egg, the resulting human zygote consists of just a single cell. But this cell soon begins to divide. By the fifteenth day after fertilization, the emerging embryo resembles a fried egg (**Figure 8-4**), a structure formed by several sheets of cells with a raised area in the middle called the *embryonic disc*—essentially the primitive body.

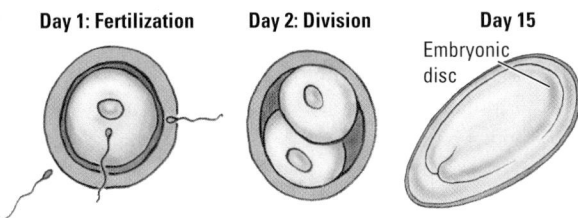

Day 1: Fertilization **Day 2: Division** **Day 15**

FIGURE 8-4 From Fertilization to Embryo
Development begins at fertilization (day 1), with the formation of the zygote. On day 2, the zygote begins to divide. On day 15, the raised embryonic disc begins to form. Information from K. L. Moore (1998). *The developing human: Clinically oriented embryology* (4th ed., p. 61). Philadelphia: Saunders.

By day 21, 3 weeks after conception, primitive neural tissue, the **neural plate**, occupies part of the outermost layer of embryonic cells. First the neural plate folds to form the *neural groove*, detailed in **Figure 8-5**. The neural groove then curls to form the **neural tube**, much as you can curl a flat sheet of paper to make a cylinder.

FIGURE 8-3 Embryonic Vertebrate Nervous System Forebrain, midbrain, and hindbrain are visible in the human embryo at about 28 days, as is the remaining neural tube, which will form the spinal cord.

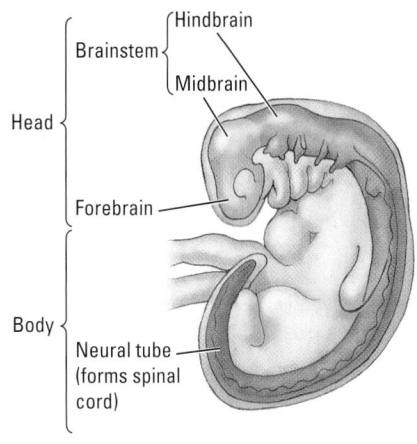

Prenatal Stages

Zygote	Fertilization to 2 weeks
Embryo	2 to 8 weeks
Fetus	9 weeks to birth

neural plate Primitive neural tissue that gives rise to the neural tube.

neural tube Structure in the early stage of brain development from which the brain and spinal cord develop.

FIGURE 8-5 Formation of the Neural Tube A long depression, the neural groove, first forms in the neural plate. By day 21, the primitive brain and neural groove are visible. On day 23, the neural tube is forming as the neural plate collapses inward along the length of the embryo's dorsal surface. The embryo is shown in a photograph at 24 days.

(A) Day 9   **(B) Day 10**   **(C) Day 11**

FIGURE 8-6 Neural Tube Development
Scanning electron micrographs show the
neural tube closing in a mouse embryo.
Reproduced with the permission of Prof. Dr. R. E. Poelmann,
Dept. Cardiology, Leiden University Medical Center, Institute
of Biology IBL, University of Leiden, Leiden, The Netherlands.

Adult stem cells that line the subventricular
zone also are located in the hippocampus,
spinal cord, and retina.

The cells that form the neural tube can be regarded as the nursery for the rest of the central nervous system. The open region in the tube's center remains open and matures into the brain's ventricles and the spinal canal. The micrographs in **Figure 8-6** show the neural tube closing in a mouse embryo.

The human body and nervous system change rapidly in the next 3 weeks (**Figure 8-7**). By 7 weeks (49 days), the embryo begins to resemble a miniature person. The brain looks distinctly human by about 100 days after conception, but it does not begin to form gyri and sulci until about 7 months. By the end of the ninth month, the fetal brain has the gross appearance of the adult human brain, but its cellular structure is different.

Origins of Neurons and Glia

The neural tube is the brain's nursery. **Neural stem cells** lining it have an extensive capacity for self-renewal. When a stem cell divides, it produces two stem cells; one dies and the other lives to divide again. This process repeats again and again throughout life. In an adult human, neural stem cells line the ventricles, forming the **subventricular zone.**

If lining the ventricles were all that stem cells did throughout the decades of a human life, they would seem very odd cells to possess. But neural stem cells have a function beyond self-renewal: they give rise to **progenitor cells (precursor cells)**, which also can divide. As shown in **Figure 8-8**, progenitor cells eventually produce nondividing cells known as **neuroblasts** and **glioblasts**. In turn, neuroblasts and glioblasts mature into neurons and glia. Neural stem cells, then, are *multipotent*: they give rise to all the many specialized cell types in the CNS.

Sam Weiss and his colleagues (1996) discovered that stem cells remain capable of producing neurons and glia not just into early adulthood but even in an aging brain. This important discovery implies that neurons that die in an adult brain should be replaceable. But neuroscientists do not yet know how to instruct stem cells to replace them.

One possibility is to make use of signals that the brain typically uses to control stem cell production in adults. For example, the level of the neuropeptide *prolactin* increases when

FIGURE 8-7 Prenatal Brain
Development The developing human
brain undergoes a series of embryonic
and fetal stages. You can identify the
forebrain, midbrain, and hindbrain by color
(review Figure 8-3) as they develop in
the course of gestation. At 6 months, the
developing forebrain has enveloped the
midbrain structures. Research from Cowan, W. M.
(1979). The development of the brain. *Scientific American*,
241(3), p. 116.

Cell type	Process
Stem	Self-renewal
Progenitor	Progenitor produced
Blast	Neuroblasts and glioblasts produced
Specialized	Neurons and glia differentiate

Neural · Glial

Interneuron · Pyramidal neuron · Oligodendroglia · Astrocyte

FIGURE 8-8 Origin of Brain Cells Cells in the brain begin as multipotential stem cells, develop into precursor cells, then produce blasts that finally develop into specialized neurons or glia.

neural stem cell Self-renewing multipotential cell that gives rise to any of the different types of neurons and glia in the nervous system.

subventricular zone Lining of neural stem cells surrounding the ventricles in adults.

progenitor cell (precursor cell) Derived from a stem cell; it migrates and produces a neuron or a glial cell.

neuroblast Product of a progenitor cell that gives rise to any of the different types of neurons.

glioblast Product of a progenitor cell that gives rise to different types of glial cells.

female mice are pregnant and stimulates the fetal brain to produce more neurons (Shingo et al., 2003). These naturally occurring hormonal signals have been shown to replace lost neurons in brain-injured laboratory animals.

How does a stem cell know to become a neuron rather than a skin cell? In each cell, certain genes are expressed (turned on) by a signal, and those genes then produce a particular cell type. *Gene expression* means that a formerly dormant gene is activated so that the cell makes a specific protein. You can easily imagine that certain proteins produce skin cells, whereas other proteins produce neurons.

The specific signals for gene expression are largely unknown but probably are chemical, and they form the basis of epigenetics. A common epigenetic mechanism that suppresses gene expression during development is *gene methylation*, or *DNA methylation*. Here a methyl group (CH_3) attaches to the nucleotide base cytosine lying next to guanine on the DNA sequence. It is relatively simple to quantify gene methylation in different phenotypes, reflecting either an increase or a decrease in overall gene expression.

Methylation alters gene expression dramatically during development. Prenatal stress can reduce gene methylation by 10 percent. This means that prenatally stressed infants express 2000 more genes (of the more than 20,000 in the human genome) than unstressed infants (Mychasiuk et al., 2011). Other epigenetic mechanisms, such as histone modification and mRNA modification, can regulate gene expression, but these mechanisms are more difficult to quantify.

Thus, the chemical environment of a brain cell is different from that of a skin cell: different genes in these cells are activated, producing different proteins and different cell types. The chemical environments needed to trigger cellular differentiation could be produced by the activity of neighboring cells or by chemicals, such as hormones, that are transported in the bloodstream.

Gene Methylation Figure 3-25 contrasts the mechanisms of histone and mRNA modification to DNA methylation.

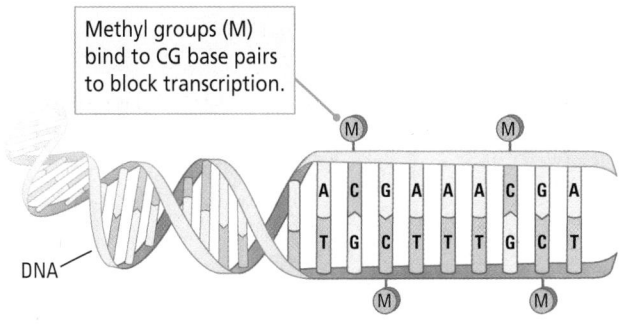

Methyl groups (M) bind to CG base pairs to block transcription.

DNA

The differentiation of stem cells into neurons must require a series of gene-activating signals. A chemical signal must induce stem cells to produce progenitor cells; another chemical signal must induce the progenitor cells to produce either neuroblasts or glioblasts. Finally, a chemical signal—perhaps a set of signals—must induce the genes to make a particular type of neuron.

Compounds that signal cells to develop in particular ways are **neurotrophic factors** (-*trophic* means *nourishing*). By removing stem cells from an animal's brain and placing those cells in solutions that keep them alive, researchers can study how neurotrophic factors function. One compound, *epidermal growth factor* (EGF), when added to the stem cell culture stimulates production of progenitor cells. Another compound, *basic fibroblast growth factor* (bFGF, or FGF-2), stimulates progenitor cells to produce neuroblasts.

At this point, the destiny of a given neuroblast is undetermined. The blast can become any type of neuron if it receives the right chemical signals. The body relies on a general-purpose neuron that matures into a specific cell type in a particular location when exposed to certain neurotrophic factors.

This flexibility makes brain development simpler than it would be if each different cell type, as well as the number of cells of each type, had to be specified precisely in an organism's genes. In the same way, building a house from all-purpose two-by-fours that can be cut to any length as needed is easier than specifying in a blueprint a precise number of precut pieces of lumber that can be used only in a certain location.

Neuronal Growth and Development

The human brain requires approximately 10 billion (10^{10}) cells to form just the cortex that blankets a single hemisphere. This means it must produce about 250,000 neurons per minute at the peak of prenatal brain development. But as **Table 8-1** shows, this rapid formation of neurons (neurogenesis) and glia (gliogenesis) is just the first step in brain growth. These new cells must travel to the correct destination (*migration*), they must differentiate into the right type of neuron or glial cell, and the neurons then must grow dendrites and axons and form synapses.

The brain also prunes unnecessary cells and connections, sculpting itself according to the particular person's experiences and needs. We consider these stages in brain development next, focusing on cortical development, because neuroscientists know more about development of the cortex than of any other area of the human brain. The principles derived from our examination of the cortex, however, apply to neural growth and development in other brain regions as well.

Neuronal Generation, Migration, and Differentiation

Figure 8-9 shows that neurogenesis is largely complete after about 5 months of gestation. (Some growth continues until about 5 years of age.) An important exception is the hippocampus, where new neurons continue to develop throughout life.

Until after full-term birth, however, the fetal brain is especially delicate and extremely vulnerable to injury, *teratogens* (chemicals that cause malformations), and trauma. Apparently, the developing brain can more easily cope with injury earlier, during neurogenesis, than it can during the later stages of cell migration or cell differentiation, when cell maturation begins (see Table 8-1). One reason may be that once neurogenesis has slowed, it is very hard to start it up again. If neurogenesis is still progressing at a high rate, more neurons can be made to replace injured ones, or perhaps existing neurons can be allocated differently. The absence of neurogenesis in adulthood, other than in the hippocampus, also explains why adult brain tumors arise from glial cells, which are generated throughout adulthood, rather than from neurons. In contrast, brain tumors in young children are sometimes neuronal, reflecting some lingering neurogenesis.

TABLE 8-1 Stages of Brain Development

1	Cell birth (neurogenesis; gliogenesis)
2	Cell migration
3	Cell differentiation
4	Cell maturation (dendrite and axon growth)
5	Synaptogenesis (formation of synapses)
6	Cell death and synaptic pruning
7	Myelogenesis (formation of myelin)

In Focus 8-1, investigators used cortical development as a measure of SES's effects.

Focus 11-2 describes outcomes resulting from cerebral palsy, caused by brain trauma acquired perinatally.

FIGURE 8-9 Prenatal Development of the Human Cerebral Cortex Brain weight and body weight increase rapidly and in proportion. The cortex begins to form about 6 weeks after conception, with neurogenesis largely complete by 25 weeks. Neural migration and cell differentiation begin at about 8 weeks and are largely complete by about 29 weeks. Neuron maturation, including axon and dendrite growth, begins at about 20 weeks and continues until well after birth. Information from M. Marin-Padilla (1993). Pathogenesis of late-acquired leptomeningeal heterotopias and secondary cortical alterations: A Golgi study. In A. M. Galaburda (Ed.), *Dyslexia and development: Neurobiological aspects of extraordinary brains.* Cambridge, MA: Harvard University Press.

The hippocampus (see Figure 2-25) is critical to memory (Section 14-3) and vulnerable to stress (Section 6-5).

Cell migration begins shortly after the first neurons are generated and continues for about 6 weeks in the cerebral cortex (and throughout life in the hippocampus). Cell differentiation, in which neuroblasts become specific types of neurons, follows migration. Cell differentiation is essentially complete at birth, although neuron maturation, which includes the growth of dendrites, axons, and synapses, goes on for years and in some parts of the brain may continue throughout adulthood.

The cortex is organized into layers distinctly different from one another in their cellular makeup. How does this arrangement of differentiated areas develop? Neuroscientist Pasko Rakic and his colleagues (e.g., Geschwind & Rakic, 2013) have been finding answers to this question for more than four decades. Apparently, the subventricular zone contains a primitive cortical map that predisposes cells formed in a certain ventricular region to migrate to a certain cortical location. One subventricular region may produce cells destined to migrate to the visual cortex; another might produce cells destined to migrate to the frontal lobes, for example.

How do the migrating cells know where to find these different parts of the cortex? They follow a path made by **radial glial cells**. A glial fiber from each of these path-making cells extends from the subventricular zone to the cortical surface, as illustrated in **Figure 8-10A**. The close-up views in Figure 8-10B and C show that neural cells from a given subventricular region need only follow the glial road to end up in the correct location.

neurotrophic factor A chemical compound that supports growth and differentiation in developing neurons and may act to keep certain neurons alive in adulthood.

radial glial cell Path-making cell that a migrating neuron follows to its appropriate destination.

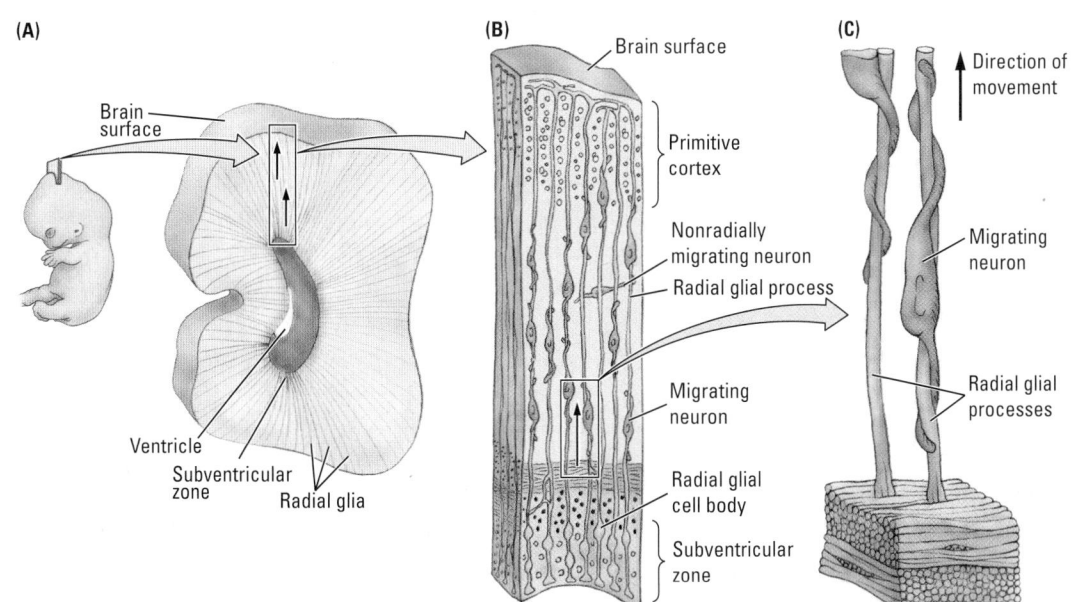

FIGURE 8-10 Neuronal Migration **(A)** Neuroscientists hypothesize that the cortical map is represented in the subventricular zone. **(B)** Radial glial fibers extend from the subventricular zone to the cortical surface. **(C)** Neurons migrate along the radial glial fibers that take them from the protomap in the subventricular zone to the corresponding region in the cortex. Information from P. Rakic (1974). Neurons in rhesus monkey cerebral cortex: Systematic relation between time of origin and eventual disposition. *Science, 183,* p. 425.

As the brain grows, the glial fibers stretch but still go to the same place. Figure 8-10B also shows a cell moving across the radial glial fibers. Although most cortical neurons follow the radial glial fibers, a small number appear to migrate by seeking some type of chemical signal. Researchers do not yet know why these cells function differently.

Cortical layers develop from the inside out, much like adding layers to a tennis ball. The neurons of innermost layer VI migrate to their locations first, followed by those destined for layer V and so on, as successive waves of neurons pass earlier-arriving neurons to assume progressively more exterior positions in the cortex. Cortex formation is a bit like building a house from the ground up until you reach the roof. The materials needed to build higher floors must pass through lower floors to get to their destinations.

To facilitate house construction, each new story has a blueprint-specified dimension, such as 10 feet high. How do neurons determine how thick a cortical layer should be? This is a tough question, especially when you consider that the cortical layers are not all the same thickness.

Local environmental signals—chemicals produced by other cells—likely influence the way cells form layers in the cortex. These intercellular signals progressively restrict the choice of traits a cell can express, as illustrated in **Figure 8-11**. Thus, the emergence of distinct cell types in the brain results not from the unfolding of a specific genetic program but rather from the interaction of genetic instructions, timing, and signals from other cells in the local environment.

Figure 2-22 contrasts the sensory and motor cortices' six distinct layers and their functions.

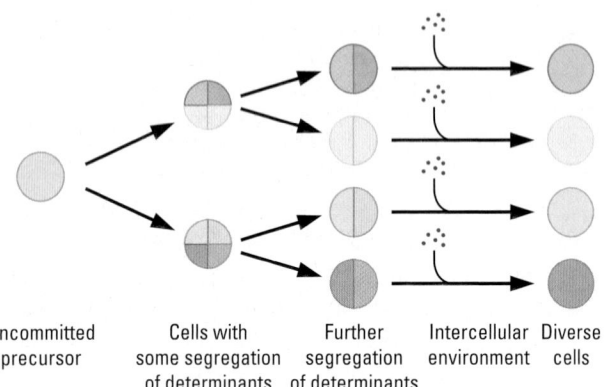

Uncommitted precursor | Cells with some segregation of determinants | Further segregation of determinants | Intercellular environment | Diverse cells

FIGURE 8-11 Cellular Commitment As also shown in Figure 8-8, precursor cells have unlimited possibilities, but as they develop, interacting genetic, maturational, and environmental influences increasingly steer them toward developing into a particular cell type.

Neuronal Maturation

After neurons migrate to their destination and differentiate, they begin to mature by (1) growing dendrites to provide surface area for synapses with other cells and (2) extending their axons to appropriate targets to initiate synapse formation.

Two events take place in dendrite development: dendritic arborization (branching) and the growth of dendritic spines. As illustrated in **Figure 8-12**, dendrites in newborn babies begin as individual processes protruding from the cell body. In the first 2 years of life, dendrites develop increasingly complex extensions that look much like leafless tree branches: they undergo arborization. The dendritic branches then begin to form spines, where most synapses on dendrites are located.

Although dendritic development begins prenatally in humans, it continues for a long time after birth, as Figure 8-12 shows. Dendritic growth proceeds at a slow rate, on the order of microns (μm, millionths of a meter) per day. Contrast this with the development of axons, which grow on the order of a millimeter per day, about a thousand times faster.

FIGURE 8-12 Neuronal Maturation in Cortical Language Areas In postnatal cortical differentiation—shown here around Broca's area, which controls speaking—neurons begin with simple dendritic fields that become progressively more complex until a child reaches about 2 years old. Brain maturation thus parallels a behavioral development: the emergence of language.
Figure from *Biological Foundations of Language* (pp. 160–161), by E. Lenneberg, 1967, New York: Wiley.

Newborn   1   3   6   15   24
Age (months)

The disparate developmental rates of axons and dendrites are important, because the faster-growing axon can reach its target cell before the cell's dendrites are completely formed. Thus the axon may play a role in dendritic differentiation and ultimately in neuron function—for example, as part of the brain's visual, motor, or language circuitry. Abnormalities in the maturation rate can produce abnormalities in patterns of neural connectivity, as explained in Clinical Focus 8-2, Autism Spectrum Disorder.

autism spectrum disorder (ASD) Range of cognitive symptoms from mild to severe that characterize autism; severe symptoms include greatly impaired social interaction, a bizarre and narrow range of interests, marked abnormalities in language and communication, and fixed, repetitive movements.

CLINICAL FOCUS 8-2

Autism Spectrum Disorder

In the 1940s, Leo Kanner and Hans Asperger first used the term *autism* (from the Greek *autos*, meaning *self*) to describe children who seem to live in their own world. Some were classified as intellectually disabled; others seemed to function intellectually.

The contemporary term, **autism spectrum disorder** (ASD), accommodates this behavioral range to include children with mild and severe symptoms. Severe symptoms include greatly impaired social interaction, a bizarre and narrow range of interests, marked abnormalities in language and communication, and fixed, repetitive movements.

The autism spectrum includes classic autism and related disorders. *Asperger syndrome*, for example, is distinguished by an obsessive interest in a single topic or object to the exclusion of nearly any other. Children with Asperger are socially awkward and also usually have delayed motor skill development. *Rett syndrome*, characterized by poor expressive language and clumsy hand use, almost exclusively affects girls.

The rate of ASD has been rising over the past four decades, from fewer than 1 person in 2000 in 1980 to the 2014 estimate of the Centers for Disease Control that as many as 1 in 68 children has some form of autism. The actual incidence may be as high as 1 in 50 (Blumberg et al., 2013). The cause of this increased incidence is uncertain. Suggestions include changes in diagnostic criteria, diagnosis of children at a younger age, and epigenetic influences. Although it knows neither racial nor ethnic nor social boundaries, ASD is four times as prevalent in boys as in girls.

The behavior of many children with ASD is noticeable from birth. To avoid physical contact, these babies arch their backs and pull away from caregivers or grow limp when held. But approximately one-third of children develop typically until somewhere between 1 and 3 years of age, when symptoms of autism emerge.

Perhaps the most recognized characteristics of ASD are failure to interact socially, repetitive rocking or hand flapping, impairments in language development, and resistance to any change in routine. Some children on the autism spectrum are severely impaired; others learn to function quite well. Still others display *savant syndrome*, a narrow range of exceptional abilities such as in music, art, or mathematics, often accompanied by severe cognitive deficits.

The brains of children diagnosed with ASD look remarkably typical. One emerging view is that these brains are characterized by unusual neuronal maturation rates. MRI studies show that at about 6 months of age, the autistic brain's growth rate accelerates to the point that its total volume is 6 percent to 10 percent greater than that of typical children.

Excessive brain volume is especially clear in the amygdala (Nordahl et al., 2012) and in the temporal and frontal lobes, the latter showing greater gray matter volume (see the review by Chen et al., 2011). The subcortical amygdala plays an important role in generating fear,

and the social withdrawal component of ASD may be related to the enlarged amygdala.

Accelerated brain growth associated with enlarged regions suggests that connections between cerebral regions are atypical, which would in turn produce atypical functioning. What leads to such brain development? More than 100 genetic differences have been described in children with ASD, so it is clear that no "autism gene" is at work.

The mechanism that translates genetic irregularities into the autistic brain is unknown but is likely to include epigenetic factors that could be prenatal, postnatal, or both. Women have an increased risk of giving birth to a child who develops ASD if they are exposed to rubella (German measles) in the first trimester of pregnancy. Researchers also suspect that industrial toxins can trigger autism, but the cause or causes remain uncertain.

No medical interventions exist for ASD. Behavioral therapies are the most successful, provided they are intense (20 to 40 hours per week) and the therapists are trained practitioners. The earlier interventions begin, the better the prognosis. Neuroscience has so far offered little insight into why behavioral therapies are effective, although in an animal model of autism, Raza et al. (2015) showed that tactile stimulation from birth until weaning reverses many morphological abnormalities in cortical neurons, suggesting a possible mechanism.

Autism may appear puzzling because no evolutionary advantage for its symptoms is apparent, but perhaps one exists. Characteristically, children with ASD are overly focused on specific tasks or information. The ability to concentrate on a complex problem for extended periods, it is suggested, is the basis for humankind's development and for cultural advances.. But too much of such a good thing may lead to conditions such as ASD.

Kim Gunkel/Getty Images

Children with ASD often look typical, but some physical anomalies do characterize the condition. The corners of the mouth may be low compared with the upper lip (left), and the tops of the ears may flop over (right). The ears may be a bit lower than average and have an almost square shape.

growth cone Growing tip of an axon.

filopod (pl. **filopodia**) Process at the end of a developing axon that reaches out to search for a potential target or to sample the intercellular environment.

cell adhesion molecule (CAM) A chemical molecule to which specific cells can adhere, thus aiding in migration.

tropic molecule Signaling molecule that attracts or repels growth cones.

netrin Member of the only class of tropic molecules yet isolated.

neural Darwinism Hypothesis that the processes of cell death and synaptic pruning are, like natural selection in species, the outcome of competition among neurons for connections and metabolic resources in a neural environment.

apoptosis Genetically programmed cell death.

FIGURE 8-13 Seeking a Path **(A)** At the tip of this axon, nurtured in a culture, a growth cone sends out filopodia seeking specific molecules to guide the axon's direction of growth. **(B)** Filopodia guide the growth cone toward a target cell that is releasing cell adhesion or tropic molecules, represented in the drawing by red dots.

Axon-appropriate connections may be millimeters or even a meter away in the developing brain, and the axon must find its way through complex cellular terrain to make them. Axon connections present a significant engineering problem for the developing brain. Such a task could not possibly be specified in a rigid genetic program. Rather, genetic–environmental interaction is at work again, as various molecules that attract or repel the approaching axon tip guide the formation of axonic connections.

Santiago Ramón y Cajal was the first scientist to describe this developmental process a century ago. He called the growing tips of axons **growth cones**. **Figure 8-13**A shows that as growth cones extend, they send out shoots, analogous to fingers reaching out to find a pen on a cluttered desk. When one shoot, a **filopod** (pl. *filopodia*), reaches an appropriate target, the others follow.

Growth cones are responsive to cues from two types of molecules (Figure 8-13B):

1. **Cell adhesion molecules** (CAMs) are cell-manufactured molecules that either lie on the target cell's surface or are secreted into the intercellular space. Some provide a surface to which growth cones can adhere, hence the name cellular adhesion molecule; others serve to attract or repel growth cones.

2. **Tropic molecules**, produced by the targets the axons' growth cones are seeking (*-tropic* means *moving toward*; pronounced as *trope*, not *tropical*), essentially tell growth cones to come on over here. They likely also tell other growth cones seeking different targets to keep away.

Although Ramón y Cajal predicted them more than 100 years ago, tropic molecules have proved difficult to find. So far, only one group, **netrins** (from Sanskrit for *to guide*), has been identified in the brain. Given the enormous number of brain connections and the great complexity in wiring them, many other types of tropic molecules undoubtedly will be found.

Do not confuse *tropic* (guiding) molecules with the *trophic* (nourishing) molecules, discussed earlier, which support neuronal growth.

Synaptic Development

The number of synapses in the human cerebral cortex is staggering, on the order of 10^{14}, or 100,000 trillion. A genetic program that assigns each synapse a specific location could not possibly determine each spot for this huge number. As with all stages of brain development, only the general outlines of neuronal connections in the brain are likely to be genetically predetermined. The vast array of specific synaptic contacts is then guided into place by a variety of local environmental cues and signals.

A human fetus displays simple synaptic contacts in the fifth gestational month. By the seventh gestational month, synaptic development on the deepest cortical neurons is extensive. After birth, synapse numbers increase rapidly. In the visual cortex, synaptic density almost doubles between ages 2 months and 4 months and then continues to increase until age 1 year.

Cell Death and Synaptic Pruning

To carve statues, sculptors begin with blocks of stone and chisel away the unwanted pieces. The brain does something similar during cell death and synaptic pruning. The chisel in the brain could be a genetic signal, experience, reproductive hormones, stress, even SES. The effect of these chisels can be seen in changes in cortical thickness over time, as illustrated in **Figure 8-14**, an atlas of brain images. The cortex actually becomes measurably thinner in a caudal–rostral (back-to-front) gradient, a process that is probably due both to synaptic pruning and to white matter expansion. This expansion stretches the cortex, leading to increased surface area, as illustrated in Research Focus 8-1.

The graph in **Figure 8-15** plots this rise and fall in synaptic density. Pasko Rakic (1974) estimated that at the peak of synapse loss, a person may lose as many as 100,000 per second. Synapse elimination is extensive. Peter Huttenlocher (1994) estimated it at 42 percent in the human cortex. We can only wonder what the behavioral consequence of this rapid synaptic loss might be. It is probably no coincidence that children, especially toddlers and adolescents, seem to change moods and behaviors quickly.

How does the brain eliminate excess neurons? The simplest explanation is competition, sometimes referred to as **neural Darwinism**. Charles Darwin believed that one key to evolution is the variation it produces in the traits possessed by a species. Those whose traits are best suited to the local environment are most likely to survive. From a Darwinian perspective, then, more animals are born than can survive to adulthood, and environmental pressures weed out the less-fit ones. Similar pressures cause neural Darwinism.

What exactly causes this cellular weeding out in the brain? It turns out that when neurons form synapses, they become somewhat dependent on their targets for survival. In fact, deprived of synaptic targets, neurons eventually die. They die because target cells produce neurotrophic (nourishing) factors absorbed by the axon terminals that function to regulate neuronal survival. *Nerve growth factor* (NGF), for example, is made by cortical cells and absorbed by cholinergic neurons in the basal forebrain.

If many neurons compete for a limited amount of a neurotrophic factor, only some can survive. The death of neurons deprived of a neurotrophic factor is different from the cell death caused by injury or disease. When neurons are deprived of a neurotrophic factor, certain genes seem to be expressed, resulting in a message for the cell to die. This programmed process is called **apoptosis**.

Apoptosis accounts for the death of overabundant neurons, but it does not account for the synaptic pruning from cells that survive. In 1976, French neurobiologist Jean-Pierre Changeux proposed a theory for synapse loss that also is based on competition (Changeux & Danchin, 1976). According to Changeux, synapses persist into adulthood only if they have become members of functional neural networks. If not, they are eventually eliminated from the brain. We can speculate that environmental factors such as hormones, drugs, and experience would influence active neural circuit formation and thus influence synapse stabilization and pruning.

In addition to outright errors in synapse formation that give rise to synaptic pruning, subtler changes in neural circuits may trigger the same process. One such change accounts for the findings of Janet Werker and Richard Tees (1992), who studied the ability of infants to discriminate speech sounds taken from widely disparate languages, such as English, Hindi (from India), and Salish (a Native American language). Their results show that young infants can discriminate speech sounds of different languages without previous experience, but their ability to do so declines in the first year of life. An explanation for this declining ability

FIGURE 8-14 Progressive Changes in Cortical Thickness MRI scans track the maturation of gray matter in typical development, revealing the length and pattern of maturation from the back of the cortex to the front. Cortical thinning and increased surface area progress together.
Courtesy Paul M Thompson/Laboratory of Neuro Imaging, Keck School of Medicine of USC.

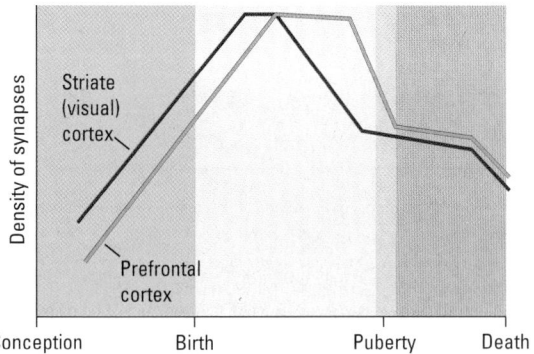

FIGURE 8-15 Synapse Formation and Pruning Changes in the relative density of synapses in the human visual cortex and prefrontal cortex (its frontmost part) as a function of age. Data from J.-P. Bourgeois (2001). Synaptogenesis in the neocortex of the newborn: The ultimate frontier for individuation?" In C. A. Nelson and M. Luciana (Eds.), *Handbook of developmental cognitive neuroscience*. Cambridge, MA: MIT Press.

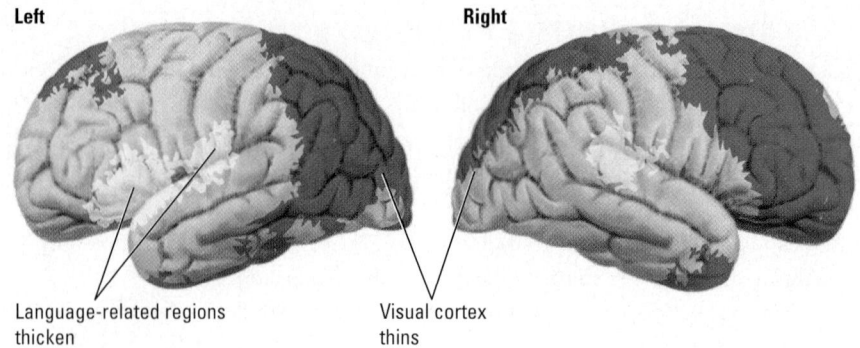

FIGURE 8-16 Gray Matter Thickness Brain maps showing the statistical significance of yearly change in cortical thickness measures taken from MRIs. Shading represents increasing (white) or decreasing (red) cortical thickness. Research from E. R. Sowell, P. M. Thompson, and A. W. Toga (2004). Mapping changes in the human cortex throughout the span of life. *The Neuroscientist, 10,* 372–392.

Three-dimensional atlases guide researchers to brain regions' precise locations (Section 7-1). More in Sections 12-4 and 15-3 on how the DLPFC functions.

is that synapses encoding speech sounds not typically encountered in an infant's daily environment are not active simultaneously with other speech-related synapses. As a result, they are eliminated.

Synaptic pruning may also allow the brain to adapt more flexibly to environmental demands. Human culture is probably the most diverse and complex environment with which any animal must cope. Perhaps the flexibility in cortical organization achieved by the mechanism of selective synaptic pruning is a necessary precondition for successful development in a cultural environment.

Synaptic pruning may also be a precursor related to different perceptions that people develop about the world. Consider, for example, the obvious differences in Eastern and Western philosophies about life, religion, and culture. Given the cultural differences to which people in the East and West are exposed as their brain develops, imagine how different their individual perceptions and cognitions may be. Considered together as a species, however, we humans are far more alike than we are different.

An important and unique characteristic common to all humans is language. As illustrated in Figure 8-14, the cortex generally thins from age 5 to 20. The sole exception: major language regions of the cortex actually show an *increase* in gray matter. **Figure 8-16** contrasts the thinning of other cortical regions with the thickening of language-related regions (O'Hare & Sowell, 2008). A different pattern of development for brain regions critical in language processing makes sense, given language's unique role in cognition and the long learning time.

Unique Aspects of Frontal Lobe Development

The imaging atlas in Figure 8-14 confirms that the frontal lobe is the last brain region to mature. Since the atlas was compiled, neuroscientists have confirmed that frontal lobe maturation extends far beyond its age 20 boundary, including in the **dorsolateral prefrontal cortex.** The DLPFC, which comprises Brodmann areas 9 and 46, makes reciprocal connections with posterior parietal cortex and the superior temporal sulcus: it selects behavior and movement with respect to temporal memory. Zdravko Petanjek and colleagues (2011) analyzed synaptic spine density in the DLPFC in a large sample of human brains ranging in age at death from newborn to age 91 years.

The analysis confirms that dendritic spine density, a good measure of the number of excitatory synapses, is two to three times greater in children than in adults and that spine density begins to decrease during puberty. The analysis also shows that dendritic spines continue to be eliminated well beyond age 20, stabilizing at the adult level around age 30. Two important correlates attend slow frontal lobe development:

1. *The frontal lobe is especially sensitive to epigenetic influences* (Kolb et al., 2012). In a study of more than 170,000 people, Robert Anda and colleagues (Anda et al., 2006) show that

such *aversive childhood experiences* (ACEs) as verbal or physical abuse, a family member's addiction, or loss of a parent are predictive of physical and mental health in middle age. People with two or more ACEs, for example, are 50 times more likely to acquire addictions or attempt suicide. Women with two or more ACEs are 5 times more likely to have been sexually assaulted by age 50. We hypothesize that early aversive experiences, such as sexual assault, promote these ACE-related susceptibilities by compromising frontal lobe development. Abnormal frontal lobe development would make a person less likely to judge such a situation as dangerous.

2. *The trajectory of frontal lobe development correlates with adult intelligence.* Philip Shaw and his colleagues (2006) used a longitudinal design, administering multiple structural MRIs to participants over time. The results show that it is not the thickness of the frontal cortex in adulthood that predicts IQ score but rather the change in trajectory of cortical thickness (**Figure 8-17**). Children who score highest in intelligence show the greatest plastic changes in the frontal lobe over time. These changes are likely to reflect strong epigenetic influences.

You can view and answer the ACE questionnaire at http://www.theannainstitute.org/Finding Your ACE Score.pdf

Glial Development

Astrocytes and oligodendrocytes begin to develop after most neurogenesis is complete and continue to develop throughout life. CNS axons can function before they are myelinated by oligodendria, but healthy adult function is attained only after myelination is complete. Consequently, myelination is a useful rough index of cerebral maturation.

In the early 1920s, Paul Flechsig noticed that cortical myelination begins just after birth and continues until at least 18 years of age. He also noticed that some cortical regions were myelinated by age 3 to 4 years, whereas others showed virtually no myelination at that time. **Figure 8-18** shows one of Flechsig's cortical maps with areas shaded according to earlier or later myelination.

Flechsig hypothesized that the earliest-myelinating areas control simple movements or sensory analyses, whereas the latest-myelinating areas control the highest mental functions. MRI analyses of myelin development in the cortex show that white matter thickness largely

Astrocytes nourish and support neurons; oligodendroglia form myelin in the CNS (see Table 3-1).

dorsolateral prefrontal cortex (DLPFC) Brodmann areas 9 and 46; makes reciprocal connections with posterior parietal cortex and the superior temporal sulcus; responsible for selecting behavior and movement with respect to temporal memory.

FIGURE 8-17 Frontal Lobe Development and IQ Score The trajectory of frontal lobe development from ages 7 to 16 years correlates with dynamic changes in cortical thickness. Colors on the scans scale to the magnitude of differences between individuals with average and superior intelligence. Purple shows thinner cortex in the individuals with higher IQ scores; red, yellow, and green show progressively increasing cortical thickness in those individuals. At age 7, they have a thinner frontal cortex that rapidly thickens to peak at age 13, then wanes later in adolescence. P. Shaw, D. Greenstein, J. Lerch, L. Clasen, R. Lenroot et al. Intellectual ability and cortical development in children and adolescents, *Nature, 440*, pp. 676–679 Mar 30, 2006, permission conveyed through Copyright Clearance Center, Inc.

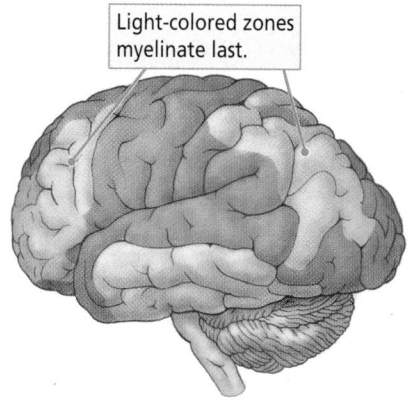

FIGURE 8-18 Progress of Myelination The fact that the light-colored zones are very late to myelinate led Flechsig to propose that they are qualitatively different in function from those that mature earlier.

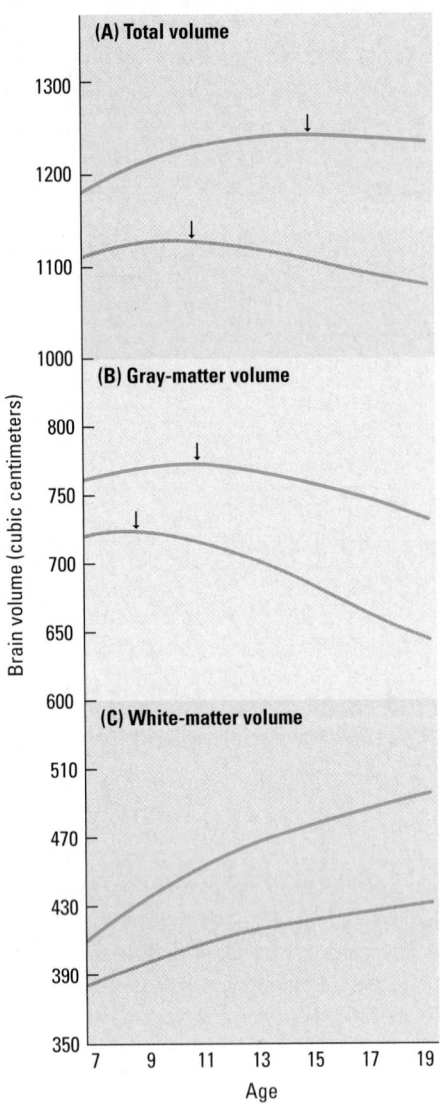

FIGURE 8-19 Sex Differences in Brain Development Mean brain volume by age in years for males (green) and females (orange). Arrows above the curves indicate that females show more rapid growth than males, reaching maximum overall volume (**A**) and gray matter volume (**B**) sooner. Decreasing gray matter corresponds to cell and synaptic loss. Increasing white matter volume (**C**) largely corresponds to myelin development. Information from R. K. Lenroot, N. Gogtay, D. K. Greenstein, E. M. Wells, G. L. Wallace, L. S. Clasen, et al. (2007). Sexual dimorphism of brain development trajectories during childhood and adolescence. NeuroImage, 36, 1065–1073.

does correspond to the progress of myelination, confirming Flechsig's ideas. Myelination continues until at least 20 years of age, as illustrated in **Figure 8-19**, which contrasts total brain volume, gray matter volume, and white matter volume during brain development in females and males.

8-2 REVIEW

Neurobiology of Development

Before you continue, check your understanding.

1. The central nervous system begins as a sheet of cells, which folds inward to form the _____.

2. The growth of neurons is referred to as _____, whereas formation of glial cells is known as _____.

3. Growth cones are responsive to two types of cues: _____ and _____.

4. The adolescent period is characterized by two ongoing processes of brain maturation: _____ and _____.

5. What is the functional significance of the prolonged development of the frontal lobe?

Answers appear at the back of the book.

For additional study tools, visit 🌀 LaunchPad:
www.macmillanhighered.com/launchpad/kolb5e

8-3 Using Emerging Behaviors to Infer Neural Maturation

As brain areas mature, a person's behaviors correspond to the functions of the maturing areas. Stated differently, behaviors cannot emerge until the requisite neural machinery has developed. When that machinery is in place, however, related behaviors develop quickly through stages and are shaped significantly by epigenetic factors.

Researchers have studied these interacting changes in the brain and behavior, especially in regard to the emergence of motor skills, language, and problem solving in children. We now explore development in these three areas.

Motor Behaviors

Developing locomotion skills are easy to observe in human infants. At first, babies cannot move about independently, but eventually, they roll over, then crawl, then walk.

Other motor skills develop in less obvious but no less systematic ways. Shortly after birth, infants are capable of flexing their arms in such a way that they can scoop something toward their body, and they can direct a hand, as toward a breast when suckling. Between 1 and 3 months of age, babies also begin to make spontaneous hand and digit movements consisting of almost all the skilled finger movements they will make as an adult, a kind of motor babbling.

These movements at first are directed toward handling parts of their body and their clothes (Wallace & Whishaw, 2003). Only then are reaching movements directed toward objects in space. Tom Twitchell (1965) studied and described how the ability to reach for objects and grasp them progresses in stages, illustrated in **Figure 8-20**.

Between 8 and 11 months, infants' grasping becomes more sophisticated as the pincer grasp, employing the index finger and the thumb, develops. The pincer grasp is significant developmentally: it allows babies to make the very precise finger movements needed to manipulate small objects. What we see then, is a sequence in the development of grasping: first scooping, then grasping with all of the fingers, then grasping with independent finger movements.

If increasingly well-coordinated grasping depends on the emergence of certain neural machinery, anatomical changes in the brain should accompany the emergence of these motor behaviors. Such changes do take place, especially in the development of dendritic arborizations and in fiber connections between neocortex and spinal cord. And a correlation has been found between myelin formation and the ability to grasp (Yakovlev & Lecours, 1967).

In particular, a group of axons from motor cortex neurons myelinate at about the same time that whole-hand reaching and grasping develop. Another group of motor cortex neurons known to control finger movements myelinates at about the time that the pincer grasp develops. MRI studies of changes in cortical thickness show that increased motor dexterity is associated with decreased cortical thickness in the hand region of the left motor cortex of right-handers (**Figure 8-21**A).

We can now make a simple prediction. If specific motor cortex neurons are essential for adultlike grasping movements to emerge, removing those neurons should make an adult's grasping ability similar to a young infant's, which is in fact what happens.

A classic symptom of motor cortex damage, detailed in Section 11-1, is permanent loss of the pincer grasp.

2 months

| Orients hand toward an object and gropes to hold it. |

4 months

| Grasps appropriately shaped object with entire hand. |

10 months

| Uses pincer grasp with thumb and index finger opposed. |

FIGURE 8-20 Development of the Grasping Response of Infants
Information from T. E. Twitchell (1965). The automatic grasping response of infants. *Neuropsychologia, 3,* p. 251.

Language Development

The gradual series of developments that accompanies speech acquisition has usually progressed significantly by age 3 or 4. According to Eric Lenneberg (1967), children reach certain important speech milestones in a fixed sequence and at constant chronological ages. Children start to form a vocabulary by 12 months. This 5-to-10-word repertoire typically doubles over the next 6 months. By 2 years, vocabulary will range from 200 to 300 words that include mostly everyday objects. In another year, vocabulary approaches 1000 words and begins to include simple sentences. At 6 years, children boast a vocabulary of about 2500 words and can understand more than 20,000 words en route to an adult vocabulary of more than 50,000 words.

Although language skills and motor skills generally develop in parallel, the capacity for language depends on more than the ability to make controlled movements of the mouth, lips, and tongue. Precise movements of the muscles controlling these body parts develop well before children can speak. Furthermore, even when children have sufficient motor skill to articulate most words, their vocabulary does not rocket ahead but rather progresses gradually.

A small proportion of children (about 1 percent) have typical intelligence and motor skill development, yet their speech acquisition is markedly delayed. Such children may not begin to speak in phrases until after age 4, despite an apparently healthy environment and the absence of any obvious neurological signs of brain damage. Because the timing of speech onset appears universal in the remaining 99 percent of children across all cultures, something different has likely taken place in the brain maturation of a child with late language acquisition. Specifying what that difference is—that is hard.

FIGURE 8-21 Correlations Between Gray Matter Thickness and Behavior **(A)** Red shading corresponds to regions showing significant cortical thinning correlated with improved motor skills. **(B)** White shading corresponds to regions showing significant cortical thickening correlated with improved language skills. **(C)** Red shading shows regions of decreased cortical thickness correlated with improved vocabulary scores. (A) and (B) Research from L. H. Lu, C. M. Leonard, P. M. Thompson, E. Kan, J. Jolley, et al. (2007). Normal developmental changes in inferior frontal gray matter are associated with improvement in phonological processing. A longitudinal MRI analysis. *Cerebral Cortex, 17,* pp. 1092–1099. (C) Research from Elizabeth R. Sowell, Paul M. Thompson, Christiana M. Leonard, Suzanne E. Welcome, Eric Kan, and Arthur W. Toga. Longitudinal Mapping of Cortical Thickness and Brain Growth in Normal Children. *J. Neurosci.* 2004 24: 8223–8231. Figure 9.

(A)

(B)

(C)

Focus 7-1 describes research on newborns' reactions to language.

Because the age of language onset is usually between 1 and 2 and language acquisition is largely complete by age 12, the best strategy considers how the cortex is different before and after these two milestones. By age 2, cell division and migration are complete in the language zones of the cerebral cortex. The major changes that take place from age 2 to 12 are in neuronal connectivity and myelination of the speech zones.

Changes in dendritic complexity in these areas are among the most impressive in the brain. Recall from Figure 8-12 that the axons and dendrites of the speech zone called Broca's area are simple at birth but grow dramatically denser at age 15 to 24 months. This neuronal development correlates with an equally dramatic change in language ability, given that a baby's vocabulary starts to expand rapidly at about age 2.

We can therefore infer that language development may be constrained, at least in part, by the maturing language areas in the cortex. Individual differences in the speed of language acquisition may be accounted for by differences in this neural development. Children with early language ability may have an early-maturing speech zone, whereas it may develop later in children with delayed language onset.

Results of MRI studies of the language cortex show that, in contrast with the thinning of motor cortex associated with enhanced dexterity shown in Figure 8-21A, a *thickening* of the left inferior frontal cortex areas associated with enhanced phonological processing (understanding speech sounds), as shown in Figure 8-21B. The unique association between cortical thickening and phonological processing is not due to a general relation between all language functions and cortical thickening, however. Figure 8-21C shows significant thinning of diffuse cortical regions associated with better vocabulary—regions outside the language areas—and vocabulary is one of the best predictors of general intelligence.

Development of Problem-Solving Ability

The first researcher to try to identify discrete stages of cognitive development was Swiss psychologist Jean Piaget (1952). He realized that he could infer children's understanding of the world by observing their behavior. For example, a baby who lifts a cloth to retrieve a hidden toy shows an understanding that objects continue to exist even when out of sight. This understanding of *object permanence* is revealed by the behavior of the infant in the upper row of photographs in **Figure 8-22**.

FIGURE 8-22 Two Stages of Cognitive Development The infant shows that she understands object permanence—that things continue to exist when they are out of sight (top). This girl does not yet understand the principle of conservation of liquid volume. Beakers with identical volumes but different shapes seem to her to hold different amounts of liquid (bottom).

An absence of understanding also can be seen in children's behavior, as shown by the actions of the 5-year-old girl in the lower row of photographs in Figure 8-22. She was shown two identical beakers with identical volumes of liquid, then watched as one beaker's liquid was poured into a shorter, wider beaker. When asked which beaker contained more liquid, she pointed to the taller beaker, not understanding that the amount of liquid remains constant despite the difference in appearance. Children display an understanding of this principle, the *conservation of liquid volume*, at about age 7.

By studying children engaged in such tasks, Piaget concluded that cognitive development is a continuous process. Children's strategies for exploring the world and their understanding of it are constantly changing. These changes are not simply the result of acquiring specific pieces of new knowledge. Rather, at certain points in development, fundamental changes take place in the organization of a child's strategies for learning about the world and for solving problems. With these developing strategies comes new understanding.

Piaget identified four major stages of cognitive development, summarized in **Table 8-2**:

- Stage I is the *sensorimotor* period, from birth to about 18 to 24 months of age. During this time, babies learn to differentiate themselves from the external world, come to realize that objects exist even when out of sight, and gain some understanding of cause and effect.

- Stage II, the *preoperational* period, takes place at age 2 to 6 years. Children gain the ability to form mental representations of things in their world and to represent those things in words and drawings.

- Stage III is the period of *concrete operations*, typically 7 to 11 years. Children learn to mentally manipulate ideas about material (concrete) things such as volumes of liquid, dimensions of objects, and arithmetic problems.

- Stage IV, the period of *formal operations*, is attained sometime after age 11. Children are now able to reason in the abstract, not just in concrete terms.

If we take Piaget's stages as rough approximations of qualitative changes that take place in children's thinking as they grow older, we can ask what neural changes might underlie them. One place to look for brain changes is in the relative rate of brain growth.

After birth, brain and body do not grow uniformly but rather during irregularly occurring periods commonly called **growth spurts**. In his analysis of ratios of brain weight to body

growth spurt Sporadic period of sudden growth that lasts for a finite time.

TABLE 8-2 Piaget's Stages of Cognitive Development

Approximate typical age range (yr)	Description of stage	Developmental phenomena
0–2	*I: Sensorimotor* Experiences the world through senses and actions (looking, touching, mouthing)	Object permanence Stranger anxiety
2–6	*II: Preoperational* Represents things with words and images but lacks logical reasoning	Pretend play Egocentrism Language development
7–11	*III: Concrete operational* Thinks logically about concrete events; grasps concrete analogies and performs arithmetical operations	Conservation Mathematical transformations
12+	*IV: Formal operational* Reasons abstractly	Abstract logic Potential for mature moral reasoning

▶ EXPERIMENT **8-1**

Question: In what sequence do the forebrain structures required for learning and memory mature?

Procedure

I. Displacement task

II. Nonmatching-to-sample learning task

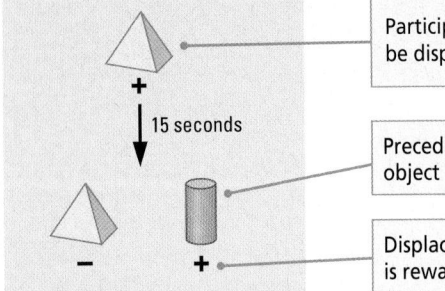

Participant is shown object that can be displaced for a food reward (+).

15 seconds

Preceding object and new object are presented.

Displacement of new object is rewarded with food.

III. Concurrent-discrimination learning task

By trial and error, participants determine which object in each of 20 pairs should be displaced for a reward of food.

In later trials, the same participants were presented with the pairs from Day 1, both to learn and to recall which object in each pair should be displaced for the food reward.

Results

Both human and monkey infants learn the concurrent-discrimination task at a younger age than the nonmatching-to-sample task.

Conclusion: Neural structures underlying the concurrent-discrimination task mature sooner than those underlying the nonmatching-to-sample task

Research from W. H. Overman, J. Bachevalier, M. Turner, and A. Peuster (1992). Object recognition versus object discrimination: Comparison between human infants and infant monkeys. *Behavioral Neuroscience, 106*, p. 18.

weight, Herman Epstein (1979) found consistent spurts in brain growth between 3 and 10 months (accounting for an increase of 30 percent in brain weight by age 18 months) as well as ages 2 to 4, 6 to 8, 10 to 12, and 14 to 16+ years. The increments in brain weight were about 5 percent to 10 percent in each of these 2-year periods.

Brain growth takes place without a concurrent increase in the number of neurons, and so it is most likely due to the growth of glial cells, blood vessels, myelin, and synapses. Although synapses themselves would be unlikely to add much weight to the brain, their growth is accompanied by increased metabolic demands that cause neurons to become larger, new blood vessels to form, and new astrocytes to be produced for neuronal support and nourishment.

We would expect such an increase in cortical complexity to generate more complex behaviors, so we might predict significant, perhaps qualitative, changes in cognitive function during each growth spurt. The first four brain growth spurts Epstein identified coincide nicely with the four main stages of cognitive development Piaget described. Such correspondence suggests significant alterations in neural functioning with the onset of each cognitive stage.

At the same time, differences in the rate of brain development, or perhaps in the rate at which specific groups of neurons mature, may account for individual differences in the age at which the various cognitive advances identified by Piaget emerge. Although Piaget did not identify a fifth stage of cognitive development in later adolescence, a growth spurt that occurs then implies one.

Growth spurts are superficial measures of changes taking place in the brain. To link them to cognitive development, we need to know at a deeper level what neural events are contributing to brain growth and just where they are taking place. A way to find out is to observe healthy children's attempts to solve specific problems that are diagnostic of damage to discrete brain regions in adults. If children perform a particular task poorly, then whatever brain region regulates that task must not yet be mature. Similarly, if children can perform one task but not another, the tasks apparently require different brain structures, and these structures must mature at different rates.

William Overman and Jocelyne Bachevalier (Overman et al., 1992) used this logic to study the development of forebrain structures required for learning and memory in young children and in monkeys. The Procedure section of **Experiment 8-1** shows the three intelligence test items presented to their participants. The first task was simply to learn to displace an object to obtain a food reward. When participants had learned the *displacement* task, they were trained in two more tasks believed to measure temporal lobe and basal ganglia functioning, respectively.

In the *nonmatching-to-sample* task, participants were shown an object they could displace to receive a food reward. After a brief (15-second) delay, two objects were presented: the first object and a novel object. The participants then had to displace the novel object to obtain the food reward. Nonmatching to sample is thought to measure object recognition, which is a temporal lobe function. The participant can find the food only by recognizing the original object and not choosing it.

In the third task, *concurrent discrimination*, participants were presented with a pair of objects and had to learn that one object in that pair was always associated with a food reward, whereas the other object was never rewarded. The task was made more difficult by sequentially giving participants 20 different object pairs. Each day, they were presented with one trial per pair. Concurrent discrimination is thought to measure trial-and-error learning of specific object information, a function of the basal ganglia.

Adults easily solve both the nonmatching and the concurrent tasks but report that the concurrent task is more difficult because it requires remembering far more information. The key question developmentally is whether there is a difference in the ages at which children (or monkeys) can solve these two tasks.

It turns out that children can solve the concurrent task by about 12 months of age, but not until about 18 months can they solve what most adults believe to be the easier nonmatching task. These results imply that the basal ganglia, the critical area for the concurrent discrimination task, mature more quickly than the temporal lobe, the critical region for the nonmatching-to-sample task.

A Caution about Linking Correlation to Causation

Throughout this section we have described research results implying that changes in the brain cause changes in behavior. Neuroscientists assert that by looking at behavioral development and brain development in parallel, they can make some inferences regarding the causes of behavior. Bear in mind, however, that the fact that two things correlate (take place together) does not prove that one of them causes the other.

The correlation–causation problem raises red flags in brain and behavior studies, because research in behavioral neuroscience, by its very nature, is often based on correlations. Nevertheless, correlational studies, especially of development, have proved a powerful source of insight into the principles of brain and behavior.

(8-3) REVIEW

Using Emerging Behaviors to Infer Neural Maturation

Before you continue, check your understanding.

1. The last stage in motor development in infants is the ability to make _____.

2. Language development is correlated with cortical thinning related to _____ and cortical thickening related to _____.

3. Brain growth spurts correlate with _____.

4. The nonmatching-to-sample task is believed to measure the function of the _____; the concurrent-discrimination learning task is believed to measure the function of the _____.

5. Describe a major challenge in inferring changes in brain development from the emergence of behaviors.

Answers appear at the back of the book.

8-4 Brain Development and the Environment

Developing behaviors are shaped not only by the maturation of brain structures but also by each person's environment and experience. Neuroplasticity suggests that the brain is pliable and can be molded, at least at the microscopic level. Brains exposed to different environmental experiences are molded in different ways. Culture is an important aspect of the human environment, so culture must help to mold the human brain. We would therefore expect people raised in widely differing cultures to acquire brain structure differences that have lifelong effects on their behavior.

The brain is plastic in response not only to external events but also to events within a person's body, including the effects of hormones, injury, and genetic mutations. The developing brain early in life is especially responsive to these internal factors, which in turn alter how the brain responds to external experiences. In this section, we explore a whole range of external and internal environmental influences on brain development. We start with a question: Exactly how does experience alter brain structure?

Section 1-5 summarizes humanity's acquisition of culture.

Experience and Cortical Organization

Researchers can study the effects of experience on the brain and behavior by placing laboratory animals in different environments and observing the results. In one of the earliest such studies, Donald Hebb (1947) took a group of young laboratory rats home and let them grow up in his kitchen. A control group grew up in standard laboratory cages at McGill University.

The home-reared rats had many experiences that the caged rats did not, including being chased with a broom by Hebb's less-than-enthusiastic wife. Subsequently, Hebb gave both groups a rat-specific intelligence test that consisted of learning to solve a series of mazes, collectively known as Hebb–Williams mazes. **Figure 8-23** shows a sample maze. Home-reared rats performed far better on these tasks than caged rats did. Hebb therefore concluded that experience must influence intelligence.

The Hebb synapse, diagrammed in Section 15-1, visualizes his predictions about synaptic plasticity. Section 14-4 elaborates Hebb's contributions to learning theory.

On the basis of his research, Hebb reasoned that people reared in a stimulating environment will maximize their intellectual development, whereas people raised in impoverished or under-resourced environments, such as those described in the SES study in Research Focus 8-1, will not reach their intellectual potential. Although a generalization, Hebb's reasoning seems logical. How do we define environments that may be stimulating or impoverished?

People living in slums typically have few formal educational resources—decidedly not an enriched setting—but that does not mean that the environment offers no cognitive stimulation or challenge. On the contrary, people raised in slums are better adapted for survival in a slum than are people raised in upper-class homes. Does this adaptability make them more intelligent in a certain way? Could it make them more resilient?

FIGURE 8-23 Hebb–Williams Maze In this version of the maze, a rat is placed in the start box (S) and must learn to find the food in the goal box (G). Investigators can reconfigure the walls of the maze to set new problems. Rats raised in complex environments solve such mazes much faster than do rats raised in standard laboratory cages.

Slum dwellers may not be well adapted for college life, however. This is probably closer to what Hebb had in mind when he referred to a slum environment as limiting intellectual potential. Indeed, Hebb's logic led to the development of preschool television programs, such as *Sesame Street*, that offer enrichment for children who would otherwise have little preschool exposure to reading.

At 36 months of age, on average, the vocabulary of children from a low-SES environment is less than one-third that of high-SES children (400 versus 1200 words). This difference grows wider as children develop. It is hypothesized to result from less direct conversation with caregivers and less reading to the children by caregivers. The weaker language skills demonstrated by children of low SES is related to the size of cortical language areas as early as age 5 years (Raizada et al., 2008). Patricia Kuhl (2011) makes the important point that SES itself is not the variable driving effects on language and brain development. Rather, SES is likely a proxy for the opportunity to learn language, a point that takes us back to James Heckman's thesis in Research Focus 8-1.

Seven decades ago, Hebb's studies used complex stimulating environments, but much simpler experiences can also influence brain development. Tactile stimulation of human infants is important not only for bonding with caregivers but also for stimulating brain development. For example, tactile stimulation of premature infants in incubators speeds their growth and allows for quicker release from the hospital. Laboratory studies show that brushing infant rats for 15 minutes 3 times per day for the first 3 weeks of life also speeds up growth and development. The animals show enhanced motor and cognitive skills in adulthood as well. Tactile stimulation also dramatically improves recovery from brain injury incurred early in development.

The idea that early experience can change later behavior seems sensible enough, but we are left to question why experience should make such a difference. One reason is that experience changes neuronal structure, which is especially evident in the cortex. Neurons in the brains of animals raised in complex environments, such as that shown in **Figure 8-24**A, are larger and richer in synapses than are those of animals reared in barren cages (Figure 8-24B). Similarly, 3 weeks of tactile stimulation increases synapse numbers all over the cortex in adulthood.

(A)   **(B)**

Laboratory housed   Complex-environment housed

FIGURE 8-24 Enriched Environment, Enhanced Development **(A)** A complex environment for a group of about six rats allows the animals to move about and to interact with one another and with toys that are changed weekly. **(B)** Representative neurons from the parietal cortex of a laboratory-housed rat and a complex-environment-housed rat; the latter has about 25 percent more dendritic space for synapses.

Presumably, increased synapse numbers result from increased sensory processing in a complex and stimulating environment. The brains of animals raised in complex settings also display more (and larger) astrocytes. Although complex-rearing studies do not address the effects of human culture directly, making predictions about human development on the basis of their findings is easy. We know that experience can modify the brain, so we can predict that different experiences might modify the brain differently. Take language development, for example, as Research Focus 8-3, Increased Cortical Activation for Second Languages, on page 268, explains.

Like early exposure to language during development, early exposure to music alters the brain. Perfect (absolute) pitch, or the ability to re-create a musical note without external reference is believed to require musical training during an early period, when brain development is most sensitive to this experience. Similarly, adults exposed only to Western music since childhood usually find Eastern music peculiar, even nonmusical, on first encountering it. Both examples demonstrate that early exposure to music alters neurons in the auditory system (see Levitin & Rogers, 2005).

Such loss of plasticity does not mean that the adult human brain grows fixed and unchangeable. Adults' brains are influenced by exposure to new environments and experiences, although more slowly and less extensively than children's brains are. In fact, evidence reveals that experience affects the brain well into old age: good news for those of us who are no longer children.

It is becoming clear as well that prenatal events can modify brain development. The consensus is that perinatal adversity, such as gestational stress at or near birth, is a significant risk factor for later behavioral disorders (see Bock et al., 2014). Even events such as stress or drug use that occur *before* conception can lead to epigenetic effects in offspring. Examples include abnormalities in neural organization and behavior (e.g., Harker et al., 2015). Although such effects are usually presumed to come from maternal exposure before conception, increasing evidence from research on humans points to paternal preconception experience also modifying children's brain development, perhaps including acquisition of fetal alcohol spectrum disorder (FASD).

Focus 5-5 describes some structural changes neurons undergo as a result of learning.

Figure 15-11 shows enhanced nerve tract connectivity in people with perfect pitch.

Focus 6-2 details FASD.

RESEARCH F⊙CUS 8-3

Increased Cortical Activation for Second Languages

Most of the world's population is bilingual, but people rarely learn their second language as early as their first. Denise Klein and her colleagues (2006) used both PET and fMRI to determine whether native and second languages differ in cortical activation.

The two languages overlap greatly in neural representation, but when participants are asked to repeat words, the second language shows greater activation in motor regions such as the striatum and cerebellum as well as in the frontal and temporal language regions. The investigators speculate that the second language places greater articulatory demands on the speaker. These demands correspond to the increased neural involvement in motor as well as language areas, as shown in the illustration.

Further support for Klein and colleagues' conclusions from these imaging studies comes from a review of cortical mapping studies of bilingual patients undergoing neurosurgery. Carlo Giussani and his colleagues (2007) conclude that although all studies show language representation grossly located in the same cortical regions, distinct language-specific areas exist in the frontal and temporoparietal language regions. Section 15-6 concludes with updates on these findings.

Blue regions show increased activation in neural motor structures when the person is speaking a second language. Copyright © 2005 Wiley-Liss, Inc. Word and Nonword Repetition in Bilingual Subjects: A PET Study. Denise Klein, Kate E. Watkins, Robert J. Zatorre, and Brenda Milner, *Human Brain Mapping* 27: 153–161 (2006). Permission conveyed through Copyright Clearance Center, Inc.

| Ventral striatum | Caudate nucleus | Anterior insula | Ventral premotor |

4.00
3.63
3.25
2.88
2.50

Experience and Neural Connectivity

Experience can actually sculpt the brain prenatally, as studies of the developing visual system illustrate clearly. Consider the anatomical challenge of connecting the eyes to the rest of the visual system. A simple analogy will help. Imagine that students in a large lecture hall are each viewing the front of the room (the visual field) through a small cardboard tube, such as an empty paper towel roll. If each student looks directly ahead, he or she will see only a small bit of the total visual field.

Essentially, this is how the photoreceptor cells in the eyes act. Each cell sees only a small bit of the visual field. The problem is putting all of the bits together to form a complete picture. To do so, analogously to students sitting side by side, receptors that see adjacent views must send their information to adjacent regions in the various parts of the brain's visual system, such as the midbrain. How do they accomplish this feat?

Roger Sperry (1963) suggested the **chemoaffinity hypothesis**, the idea that specific molecules in different cells in various midbrain regions give each cell a distinctive chemical identity. Each cell has an identifiable biochemical label. Presumably, incoming axons seek out a specific chemical, such as the tropic factors discussed in Section 8-2, and consequently land in the correct general midbrain region.

Many experiments have shown this process to take place prenatally as the eye and brain are developing. But the problem is that chemical affinity directs incoming axons only to a general location. To return to our two adjacent retinal cells, how do they now place themselves in the precisely correct position?

Here is where postnatal experience comes in: fine-tuning of neural placement is believed to be activity-dependent. Because adjacent receptors tend to be activated at the

Section 9-2 describes visual system anatomy. Figure 2-18 details midbrain structures.

same time, they tend to form synapses on the same neurons in the midbrain after chemoaffinity has drawn them to a general midbrain region. **Figure 8-25** illustrates this process. Neurons A and G are unlikely to be activated by the same stimulus, so they seldom fire synchronously. Neurons A and B, in contrast, are apt to be activated by the same stimuli, as are B and C. Through this simultaneous activity and with the passage of time, cells eventually line up correctly in the connections they form.

Now consider what happens to axons coming from different eyes. Although the neural inputs from the two eyes may be active simultaneously, cells in the same eye are more likely to be active together than are cells in different eyes. The net effect is that inputs from the two eyes tend to organize themselves into neural bands, called *columns*, that represent the same region of space in each eye, as shown on the left in **Figure 8-26** on page 270. Formation of these segregated cortical columns therefore depends on the patterns of coinciding electrical activity on the incoming axons.

If experience is abnormal—if one eye is covered during a crucial time in development, for example—then the neural connections will not be guided appropriately by experience. As shown at the right in Figure 8-26, the effect of suturing one eye closed has the most disruptive effect on cortical organization in kittens between 30 and 60 days after birth. In a child who has a lazy eye, visual input from that eye does not contribute to fine-tuning the neural connections as it should. So the details of those connections develop abnormally, much as if the eye had been covered. The resulting loss of sharpness in vision is **amblyopia**.

To summarize, an organism's genetic blueprint is vague in regard to exactly which connections in the brain go to exactly which neurons. Experience fine-tunes neural connectivity by modifying those details.

Critical Periods for Experience and Brain Development

The preceding examples of perfect pitch and visual connectivity show that for healthy development, specific sensory experiences occurring at particular times are especially important. A time during which brain development is most sensitive to a specific experience is called either a **critical period** or a *sensitive period*.

The absence of appropriate sensory experience during a critical period may result in abnormal brain development, leading to abnormal behavior that endures even into adulthood. Our colleague Richard Tees offered an analogy to help explain the concept. He pictured the developing animal as a little train traveling past an environmental setting, perhaps the Rocky Mountains. All the windows are closed at the beginning of the journey (prenatal development), but at particular stages of the trip, the windows in certain cars open, exposing the occupants (different parts of the brain) to the outside world. Some windows open to expose the brain to specific sounds, others to certain smells, others to particular sights, and so on.

This exposure affects the brain's development, and the absence of any exposure through an open window severely disturbs that development. As the journey continues, the windows become harder to open until finally they close permanently. This does not mean that the brain can no longer change, but changes become much harder to induce.

Now imagine two different trains, one headed through the Rocky Mountains and another, the Orient Express, traveling across Eastern Europe. The views from the windows are very different, and the effects on the brain are correspondingly different. In other words, not

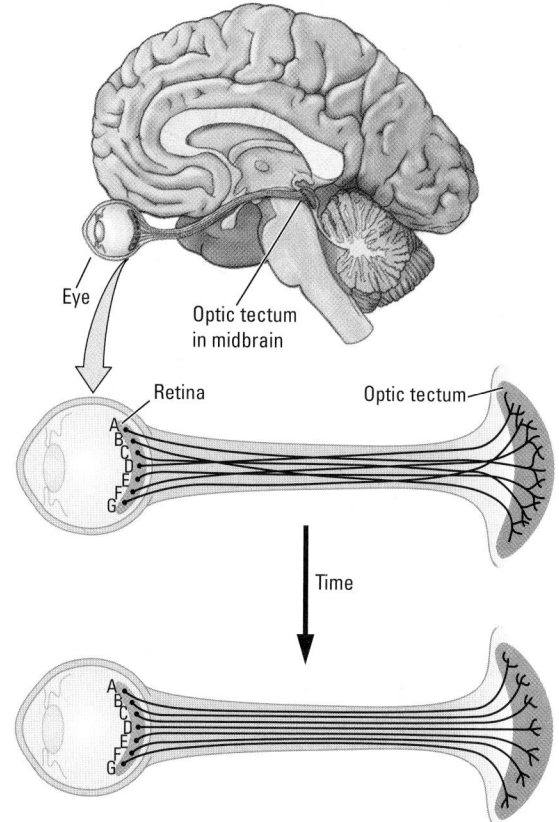

FIGURE 8-25 Chemoaffinity in the Visual System Neurons A through G project from the retina to the tectum in the midbrain. The activities of adjacent neurons (C and D, say) are more likely to coincide than are the activities of widely separated neurons such as A and G. As a result, adjacent retinal neurons are more likely to establish permanent synapses on the same tectal neurons. By using chemical signals, axons grow to the approximate location in the tectum (top). The connections become more precise with the passage of time (bottom).

chemoaffinity hypothesis Proposal that neurons or their axons and dendrites are drawn toward a signaling chemical that indicates the correct pathway.

amblyopia Condition in which vision in one eye is reduced as a result of disuse; usually caused by a failure of the two eyes to look in the same direction.

critical period Developmental window during which some event has a long-lasting influence on the brain; also, *sensitive period*.

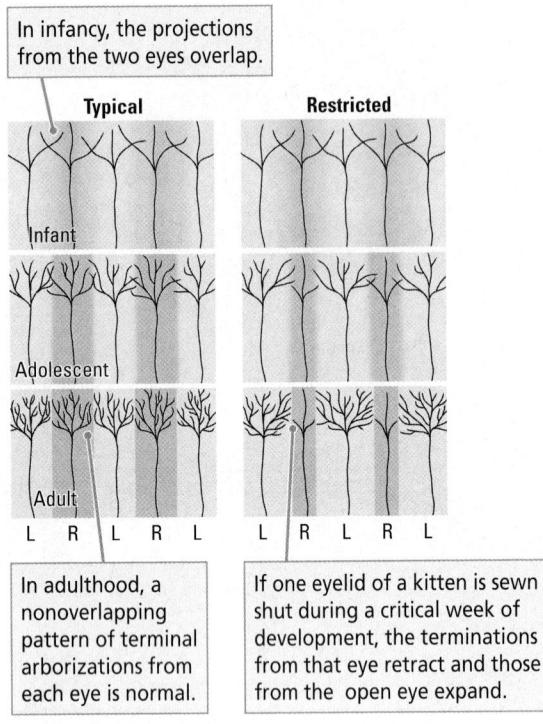

In infancy, the projections from the two eyes overlap.

Typical   Restricted

Infant

Adolescent

Adult

L R L R   L R L R

In adulthood, a nonoverlapping pattern of terminal arborizations from each eye is normal.

If one eyelid of a kitten is sewn shut during a critical week of development, the terminations from that eye retract and those from the open eye expand.

FIGURE 8-26 Ocular Dominance Columns Typically in the postnatal development of the cat brain, axons from each eye enter the cortex, where they grow large terminal arborizations. (L, left eye; R, right eye).

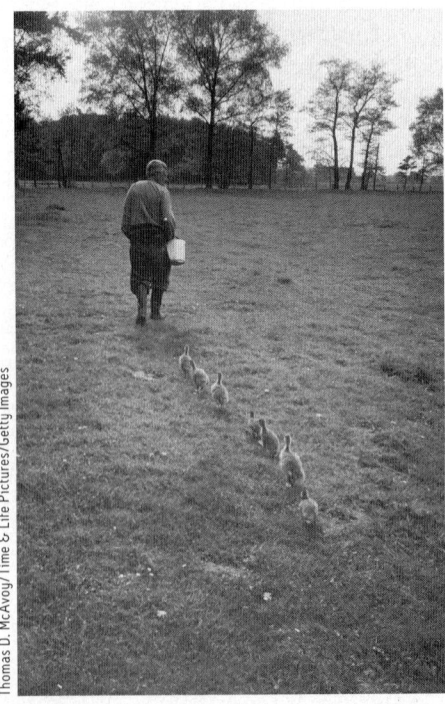

Thomas D. McAvoy/Time & Life Pictures/Getty Images

FIGURE 8-27 Strength of Imprinting Ethologist Konrad Lorenz followed by goslings that imprinted on him. He was the first object that the geese encountered after hatching, so he became their "mother."

only is the brain altered by the experiences it has during a critical period, but the particular kinds of experiences encountered matter too.

An extensively studied, related behavior is **imprinting**, a critical period during which an animal learns to restrict its social preferences to a specific class of objects, usually the members of its own species. In birds, such as chickens and waterfowl, the critical period for imprinting often comes shortly after hatching. Typically, the first moving object a young hatchling sees is a parent or sibling, so the hatchling's brain appropriately imprints to its own species.

Appropriate imprinting is not inevitable. Konrad Lorenz (1970) demonstrated that if the first animal or object that baby goslings encounter is a person, the goslings imprint to that person as though he or she were their mother. **Figure 8-27** shows a flock of goslings that imprinted to Lorenz and followed him wherever he went. Incorrect imprinting has long-term consequences for the hatchlings. They often direct their subsequent sexual behavior toward humans. A Barbary dove that had become imprinted to Lorenz directed its courtship toward his hand and even tried to copulate with the hand if it was held in a certain orientation.

Birds can imprint not just to humans but also to inanimate objects, especially moving objects. Chickens have been induced to imprint to a milk bottle sitting on the back of a toy train moving around a track. But the brain is not entirely clueless when it comes to selecting an imprinting target. Given a choice, young chicks will imprint on a real chicken over any other stimulus.

This quick acquisition and its permanent behavioral consequences suggest that during imprinting, the brain makes a rapid change of some kind, probably a structural change given the permanence of the new behavior. Gabriel Horn and his colleagues at Cambridge University (1985) tried to identify the changes in chicks' brains during imprinting. The results of Horn's electron microscopic studies show that synapses in a specific forebrain region enlarge with imprinting. Thus, imprinting seems a good model for studying brain plasticity during development, in part because the changes are rapid, related to specific experience, and localized in the brain.

As noted in Section 8-3, brain development can be affected by either parent's experiences before conception or those of the mother or fetus during gestation. Because developmental events change so dramatically and quickly in utero, we should not be surprised that the effects of fetal experiences vary with the precise developmental stage. As a rule, the CNS is especially sensitive during gestational weeks 4 to 8, as the neural tube forms. It remains sensitive through the period of cerebral neurogenesis, which continues until the end of the second trimester. Robbin Gibb and her colleagues (2014) have shown that housing pregnant rats in complex environments, as in Figure 8-24A, results in the offspring showing increased dendritic spine density in the cortex, as though the animals had been placed in the environment in adulthood.

Abnormal Experience and Brain Development

If complex or enriched experiences can stimulate brain growth and influence later behavior, severely restricted experiences seem likely to retard both brain growth and behavior. To study the effects of such restrictions, Donald Hebb and his colleagues (Clarke et al., 1951) placed young Scottish terriers in the dark with as little stimulation as possible and compared their behavior to that of dogs raised in a typical environment.

When the dogs raised in the barren environment, obviously unethical by today's standards, were later removed from it, their behavior was highly unusual. They showed virtually no reaction to people or other dogs and appeared to have lost any pain sensation. Even sticking pins in them (equally unethical) produced no response. When given a dog version of the

Hebb–Williams intelligence test for rats, these dogs performed terribly and were unable to learn some tasks that dogs raised in more stimulating settings learned easily.

Results of subsequent studies show specifically that depriving young animals of visual input or of maternal contact has devastating consequences for their behavioral development and presumably for their brain development. Austin Riesen (1982) and his colleagues extensively studied animals raised in the dark. They found that even though the animals' eyes still work, they may be functionally blind after early visual deprivation. An absence of visual stimulation results in the atrophy of dendrites on cortical neurons, essentially the opposite of the results observed in the brains of animals raised in complex and stimulating environments.

Not only does the absence of specific sensory inputs adversely affect brain development; so do more complex atypical experiences. In the 1950s, Harry Harlow (1971) began the first systematic laboratory studies of analogous deprivation in laboratory animals. Harlow showed that infant monkeys raised without maternal (or paternal) contact develop grossly atypical intellectual and social behaviors in adulthood.

Harlow separated baby monkeys from their mothers shortly after birth and raised them in individual cages. Perhaps the most stunning effect occurred in adulthood, when these animals were totally unable to establish normal relations with other animals. Unfortunately, Harlow did not analyze the deprived monkeys' brains. We would predict atrophy of cortical neurons, especially in the frontal lobe regions related to social behavior. Harlow's student Stephen Suomi continues to study early experiences in monkeys at the U.S. National Institute of Child Health and Human Development. He has found a wide variety of hormonal and neurological abnormalities among motherless monkeys, including epigenetic changes (see the review by Suomi, 2011).

Children in a barren environment or abused or neglected are at a serious disadvantage later in life. Proof is the hampered intellectual and motor development displayed by children raised in dreadful circumstances such as those described in Clinical Focus 8-4, Romanian Orphans, on page 272. Although some argue that children can succeed in school and in life if they really want to, abnormal developmental experiences can clearly alter the brain irrevocably. As a society, we cannot be complacent about the environment to which our children are exposed.

Early exposure to stress, including prenatally, also has major effects on a child's later behavior. Stress can alter the expression of certain genes, such as those related to serotonin (5-hydroxytryptamine, or 5-HT) reuptake. Early alteration in serotonin activity can severely alter how the brain responds to stressful experiences later in life.

Stress early in life may predispose people to develop behavioral disorders, such as depression (Sodhi & Sanders-Bush, 2004). Early stress can also leave a lasting imprint on brain structure: the amygdala is enlarged and the hippocampus is small (Salm et al., 2004). Changes in frontal lobe anatomy have been associated with the development of depressive and anxiety disorders and may be linked to the epigenetic effects described in Section 8-2.

Prenatal experiences also can lead to abnormal behavior in children and adults. Exposing the fetus to alcohol, especially in the first two trimesters, can lead to FASD, as can excessive alcohol use by either parent before conception. Similarly, children exposed in utero to radiation in the aftermath of the 1986 accident at the Chernobyl nuclear power plant later developed a range of cognitive disorders, including lowered IQ scores. Effects were most severe if they had been exposed during gestational weeks 8 to 25, the critical period of cerebral neurogenesis (Nyagu et al., 1998).

Hormones and Brain Development

The determination of sex is largely genetic. In mammals, the Y chromosome in males controls the process by which an undifferentiated, primitive gonad develops into testes,

imprinting Formation of an attachment by an animal to one or more objects or animals at a critical period in development.

Section 6-5 explains the neurobiology of the stress response. Section 16-4 connects mood and reactivity to stress.

Romanian Orphans

In the 1970s, Romania's Communist regime outlawed all forms of birth control and abortion. The natural result was more than 100,000 unwanted children in state-run orphanages. The conditions were appalling.

The children were housed and clothed but given virtually no environmental stimulation. Mostly they were confined to cots with few, if any, playthings and virtually no personal interaction with overworked caregivers, who looked after 20 to 25 children at once. Bathing often consisted of being hosed down with cold water.

After the Communist government fell, the outside world intervened. Hundreds of these children were placed in adoptive homes throughout the world, especially in the United States, Canada, and the United Kingdom. Studies of these severely deprived children on arrival in their new homes document malnourishment, chronic respiratory and intestinal infections, and severe developmental impairments.

A British study by Michael Rutter (1998) and his colleagues assessed the orphans at two standard deviations below age-matched children for weight, height, and head circumference (taken as a very rough measure of brain size). Scales of motor and cognitive development assessed most of the children in the impaired range.

The improvement these children showed in the first 2 years after placement in their adoptive homes was nothing short of spectacular. Average height and weight advanced to nearly normal, although head circumference remained below normal. Many tested in the normal range of motor and cognitive development. But a significant number were still considered intellectually impaired. What caused these individual differences in recovery from the past deprivation?

The key factor was age at adoption. Children adopted before 6 months of age did significantly better than those adopted later. In a Canadian study by Elenor Ames (1997), Romanian orphans who were adopted before 4 months of age and then tested at age 4½ had an average Stanford–Binet IQ score of 98. Age-matched Canadian controls had an average score of 109. Brain imaging studies showed that children adopted at an older age had a smaller brain than normal.

Charles Nelson and his colleagues (Berens & Nelson, 2015; Nelson et al., 2007; Smyke et al., 2012) analyzed cognitive and social development as well as event-related potential (ERP) measures in a group of children who had remained in Romania. Whether the children had moved to foster homes or remained in institutions, the studies reveal severe abnormalities at about 4 years of age. The age at adoption was again important, but in the Nelson studies the critical age appears to be before 24 months rather than 6 months, as in the earlier studies.

The inescapable conclusion is that the human brain may be able to recover from a brief period of extreme deprivation in early infancy, but periods longer than 24 months produce significant developmental abnormalities that cannot be overcome completely. The studies of Romanian orphans make clear that the developing brain requires stimulation for healthy development. Although the brain may be able to catch up after a brief deprivation, severe deprivation lasting many months results in a small brain and associated behavioral abnormalities, especially in cognitive and social skills.

Romanian orphans warehoused in the 1970s and 1980s endured the conditions shown in this photograph. The utter absence of stimuli hampered their normal brain development.

---

illustrated in **Figure 8-28**. The genitals begin to form in the seventh week after conception, but they appear identical (indifferent) in the two sexes at this early stage. No *sexual dimorphism*, or structural difference, yet exists. The testes subsequently secrete the sex hormone **testosterone**, which stimulates development of male reproductive organs and later, in puberty, the appearance of male secondary sexual characteristics such as facial hair and deepening of the voice.

Gonadal (sex) hormones change the genetic activity of certain cells, most obviously those that form the genitals, but neural cells also respond to them. Regions of the embryonic brain thus also may begin to show sexual dimorphism as testosterone secretion begins, about 60 days after conception. What does sexual differentiation have to do with brain development? Although the answer is largely hormonal, genetic influences contribute, too.

Testosterone stimulates sexual differentiation in male embryos. In its absence, female embryos develop. Prenatal exposure to gonadal hormones shapes male and female brains differently, because these hormones activate different genes in the two sexes. Experience, then, affects male and female brains differently. Clearly, genes and experience begin to shape the developing brain very early.

Sections 6-5 and 12-5 detail the actions of gonadal hormones, including testosterone.

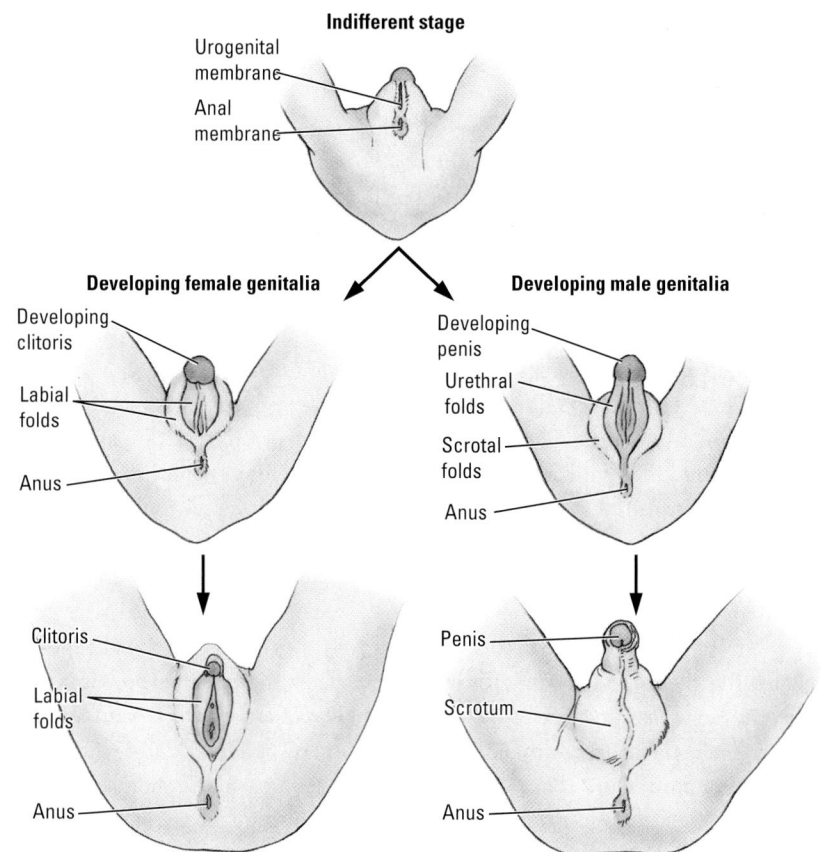

FIGURE 8-28 Sexual Differentiation in the Human Infant Early in the indifferent stage, male and female human embryos are identical (top). In the absence of testosterone, female structures emerge (left). In response to testosterone, genitalia begin to develop into male structures at about 60 days (right). Parallel changes take place in the embryonic brain in response to the absence or presence of testosterone.

Gonadal Hormones and Brain Development

Testosterone, the best-known **androgen** (the class of hormones that stimulates or controls masculine characteristics), is released during a brief period of prenatal brain development. Subsequently, it alters the brain much as it alters the sex organs. This process is **masculinization**.

Testosterone does not affect all body organs or all brain regions, but it does affect many brain regions in many ways. It affects the number of neurons formed in certain brain areas, reduces the number of neurons that die, increases cell growth, increases or reduces dendritic branching and synaptic growth, and regulates synaptic activity, among other effects.

Estrogens, the sex hormones responsible for the female's distinguishing characteristics, also probably influence postnatal brain development. Jill Goldstein and her colleagues found sex differences in the volume of cortical regions known to have differential levels of receptors for testosterone (androgen receptors) and estrogen, respectively, as shown in **Figure 8-29** (Goldstein et al., 2001). Orange areas in the figure are larger in females, and green areas are larger in males. Clearly, a male brain and a female brain are not the same. Hormones alter brain development, and clear sex differences appear in the rate of brain development (see Figure 8-19).

Testosterone's effects on brain development were once believed unimportant, because this hormone was thought primarily to influence brain regions related to sexual behavior, not regions of higher functions.

testosterone Sex hormone secreted by the testes and responsible for the distinguishing characteristics of the male.

androgen Class of hormones that stimulates or controls masculine characteristics.

masculinization Process by which exposure to androgens (male sex hormones) alters the brain, rendering it identifiably male.

estrogens Variety of sex hormones responsible for the distinguishing characteristics of the female.

FIGURE 8-29 Sex Differences in Brain Volume Cerebral areas related to sex differences in the distribution of estrogen (orange) and androgen (green) receptors in the developing brain correspond to areas of relatively larger cerebral volumes in adult women and men. Information from J. M. Goldstein, L. J. Seidman, N. J. Horton, N. Makris, D. N. Kennedy et al. (2001). Normal sexual dimorphism of the adult human brain assessed by in vivo magnetic resonance imaging. *Cerebral Cortex, 11,* 490–497.

Lateral view   Medial view

This belief is false. Testosterone changes cell structure in many cortical regions, with diverse behavioral consequences that include influences on cognitive processes.

Jocelyne Bachevalier adapted her method, shown in Experiment 8-1 on page 264, by training infant male and female monkeys in the concurrent discrimination task. The animal has to learn which of two objects in a series of pairs conceals a food reward. Bachevalier also trained the animals in another task, *object reversal learning*. The task is to learn that one object always conceals a food reward, whereas another object never does. After the animal learns this pattern, the reward contingencies are reversed so that the particular object that has always been rewarded is now never rewarded, and the formerly unrewarded object now conceals the reward. When the animal learns this new pattern, the contingencies are reversed again, and so on for five reversals.

Bachevalier found that 2½-month-old male monkeys were superior to female monkeys on the object reversal task, but females did better on the concurrent task. Apparently, the different brain areas required for these two tasks mature at different rates in male and female monkeys. Bachevalier later tested additional male monkeys whose testes had been removed at birth and so were no longer exposed to testosterone. These animals performed like females on the tasks, which implies that testosterone was influencing the brain development rate in areas related to certain cognitive behaviors.

Bachevalier and her colleague William Overman (Overman et al., 1996) repeated the experiment with children 15 to 30 months old. The results were the same: boys were superior at the object reversal task and girls were superior at the concurrent task. The investigators found no such male–female performance differences among children 32 to 55 months of age. Presumably, the brain regions required for both tasks had matured in both boys and girls. At the earlier age, however, gonadal hormones seemed to influence the maturation rate in certain brain regions, just as they had in the baby monkeys.

Lifelong Effects of Gonadal Hormones

Although gonadal hormones' biggest effects on the brain may come during early development, their role there is by no means finished in infancy. Both testosterone and estrogen (which females' ovaries produce in large quantities) continue to influence brain structure throughout an animal's life. In fact, removal of the ovaries in middle-aged laboratory rats leads to marked growth of dendrites and glial cells in the cortex. This finding of widespread neural change in the cortex associated with estrogen loss has implications for treating postmenopausal women with hormone replacement therapy, which may reverse the plastic changes.

Gonadal hormones also affect how the brain responds to environmental events. For instance, among rats housed in complex environments, males show more dendritic growth in neurons of the visual cortex than do females (Juraska, 1990). In contrast, females housed in this setting show more dendritic growth in the hippocampus than males do. Apparently, the same experience can affect the male and female brain differently owing to the mediating influence of gonadal hormones.

As females and males develop, then, their brains continue to diverge more and more, much like a fork in a road. After you set out on one path, your direction is forever changed, as the roads increasingly course farther apart.

To summarize, gonadal hormones alter basic neuronal development, shape experience-dependent changes in the brain, and influence neuronal structure throughout our lifetimes. Those who believe that behavioral differences between males and females are solely the result of environmental experiences must consider these neural effects of sex hormones.

Details on sexual orientation and gender identity appear in Section 12-5.

In part, it is true that environmental factors exert a major influence. But one reason they do so may be that male and female brains are different to start with. Even the same events experienced by structurally different brains may lead to different effects on those brains. Evidence shows that significant experiences, such as prenatal stress, produce markedly different changes in gene expression in the frontal cortex of male and female rats (Mychasiuk et al., 2011).

Another key question related to hormonal influences on brain development is whether any sex differences in brain organization might be independent of hormonal action. In other words, are differences in the action of sex chromosome genes unrelated to sex hormones? Although little is known about such genetic effects in humans, studies of birds clearly show that genetic effects on brain cells may indeed contribute to sex differentiation.

Songbirds have an especially interesting brain dimorphism: in most species, males sing and females do not. This behavioral difference between the sexes is directly related to a neural birdsong circuit present in males but not in females. Robert Agate and his colleagues (2003) studied the brain of a rare *gynandromorph* zebra finch, shown in **Figure 8-30**. This bird exhibits physical characteristics of both sexes.

Genetic analysis shows that cells on one half of the bird's brain and body are genetically female and on the other half are genetically male. The two sides of the gynandromorph's body and brain were exposed to the same hormones during prenatal development. Thus, the effect of male and female genes on the birdsong circuit can be examined to determine how the genes and hormones might interact.

If the sex difference in the birdsong circuit were totally related to the presence of hormones prenatally, then the two sides of the brain should be equally masculine or feminine. Agate's results confirm the opposite: the neural song circuit is masculine on the male side of the brain. Only a genetic difference that was at least partly independent of hormonal effects could explain such a structural difference in the brain.

Adolescent Onset of Mental Disorders

Adolescence is a time of rapid brain change related both to pubertal hormones and to psychosocial stress. Relationships with parents and peers are among the prime stressors, as is school. Add to this the finding, charted in **Figure 8-31**, that the peak age of onset for any mental disorder is estimated at 14 years (Paus et al., 2008).

Figure 8-31 reveals that age of onset differs across disorders. However, anxiety disorders, psychoses (including schizophrenia), bipolar disorder, depression, eating disorders, and substance abuse most commonly emerge by or during adolescence. From an evolutionary perspective, neurobiological and associated behavioral changes linked with the period we define as adolescence are designed to optimize the brain for challenges that lie ahead in adulthood. But the brain's plasticity in adolescence can also make it vulnerable to psychopathologies that can endure for the rest of the individual's life.

Gut Bacteria and Brain Development

We have emphasized factors that affect CNS development directly, but a less direct route exerts itself via the enteric nervous system. The ENS sends information to the brain that affects our mental state. The brain in turn can modify gut function.

An important component of the ENS is the microbiome, the bacteria in the gut with which the ENS interacts. About 10^{14} microbiota populate the adult gut, which means that microbiota outnumber the host body cells by a factor of 10. But in utero, the fetus's gut is sterile. It is only at birth that trillions of microbes from the mother's vaginal and anal fluids, and later from her skin, invade the baby's body and start to grow.

Many neurodevelopmental disorders, including autism, may be related to an atypical microbiome early in life (e.g., Finegold et al., 2012). Elaine Hsiao and her colleagues (2013) studied a mouse model known to display features of ASD. These mice produce few social auditory vocalizations, about one-third the normal levels. Manipulation of their gut bacteria restored the vocalizations to normal levels, demonstrating that gut bacteria can alter behavior. Other neurodevelopmental disorders may involve microbiome abnormalities as well.

FIGURE 8-30 Gynandromorph This rare zebra finch has dull female plumage on one side of the body and bright male plumage on the other side. Neural, not gonadal, origin of brain sex differences in a gynandromorphic finch. Agate RJ, Grisham W, Wade J, Mann S, Wingfield J, Schanen C, Palotie A, Arnold AP. *Proc Natl Acad Sci U S A.* 2003 Apr 15; 100 (8): 4873-8. Copyright (2003) National Academy of Sciences, U.S.A.

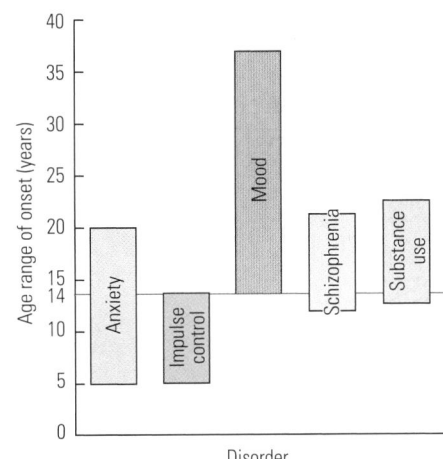

FIGURE 8-31 Emergence of Mental Disorders in Adolescence Data from T. Paus, M. Keshavan, and J. N. Giedd (2008). Why do so many psychiatric disorders emerge during adolescence? *Nature Reviews Neuroscience, 9,* pp. 947–957.

Section 2-5 introduces the ENS and microbiome.

FIGURE 8-32 Time-Dependent Effects Damage to the rat's frontal cortex on the day of birth leads to cortical neurons with simple dendritic fields and sparse growth of spines in the adult (left). In contrast, damage to the frontal cortex at 10 days of age leads to cortical neurons with expanded dendritic fields and denser spines than normal in adults (right).

Information from B. Kolb and R. Gibb (1993). Possible anatomical basis of recovery of function after neonatal frontal lesions in rats. *Behavioral Neuroscience, 107,* p. 808.

Injury and Brain Development

Dating to the late 1800s, infants and children were generally believed to show better recovery from brain injury than adults. In the 1930s, Donald Hebb studied children with major birth-related injuries to the frontal lobes and found them to have severe and permanent behavioral abnormalities in adulthood. He concluded that brain damage early in life can alter the brain's subsequent development and actually may be worse than injury later in life.

Have other studies confirmed Hebb's conclusion? Few anatomical studies of humans with early brain injuries exist, but we can make some general predictions from studying laboratory animals. In general, early brain injuries do produce atypical brains, especially at certain critical periods in development.

For humans, the worst time appears to be in the last half of the intrauterine period and the first couple of months after birth. Rats and cats that are injured at a comparable time have a significantly smaller brain than average, and their cortical neurons show general atrophy relative to healthy brains, as illustrated on the left in **Figure 8-32**. Behaviorally, these animals appear cognitively deficient over a wide range of skills.

Injury to the developing brain is not always devastating. For example, researchers have known for more than 100 years that children with brain injuries in the first couple of years after birth almost never have the severe language disturbances common to adults with equivalent injuries. Animal studies help explain why.

Whereas damage to the rat brain in the developmental period comparable to the last few months of gestation in humans produces widespread cortical atrophy, damage at a time in rat brain development roughly comparable to ages 6 months to 2 years in humans actually produces more dendritic development in rats (Figure 8-32 at right). Furthermore, these animals show dramatic recovery of functions, which implies that during development the brain has a capacity to compensate for injury. Parallel studies in cats have shown extensive reorganization of cortex-to-cortex connections after early injury to the visual cortex (see the review by Payne and Lomber, 2001).

Drugs and Brain Development

The U.S. National Institute on Drug Abuse (2012) estimates that 16 percent of babies born alive in the United States today are exposed to nicotine in utero. Similar statistics on alcohol consumption by pregnant mothers are not available, but the effects of alcohol on the fetus are well documented. Even low doses of commonly prescribed drugs, including antidepressants, antipsychotics, and pain-killers, appear to alter prenatal neuron development in the prefrontal cortex. It manifests after birth in abnormalities in behaviors controlled by the affected regions (see the review by Halliwell et al., 2009).

NIDA also estimates that 5.5 percent of expectant mothers, approximately 221,000 pregnant women each year in the United States, use an illicit drug at least once in the course of their pregnancy. Among pregnant teenagers aged 15 to 17, that figure climbs to 16%, or about 14,000 women. And what about caffeine and nicotine? More than likely most children were exposed to caffeine (from coffee, tea, cola, energy drinks, and chocolate) in utero and about 16% were exposed to nicotine. Laboratory animal studies have shown that prenatal exposure to nicotine alters the brain's response to complex housing: the brain appears less plastic (e.g., Mychasiuk et al., 2014).

Section 6-3 reviews nicotine's prominence as a gateway drug.

The precise effects of prenatal drug intake on brain development are poorly understood, but the overall conclusion from current knowledge is that children with prenatal exposure to a variety of psychoactive drugs have an increased likelihood of later drug use (e.g., Minnes et al., 2014). Although, again, childhood disorders are poorly studied, many experts suggest that they—learning disabilities and ADHD are examples—may be related to prenatal exposure to drugs such as nicotine or caffeine or both. As Carl Malanga and Barry Kosofsky

Focus 7-4 details ADHD and Focus 14-1 details dyslexia.

(2003) note poignantly, society at large does not yet fully appreciate the impact that prenatal drug exposure can have on the lives of its children.

Other Sources of Abnormal Brain Development

The nervous system need not be damaged by external forces to develop abnormally. Many genetic aberrations are believed to result in abnormalities in brain development and ultimately brain structure. *Spina bifida*, in which the genetic blueprint goes awry and the neural tube does not close completely, leads to an incompletely formed spinal cord. After birth, unless treated with folic acid, children with spina bifida usually have serious motor problems.

Imagine what happens if some genetic aberration causes improper closure of the front end of the neural tube. Because the front end of the neural tube forms the brain (see Figure 8-5), this failure results in gross abnormalities in brain development known as **anencephaly**. Affected infants die soon after birth.

Atypical brain development can be much subtler than anencephaly. For example, if cells do not migrate to their correct locations, and if these mispositioned cells do not subsequently die, they can disrupt brain function and may lead to disorders ranging from seizures to schizophrenia (see review by Guerrini et al., 2007). In a variety of conditions, neurons fail to differentiate normally. In certain cases, neurons fail to produce long dendrites or spines, which results in abnormal brain connectivity and developmental disabilities.

The opposite condition also is possible: neurons continue to make dendrites and form connections with other cells until the neurons are extraordinarily large. The functional consequences of all the newly formed connections can be devastating. Excitatory synapses in the wrong location effectively short-circuit a neuron's function.

Subtle abnormal events also can be devastating, even terminal. **Sudden infant death syndrome** (SIDS), the unexplained death while asleep of a seemingly healthy infant less than 1 year old, kills about 2500 babies yearly in the United States alone. Postmortem studies reveal that SIDS victims are more likely than other babies to have a particular gene variation that makes the serotonin transporter unusually efficient. Normally, the serotoninergic system helps to stimulate a respiratory mechanism that responds to high carbon dioxide levels in the blood and acts to expel the gas.

In babies who die of SIDS, serotonin is cleared from the synapse more rapidly than normal. This action makes 5-HT less effective in regulating life-threatening events such as carbon dioxide buildup during sleep. Babies can breathe excessive levels of carbon dioxide that is trapped in their bedding, for example, and suffocate.

In addition to the serotonin transporter abnormality, David Paterson and his colleagues (2006) found an abnormally low occurrence of $5\text{-}HT_{1A}$ receptors in SIDS victims' brains. The researchers found that boys have significantly fewer $5\text{-}HT_{1A}$ receptors than do females, a result consistent with higher SIDS mortality in boys. Hannah Kinney (2009) speculates that the primary defect is increased numbers of 5-HT cells, possibly arising during fetal development and owing to unknown causes, but augmented by adverse prenatal exposure to alcohol, nicotine, and/or other factors. This defect leads to the changes in $5\text{-}HT_{1A}$ receptors.

A curious consequence of abnormal brain development is that behavioral effects may emerge only as the brain matures and the maturing regions begin to play a greater role in behavior. This consequence is true especially of frontal lobe injuries. The frontal lobes continue to develop into early adulthood (see Figure 8-17), and often not until adolescence do the effects of frontal lobe abnormalities become noticeable.

Schizophrenia is a disease characterized by its slow development, usually not becoming obvious until late adolescence. Clinical Focus 8-5, Schizophrenia on page 278, relates disease progress and its possible origin.

anencephaly Failure of the forebrain to develop.

sudden infant death syndrome (SIDS) Unexplained death while asleep of a seemingly healthy infant less than 1 year old.

Section 16-4 describes the schizophrenic brain and Section 5-3 a possible relation to excessive DA or 5-HT activity in that brain.

Schizophrenia

When Mrs. T. was 16 years old, she began to experience her first symptom of schizophrenia: a profound feeling that people were staring at her. These bouts of self-consciousness soon forced her to end her public piano performances. Her self-consciousness led to withdrawal, then to fearful delusions that others were speaking about her behind her back, and finally to suspicions that they were plotting to harm her.

At first Mrs. T.'s illness was intermittent, and the return of her intelligence, warmth, and ambition between episodes allowed her to complete several years of college, to marry, and to rear three children. She had to enter a hospital for her illness for the first time at age 28, after the birth of her third child, when she began to hallucinate.

Now, at 45, Mrs. T. is never entirely well. She has seen dinosaurs on the street and live animals in her refrigerator. While hallucinating, she speaks and writes in an incoherent, but almost poetic way. At other times, she is more lucid, but even then the voices she hears sometimes lead her to do dangerous things, such as driving very fast down the highway in the middle of the night, dressed only in a nightgown. . . . At other times and without any apparent stimulus, Mrs. T. has bizarre visual hallucinations. For example, she saw cherubs in the grocery store. These experiences leave her preoccupied, confused, and frightened, unable to perform such everyday tasks as cooking or playing the piano. (Gershon & Rieder, 1992, p. 127)

It has always been easier to identify schizophrenic behavior than to define schizophrenia. Perhaps the one universally accepted criterion for its diagnosis is the absence of other neurological disturbances or affective (mood) disorders that could cause a person to lose touch with reality—a definition by default.

Symptoms of schizophrenia vary, suggesting that biological abnormalities also vary from person to person. Most patients appear to stay at a fairly stable level after the first few years of symptoms, with little evidence of a decline in neuropsychological functioning. Symptoms come and go, much as for Mrs. T., but the severity is relatively constant after the first few episodes.

Numerous studies have investigated the brains of schizophrenia patients, both in MRI and CT scans and in autopsies. Although the results vary, most neuroscientists agree that schizophrenic brains weigh less than normal and have enlarged ventricles. Research findings also suggest that brains affected by schizophrenia have smaller frontal lobes (or at least a reduction in the number of neurons in the prefrontal cortex) and thinner parahippocampal gyri.

Joyce Kovelman and Arnold Scheibel (1984) found abnormalities in the orientation of hippocampal neurons in people with schizophrenia. Rather than the consistently parallel orientation of neurons in this region characteristic of healthy brains, schizophrenic brains have a more haphazard organization, as shown in the accompanying drawings.

Evidence is increasing that the abnormalities observed in schizophrenic brains are associated with disturbances of brain development. William Bunney and his colleagues (1997) suggested that at least a subgroup of those with schizophrenia underwent either environmental insults or some type of abnormal gene activity in the fourth to sixth month of fetal development.

These events are thought to result in abnormal cortical development, particularly in the frontal lobes. Later in adolescence, as the frontal lobes approach maturity, the person begins to have symptoms deriving from this abnormal prenatal development.

Hippocampus

Pyramidal cell orientation in the hippocampus of (A) a healthy brain and (B) a schizophrenic brain. Research from J. A. Kovelman and A. B. Scheibel (1984.) A neurohistologic correlate of schizophrenia. *Biological Psychiatry, 19,* p. 1613.

Organized (healthy) pyramidal neurons   Disorganized (schizophrenic) pyramidal neurons

Developmental Disability

Impaired cognitive functioning accompanies abnormal brain development. Impairment may range from mild, allowing an almost normal lifestyle, to severe, requiring constant care. As summarized in **Table 8-3**, such developmental disability can result from chronic malnutrition, genetic abnormalities such as Down syndrome, hormonal abnormalities, brain injury, or neurological disease. Different causes produce different abnormalities in brain organization, but the critical similarity across all types of developmental disability is that the brain is not normal.

Dominique Purpura (1974) conducted one of the few systematic investigations of developmentally disabled children's brains. Purpura used Golgi stain to examine the neurons of children who had died of accident or disease unrelated to the nervous system. When he examined the brains of children with various forms of intellectual disability, he found that dendrite growth was stunted and the spines very sparse relative to dendrites from children of typical intelligence, as illustrated in **Figure 8-33**.

Figure 3-22 illustrates trisomy, the chromosomal abnormality that causes Down syndrome.

TABLE 8-3 Causes of Developmental Disability

Cause	Example mechanism	Example condition
Abnormal embryonic development	Exposure to a toxin	FASD
Birth trauma	Anoxia (oxygen deprivation)	Cerebral palsy
Chronic malnutrition	Abnormal brain development	Kwashiorkor
Drugs (e.g., valproate)	Neural tube defects	Spina bifida ASD
Environmental abnormality	Sensory deprivation	Children in Romanian orphanages
Genetic abnormality	Error of metabolism Chromosomal abnormality	Phenylketonuria Down syndrome
Prenatal disease	Infection	Rubella (German measles) Retardation

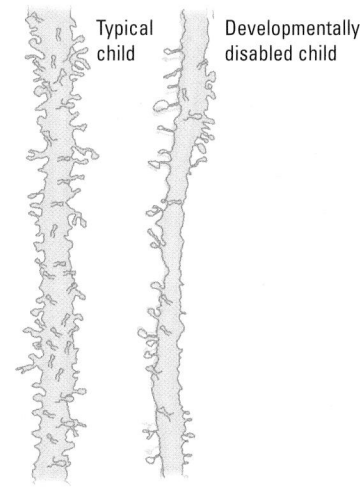

FIGURE 8-33 Neuronal Contrast Representative dendritic branches from cortical neurons in a child of typical intelligence (left) and a developmentally disabled child (right), whose neurons are thinner and have far fewer spines. Information from D. P. Purpura (1974). Dendritic spine "dysgenesis" and mental retardation. *Science, 186*, p. 1127.

The simpler neuronal structure probably indicates a marked reduction in the number of brain connections, which presumably caused the developmental disability. Variation in both the nature and the extent of neuronal abnormality in different children would lead to different behavioral syndromes.

(8-4) REVIEW

Brain Development and the Environment

Before you continue, check your understanding.

1. The idea that specific molecules in different cells in various midbrain regions give each cell a distinctive chemical identity is known as the _____.

2. Subnormal visual stimulation to one eye during early development can lead to a loss of acuity, known as _____.

3. The hormone _____ masculinizes the brain during development.

4. The brain's sensitivity to experience is highest during _____.

5. Why do so many mental disorders appear during adolescence?

Answers appear at the back of the book.

For additional study tools, visit 🐨 LaunchPad:
www.macmillanhighered.com/launchpad/kolb5e

(8-5) How Do Any of Us Develop a Normal Brain?

When we consider the brain's complexity, the less-than-precise process of brain development, and the myriad factors—from SES to gut bacteria—that can influence development, we are left to marvel at how so many of us end up with brains that pass for normal. We all must have had neurons that migrated to wrong locations, made incorrect connections, were exposed to viruses or other harmful substances. If the brain were as fragile as it might seem, to end up with a normal brain would be almost impossible.

Apparently, animals have evolved a substantial capacity to repair minor abnormalities in brain development. Most people have developed in the range that we call normal because the human brain's plasticity and regenerative powers overcome minor developmental deviations.

By initially overproducing neurons and synapses, the brain gains the capacity to correct errors that might have arisen accidentally.

These same plastic properties later allow us to cope with the ravages of aging. Neurons are dying throughout our lifetime. By age 60, investigators ought to see significant effects from all this cell loss, especially considering the cumulative results of exposure to environmental toxins, drugs, traumatic brain injuries, and other neural insults. But this is not what happens.

Although some teenagers may not believe it, relatively few 60-year-olds are demented. By most criteria, the 60-year-old who has been intellectually active throughout adulthood is likely to be much wiser than the 18-year-old whose brain has lost relatively few neurons. A 60-year-old chess player will have a record of many more chess matches from which to draw game strategies than does an 18-year-old, for example.

Clearly, some mechanism must enable us to compensate for loss and minor injury to our brain cells. This capacity for plasticity and change, for learning and adapting, is arguably the most important characteristic of the human brain during development and throughout life.

We return to learning, memory, and neuroplasticity in Chapter 14.

SUMMARY

8-1 Three Perspectives on Brain Development

Nervous system development entails more than the unfolding of a genetic blueprint. Development is a complex dance of genetic and environmental events that interact to sculpt the brain to fit within a particular cultural and environmental context. We can approach this dance from three perspectives: (1) correlating emerging brain structures with emerging behaviors, (2) correlating new behaviors with neural maturation, and (3) identifying influences on brain and behavior.

8-2 Neurobiology of Development

Human brain maturation is a long process, lasting as late as age 30. Neurons, the units of brain function, develop a phenotype, migrate, and, as their processes elaborate, establish connections with other neurons even before birth. The developing brain produces many more neurons and connections than it needs and then prunes back in toddlerhood and again in adolescence and early adulthood to a stable level maintained by some neurogenesis throughout the life-span. Experiences throughout development can trigger epigenetic mechanisms, such as gene methylation, that alter gene expression.

8-3 Using Emerging Behaviors to Infer Neural Maturation

Throughout the world, across the cultural spectrum, from newborn to adult, we all develop through similar behavioral stages. As infants develop physically, motor behaviors emerge in a predictable sequence from gross, poorly directed movements toward objects to controlled pincer grasps to pick up objects as small as pencils by about 11 months. Cognitive behaviors also develop through stages of logic and problem solving. Beginning with Jean Piaget, researchers have identified and characterized four or more distinct stages of cognitive development. Each stage can be identified by specific behavioral tests.

Behaviors emerge as the neural systems that produce them develop. Matching the median timetables of neurodevelopment with observed behavior infers the hierarchical relation between brain structure and brain function. Motor behaviors emerge in synchrony with maturating motor circuits in the cerebral cortex, basal ganglia, and cerebellum, as well as in the connections from these areas to the spinal cord. Similar correlations between emerging behaviors and neuronal development accompany the maturation of cognitive behavior as neural circuits in the frontal and temporal lobes mature in early adulthood.

8-4 Brain Development and the Environment

The brain is most plastic during its development, and neuronal structures and their connections can be molded by various factors throughout development. The brain's sensitivity to factors such as external events, quality of environment, tactile stimulation, drugs, gonadal hormones, stress, and injury varies over time. At critical periods in the course of development, beginning prenatally, different brain regions are particularly sensitive to different events.

Brain perturbations in the course of development from, say, anoxia, trauma, or toxins can alter brain development significantly; can result in severe behavioral abnormalities, including intellectual disability; and may be related to such disorders as ASD or SIDS. Other behavioral disorders emerge in adolescence, a time of prolonged frontal lobe change.

8-5 How Do Any of Us Develop a Normal Brain?

The brain has a substantial capacity to repair or correct minor abnormalities, allowing most people to develop normal behavioral repertoires and to maintain brain function throughout life.

KEY TERMS

↪ Visit LaunchPad to access the e-Book, videos, LearningCurve adaptive quizzing, flashcards, and more.

www.macmillanhighered.com/launchpad/kolb5e

CHAPTER 9

How Do We Sense, Perceive, and See the World?

Katherine Streeter

Migraines and a Case of Blindsight

D. B.'s recurring headaches began at about age 14. A visual aura warned of a headache's approach: an oval area of flashing (scintillating) light appeared just left of center in his field of vision. Over the next few minutes, the oval enlarged. After about 15 minutes, the flashing light vanished, and D. B. was blind in the region of the oval.

D. B. described the oval as an opaque white area surrounded by a rim of color. A headache on the right side of his head followed and could persist for as long as 48 hours. D. B. usually fell asleep before that much time elapsed. When he awakened, the headache was gone and his vision was normal again.

D. B. was subject to severe *migraine*, a recurrent headache usually on one side of the head. Migraines vary in severity, frequency, and duration and are often accompanied by nausea and vomiting. Migraine is perhaps the most common of all neurological disorders, affecting some 5 to 20 percent of the population at some time in their life.

Auras may be auditory or tactile as well as visual and may result in an inability to move or to talk. After an aura passes, most have a severe headache caused by a dilation of cerebral blood vessels. The headache is usually limited to one side of the head, just as the aura is on one side of the visual field. Left untreated, migraines may last for hours or even days.

D. B.'s attacks continued at intervals of about 6 weeks for 10 years. After one attack, he was left with a small blind spot, or *scotoma*, illustrated in the accompanying photographs. When D. B. was 26 years old, a neurologist found that a collection of abnormal blood vessels at the back of his right occipital lobe was causing the migraine attacks—a most unusual cause.

By the time he was 30, the migraines had begun to interfere with his family life, social life, and job. No drug treatment was effective, so D. B. had the malformed blood vessels surgically removed. The operation relieved his pain and generally improved his life, but a part of his right occipital lobe, deprived of blood, had died. D. B. was blind in the left half of his visual field: as he looks at the world through either eye, he is unable to see anything left of the midline.

Lawrence Weizkrantz (1986) made a remarkable discovery about D. B.'s blindness. D. B. could not identify objects in his blind area but could very accurately tell whether a light had blinked on there and even where the light was. Apparently, D. B.'s brain knew when a light blinked and where it appeared. This phenomenon is called *blindsight*. D. B.'s brain knew more than he was aware of consciously. D. B.'s case provides an excellent example of the parallel streams of visual processing in the cortex. His system for processing objects was impaired, but his system for locating objects in space was not.

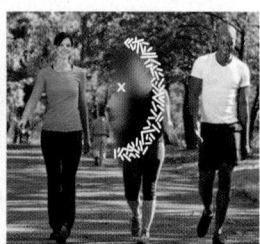

Tyler Olson/Shutterstock

X = Fixation point

As a typical migraine scotoma develops, a person looking at the small white × in the photograph at the far left would first see a small patch of lines. This striped area continues growing outward, leaving an opaque area (scotoma) where the stripes were, almost completely blocking the visual field within 15 to 20 minutes. Normal vision returns shortly thereafter.

As you look at the photograph in Clinical Focus 9-1, Migraines and a Case of Blindsight, you see three people—two women and a man—who appear to be walking and talking on a warm summer day. Trees appear in the background, clearly behind the people. It is tempting to believe that this visual image is transferred whole to the brain, where we see it.

But how could the nervous system do this? There is no viewing screen in the brain. Instead, the nervous system must construct the image from bits of information, such as shape and color. Then the brain must put it all together to form what we perceive as a complete image. The neural reconstruction is not a passive image such as a TV screen projects. Rather, the brain continuously employs memories, both to interpret moment-to-moment sensory information and to predict the immediate future.

D. B.'s case demonstrates that we are consciously aware of only part of the visual information our brain is processing. This *selective awareness* is an important working principle behind human sensation and perception. Weizkrantz, a world-renowned visual neuroscientist at Oxford University, detected it in the visual system only because of D. B.'s injury.

We are in fact unaware of much of the sensory processing that takes place in the neural pathways for vision, hearing, touch, taste, and smell. All our senses convert energy into neural activity that has meaning for us. We begin this chapter with a general summary of sensation and perception that explores how this energy conversion takes place.

The ability to lose conscious visual perception while retaining unconscious vision, as D. B. did, leads us to the chapter's central question: How do we see the world? We begin by overviewing visual system anatomy. Next we consider the connections between the eyes and the sections of the brain that process visual information.

Turning to the perceptual experience of sight, we focus on how neurons respond to visual input and enable the brain to perceive features such as color, shape, and movement. At the chapter's end, we explore vision's culmination: understanding what we see. How do we infuse light energy with meaning to grasp the content of written words or to see the beauty in a painting? Read on.

Vision is this chapter's main topic; hearing is Chapter 10's. Section 11-4 covers body senses and balance. Section 12-2 explains smell and taste.

9-1 Nature of Sensation and Perception

We may believe that we see, hear, touch, smell, and taste real things in a real world. In fact, the only input our brain receives from the "real" world is a series of action potentials passed along the neurons that form our various sensory pathways. Although we experience visual and body sensations as fundamentally different from one another, the nerve impulses coursing in the neurons of these two sensory systems are quite similar, as are the neurons themselves.

Neuroscientists understand how nerves can turn energy, such as light waves, into nerve impulses. They also know the pathways those nerve impulses take to reach the brain. But they do not know how we end up perceiving one set of nerve impulses as what the world looks like and another set as what makes us move.

How much of what you know comes through your senses? Taken at face value, this question seems reasonable. At the same time, we realize that our senses can deceive us—that two people can look at the same optical illusion and see very different images, that a person dreaming typically does not think that the dream images are real, that you often do not think that a picture of you looks like you. Many scientists think that much of what we know comes to us through our senses, but they also think that our brains actively transform sensory information into forms that help us to adapt and are thus behaviorally useful.

Our sensory systems appear to be extremely diverse: vision, audition, touch, taste, and olfaction appear to have little in common at first glance. Although our perceptions and behaviors in relation to them differ, each sensory system is organized on a similar hierarchical plan. We now consider the features common to the sensory systems—receptors, neural relays between receptor and neocortex, sensory coding and representation, and perception.

Sensory Receptors

Sensory receptor neurons are specialized to transduce (convert) sensory energy—light, for example—into neural activity. If we put flour into a sieve and shake it, the more finely milled particles fall through the holes, whereas the coarser particles and lumps do not. Sensory receptors are designed to respond only to a narrow band of energy—analogous to particles of certain sizes—within each modality's energy spectrum. Each sensory system's receptors are specialized to filter a different form of energy:

- For vision, the photoreceptors in the retina convert light energy into chemical energy, which is in turn converted into action potentials.

- In the auditory system, air pressure waves are first converted into mechanical energy, which activates the auditory receptors that produce action potentials in auditory receptor neurons.

Vision begins in the photoreceptor cells, the rods and cones shown here. Section 9-2 details how they work.

SPL/Science Source

receptive field Sensory region that stimulates a receptor cell or neuron.

optic flow Streaming of visual stimuli that accompanies an observer's movement through space.

auditory flow Change heard as a person and a source of sound move relative to one another.

An animal's perception of the world depends on its nervous system's complexity and organization.

- In the somatosensory system, mechanical energy activates receptors sensitive to touch, pressure, or pain. These somatosensory receptors in turn generate action potentials in somatosensory receptor neurons.

- For taste and olfaction, various chemical molecules in the air or in food fit themselves into receptors of various shapes to activate action potentials in the respective receptor neurons.

Were our visual receptors somewhat different, we would be able to see in the ultraviolet as well as the visible parts of the electromagnetic spectrum, as honeybees and butterflies can. Receptors in the human ear respond to a wide range of sound waves, but elephants and bats can hear and produce sounds far below and above, respectively, the range humans can hear. In fact, in comparison with those of other animals, human sensory abilities are about average.

Even our pet dogs have "superhuman" powers: they can detect trace odors; hear low-range sounds, as elephants do; and see in the dark. We can hold up only our superior color vision. Thus, for each species and its individual members, sensory systems filter the inputs to produce an idiosyncratic representation of reality.

Receptive Fields

Every sensory receptor organ and cell has a **receptive field**, a specific part of the world to which it responds. If you fix your eyes on a point directly in front of you, for example, what you see of the world is the scope of your eyes' receptive field. If you close one eye, the visual world shrinks. What the remaining eye sees is the receptive field for that eye.

Each photoreceptor cell in the eye points in a slightly different direction and so has a unique receptive field. You can grasp the conceptual utility of the receptive field by considering that the brain uses information from each sensory receptor's receptive field not only to identify sensory information but also to contrast the information each receptor field is providing.

Receptive fields not only sample sensory information but also help locate events in space. Because adjacent receptive fields may overlap, the contrast between their responses to events help us localize sensations. This spatial dimension of sensory information produces cortical patterns and maps that form each person's sensory reality.

Our sensory system is organized to tell us both what is happening in the world around us and what in the world we are doing ourselves. When you move, you change the perceived properties of objects, and you sense things that have little to do with the external world. When we run, visual stimuli appear to stream by us, a stimulus configuration called **optic flow**. When you move past a sound source, you hear an **auditory flow**, a gradual shift in sound intensity that takes place because of your changing location. Optic flow and auditory flow are useful for telling us how fast we are going, whether we are going in a straight line or up or down, and whether we or an object in the world is moving.

Try this experiment. Slowly move your hand back and forth before your eyes and gradually increase its speed. Eventually, your hand will get a little blurry, because your eye movements are not quick enough to follow its movement. Now keep your hand still and move your head back and forth. The image of your hand remains clear. When receptors in the inner ear inform your visual system that your head is moving, the visual system compensates for the head movements, and you observe the hand as a stationary image.

Tyler Olson/Shutterstock

Receptive Fields In vision, each photoreceptor neuron has a unique receptive field that partially overlaps adjacent fields, diagrammed for another class of retinal neurons in Figure 9-27.

Receptor Density and Sensitivity

Receptor density is particularly important for determining a sensory system's sensitivity. For example, tactile receptors on the fingers are numerous compared with those on the arm. The difference explains why fingers can discriminate touch remarkably well and the arm cannot.

Our sensory systems use different receptors to enhance sensitivity under different conditions. For example, the visual system uses different sets of receptors to respond to light and color. Color photoreceptors are small and densely packed to make sensitive color discriminations in bright light. Receptors for black–white vision are larger and more scattered, but their sensitivity to light—say, a lighted match at a distance of 2 miles on a dark night—is truly remarkable.

Differences in density of sensory receptors determine many animals' special abilities—dogs' excellent olfactory ability and the excellent tactile ability of raccoons' digits. Variations in receptor density in the human auditory receptor organ may explain such abilities as perfect pitch, displayed by some musicians.

Neural Relays

Inasmuch as receptors are common to each sensory system, all receptors connect to the cortex through a sequence of three or four intervening neurons. The visual and somatosensory systems have three relays, and the auditory system has four. Information can be modified at various stages in the relay, allowing the sensory system to mediate different responses. Once again, this is very different from the sensory images on a TV screen or from an audio system: information is being modified repeatedly as the brain constructs the image or sound.

Neural relays also allow sensory systems to interact. There is no straight-through point-to-point correspondence between one neural relay and the next; rather, each successive relay recodes the activity. Sensory neural relays are central to the hierarchy of motor responses in the brain.

Some of the three or four relays in each sensory system are in the spinal cord; others, in the brainstem; and still others, in the neocortex. At each level, the relay allows a sensory system to produce relevant actions that define the hierarchy of our motor behavior. For example, the first relay for pain receptors in the spinal cord is related to reflexes that produce withdrawal of a body part from a painful stimulus. Thus, even after section of the spinal cord from the brain, a limb still withdraws from a painful stimulus.

A dramatic effect of sensory interaction is the visual modification of sound. If a person hears a speech syllable such as *ba* while observing someone who is articulating *ga*, the listener hears not the actual sound *ba* but a hybrid sound, *da*. The viewed lip movements modify the listener's auditory perception.

This interaction effect is potent: it highlights the fact that a speaker's facial gestures influence our perception of speech sounds. As Roy Hamilton and his coworkers (2006) described, synchrony of gestures and sounds is an important aspect of language acquisition. The difficulty of learning a foreign language can relate to the difficulty of blending a speaker's articulation movements with the sounds the speaker produces.

Sensory Coding and Representation

After it has been transduced, all information from all sensory systems is encoded by action potentials that travel along peripheral nerves in the somatic nervous system until they enter the spinal cord or brain. From there the action potentials travel on nerve tracts within the central nervous system. Every bundle carries the same kind of signal. How do action potentials encode different sensations? (How does vision differ from touch?) How do they encode the features of particular sensations? (How does purple differ from blue?)

Parts of these questions seem easy to answer; others pose a fundamental challenge to neuroscience. The presence of a stimulus can be encoded by an increase or decrease in a neuron's discharge rate, and the amount of increase or decrease can encode stimulus intensity. As detailed in Section 9-4, qualitative visual changes, such as from red to green, can be encoded by activity in different neurons or even by different levels of discharge in the same neuron. (For example, more activity might signify redder and less activity, greener.)

What is less clear is how we perceive such sensations as touch, sound, and smell as different from one another. Part of the explanation is that each sensation is processed in its own distinct cortical region. Also, we learn through experience to distinguish them. Third, each sensory system has a preferential link with certain reflexive movements, constituting a separate wiring that helps keep each system distinct at all levels of neural organization.

Craig Lovell/Eagle Visions Photography/Alamy

Section 10-4 explains how we perceive music.

Recall the principle from Section 2-6: brain systems are organized hierarchically and in parallel.

Recall the principle from Section 2-6: the nervous system works by juxtaposing excitation and inhibition.

Sensory Homunculus (plaster), English School, (20th century)/Natural History Museum, London, UK/The Bridgeman Art Library

This curious figure reflects the topographic map in the sensorimotor cortex. Disproportionately large areas control body parts we use to make the most-skilled movements. See Sections 11-2 and 11-6. Section 15-6 details synesthesia.

FIGURE 9-1 Perceptual Illusions **(A)** Edgar Rubin's ambiguous reversible image can be perceived as a vase or as two faces. **(B)** Likewise ambiguous in the photo, each cheetah's head can be perceived as belonging to either cheetah's body.

(A)

(B)

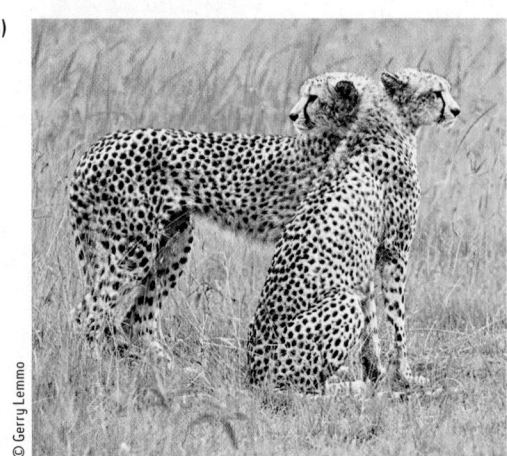

© Gerry Lemmo

For example, pain stimuli produce withdrawal responses, and fine-touch and pressure stimuli produce approach responses.

The distinctions among the sensory systems, however, are not always clear: some people hear in color or identify smells by how the smells sound to them. This mixing of the senses is called *synesthesia*. Anyone who has shivered when hearing a piece of music or at the noise chalk or fingernails can make on a blackboard has felt sound.

In most mammals, the neocortex represents the sensory field of each modality—vision, hearing, touch, smell, or taste—as a spatially organized neural representation of the external world. This **topographic map** is a neural–spatial representation of the body or of the areas of the sensory world perceived by a sensory organ. All mammals have at least one primary cortical area for each sensory system. Additional areas are usually referred to as *secondary*, because most of the information that reaches these areas is relayed through the primary area. Each additional representation is probably dedicated to encoding one specific aspect of the sensory modality. For vision, different additional representational areas may take part in perceiving color, movement, and form.

Perception

Sensation is far more than the simple registration of physical stimuli from the environment by the sensory organs. Compared with the richness of actual sensation, our description of sensory neuroanatomy and function is bound to seem sterile. Part of the reason for the disparity is that our sensory impressions are affected by the context in which they take place, by our emotional state, and by our past. All these factors contribute to **perception**, the subjective experience of sensation—how we interpret what we sense. Perception is more interesting to neuropsychologists than is sensation.

Clear proof that perception is more than sensation lies in the fact that different people transform the same sensory stimulation into totally different perceptions. The classic demonstration is an ambiguous image such as the well-known Rubin's vase shown in **Figure 9-1A**. This image may be perceived either as a vase or as two faces. If you fix your eyes on the center of the picture, the two perceptions will alternate, even though the sensory stimulation remains constant.

Similarly, the photograph of two cheetahs in Figure 9-1B is ambiguous. Which head goes with which cheetah? As with the Rubin's vase, the two perceptions may alternate. Such ambiguous images and illusions demonstrate the workings of complex perceptual phenomena and enlighten our insight into our cognitive processes.

(9-1) **REVIEW**

Nature of Sensation and Perception

Before you continue, check your understanding.

1. _____ are energy filters that transduce incoming physical energy into neural activity.

2. _____ fields locate sensory events. Receptor _____ determines sensitivity to sensory stimulation.

3. We distinguish one sensory modality from another by its _____ .

4. Sensation registers physical stimuli from the environment by the sensory organs. Perception is the _____ .

5. How is the anatomical organization similar for each sense?

Answers appear at the back of the book.

9-2 The Visual System's Functional Anatomy

Our primary sensory experience is visual. Far more of the human brain is dedicated to vision than to any other sense. Understanding the visual system's organization, then, is key to understanding human brain function. To build this understanding, we begin by following the routes visual information takes into and within the brain. This exercise is a bit like traveling a road to discover where it goes. As you trace the route, keep in mind the photograph in Focus 9-1 (page 284) and what the different levels of the visual system are doing to capture that image in the brain.

Structure of the Retina

Light energy travels from the outside world through the pupil and into the eye, where it strikes a light-sensitive surface, the **retina**, at the back of the eye (**Figure 9-2**). From this stimulation of **photoreceptor** cells on the retina, we begin to construct a visual world. If you are familiar with the properties of the electromagnetic spectrum and with the structure of the eye, read on. To refresh your knowledge of these topics, read The Basics: Visible Light and the Structure of the Eye on pages 290–291 before you continue.

Figure 9-2 includes a photograph of the retina, which is composed of photoreceptors beneath a layer of neurons connected to them. The neurons lie in front of the photoreceptor cells, but they do not prevent incoming light from being absorbed by those receptors, because the neurons are transparent and the photoreceptors are extremely sensitive to light. In addition, special glial cells in the retina called *Müller cells* span from the retina's inner membrane at the front to the photoreceptors at the back of the retina and act as optical fibers, channeling light to the buried photoreceptors.

Together, the photoreceptor cells and the retinal neurons perform some amazing functions. They translate light into action potentials, discriminate wavelengths so that we can distinguish colors, and work in a range of light intensities from bright to dim. These cells afford visual precision sufficient for us to see a human hair lying on the page of this book from a distance of 18 inches.

As in a camera, the image of objects projected onto the retina is upside down and backward. This flip-flopped orientation poses no problem for the brain. Remember, the brain is constructing the outside world, so it does not really care how the image is oriented initially. In fact, the brain can make adjustments regardless of the orientation of the images that it receives.

If for several days you were to wear glasses that invert visual images, the world would first appear upside down but then would suddenly appear right side up again because your brain would correct the distortion (Held, 1968). Curiously, when you removed the glasses, the world would temporarily seem upside down once more, because your brain at first would be unaware that you had tricked it again. Eventually, though, your brain would solve this puzzle too, and the world would flip back to the correct orientation.

Fovea

Try this experiment. Focus on the print at the left edge of this page. The words will be clearly legible. Now, while holding your eyes still, try to read the words on the right side of the page. It will be very difficult, even impossible, even though you can see that words are there.

topographic map Spatially organized neural representation of the external world.

sensation Registration by the sensory organs of physical stimuli from the environment.

perception Subjective interpretation of sensations by the brain.

retina Light-sensitive surface at the back of the eye consisting of neurons and photoreceptor cells.

photoreceptor Specialized retinal neuron that transduces light into neural activity.

Virtually all retinal neurons are insensitive to light so are unaffected by light passing through them.

FIGURE 9-2 Central Focus This cross section through the retina **(A)** shows the depression at the fovea—also shown in the scanning electron micrograph **(B)**—where photoreceptors are packed most densely and where our vision is clearest.

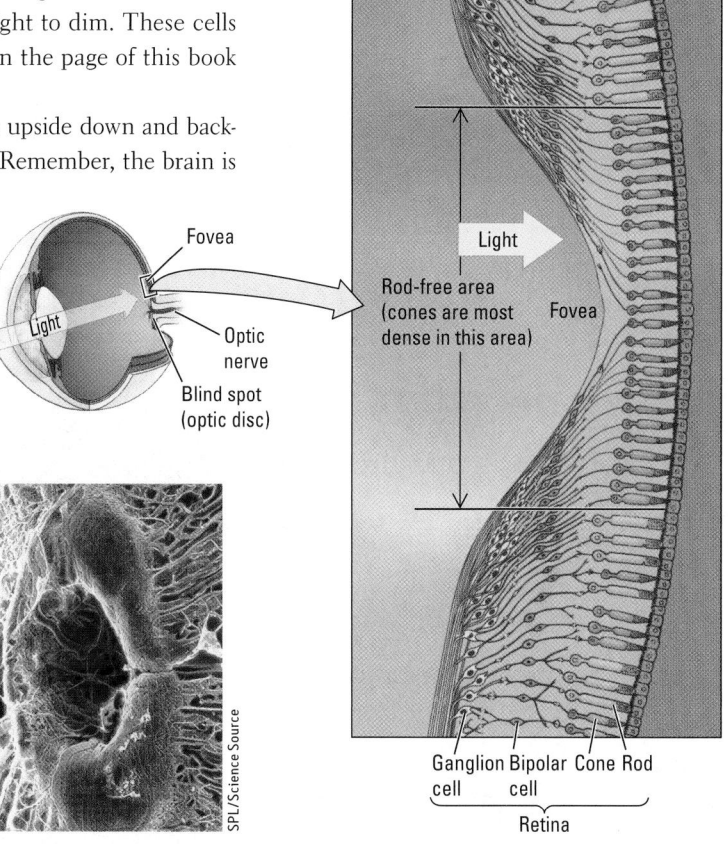

Fovea
Light
Optic nerve
Blind spot (optic disc)

Light
Rod-free area (cones are most dense in this area)
Fovea

Ganglion cell   Bipolar cell   Cone   Rod
Retina

SPL/Science Source

THE BASICS ▄

Visible Light and the Structure of the Eye

The brain's visual system analyzes visible light—the part of the electromagnetic (EM) spectrum that the human eye evolved to capture and focus.

Light: The Stimulus for Vision

Light can enter the eye directly from a source that produces it—a lamp, for example, or the sun—or indirectly after reflecting from a surface—the pages of a book, for example, or the surface of water. As illustrated in Electromagnetic Spectrum, not all light waves are the same length, and only a sliver of the EM spectrum is visible to us. If our photoreceptors could detect light in the shorter ultraviolet or longer infrared wavelengths, we would see additional colors.

Structure of the Eye

The range of light visible to humans is constrained not by the properties of light waves but rather by the properties of our visual receptors. How do photoreceptor cells in the retina absorb light energy and initiate the processes leading to vision? How the Eye Works illustrates the eye's structure and shows how its design captures and focuses light.

Optical Errors of Refraction

A web of muscles adjusts the shape of the eye's lens to bend light to greater or lesser degrees, which allows near or far images to be focused on the retina. When images are not properly focused, we need corrective lenses.

The eye, like a camera, works correctly only when sufficient light passes through the lens and is focused on the receptor surface—the retina in the eye or the light-sensitive material in the camera. If the focal point of the light falls slightly in front of the receptor surface or slightly behind it, a refractive error causes objects to appear blurry. Refractive errors in the eye are of two basic types, diagrammed in Refractive Errors.

Myopia (nearsightedness) afflicts about 50 percent of young people in the developed world. Hyperopia (farsightedness) is a less common refractive error, but as people age, the lens loses its elasticity and consequently becomes unable to refract light from nearby objects correctly. This form of hyperopia, called presbyopia (old-sightedness), is so common that you rarely find people older than 50 who do not need glasses to see up close, especially for reading.

It is also common to see young children wearing corrective lenses. The incidence of myopia in the United States has doubled in the past 40 years to about 42 percent. It is even higher in Northern Europe (50 percent) and Asia (50 percent to 80 percent). Two factors probably account for the increase.

First, more young people are attending school longer and thus are doing more close work, especially reading. Close work strains the eye muscles. Second, people are spending less and less time outdoors in bright light. Bright light makes the pupil contract, which improves visual depth of field: your eyes focus better. Children should probably spend at least 2 hours each day outside in bright light. Consider that myopia is less common in countries such as Australia (17 percent), where bright light is plentiful.

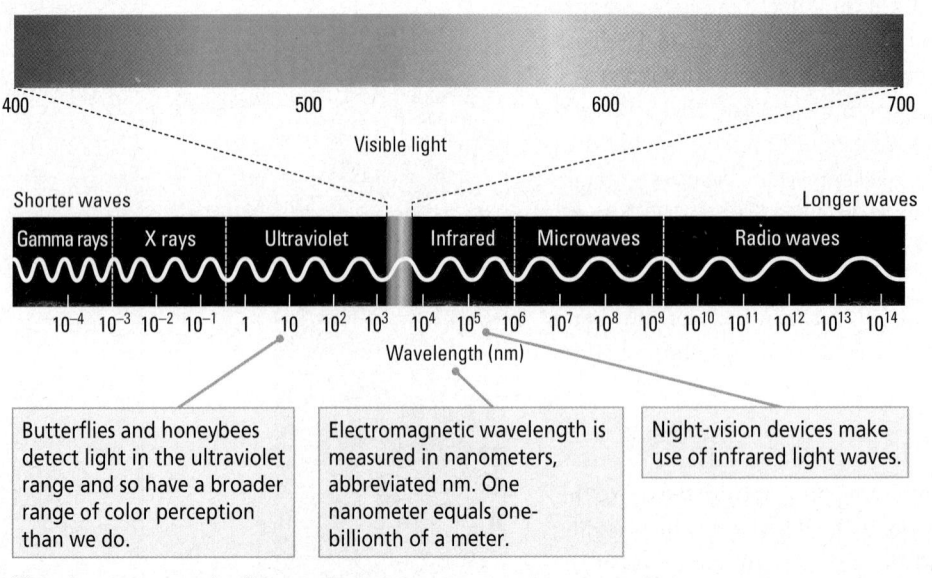

The electromagnetic energy visible to humans varies in wavelength from about 400 to 700 nanometers. We perceive the shortest visible wavelengths as deep purple. As wavelength increases, perceived color morphs from violet to blue to green to yellow, orange, and red: the colors of the rainbow.

Butterflies and honeybees detect light in the ultraviolet range and so have a broader range of color perception than we do.

Electromagnetic wavelength is measured in nanometers, abbreviated nm. One nanometer equals one-billionth of a meter.

Night-vision devices make use of infrared light waves.

Electromagnetic Spectrum

How the Eye Works

A photograph of the retina's surface shows blood vessels emerging from the blind spot and their near absence around the fovea.

Fovea

Blind spot

Retina

Ralph Eagle/Science Source

The *sclera* forms the eyeball, the white of the eye. The *cornea* is the eye's clear outer covering. The colored *iris* opens and closes to allow more or less light through a hole, the *pupil*. The *lens* focuses light.

In the *retina*, light energy initiates neural activity. At the center of the retina, the *fovea* is the region of sharpest vision and has the densest distribution of photoreceptors specialized for color.

Chetty Thomas/Shutterstock

Retina

Sclera

Cornea

Iris

Pupil

Lens

Fovea

Optic disc (blind spot)

Blood vessels

Optic nerve

The *optic disc*, where blood vessels enter the eye and the axons that form the *optic nerve* leave the eye, has no receptors and thus forms a *blind spot*. The optic nerve conveys information from the eye to the brain.

The cornea and lens of the eye, like the lens of a camera, focus light rays to project a backward, inverted image on a light-receptive surface.

Lenses

As light enters the eye, it is bent first by the cornea, travels through the pupil, and is then bent again by the lens. The curvature of the cornea is fixed, whereas small muscles adjust the curvature of the lens to focus nearby or far away.

Refractive Errors

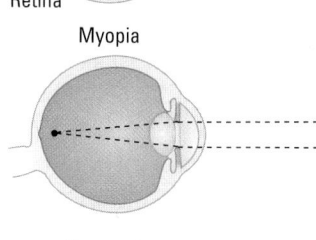

Normal

Retina

In normal vision, the lens focuses incoming light directly on the retina.

Myopia

People with myopia cannot bring distant objects into clear focus because the focal point of light falls short of the retina. Most commonly caused by the normally round eyeball being elongated, nearsightedness can also be caused by excessive curvature of the front of the cornea.

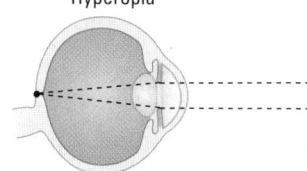

Hyperopia

People with hyperopia cannot focus on nearby objects because the focal point of light falls beyond the retina. Whereas the myopic eyeball may be too long, the hyperoptic eyeball may be too short. Farsightedness may also be due to the fact that the lens is too flat to refract light adequately.

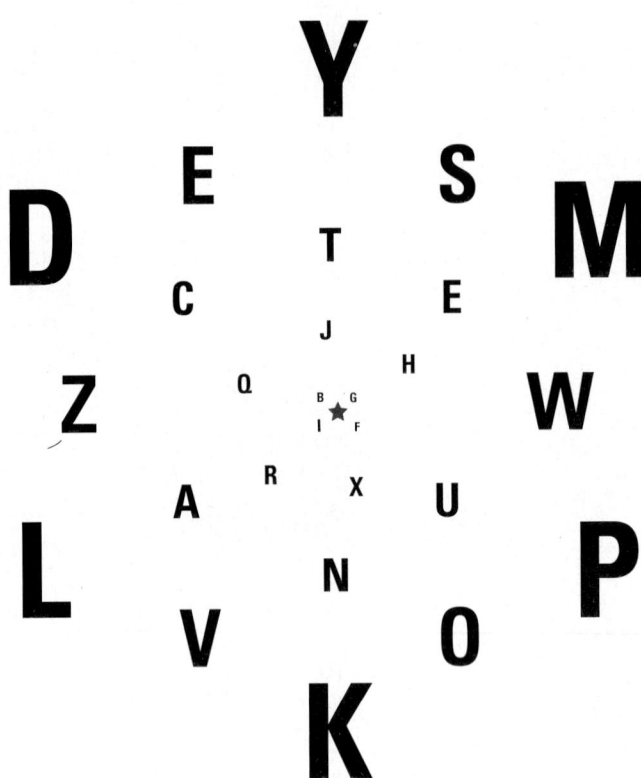

FIGURE 9-3 Acuity Across the Visual Field Focus on the star in the middle of the chart to demonstrate the relative sizes of letters legible in the central field of vision compared with the peripheral field.

The lesson is that our vision is better in the center of the visual field than at the margins, or *periphery*. Letters at the periphery must be much larger than those in the center for us to see them as well. **Figure 9-3** shows how much larger. The difference is due partly to the fact that photoreceptors are more densely packed at the center of the retina, in a region known as the **fovea**. Figure 9-2 shows that the retinal surface is depressed at the fovea. This depression is formed because many optic nerve fibers skirt the fovea to facilitate light access to its receptors.

Blind Spot

Now try another experiment. Stand with your head over a tabletop and hold a pencil in your hand. Close one eye. Stare at the edge of the tabletop nearest you. Now hold the pencil in a horizontal position and move it along the edge of the table, with the eraser on the table. Beginning at a point approximately below your nose, move the pencil slowly along the table in the direction of the open eye.

When you have moved the pencil about 6 inches, the eraser will vanish. You have found your **blind spot**, a small area of the retina also known as the *optic disc*. This is the area where blood vessels enter and exit the eye and where fibers leading from retinal neurons form the optic nerve, which goes to the brain. There are therefore no photoreceptors in this part of the retina. You can use **Figure 9-4** to demonstrate the blind spot in another way.

Fortunately, your visual system solves the blind spot problem: your optic disc is in a different location in each eye. The optic disc is lateral to the fovea in each eye, which means that it is left of the fovea in the left eye and right of the fovea in the right eye. Because the two eyes' visual fields overlap, the right eye can see the left eye's blind spot and vice versa.

Using both eyes together, then, you can see the whole visual world. For people blind in one eye, the sightless eye cannot compensate for the blind spot in the functioning eye. Still, the visual system compensates for the blind spot in several other ways, and so these people have no sense of a hole in their field of vision.

The blind spot is of particular importance in neurology. It allows neurologists to indirectly view the condition of the optic nerve while providing a window on events in the brain. If intracranial pressure increases, as occurs with a tumor or brain abscess (an infection), the optic disc swells, leading to *papilledema* (swollen disc). The swelling occurs in part because, like all neural tissue, the optic nerve is surrounded by cerebrospinal fluid. Pressure inside the cranium can displace CSF around the optic nerve, causing swelling at the optic disc.

Another cause of papilledema is inflammation of the optic nerve itself, a condition known as *optic neuritis*. Whatever the cause, a person with a swollen optic disc usually loses vision owing to pressure on the optic nerve. If the swelling is due to optic neuritis, probably the most common neurological visual disorder, the prognosis for recovery is good.

FIGURE 9-4 Find Your Blind Spot Hold this book 30 centimeters (about 12 inches) away from your face. Shut your left eye and look at the cross with your right eye. Slowly bring the page toward you until the red spot in the center of the yellow disc disappears and the entire disc appears yellow. The red spot is now in your blind spot. Your brain replaces the area with the surrounding yellow to fill in the image. Turn the book upside down to test your left eye.

Photoreceptors

The retina's photoreceptor cells convert light energy first into chemical energy and then into neural activity. Light striking a photoreceptor triggers a series of chemical reactions that lead to a change in membrane potential (electrical charge) that in turn leads to a change in the release of neurotransmitter onto nearby neurons.

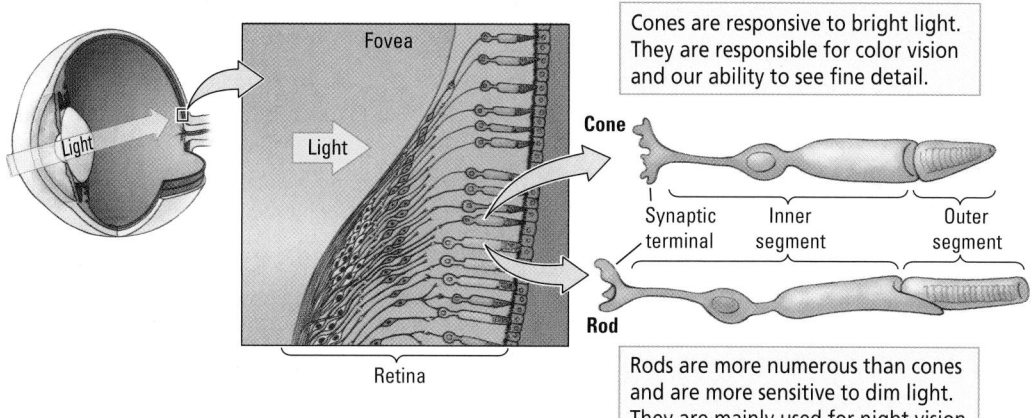

Cones are responsive to bright light. They are responsible for color vision and our ability to see fine detail.

Rods are more numerous than cones and are more sensitive to dim light. They are mainly used for night vision.

SPL/Science Source

FIGURE 9-5 Photoreceptor Cells Rods and cones are tubelike structures, as the scanning electron micrograph at right shows. They differ, especially in the outer segment that contains the light-absorbing visual pigment. Rods are especially sensitive to broad-spectrum luminance; and cones, to particular wavelengths of light.

Rods and cones, the two types of photoreceptors shown in **Figure 9-5**, differ in many ways. They are structurally different. Rods are longer than cones and cylindrical at one end, whereas cones have a tapered end. **Rods** are more numerous than cones; are sensitive to low levels of brightness (luminance), especially in dim light; and function mainly for night vision (see Clinical Focus 9-2, Visual Illuminance). **Cones** do not respond to dim light, but they are highly responsive to bright light. Cones mediate both color vision and our ability to see fine detail (visual acuity).

Rods and cones are unevenly distributed over the retina. The fovea has only cones, but their density drops dramatically beyond the fovea. For this reason, our vision is not so sharp at the edges of the visual field, as demonstrated in Figure 9-3.

A final difference between rods and cones is in their light-absorbing pigments. All rods have the same pigment. Each cone has one of three pigments. These four pigments, one in the rods and three in the cones, form the basis for our vision.

As shown on the spectrum in **Figure 9-6**, the three cone pigments absorb light across a range of visible frequencies, but each is most responsive to a small range of wavelengths—short (bluish light), medium (greenish light), and long (reddish light). As you can see on the background spectrum in Figure 9-6, however, if you were to look at lights with wavelengths of 419, 531, and 559 nanometers (nm), they would not appear blue, green, and red but rather blue-green, yellow-green, and orange. Remember, though, that you are looking at the lights with all three of your cone types and that each cone pigment responds to light across a range of frequencies, not just to its frequency of maximum absorption.

Both the presence of three cone receptor types and their relative numbers and distribution across the retina contribute to our perception of color. As **Figure 9-7** shows, the three cone types are distributed more or less randomly across the retina, making our ability to perceive different colors fairly constant across the visual field. The numbers of red and green cones are approximately equal, but blue cones are fewer. As a result, we are not as sensitive to wavelengths in the blue part of the visible spectrum as we are to red and green wavelengths.

fovea Central region of the retina specialized for high visual acuity; its receptive fields are at the center of the eye's visual field.

blind spot Retinal region where axons forming the optic nerve leave the eye and blood vessels enter and leave; has no photoreceptors and is thus said to be blind.

rod Photoreceptor specialized for functioning at low light levels.

cone Photoreceptor specialized for color and high visual acuity.

A nanometer (nm) is one-billionth of a meter.

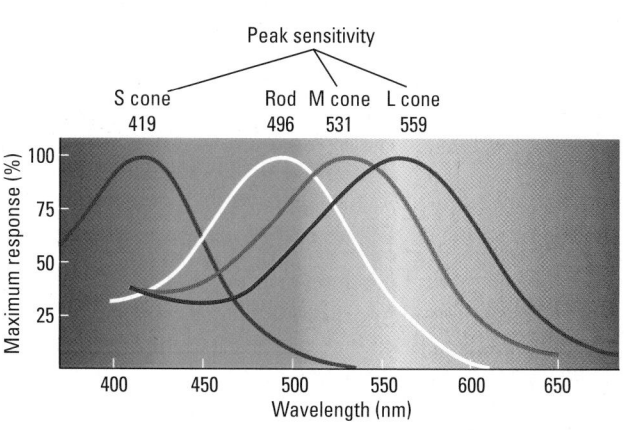

FIGURE 9-6 Range and Peak Sensitivity Our color perception corresponds to the summed activity of the three cone types: S cones, M cones, and L cones (for short, medium, and long wavelengths). Each type is most sensitive to a narrow range of the visible spectrum. Rods (white curve) prefer a range of wavelengths centered on 496 nm but do not contribute to our color perception. Rod activity is not summed with the cones in the color vision system.

Visual Illuminance

The eye, like a camera, works correctly only when sufficient light passes through the lens and is focused on the receptor surface—the retina of the eye or the light-sensitive surface in the camera. Too little light entering the eye or the camera produces a problem of *visual illuminance*: it is hard to see any image at all.

Visual illuminance is typically a complication of aging eyes, It cannot be cured by corrective lenses. As we age, the eye's lens and cornea allow less light through, so less light strikes the retina. Don Kline (1994)

estimated that between ages 20 and 40, people's ability to see in dim light drops by 50 percent; and by a further 50 percent over every 20 additional years. As a result, seeing in dim light becomes increasingly difficult, especially at night.

The only solution to compensate for visual illuminance is to increase lighting. Night vision is especially problematic. Not surprisingly, statistics show a marked drop in the number of people driving at night in each successive decade after age 40.

These photographs represent the typical drop in luminance between age 20 (left) and age 60 (right).

FIGURE 9-7 Retinal Receptors The retinal mosaic of rods and three cone types. This diagram represents the distribution near the fovea, where cones outnumber rods. Red and green cones outnumber the blue.

Other species that have color vision similar to humans' also have three types of cones with three color pigments. Because of slight variations in these pigments, the exact frequencies of maximum absorption differ among species. For humans, the exact frequencies are not identical with the numbers given earlier, which are an average across mammals. They are actually 426 and 530 nm for the blue and green cones, respectively, and 552 or 557 nm for the red cone. The two peak sensitivity levels of red cones represent the two variants that humans have evolved. The difference in these two red cones appears minuscule, but it does make a functional difference in some females' color perception.

The gene for the red cone is carried on the X chromosome. Males have only one X chromosome, so they have only one of these genes and only one type of red cone. The situation is more complicated for females, who possess two X chromosomes. Although most women have only one type of red cone, those who have both are more sensitive than the rest of us to color differences at the red end of the spectrum. We could say that women who have both red cone types have a slightly rosier view of the world: their color receptors construct a world with a richer range of red experiences. But they also have to contend with seemingly peculiar color coordination by others.

Types of Retinal Neurons

Photoreceptors are connected to two layers of retinal neurons. In the procession from the rods and cones toward the brain shown in **Figure 9-8**, the first layer contains three cell types: *bipolar, horizontal,* and *amacrine*. Horizontal cells link photoreceptors with bipolar cells, whereas amacrine cells link bipolar cells with cells in the second neural layer, the **retinal ganglion cells** (RGCs). RGC axons collect in a bundle at the optic disc and leave the eye to form the optic nerve.

FIGURE 9-8 Retinal Cells Neurons in the retina—bipolar, horizontal, amacrine, and ganglion cells—form two layers moving outward from the rods and cones at the retinal surface. Light must pass through both transparent neuron layers to reach the photoreceptors.

Retinal ganglion cells fall into two major categories, called M and P cells in the primate retina. The designations derive from the distinctly different cell populations in the visual thalamus to which these two classes of RGCs send their axons. As shown in **Figure 9-9**, one population consists of **magnocellular cells** (hence M); the other consists of **parvocellular cells** (hence P). The larger M cells receive their input primarily from rods and so are sensitive to light but not to color. The smaller P cells receive their input primarily from cones and so are sensitive to color.

M cells are found throughout the retina, including the periphery, where we are sensitive to movement but not to color or fine detail. P cells are found largely in the region of the fovea, where we are sensitive to color and fine details. As we follow the ganglion cell axons into the brain, you will see that these two categories of RGCs maintain their distinctiveness throughout the visual pathways.

In Latin, *magno* means *large* and *parvo* means *small*.

FIGURE 9-9 Visual Thalamus The optic nerves connect with the lateral geniculate nucleus of the thalamus. The LGN has six layers: two magnocellular layers, which receive input mainly from rods, and four parvocellular layers, which receive input mainly from cones.

retinal ganglion cell (RGC) One of a group of retinal neurons with axons that give rise to the optic nerve.

magnocellular (M) cell Large visual system neuron sensitive to moving stimuli.

parvocellular (P) cell Small visual system neuron sensitive to differences in form and color.

optic chiasm Junction of the optic nerves, one from each eye, at which the axons from the nasal halves of the retinas cross to the brain's opposite side.

Visual Pathways

RGCs form the optic nerve, the road into the brain. This road forks off to several places. The destinations of these branches give us clues to what the brain is doing with visual input and how the brain constructs our visual world.

Crossing the Optic Chiasm

We begin with the optic nerves, one exiting from each eye. Just before entering the brain, the optic nerves partly cross, forming the **optic chiasm**.

About half the fibers from each eye cross in such a way that the left half of each optic nerve goes to the left side of the brain, and the right half goes to the brain's right side, as diagrammed in **Figure 9-10**. The medial path of each retina, the *nasal retina*, crosses to the opposite side. The lateral path, the *temporal retina*, travels straight back on the same side.

The optic chiasm gets its name from the shape of the Greek letter chi (Χ) (pronounced *ki*).

By connecting both eyes with both hemispheres, our visual system represents the world seen through two eyes as a single perception.

Because light that falls on the right half of each retina actually comes from the left side of the visual field, information from the left visual field goes to the brain's right hemisphere, and information from the right visual field goes to the left hemisphere. Thus, half of each retina's visual field is represented on each side of the brain.

Three Routes to the Visual Brain

Two main pathways lead to the visual cortex in the occipital lobe: the geniculostriate pathway for processing the object's image and the tectopulvinar pathway for directing rapid eye movements. Another smaller pathway tracks into the hypothalamus.

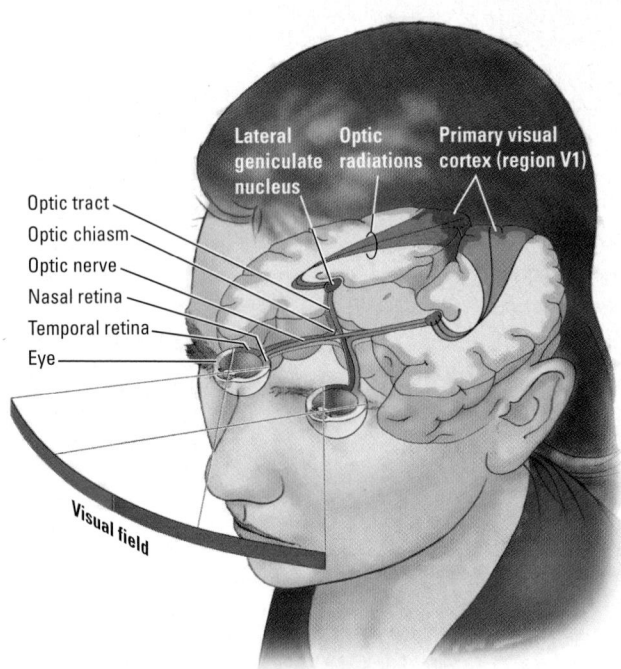

FIGURE 9-10 Crossing the Optic Chiasm This dorsal view shows the visual pathway from each eye to the primary visual cortex of each hemisphere. Information from the right side of the visual field (blue) moves from the two left halves of the retinas, ending in the left hemisphere. Information from the left side of the visual field (red) hits the right halves of the retinas and travels to the right side of the brain.

Figure 13-6 maps the retinohypothalamic tract into the SCN.

GENICULOSTRIATE SYSTEM On entering the brain, the RGC axons separate, forming the two distinct pathways shown in **Figure 9-11**. All of the P ganglion axons and some of the M ganglion axons form a pathway called the **geniculostriate system**. This pathway goes from the retina to the lateral geniculate nucleus (LGN) of the thalamus and then to layer IV of the primary visual cortex in the occipital lobe.

When stained, the primary visual cortex shows a broad stripe across it in layer IV and so is known as **striate** (striped) **cortex** (**Figure 9-12**). The geniculostriate system therefore bridges the thalamus (geniculate) and the striate cortex. From the striate cortex, the axon pathway divides. One route goes to vision-related regions of the parietal lobe, and another route goes to vision-related regions of the temporal lobe.

TECTOPULVINAR SYSTEM The second pathway leading from the eye is formed by the axons of the remaining M ganglion cells. These cells send their axons to the midbrain's superior colliculus, which sends connections to the pulvinar region of the thalamus. This pathway is therefore known as the **tectopulvinar system** because it runs from the eye through the midbrain tectum to the pulvinar (see Figure 9-11). The pulvinar sends connections to the parietal and temporal lobes, bypassing the occipital visual areas.

RETINOHYPOTHALAMIC TRACT Between 1 percent and 3 percent of RGCs are unique in that they are *photosensitive*: they act as photoreceptors. These *pRGCs*, which contain the pigment melanopsin, absorb blue light at a wavelength (between 460 and 480 nm) different from the wavelengths of rods or cones (see Figure 9-6). Axons of pRGCs form a small third visual pathway, the **retinohypothalamic tract**.

The retinohypothalamic tract synapses in the tiny suprachiasmatic nucleus (SCN) in the hypothalamus, next to the optic chiasm. Photosensitive RGCs participates both in regulating circadian rhythms and in the pupillary reflex that expands and contracts the pupil in response to the amount of light falling on the retina. Farhan Zaidi and colleagues (2007) studied two profoundly blind subjects who lack functional rods and cones. The researchers found that stimulation with 480-nm (blue) light increases alertness and appears to play some rudimentary role in visual awareness.

Dorsal and Ventral Visual Streams

The geniculostriate and tectopulvinar pathways extend into the visual brain. Each eventually leads to either the parietal lobe or the temporal lobe. Our next task is to determine the role each lobe plays in building our visual world. As we look at

FIGURE 9-11 Main Visual Pathways into the Brain The optic nerve follows (1) the geniculostriate path to the primary visual cortex and (2) the tectopulvinar path to the temporal and parietal lobes. (The LGN of the thalamus is part of the diencephalon, shown in Figure 2-19; the superior colliculus in the tectum is part of the midbrain, shown in Figure 2-18.)

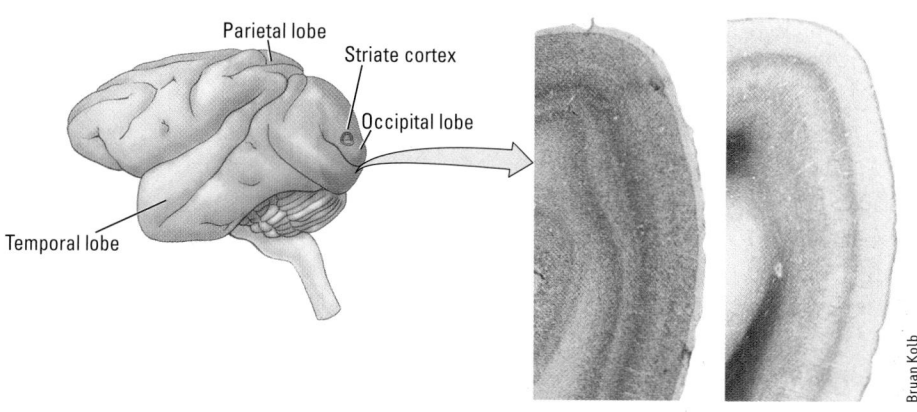

Bryan Kolb

FIGURE 9-12 Striate Cortex Area V1 is also called the *striate cortex* because sections appear striated (striped) when stained with either a cell body stain (left) or a myelin stain (right). The sections shown here come from a rhesus monkey's brain.

geniculostriate system Projections from the retina to the lateral geniculate nucleus to the visual cortex.

striate cortex Primary visual cortex (V1) in the occipital lobe; shows stripes (striations) on staining.

tectopulvinar system Projections from the retina to the superior colliculus to the pulvinar (thalamus) to the parietal and temporal visual areas.

retinohypothalamic tract Neural route formed by axons of photosensitive retinal ganglion cells (pRGCs) from the retina to the suprachiasmatic nucleus; allows light to entrain the SCN's rhythmic activity.

ventral stream Visual processing pathway from V1 to the temporal lobe for object identification and perceiving related movements.

dorsal stream Visual processing pathway from V1 to the parietal lobe; guides movements relative to objects.

the photograph in Clinical Focus 9-1, we can identify objects, and we can point to them. Identifying and pointing are different functions.

Having identified the temporal lobe and parietal lobe visual pathways, researchers went searching for their possible functions. Why would evolution produce two different destinations for these neural pathways? Each route must produce visual knowledge for a different purpose.

David Milner and Mel Goodale (2006) proposed that these two purposes are to identify a stimulus (the *what* function) and to control movement to or away from the stimulus (the *how* function). This *what–how* distinction came from an analysis of the routes visual information takes when it leaves the striate cortex. **Figure 9-13** shows the two distinct visual pathways that originate in the striate cortex, one progressing to the temporal lobe and the other to the parietal lobe. The pathway to the temporal lobe is the **ventral stream**, whereas the pathway to the parietal lobe is the **dorsal stream**.

Both the geniculostriate and the tectopulvinar pathways contribute to the dorsal and ventral streams. To understand how the two streams function, we return to the details of how visual input from the eyes contributes to them.

Geniculostriate Pathway

The RGC fibers from the two eyes distribute their connections to the two lateral geniculate nuclei (left and right) of the thalamus. At first glance, this appears to be an unusual arrangement. As seen in Figure 9-10, the fibers from the left half of each retina go to the left LGN; those from the right half of each retina go to the right LGN. But the fibers from each eye do not go to exactly the same LGN location.

Each LGN has six layers, and the projections from the two eyes go to different layers, as illustrated in anatomical context in Figure 9-9 and diagrammed in **Figure 9-14**. Layers 2, 3, and 5 receive fibers from the ipsilateral eye (the eye on the same side), whereas layers 1, 4, and 6 receive fibers from the contralateral eye (the eye on the opposite side). This arrangement provides both for combining the information from the two eyes and for segregating the information from the P and M ganglion cells.

Axons from the P cells go only to layers 3 through 6 (the parvocellular layers). Axons from the M cells go only to layers 1 and 2 (the magnocellular layers). Because the P cells are responsive to color and fine detail, LGN layers 3 through 6 must be processing information about color and form. In contrast, the M cells mostly process information about movement, so layers 1 and 2 must deal with movement.

Just as there are six layers in the thalamic LGN (numbered 1 through 6), there are also six layers in the striate cortex (numbered I through VI). That there happen to be six layers in

FIGURE 9-13 Visual Streaming Information travels from the occipital visual areas to the parietal and temporal lobes, forming the dorsal (*how*) and ventral (*what*) streams, respectively.

Figure 2-22 maps layers I through VI in the primary motor and sensory cortices.

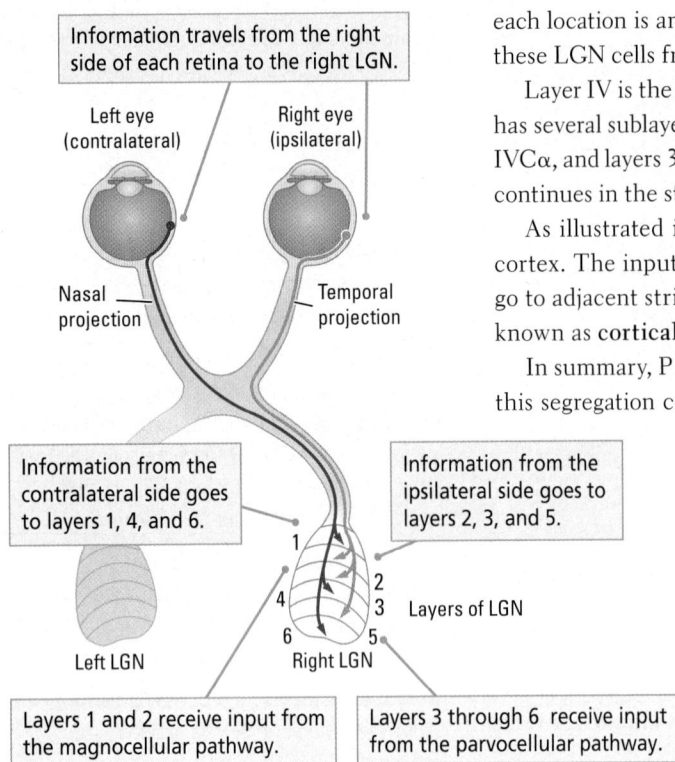

Information travels from the right side of each retina to the right LGN.

Left eye (contralateral)

Right eye (ipsilateral)

Nasal projection

Temporal projection

Information from the contralateral side goes to layers 1, 4, and 6.

Information from the ipsilateral side goes to layers 2, 3, and 5.

1
4   2
6   3   Layers of LGN
5

Left LGN

Right LGN

Layers 1 and 2 receive input from the magnocellular pathway.

Layers 3 through 6 receive input from the parvocellular pathway.

FIGURE 9-14 Geniculostriate Pathway

Many textbooks emphasize the *how* pathway as a *where* function. Because *where* is both a property of *what* a stimulus is and a cue for *how* to control movement, we use Milner and Goodale's *what–how* distinction.

each location is an accident of evolution found in all primate brains. Let us now see where these LGN cells from the thalamus send their connections within the visual cortex.

Layer IV is the main afferent (incoming) layer of the cortex. In the visual cortex, layer IV has several sublayers, two of which are known as IVCα and IVCβ. LGN layers 1 and 2 go to IVCα, and layers 3 through 6 go to IVCβ. A distinction between the P and M functions thus continues in the striate cortex.

As illustrated in **Figure 9-15**, input from the two eyes also remains separated in the cortex. The input from the ipsilaterally and contralaterally connected parts of the LGN go to adjacent strips of occipital cortex. These strips, which are about 0.5 mm across, are known as **cortical columns**.

In summary, P and M retinal ganglion cells send separate pathways to the thalamus, and this segregation continues in the striate cortex. The left and right eyes also send separate pathways to the thalamus, and these pathways, too, remain segregated in the striate cortex.

Tectopulvinar Pathway

To review, magnocellular RGCs found throughout the retina receive input primarily from the rods and so are sensitive to light but not to color. M cells in the periphery of the retina are sensitive to movement but not to color or fine details. In the brain, some M cells join P cells to form the geniculostriate pathway. The tectopulvinar pathway is formed by the axons of the remaining M cells.

These M cells send their axons to the superior colliculus in the midbrain's tectum. One function of the tectum is to produce orienting movements—to detect stimuli and shift the eyes toward them. The superior colliculus sends connections to the pulvinar region of the thalamus. The medial pulvinar sends connections to the parietal lobe, and the lateral pulvinar sends connections to the temporal lobe. One type of information that these connections are conveying is related to *where*. Where is important in both the *what* and *how* visual streams.

The *where* function of the tectopulvinar system is useful in understanding D. B.'s blindsight, described in Clinical Focus 9-1. His geniculostriate system was disrupted by surgery, but his tectopulvinar system was not, which allowed him to identify the location of stimuli (*where*) that he could not identify (*what*).

Lateral geniculate nucleus

Horizontal section of striate cortex

Right eye Left eye

Left eye

1
2 — M layers

3
4
5 — P layers
6

Ocular dominance columns

I
II
III
IVCα
IVCβ
V
VI

Cortical visual area 1

FIGURE 9-15 Maintaining Separate Visual Input
Left: Information from the eyes is segregated by layers in the LGN, which maintains this segregation in its projections from the thalamus to the primary visual cortex. Information from each eye travels to adjacent regions in cortical layer IV. Right: A horizontal plane through striate cortex shows a zebralike effect of alternating left and right eye regions.

Occipital Cortex

Our route down the visual pathways has led us from the retina all the way back to the occipital lobe and into the parietal and temporal lobes. Now we explore how visual information proceeds from the striate cortex through the rest of the occipital lobe to the dorsal and ventral streams.

(A) Medial view of functional areas

V3A
V3
V2
V1
V2
V4
V3
V3A

(B) Lateral view of functional areas

V3A
V3
V2
V1
V2
V3
V3A
V4
V5

V1 = Primary visual cortex
V2–V5 = Extrastriate cortex

FIGURE 9-16 Visual Regions of the Occipital Lobe

cortical column Anatomic organization that represents a functional unit six cortical layers deep and approximately 0.5 mm square, perpendicular to the cortical surface.

primary visual cortex (V1) Striate cortex in the occipital lobe that receives input from the lateral geniculate nucleus.

extrastriate (secondary visual) cortex (V2–V5) Visual cortical areas in the occipital lobe outside the striate cortex.

blob Region in V1 that contains color-sensitive neurons, as revealed by staining for cytochrome oxidase.

As shown in **Figure 9-16**, the occipital lobe is composed of at least six visual regions: V1, V2, V3, V3A, V4, and V5. The striate cortex is region **V1**, the **primary visual cortex**. The remaining occipital visual areas form the **extrastriate cortex**, with each region processing specific features of visual information. Because each occipital region has a unique cytoarchitecture (cellular structure) and unique inputs and outputs, we can infer that each must be doing something different from the others.

As shown in Figures 9-12 and 9-15, a remarkable feature of region V1 is its striations—its distinctly visible layers. When Margaret Wong-Riley and her colleagues (1993) stained region VI for the enzyme cytochrome oxidase, which has a role in cell metabolism, they found an unexpected heterogeneity. So they sectioned the V1 layers in such a way that each cortical layer was in one plane of section, much like peeling off the layers of an onion and laying them flat on a table. The surface of each flattened layer can then be viewed from above.

The heterogeneous cytochrome staining now appears as random blobs in the V1 layers, as diagrammed in **Figure 9-17**. These darkened regions have in fact become known as **blobs**, the less-dark regions separating them as *interblobs*. Blobs and interblobs serve different functions. Neurons in the blobs take part in color perception; neurons in the interblobs participate in perception of form and motion. Within region V1, then, input arriving from the P cell and M cell pathways of the geniculostriate system is segregated into three separate types of information: color, form, and motion.

All three types of information move from region V1 to the adjoining region V2. Here, the color, form, and motion inputs remain segregated, again seen through the pattern of cytochrome oxidase staining. But as Figure 9-17 shows, the staining pattern in region V2 differs from that in region V1. Region V2 has a pattern of thick and thin stripes intermixed with pale zones. The thick stripes receive input from the movement-sensitive neurons in

All mammals have at least one primary cortical area for each sensory system. The primary area relays most information that reaches secondary areas.

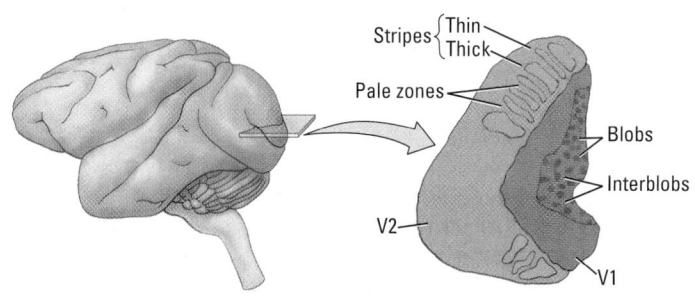

Stripes { Thin
Thick
Pale zones
Blobs
Interblobs
V2
V1

FIGURE 9-17 Heterogeneous Layering Blobs in region V1 and stripes in region V2 are illustrated in this drawing of a flattened section through the visual cortex of a monkey. The blobs and stripes are revealed by a special stain for cytochrome oxidase, a marker for mitochondria, the organelles in cells that gather, store, and release energy.

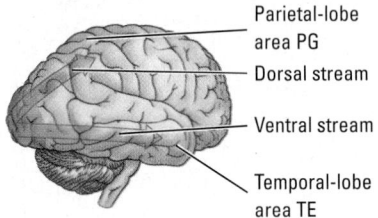

FIGURE 9-18 Charting the Visual Streams   The dorsal stream, which controls visual action (top), begins in region V1 and flows through V2 to the other occipital areas and finally to the parietal cortex, ending in area PG. The ventral stream, which controls object recognition (bottom), begins in region V1 and flows through V2 to the other occipital areas and finally to the temporal cortex, ending in area TE. Information from the blobs and interblobs in V1 flows to the thick, thin, and pale zones of V2 and then to regions V3 and V4 to form the ventral stream. Information in the thick and pale zones goes to regions V3A and V5 to form the dorsal stream.

region V1; the thin stripes receive input from V1's color-sensitive neurons; and the pale zones receive input from V1's form-sensitive neurons.

As charted in **Figure 9-18**, the visual pathways proceed from region V2 to the other occipital regions and then to the parietal and temporal lobes, forming the dorsal and ventral streams. Although many parietal and temporal regions take part, the major regions are region G in the parietal lobe (thus called region PG) and region E in the temporal lobe (thus called region TE).

The simple records of color, form, and motion from the occipital regions are assembled in the dorsal and ventral streams to produce a rich, unified visual world of complex objects, such as faces and paintings, and complex skills, such as bike riding and ball catching. We can think of the complex representations of the dorsal and ventral streams as consisting of *how* functions and *what* functions. *How* is looking at, reaching for, and grasping; *what* is the spoon.

Vision Beyond the Occipital Cortex

Visual processing that begins in occipital cortex continues via the ventral and dorsal streams into the temporal and parietal visual cortex. Each region has multiple areas specialized for specific visual functions. For example, **Figure 9-19**A shows two regions on the ventral surface

FIGURE 9-19 Vision Beyond the Occipital Cortex   **(A)** In the temporal lobe, the fusiform face area (FFA) processes faces, and the parahippocampal place area (PPA) processes scenes. **(B)** In the parietal lobe, the lateral intraparietal area (LIP) contributes to eye movements; the anterior intraparietal area (AIP) is involved in visual control of grasping; and the parietal reach region (PRR) participates in visually guided reaching.

(A) Republished with permission of Hasson, U., Y. Nir, I. Levy, G. Fuhrmann, and R. Malach. Intersubject synchronization of cortical activity during natural vision. *Science* 303:1634–1640, 2004, permission conveyed through Copyright Clearance Center, Inc.

of the temporal lobes. One is specialized for recognizing faces (fusiform face area, or FFA), the other for analyzing landmarks such as buildings or trees (parahippocampal place area, or PPA). As we gaze at the photograph in Clinical Focus 9-1 (p. 284), then, the three faces activate the FFA and the trees engage the PPA. Figure 9-19B shows three regions in the parietal lobe related to eye movements (lateral intraparietal area, or LIP) and visual control of grasping (anterior intraparietal area, or AIP). The parietal reach region (PRR) has a role in visually guided reaching movements.

Damage to these regions can produce surprisingly specific deficits. For example, damage to the FFA leads to **facial agnosia**, or *prosopagnosia*, a condition in which an individual cannot recognize faces. We saw one patient with prosopagnosia so severe that she could not recognize her identical twin sister's face. Curiously, her other visual functions seemed to be normal.

Literally, *agnosia* means *not knowing*. Section 15-7 ties conditions like agnosia to the search for a neural basis of consciousness.

(9-2) REVIEW

The Visual System's Functional Anatomy

Before you continue, check your understanding.

1. Neurons that project into the brain from the retina and form the optic nerve are called

   _____ .

2. _____ retinal ganglion cells receive input mostly from cones and carry information about color and fine detail, whereas _____ retinal ganglion cells receive input mostly from rods and carry information about light but not color.

3. The two major pathways from the retina into the brain are _____ and

   _____ .

4. Damage to the fusiform face area in the temporal lobe can produce _____ .

5. Contrast the paths and functions of the dorsal and ventral streams.

Answers appear at the back of the book.

For additional study tools, visit 🐾 **LaunchPad**:
www.macmillanhighered.com/launchpad/kolb5e

(9-3) Location in the Visual World

As we move about from place to place, we encounter objects in specific locations. If we had no awareness of location, the world would be a bewildering mass of visual information. The next leg of our journey down the neural roads traces how the brain constructs a spatial map. In Clinical Focus 9-1, the photograph has a left and a right, an up and a down. All these elements must be coded separately in the brain.

Neural coding of location begins in the retina and is maintained throughout all visual pathways. To understand how this spatial coding is accomplished, imagine your visual world as seen by your two eyes. Imagine the large red and blue rectangles in **Figure 9-20** as a wall. Focus your gaze on the black cross in the middle of the wall.

The part of the wall that you can see without moving your head is your **visual field**. It can be divided into two halves, the left and right visual fields, by drawing a vertical line through the middle of the black cross. Now recall from Figure 9-10 that the left half of each retina looks at the right side of the visual field, whereas the right half of each retina looks at the visual field's left side. Thus, input from the right visual field goes to the left hemisphere, and input from the left visual field goes to the right hemisphere.

Therefore, the brain can easily determine whether visual information lies to the left or right of center. If input goes to the left hemisphere, the source must be in the right visual field; if input goes to the right hemisphere, the source must be in the left visual field. This

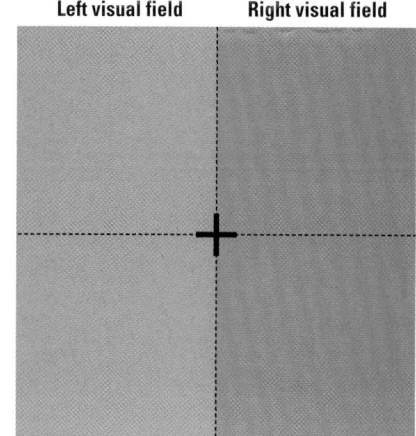

FIGURE 9-20 Visual-Field Demonstration As you focus on the cross at center, information at the left of this focal point forms the left visual field (red) and travels to the right hemisphere. Information to the right of the focal point forms the right visual field (blue) and travels to the left hemisphere. The visual field can be split horizontally as well: information above the focal point is in the upper visual field and that below the focal point is in the lower visual field.

---

facial agnosia Face blindness—the inability to recognize faces; also called *prosopagnosia*.

visual field Region of the visual world seen by the eyes.

arrangement tells you nothing about the precise location of an object in the left or right side of the visual field, however. To understand how precise spatial localization is accomplished, we must return to the retinal ganglion cells.

Coding Location in the Retina

Look again at Figure 9-8 and you can see that each RGC receives input through bipolar cells from several photoreceptors. In the 1950s, Stephen Kuffler, a pioneer in visual system physiology, made an important discovery about how photoreceptors and retinal ganglion cells are linked (Kuffler, 1952). By shining small spots of light on the receptors, he found that each ganglion cell responds to stimulation on just a small circular patch of the retina—the ganglion cell's receptive field.

A ganglion cell's receptive field is therefore the retinal region on which it is possible to influence that cell's firing. Stated differently, the receptive field represents the outer world as seen by a single cell. Each RGC sees only a small bit of the world, much as you would if you looked through a narrow cardboard tube. The visual field is composed of thousands of such receptive fields (illustrated on page 286).

Now let us consider how receptive fields enable the visual system to interpret an object's location. Imagine that the retina is flattened like a piece of paper. When a tiny light shines on different parts of the retina, different ganglion cells respond. For example, when a light shines on the top left corner of the flattened retina, a particular RGC responds because that light is in its receptive field. Similarly, when a light shines on the top right corner, a different RGC responds.

By using this information, we determine the location of a light on the retina by the ganglion cell it activates. Another location device is determining where the light must come from to hit a particular place on the retina. Light coming from above hits the bottom of the retina after passing through the eye's lens, and light from below hits the top of the retina. Information at the top of the visual field stimulates ganglion cells on the bottom of the retina; information at the bottom of the field stimulates ganglion cells on the top of the retina.

Location in the Lateral Geniculate Nucleus and Region V1

Now consider the connection from the ganglion cells to the lateral geniculate nucleus. In contrast to the retina, the LGN is not a thin sheet; it is shaped more like a sausage. We can compare it to a stack of sausage slices, with each slice representing a layer of cells.

Figure 9-21 shows how the connections from the retina to the LGN can represent location. A retinal ganglion cell that responds to light in the top left region of the retina connects to the left side of the first card. A retinal ganglion cell that responds to light in the bottom right region of the retina connects to the right side of the last card. In this way, the location of left–right and top–bottom information is maintained in the LGN.

Like the ganglion cells, each LGN cell has a receptive field—the region of the retina that influences its activity. If two adjacent retinal ganglion cells synapse on a single LGN cell, the receptive field of that LGN cell will be the sum of the two ganglion cells' receptive fields. As a result, the receptive fields of LGN cells are bigger than those of RGCs.

The LGN projection to the striate cortex (region V1) also maintains spatial information. As each LGN cell, representing a particular place, projects to region V1, a spatially organized neural representation—a topographic map—is produced in the cortex. As illustrated in **Figure 9-22**, this representation is essentially a map of the visual world.

The central part of the visual field is represented at the back of the brain, whereas the periphery is represented more anteriorly. The upper part of the visual field is represented at the bottom of region V1 and the lower part at the top of V1. The other regions of the visual cortex (such as V3, V4, and V5) have topographical maps similar to that of V1.

Like a camera lens, the lens in the eye focuses light rays to project a backward, inverted image on a light-receptive surface (see How the Eye Works in The Basics, p 291).

FIGURE 9-21 Receptive Field Projection Information from a receptive field in the retina retains its spatial relation when sent to the lateral geniculate nucleus. Information at the top of the visual field goes to the top of the LGN; information from the bottom of the visual field goes to the bottom of the LGN; and information from the left or right goes to the left or right of the LGN, respectively.

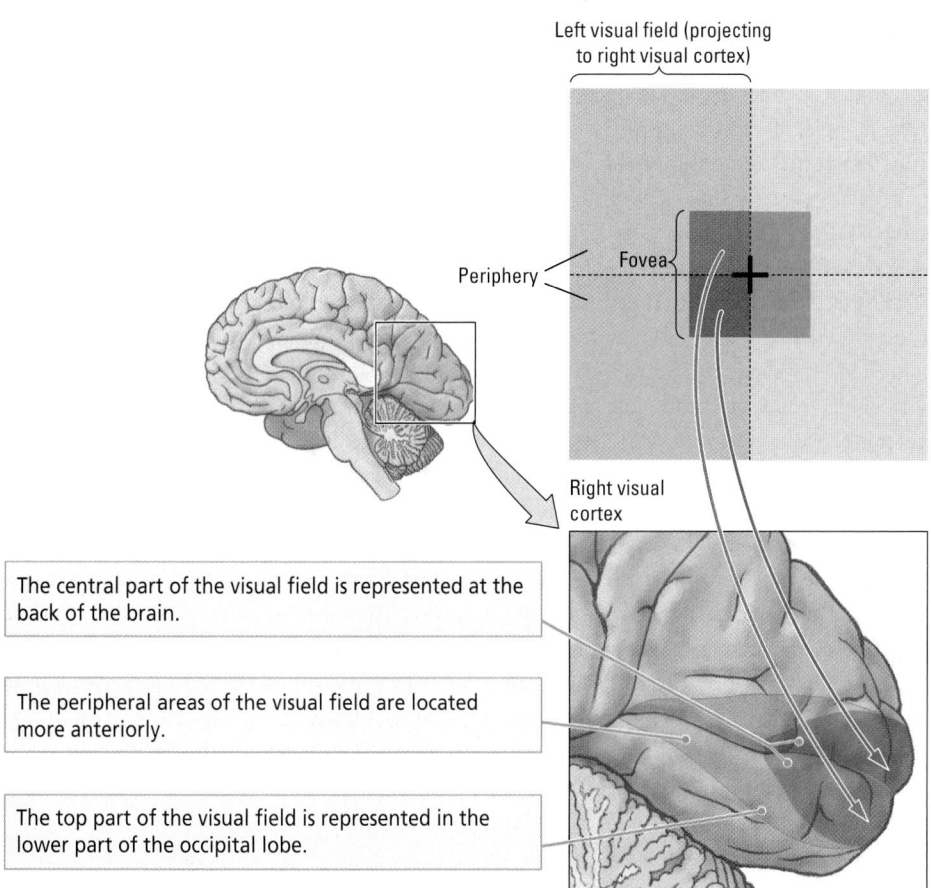

Left visual field (projecting to right visual cortex)

Periphery

Fovea

Right visual cortex

The central part of the visual field is represented at the back of the brain.

The peripheral areas of the visual field are located more anteriorly.

The top part of the visual field is represented in the lower part of the occipital lobe.

FIGURE 9-22 Topographic Organization of Region V1 The fovea sends information to a disproportionately large part of the occipital cortex, which is why visual acuity is best in the central part of the visual field.

FIGURE 9-23 Receptive-Field Hierarchy

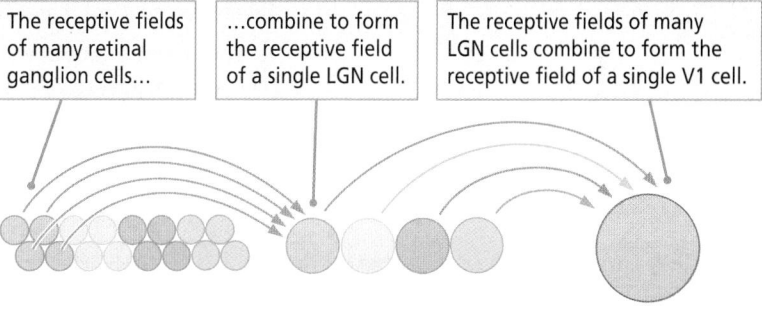

The receptive fields of many retinal ganglion cells...

...combine to form the receptive field of a single LGN cell.

The receptive fields of many LGN cells combine to form the receptive field of a single V1 cell.

Thus the V1 neurons must project to the other regions in an orderly manner, just as the LGN neurons project to region V1 in an orderly way.

Within each visual cortical area, each neuron's receptive field corresponds to the part of the retina to which the neuron is connected. As a rule of thumb, cells in the cortex have much larger receptive fields than RGCs do. This large field size means that the receptive field of a cortical neuron must be composed of the receptive fields of many RGCs, as illustrated in **Figure 9-23**.

One additional wrinkle pertains to the organization of topographic maps. Harry Jerison (1973) proposed the principle of proper mass, which states that the amount of neural tissue responsible for a particular function is proportional to the amount of neural processing that function requires. The more complex a function is, the larger a specific region performing that function must be. The visual cortex provides some good examples.

You can see in Figure 9-22 that not all parts of the visual field are equally represented in region V1. The small central part of the visual field seen by the fovea is represented by a larger area in the cortex than the visual field's periphery, even though the periphery covers a much larger area. In accord with Jerison's principle, we would predict more processing of foveal information than of peripheral information in region V1. This prediction makes intuitive sense because we can see more clearly in the center of the visual field than at the periphery (see Figure 9-3). In other words, sensory areas that have more cortical representation provide a more detailed construct of the external world.

In Figure 1-14, we apply Jerison's ideas to relative differences in overall brain size across mammals.

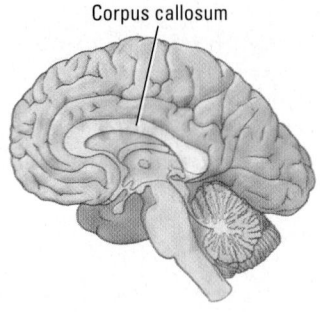

Corpus callosum

Section 15-4 describes the revelations learned from studying split-brain patients, whose corpus callosa have been severed.

FIGURE 9-24 Callosal Connections Darker areas show regions of the rhesus monkey cortex that receive projections from the opposite hemisphere through the corpus callosum.

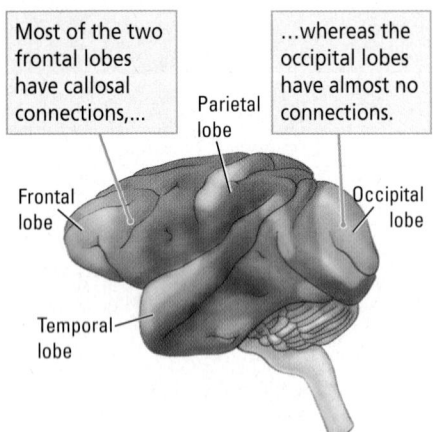

Most of the two frontal lobes have callosal connections,...

...whereas the occipital lobes have almost no connections.

Parietal lobe

Frontal lobe

Occipital lobe

Temporal lobe

Visual Corpus Callosum

Topographic mapping based on neuronal receptive fields is an effective way for the brain to code object location. But if the left visual field is represented in the right cerebral hemisphere and the right visual field is represented in the left cerebral hemisphere, how are the two halves of the visual field ultimately merged into a unified representation? After all, we have the subjective impression not of two independent visual fields but rather of a single, continuous field of vision.

The answer to how this unity is accomplished lies in the corpus callosum, which binds the two sides of the visual field together at the midline. Until the 1950s, its function was largely a mystery. Physicians had occasionally cut the corpus callosum to control severe epilepsy or to reach a very deep tumor, but patients did not appear much affected by this surgery. The corpus callosum clearly linked the two hemispheres of the brain, but exactly which parts were connected was not yet known.

We now realize that the corpus callosum connects only certain brain structures. As shown in **Figure 9-24**, the frontal lobes have many callosal connections, but the occipital lobes have almost none. If you think about it, there is no reason for a neuron in the visual cortex that is looking at one place in the visual field to be concerned with what another neuron in the opposite hemisphere is looking at in another part of the visual field.

Cells that lie along the midline of the visual field are an exception, however. These cells look at adjacent places in the visual field, one slightly to the left of center and one slightly to the right. Callosal connections between such cells zip the two visual fields together by combining their receptive fields to overlap at the midline. The two fields thus become one.

(9-3) **REVIEW**

Location in the Visual World

Before you continue, check your understanding.

1. The characteristic of visual receptive fields that allows us to detect exactly where a light source is coming from is their _____.

2. List four types of cells that have visual receptive fields: _____, _____, _____, and _____.

3. Inputs to different parts of cortical region V1 from different parts of the retina essentially form a _____ of the visual world within the brain.

4. The two sides of the visual world are bound together as one perception by the _____.

5. How does Jerison's principle of proper mass apply to the visual system?

Answers appear at the back of the book.

For additional study tools, visit 🐨 LaunchPad:
www.macmillanhighered.com/launchpad/kolb5e

(9-4) Neuronal Activity

Individual neurons make up the visual system pathways. By studying how these cells behave when their receptive fields are stimulated, we can begin to understand how the brain processes the features of the visual world beyond the location of a light. We first examine how neurons in the ventral stream respond to objects' shapes and colors, then briefly consider how neurons in the dorsal stream direct vision for action.

Seeing Shape

Imagine a microelectrode placed near a neuron somewhere in the visual pathway from retina to cortex. The microelectrode is recording changes in the neuron's firing rate. This cell occasionally fires spontaneously, producing action potentials with each discharge. Assume that the neuron discharges, on average, once every 0.08 second. Each action potential is brief, on the order of 1 millisecond.

If we plot action potentials spanning 1 s, we see only spikes in the record because the action potentials are so brief. **Figure 9-25**A is a single cell recording of 12 spikes in the span of 1 second. If the firing rate of this cell increases, we see more spikes (Figure 9-25B). If the firing rate decreases, we see fewer spikes (Figure 9-25C). The increase in firing is the result of neuronal excitation, whereas the decrease indicates inhibition. Excitation and inhibition, of course, are the principal information transfer mechanisms in the nervous system.

Now suppose we present a stimulus to the neuron by illuminating its receptive field in the retina, perhaps by shining a light on a blank screen within the cell's visual field. We might place before the eye a straight line positioned at a 45° angle. The cell could respond to this stimulus either by increasing or decreasing its firing rate. In either case, we would conclude that the cell is generating information about the line.

The same cell could show excitation to one stimulus, inhibition to another stimulus, and no reaction at all to a third. The cell could be excited by lines oriented 45° to the left and inhibited by lines oriented 45° to the right. Similarly, the cell could be excited by stimulation in one part of its receptive field (such as the center) and inhibited by stimulation in another part (such as the periphery).

Finally, we might find that the cell's response to a particular stimulus is selective. Such a cell would be telling us about the importance of the stimulus to the animal. For instance, the cell might be excited when a stimulus is presented with food but inhibited when the same stimulus is presented alone. In each case, the cell is selectively sensitive to characteristics in the visual world.

Neurons at each level of the visual system have distinctly different characteristics and functions. Our goal is not to look at each neuron type but rather to consider generally how some typical neurons at each level differ from one another in their contributions to processing shape. We focus on neurons in three areas: the ganglion cell layer of the retina, the primary visual cortex, and the temporal cortex.

Processing in RGCs

Neurons in the retina do not detect shape, because their receptive fields are minuscule dots. Each retinal ganglion cell responds only to the presence or absence of light in its receptive field, not to shape. Shape is constructed by processes in the cortex from the information that those ganglion cells pass on about events in their receptive fields.

The receptive field of a ganglion cell has a concentric circle arrangement, as illustrated in **Figure 9-26**A. A spot of light falling in the receptive field's central circle excites some of these cells, whereas a spot of light falling in the receptive field's surround (periphery) inhibits the cell. A spot of light falling across the entire receptive field weakly increases the cell's firing rate.

This type of neuron is called an *on-center cell*. Other RGCs, called *off-center cells*, have the opposite arrangement, with light in the center of the receptive field inhibiting, light in the surround exciting, and light across the entire field producing weak inhibition (Figure 9-26B). The on–off arrangement of RGC receptive fields makes these cells especially responsive to tiny spots of light.

This description of ganglion cell receptive fields might mislead you into thinking that they form a mosaic of discrete little circles on the retina. In fact, neighboring retinal ganglion cells receive their inputs from an overlapping set of photoreceptors. As a result, their receptive fields overlap, as illustrated in **Figure 9-27**. In this way, a small spot of light shining on the retina is likely to produce activity in both on-center and off-center RGCs.

Figure 4-6 diagrams how microelectrodes work.

FIGURE 9-25 Recording Neuronal Stimulation Each action potential is represented by a spike. **(A)** In a 1-s period at this neuron's baseline firing rate, 12 spikes were recorded. **(B)** A firing rate over baseline signals excitation. **(C)** A firing rate under baseline signals inhibition.

(A) On-center cell's receptive field

Response of cell to stimulus at left

Light strikes center

0   1   Excitation   2   3
Time (seconds)

Light strikes surround

0   1   Inhibition   2   3
Time (seconds)

(B) Off-center cell's receptive field

Light strikes center

0   1   Inhibition   2   3
Time (seconds)

Light strikes surround

0   1   Excitation   2   3
Time (seconds)

FIGURE 9-26 On—Off Receptivity **(A)** In the receptive field of an RGC with an on-center and off-surround, a spot of light shining on the center excites the neuron, but a spot of light in the surround inhibits it. When the light in the surround is turned off, firing rate increases briefly—an offset response. A light shining in both the center and the surround would produce a weak increase in firing. **(B)** In the receptive field of an RGC with an off-center and on-surround, light in the center produces inhibition, light on the surround produces excitation, and light across the entire field produces weak inhibition.

luminance contrast Amount of light an object reflects relative to its surroundings.

How can on-center and off-center ganglion cells tell the brain anything about shape? The answer is that a ganglion cell tells the brain about the amount of light hitting a certain spot on the retina compared with the average amount of light falling on the surrounding retinal region. This comparison is known as **luminance contrast**. Luminance is the amount of visible light reflected to the eye from a surface, and contrast is the difference in luminance between adjacent parts of that surface. The photograph in Focus 9-1 (p. 284) shows us two clear differences in luminance contrast. On the left, the woman's pink top contrasts sharply with her black slacks, but the sleeve on the right contrasts far less with the background. It does not appear as bright.

To understand how luminance contrast tells the brain about shape, consider the hypothetical population of on-center ganglion cells represented in **Figure 9-28**. Their receptive fields are distributed across the retinal image of a light–dark edge. Some of the ganglion cells' receptive fields are in the dark area, others are in the light area, and still others' fields straddle the edge of the light.

The ganglion cells with receptive fields in the dark or light areas are least affected because they receive either no stimulation or stimulation of both the excitatory and

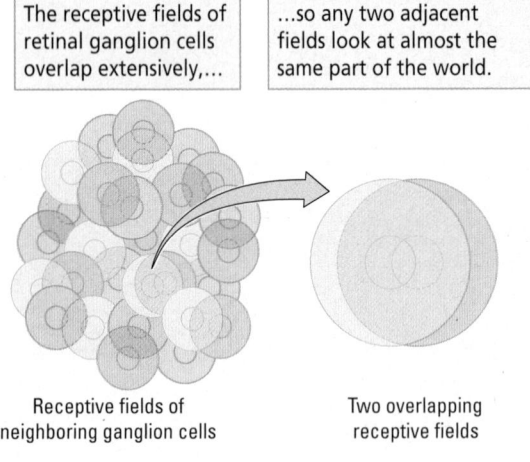

The receptive fields of retinal ganglion cells overlap extensively,...   ...so any two adjacent fields look at almost the same part of the world.

Receptive fields of neighboring ganglion cells

Two overlapping receptive fields

FIGURE 9-27 Overlapping Receptive Fields

FIGURE 9-28 Activity at the Margins Responses of a hypothetical population of on-center ganglion cells whose receptive fields (A–E) are distributed across a light–dark edge. The activity of the cells along the edge is most affected relative to those away from the edge. Information from D. Purves, G. J. Augustine, D. Fitzpatrick, L. C. Katz, A.-S. LaMantia, & J. O. McNamara (Eds.). (1997). *Neuroscience*, (1st ed., p. 195). Sunderland, MA: Sinauer.

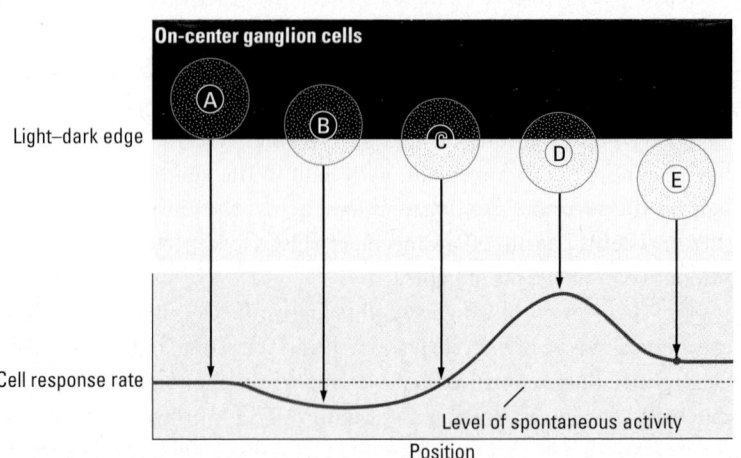

On-center ganglion cells

Light–dark edge

Cell response rate

Level of spontaneous activity

Position

(A) Horizontally aligned preferred orientation   **(B) Oblique preferred orientation**

FIGURE 9-29 Typical Receptive Fields for Simple V1 Cells Simple cells respond to a bar of light in a particular orientation, such as **(A)** horizontal or **(B)** oblique. The position of the bar in the visual field is important, because the cell either responds (ON) or does not respond (OFF) to light in adjacent visual field regions.

the inhibitory regions of their receptive fields. The ganglion cells most affected by the stimulus are those lying along the edge. Ganglion cell B is inhibited because the light falls mostly on its inhibitory surround, and ganglion cell D is excited because its entire excitatory center is stimulated but only part of its inhibitory surround is.

Consequently, information transmitted from retinal ganglion cells to the visual areas in the brain does not give equal weight to all visual field regions. Rather, it emphasizes regions containing differences in luminance—areas along the edges. So RGCs are really sending signals about edges, and edges form shapes.

Processing Shape in the Primary Visual Cortex

Now consider cells in region V1 that receive their visual inputs from LGN cells, which in turn receive theirs from retinal ganglion cells. As you read on, think about how these cortical cells are responding to the Clinical Focus 9-1 photograph. Because each V1 cell receives input from multiple RGCs, the receptive fields of the V1 neurons are much larger than those of retinal neurons. Consequently, V1 cells respond to stimuli more complex than simply light on or light off. In particular, these cells are maximally excited by bars of light oriented in a particular direction rather than by spots of light. These V1 cells are therefore called *orientation detectors*.

Like the ganglion cells, some orientation detectors have an on–off receptive-field arrangement, but the arrangement is rectangular rather than circular. Visual cortex cells with this property are known as *simple cells*. Typical receptive fields for simple cells in V1 are shown in **Figure 9-29**.

Simple cells are not the only kind of orientation detector in the primary visual cortex; several functionally distinct types of neurons populate region V1. For instance, the receptive fields of *complex cells*, such as those in **Figure 9-30**, are maximally excited by bars of light moving in a particular direction through the visual field. A *hypercomplex cell*, like a complex cell, is maximally responsive to moving bars but also has a strong inhibitory area at one end of its receptive field. As illustrated in **Figure 9-31**, a bar of light landing on the right side of

FIGURE 9-30 Receptive Field of a Complex Cell Unlike a simple cell's on–off response pattern, a complex cell in V1 shows the same response throughout its circular receptive field, responding best to bars of light moving at a particular angle. The response is reduced or absent with the bar of light at other orientations.

Hypercomplex cell's receptive field

No stimulus / Baseline response

ON / Strong response

ON / Strong response

ON / Weak response

ON / No response

FIGURE 9-31 Receptive Field of a Hypercomplex Cell A hypercomplex cell in V1 responds to a moving bar of light in a particular orientation (horizontal, e.g.) anywhere in the excitatory (ON) part of its receptive field. If most of the bar extends into the inhibitory area (OFF), however, the response is inhibited.

the hypercomplex cell's receptive field excites the cell; but if, for example, the bar lands mainly on the inhibitory area to the left, the cell's firing is inhibited.

Each class of V1 neurons responds to bars of light in some way, yet this response results from input originating in retinal ganglion cells that respond maximally not to bars but to spots of light. How does this conversion from responding to spots to responding to bars take place? An example will help explain the process.

A thin bar of light falls on the retinal photoreceptors, striking the receptive fields of perhaps dozens of retinal ganglion cells. The input to a V1 neuron comes from a group of ganglion cells that happen to be aligned in a row, as in **Figure 9-32**. That V1 neuron is activated (or inhibited) only when a bar of light hitting the retina strikes that particular row of ganglion cells. If the bar of light shines at a slightly different angle, only some of the retinal ganglion cells in the row are activated, so the V1 neuron is excited only weakly.

Figure 9-32 illustrates the connection between light striking the retina in a certain pattern and the activation of a simple cell in the primary visual cortex, one that responds to a bar of light in a particular orientation. Using the same logic, we can also diagram the retinal receptive fields of complex or hypercomplex V1 neurons. Try it as an exercise yourself by adapting the format in Figure 9-32.

A characteristic of cortical structure is that the neurons are organized into functional columns. The connectivity pattern in a column is vertical: inputs arrive in layer IV, then connect with cells in the other layers. **Figure 9-33** shows such a column, a 0.5-mm-diameter strip of cortex that includes representative neurons and their connections.

Neurons within a cortical column have similar functions. For example, **Figure 9-34**A shows that neurons within the same column respond to lines oriented in the same direction. Adjacent columns house cells responsive to different line orientations. Figure 9-34B shows the cortical columns of input coming from each

Each circle represents the receptive field of a ganglion cell.

Stimulation of a subset of on-center ganglion cells excites a V1 neuron through connections in the LGN (not shown here).

Strong response

V1 neuron

Weak response

V1 neuron

FIGURE 9-32 V1 Receptivity A V1 cell responds to a row of ganglion cells in a particular orientation on the retina. The bar of light strongly activates a row of ganglion cells, each connected through the LGN to a V1 neuron. The activity of this V1 neuron is most affected by a bar of light at a 45° angle.

eye, discussed earlier, called **ocular dominance columns**. So V1 has both orientation columns housing neurons of similar sensitivity and ocular dominance columns with input from one eye or the other.

Processing Shape in the Temporal Cortex

Consider neurons along the ventral stream in temporal lobe region TE. Rather than being responsive to spots or bars of light, TE neurons are maximally excited by complex visual stimuli, such as faces (see Figure 9-19A) or hands, and can be remarkably specific in their responsiveness. They may be responsive to particular faces seen head-on, to faces viewed in profile, to the posture of the head, or even to particular facial expressions.

How far does this specialized responsiveness extend? Would it be practical to have visual neurons in the temporal cortex specialized to respond to every conceivable feature of objects? Keiji Tanaka (1993) approached this question by presenting monkeys with many three-dimensional representations of animals and plants to find stimuli that are effective in activating particular neurons of the inferior temporal cortex.

Having identified stimuli that were especially effective, such as faces or hands, he then wondered which specific features of those stimuli are critical to stimulating the neurons. Tanaka found that most neurons in area TE require rather complex features for their activation. These features include a combination of characteristics such as orientation, size, color, and texture. Furthermore, neurons with similar but not identical responsiveness to particular features tend to cluster in columns, as shown in **Figure 9-35**.

Apparently, then, an object is represented not by the activity of a single neuron but rather by the activity of many neurons with slightly varying stimulus specificity. These neurons are grouped in a column. This finding is important because it provides an explanation for *stimulus equivalence*, recognizing an object as remaining the same despite being viewed from different orientations.

Think of how the representation of objects by multiple neurons in a column can produce stimulus equivalence. If each neuron in the column module varies slightly in regard to the features to which it responds but the effective stimuli largely overlap, the effect of small

FIGURE 9-33 Neural Circuit in a Column in the Visual Cortex In this three-dimensional view, sensory inputs enter the cortical column at layer VI (bottom) and terminate on stellate cells in layer IV that synapse with pyramidal cells in layers III and V. The information flow is vertical. Axons of the pyramidal cells leave the column to join other columns or structures. Information from J. Szentagothai (1975). The "module-concept" in cerebral architecture. *Brain Research*, 95, p. 490.

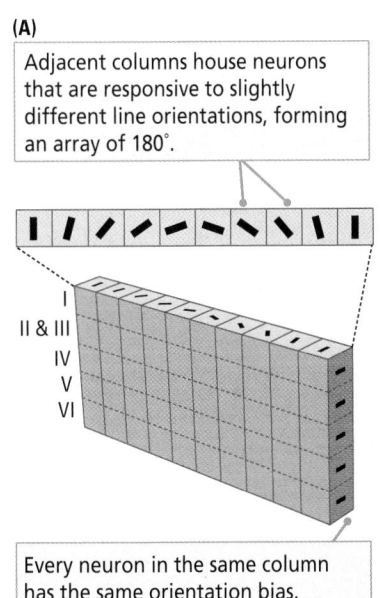

(A)

Adjacent columns house neurons that are responsive to slightly different line orientations, forming an array of 180°.

Every neuron in the same column has the same orientation bias.

FIGURE 9-34 Organization of Functional Columns in V1

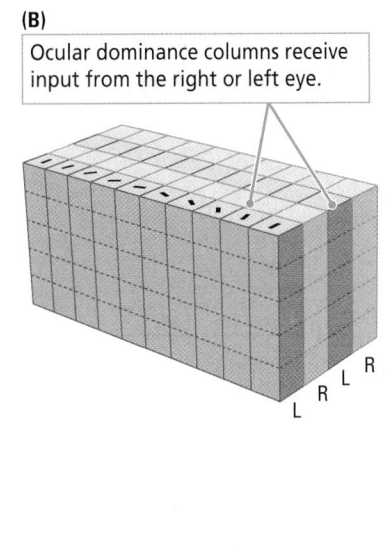

(B)

Ocular dominance columns receive input from the right or left eye.

ocular dominance column Functional column in the visual cortex maximally responsive to information coming from one eye.

Neurons in the temporal lobe form columns that respond to categories of shapes.

Temporal lobe

I
II & III
IV
V
VI

FIGURE 9-35 Columnar Organization of Area TE Neurons with similar but slightly different pattern selectivity cluster in vertical columns, perpendicular to the cortical surface.

Section 1-4 recounts several ideas on how the primate lifestyle, including diet, encouraged the evolution of complex nervous systems.

(A)

(B)

changes in incoming visual images will be minimized and we will continue to perceive an object as itself.

The stimulus specificity of neurons in the inferior temporal cortex in monkeys shows remarkable neuroplasticity. If monkeys are trained to discriminate particular shapes to obtain a food reward, not only do they improve their discriminatory ability but neurons in the temporal lobe also modify their preferred stimuli to fire maximally to some of the stimuli used in training. This result shows that the temporal lobe's role in visual processing is not determined genetically but is instead subject to experience, even in adults.

We can speculate that this neuroplastic characteristic evolved because it allows the visual system to adapt to a changing visual environment. Think of how different the demands on your visual recognition abilities are when you move from a dense forest to a treeless plain to a city street. The visual neurons of your temporal cortex can adapt to these differences (Tanaka, 1993). Experience-dependent visual neurons ensure in addition that people can identify visual stimuli that were never encountered as the human brain evolved.

The preferred stimuli of neurons in the primary visual cortex are not modified by experience. This implies that the stimulus preferences of V1 neurons are genetically programmed. Regardless, the functions of the V1 neurons underlie the more complex and flexible characteristics of the inferior temporal cortex neurons.

Seeing Color

Scientists have long wondered why—and how—we see a world so rich in color. One hypothesis on the *why* is that color vision evolved first in the great apes, specifically in apes that eat fruit. Chimpanzees and humans are members of this family. Over their evolution, both species have faced plentiful competition for ripe fruits—from other animals, insects, and each other. Scientists suspect that color vision gave the great apes a competitive evolutionary advantage.

An explanation of color vision has its roots in the Renaissance 600 years ago in Italy. Painters of the time discovered that they could obtain the entire range of colors in the visual world by mixing only three colors of paint (red, blue, and yellow). This is the process of *subtractive color mixing* shown in **Figure 9-36**A.

We now know that such trichromatic color mixing is a property of the cones in the retina. Subtractive color mixing works by removing light from the mix. This is why matte black surfaces reflect no light: the darker the color, the less light it contains.

Conversely, *additive color mixing* increases light to make color (Figure 9-36B). The lighter the color, the more light it contains, which is why a white surface reflects the entire visible spectrum. Unlike those of paint, the primary colors of light are red, blue, and green. Light of different wavelengths stimulates the three cone receptor types in different ways. It is the ratio of activity of these three receptor types that forms our impressions of colors.

Trichromatic Theory

According to the **trichromatic theory**, the color we see—say, blue at short 400-nanometer wavelengths, green at medium 500 nm, and red at long 600 nm—is determined by the relative responses of the corresponding cone types (see Figure 9-6). If all three types are equally active, we see white.

Trichromatic theory predicts that if we lack one cone receptor type, we cannot process as many colors as we could with all three. This is exactly what happens when a person is born with only two cone types. The colors this person cannot perceive depend on which receptor type is missing, as illustrated in Research Focus 9-3, Color-Deficient Vision.

FIGURE 9-36 Color Mixing **(A)** Subtractive color mixing absorbs light waves that we see as red, blue, or yellow. When all visible wavelengths are absorbed, we see black. **(B)** Additive color mixing reflects light waves that we see as red, blue, and green. When all visible wavelengths are reflected, we see white.

RESEARCH F◉CUS 9-3

Color-Deficient Vision

Most people's retinas contain three cone types. These people have trichromatic vision. But some people are missing one or more cone types and are thus often mistakenly said to be color-blind. Mistakenly, because people who have two types of cones still can distinguish lots of colors, just not as many as people with three cones can.

To have no color vision at all, one would have to have only one type of photoreceptor, rods. This is a rare occurrence, but we do have a friend who has no concept of color. It has led to a lifetime of practical jokes, because others (especially his wife) must choose clothing colors that coordinate for him to wear.

The complete lack of red cones leads to a condition called *protanopia*; the lack of green cones is *deuteranopia*; the lack of blue cones is *tritanopia*. The frequency of each condition is about 1 percent in men and 0.01 percent in women. Having only a partial lack of one cone type, most commonly the green cone, also is possible. This condition afflicts about 5 percent of men and 0.4 percent of women.

The illustration provides a simple approximation, compared with trichromats (left), of what people with protanopia (center) or deuteranopia (right) see. They still see plenty of color, but that color is largely different from the color trichromats see. Many domestic animals (dogs, cats, and horses among them) have deuteranopia, which actually gives them an advantage in seeing objects that appear camouflaged to trichromats. In fact, the military often use humans with deuteranopia to help see through camouflage.

Image as viewed by a trichromat observer

Protanopia: image as viewed by an observer lacking red cones

Deuteranopia: image as viewed by an observer lacking green cones

Dr. Terrace L. Waggoner/www.ColorVisionTesting.com

The mere presence of cones in an animal's retina does not mean that the animal has color vision. It simply means that the animal has photoreceptors particularly sensitive to light. Many animals lack color vision as we know it, but the only animal with eyes known to have no cones at all is a fish, the skate.

trichromatic theory Explanation of color vision based on the coding of three primary colors: red, green, and blue.

Opponent Processes

Although the beginning of color perception in the cones follows the trichromatic model, succeeding levels of color processing use a different strategy. Try staring first at the red and blue box in **Figure 9-37** for about 30 seconds then at the white box next to it. When you shift your

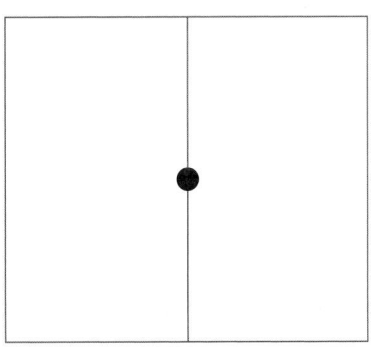

FIGURE 9-37 Demonstrating Opposing Color Pairs Stare at the rectangle on the left for about 30 seconds. Then stare at the white box on the right. You will see an afterimage of green on the red side and of yellow on the blue side.

FIGURE 9-38 Opponent-Color Contrast Response **(A)** A red–green color-sensitive RGC responds weakly to white light on its center and surround because red and green cones absorb white light to similar extents, so their inputs cancel out. **(B)** The cell responds strongly to a spot of red light in its center as well as to red's paired wavelength, green, in the surround. **(C)** It is strongly inhibited by a small spot of green in its center. **(D)** The RGC responds very strongly to simultaneous illumination of the center with red and the surround with green. **(E)** It is completely inhibited by the simultaneous illumination of the center with green and the surround with red.

gaze to the white surface, you will see an afterimage in the colors opposite to red and blue—green and yellow. Conversely, if you stare at a green and yellow box and then shift to white, you will see a red and blue afterimage. Such afterimages lead to the sense that there are actually four basic colors (red, green, yellow, and blue).

A characteristic of RGCs explains the two opposing pairs of four basic colors. Remember that RGCs have an on–off and center–surround organization. Stimulation to the center of the cell's receptive field is either excitatory (in some cells) or inhibitory (in other cells), whereas stimulation to the periphery of the receptive field has the opposite effect (see Figure 9-26).

This arrangement can be adapted to produce color-opponent cells. If one wavelength of light produced excitation and another inhibition, cells would evolve that are excited by red and inhibited by green (or vice versa), as would cells that are excited by blue and inhibited by yellow (or vice versa). Red–green and blue–yellow would therefore be linked to each other as color opposites, or opponents.

In fact, about 60 percent of human retinal ganglion cells are color-sensitive in this way, with the center responsive to one wavelength and the surround to another. The most common **opponent-process** pairing, shown in **Figure 9-38**, is medium-wavelength (green) versus long-wavelength (red), but we also have blue versus yellow RGCs. Most likely, opponent-process cells evolved to enhance the relatively small differences in spectral absorption among the three cone types.

Cortical neurons in region V1 also respond to color in an opponent-process manner reminiscent of retinal ganglion cells. Recall that color inputs in the primary visual cortex go to the blobs that appear in sections stained for cytochrome oxidase (see Figure 9-17). These blobs are where the color-sensitive cells are found.

Figure 9-39 models how the color-sensitive cells in the blobs are inserted amid the orientation-sensitive and ocular dominance columns. The primary visual cortex thus appears to be organized into modules that include ocular dominance and orientation-sensitive columns as well as blobs. Think of V1 as composed of several thousand modules, each analyzing color and contour for a particular visual region. This organization allows the primary visual cortex to perform several functions concurrently.

How do neurons in the visual system beyond V1 process color? You have already learned that cells in region V4 respond to color, but in contrast with the cells in region V1, these

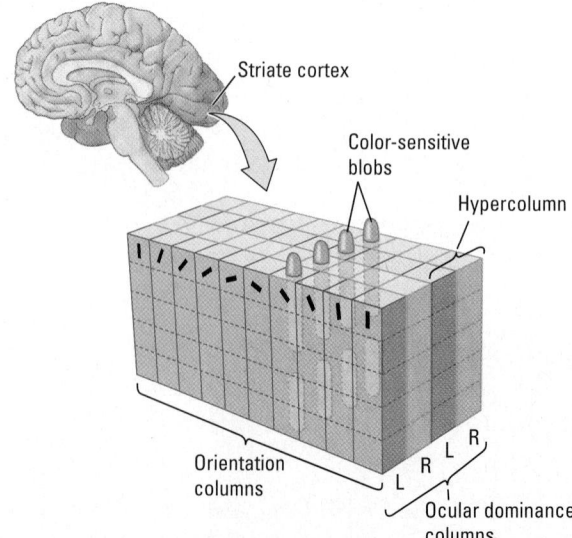

FIGURE 9-39 V1 Modules A model of striate cortex showing the orientation-sensitive columns, ocular dominance columns, and color-sensitive blobs as composed of two hypercolumns. Each consists of a full set (red and blue) of orientation-sensitive columns spanning 180° of preferred angle as well as a pair of blobs. All cells in the hypercolumn share the same receptive field.

V4 cells do not respond to particular wavelengths. Rather, they are responsive to different perceived colors, with the center of the field being excited by a certain color and the surround being inhibited.

Speculation swirls about the function of these V4 cells. One idea is that they are important for **color constancy**, the property of perception whereby colors appear to remain the same relative to one another despite changes in light. For instance, were you to look at a bowl of fruit through light-green glasses, the fruit would take on a greenish tinge, but bananas would still look yellow relative to red apples. If you removed all the fruit except the bananas and looked at them through the tinted glasses, the bananas would appear green because the color you perceive is isolated relative to any other. Monkeys with V4 lesions lose color constancy, though they can discriminate different color wavelengths.

Color Constancy Depending on the viewer, the dress in the center photo is perceived as either white and gold or blue and black. The image is color-balanced, at left, to show the dress as white and gold, at right, as blue and black. Which is the original?

Neuronal Activity in the Dorsal Stream

A striking characteristic of many cells in the visual areas of parietal cortex is that they are virtually silent to visual stimulation when a person is under anesthesia. This is true of neurons in the posterior parietal regions of the dorsal stream. In contrast, cells in the visual temporal cortex do respond to visual stimulation when a person is anesthetized.

The silence on the part of neurons in the posterior parietal cortex under anesthesia makes sense if their role is to process visual information for action. In the absence of action when a person is unconscious, there is no need for processing. Hence, the cells are quiescent.

Cells in the dorsal stream are of many types, their details varying with the nature of the movement in which a particular cell takes part. One interesting cell category processes the visual appearance of an object to be grasped. If a monkey is going to pick up an apple, for instance, these cells respond even when the monkey is only looking at the apple. The cells do not respond when the monkey encounters the same apple if no movement is to be made.

These dorsal stream cells also respond if the monkey merely watches another monkey making movements to pick up the apple. Apparently, the cells have some understanding of what is happening in the external world. But that understanding is always related to action performed with respect to visually perceived objects. These cells led David Milner and Mel Goodale (2006) to conclude that the dorsal stream is a *how* visual system.

opponent process Explanation of color vision that emphasizes the importance of the apparently opposing color pairs: red versus green and blue versus yellow.

color constancy Phenomenon whereby an object's perceived color tends to remain constant relative to other colors, regardless of changes in illumination.

(9-4) **REVIEW**

Neuronal Activity

Before you continue, check your understanding.

1. Neurons in the primary visual cortex respond to properties of shapes, especially to _____ oriented in a certain direction.

2. Recognition of complex visual stimuli such as faces is completed in the _____ lobe.

3. The idea that the color we see is determined by the relative responses of the three cone types in the retina is called _____ .

4. Retinal ganglion cells mediate color vision by _____ processes.

5. Describe the opponent process in the retinal ganglion cells.

Answers appear at the back of the book.

The blue and black dress at right is the original.

9-5 The Visual Brain in Action

Anatomical and physiological studies of brain systems leave one key question unanswered: How do all of the cells in these systems act together to produce a particular function? One way to answer this question is to evaluate what happens when parts of the visual system are dysfunctional. Then we can see how these parts contribute to the workings of the whole. We use this strategy to examine the neuropsychology of vision—the study of the visual brain in action.

Injury to the Visual Pathway Leading to the Cortex

What happens when parts of the visual pathway leading from the eye to the cortex are injured? For instance, destruction of the retina or optic nerve of one eye produces *monocular blindness*, the loss of sight in that eye. Partial destruction of the retina or optic nerve produces a partial loss of sight in one eye, restricted to the visual field region that has severed connections to the brain.

Injuries to the visual pathway beyond the eye also produce blindness. For example, complete cuts of the optic tract, the LGN, or cortical region V1 result in **homonymous hemianopia**, blindness of one entire side of the visual field, as shown in **Figure 9-40A**. We encountered this syndrome in Focus 9-1, the story of D. B.'s lesion in region V1. Should a lesion in one of these areas be partial, as is often the case, the result is **quadrantanopia**, destruction of only a part of the visual field, illustrated in Figure 9-40B.

Figure 9-40C shows that small lesions in V1 often produce small blind spots, or **scotomas**, in the visual field. Focus 9-1 observes that scotomas can be a warning symptom for migraine sufferers. But brain-injured people are often totally unaware of them. One reason is that the eyes are usually moving.

We make tiny, involuntary eye movements almost constantly. Because of this usually constant eye motion, called *nystagmus*, a scotoma moves about the visual field, allowing the intact brain regions to perceive all the information in that field. If the eyes are temporarily held still, the visual system actually compensates for a scotoma through pattern completion—filling in the hole, so to speak—so that the people and objects in the visual world are perceived as whole. The result: a seemingly normal set of perceptions.

The visual system may cover up a scotoma so successfully that its presence can be demonstrated to the patient only by tricking the visual system. The trick is to place an object entirely within the scotoma and without allowing the patient to shift gaze, asking what the object is. If the patient reports seeing nothing, to confirm the existence of a blind area the examiner moves the object out of the scotoma so that it suddenly appears in the intact region of the visual field.

This technique is similar to demonstrating the presence of the blind spot that is due to the optic disc (as in Figure 9-4). When a person is looking at an object with only one eye, the brain compensates for the scotoma in the same way as for the optic disc's blind spot. As a result, the person does not notice the scotoma.

Thus the type of blindness offers clues about where in the visual pathway the cause of the problem lies. If the loss of vision is in one eye only, the problem must be in that eye or its optic nerve;

FIGURE 9-40 Consequences of Lesions in Region V1 The shaded areas indicate regions of visual loss. **(A)** A complete lesion of V1 in the left hemisphere results in hemianopia affecting the right visual field. **(B)** A large lesion of the lower lip of the calcarine fissure produces quadrantanopia that affects most of the upper right visual quadrant. **(C)** A smaller lesion of the lower lip of the calcarine fissure results in a smaller scotoma.

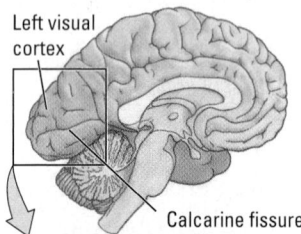
Left visual cortex
Calcarine fissure

(A) Hemianopia

Injury

(B) Quadrantanopia

Injury

(C) Scotoma
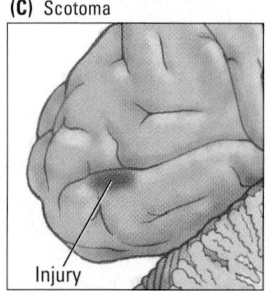
Injury

Left visual field   Right visual field

Glowimages/Getty Images

if the vision loss affects both eyes, the problem most likely is in the brain. Many people have difficulty understanding why a person with damage to the visual cortex has difficulty with both eyes. They fail to realize that the visual field, not the eye, is represented in the brain.

Beyond region V1, the nature of visual loss caused by injury is considerably more complex. It is also very different in the ventral and dorsal streams. We therefore look at each pathway separately.

Injury to the *What* Pathway

We have encountered an example of damage to the *what* pathway: the case of D. B. in Focus 9-1. He appeared to be blind in his affected visual field but could point to the location of blinking lights in that field, suggesting that some part of his visual system was working. An even more dramatic example of ventral stream injury comes from the case of D. F., a 35-year-old woman who, while taking a shower, was poisoned by carbon monoxide (CO) from a faulty gas-fueled water heater. The length of her exposure is unclear, but when her roommate found her, the shower was running cold. CO poisoning can cause several kinds of neurological damage, as discussed in Clinical Focus 9-4, Carbon Monoxide Poisoning; the result for D. F. was an extensive lesion of the lateral occipital region, including cortical tissue in the ventral visual pathway.

D. F.'s principal deficit was **visual-form agnosia**, an inability to recognize objects, real or drawn (see Farah, 1990). Not only was D. F. unable to recognize objects, especially line drawings of objects, she could neither estimate their size and their orientation nor

homonymous hemianopia Blindness of an entire left or right visual field.

quadrantanopia Blindness of one quadrant of the visual field.

scotoma Small blind spot in the visual field caused by migraine or by a small lesion of the visual cortex.

visual-form agnosia Inability to recognize objects or drawings of objects.

Section 9-2 describes damage to the temporal lobe area that causes facial agnosia.

Carbon Monoxide Poisoning

Brain damage from carbon monoxide (CO) poisoning is usually caused either by a faulty furnace or by motor vehicle exhaust fumes. The blood absorbs carbon monoxide gas, resulting in swelling and bleeding of the lungs and anoxia (loss of oxygen) in the brain. The cerebral cortex, hippocampus, cerebellum, and striatum are especially sensitive to CO-induced anoxia.

Only a small proportion of people who are subjected to CO poisoning have permanent neurological symptoms. Among those who do, the symptoms are highly variable. Most common are cortical blindness and various agnosias, as seen in case D. F. Many also have language difficulties.

The peculiarities of the language difficulties are shown clearly in a young woman whose case was described by Norman Geschwind (1972). Geschwind studied this patient for 9 years after her accidental poisoning. She required complete nursing care during this time, never uttered spontaneous speech, and did not comprehend spoken language. Nonetheless, she could repeat with perfect accuracy sentences that had just been said to her.

She could also complete certain well-known phrases. For example, if she heard "Roses are red," she would say, "Roses are red, violets are blue, sugar is sweet, and so are you." She could also learn new songs. She did not appear to understand the content of the songs, yet with only a few repetitions, she began to sing along. Eventually, she could sing the song spontaneously, making no errors in either words or melody.

Postmortem examination of this woman's brain found that although the parietal and temporal lobes were damaged extensively, as shown in the accompanying diagram, her speech areas were intact. Geschwind proposed that she could not comprehend speech because the words she heard did not arouse associations in other parts of her cortex.

She could, however, repeat sentences because the internal connections of the speech regions were undamaged. Geschwind did not comment on whether this woman had agnosia, but it is likely that she did. The difficulty would be in diagnosing agnosia in a person who is unable to communicate.

Areas damaged by carbon monoxide poisoning are shown in red in this postmortem diagram of Geschwind's patient's brain.

Original   J. W.'s copy

Marlene Behrmann, Director Cognitive Neuroscience Lab, Carnegie Mellon University

FIGURE 9-41 Injury to the Ventral Stream J. W. survived a severe heart attack while exercising and later, anoxia. Subsequently, he was unable to recognize the simple line drawings on the left and copied them poorly (right).

FIGURE 9-42 Visual Guidance You may consciously reach for an object such as a pen or a mug, but your hand forms the appropriate posture automatically, without your conscious awareness. Figure 11-1 details this type of sequentially organized movement.

Section 11-5 details the somatic senses, including proprioception, or body awareness.

optic ataxia Deficit in the visual control of reaching and other movements.

copy drawings. Likewise, as **Figure 9-41** illustrates, patient J. W. also fails to recognize or copy simple drawings.

Clearly, D. F.'s lesion interfered with her ventral stream *what* pathway. Remarkably, despite her inability to identify objects or to estimate their size and orientation, D. F. retained the capacity, illustrated in **Figure 9-42**, to appropriately shape her hand when reaching out to grasp something. Goodale, Milner, and their research colleagues (1991) studied D. F. extensively for years and devised a way to demonstrate D. F.'s skill at reaching for objects.

The middle column in **Figure 9-43** shows the grasp patterns of a control participant (S. H.) when she picks up something irregularly shaped. S. H. grasps the object along whichever of the two axes makes it easier to pick up. When D. F. is presented with the same task, shown in the left-hand column, she is as good as S. H. at placing her index finger and thumb on appropriately opposed grasp points.

Clearly, D. F. remains able to use the structural features of objects to control her visually guided grasping movements, even though she is unable to interpret these same features. This result demonstrates once more that we are consciously aware of only a small part of the sensory processing that goes on in the brain. Furthermore, D. F.'s ability to use structural features of objects for guiding movement but not for perceiving shapes again shows us that the brain has separate systems for each type of visual operation.

D. F.'s lesion is quite far back in the ventral visual pathway. More anterior lesions produce other deficits, depending on the exact location. For example, J. I., described by Oliver Sacks and Robert Wasserman (1987), was an artist who developed complete color deficiency owing to a cortical lesion presumed to be in region V4. His principal symptom was *achromatopsia*, or color agnosia. Despite his inability to distinguish any colors whatsoever, J. I.'s vision appeared otherwise unaffected.

Similarly, L. M., a woman described by Josef Zihl and his colleagues (1983), lost her ability to detect movement after a lesion presumed to be in region V5. In her case, objects either vanished when they moved or appeared frozen despite their movement. L. M. had particular difficulty pouring tea into a cup, because the fluid appeared to be frozen in midair. Yet she could read, write, and recognize objects, and she appeared to have normal form vision—until objects moved.

These varied cases demonstrate that cortical injuries in the ventral stream all somehow interfere with determining what things are or are like or are doing. In each case, the symptoms are somewhat different, however, which is thought to be indicative of damage to different subregions or substreams of the ventral visual pathway.

Injury to the *How* Pathway

In 1909, R. Bálint described a rather peculiar set of visual symptoms associated with a bilateral parietal lesion. The patient had full visual fields and could recognize, use, and name objects, pictures, and colors normally. But he had a severe deficit in visually guided reaching, even though he could still make accurate movements directed toward his own body (presumably guided by tactile or proprioceptive feedback from his joints). Bálint called this syndrome **optic ataxia**.

Since Bálint's time, many descriptions of optic ataxia associated with parietal injury have been recorded. Goodale has studied several such patients, one of whom is a woman identified as R. V. (Milner & Goodale, 2006). In contrast with patient D. F.'s visual form agnosia, R. V.'s perception of drawings and objects was normal, but she could not guide her hand to reach for objects.

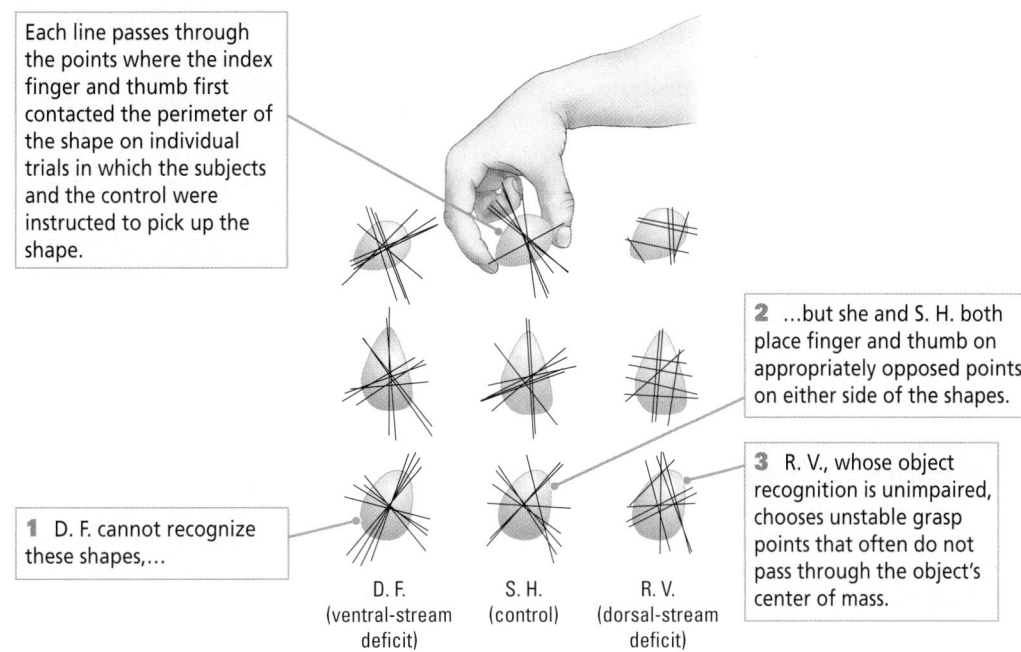

Each line passes through the points where the index finger and thumb first contacted the perimeter of the shape on individual trials in which the subjects and the control were instructed to pick up the shape.

2 ...but she and S. H. both place finger and thumb on appropriately opposed points on either side of the shapes.

1 D. F. cannot recognize these shapes,...

3 R. V., whose object recognition is unimpaired, chooses unstable grasp points that often do not pass through the object's center of mass.

D. F.
(ventral-stream deficit)

S. H.
(control)

R. V.
(dorsal-stream deficit)

FIGURE 9-43 Grasp Patterns The Milner–Goodale experiments confirm that the brain has different systems for visual object recognition and visual guidance of movement. Information from A. D. Milner & M. A. Goodale (1995). *The Visual Brain in Action* (p. 127). Oxford: Oxford University Press.

The rightmost column in Figure 9-43 shows that, when asked to pick up the same irregularly shaped objects that D. F. could grasp normally, R. V. often failed to place her fingers on the appropriate grasp points, even though she could distinguish the objects easily. In other words, although R. V.'s perception of an object's features was normal for the task of describing that object, her perception was not normal for the task of visually guiding her hand to reach for the object.

To summarize, people with damage to the parietal cortex in the dorsal visual stream can see perfectly well, yet they cannot accurately guide their movements on the basis of visual information. Guidance of movement is the dorsal stream's function. In contrast, people with damage to the ventral stream cannot perceive objects, because object perception is a ventral stream function. Yet these same people can guide their movements to objects on the basis of visual information.

The first kind of patient, like R. V., has an intact ventral stream that analyzes the visual characteristics of objects. The second kind of patient, like D. F., has an intact dorsal stream that visually directs movements. Comparing the two types of cases enables us to infer the visual functions of the dorsal and ventral streams.

(9-5) **REVIEW**

The Visual Brain in Action

Before you continue, check your understanding.

1. Cuts completely through the optic tract, LGN, or V1 produce _____ .

2. Small lesions of V1 produce small blind spots called _____ .

3. Destruction of the retina or the optic nerve of one eye produces _____ .

4. The effect of severe deficits in visually guided reaching is called _____ .

5. Contrast the effects of injury to the dorsal stream and the effects of injury to the ventral stream.

Answers appear at the back of the book.

SUMMARY

9-1 Nature of Sensation and Perception

Sensory systems allow animals, including ourselves, to adapt. Animals adapted to different environments vary widely in their sensory abilities. What is distinctive about humans is the extent to which we can transform sensations into perceptual information to mediate aspects of language, music, and culture. For each sense, mammals represent the world in topographic maps that form neural-spatial representations in the cortex.

9-2 The Visual System's Function Anatomy

Like all sensory systems, vision begins with receptor neurons. The visual photoreceptors (rods and cones) at the back of the eye in the retina transduce the physical energy of light waves into neural activity.

Rods are sensitive to dim light. Cones, which are sensitive to bright light, mediate color vision. Each of the three cone types is maximally sensitive to a different wavelength—short, medium, or long. We see these wavelengths, respectively, as the colors blue, green, or red; thus the short, medium, and long cone receptors often are referred to as blue, green, or red.

Retinal ganglion cells receive input from photoreceptors through bipolar cells and send their axons out from the retinas to form the optic nerve. P ganglion cells receive input mostly from cones and convey information about color and fine detail. M cells receive input from rods and convey information about luminance and movement but not color.

The optic nerve forms two distinct major routes into the brain. The geniculostriate pathway synapses first in the thalamic LGN nucleus, then in V1. The tectopulvinar pathway synapses first in the midbrain's tectum (superior colliculus), then in the pulvinar of the thalamus, and finally in the temporal and parietal visual cortex areas. A few optic nerve fibers also form the retinohypothalamic tract, which functions in part to control circadian rhythms.

Among the visual regions in the occipital cortex, V1 and V2 carry out multiple functions; the remaining regions (V3, V3A, V4, and V5) are specialized. Visual information flows from the thalamus to V1 and V2, then divides to form the visual stream pathways. The unconscious dorsal stream aids in guiding movements visually, whereas the conscious ventral stream aids in visual object perception.

9-3 Location in the Visual World

At each step along the visual pathways, neuronal activities are distinctly different; it is the summed neural activity in all regions that produces our visual experience. Each functional column in the cortical visual regions is about 0.5 mm in diameter and extends to the depth of the cortex. The visual system cortical columns are specialized for processes such as analyzing line orientation or comparing similar shapes as complex as faces.

9-4 Neuronal Activity

Neurons in the ventral stream are selective for aspects of shape. Those in the visual cortex are maximally responsive to lines of different orientations. Upstream, cells in the inferior temporal cortex are responsive to shapes, some abstract, and in other cases, to concrete forms as complex as hands or faces.

Cones in the retina are maximally responsive to different light wavelengths, roughly corresponding to colors we perceive as green, blue, and red. At the next level, RGCs' center-surround organization facilitates their opponent-process function: the cells are excited by one hue and inhibited by another, as for example, red versus green; blue versus yellow.

Color-sensitive cells in V1, located in the blobs, also have opponent-process properties. Cells in region V4 respond to colors that we perceive rather than to particular visible light wavelengths. Both the luminance and the color of nearby objects influence the colors we perceive.

9-5 The Visual Brain in Action

Upon entering the brain, information from the left and right visual fields proceeds on the optic nerve to the brain's right and to its left sides, respectively. As a result of these contralateral connections, damage to the visual areas on one side of the brain results in visual disturbance in both eyes, because half of each retina's visual field is represented on each side of the brain.

Specific visual functions are localized to different brain regions, so local damage results in the loss of a particular function. Damage to region V4 produces a loss of color constancy, for example; damage to regions in the parietal cortex inhibits the contralateral hand's grasping ability.

As summarized in the illustration, the visual streams perform distinct functions: (A) object recognition (the *what*) in the ventral stream and (B) visual action (the *how*) in the dorsal stream. We are largely unconscious of the dorsal stream's ongoing online analyses, that allow us to make accurate movements in relation to objects.

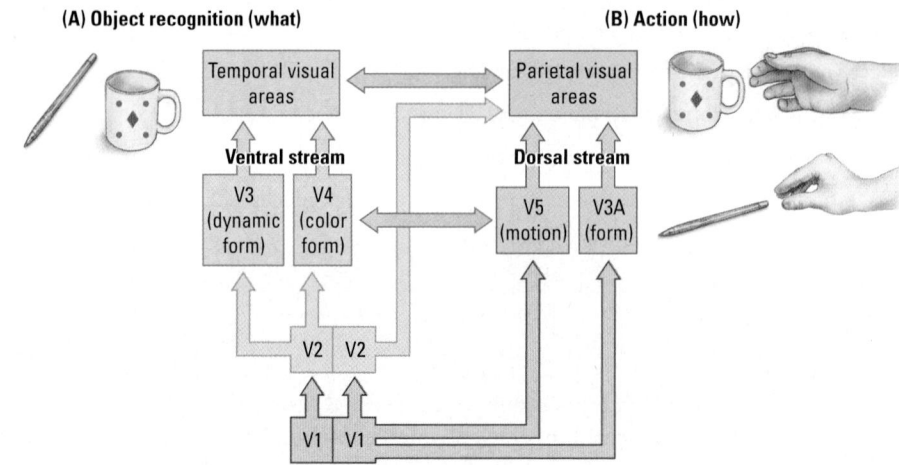

(A) The ventral stream begins in V1 and flows through V2 to V3 and V4, then into the temporal visual areas. (B) The dorsal stream begins in V1 and flows through V5 and V3A to the posterior parietal visual areas. Double-headed arrows show information flow between the two streams—between recognition and action, perception and behavior.

KEY TERMS

auditory flow, p. 286

blind spot, p. 293

blob, p. 299

color constancy, p. 313

cone, p. 293

cortical column, p. 299

dorsal stream, p. 297

extrastriate (secondary visual) cortex (V2–V5), p. 299

facial agnosia, p. 301

fovea, p. 293

geniculostriate system, p. 297

homonymous hemianopia, p. 315

luminance contrast, p. 306

magnocellular (M) cell, p. 295

ocular dominance column, p. 309

opponent process, p. 313

optic ataxia, p. 316

optic chiasm, p. 295

optic flow, p. 286

parvocellular (P) cell, p. 295

perception, p. 289

photoreceptor, p. 289

primary visual cortex (V1), p. 299

quadrantanopia, p. 315

receptive field, p. 286

retina, p. 289

retinal ganglion cell (RGC), p. 295

retinohypothalamic tract, p. 297

rod, p. 293

scotoma, p. 315

sensation, p. 289

striate cortex, p. 297

tectopulvinar system, p. 297

topographic map, p. 289

trichromatic theory, p. 311

ventral stream, p. 297

visual field, p. 301

visual-form agnosia, p. 315

⬆ Visit 🅜 LaunchPad to access the e-Book, videos, 🅜 LearningCurve adaptive quizzing, flashcards, and more.

www.macmillanhighered.com/launchpad/kolb5e

How Do We Hear, Speak, and Make Music?

Streeter

Katherine Streeter

Evolution of Language and Music

The finding that modern humans (*Homo sapiens*) made music early on implies that music has been important in our evolution. Behavioral scientists have shown that music plays as central a role in our social and emotional lives as language does.

Thomas Geissmann (2001) noted that among most of the 26 species of singing primates, males and females sing duets. All singing primates are monogamous, suggesting that singing may somehow relate to sexual behaviors. Music may also play a role in primates' parenting behaviors.

The human brain is specialized for analyzing certain aspects of music in the right temporal lobe, which complements the left temporal lobe specialization for analyzing aspects of speech. Did music and language evolve simultaneously in our species? Possibly.

Neanderthals (*Homo neanderthalensis*) have long fascinated researchers. The species originated about 300,000 years ago and disappeared about 30,000 years ago. During some of that time they coexisted in Europe and the Middle East with *Homo sapiens,* whom they resembled in many ways because they shared a common ancestor. In some locales, the two species may have shared resources and tools.

Researchers long hypothesized that Neanderthal culture was significantly less developed than that of early modern humans. Yet Neanderthals had a brain as large as or larger than that of *Homo sapiens,* with whom they appear to have shared many cultural similarities. Neanderthals buried their dead with artifacts, which implies that they held spiritual beliefs, but we have no conclusive evidence that they made visual art. In contrast, *Homo sapiens* began painting on cave walls some 30,000 years ago, near the end of the Neanderthal era.

Anatomically, some skeletal analyses of the larynx suggest that Neanderthals' articulated language ability was less well developed than their *Homo sapiens* contemporaries'. What about music? It appears that Neanderthals did make music.

Shown in the accompanying photo is the bone flute found in 1995 by Ivan Turk, a paleontologist at the Slovenian Academy of Sciences in Ljubljana. Turk was excavating a cave in northern Slovenia used by Neanderthals long ago as a hunting camp. Buried in the cave among a cache of stone tools was the leg bone of a young bear that looked as if it had been fashioned into a flute.

The bone has holes aligned along one side that could not have been made by gnawing animals. Rather, the holes' spacing resembles positions found on a modern flute. But the bone flute is at least 43,000 years old—perhaps as old as 82,000 years. All the evidence suggests that Neanderthals, not modern humans, made the instrument.

Bob Fink, a musicologist, analyzed the flute's musical qualities. He found that an eight-note scale similar to a do-re-mi scale could be played on the flute, but compared with the scale most familiar in European music, one note was slightly off. That blue note, a staple of jazz, is standard in musical scales throughout Africa and India today.

The similarity between Neanderthal and contemporary musical scales encourages us to speculate about the brain that conceived this ancient flute. Like modern humans, Neanderthals probably had complementary hemispheric specialization for language and music. This may have contributed to the two species cohabitating and to interbreeding that led to 1 to 4 percent of alleles being of Neanderthal origin in humans whose lineages, in the last 30,000 years, come from outside of Africa.

Archive of the Institute of Archaeology ZRC SAZU, photo: Marko Zaplatil

Ancient Bone Flute The hole alignment in this piece of bear femur, found in a cave in northern Slovenia, suggests that Neanderthals made a flute from the bone and made music with the flute.

Language is independent of making or perceiving sounds, as sign language demonstrates. In this chapter, however, language refers to speech.

Language and music are universal among humans. The oral language of every known culture follows similar basic structural rules, and people in all cultures make and enjoy music. Music and language allow us both to organize and to interact socially. Like music, language probably improves parenting. People who can communicate their intentions to one another and to their children presumably are better parents.

Humans' capacities for language and music are linked conceptually because both are based on sound. Understanding how and why we engage in speech and music is this chapter's goal. We first examine the physical energy that we perceive as sound, then how the human ear and nervous system detect and interpret sound. We next examine the complementary neuroanatomy of human language and music processing. Finally, we investigate how two other species, birds and bats, interpret and utilize auditory stimuli.

(10-1) Sound Waves: Stimulus for Audition

What we experience as sound is the brain's construct, as is what we see. Without a brain, sound and sight do not exist. When you strike a tuning fork, the energy of its vibrating prongs displaces adjacent air molecules. **Figure 10-1** shows how, as one prong moves to the left, air molecules to the left compress (grow more dense) and air molecules to the right become more rarefied (grow less dense). The opposite happens when the prong moves to the right. The undulating energy generated by this displacement of molecules causes *compression waves* of changing air pressure to emanate from the fork. These **sound waves** move through compressible media—air, water, ground—but not through the vacuum of outer space.

The top graph in **Figure 10-2** represents waves of changing air pressure emanating from a tuning fork by plotting air molecule density against time at a single point. The bottom graph shows how the energy from the right-hand prong of the tuning fork moves to make the air pressure changes associated with a single cycle. A *cycle* is one complete peak and valley on the graph—the change from one maximum or minimum air pressure level of the sound wave to the next maximum or minimum level, respectively.

Physical Properties of Sound Waves

Light is electromagnetic energy we see; sound is mechanical energy we hear. Sound wave energy has three physical attributes—*frequency, amplitude,* and *complexity*—produced by the displacement of air molecules and summarized in **Figure 10-3.** The auditory system analyzes each property separately, just as the visual system analyzes color and form separately.

Sound Wave Frequency

Sound waves in air travel at a fixed speed of 1100 feet (343 meters) per second and more than four times faster in water, but sound energy varies in wavelength. **Frequency** is the number of cycles a wave completes in a given amount of time. Sound wave frequencies are measured in cycles per second, called **hertz** (Hz), for the German physicist Heinrich Rudolph Hertz.

One hertz is 1 cycle per second, 50 hertz is 50 cycles per second, 6000 hertz is 6000 cycles per second, and so on. Sounds we perceive as low pitched have fewer wave frequencies

The nervous system produces movement within a perceptual world the brain constructs.

sound wave Mechanical displacement of molecules caused by changing pressure that possesses the physical properties of frequency, amplitude, and complexity. Also *compression wave.*

frequency Number of cycles a wave completes in a given time.

hertz (Hz) Measure of sound wave frequency (repetition rate); 1 hertz equals 1 cycle per second.

Section 9-4 explains how we see shapes and colors.

FIGURE 10-1 How a Tuning Fork Produces Sound Waves **(A)** The fork is still, and air molecules are distributed randomly. **(B)** When struck, the fork's right arm moves to the left; air on the leading edge compresses and air on the trailing edge rarefies. **(C)** As the arm rebounds, air to the right compresses and air to the left rarefies.

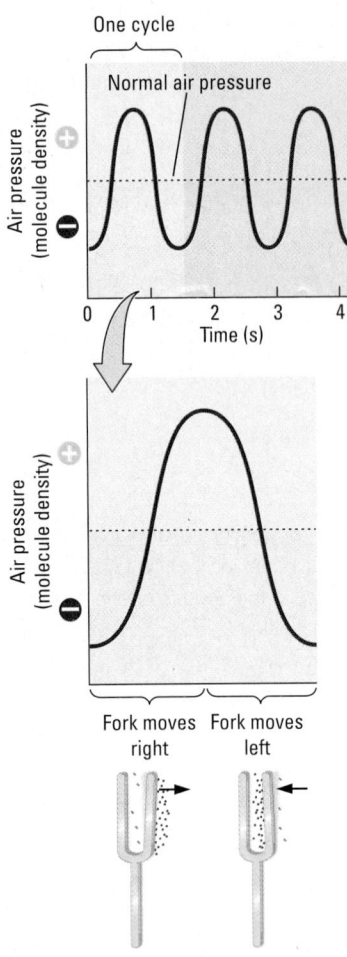

FIGURE 10-2 Visualizing a Sound Wave Air molecule density plotted against time at a single point relative to the tuning fork's right prong. Physicists call the resulting cyclical waves *sine waves*.

Section 8-4 suggests a critical period in brain development most sensitive to musical training. Figure 15-11 shows enhanced connectivity in people with perfect pitch.

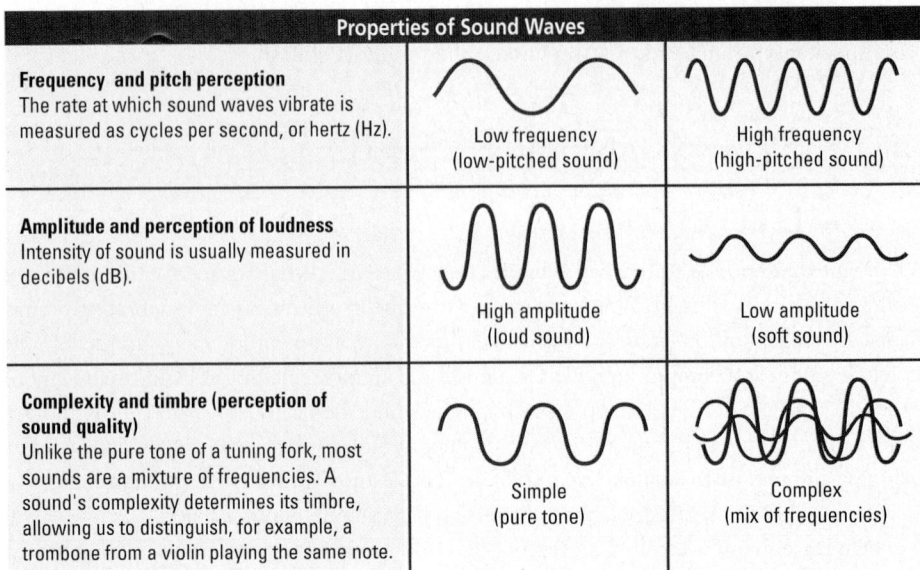

Properties of Sound Waves		
Frequency and pitch perception The rate at which sound waves vibrate is measured as cycles per second, or hertz (Hz).	Low frequency (low-pitched sound)	High frequency (high-pitched sound)
Amplitude and perception of loudness Intensity of sound is usually measured in decibels (dB).	High amplitude (loud sound)	Low amplitude (soft sound)
Complexity and timbre (perception of sound quality) Unlike the pure tone of a tuning fork, most sounds are a mixture of frequencies. A sound's complexity determines its timbre, allowing us to distinguish, for example, a trombone from a violin playing the same note.	Simple (pure tone)	Complex (mix of frequencies)

FIGURE 10-3 Physical Dimensions of Sound Waves The frequency, amplitude, and complexity of sound wave sensations correspond to the perceptual dimensions of pitch, loudness, and timbre.

(fewer cycles per second), whereas sounds that we perceive as high pitched have more wave frequencies (many cycles per second), as shown in the top panel of Figure 10-3.

Just as we can perceive light only at visible wavelengths, we can perceive sound waves only in the limited range of frequencies plotted in **Figure 10-4**. Healthy young adult humans' hearing range is from about 20 to 20,000 hertz. Many animals communicate with sound: their auditory system is designed to interpret their species-typical sounds. After all, what is the point in making complicated songs or calls if other members of your species cannot hear and interpret them?

The range of sound wave frequencies heard by different species varies extensively. Some (such as frogs and birds) have a rather narrow hearing range; others (such as dogs, whales, and humans) have a broad range. Some species use extremely high frequencies (bats are off the scale in Figure 10-4); others (fish, for example) use the low range.

The auditory systems of whales and dolphins are responsive to a remarkably wide range of sound waves. Characteristics at the extremes of these frequencies allow marine mammals to use them in different ways. Very low frequency sound waves travel long distances in water. Whales produce them for underwater communication over hundreds of miles. High-frequency sound waves echo and form the basis of sonar. Dolphins produce them in bursts, listening for the echoes that bounce back from objects. The echoes help the dolphins to navigate and locate prey.

Differences in sound wave frequencies become differences in pitch when heard. Each note in a musical scale must have a different frequency, because each has a different pitch. Middle C on the piano, for instance, has a frequency of 264 hertz.

Most people can discriminate between one musical note and another, but some can actually name any note they hear (A, B flat, C sharp, and so forth). This *perfect* (or *absolute*) *pitch* runs in families, suggesting a genetic influence. On the side of experience, most people who develop perfect pitch also receive musical training in matching pitch to note from an early age.

Sound Wave Amplitude

Sound waves vary not only in frequency, which causes differences in perceived pitch, but also in **amplitude** (strength), which causes differences in perceived *intensity,* or *loudness.* If you hit a tuning fork lightly, it produces a tone with a frequency of, say, 264 hertz (middle C).

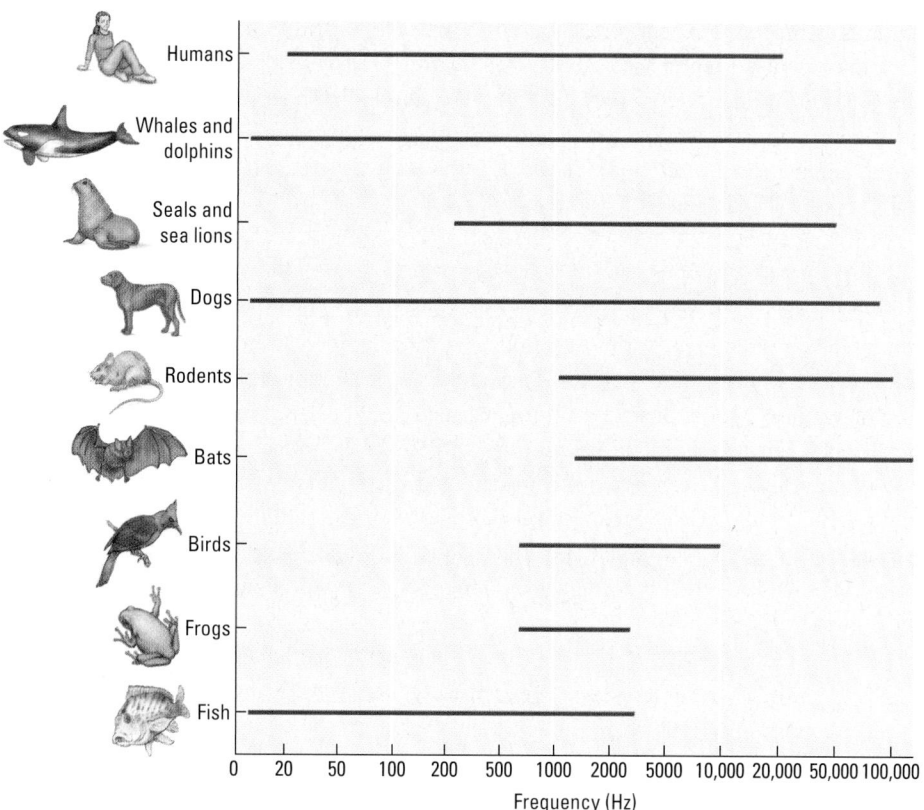

FIGURE 10-4 Hearing Ranges among Animals Frogs and birds hear a relatively narrow range of frequencies; whales' and dolphins' ranges are extensive, as are dogs'. Humans' hearing range is broad, yet we do not perceive many sound frequencies that other animals can both make and hear.

If you hit it harder, the frequency remains 264 hertz, but you also transfer more energy into the vibrating prong, increasing its amplitude.

The fork now moves farther left and right but at the same frequency. Increased air molecule compression intensifies the energy in a sound wave, which amps the sound—makes it louder. Differences in amplitude are graphed by increasing the height of a sound wave, as shown in the middle panel of Figure 10-3.

Sound wave amplitude is usually measured in **decibels (dB)**, the strength of a sound relative to the threshold of human hearing as a standard, pegged at 0 decibels **(Figure 10-5)**. Typical speech sounds, for example, measure about 40 decibels. Sounds that register more than about 70 dB we perceive as loud; those of less than about 20 dB we perceive as soft, or quiet.

The human nervous system evolved to be sensitive to soft sounds and so is actually blown away by extremely loud ones. People regularly damage their hearing through exposure to very loud sounds (such as rifle fire at close range) or even by prolonged exposure to sounds that are only relatively loud (such as at a live concert). Prolonged exposure to sounds louder than 100 decibels is likely to damage our hearing.

Rock bands, among others, routinely play music that registers higher than 120 decibels and sometimes as high as 135 decibels. Drake-Lee (1992) found that rock musicians had a significant loss of sensitivity to sound waves, especially at about 6000 hertz. After a typical 90-minute concert, this loss was temporarily far worse—as much as a 40-fold increase in

amplitude Stimulus intensity; in audition, roughly equivalent to loudness, graphed by the increasing height of a sound wave.

decibel (dB) Measure of the relative physical intensity of sounds.

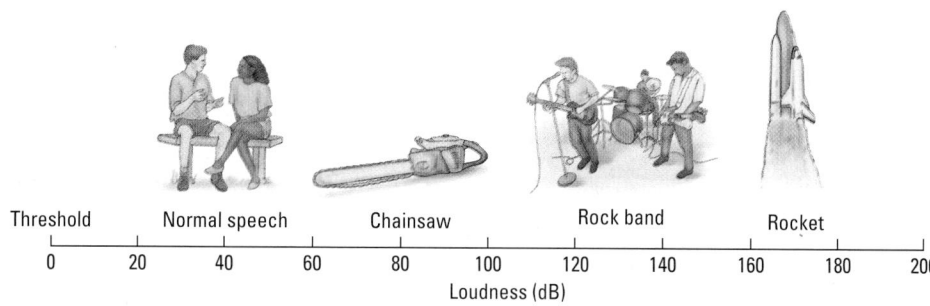

FIGURE 10-5 Sound Intensity

sound pressure was needed to reach a musician's hearing threshold. But rock concerts are not the only music venue that can damage hearing. Teie (1998) reports that symphony orchestras also produce dangerously high sound levels and that hearing loss is common among symphony musicians. Similarly, prolonged listening through headphones or earbuds to music played loudly on personal music players is responsible for significant hearing loss in many young people (Daniel, 2007).

Sound Wave Complexity

Sounds with a single frequency wave are *pure tones,* much like those that emanate from a tuning fork or pitch pipe, but most sounds mix wave frequencies together in combinations called *complex tones* (see Figure 10-3, bottom panel). To better understand the blended nature of a complex tone, picture a clarinetist, such as Don Byron in **Figure 10-6,** playing a steady note. The upper graph in Figure 10-6 represents the sound wave a clarinet produces.

The waveform pattern is more complex than the simple, regular waves visualized in Figures 10-2 or 10-3. Even when a musician plays a single note, the instrument is making a complex tone. Using a mathematical technique known as Fourier analysis, we can break down this complex tone into its many component pure tones, the numbered waves traced at the bottom of Figure 10-6.

FIGURE 10-6 Breaking Down a Complex Tone The waveform of a single note (top) from Don Byron's clarinet and the simple sound waves— the fundamental frequency (middle) and overtones (bottom)—that make up the complex tone.

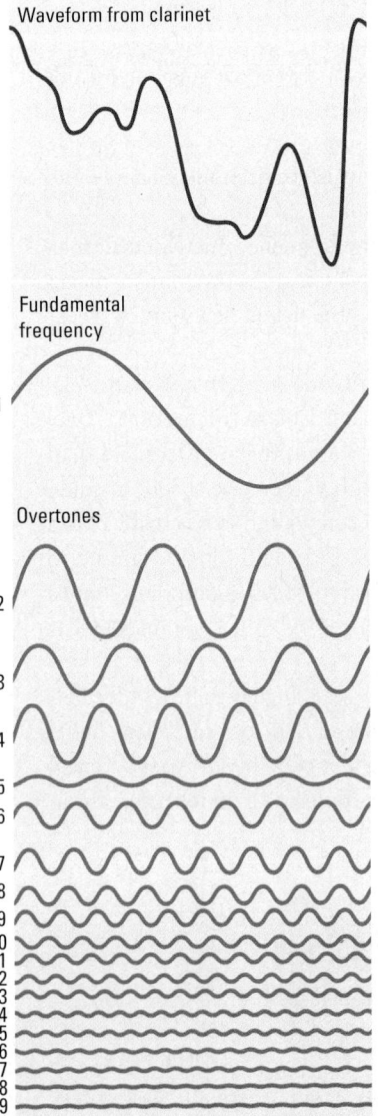

Waveform from clarinet

Fundamental frequency

Simple waves that make up sound of clarinet

Overtones

1
2
3
4
5
6
7
8
9
10
11
12
13
14
15
16
17
18
19
20

Craig Lovell/Eagle Visions Photography/Alamy

The *fundamental frequency* (wave 1) is the rate at which the complex waveform pattern repeats. Waves 2 through 20 are *overtones,* a set of higher-frequency sound waves that vibrate at whole-number (integer) multiples of the fundamental frequency. Different musical instruments sound unique because they produce overtones of different amplitudes. Among the clarinet's overtones, represented by the heights of the blue waves in Figure 10-6, wave 5 is low amplitude, whereas wave 2 is high amplitude.

As primary colors blend into near-infinite variety, so pure tones blend into complex tones. Complex tones emanate from musical instruments, from the human voice, from birdsong, and from machines or repetitive mechanisms that make rhythmic buzzing or humming sounds. A key feature of complex tones, besides being made up of two or more pure tones, is periodicity: the fundamental frequency repeats at regular intervals. Sounds that are aperiodic, or random, we call *noise.*

Perception of Sound

Visualize what happens when you toss a pebble into a pond. Waves of water emanate from the point where the pebble enters the water. These waves produce no audible sound. But if your skin were able to convert the water wave energy (sensation) into neural activity that stimulated your auditory system, you would hear the waves when you placed your hand in the rippling water (perception). When you removed your hand, the sound would stop.

The pebble hitting the water is much like a tree falling to the ground, and the waves that emanate from the pebble's entry point are like the air pressure waves that emanate from the place where the tree strikes the ground. The frequency of the waves determines the pitch of the sound heard by the brain, whereas the height (amplitude) of the waves determines the sound's loudness.

Our sensitivity to sound waves is extraordinary. At the threshold of human hearing, we can detect the displacement of air molecules of about 10 picometers. We are rarely in an environment where we can detect such a small air pressure change: there is usually too much background noise. A quiet, rural setting is probably as close as we ever get to an environment suitable for testing the acuteness of our hearing. The next time you visit the countryside, take note of the sounds you can hear. If there is no sound competition, you can often hear a single car engine miles away.

In addition to detecting minute changes in air pressure, the auditory system is also adept at simultaneously perceiving different sounds. As you read this chapter, you can differentiate all sorts of sounds around you—traffic on the street, people talking next door, your air conditioner humming, footsteps in the hall. As you listen to music, you detect the sounds of different instruments and voices.

You can perceive more than one sound simultaneously because each frequency of change in air pressure (each different sound wave) stimulates different neurons in your auditory system. Sound perception is only the beginning of your auditory experience. Your brain interprets sounds to obtain information about events in your environment, and it analyzes a sound's meaning. Your use of sound to communicate with other people through both language and music clearly illustrate these processes.

1 picometer = one-trillionth of a meter

Properties of Language and Music as Sounds

Language and music differ from other auditory sensations in fundamental ways. Both convey meaning and evoke emotion. Analyzing meaning in sound is a considerably more complex behavior than simply detecting a sound and identifying it. The brain has evolved systems that analyze sounds for meaning, speech in the left temporal lobe and music in the right.

Infants are receptive to speech and musical cues before they have any obvious utility, which suggests both the innate presence of these skills and the effects of prenatal experiences. Humans have an amazing capacity for learning and remembering linguistic and musical information. We are capable of learning a vocabulary of tens of thousands of words, often in many languages, and a capacity for recognizing thousands of songs.

Language facilitates communication. We can organize our complex perceptual worlds by categorizing information with words. We can tell others what we think and know and imagine. Imagine the efficiency that gestures and language added to the cooperative food hunting and gathering behaviors of early humans.

All these benefits of language seem obvious, but the benefits of music may seem less straightforward. In fact, music helps us to regulate our own emotions and to affect the emotions of others. After all, when do people most commonly make music? We sing and play music to communicate with infants and put children to sleep. We play music to enhance social interactions and gatherings and romance. We use music to bolster group identification—school songs and national anthems are examples. Music as we know it is unique to humans. Studies of nonhumans provide little evidence for preferences for human music over other sounds.

Another characteristic that distinguishes speech and musical sounds from other auditory inputs is their delivery speed. Nonspeech and nonmusical noise produced at a rate of about five segments per second is perceived as a buzz. (A sound segment is a distinct unit of sound.) Normal speed for speech is on the order of 8 to 10 segments per second, and we are capable of understanding speech at nearly 30 segments per second. Speech perception at these higher rates is astounding, because the input speed far exceeds the auditory system's ability to transmit all the speech segments as separate pieces of information.

Elvis Presley's memory for lyrics suits his legend: while serving in the U.S. Army, he wagered all comers that he could sing any song they named. Elvis never lost a bet.

Loomis Dean/Time Life Pictures/Getty Images

Properties of Language

Experience listening to a particular language helps the brain to analyze rapid speech, which is one reason people who are speaking languages unfamiliar to you often seem to be talking incredibly fast. Your brain does not know where the foreign words end and begin, so they seem to run together in a rapid-fire stream.

A unique characteristic of our perception of speech sounds is our tendency to hear variations of a sound as if they were identical, even though the sound varies considerably from one context to another. For instance, the English letter *d* is pronounced differently in the words *deep*, *deck*, and *duke*, yet a listener perceives the pronunciations to be the same *d* sound.

The auditory system must therefore have a mechanism for categorizing sounds as being the same despite small differences in pronunciation. Experience must affect this mechanism, because different languages categorize speech sounds differently. A major obstacle to mastering a foreign language after age 10 is the difficulty of learning which sound categories are treated as equivalent.

Properties of Music

As with other sounds, the subjective properties that people perceive in musical sounds differ from one another. One subjective property is *loudness*, the magnitude of the sound as judged by a person. Loudness is related to the amplitude of a sound wave measured in decibels, but loudness is also subjective. What is very loud music for one person may be only moderately loud for another, whereas music that seems soft to one listener may not seem at all soft to someone else. Your perception of loudness also changes with context. After you've slowed down from driving fast on a highway, for example, your car's music system seems louder. The reduction in road noise alters your perception of the music's loudness.

Another subjective property of musical sounds is *pitch*, the position of each tone on a musical scale as judged by the listener. Although pitch is clearly related to sound wave frequency, there is more to it than that. Consider the note middle C as played on a piano. This note can be described as a pattern of sound frequencies, as is the clarinet note in Figure 10-6.

Like the note played on the piano, any musical note is defined by its fundamental frequency—the lowest frequency of the sound wave pattern, or the rate at which the overall pattern repeats. For middle C, the fundamental frequency is 264 Hertz, and the sound waves for notes C, E, and G, as measured by a spectrograph, are shown in **Figure 10-7**. Notice that by convention sound wave spectrographs are measured in kilohertz (kHz), or thousands of hertz. Thus, if we look at the fundamental frequency for middle C, it is the first large wave on the left, at 0.264 kilohertz. The fundamental frequencies for E and G are 0.330 and 0.392 kilohertz, respectively.

An important feature of the human brain's analysis of music is that middle C is perceived as being the same note whether it is played on a piano or on a guitar, even though the sounds of these instruments differ widely. The right temporal lobe extracts pitch from sound, whether the sound is speech or music. In speech, pitch contributes to the perceived melodic tone of a voice, or **prosody**.

A final property of musical sound is *quality*, or *timbre*, the perceived characteristics that distinguish a particular sound from all others of similar pitch and loudness. We can easily distinguish the timbre of a violin from that of a trombone, even if both instruments are playing the same note at the same loudness. The quality of their sounds differs.

Auditory constancy is reminiscent of the visual system's capacity for object constancy; see Section 9-4.

FIGURE 10-7 Fundamental Frequencies of Piano Notes Waveforms of the notes C, E, and G as played on a piano and recorded on a spectrograph. The first wave in each graph is the fundamental frequency; the secondary waves are the overtones.

Courtesy Drew Rendall, University of New Brunswick

(10-1) REVIEW

Sound Waves: Stimulus for Audition

Before you continue, check your understanding.

1. The physical stimulus for audition, produced by changes in _____, is a form of mechanical energy converted in the ear to neural activity.

2. Sound waves have three physical attributes: _____, _____, and _____.

3. Four properties of musical sounds are _____, _____, _____, and _____.

4. Sound is processed in the _____ lobes.

5. What distinguishes speech and musical sounds from other auditory inputs?

Answers appear at the back of the book.

For additional study tools, visit 🅜 LaunchPad:
www.macmillanhighered.com/launchpad/kolb5e

10-2 Functional Anatomy of the Auditory System

To understand how the nervous system analyzes sound waves, we begin by tracing the pathway sound energy takes to and through the brain. The ear collects sound waves from the surrounding air and converts their mechanical energy to electrochemical neural energy, which begins a long route through the brainstem to the auditory cortex.

Before we can trace the journey from ear to cortex, we must ask what the auditory system is designed to do. Because sound waves have the properties frequency, amplitude, and complexity, we can predict that the auditory system is structured to decode these properties. Most animals can tell where a sound comes from, so some mechanism must locate sound waves in space. Finally, many animals, including humans, not only analyze sounds for meaning but also make sounds. Because the sounds they produce are often the same as the ones they hear, we can infer that the neural systems for sound production and analysis must be closely related.

In humans, the evolution of sound-processing systems for both language and music was accompanied by enhancement of specialized cortical regions, especially in the temporal lobes. In fact, a major difference between the human and the monkey cortex is a marked expansion of auditory areas in humans.

Monkey

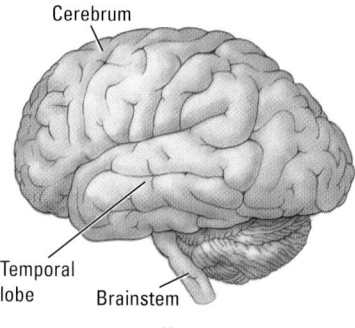

Human

Structure of the Ear

The ear is a biological masterpiece in three acts: outer ear, middle ear, and inner ear, all illustrated in **Figure 10-8.**

Processing Sound Waves

Both the *pinna,* the funnel-like external structure of the outer ear, and the external ear canal, which extends a short distance from the pinna inside the head, are made of cartilage and flesh. The pinna is designed to catch sound waves in the surrounding environment and deflect them into the external ear canal. To enhance sound detection when we want to hear better, we often cup a hand around the pinna.

Because it narrows from the pinna, the external canal amplifies sound waves and directs them to the *eardrum* at its inner end. When sound waves strike the eardrum, it vibrates, the rate of vibration varying with the frequency of the waves. On the inner side of the eardrum, as depicted in Figure 10-8, is the middle ear, an air-filled chamber that contains the three smallest bones in the human body, connected in a series.

These three **ossicles** are called the *hammer,* the *anvil,* and the *stirrup* because of their distinctive shapes. The ossicles attach the eardrum to the *oval window,* an opening in the bony casing of the **cochlea,** the inner ear structure containing the auditory receptor cells.

prosody Melodic tone of the speaking voice.

ossicle Bone of the middle ear; includes malleus (hammer), incus (anvil), and stapes (stirrup).

cochlea Inner ear structure containing the auditory receptor cells.

FIGURE 10-8 Anatomy of the Human Ear Sound waves gathered into the outer ear are transduced from air pressure into mechanical energy in the middle ear ossicles then into electrochemical activity in the inner ear cochlea. Inner hair cells embedded in the basilar membrane (the organ of Corti) are tipped by cilia. Movements of the basilar and tectorial membranes displace the cilia, leading to changes in the inner hair cells' membrane potentials and resultant activity of auditory bipolar neurons.

Cochlea actually means *snail shell* in Latin.

These receptor cells and the cells that support them are collectively called the *organ of Corti,* shown in detail in Figure 10-8.

When sound waves vibrate the eardrum, the vibrations are transmitted to the ossicles. The leverlike action of the ossicles amplifies the vibrations and conveys them to the membrane that covers the cochlea's oval window. As Figure 10-8 shows, the cochlea coils around itself and looks a bit like a snail shell. Inside its bony exterior, the cochlea is hollow, as the cross-sectional drawing reveals.

The hollow cochlear compartments are filled with lymphatic fluid, and floating in its midst is the thin **basilar membrane.** Embedded in a part of the basilar membrane are outer and inner **hair cells.** At the tip of each hair cell are several filaments called *cilia,* and the cilia of the outer hair cells are embedded in the overlying tectorial membrane. The inner hair cells loosely contact this *tectorial membrane.*

Pressure from the stirrup on the oval window makes the cochlear fluid move because a second membranous window in the cochlea (the *round window*) bulges outward as the stirrup presses inward on the oval window. In a chain reaction, the waves traveling through the cochlear fluid bend the basilar and tectorial membranes, and the bending membranes stimulate the cilia at the tips of the outer and inner hair cells.

Transducing Sound Waves into Neural Impulses

How does the conversion of sound waves into neural activity code the various properties of sound that we perceive? In the late 1800s, the German physiologist Hermann von Helmholtz

(A) Uncoiling of cochlea

Basilar membrane

20,000   4000   1000   100
Hertz

(B) Uncoiled cochlea

Cochlear base

| A narrow, thick base is tuned for high frequencies. |

| A wide, thin apex is tuned for low frequencies. |

Basilar membrane

| Sound waves at medium frequencies cause peak bending of the basilar membrane at this point. |

FIGURE 10-9 Anatomy of the Cochlea **(A)** The basilar membrane is maximally responsive to frequencies mapped as the cochlea uncoils. **(B)** Sound waves of different frequencies produce maximal displacement of the basilar membrane (shown uncoiled) at different locations.

proposed that sound waves of different frequencies cause different parts of the basilar membrane to resonate. Von Helmholtz was partly correct. Actually, all parts of the basilar membrane bend in response to incoming waves of any frequency. The key is where the peak displacement takes place (**Figure 10-9**).

This solution to the coding puzzle was determined in 1960, when George von Békésy observed the basilar membrane directly. He saw a traveling wave moving along the membrane all the way from the oval window to the membrane's apex. The coiled cochlea in Figure 10-9A maps the frequencies to which each part of the basilar membrane is most responsive. When the oval window vibrates in response to the vibrations of the ossicles, shown beside the uncoiled membrane in Figure 10-9B, it generates waves that travel through the cochlear fluid. Békésy placed little grains of silver along the basilar membrane and watched them jump in different places to different frequencies of incoming waves. Higher wave frequencies caused maximum peaks of displacement near the base of the basilar membrane; lower wave frequencies caused maximum displacement peaks near the membrane's apex.

As a rough analogy, consider what happens when you shake a rope. If you shake it quickly, the waves in the rope are small and short and the peak of activity remains close to the base—the hand holding the rope. But if you shake the rope slowly, with a broader movement, the longer waves reach their peak farther along the rope—toward the apex. The key point is that, although both rapid and slow shakes produce movement along the rope's entire length, the point of maximum displacement depends on whether the wave movements are rapid or slow.

This same response pattern holds for the basilar membrane and sound wave frequency. All sound waves cause some displacement along the entire length of the membrane, but the amount of displacement at any point varies with the sound wave's frequency. In the human cochlea, shown uncoiling in Figure 10-9A, the basilar membrane near the oval window is maximally affected by frequencies as high as about 20,000 hertz, the upper limit of our hearing range. The most effective frequencies at the membrane's apex register less than 100 hertz, closer to our lower limit of about 20 Hz (see Figure 10-4).

Intermediate frequencies maximally displace points on the basilar membrane between its ends, as shown in Figure 10-9B. When a wave of a certain frequency travels down the basilar membrane, hair cells at the point of peak displacement are stimulated, resulting in a maximal neural response in those cells. An incoming signal composed of many frequencies causes several points along the basilar membrane to vibrate and excites hair cells at all these points.

Not surprisingly, the basilar membrane is much more sensitive to changes in frequency than is the rope in our analogy, because the basilar membrane varies in thickness along its entire length. It is narrow and thick at the base, near the oval window, and wider and thinner at its tightly coiled apex. The combination of varying width and thickness enhances the effect of small frequency differences. As a result, the cochlear receptors can code small differences in sound wave frequency as neural impulses.

basilar membrane Receptor surface in the cochlea that transduces sound waves into neural activity.

hair cell Specialized neurons in the cochlea tipped by cilia; when stimulated by waves in the cochlear fluid, the cilia bend and generate graded potentials in inner hair cells, the auditory receptor cells.

Auditory Receptors

Two kinds of hair cells transform sound waves into neural activity. Figure 10-8 (bottom left) shows the anatomy of the inner hair cells; **Figure 10-10** illustrates how sound waves stimulate them. A young person's cochlea has about 12,000 outer and 3500 inner hair cells. The numbers fall off with age. Only the inner hair cells act as auditory receptors, and their numbers are small considering how many different sounds we can hear. As diagrammed in Figure 10-10, both outer and inner hair cells are anchored in the basilar membrane. The tips of the cilia of outer hair cells are attached to the overlying tectorial membrane, but the cilia of the inner hair cells only loosely touch that membrane. Nevertheless, the movement of the basilar and tectorial membranes causes the cochlear fluid to flow past the cilia of the inner hair cells, bending them back and forth.

Animals with intact outer hair cells but no inner hair cells are effectively deaf. That is, they can perceive only very loud, low-frequency sounds via the somatosensory system. You may have experienced this feeling when a subwoofer or a passing truck caused vibrations in your chest. Inner hair cells can be destroyed by prolonged exposure to intense sound pressure waves, infections, diseases, or certain chemicals and drugs. Inner hair cells do not regenerate; thus once the inner hair cells have died hearing loss is permanent.

Outer hair cells function by sharpening the cochlea's resolving power, contracting or relaxing and thereby changing tectorial membrane stiffness. That's right: the outer hair cells have a motor function. While we typically think of sensory input preceding motor output, in fact, motor systems can influence sensory input. The pupil contracts or dilates to change the amount of light that falls on the retina, and the outer hair cells contract or relax to alter the physical stimulus detected by the inner hair cells.

How this outer hair cell function is controlled is puzzling. What stimulates these cells to contract or relax? The answer seems to be that through connections with axons in the auditory nerve, the outer hair cells send a message to the brainstem auditory areas and receive a reply that causes the cells to alter tension on the tectorial membrane. In this way, the brain helps the hair cells to construct an auditory world. The outer cells are also part of a mechanism that modulates auditory nerve firing, especially in response to intense sound pressure waves, and thus offers some protection against their damaging effects.

A final question remains: How does movement of the inner hair cell cilia alter neural activity? The neurons of the auditory nerve have a spontaneous baseline rate of firing action potentials, and this rate is changed by the amount of neurotransmitter the hair cells release. It turns out that movement of the cilia changes the inner hair cell's polarization and its rate of neurotransmitter release. Inner hair cells continuously leak calcium, and this leakage causes a small but steady amount of neurotransmitter release into the synapse. Movement of the cilia in one direction results in depolarization: calcium channels open and release more neurotransmitter onto the dendrites of the cells that form the auditory nerve, generating more nerve impulses. Movement of the cilia in the other direction hyperpolarizes the cell membrane and transmitter release decreases, thus decreasing activity in auditory neurons.

Inner hair cells are amazingly sensitive to the movement of their cilia. A movement sufficient to allow sound wave detection is only about 0.3 nm, about the diameter of a large atom! Such sensitivity helps to explain why our hearing is so incredibly sensitive. Clinical Focus 10-2, Otoacoustic Emissions, describes a consequence of cochlear function.

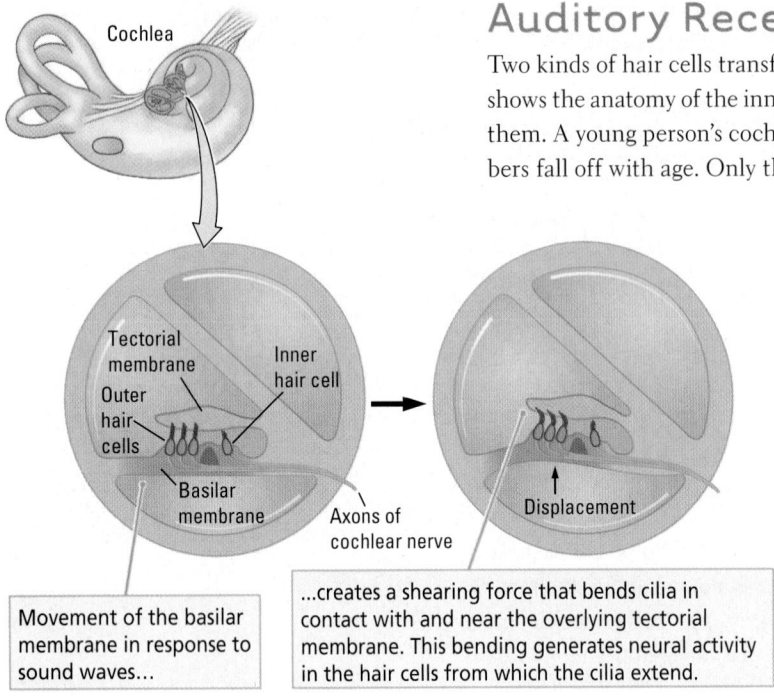

FIGURE 10-10 Transducing Waves into Neural Activity Movement of the basilar membrane produces a shearing force in the cochlear fluid that bends the cilia, leading to the opening or closing of calcium channels in the outer hair cells. An influx of calcium ions leads the inner hair cells to release neurotransmitter, stimulating increased action potentials in auditory neurons.

Section 4-2 reviews phases of the action potential and its propagation as a nerve impulse.

Labels in figure:
- Cochlea
- Tectorial membrane
- Inner hair cell
- Outer hair cells
- Basilar membrane
- Axons of cochlear nerve
- Displacement

Movement of the basilar membrane in response to sound waves...

...creates a shearing force that bends cilia in contact with and near the overlying tectorial membrane. This bending generates neural activity in the hair cells from which the cilia extend.

Otoacoustic Emissions

While the ear is exquisitely designed to amplify and convert sound waves into action potentials, it is unique among the sensory organs. The ear also *produces* the physical stimulus it is designed to detect! A healthy cochlea produces sound waves called **otoacoustic emissions.**

The cochlea acts as an amplifier. The outer hair cells amplify sound waves, providing an energy source that enhances cochlear sensitivity and frequency selectivity. Not all the energy the cochlea generates is dissipated within it. Some escapes toward the middle ear, which works efficiently in both directions, thus setting the eardrum in motion. The eardrum then acts as a loudspeaker, radiating sound waves—the otoacoustic emissions—out of the ear.

Sensitive microphones placed in the external ear canal can detect both types of otoacoustic emissions, spontaneous and evoked. As the name implies, *spontaneous otoacoustic emissions* occur without external stimulation. *Evoked otoacoustic emissions*, generated in response to sound waves, are important because evoked emissions are useful for assessing hearing impairments.

A simple, noninvasive test can detect and evaluate evoked otoacoustic emissions in newborns and children who are too young to take conventional hearing tests, as well as in people of any age. A small speaker and microphone are inserted into the ear. The speaker emits a click sound, and the microphone detects the resulting evoked emission without damaging the delicate workings of the inner ear. Missing or abnormal evoked emissions predict a hearing deficit. Many wealthy countries now sponsor universal programs to test the hearing of all newborn babies using otoacoustic emissions.

Otoacoustic emissions serve a useful purpose, but even so, they play no direct role in hearing. They are considered an *epiphenomenon*—a secondary phenomenon that occurs in parallel with or above (*epi*) a primary phenomenon.

Pathways to the Auditory Cortex

Inner hair cells in the organ of Corti synapse with neighboring bipolar cells, the axons that form the auditory (cochlear) nerve. The auditory nerve in turn forms part of the eighth cranial nerve, the auditory vestibular nerve that governs hearing and balance. Whereas ganglion cells in the eye receive inputs from many receptor cells, bipolar cells in the ear receive input from but a single inner hair cell receptor.

Cochlear-nerve axons enter the brainstem at the level of the medulla and synapse in the cochlear nucleus, which has ventral and dorsal subdivisions. Two nearby structures in the hindbrain (brainstem), the superior olive (a nucleus in the olivary complex) and the trapezoid body, receive connections from the cochlear nucleus, as charted in **Figure 10-11.** Projections from the cochlear nucleus connect with cells on the same side of the brain as well as with cells on the opposite side. This arrangement mixes the inputs from the two ears to form a single sound perception.

Both the cochlear nucleus and the superior olive send projections to the inferior colliculus in the dorsal midbrain. Two distinct pathways emerge from the inferior colliculus, coursing to the **medial geniculate nucleus** in the thalamus. The ventral region of the medial geniculate nucleus projects to the **primary auditory cortex (area A1),** whereas the dorsal region projects to the auditory cortical regions adjacent to area A1.

Analogous to the two distinct visual pathways—the ventral stream for object recognition and the dorsal stream for visual control of movement—a similar distinction exists in the auditory cortex (Romanski et al., 1999). Just as we can identify objects by their sound characteristics, we can direct our movements by the sound we hear. The role of sound in guiding movement is less familiar to sight-dominated people than it is to the blind. Nevertheless, the ability exists in us all. Imagine waking up in the dark and reaching to pick up a ringing telephone or to turn off an alarm clock. Your hand automatically forms the appropriate shape in response to just the sound you have heard. That sound is guiding your movements much as a visual image guides them.

Relatively little is known about the what–how auditory pathways in the cortex. One appears to continue through the temporal lobe, much like the ventral visual pathway, and plays a role in identifying auditory stimuli. A second auditory pathway apparently goes to the posterior parietal region, where it forms a dorsal route for the auditory control of movement. It appears as well that auditory information can gain access to visual cortex, as illustrated in Research Focus 10-3, Seeing with Sound.

Figure 2-27 lists and locates the cranial nerves, and in its caption is a mnemonic for remembering them in order.

otoacoustic emissions Spontaneous or evoked sound waves produced within the ear by the cochlea and escape from the ear.

medial geniculate nucleus Major thalamic region concerned with audition.

primary auditory cortex (area A1) Asymmetrical structures within Heschl's gyrus in the temporal lobes; receive input from the ventral region of the medial geniculate nucleus.

Figure 9-13 maps the visual pathways through the cortex.

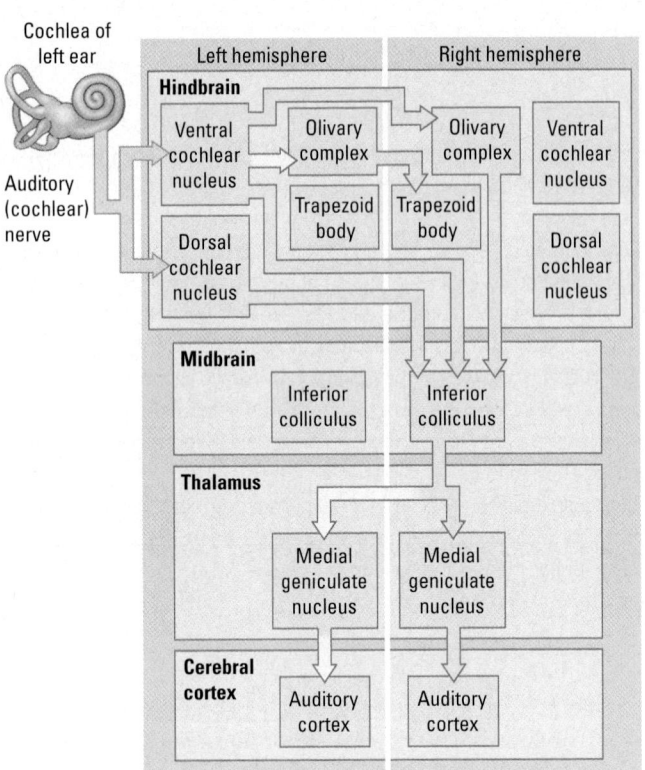

FIGURE 10-11 Auditory Pathways Auditory inputs cross to the hemisphere opposite the ear in the hindbrain and midbrain, then recross in the thalamus. In this way, the information from each ear reaches both hemispheres. Multiple nuclei process inputs en route to the auditory cortex, charted here for the left ear.

Auditory Cortex

In humans, the primary auditory cortex (A1) lies within Heschl's gyrus, surrounded by secondary cortical areas (A2), as shown in **Figure 10-12A**. The secondary cortex lying behind Heschl's gyrus is called the *planum temporale* (Latin for *temporal plane*).

In right-handed people, the planum temporale is larger on the left than it is on the right side of the brain, whereas Heschl's gyrus is larger on the right side than on the left. The cortex of the left planum forms a speech zone known as **Wernicke's area** (the posterior speech zone), whereas the cortex of the larger right-hemisphere Heschl's gyrus has a special role in analyzing music.

These hemispheric differences mean that the auditory cortex is anatomically and functionally asymmetrical. Although cerebral asymmetry is not unique to the auditory system, it is most obvious here because auditory analysis of speech takes place only in the left hemisphere of right-handed people. About 70 percent of left-handed people have the same anatomical asymmetries as right-handers, an indication that speech organization is not strictly related to hand preference. Language, including speech and other functions such as reading and writing, also is asymmetrical, although the right hemisphere also contributes to these broader functions.

The remaining 30 percent of left-handers fall into two distinct groups. The organization in about half of these people is opposite that of right-handers. The other half has some

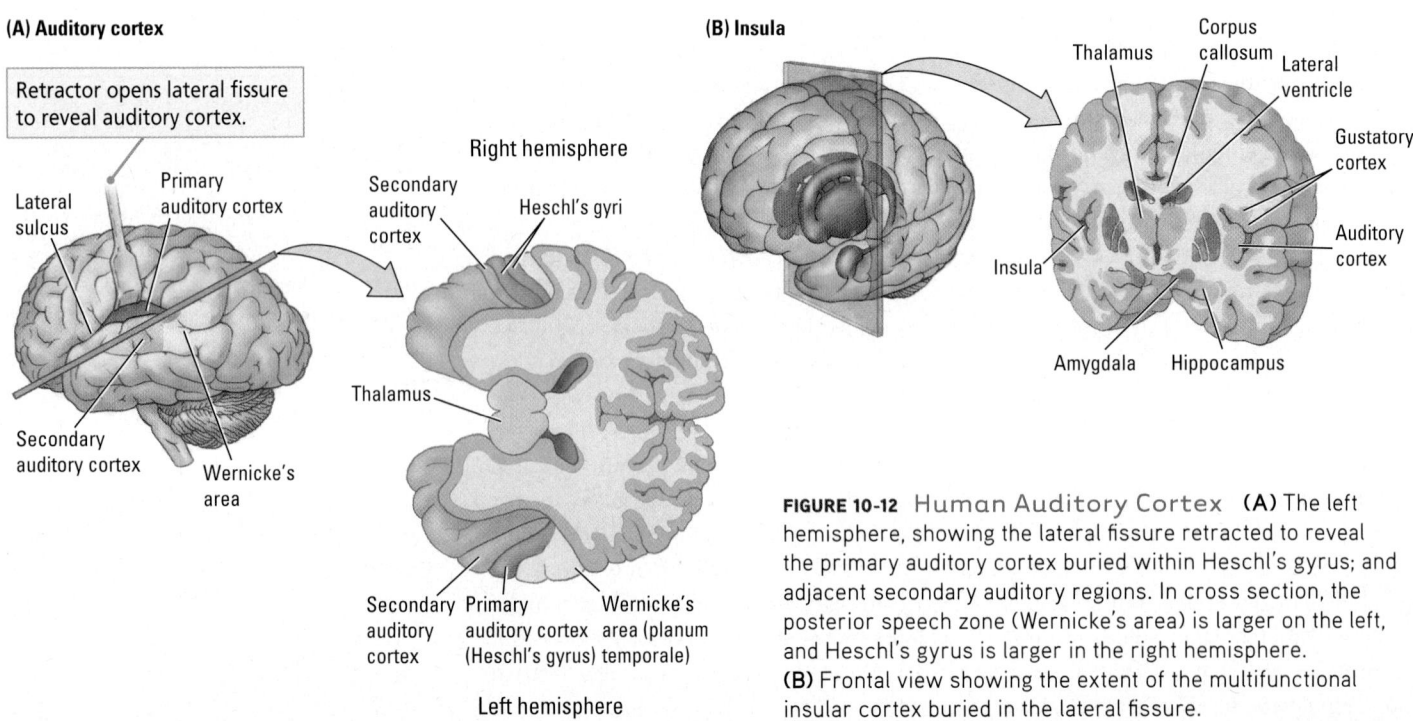

(A) Auditory cortex

(B) Insula

FIGURE 10-12 Human Auditory Cortex **(A)** The left hemisphere, showing the lateral fissure retracted to reveal the primary auditory cortex buried within Heschl's gyrus; and adjacent secondary auditory regions. In cross section, the posterior speech zone (Wernicke's area) is larger on the left, and Heschl's gyrus is larger in the right hemisphere.
(B) Frontal view showing the extent of the multifunctional insular cortex buried in the lateral fissure.

Seeing with Sound

As detailed in Section 10-5, echolocation, the ability to use sound to locate objects in space, has been extensively studied in species such as bats and dolphins. But it was reported more than 50 years ago that some blind people also echolocate.

More recently, anecdotal reports have surfaced of blind people who navigate around the world using clicks made with their tongues and mouths then listening to the returning echoes. Videos, such as the 45-minute documentary at https://www.youtube.com/watch?v=AiBeLoB6CKE, show congenitally blind people riding a bicycle down a street with silent obstacles such as parked cars. But how do they do this, and what part of the brain enables it?

Behavioral studies of blind people reveal that echolocators make short, spectrally broad clicks by moving the tongue backward and downward from the roof of the mouth directly behind the teeth. Skilled echolocators can identify properties of objects that include position, distance, size, shape, and texture (Teng & Whitney, 2011).

Thaler and colleagues (2011) investigated the neural basis of this ability using fMRI. They studied two blind echolocation experts and compared brain activity for sounds that contain both clicks and returning echoes with brain activity for control sounds that did not contain the echoes. The participants use echolocation to localize objects in the environment, but more important, they also perceive the object's shape, motion—even its identity!

When the blind participants listened to recordings of their echolocation clicks and echoes compared to silence, both the auditory cortex and the primary visual cortex showed activity. Sighted controls showed activation only in the auditory cortex. Remarkably, when the investigators compared the controls' brain activity to recordings that contained echoes

versus those that did not, the auditory activity disappeared. By contrast, as illustrated in the figure, the blind echolocators showed activity only in the visual cortex when sounds with and without echoes were compared. Sighted controls (findings not shown) showed no activity in either the visual or auditory cortex in this comparison.

These results suggest that blind echolocation experts process click–echo information using brain regions typically devoted to vision. Thaler and his colleagues propose that the primary visual cortex is performing a spatial computation using information from the auditory cortex.

Future research may determine how this process works. More immediately, the study suggests that echolocation could be taught to blind and visually impaired people to provide them increased independence in their daily life.

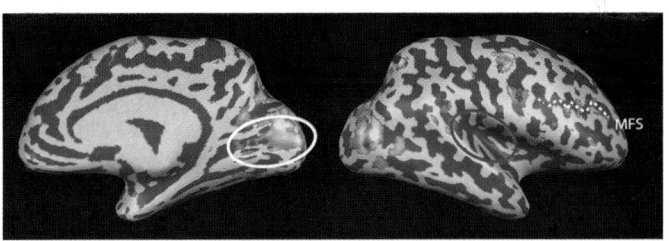

Seeing with Sound When cortical activation for sound with and without echoes is imaged in a blind echolocator, only the visual cortex shows activation (left) relative to the auditory cortex (right). Research from Thaler, L., Arnott, S. R., & Goodale, M. A. (2011), Neural correlates of natural human echolocation in early and late blind echolocation experts. *PLoS ONE, 6,* (5)e20162. doi:10.1371/journal.pone.0020162

---

idiosyncratic bilateral speech representation. That is, about 15 percent of all left-handed people have some speech functions in one hemisphere and some in the other hemisphere.

Localization of language on one side of the brain is an example of **lateralization.** Note here simply that, in neuroanatomy, if one hemisphere is specialized for one type of analysis—as, for example, the left hemisphere is for language—the other hemisphere has a complementary function: the right hemisphere appears to be lateralized for music.

The temporal lobe sulci enfold a volume of cortical tissue far more extensive than the auditory cortex (Figure 10-12B). Buried in the lateral fissure, cortical tissue called the **insula** contains not only lateralized regions related to language but also areas controlling taste perception (the gustatory cortex) and areas linked to the neural structures underlying social cognition. As you might expect, injury to the insula can produce such diverse deficits as disturbance of both language and taste.

Wernicke's area Secondary auditory cortex (planum temporale) lying behind Heschl's gyrus at the rear of the left temporal lobe; regulates language comprehension. Also *posterior speech zone.*

lateralization Localization of function primarily on one side of the brain.

insula Multifunctional cortical tissue located within the lateral fissure; contains language- and taste perception–related regions and neural structures underlying social cognition.

10-2 REVIEW

Functional Anatomy of the Auditory System

Before you continue, check your understanding.

1. Incoming sound wave energy vibrates the eardrum, which in turn vibrates the

   _____ .

2. The auditory receptors are the _____, found in the _____ .

3. The motion of the cochlear fluid causes displacement of the _____ and _____ membranes.

4. The axons of bipolar cells from the cochlea form the _____ nerve, which is part of the _____ cranial nerve.

5. The auditory nerve originating in the cochlea projects to various nuclei in the brainstem; then it projects to the _____ in the midbrain and the _____ in the thalamus.

6. Describe the asymmetrical structure and functions of the auditory cortex.

Answers appear at the back of the book

For additional study tools, visit 🌐 **LaunchPad:**
www.macmillanhighered.com/launchpad/kolb5e

(10-3) Neural Activity and Hearing

We now turn to the neuronal activity in the auditory system that produces our perception of sound. Neurons at different levels in this system serve different functions. To get an idea of what individual hair cells and cortical neurons do, we consider how the auditory system codes sound wave energy so that we perceive pitch, loudness, location, and pattern.

Hearing Pitch

Recall that perception of pitch corresponds to the frequency (repetition rate) of sound waves measured in hertz (cycles per second). Hair cells in the cochlea code frequency as a function of their location on the basilar membrane. In this **tonotopic representation,** hair cell cilia at the base of the cochlea are maximally displaced by high-frequency waves, which we hear as high-pitched sounds; those at the apex are displaced the most by low-frequency waves, which we hear as low-pitched sounds. Because each bipolar-cell axon that forms the cochlear nerve is connected to only one inner hair cell, the bipolar cells convey information about the spot on the basilar membrane, from apex to base, that is being stimulated.

Tonotopic literally means of a tone place.

Recordings from single fibers in the cochlear nerve reveal that although each axon transmits information about only a small part of the auditory spectrum, each cell does respond to a range of sound wave frequencies—if the wave is sufficiently loud. That is, each hair cell is maximally responsive to a particular frequency and also responds to nearby frequencies, but the sound wave's amplitude must be greater (louder) for those nearby frequencies to excite the receptor's membrane potential.

A hair cell's frequency range parallels a photoreceptor's response to light wavelengths. See Figure 9-6.

We can plot this range of hair cell responses to different frequencies at different amplitudes as a tuning curve. As graphed in **Figure 10-13,** each hair cell receptor is maximally sensitive to a particular wavelength but still responds somewhat to nearby wavelengths.

FIGURE 10-13 Tuning Curves Graphs plotted by the sound wave frequency and amplitude energy required to increase the firing rate of two axons in the cochlear nerve. The lowest point on each tuning curve is the frequency to which that hair cell is most sensitive. The curve at left is centered on a frequency of 1000 Hz, the midrange of human hearing; the curve at right is centered on a frequency of 10,000 Hz, in the high range.

Corresponds to apex of cochlea

Corresponds to base of cochlea

FIGURE 10-14 Tonotopic Representation of Area A1 A retractor holds the lateral fissure open to reveal the underlying primary auditory cortex. The anterior end of area A1 corresponds to the apex of the cochlea, hence low frequencies. The posterior end corresponds to the base of the cochlea, hence high frequencies.

Bipolar cell axons in the cochlea project to the cochlear nucleus in an orderly manner (see Figure 10-11). Axons entering from the base of the cochlea connect with one location; those entering from the middle connect to another location; and those entering from the apex connect to yet another. Thus the basilar membrane's tonotopic representation is reproduced in the hindbrain cochlear nucleus.

This systematic representation is maintained throughout the auditory pathways and into the primary auditory cortex. **Figure 10-14** shows the distribution of projections from the base and apex of the cochlea across area A1. Similar tonotopic maps can be constructed for each level of the auditory system.

This systematic auditory organization has enabled the development of **cochlear implants**—electronic devices surgically inserted in the inner ear that serve as prostheses to allow deaf people to hear (see Loeb, 1990). Cochlear implants are no cure for deafness but rather are a hearing substitute. In **Figure 10-15**, a miniature microphonelike processor secured to the skull detects the component frequencies of incoming sound waves and sends them to the appropriate place on the basilar membrane through tiny wires. The nervous system does not distinguish between stimulation coming from this artificial device and stimulation coming through the middle ear.

As long as appropriate signals go to the correct locations on the basilar membrane, the brain will hear. Cochlear implants work well, allowing the deaf to detect even the fluctuating pitches of speech. Their success corroborates the tonotopic representation of pitch in the basilar membrane.

tonotopic representation In audition, structural organization for processing of sound waves from lower to higher frequencies.

cochlear implant Electronic device implanted surgically into the inner ear to transduce sound waves to neural activity and allow a deaf person to hear.

Semicircular canals

Ossicles

Auditory nerve

Cochlea

Electrode contacts

Eardrum

External ear canal

Coil

Implant

Microphone

Audio processor

Pinna

Wire

FIGURE 10-15 Tonotopic Technology A cochlear implant captures incoming sound wave stimulation via a microphone worn behind the ear. An audio processor converts the frequencies into electric current and stimulates the correct locations on the basilar membrane.

Even so, the quality of sound cochlear implants create is impoverished relative to natural hearing. Adults who lose their hearing and then get cochlear implants describe the sounds as "computerized" and "weird." Many people with implants find music unpleasant and difficult to listen to. Graeme Clark (2015) developed a prototype high-fidelity cochlear implant with 50 electrodes to increase basilar membrane stimulation. His goal is achieving better music perception and enhanced ability to discern specific voices in noisy rooms.

One minor difficulty with frequency detection is that the human cochlea does not respond in a tonotopic manner to frequencies below about 200 Hz, yet we can hear frequencies as low as 20 Hz. At its apex, all the cells respond to movement of the basilar membrane, but they do so in proportion to the frequency of the incoming wave (see Figure 10-9B). Higher rates of bipolar cell firing signal a higher frequency, whereas lower rates of firing signal a lower frequency.

Why the cochlea uses a different system to differentiate pitch within this range of very low frequency sound waves is not clear. It probably has to do with the physical limitations of the basilar membrane. Discriminating among low-frequency sound waves is vital to animals such as elephants and whales, which depend on these frequencies to communicate. These species most likely have more neurons at the apex of the basilar membrane than we humans do.

Detecting Loudness

The simplest way for cochlear (bipolar) cells to indicate sound wave intensity is to fire at a higher rate when amplitude is greater, which is exactly what happens. More intense air pressure changes produce more intense basilar membrane vibrations and therefore greater shearing of the cilia. Increased shearing leads to more neurotransmitter released onto bipolar cells. As a result, the bipolar axons fire more frequently, telling the auditory system that the sound is getting louder.

Detecting Location

Psychologist Albert Bregman devised a visual analogy to describe what the auditory system is doing when it detects sound location:

> Imagine a game played at the side of a lake. Two small channels are dug, side by side, leading away from the lake, and the lake water is allowed to fill them up. Partway up each channel, a cork floats, moving up and down with the waves. You stand with your back to the lake and are allowed to look only at the two floating corks. Then you are asked questions about what is happening on the lake. Are there two motorboats on the lake or only one? Is the nearer one going from left to right or right to left? Is the wind blowing? Did something heavy fall into the water? You must answer these questions just by looking at the two corks. This would seem to be an impossible task. Yet consider an exactly analogous problem. As you sit in a room, a lake of air surrounds you. Running off this lake, into your head, are two small channels – your ear canals. At the end of each is a membrane (the ear drum) that acts like the floating corks in the channels running off the lake, moving in and out with the sound waves that hit it. Just as the game at the lakeside offered no information about the happenings on the lake except for the movements of the corks, the sound-producing events in the room can be known by your brain only through the vibrations of your two eardrums. (Bregman, 2005, p. 35)

We estimate the location of a sound both by taking cues derived from one ear and by comparing cues received at both ears. The fact that each cochlear nerve synapses on both sides of the brain provides mechanisms for locating a sound source. In one mechanism, neurons in the brainstem compute the difference in a sound wave's arrival time at each ear—the *interaural time difference* (ITD). Differences in arrival time need not be large to be detected. If two sounds presented through earphones are separated in time by as little as 10 microseconds, the listener will perceive that a single sound came from the leading ear.

This computation of left-ear–right-ear arrival times is carried out in the medial part of the superior olivary complex (see Figure 10-11). Because these hindbrain cells receive inputs from each ear, they can compare exactly when the signal from each ear reaches them.

Figure 10-16 shows how sound waves originating on the left reach the left ear slightly before they reach the right ear. As the sound source moves from the side of the head toward the middle, a person has greater and greater difficulty locating it: the ITD becomes smaller and smaller until there is no difference at all. When we detect no difference, we infer that the sound is either directly in front of us or directly behind us. To locate it, we turn our head, making the sound waves strike one ear sooner. We have a similar problem distinguishing between sounds directly above and below us. Again, we solve the problem by tilting our head, thus causing the sound waves to strike one ear before the other.

Another mechanism used by the auditory system to detect the source of a sound is the sound's relative loudness on the left and the right—the *interaural intensity difference* (IID). The head acts as an obstacle to higher-frequency sound waves, which do not easily bend around the head. As a result, higher-frequency waves on one side of the head are louder than on the other. The lateral part of the superior olive and the trapezoid body detect this difference. Again, sound waves coming from directly in front or behind or from directly above or below require the same solution: tilting or turning the head.

Head tilting and turning take time, which is important for animals, such as owls, that hunt using sound. Owls need to know the location of a sound simultaneously in at least two directions—right or left and above or below. Owls, like humans, can orient in the horizontal plane to sound waves by using ITD. Additionally, the owl's ears have evolved to detect the relative loudness of sound waves in the vertical plane. As diagrammed in **Figure 10-17**, owls' ears are slightly displaced vertically. This solution allows owls to hunt entirely by sound in the dark. Bad news for mice.

Detecting Patterns in Sound

Music and language are perhaps the primary sound wave patterns that humans recognize. Perceiving sound wave patterns as meaningful units thus is fundamental to our auditory analysis. Because music perception and language perception are lateralized in the right and left temporal lobes, respectively, we can guess that neurons in the right and left temporal cortex take part in pattern recognition and analysis of both auditory experiences. Studying the activities of auditory neurons in humans is not easy, however.

Most of what neuroscientists know comes from studies of how individual neurons respond in nonhuman primates. Both human and nonhuman primates have a ventral and

Extra distance that sound must travel to reach the right ear.

FIGURE 10-16 Locating a Sound Compression waves originating on the left side of the body reach the left ear slightly before the right. The ITD is small, but the auditory system can discriminate it and fuse the dual stimuli so that we perceive a single, clear sound coming from the left. Horizontal orienting is *azimuth detection;* vertical orienting is *elevation detection.*

Facial ruff   Ear-canal opening

Ear opening

Ear opening

FIGURE 10-17 Hunting by Ear Left: In the dark, a barn owl aligns its talons with the body axis of the mouse it is about to catch. Center: The owl's facial ruff collects and funnels sound waves into ear canal openings through tightly feathered troughs above and below the eyes. The owl's left ear is more sensitive to sound waves from the left and below because the ear canal is higher on the left side and the trough is tilted down. The right-side ear canal is lower and the trough tilts up, making the right ear more sensitive to sound waves from the right and above. Right: The boreal owl's asymmetric skull produces a similar auditory asymmetry. Information from E. I. Knudsen (1981). The hearing of the barn owl. *Scientific American, 245*(6), p. 115.

Audition for action parallels unconscious visually guided movements by the dorsal stream; see Figure 9-42.

dorsal cortical pathway for audition. Neurons in the ventral pathway decode spectrally complex sounds—referred to by some investigators as *auditory object recognition*—including the meaning of speech sounds for people and species-typical vocalizations in monkeys (for a review, see Rauschecker, 2012). Less is known about the properties of neurons in the dorsal auditory stream, but this path clearly has a role in integrating auditory and somatosensory information to control speech production. We could call it *audition for action*.

(10-3) REVIEW

Neural Activity and Hearing

Before you continue, check your understanding.

1. Bipolar neurons in the cochlea form _____ maps that code sound wave frequencies.

2. Loudness is decoded by the firing rate of cells in the _____ .

3. Detecting the location of a sound is a function of neurons in the _____ and _____ of the brainstem.

4. The function of the dorsal auditory pathway can be described as _____ .

5. Explain how the brain detects a sound's location.

Answers appear at the back of the book.

For additional study tools, visit LaunchPad:
www.macmillanhighered.com/launchpad/kolb5e

(10-4) Anatomy of Language and Music

This chapter began with the evolutionary implications of discovering a flute made by Neanderthals (see Focus 10-1). That Neanderthals made flutes implies not only that they processed musical sound wave patterns but also that they made music. In our brain, musical ability is generally a right-hemisphere specialization complementary to language ability, lateralized to the left hemisphere in most people.

No one knows whether these complementary systems evolved together in the hominid brain, but it is highly likely. Language and music abilities are highly developed in the modern human brain. Although little is known about how each is processed at the cellular level, electrical stimulation and recording and blood flow imaging studies yield important insights into the cortical regions that process them. We investigate such studies next, focusing first on how the brain processes language.

Section 7-4 surveys functional brain imaging methods; Section 7-2 reviews methods for measuring its electrical activity.

Processing Language

An estimated 5000 to 7000 human languages are spoken in the world today, and probably many more have gone extinct in past millennia. Researchers have wondered whether the brain has a single system for understanding and producing any language, regardless of its structure, or whether disparate languages, such as English and Japanese, are processed differently. To answer this question, it helps to analyze languages to determine just how fundamentally similar they are, despite their obvious differences.

Uniformity of Language Structure

Foreign languages often seem impossibly complex to those who do not speak them. Their sounds alone may seem odd and difficult to make. If you are a native English speaker, for instance, Asian languages, such as Japanese, probably sound especially melodic and almost without obvious consonants to you, whereas European languages, such as German or Dutch, may sound heavily guttural.

Even within such related languages as Spanish, Italian, and French, marked differences can make learning one of them challenging, even if the student already knows another. Yet as real as all these linguistic differences may be, they are superficial. The similarities among human languages, although not immediately apparent, are actually far more fundamental than their differences.

Noam Chomsky (1965) is usually credited as the first linguist to stress similarities over differences in human language structure. In a series of books and papers written over the past half-century, Chomsky has made a sweeping claim, as have researchers such as Steven Pinker (1997) more recently. They argue that all languages have common structural characteristics stemming from a genetically determined constraint, and these common characteristics form the basis of universal grammar theory. Humans, apparently, have a built-in capacity for learning and using language, just as we have for walking upright.

Chomsky was greeted with deep skepticism when he first proposed this idea in the 1960s, but it has since become clear that the capacity for human language is indeed genetic. An obvious piece of evidence: language is universal in human populations. All people everywhere use language.

A language's complexity is unrelated to its culture's technological complexity. The languages of technologically unsophisticated peoples are every bit as complex and elegant as the languages of postindustrial cultures. Nor is the English of Shakespeare's time inferior or superior to today's English; it is just different.

Another piece of evidence that Chomsky adherents cite for the genetic basis of human language is that humans learn language early in life and seemingly without effort. By about 12 months of age, children everywhere have started to speak words. By 18 months, they are combining words, and by age 3 years, they have a rich language capability.

Perhaps the most amazing thing about language development is that children are not formally taught the structure of their language, just as they are not taught to crawl or walk. They just do it. As toddlers, they are not painstakingly instructed in the rules of grammar. In fact, their early errors—sentences such as "I goed to the zoo"—are seldom even corrected by adults. Yet children master language rapidly. They also acquire language through a series of stages that are remarkably similar across cultures. Indeed, the process of language acquisition plays an important role in Chomsky's theory of its innateness—which is not to say that language development is not influenced by experience.

At the most basic level, children learn the language or languages that they hear spoken. In an English household, they learn English; in a Japanese home, Japanese. They also pick up the language structure—the vocabulary and grammar—of the people around them, even though that structure can vary from one speaker to another. Children go through a sensitive period for language acquisition, probably from about 1 to 6 years of age. If they are not exposed to language throughout this critical period, their language skills are severely compromised. If children learn two languages simultaneously, the two share the same part of Broca's area. In fact, their neural representations overlap (Kim et al., 1997).

Both its universality and natural acquisition favor the theory for a genetic basis of human language. A third piece of evidence is the many basic structural elements common to all languages. Granted, every language has its own particular grammatical rules specifying exactly how various parts of speech are positioned in a sentence (syntax), how words are inflected to convey different meanings, and so forth. But an overarching set of rules also applies to all human languages, and the first rule is that there *are* rules.

For instance, all languages employ parts of speech that we call subjects, verbs, and direct objects. Consider the sentence *Jane ate the apple. Jane* is the subject, *ate* is the verb, and *apple* is the direct object. Syntax is not specified by any universal rule but rather is a characteristic of the particular language. In English, syntactical order (usually) is subject, verb, object; in Japanese, the order is subject, object, verb; in Gaelic, the order is verb, subject, object. Nonetheless, all have both syntax and grammar.

The existence of these two structural pillars in all human languages is seen in the phenomenon of *creolization*—the development of a new language from what was formerly

A 1-year-old's 5- to 10-word vocabulary doubles in the next 6 months and by 36 months mushrooms to 1000 words; see Section 8-3.

Focus 8-3 describes how cortical activation differs for second languages learned later in life and Section 15-6, research on bilingualism and intelligence.

a rudimentary language, or *pidgin*. Creolization took place in the seventeenth century in the Americas when slave traders and colonial plantation owners brought together, from various parts of West Africa, people who lacked a common language. The newly enslaved needed to communicate, and they quickly created a pidgin based on whatever language the plantation owners spoke—English, French, Spanish, or Portuguese.

The pidgin had a crude syntax (word order) but lacked a real grammatical structure. The children of the slaves who invented this pidgin grew up with caretakers who spoke only pidgin to them. Yet within a generation, these children had developed their own creole, a language complete with a genuine syntax and grammar.

Clearly, the pidgin invented of necessity by adults was not a learnable language for children. Their innate biology shaped a new language similar in basic structure to all other human languages. All creolized languages seem to evolve in a similar way, even though the base languages are unrelated. This phenomenon can happen only because there is an innate biological component to language development.

Localizing Language in the Brain

Finding a universal basic language structure set researchers on the search for an innate brain system that underlies language use. By the late 1800s, it had become clear that language functions were at least partly localized—not just within the left hemisphere but to specific areas there. Clues that led to this conclusion began to emerge early in the nineteenth century, when neurologists observed patients with frontal lobe injuries who had language difficulties.

Then, in 1861, the French physician Paul Broca confirmed that certain language functions are localized in the left hemisphere. Broca concluded, on the basis of several postmortem examinations, that language is localized in the left frontal lobe, in a region just anterior to the central fissure. A person with damage in this area is unable to speak despite both an intact vocal apparatus and normal language comprehension. The confirmation of **Broca's area** was significant because it triggered the idea that the left and right hemispheres might have different functions.

Other neurologists of the time believed that Broca's area might be only one of several left-hemisphere regions that control language. In particular, they suspected a relation between hearing and speech. Proving this suspicion correct, Karl Wernicke later described patients who had difficulty comprehending language after injury to the posterior region of the left temporal lobe, identified as Wernicke's area in **Figure 10-18**.

Section 7-1 links Broca's observations to his contributions to neuropsychology.

FIGURE 10-18 Neurology of Language **(A)** In Wernicke's model of speech recognition, stored sound images are matched to spoken words in the left posterior temporal cortex, shown in yellow. **(B)** Speech is produced through the connection that the arcuate fasciculus makes between Wernicke's area and Broca's area.

In Section 10-2 we identified Wernicke's area as a speech zone (see Figure 10-12A). Damage to any speech area produces some form of **aphasia,** the general term for any inability to comprehend or produce language despite the presence of otherwise normal comprehension and intact vocal mechanisms. At one extreme, people who suffer *Wernicke's aphasia* can speak fluently, but their language is confused and makes little sense, as if they have no idea what they are saying. At the other extreme, a person with *Broca's aphasia* cannot speak despite normal comprehension and intact physiology.

Wernicke went on to propose a model, diagrammed in Figure 10-18A, for how the two language areas of the left hemisphere interact to produce speech. He theorized that images of words are encoded by their sounds and stored in the left posterior temporal cortex. When we hear a word that matches one of those sound images, we recognize it, which is how Wernicke's area contributes to speech comprehension.

To *speak* words, Broca's area in the left frontal lobe must come into play, because the motor program to produce each word is stored in this area. Messages travel to Broca's area from Wernicke's area through the *arcuate fasciculus*, a fiber pathway that connects the two regions. Broca's area in turn controls articulation of words by the vocal apparatus, as diagrammed in Figure 10-18B.

Wernicke's model provided a simple explanation both for the existence of two major language areas in the brain and for the contribution each area makes to the control of language. But the model was based on postmortem examinations of patients with brain lesions that were often extensive. Not until neurosurgeon Wilder Penfield's pioneering studies, begun in the 1930s, were the left hemisphere language areas clearly and accurately mapped.

Auditory and Speech Zones Mapped by Brain Stimulation

It turns out, among Penfield's discoveries, that neither is Broca's area the independent site of speech production nor is Wernicke's area the independent site of language comprehension. Electrical stimulation of either region disrupts both processes.

Penfield took advantage of the chance to map the brain's auditory and language areas when he operated on patients undergoing elective surgery to treat epilepsy unresponsive to antiseizure medication. The goal of this surgery is to remove tissues where the abnormal discharges are initiated without damaging the areas responsible for linguistic ability or vital sensory or motor functioning. To determine the locations of these critical regions, Penfield used a weak electrical current to stimulate the brain surface. By monitoring the patient's responses during stimulation in different locations, Penfield could map brain functions along the cortex.

Typically, two neurosurgeons perform the operation under local anesthesia applied to the skin, skull, and dura mater (Penfield is shown operating in **Figure 10-19A**) as a neurologist analyzes the electroencephalogram in an adjacent room. Patients, who are awake, are asked to contribute during the procedure, and the effects of brain stimulation in specific regions can be determined in detail and mapped. Penfield placed tiny numbered tickets on different parts of the brain's surface where the patient noted that stimulation had produced some noticeable sensation or effect, producing the cortical map shown in Figure 10-19B.

When Penfield stimulated the auditory cortex, patients often reported hearing such sounds as a ringing that sounded like a doorbell, a buzzing noise, or a sound like birds chirping. This result is consistent with later single-cell recordings from the auditory cortex in nonhuman primates. Findings in these later studies showed that the auditory cortex participates in pattern recognition.

Penfield also found that stimulation in area A1 seemed to produce simple tones—ringing sounds, and so forth—whereas stimulation in the adjacent auditory cortex (Wernicke's area) was more apt to cause some interpretation of a sound—ascription of a buzzing sound to a familiar source such as a cricket, for instance. There was no difference in the effects of stimulation of the left or right auditory cortex, and the patients heard no words when the brain was stimulated.

Broca's area Anterior left hemisphere speech area that functions with the motor cortex to produce movements needed for speaking.

aphasia Inability to speak or comprehend language despite the presence of normal comprehension and intact vocal mechanisms. *Broca's aphasia* is the inability to speak fluently despite the presence of normal comprehension and intact vocal mechanisms. *Wernicke's aphasia* is the inability to understand or to produce meaningful language even though word production remains intact.

Section 7-1 describes brain stimulation techniques used in neuroscience research.

(A)

(B)

Central sulcus

Lateral fissure

Courtesy Penfield Archive, Montreal Neurological Institute, McGill University

FIGURE 10-19 Mapping Cortical Functions **(A)** Neurosurgery for eligible epilepsy patients who failed to respond to antiseizure medications. The patient is fully conscious, lying on his right side, and kept comfortable with local anesthesia. Wilder Penfield stimulates discrete cortical areas in the patient's exposed left hemisphere. In the background, a neurologist monitors an EEG recorded from each stimulated area to help identify the epileptogenic focus. The anesthetist (seated) observes the patient's responses to the cortical stimulation. **(B)** A drawing overlies a photograph of the patient's exposed brain. The numbered tickets identify points Penfield stimulated to map the cortex in this patient's brain. At points 26, 27, and 28, a stimulating electrode disrupted speech. Point 26 presumably is in Broca's area, 27 is the motor cortex facial control area, and 28 is in Wernicke's area.

Sometimes, however, stimulation of the auditory cortex produced effects other than sound perceptions. Stimulation of one area, for example, might cause a patient to feel deaf, whereas stimulation of another area might produce a distortion of sounds actually being heard. As one patient exclaimed after a certain region had been stimulated, "Everything you said was mixed up!"

Penfield was most interested in the effects of brain stimulation not on simple sound wave processing but on language. He and later researchers used electrical stimulation to identify four important cortical regions that control language. The two classic regions—Broca's area and Wernicke's area—are left-hemisphere regions. Located on both sides of the brain are the other two major language use regions: the dorsal area of the frontal lobes and the areas of the motor and somatosensory cortex that control facial, tongue, and throat muscles and sensations. Although the effects on speech vary depending on the region, stimulating any of them disrupts speech in some way.

Clearly, much of the left hemisphere takes part in audition. **Figure 10-20** shows those areas that Penfield found engaged in some way in processing language. In fact, Penfield mapped cortical language areas in two ways, first by disrupting speech, then by eliciting speech. Not surprisingly, damage to any speech area produces some form of aphasia.

DISRUPTING SPEECH Penfield expected that electrical current might disrupt ongoing speech by effectively short-circuiting the brain. To test his hypothesis, he stimulated different cortical regions while the patient was speaking. In fact, the speech disruptions took several forms, including slurring, word confusion, and difficulty in finding the right word. Such aphasias are detailed in Clinical Focus 10-4, Left-Hemisphere Dysfunction.

Electrical stimulation of the **supplementary speech area** on the dorsal surface of the frontal lobe (shown in Figure 10-20) can even stop ongoing speech completely, a reaction that Penfield called *speech arrest*. Stimulation of other cortical regions far removed from

Supplementary speech area (vocalization or speech arrest)

Areas controlling facial movement or sensation (vocalization or speech arrest)

Aphasia

Broca's area (aphasia)

A1 (sounds heard)

Wernicke's area (aphasia)

FIGURE 10-20 Cortical Regions That Control Language This map, based on Penfield's extensive study, summarizes the left-hemisphere areas where direct stimulation may disrupt speech or elicit vocalization. Information from W. Penfield & L. Roberts (1956). *Speech and brain mechanisms* (p. 201). London: Oxford University Press.

Left-Hemisphere Dysfunction

Susan S., a 25-year-old college graduate and mother of two, had epilepsy. When she had a seizure, which was almost every day, she lost consciousness for a short period during which she often engaged in repetitive behaviors, such as rocking back and forth.

Medication can usually control such seizures, but the drugs were ineffective for Susan. The attacks disrupted her life: they prevented her from driving and restricted the types of jobs she could hold. So Susan decided to undergo neurosurgery to remove the region of abnormal brain tissue that was causing the seizures.

The procedure has a high success rate. Susan's surgery entailed removal of a part of the left temporal lobe, including most of the cortex in front of the auditory areas. Although it may seem a substantial amount of the brain to cut away, the excised tissue is usually abnormal, so any negative consequences typically are minor.

After the surgery, Susan did well for a few days; then she started to have unexpected and unusual complications. As a result, she lost the remainder of her left temporal lobe, including the auditory cortex and Wernicke's area. The extent of lost brain tissue resembles that shown in the accompanying MRI.

Courtesy of George Jallo/ Johns Hopkins Hospital

Postoperative MRI of a patient who has lost most of the left hemisphere.

Susan no longer understood language, except to respond to the sound of her name and to speak just one phrase: I love you. Susan was also unable to read, showing no sign that she could even recognize her own name in writing.

To find ways to communicate with Susan, Bryan Kolb tried humming nursery rhymes to her. She immediately recognized them and could say the words. We also discovered that her singing skill was well within the normal range and she had a considerable repertoire of songs.

Susan did not seem able to learn new songs, however, and she did not understand messages that were sung to her. Apparently, Susan's musical repertoire was stored and controlled independently of her language system.

---

the temporal and frontal speech areas has no effect on ongoing speech, with the exception of motor cortex regions, shown in Figure 10-20, that control facial movements. This exception makes sense because talking requires movement of facial, tongue, and throat muscles.

ELICITING SPEECH The second way Penfield mapped language areas was to stimulate the cortex when a patient was not speaking. Here the goal was to see if stimulation caused the person to utter a speech sound. Penfield did not expect to trigger coherent speech; cortical electrical stimulation is not physiologically normal and so probably would not produce actual words or word combinations. His expectation was borne out.

Stimulation of regions on both sides of the brain—for example, the supplementary speech areas—produces a sustained vowel cry, such as *Oooh* or *Eee*. Stimulation of the facial areas in the motor and somatosensory cortices produces some vocalization related to mouth and tongue movements. Stimulation outside these speech-related zones produces no such effects.

Auditory Cortex Mapped by Positron Emission Tomography

To study the metabolic activity of brain cells engaged in tasks such as processing language, researchers use PET, a brain-imaging technique that detects changes in brain blood flow. Among the many PET studies of auditory stimulation, a series conducted by Robert Zatorre and his colleagues (1992, 1996) serves as a good example. These researchers hypothesized that simple auditory stimulation, such as bursts of noise, are analyzed by area A1, whereas more complex auditory stimulation, such as speech syllables, are analyzed in adjacent secondary auditory areas.

The researchers also hypothesized that performing a discrimination task for speech sounds would selectively activate left-hemisphere regions. This selective activation is exactly what they found. **Figure 10-21**A shows increased activity in the primary auditory cortex

supplementary speech area Speech production region on the left frontal lobe dorsal surface.

Section 7-4 details procedures used to obtain a PET scan.

(A) Listening to bursts of noise

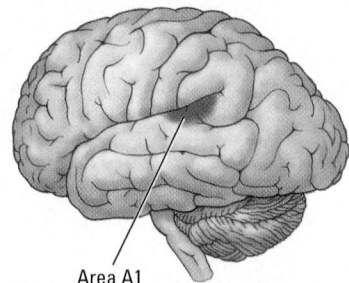

Area A1

(B) Listening to words

Wernicke's area

(C) Discriminating speech sounds

Broca's area

FIGURE 10-21 Cortical Activation in Language–Related Tasks **(A)** Passively listening to noise bursts activates the primary auditory cortex. **(B)** Listening to words activates the posterior speech zone, including Wernicke's area. **(C)** Making a phonetic discrimination activates the frontal region, including Broca's area.

in response to bursts of noise, whereas secondary auditory areas are activated by speech syllables (Figure 10-21B and C).

Both types of stimuli produced responses in both hemispheres but with greater activation in the left hemisphere for the speech syllables. These results imply that area A1 analyzes all incoming auditory signals, speech and nonspeech, whereas the secondary auditory areas are responsible for some higher-order signal processing required for analyzing language sound patterns.

As Figure 10-21C shows, the speech sound discrimination task yielded an intriguing additional result: Broca's area in the left hemisphere was also activated. This frontal lobe region's involvement during auditory analysis may seem surprising. In Wernicke's model, Broca's area is considered the storage area for motor programs needed to produce words. It is not usually a region thought of as a site of speech sound discrimination.

A possible explanation is that to determine that the *g* in *bag* and the one in *pig* are the same speech sound, the auditory stimulus must be related to how the sound is actually articulated. That is, speech sound perception requires a match with the motor behaviors associated with making the sound.

This role for Broca's area in speech analysis is confirmed further when investigators ask people to determine whether a stimulus is a word or a nonword (e.g., *tid* versus *tin* or *gan* versus *tan*). In this type of study, information about how the words are articulated is irrelevant, and Broca's area need not be recruited. Imaging reveals that it is not.

Processing Music

Although Penfield did not study the effect of brain stimulation on musical analysis, many researchers study musical processing in brain-damaged patients. Clinical Focus 10-5, Cerebral Aneurysms, describes one such case. Collectively, the results of these studies confirm that musical processing is in fact largely a right-hemisphere specialization, just as language processing is largely a left-hemisphere one.

Localizing Music in the Brain

A famous patient, the French composer Maurice Ravel (1875–1937), provides an excellent example of right-hemisphere predominance for music processing. *Boléro* is perhaps Ravel's best-known work. At the peak of his career, Ravel had a left-hemisphere stroke and developed aphasia. Yet many of his musical skills remained intact post-stroke because they were localized to the right hemisphere. He could still recognize melodies, pick up tiny mistakes in music he heard, and even judge the tuning of pianos. His music perception was largely intact.

Skills that had to do with producing music, however, were among those destroyed. Ravel could no longer recognize written music, play the piano, or compose. This dissociation of music perception and music production may parallel the dissociation of speech comprehension and speech production in language. Apparently, the left hemisphere plays at least some role in certain aspects of music processing, especially those that have to do with making music.

Cerebral Aneurysms

C. N. was a 35-year-old nurse described by Isabelle Peretz and her colleagues (1994). In December 1986, C. N. suddenly developed severe neck pain and headache. A neurological examination revealed an aneurysm in the middle cerebral artery on the right side of her brain.

An *aneurysm* is a bulge in a blood vessel wall caused by weakening of the tissue, much like the bulge that appears in a bicycle tire at a weakened spot. Aneurysms in a cerebral artery are dangerous: if they burst, severe bleeding and consequent brain damage result.

In February 1987, C. N.'s aneurysm was surgically repaired, and she appeared to have few adverse effects. Postoperative brain imaging revealed, however, that a new aneurysm had formed in the same location but in the middle cerebral artery on the opposite side of the brain. This second aneurysm was repaired 2 weeks later.

After her surgery, C. N. had temporary difficulty finding the right word when she spoke, but more important, her perception of music was deranged. She could no longer sing, nor could she recognize familiar tunes. In fact, singers sounded to her as if they were talking instead of singing. But C. N. could still dance to music.

A brain scan revealed damage along the lateral fissure in both temporal lobes. The damage did not include the primary auditory cortex, nor did it include any part of the posterior speech zone. For these reasons, C. N. could still recognize nonmusical sound patterns and showed no evidence of language disturbance. This finding reinforces the hypothesis that nonmusical sounds and speech sounds are analyzed in parts of the brain separate from those that process music.

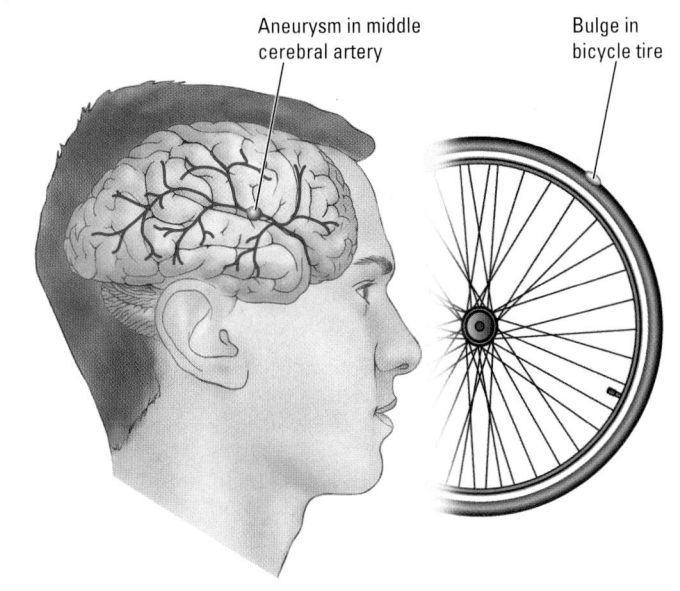

Aneurysm in middle cerebral artery

Bulge in bicycle tire

To find out more about how the brain carries out the perceptual side of music processing, Zatorre and his colleagues (1994) conducted PET studies. When participants listened simply to bursts of noise, Heschl's gyrus became activated (**Figure 10-22**A), but perception of melody triggers major activation in the right-hemisphere auditory cortex lying in front of Heschl's gyrus (Figure 10-22B), as well as minor activation in the same left-hemisphere region (not shown).

In another test, participants listened to the same melodies. The investigators asked them to indicate whether the pitch of the second note was higher or lower than that of the first note. During this task, which necessitates short-term memory of what was just heard, blood flow in the right frontal lobe increased (Figure 10-22C). As with language, then, the frontal lobe plays a role in auditory analysis when short-term memory is required. People with enhanced or impaired musical abilities show differences in frontal lobe organization, as demonstrated in Research Focus 10-6, The Brain's Music System.

As noted earlier, the capacity for language is innate. Sandra Trehub and her colleagues (1999) showed that music may be innate as well, as we hypothesized at the beginning of the chapter.

FIGURE 10-22 Cortical Activation in Music–Related Tasks **(A)** Passively listening to bursts of noise activates Heschl's gyrus. **(B)** Listening to a melody activates the secondary auditory cortex. **(C)** Making relative pitch judgments about two notes in each melody activates a right frontal lobe area.

(A) Listening to bursts of noise

Heschl's gyrus

(B) Listening to melodies

A2

(C) Comparing pitches

Frontal lobe

The Brain's Music System

Nonmusicians enjoy music and have musical ability. Musicians show an enormous range of ability: some have perfect pitch and some do not, for example. About 4 percent of the population is tone deaf. Their difficulties, characterized as **amusia**—an inability to distinguish between musical notes—are lifelong.

Robert Zatorre and his colleagues (Bermudez et al., 2009; Hyde et al., 2007) have used MRI to look at differences among the brains of musicians, nonmusicians, and amusics. MRIs of the left and right hemispheres show that compared to nonmusicians, musicians' cortical thickness is greater in dorsolateral frontal and superior temporal regions. Curiously, musicians with perfect pitch have thinner cortex in the posterior part of the dorsolateral frontal lobe. Thinner appears to be better for some music skills.

Compared to nonmusicians then, musicians with thicker than normal cortex must have enhanced neural networks in the right-hemisphere frontal–temporal system linked to performing musical tasks. But thicker than normal cortex can bestow both advantage and impairment.

Analysis of amusic participants' brains showed thicker cortex in the right frontal area and in the right auditory cortex regions. Some abnormality in neuronal migration during brain development is likely to have

led to an excess of neurons in the right frontal–temporal music pathway of the amusics. Their impaired music cognition is the result.

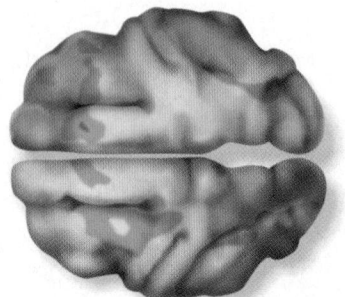

Right hemisphere

Left hemisphere

Compared to nonmusicians and amusics, musicians' thicker cortex, shown in the green, yellow, and red areas, contributes to performance. Focus 14-5 describes how playing music can affect sensorimotor maps in the cortex. Research from P. Bermudez, J. P. Lerch, A. C. Evans, & R. J. Zatorre (2009). Neuroanatomical correlates of musicianship as revealed by cortical thickness and voxel-based morphometry. *Cerebral Cortex, 7,* 1583–1596.

---

amusia Tone deafness—inability to distinguish between musical notes.

The brain may be tuned prenatally to the language it will hear at birth; see Focus 7-1.

At: https://www.youtube.com/watch?v=eNpoVeLfMKg, watch as Parkinson patients step to the beat of music to improve their gait length and walking speed.

More on music as therapy in Focus 5-2 and the dance class for Parkinson patients pictured on page 160. Sections 16-2 and 16-3 revisit music therapy.

Trehub found that infants show learning preferences for musical scales versus random notes. Like adults, children are sensitive to musical errors, presumably because they are biased for perceiving regularity in rhythms. Thus, it appears that the brain is prepared at birth for hearing both music and language, and presumably it selectively attends to these auditory signals.

Music as Therapy

The power of music to engage the brain has led to its use as a therapeutic tool for brain dysfunctions. The best evidence of its effectiveness lies in studies of motor disorders such as stroke and Parkinson disease (Johansson, 2012). Listening to rhythm activates the motor and premotor cortex and can improve gait and arm training after stroke. Musical experience reportedly also enhances the ability to discriminate speech sounds and to distinguish speech from background noise in patients with aphasia.

Music therapy also appears to be a useful complement to more traditional therapies, especially when there are problems with mood, such as in depression or brain injury. This may prove important in the treatment of stroke and traumatic brain injury, with which depression is a common complication in recovery. Music therapy also has positive effects following major surgery, both in adults and children, by reducing both their pain perception and the amount of pain medication they use (Sunitha Suresh et al., 2015). With all these applications, perhaps researchers will decide to use noninvasive imaging to determine which brain areas music therapy recruits.

10-4 REVIEW

Anatomy of Language and Music

Before you continue, check your understanding.

1. The human auditory system has complementary specialization for the perception of sounds: left for _____ and right for _____.

2. The three frontal lobe regions that participate in producing language are _____, _____, and _____ .

3. _____ area identifies speech syllables and words and stores their representations in that location.

4. _____ area matches speech sounds to the motor programs necessary to articulate them.

5. At one end of the spectrum for musical ability are people with _____ and at the other are people who are _____ .

6. What evidence supports the idea that language is innate?

Answers appear at the back of the book.

For additional study tools, visit 🐢 **LaunchPad**:
www.macmillanhighered.com/launchpad/kolb5e

(10-5) Auditory Communication in Nonhuman Species

Sound has survival value. You will appreciate this if you've ever narrowly escaped becoming an accident statistic by crossing a busy intersection on foot while listening to a music player or talking on a cell phone. Audition is as important a sense to many animals as vision is to humans. Many animals also communicate with other members of their species by using sound, as humans do.

Here we consider just two types of auditory communication in nonhumans: birdsong and echolocation. Each provides a model for understanding different aspects of brain–behavior relations in which the auditory system plays a role.

Birdsong

Of about 8500 living bird species, about half are considered songbirds. Birdsong has many functions, including attracting mates (usually employed by males), demarcating territories, and announcing location or even just presence. Although all birds of the same species have a similar song, the song's details vary markedly from region to region, much as dialects of the same human language vary.

Parallels Between Birdsong and Language

Figure 10-23 shows sound wave spectrograms for the songs of male white-crowned sparrows that live in three localities near San Francisco. These songs differ markedly from region to region. The differences stem from the fact that song development in young birds is influenced not just by genes but also by early experience and learning. Young birds that have a good tutor can acquire more elaborate songs than can other members of their species (Marler, 1991).

These gene–experience interactions are the result of epigenetic mechanisms. For example, brain areas that control singing in adult song sparrows show altered gene expression in spring as the breeding—and singing—season begins (Thompson et al., 2012). Such studies have not yet targeted young birds, but it is safe to predict that researchers will find parallel changes.

Birdsong and human language have broad similarities beyond regional variation. Both appear to be innate yet are sculpted by experience. Both are diverse and can vary in complexity. Humans seem to have a basic template for language that is programmed into the brain, and experience adds a variety of specific structural forms to this template.

If a young bird is not exposed to song until it is a juvenile and then listens to recordings of birdsongs of various species, the young bird shows a general preference for its own species' song. This preference must mean that each bird has a species-specific song template in the brain. As for language, experience modifies the details of this birdsong template.

White-crowned sparrow

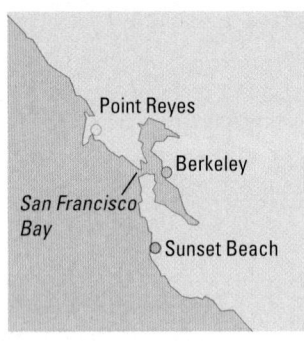
Point Reyes
Berkeley
San Francisco Bay
Sunset Beach

FIGURE 10-23 Birdsong Dialects The songs of male white-crowned sparrows recorded in three locales around San Francisco Bay are similar, but sound wave spectrograms reveal that the dialects differ. Like humans, birds acquire regional dialects. Information from P. Marler (1991). The instinct to learn. In S. Carey & R. German (Eds.), *The epigenesis of mind: Essays on biology and cognition* (p. 39), Hillsdale, NJ: Erlbaum.

Another broad similarity between birdsong and human language is their great diversity. Among birds, diversity is apparent in the sheer number of songs that a species possesses. Species such as the white-crowned sparrow have but a single song; the marsh wren has as many as 150.

The number of syllables in birdsong also varies greatly, ranging from 30 for the canary to about 2000 for the brown thrasher. Similarly, even though all modern human languages are equally complex, they vary significantly in the type and number of elements they employ. The number of meaningful patterns in speech sounds in human languages ranges from about 15 for some Polynesian languages to about 100 for some dialects spoken in the Caucasus Mountains. English has 24.

A final broad similarity between birdsong and human language lies in how they develop. In many bird species, song development is heavily influenced by experience during a critical period, just as language development is in humans. Birds also go through stages in song development, just as humans go through stages in language development. Hatchlings make noises that attract their parents' attention, usually for feeding, and human babies emit cries to signal hunger, among other things.

The fledgling begins to make noises that Charles Darwin compared to the prespeech babbling of human infants. These noises, called *subsong,* are variable in structure, low in volume, and often produced as the bird appears to doze. Presumably, subsong, like human babbling, is practice for the later development of adult communication after the bird has left the nest.

As a young bird matures, it starts to produce sound wave patterns that contain recognizable bits of the adult song. Finally, the adult song emerges. In most species, the adult song remains remarkably stable, although a few species, such as canaries, can develop a new song every year that replaces the previous year's song.

Neurobiology of Birdsong

The neurobiology of birdsong has been a topic of intense research, partly because it provides an excellent model of brain changes that accompany learning and partly because it offers insight into how sex hormones influence behavior. In the 1970s, Fernando Nottebohm and his colleagues first identified the major structures controlling birdsong, illustrated in **Figure 10-24** (Nottebohm & Arnold, 1976). The largest structures are the higher vocal control center (HVC) and the nucleus *robustus archistriatalis* (RA). The axons of the HVC connect to the RA, which in turn sends axons to the 12th cranial nerve. This nerve controls the muscles of the *syrinx,* the structure that actually produces the song.

The HVC and RA have several important and some familiar characteristics:

Shown in Figure 8-30, a rare gyandromorph zebra finch exhibits physical characteristics of both sexes.

- The structures are asymmetrical in some bird species, with those in the left hemisphere larger than those on the right. In many cases, this asymmetry is similar to the lateralized control of language in humans: if the left-hemisphere pathways are damaged, the bird stops singing, but similar injury in the right hemisphere has no effect on song.

- Birdsong structures are sexually dimorphic, that is, much larger in males than in females. In male canaries, the structures are five times as large as in the female. This sex difference is due to the hormone testosterone in males. Injection of testosterone into female birds causes the song-controlling nuclei to increase in size.

- The size of the birdsong-controlling nuclei is related to singing skill. Unusually talented singers among male canaries tend to have larger HVCs and RAs than do less-gifted singers.

- The HVC and RA contain cells that produce birdsong as well as cells responsive to hearing song, especially the song of a bird's own species.

The same structures therefore play a role in both song production and song perception. This avian neural anatomy is comparable to the overlapping roles of Broca's and Wernicke's areas in language perception and production in humans.

Echolocation in Bats

Next to rodents, bats are the most numerous mammalian order. The two general groups, or suborders, are the smaller bats (Microchiroptera) and the larger fruit-eating and flower-visiting bats (Megachiroptera), sometimes called flying foxes. Each uses a form of echolocation. Using their wings to make clicking sounds, Megachiroptera can detect large surfaces and orient in complete darkness. This rudimentary form of echolocation may be the forerunner of the highly evolved throat (laryngeal) system used in a sophisticated way by the Microchiroptera to navigate, hunt, and communicate using sound waves (Boonman et al., 2014).

Most of the 680 species of Microchiroptera feed on insects. Others live on blood (vampire bats), and some catch frogs, lizards, fishes, birds, and small mammals. These bats' auditory system is highly specialized to use echolocation not only to locate targets in the dark but also to analyze the targets' features as well as environmental features in general. Through echolocation, these bats identify prey, navigate through the leaves of trees, and locate suitable landing surfaces. **Echolocation** in the Microchiroptera works rather like sonar. The bat larynx emits bursts of sound waves at ultrasonic frequencies. The waves bounce off objects and return to the bat's ears, allowing the animal to identify what is in the surrounding environment. The bat, in other words, navigates by the echoes it hears, differentiating among the various characteristics of the echoes.

Moving objects (such as insects) give off a moving echo, smooth objects a different echo from rough objects, and so on. A key component of the bats' echolocation system is analysis of differences in echo return times. Close objects return echoes sooner than more distant objects do, and the textures of various objects' surfaces impose minute differences in return times.

A bat's cries are short (ranging from 0.3 to 200 milliseconds) and high frequency (12,000 to 200,000 Hz, charted in Figure 10-4). Most of this range lies at too high a frequency for the human ear to detect. Different bat species produce sound waves of different frequencies that depend on the animal's ecology. Bats that catch prey in the open use different frequencies from those used by bats that catch insects in foliage and from those used by bats that hunt prey on the ground.

The echolocation abilities of bats are phenomenal, as shown in **Figure 10-25.** Bats in the wild can be trained to catch small food particles thrown up into the air in the dark. These echolocating skills make the bat a most efficient hunter. The little brown bat, for instance, can capture tiny flying insects, such as mosquitoes, at the remarkable rate of two per second.

Researchers have considerable interest in the neural mechanisms of bat echolocation. Each species emits sound waves in a relatively narrow frequency range, and a bat's auditory pathway has cells specifically tuned to echoes in its species' frequency range. For example, the mustached bat sends out sound waves ranging from 60,000 to 62,000 Hz, and its auditory system has a cochlear fovea (a maximally sensitive area in the organ of Corti) that corresponds to that frequency range.

In this way, more neurons are dedicated to the frequency range used for echolocation than to any other range of frequencies. Analogously, our visual system dedicates more neurons to the retina's fovea, the area responsible for our most detailed vision. In the cortex of

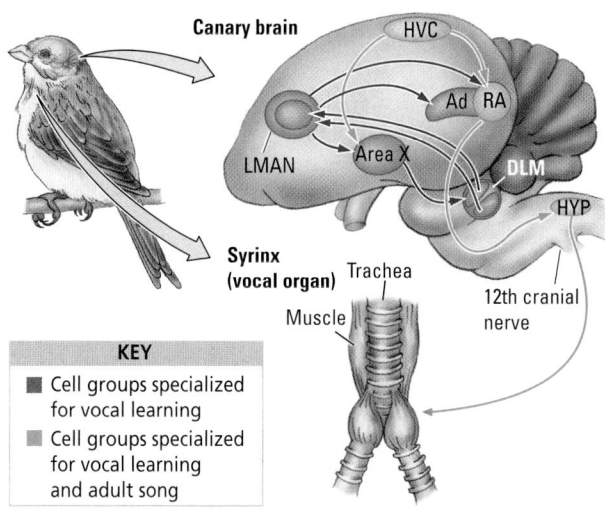

FIGURE 10-24 Avian Neuroanatomy Lateral view of the canary brain shows several left-hemisphere nuclei that control song learning. Two that are necessary both for adult singing and for learning the song are the higher vocal control center (HVC) and the nucleus robustus archistriatalis (RA). Other regions necessary for learning the song during development but not required for adult singing include the dorsal archistriatum (Ad), the lateral magnocellular nucleus of the anterior neostriatum (LMAN), area X of the avian striatum, and the medial dorsolateral nucleus of the thalamus (DLM).

KEY
- Cell groups specialized for vocal learning
- Cell groups specialized for vocal learning and adult song

Dolphins use an auditory strategy similar to bats, but in water. Focus 10-2 profiles human echolocators.

Microchiroptera

Megachiroptera

echolocation Identifying and locating an object by bouncing sound waves off it.

Figure 9-2 details the fovea's structure.

FIGURE 10-25 Born with Sonar Based entirely on auditory information, a bat with a 40-centimeter wingspan can navigate through openings in a 14-by-14-centimeter mesh made of 80-millimeter nylon thread while flying in total darkness.

© Rolf Nussbaumer/imageBROKER

the bat's brain, several distinct areas process complex echoic inputs. One area computes the distance of given targets from the animal, for instance, whereas another area computes the velocity of a moving target. This neural system makes the bat exquisitely adapted for night-time navigation.

(10-5) **REVIEW**

Auditory Communication in Nonhuman Species

Before you continue, check your understanding.

1. Song development in young birds is influenced both by genes and by early experience and learning, interactions indicative of _____.

2. In many bird species the control of song in the brain is lateralized to the _____ hemisphere.

3. Bats use _____ to locate prey in the dark. This system is much like the _____ that ships use to locate underwater objects.

4. What does the presence of dialects in birdsong in the same species demonstrate?

Answers appear at the back of the book.

For additional study tools, visit 🌐 **LaunchPad**:
www.macmillanhighered.com/launchpad/kolb5e

■ SUMMARY

Although we take language and music for granted, both play central roles in our mental lives and in our social lives. Language and music provide us ways to communicate with other people—and with ourselves. They facilitate social identification, parenting, and cultural transmission.

(10-1) **Sound Waves: The Stimulus for Audition**

The stimulus for the auditory system is the mechanical energy of sound waves that results from changes in air pressure. The ear transduces three fundamental physical qualities of sound wave energy: frequency (repetition rate), amplitude (size), and complexity. Perceptually, neural networks then translate these energies into the pitch, loudness, and timbre of the sounds that we hear.

(10-2) **Functional Anatomy of the Auditory System**

Beginning in the ear, mechanical and electrochemical systems combine to transform sound waves into auditory perceptions—what we hear. Changes in air pressure are conveyed in a mechanical chain reaction from the eardrum to the bones of the middle ear to the oval window of the cochlea and the cochlear fluid that lies behind it in the inner ear. Movements of the cochlear fluid produce movements in specific regions of the basilar membrane, leading to changes in the electrochemical activity of the auditory receptors, the inner hair cells on the basilar membrane that send neural impulses through the auditory nerve into the brain.

10-3 Neural Activity and Hearing

The basilar membrane has a tonotopic organization. High-frequency sound waves maximally stimulate hair cells at the base, whereas low-frequency sound waves maximally stimulate hair cells at the apex, enabling cochlear neurons to code sound frequencies.

Tonotopic organization analyzes sound waves at all levels of the auditory system, which also detects both amplitude and location. The firing rate of cochlear neurons codes sound amplitude, with louder sounds producing higher firing rates than softer sounds do. Location is detected by structures in the brainstem that compute differences in the arrival times and loudness of a sound in the two ears.

Cochlear hair cells synapse with bipolar neurons that form the cochlear nerve, which in turn forms part of the eighth cranial nerve. The cochlear nerve takes auditory information to three structures in the hindbrain: the cochlear nucleus, the superior olive, and the trapezoid body. Cells in these areas are sensitive to differences in both sound wave intensity and arrival times at the two ears. In this way, they enable the brain to locate a sound.

The auditory pathway continues from the hindbrain areas to the inferior colliculus of the midbrain, then to the medial geniculate nucleus in the thalamus, and finally to the auditory cortex. As for vision, dorsal and ventral pathways exist in the auditory cortex, one for pattern recognition and the other for controlling movements in auditory space. Cells in the cortex are responsive to specific sound categories, such as species-specific communication.

10-4 Anatomy of Language and Music

Despite differences in the patterns and structures of speech sounds, all human languages have the same basic foundation: syntax and grammar, which implies an innate template for creating language. Auditory areas of the left hemisphere cortex play a special role in analyzing language-related information, whereas those in the right hemisphere play a special role in analyzing music-related information. The right temporal lobe also analyzes prosody, the melodic qualities of speech.

Among several left-hemisphere language-processing areas, Wernicke's area identifies speech syllables and words and so is critically engaged in speech comprehension. Broca's area matches speech sound patterns to the motor behaviors necessary to make them and so plays a major role in speech production. Broca's area also discriminates between closely related speech sounds. Aphasias are an inability to speak (Broca's aphasia) or to comprehend language (Wernicke's aphasia) despite the presence of normal cognition and intact vocal mechanisms.

Auditory analysis of music draws more on right-hemisphere activity than on the left. Nor is music production localized to the right hemisphere: it recruits the left hemisphere as well. Music perception engages both the right temporal and frontal regions.

Music's power to engage both right- and left-hemisphere activity makes it a powerful tool for engaging the injured or dysfunctioning brain. Music therapy is playing an increasingly important role in treatment.

10-5 Auditory Communication in Nonhuman Species

Nonhuman animals have evolved specialized auditory structures and behaviors. Regions of songbirds' brains are specialized for producing and comprehending song. In many species, these regions are lateralized to the left hemisphere, analogous in a way to how language areas are lateralized to the left hemisphere in most humans. Similarities in the development of song in birds and the development of language in humans, as well as similarities in the neural mechanisms underlying both the production and the perception of birdsong and language, are striking.

Both owls and bats can fly and catch prey at night using only auditory information to guide their movement. Bats evolved a type of biosonar that allows them to map the objects in their auditory world, as humans map their visual worlds. Although some blind humans employ this strategy, the mainly auditory reality of bats, dolphins, and other echolocators is one most people can only try to imagine.

■ KEY TERMS

aphasia, p. 343

amplitude, p. 325

amusia, p. 348

basilar membrane, p. 331

Broca's area, p. 343

cochlea, p. 329

cochlear implant, p. 337

decibel (dB), p. 325

echolocation, p. 351

frequency, p. 323

hair cell, p. 331

hertz (Hz), p. 323

insula, p. 335

lateralization, p. 335

medial geniculate nucleus, p. 333

ossicle, p. 329

otoacoustic emissions, p. 333

primary auditory cortex (area A1), p. 333

prosody, p. 329

sound wave, p. 323

supplementary speech area, p. 345

tonotopic representation, p. 337

Wernicke's area, p. 335

→ Visit LaunchPad to access the e-Book, videos, LearningCurve adaptive quizzing, flashcards, and more.
www.macmillanhighered.com/launchpad/kolb5e

CHAPTER

11

How Does the Nervous System Respond to Stimulation and Produce Movement?

Katherine Streeter

355

Neuroprosthetics

Most of us seamlessly control the approximately 650 muscles that move our bodies. But if the motor neurons that control those muscles no longer connect to them, as happens in amyotrophic lateral sclerosis (ALS, or Lou Gehrig disease), movement, and eventually breathing, become impossible.

This happened to Scott Mackler, a neuroscientist and marathon runner, in his late 30s. Dependent on a respirator to breathe, he developed *locked-in syndrome:* Mackler lost virtually all ability to communicate.

ALS has no cure, and death often occurs within 5 years of diagnosis. Yet Scott Mackler beat the odds: he survived for 17 years before he died in 2013 at age 55. Mackler beat locked-in syndrome too, by learning to translate his mental activity into movement. He returned to work at the University of Pennsylvania, stayed in touch with family and friends, and even gave an interview to CBS's *60 Minutes* in 2008.

Mackler was a pioneer in *brain–computer interface* (BCI) technology. BCIs employ the brain's electrical signals to direct computer-controlled devices. BCIs are one area of **neuroprosthetics**, development of computer-assisted devices to replace lost biological function.

A *computer–brain interface* (CBI) employs electrical signals from a computer to instruct the brain. Cochlear implants that deliver sound-related signals to the inner ear to allow hearing are CBIs. *Brain–computer–brain interfaces* (BCBIs) combine the BCI and CBI approaches. BCBIs enable the brain to command robotic devices that provide it sensory feedback.

In 2008, Mackler's BCI took up to 20 s to execute a single command. Today's devices enhance processing speed and increase signal precision by using electrodes placed directly adjacent to brain cells in arrays that interface with thousands of cells. Experimental approaches use optogenetics, incorporating light-sensitive channels into cortical motor and sensory neurons. Light signals are faster than electrical signals and produce less tissue damage.

BCBIs command robotic hands to grasp objects while tactile receptors on the robot are delivering touch and other sensory information to the user. BCBIs in development also control exoskeletal devices that reach and walk and return touch, body position, and balance information to guide movement. In essence, BCBIs use variations in CNS activity to generate signals. It is unlikely, however, that in doing so they employ the signaling codes normally used by the brain in producing behavior (Daly & Huggins, 2015).

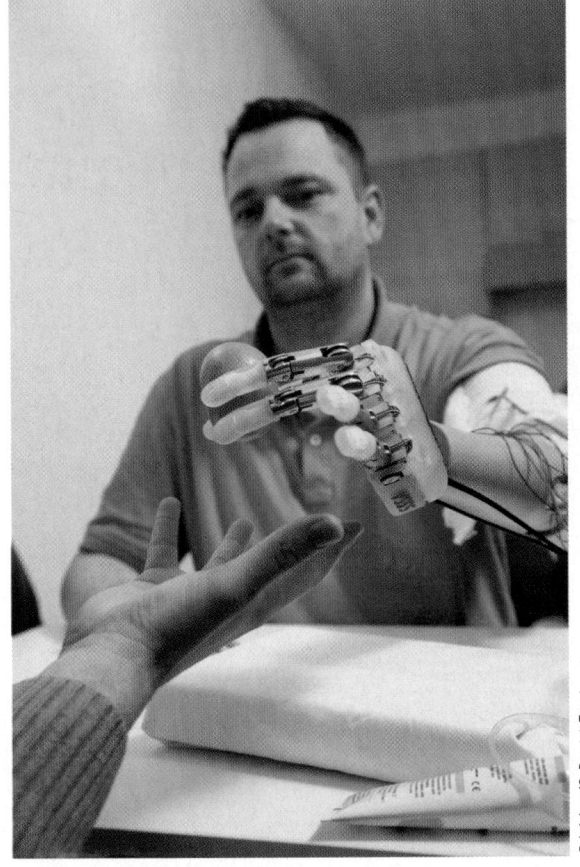

© Lifehand2, PatriziaTocci

Brain–computer–brain interfaces such as the robotic limb shown here enable the brain to command robotic devices that provide it sensory feedback.

Section 1-1 offers a simple definition of behavior: any movement in a living organism.

Movement is a defining feature of animals, and this chapter explores how the nervous system produces movement. The body senses are more closely related to movement than are the other senses. This chapter also describes how somatic sensation and movement interact at different levels of the nervous system.

At the level of the spinal cord, somatosensory information contributes to motor reflexes. In the brainstem, it contributes to movement timing and control. In the cerebrum, it contributes to complex voluntary movements. Indeed, for many functions, the other senses work through the somatosensory system to produce movement. If the motor system is a vehicle and the somatosensory system is the driver, the other sensory systems act like backseat drivers.

We begin here with movement and end with sensation. Section 4-4 begins with sensation and ends with movement.

We first consider how movement is organized in the central nervous system, then turn to how the somatic senses contribute to movement and balance. If you want to review how the motor system and somatic sensation interact before you read on, turn to The Basics: Relating the Somatosensory and Motor Systems, on pages 358–359.

11-1 A Hierarchy of Movement Control

neuroprosthetics Field that develops computer-assisted devices to replace lost biological function.

Our movements feature at least two categories of action. First we decide on a goal and choose how to achieve it; then we make moves to reach the goal. As we move, we correct movement errors that direct us away from our goal. What are the neural bases of these choices? What neural bases enable the motor system to produce our movements?

The major components of our motor system are the cerebrum (forebrain), the brainstem, and the spinal cord. The cerebrum contributes to our conscious control of movement, while the brainstem and spinal cord direct our movements. In the face of impaired brainstem or spinal cord function, the forebrain can imagine movement but can no longer produce it. Neuroprosthetic devices, described in Research Focus 11-1, can replace the movement production function provided by the brainstem and spinal cord and restore forebrain control.

Getting from decisions to movements involves most of our nervous system. **Figure 11-1** illustrates the stepwise sequence your CNS performs in the seemingly simple act of directing your hand to pick up a cup. Once you decide to pick it up, you visually inspect it to determine what part to grasp. The visual cortex relays this information through the cortical somatosensory regions to the motor regions that plan and initiate the movement. Only then does the brain send instructions to the spinal cord segments that control your arm and hand muscles.

As you grasp the cup's handle, information from sensory receptors in your fingers aids in adjusting your grip and sends information back through the spinal cord to the somatosensory cortex and from there to the motor cortex to confirm that the act is complete—you are holding the cup. Other brain regions also participate in controlling the movement. The subcortical *basal ganglia* help to produce the appropriate amount of force for grasping the cup handle, while in the brainstem, the cerebellum helps to regulate the movement's timing and accuracy.

Clearly, the movement involved in picking up a cup involves widespread CNS regions. The action also requires that higher-function regions, including those that participate in deciding to pick up the cup, work through and influence the actions of lower functional areas. Remarkably, once you have made the decision to pick up the cup, most of the movement happens automatically, without conscious control. Few of us can describe the sequence of actions or produce an accurate pantomime of the movements we make to actually grasp a

For now, remember that the entire sensorimotor system is organized hierarchically. When you reach the chapter's end, review Figure 11-1 to reinforce what you've learned.

1 Visual information required to locate the target.

2 Frontal-lobe motor areas plan the reach and command the movement.

3 Spinal cord carries information to the hand.

4 Motor neurons carry message to muscles of the hand and forearm.

5 Sensory receptors on the fingers send message to sensory cortex saying that the cup has been grasped.

6 Spinal cord carries sensory information to the brain.

7 Basal ganglia judge grasp forces, and cerebellum corrects movement errors.

8 Sensory cortex receives message that the cup has been grasped.

Motor nerve

Sensory nerve

FIGURE 11-1 Sequentially Organized Movement

THE BASICS ■

Relating the Somatosensory and Motor Systems

The intimate relationship between the motor and somatosensory systems is apparent in their close anatomical relationships. *Afferent* somatosensory information travels from the body inward via the somatic nervous system. Movement information travels out of the central nervous system via a parallel *efferent* motor system.

As diagrammed in Information Flow, when you step on a tack, the sensory signals transmitted by the SNS from the body through the spinal cord and into the brain are afferent. Efferent signals from the CNS trigger a motor response: you lift your foot.

The spinal cord connects the somatosensory and motor systems throughout the CNS. Connections Between the Nerves and the Spine shows the spinal cord in cross section. In the outer part, which consists of white matter, posterior tracts are sensory and anterior tracts are motor, with some exceptions. The inner cord is gray matter composed largely of cell bodies and shaped like a butterfly.

SNS nerves entering the spinal cord's posterior side carry information inward from the body's sensory receptors and merge into a *posterior root* as the fibers enter a spinal cord segment of the CNS. Fibers leaving the spinal cord's anterior side carry information out from the spinal cord to the

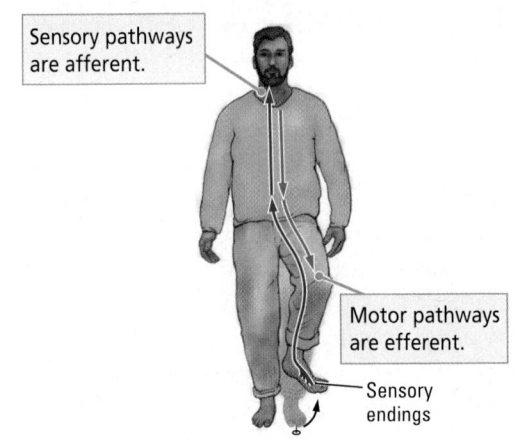

Information Flow

muscles. They, too, bundle together as the fibers exit the spinal cord, forming an *anterior root*. (Bundles of nerve fibers within the CNS are called *tracts;* outside the CNS they are called *nerves.*)

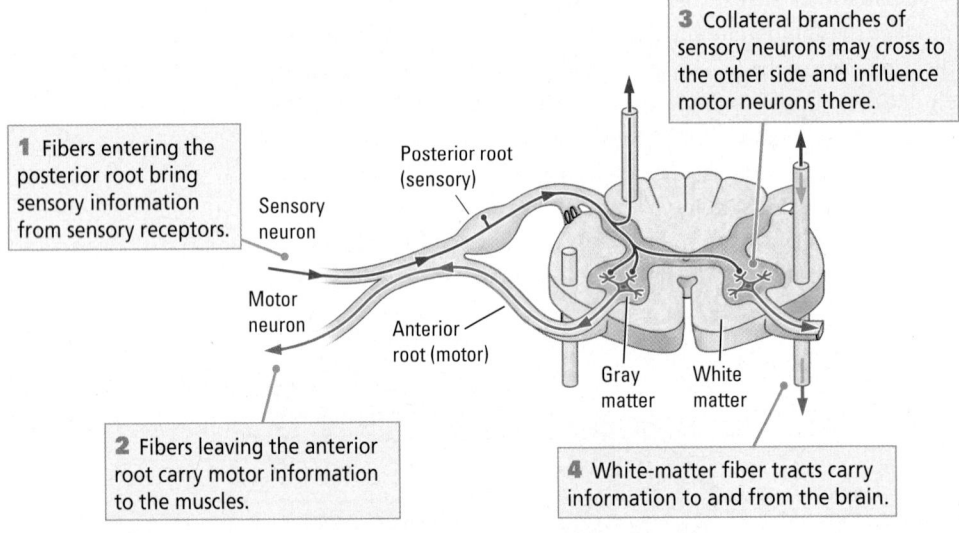

1 Fibers entering the posterior root bring sensory information from sensory receptors.

2 Fibers leaving the anterior root carry motor information to the muscles.

3 Collateral branches of sensory neurons may cross to the other side and influence motor neurons there.

4 White-matter fiber tracts carry information to and from the brain.

Posterior root (sensory)

Sensory neuron

Motor neuron

Anterior root (motor)

Gray matter   White matter

Connections Between the Nerves and the Spine

Recall the principle from Section 2-6: The CNS functions on multiple levels.

cup, although we have performed the action thousands of times (Davarpanah et al., 2015). To understand how these CNS regions work together to produce decisions and movements, we now consider the major components of the hierarchy, starting with the forebrain.

Forebrain: Initiating Movement

Complex movements consist of many acts. Consider playing basketball. At every moment, players must make decisions and perform actions. Dribble, pass, and shoot are different movement categories, and each can be performed in many ways. Skilled players choose among the categories effortlessly and blend them together seemingly without thought.

The spinal cord lies within a series of small bones called *vertebrae* categorized into the five anatomical regions diagrammed on the left in Spinal Segments and Dermatomes. Each spinal segment corresponds to a region of body surface called a *dermatome* (literally, *skin cut*), shown on the right. From top to bottom, the cervical, thoracic, lumbar, sacral, and coccygeal regions are identified by spinal segment number: C5 (cervical segment 5) at the base of the neck, for example, and L2 in the lower back.

Body and nervous system segmentation has a long evolutionary history that can be seen in spineless worms as well as in vertebrates. The cervical and lumbar dermatomes represent the human forelimbs and hind limbs. Their arrangement is sequential if you imagine a human on all fours.

Layering in the Neocortex plumbs the depths of the primary motor cortex (shown in blue) and adjacent sensory (red) cortical regions. Viewed through a microscope, the six cortical layers differ in appearance, characteristics, and functions. Layer IV is relatively thick in the sensory cortex but relatively thin in the motor cortex. Layer V is relatively thick in the motor cortex and relatively thin in the sensory cortex. Cortical layer IV is afferent and layer V is efferent, and that makes sense: sensory regions have a large input layer and motor regions, a large output layer.

Spinal Segments and Dermatomes

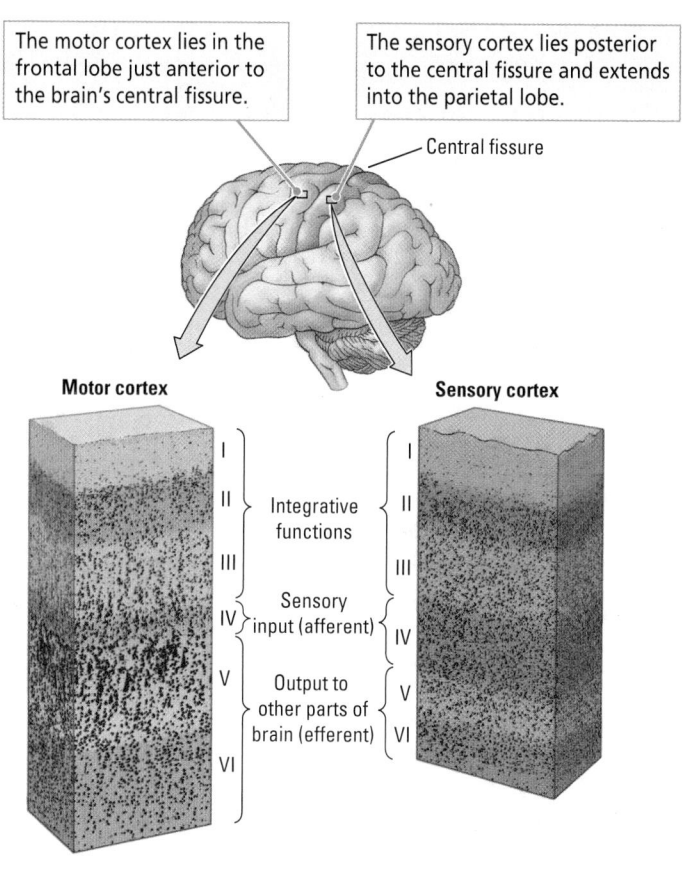

Layering in the Neocortex

An early explanation for control of such complex movements centered on feedback: after we act, we wait for feedback about how well the action has succeeded, then make the next movement. The pioneering neuroscience researcher Karl Lashley (1951), in the article "The Problem of Serial Order in Behavior," found fault with this explanation.

Lashley realized that we perform skilled movements too quickly to rely on feedback about one movement before shaping the next. The time required to receive feedback about the first movement combined with the time needed to develop a plan for the subsequent movement and send a corresponding message to muscles is simply too long for effective action. Lashley argued that movements must be performed as **motor sequences,** with the next sequence held in readiness while the ongoing one is under way.

Lashley experimented for three decades to find the location of memory in the brain. He failed.

motor sequence Movement modules preprogrammed by the brain and produced as a unit.

FIGURE 11-2 Initiating a Motor Sequence

Sections 12-4 and 15-2 explore cognitive deficits caused by frontal lobe injury.

Recall the principle from Section 2-6: Brain circuits process information hierarchically and in parallel.

All complex behaviors, including speaking, piano playing, and playing basketball, require selecting and executing multiple movements as sequences. Most of our motor learning is mastering sequences of action. As one sequence is being executed, the next sequence is being prepared to follow the first smoothly. The act of speaking illustrates this activity. When people use complex rather than simple word sequences, they are more likely to pause and make *umm* and *ahh* sounds, suggesting that it is taking them more time than usual to organize their speech sequences.

Initiating a Motor Sequence

The frontal lobes are responsible for planning and initiating motor sequences. Each frontal lobe is divided into several hierarchically arranged motor regions, including the three illustrated in **Figure 11-2**. From front to back, they are prefrontal cortex, premotor cortex, and primary motor cortex.

PREFRONTAL CORTEX Atop the hierarchy, the *prefrontal cortex* (PFC) plans our behavior. Deciding to get up at a certain hour to arrive at work on time, to stop at the library to return a book, even whether a behavior is right or wrong and whether it should be performed at all are examples. Humans with PFC injury often break social and legal rules not because they do not know the rules or the consequences of breaking them but because their decision making is faulty. The PFC does not specify the precise movements to be made. It simply specifies the goal.

PREMOTOR CORTEX To bring a plan to completion, the prefrontal cortex sends instructions to the *premotor cortex*, which produces movements coordinating many body parts. If the premotor cortex is damaged, sequences cannot be coordinated and goals cannot be accomplished. For example, the monkey on the right in **Figure 11-3** has a lesion in the dorsal premotor cortex. The monkey has been given the task of extracting a piece of food wedged in a hole in a table (Brinkman, 1984).

The monkey simply pushes the food with a finger. The food drops to the floor and is lost. The monkey has to catch the food by holding a palm beneath the hole as the food is being pushed out. But this brain-injured animal is unable to make the two complementary movements together. It can push the food with a finger and extend an open palm, but it cannot coordinate the action of its two hands, as the healthy monkey on the left can.

PRIMARY MOTOR CORTEX The *primary motor cortex* (area M1) specializes in producing focal skilled movements, such as those involving our arms, hands, and mouth. To understand its role, consider the rich array of movements we can use to grasp objects. We can hold them in one hand, with two hands, or between a hand and another part of the body, for example.

In using the precision pincer grip (**Figure 11-4**A), we hold an object between the thumb and index finger. We can perform many precision grips using the thumb and other fingers in opposition. The pincer grip not only allows us to pick up small objects easily but also allows

FIGURE 11-3 Premotor Control On a task requiring both hands, the healthy monkey can push the peanut out of a hole with one hand and catch it in the other, but 5 months after receiving a lesion of the premotor cortex, the brain-injured monkey cannot. Information from C. Brinkman (1984). Supplementary motor area of the monkey's cerebral cortex: Short- and long-term effects after unilateral ablation and the effects of subsequent callosal section. *Journal of Neuroscience, 4,* p. 925.

us to use them with considerable skill. In contrast, when using a power grip (Figure 11-4B), we hold an object with all our fingers and with more power but fewer skilled options.

People with damage to M1 have difficulty performing reaching movements and shaping their fingers correctly to perform various hand grasps. They also have difficulty performing many skilled hand, arm, and trunk movements, bringing the hand to the mouth to feed themselves, and in talking (Lang & Schieber, 2004).

Experimental Evidence for a Movement Hierarchy

The frontal lobe regions in each hemisphere that plan, coordinate, and execute different kinds of movements are hierarchically related. After the prefrontal cortex formulates a plan of action, it instructs the premotor cortex to organize the appropriate movement sequence, which the primary motor cortex executes. This hierarchy is supported by findings from studies of cerebral blood flow, which serves as an indicator of neural activity. **Figure 11-5** shows the brain regions that were active as the participants in one such study performed various tasks (Roland, 1993).

As the participants use a finger to push a lever, increased blood flow is limited to the primary somatosensory and primary motor cortex (Figure 11-5A). As the participants execute a sequence of finger movements, blood flow also increases in the premotor cortex (Figure 11-5B). And as the participants use a finger to trace their way through a maze, a task that requires coordinated movements in relation to a goal, blood flow increases in the prefrontal cortex as well (Figure 11-5C). Notice that as the participants were performing these tasks, relative blood flow increased most in the regions taking part in the required movements rather than throughout the frontal lobe.

(A) Pincer grip **(B) Whole-hand grip**

Ian Whishaw

FIGURE 11-4 Getting a Grip Figure 8-20 illustrates the development of grasping responses in infants, from the whole-hand to the pincer grip.

Section 7-4 describes imaging methods that record and measure blood flow in the brain.

(A) Simple movement

Blood flow increases in hand area of primary somatosensory and primary motor cortex when participants use a finger to push a lever.

Motor cortex | Sensory cortex

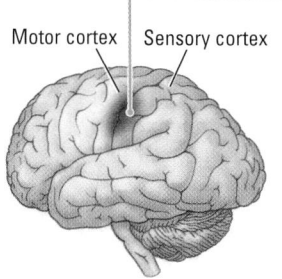

(B) Movement sequence

Blood flow increases in premotor cortex when participants perform a sequence of movements.

Dorsal premotor cortex

(C) Complex movement

When participants use a finger to find a route through a maze, blood flow also increases in prefrontal, temporal, and parietal cortex.

FIGURE 11-5 Hierarchical Movement Control in the Brain Research from P. E. Roland (1993). *Brain Activation* (p. 63). New York: Wiley-Liss.

Brainstem: Species-Typical Movement

In a series of studies, the Swiss neuroscientist Walter Hess (1957) found that the brainstem controls *species-typical behaviors*, actions displayed by every member of a species—the pecking of a robin, the hissing of a cat, or the breaching of a whale. Species-typical movements, then, are mainly innate and organized by brainstem neurons. Hess developed the technique of implanting electrodes into the brains of cats and other animals and cementing them in place. These electrodes could then be attached to stimulating leads in the freely moving animal without causing it much discomfort.

Section 1-5 introduces species-typical behavior, noting that evolutionary principles apply *across* species but not to individuals *within* a species.

▶ EXPERIMENT 11-1

Procedures

Results

Stimulating electrode in brainstem

Electrical stimulation alone produces restless behavior.

Electrical stimulation in the presence of a fist produces slight threats.

Electrical stimulation in the presence of a stuffed polecat (a type of weasel) produces vigorous threat.

Continued electrical stimulation in the presence of the stuffed polecat produces flight and screeching.

Conclusion: Stimulation of some brainstem sites produces behavior that depends on context, suggesting that an important function of the brainstem is to produce appropriate species-typical behavior.

Information from *The Collected Papers of Erich von Holst* (p. 121), translated by R. Martin, 1973, Coral Gables, FL: University of Miami Press.

By stimulating the brainstem, Hess elicited the innate movements that the animal might be expected to make. A resting cat could be induced to suddenly leap up with an arched back and erect hair as though frightened, for example, by an approaching dog. The elicited movements began abruptly when the stimulating current was turned on and ended equally abruptly when it was turned off. An animal performed such species-typical behaviors in a subdued manner when the stimulating current was low and displayed increased vigor as the stimulating current was turned up.

The actions varied, depending on the brainstem site that was stimulated. Stimulating some sites produced head turning; others, walking or running; and still others elicited displays of aggression or fear. The animal's response to a particular stimulus could be modified accordingly. For instance, when shown a stuffed toy, a cat responded to electrical stimulation of some brainstem sites by stalking it and to stimulation of other sites by showing fear and withdrawing.

Hess's experiments have been confirmed and expanded on by other researchers using many animal species. **Experiment 11-1** shows the effects of brainstem stimulation on a chicken under various conditions (von Holst, 1973). Notice the effect of context: how the neural site stimulated interacts both with the object presented and with the stimulation's duration.

With stimulation at a certain site alone, the chicken displays only restless behavior. When a fist is displayed, the same stimulation elicits slightly threatening behavior. When the display switches from a fist to a stuffed polecat, the chicken responds with vigorous threats. Finally, with continued stimulation in the presence of the polecat, the chicken flees, screeching.

Such experiments show that producing complex patterns of adaptive behavior is an important brainstem function. These adaptive patterns include movements used in eating and drinking and in sexual behavior. Animals can be induced to display survival-related behaviors when certain brainstem areas are stimulated. An animal can even be induced to eat nonfood objects, such as chips of wood, if the part of the brainstem that triggers chewing is stimulated.

Grooming illustrates how the brainstem coordinates complex action patterns (Kalueff et al., 2007). A grooming rat sits back on its haunches, licks its paws, wipes its nose with its paws, then wipes its paws across its face, and finally turns to lick the fur on its body. These movements are always performed in the same order, from the face to the shoulders and then toward the rear of the body. The next time you dry off after a shower or swimming, note the grooming sequence you use. Humans' grooming sequence is very similar to the one rats use.

The brainstem is also important for maintaining posture, standing upright, coordinating limb movements, swimming and walking, grooming the fur, and making nests. The effects

Focus 4-4 details ALS.

of damage to brainstem regions that organize many adaptive movements can be seen in the effects of **locked-in syndrome,** similar to those Scott Mackler experienced in connection with ALS (see Research Focus 11-1, Neuroprosthetics). The patient with locked-in syndrome is aware and awake but cannot move or communicate verbally because nearly all voluntary muscles except those of the eyes are completely paralyzed.

The effects of brainstem damage on behavior can also be seen in **cerebral palsy** (CP), a disorder primarily of motor function: making voluntary movements becomes difficult, whereas many aspects of conscious behavior controlled by the cortex may remain intact. CP is often caused by brainstem trauma before or shortly after birth. As described in Clinical Focus 11-2, Cerebral Palsy, trauma leading to cerebral palsy can sometimes happen in early infancy as well. Advances in neuroprosthetic technology, touch-screen technology, and remotely controlled computers all signal important steps toward allowing people with physical disabilities to become more independent.

locked-in syndrome Condition in which a patient is aware and awake but cannot move or communicate verbally because of complete paralysis of nearly all voluntary muscles except the eyes.

cerebral palsy Group of disorders that result from brain damage acquired perinatally (at or near birth).

connectome Comprehensive map of the structural connectivity (the physical wiring) of an organism's nervous system.

CLINICAL F◉CUS 11-2

Cerebral Palsy

E. S. had a cold and infection when he was about 6 months old. Subsequently, he had great difficulty coordinating his movements. As he grew up, his hands and legs were almost useless and his speech was extremely difficult to understand. E. S. was considered intellectually disabled and spent most of his childhood in a custodial school.

When E. S. was 13 years old, the school bought a computer. One teacher attempted to teach E. S. to use it by pushing the keys with a pencil held in his mouth. Within a few weeks, the teacher realized that E. S. was extremely intelligent and could communicate and complete school assignments on the computer. He eventually received a motorized wheelchair that he could control with finger movements of his right hand.

Assisted by the computer and the wheelchair, E. S. soon became almost self-sufficient and eventually attended college, where he achieved excellent grades and became a student leader. On graduation with a degree in psychology, he became a social worker and worked with children with cerebral palsy.

William Little, an English physician, first noticed in 1853 that difficult or abnormal births could lead to later motor difficulties in children. The disorder that Little described was cerebral palsy (also called *Little disease)*, a group of disorders that result from brain damage acquired perinatally (at or near birth). Cerebral palsy is common worldwide, with an incidence estimated to be 1.5 in every 1000 births. Among surviving babies who weigh less than 2.5 kilograms at birth, the incidence is much higher—about 10 in 1000.

The most common causes of cerebral palsy are birth injury, especially due to *anoxia*, a lack of oxygen, and genetic defects. Anoxia may result from a defect in the placenta, the organ that allows oxygen and nutrients to pass from mother to child in utero, or it may be caused by a tangled umbilical cord that reduces the oxygen supply to the infant during birth. Other causes include infections, hydrocephalus, seizures, and prematurity. All may produce a defect in the immature brain before, during, or just after birth.

Most children with cerebral palsy appear healthy in the first few months of life, but as the nervous system develops, motor disturbances become progressively more noticeable. Common symptoms include spasticity, an exaggerated contraction of muscles when they are stretched; dyskinesia, involuntary extraneous movements such as tremors and uncontrollable jerky twists (athetoid movements); and rigidity, or resistance to passive movement. Everyday movements are abnormal, and the affected person may be confined to a wheelchair.

As a means for investigating the relationship between brain development and susceptibility to brain injury, investigators can use an MRI-derived baby connectome that maps changing brain connections during development. A **connectome** is a comprehensive map of the structural connectivity (the physical wiring) of an organism's nervous system. The baby connectome can reveal developmental abnormalities in brain connections even at very early ages, thus expanding the time window to initiate therapeutic strategies (Castellanos et al., 2014).

Many people with cerebral palsy have successful professional careers. Dr. John Melville, second from right, monitors a CT scan and discusses the patient's progress with a colleague. Cerebral palsy has not impeded—and may have inspired—his medical career.

AP Photo/Tony Dejak

Christopher Reeve (left) portraying Superman in 1984 and (right) in 2004, 9 years after his spinal cord injury.

Scratch reflex

quadriplegia Paralysis of the legs and arms due to spinal cord injury.

paraplegia Paralysis of the legs due to spinal cord injury.

scratch reflex Automatic response in which an animal's hind limb reaches to remove a stimulus from the surface of its body.

Spinal Cord: Executing Movement

The late actor Christopher Reeve, who portrayed Superman in three 1980s films, was thrown from a horse during a riding competition in 1995. Reeve's spinal cord was severed near its upper end, at the C1–C2 level (see Spinal Segments and Dermatomes, page 359). The injury left Reeve's brain intact and functioning and his remaining spinal cord intact and functioning too, but his brain and spinal cord were no longer connected.

Other than head movements and slight movement in his shoulders, Reeve's body was completely paralyzed. He was even unable to breathe without assistance. A century ago such a severe injury would have been fatal, but modern and timely medical treatment allowed Reeve to survive for nearly a decade.

A cut high on the spinal cord, such as Christopher Reeve survived, entails paralysis and loss of sensation in the arms and legs, a condition called **quadriplegia.** If the cut is low, **paraplegia** results: paralysis and loss of sensation are confined to the legs and lower body, as described in Clinical Focus 11-3, Spinal Cord Injury, on page 365. Christopher Reeve and his late wife Dana founded the Christopher and Dana Reeve Foundation for spinal cord research. It is dedicated to improving the life and function of spinal cord–injured people and also to searching for cures for spinal cord injury.

Far from being a mere relay between the body and brain, the spinal cord contains complex motor programs. A spinal cord patient can walk on a conveyor belt if the body is supported. Indeed, Christopher Reeve was able to walk in a swimming pool, where his body was supported by water.

When a spinal cord patient's leg is moved backward on a conveyor belt, causing the foot to lose support, the limb reflexively lifts off the belt and swings forward underneath the body. As the foot touches the surface of the belt again, tactile receptors initiate the reflex that causes the foot to push against the surface and support the body's weight. In this way, several spinal reflexes work together to facilitate the complex movement of walking. Walking's reflexive organization can even be obtained in a premature or newborn baby: when held upright, the baby will perform stepping movements.

Among the complex reflexes observed in other vertebrates is the **scratch reflex.** Here, an animal reflexively scratches a part of its body in response to a stimulus from the body surface. The complexity of the scratch reflex is revealed in the movement's accuracy. Absent the brain's direction, the tip of a limb, usually a hind limb in a quadruped, can be correctly directed to the irritated body part. Typically, itching is the sensation that elicits scratching; it is likely that the sensory receptors on the skin that produce itch evolved for detecting parasites and other foreign objects. We return to itching sensations in Section 11-4.

In humans and other animals with a severed spinal cord, spinal reflexes still function, even though the spinal cord is cut off from communication with the brain. As a result, the paralyzed limbs may display spontaneous movements or spasms. But the brain can no longer guide the timing of these movements. Consequently, reflexes related to bladder and bowel control may have to be artificially stimulated by caregivers.

Spinal Cord Injury

Each year, on average, about 11,000 people in the United States and 1000 people in Canada undergo spinal cord injury (as reported by the Foundation for Spinal Cord Injury). Nearly 40 percent of these injuries occur in traffic accidents and another 40 percent occur as a result of falls. Often the spinal cord is completely severed, leaving an individual with no sensation or movement from the site of the cut downward.

Although 12,000 annual spinal cord injuries may seem like a large number, it is small relative to the number of people in the United States and Canada who undergo other kinds of nervous system damage each year. To increase public awareness of their condition and promote research into possible treatments, some, like Christopher Reeve and Canadian Rick Hansen, have been especially active.

Hansen's paraplegia resulted from a lower thoracic spinal injury in 1975. Twelve years later, to raise public awareness of the potential of people with disabilities, he wheeled himself 40,000 kilometers around the world to raise funds for the Man in Motion Legacy Trust Fund. The fund contributes to rehabilitation, wheelchair sports, and public awareness programs. In 2008 it sponsored the Blusson Spinal Cord Centre in Vancouver, Canada, the largest institution in the world dedicated to spinal cord research, housing over 300 investigators.

Spinal cord injury is usually due to trauma to the cord that results in a number of secondary degenerative processes. These processes increase the size of the lesion. Thereafter, the formation of scar tissue, a cavity, and cysts block communication between the two severed sides. Research on spinal cord injury is directed at minimizing the acute changes that take place after the insult, devising ways to facilitate neural communication across the injury, and improving mobility and home care.

Nanotechnology, the science of making and using molecular-sized tools, holds promise for both decreasing the acute effects of injury and bridging the two sides of the injury. Nanotechnology works with substances between 1 and 100 nanometers (nm) in size. (A nanometer is one billionth, or 10^{-9}, of a meter.)

Nanotubes, or nanovesicles, can be engineered to transport drugs, RNA, or new stem cells into the area of injury, where they can arrest degenerative changes and help form neural bridges across the injury (Sharma & Sharma, 2012). Nanotubes that can carry chemicals or conduct electrical impulses can be threaded into the injury through blood vessels and then into the very small capillaries within the spinal cord. Or they can be injected as molecules that self-assemble into scaffolding or tubes when they reach a target area.

Nanoscaffolding, introduced into the injury to form a bridge, can aid the regrowth of axons across the injury (Imani et al., 2015). Nanoaxons can be introduced into the region of injury to synapse with neurons on both sides of the injury and to carry messages across the injury. Because they are small, nanomedicinal substances can interface with spinal cord cells on both sides of an injury.

Stacy Pearsall/Getty Images/Aurora Creative

11-1 REVIEW

A Hierarchy of Movement Control

Before you continue, check your understanding.

1. The motor system is organized as a _____.

2. The _____ cortex plans movements, the _____ cortex organizes movement sequences to carry out the plan, and the _____ cortex executes precise movements.

3. The _____ is responsible for species-typical movements, for survival-related actions, and for posture and walking.

4. In addition to serving as a pathway between the brain and the rest of the body, the _____ independently produces reflexive movements.

5. Explain what happens when the brain is disconnected from the spinal cord and why.

Answers appear at the back of the book.

For additional study tools, visit 😊 LaunchPad:
www.macmillanhighered.com/launchpad/kolb5e

11-2 Motor System Organization

Although we humans tend to rely primarily on our hands for manipulating objects, we can still learn to handle things with other body parts, such as the mouth or a foot, if we have to. Some people without arms become proficient at using a foot for writing or painting or even for driving. What properties of the motor system allow such versatility in carrying out such skilled movements? In this section we examine first the organization of the motor cortex, then the descending pathways from the motor cortex to the brainstem and spinal cord, and finally the motor neurons that in turn connect with the body's muscles.

Motor Cortex

Section 4-1 describes the milestones that led to understanding how the nervous system uses electrical charge to convey information.

In 1870, two Prussian physicians, Gustav Fritsch and Eduard Hitzig, discovered that they could electrically stimulate the neocortex of an anesthetized dog to produce movements of the mouth, limbs, and paws on the opposite side of the dog's body. They provided the first direct evidence that the neocortex controls movement. Later researchers confirmed the finding by experimenting with a variety of animals as subjects, including rats, monkeys, and apes.

Figure 10-19 shows Penfield using brain stimulation to map the cortex.

Based on this research background, beginning in the 1930s Wilder Penfield (Penfield & Boldrey, 1958) used electrical stimulation to map the cortices of conscious human patients who were about to undergo neurosurgery. Penfield's aim was to use the results to assist in surgery. He and his colleagues confirmed that movements in humans are triggered mainly in response to stimulation of the premotor and primary motor cortices.

Mapping the Motor Cortex

Penfield summarized his results by drawing cartoons of body parts to represent the areas of the motor cortex that produce movement in those parts. The result was a **homunculus** (pl. *homunculi*; Latin for *little person*) that could be spread out across the primary motor cortex, as illustrated in **Figure 11-6.** Because the body is symmetrical, an equivalent motor homunculus is discernible in the primary motor cortex of each hemisphere, and each motor cortex mainly controls movement in the opposite side of the body. Penfield also identified another, smaller motor homunculus in the dorsal premotor area of each frontal lobe, a region sometimes referred to as the *supplementary motor cortex*.

The striking feature of the homunculus shown in **Figure 11-7** is the disproportionate relative sizes of its body parts compared with the relative sizes of actual parts of the human body. The homunculus has huge hands with an especially large thumb. Its lips and tongue are also prominent. By contrast, the trunk, arms, and legs—most of the area of a real body—are small.

These distortions illustrate that extensive areas of M1 allow precise regulation of the hands, fingers, lips, and tongue (see Figure 11-6). Body areas over which we have relatively little motor control have a much smaller representation in the motor cortex.

Another curious feature of the homunculus as laid out across the motor cortex is that the body parts are discontinuous—arranged differently from those of an actual body. The cortical area that produces eye movements is in front of the homunculus head on the motor cortex (see the top drawing in Figure 11-6), and the head is oriented with the chin up and the forehead down (bottom drawing). The tongue is below the forehead.

Motor cortex

Electrical stimulation of the motor cortex...

Homunculus

Stimulating electrode

...elicits movements of body parts corresponding to the map of the body.

Movement of body parts

FIGURE 11-6 Penfield's Homunculus Movements are topographically organized in M1. Stimulation of dorsal medial regions produces movements in the lower limbs. Stimulation in ventral regions of the cortex produces movements in the upper body, hands, and face.

Sensory Homunculus (plaster), English School, (20th century)/Natural History Museum, London, UK / The Bridgeman Art Library

FIGURE 11-7 Homuncular Man An artist's representation illustrates the disproportionate areas of the sensory and motor cortices that control different body parts.

Modeling Movement

The motor homunculus shows at a glance that relatively large areas of the brain control the body parts we use to make the most skilled movements—our hands, mouth, and eyes. This makes it useful for understanding M1's **topographic organization** (functional layout). Debate over how the motor areas represented by Penfield's homunculus might produce movement has been considerable.

An early idea was that each part of the homunculus controls muscles in that part of the body. Information from other cortical regions could be sent to the motor homunculus, and neurons in the appropriate part of the homunculus could then activate body muscles required for producing the movement. If you wanted to pick up a coin, for example, messages from the M1 finger area would instruct the fingers. More recent experiments suggest that the motor cortex represents not muscles but rather a repertoire of fundamental movement categories (Grazaino, 2006).

The drawings in **Figure 11-8** illustrate several movement categories elicited in monkeys by electrical stimulation. They include (A) ascend, descend, or jump, (B) reach to clasp, (C) defensive posture or expression, (D) hand toward mouth, (E) masticate or lick, (F) control centrally, and (G) control distally. Whole-body movements are elicited from premotor cortex, and more precise hand and mouth movements are elicited from M1. All these movements occur only when the electrical stimulation lasts long enough for the movement to take place.

Each observed movement has the same end regardless of the starting location of a monkey's limb or its other ongoing behavior. Electrical stimulation that results in the hand coming to the mouth always recruits the hand. If a weight is attached to the monkey's arm, the evoked movement compensates for the added load.

But categorized movements are inflexible: when an obstacle is placed between the hand and the mouth, the hand hits the obstacle. If stimulation continues after the hand has reached the mouth, the hand remains there for the duration of the stimulation.

homunculus Representation of the human body in the sensory or motor cortex; also any topographical representation of the body by a neural area.

topographic organization Neural spatial representation of the body or areas of the sensory world perceived by a sensory organ.

FIGURE 11-8 Natural Movement Categories Movement categories evoked by electrical stimulation of the monkey cortex and the primary motor and premotor regions from which the categories were elicited. Research from M. S. A. Graziano and T. N. Aflalo (2007). Mapping behavioral repertoire onto the cortex. *Neuron 56:* Figure 5, p. 243.

Further, broad movement categories—for example, reaching—cluster together on the motor cortex, but reaching directed to different parts of space is elicited from slightly different cortical points in the topographic reaching map.

MRI studies on human subjects suggest that the human motor cortex, like the monkey motor cortex, is organized in terms of functional movement categories (Meier et al., 2008). The motor cortex maps appear to represent basic types of movements that learning and practice can modify. In other words, the motor cortex encodes not muscle twitches but a lexicon, or dictionary, of movements. As with words and sentences, these few movements used in different combinations produce all the movements you are capable of, even in activities as complex as playing basketball.

Motor Cortex and Skilled Movement

In a study designed to investigate how neurons in the motor cortex control movement, Edward Evarts (1968) used the simple procedure illustrated in **Experiment 11-2.** He trained a monkey to flex its wrist to move a bar. Different weights could be attached to the bar. An electrode implanted in the wrist region of the monkey's motor cortex recorded the activity of neurons there.

Evarts discovered that the neurons began to discharge even before the monkey began the movement, as shown in the Results section of Experiment 11-2. Thus, they take part in planning the movement as well as initiating it. The neurons continued to discharge as the wrist moved, confirming that they play a role in producing the movement. Finally, the neurons discharged at a higher rate when the bar was loaded with a weight. This finding shows that motor cortex neurons increase a movement's force by increasing their firing rate and its duration, as stated in the experiment's Conclusion.

Evarts's findings also reveal that the motor cortex has a role in specifying the end point of a movement. Motor cortex neurons in the wrist might discharge when the monkey flexed its wrist inward but not when the wrist was extended back to its starting position. These on–off neuronal responses are a simple way of coding a desired final position of a movement. Evart's finding that motor cortex neurons are involved in planning movements is confirmed in much less formal situations. For example, recordings of a monkey's biceps muscle, which produces arm flexion, and from motor cortex neurons that produce arm flexion when stimulated, show correlated activity during a monkey's spontaneous behaviors.

The activity of motor neurons in freely moving monkeys suggests that the neurons, depending upon their location, move the body or parts of the body to specific positions (Aflalo & Graziano, 2007). For example, if some neurons are very active when a hand is moved to a specific location, they are progressively less active when the hand is moved away from that position. Thus, the neurons in the motor cortex regions illustrated in Figure 11-8 are responsible for configuring movements that achieve the same end point produced when those same neurons are electrically stimulated (Aflalo & Graziano, 2007).

▶ EXPERIMENT 11-2

Question: How does the motor cortex take part in the control of movement?

Procedure

Electrode from motor-cortex neurons to recording device

Monkey flexes wrist to rotate lever.

Pulley

Lever

Restraint

Wrist movement

Weight

Attached weight can be changed to vary force of movement.

Results

Response of motor-cortex neurons to wrist movement

No weight

Neural activity increases before movement, suggesting motor-cortex participation in planning.

Neural activity continues throughout movement, suggesting motor-cortex participation in execution.

Weight added

Movement begins

Neural activity increases over no-weight condition, suggesting that motor-cortex neurons code force of movement.

Conclusion: The motor cortex takes part in planning movement, executing movement, and adjusting the force and duration of a movement.

Research from E. V. Evarts (1968). Relation of Pyramidal Tract Activity to Force Exerted During Voluntary Movement. *Journal of Neurophysiology, 31,* p. 15.

Nevertheless, studies using human participants reveal situations in which motor cortex neurons can be active even when no overt movement occurs (Schieber, 2011). These situations include planning a movement, withholding a movement on instruction, and mental imagery. Such subthreshold activity in motor cortex neurons may underlie our ability to imagine movements without actually producing them. Subthreshold activity may also allow motor cortex neurons to control brain–computer interfaces (see Research Focus 11-1). In keeping with this idea, monkeys that are controlling an external device using brain activity are described as displaying a nearly complete absence of movement.

Plasticity in the Motor Cortex

An intimate relationship connects the activity of M1 neurons with movement of the body. The studies just described show that flexibility is part of the relationship. Flexibility underlies another property of the motor cortex: its plasticity, which contributes both to motor learning and to recovery after the motor cortex is damaged, as the following example explains.

A study by Randy Nudo and his coworkers (1996), summarized in the Procedure section of **Experiment 11-3**, illustrates change due to cortical damage. These researchers mapped the

Section 14-4 explores how motor maps change in response to learning.

Focus 2-3 describes motor disruptions that stroke causes; Section 16-3 reviews stroke treatments.

▶ EXPERIMENT 11-3

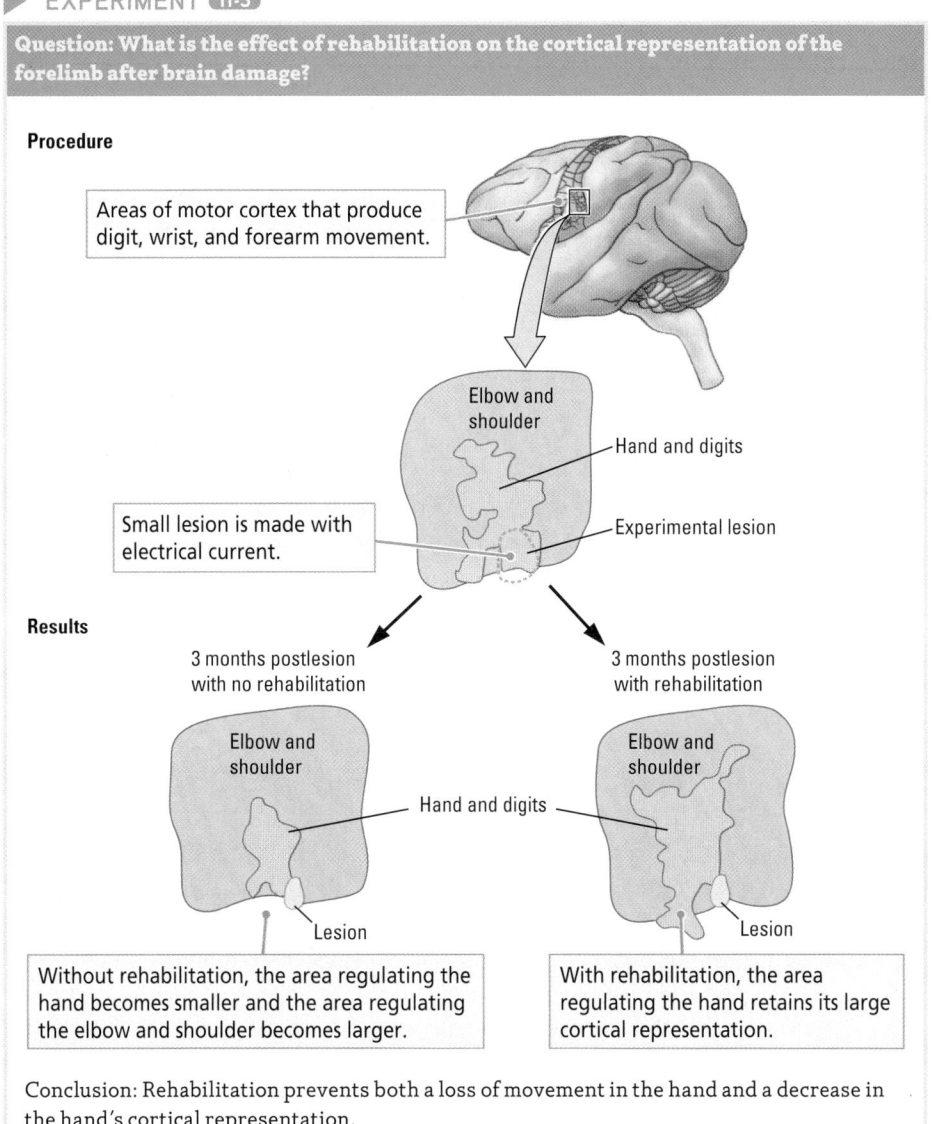

Question: What is the effect of rehabilitation on the cortical representation of the forelimb after brain damage?

Procedure

Areas of motor cortex that produce digit, wrist, and forearm movement.

Elbow and shoulder

Hand and digits

Small lesion is made with electrical current.

Experimental lesion

Results

3 months postlesion with no rehabilitation

3 months postlesion with rehabilitation

Elbow and shoulder

Elbow and shoulder

Hand and digits

Lesion

Lesion

Without rehabilitation, the area regulating the hand becomes smaller and the area regulating the elbow and shoulder becomes larger.

With rehabilitation, the area regulating the hand retains its large cortical representation.

Conclusion: Rehabilitation prevents both a loss of movement in the hand and a decrease in the hand's cortical representation.

Research from R. J. Nudo, B. M. Wise, F. SiFuentes, & G. W. Milliken (1996). Neural Substrates for the Effects of Rehabilitative Training on Motor Recovery after Ischemic Infarct. *Science, 272*, p. 1793.

Section 7-1 describes ablation techniques used by neuroscience researchers to manipulate the brain.

motor cortices of monkeys to identify the hand and digit areas. They then surgically removed a small part of the cortex that represents the digit area. After undergoing this electrolytic lesion, the monkeys used the affected hand much less, relying mainly on the good hand.

When the researchers stimulated the cortex of the monkeys 3 months later, the animals were unable to produce many lower-arm movements—including the wrist, hand, and digits—that they produced prior to the lesion. Much of the area representing the hand and lower arm had disappeared from the animals' cortical maps. The shoulder, upper arm, and elbow areas had spread out to take up what had formerly been space representing the hand and digits. The Results section of Experiment 11-3 shows this topographic change.

The experimenters wondered whether the change could have been prevented had they forced the monkeys to use the affected arm. To find out, they used the same procedure on other monkeys, except that during the postsurgery period they forced the animals to rely on the bad arm by binding the good arm in a sling.

When the experimenters reexamined these monkeys' motor maps 3 months later, they found that the hand and digit area retained its larger size. Even though no neural activity occurred in the spot with the lesion, the monkeys had gained some function in the digits that used to be connected to the damaged spot. Apparently, the remaining cortical digit area was now controlling the movement of these fingers.

Most likely, plasticity is promoted in the formation of new connections and the strengthening of existing connections among different parts of the motor homunculus. Humans who have had a stroke to the motor cortex also display plasticity-mediated recovery. They may at first be completely unable to use their contralateral forelimb, but with time and practice they may recover a great deal of movement.

As Nudo's monkey experiment illustrates, one way to enhance recovery is to restrain the good limb. **Constraint-induced therapy,** which forces use of the affected limb, is a major therapy for stroke-induced limb paralysis. Its effectiveness depends on frustration of the good limb, which promotes a concerted effort to use the bad limb and promotes neural plasticity.

Corticospinal Tracts

The main efferent pathways from the motor cortex to the brainstem to the spinal cord are the **corticospinal tracts.** The axons from these tracts originate mainly in motor cortex layer V pyramidal cells but also extend from the premotor cortex and the sensory cortex (see Layering in the Neocortex on page 359). The axons descend into the brainstem, sending collaterals to numerous brainstem nuclei, and eventually emerge on the brainstem's ventral surface, where they form a large bump on each side. These bumps, or pyramids, give the corticospinal tracts their alternative name, the *pyramidal tracts.*

At this point, some axons descending from the left hemisphere cross over to the right side of the brainstem. Likewise, some axons descending from the right hemisphere cross over to the left side of the brainstem. The remaining axons stay on their original side. This division produces two corticospinal tracts, one crossed and the other uncrossed, entering each side of the spinal cord. **Figure 11-9** illustrates the division of tracts originating in the left-hemisphere cortex. The dual tracts on each side of the brainstem descend into the spinal cord, forming the two spinal cord tracts.

The cross section of a spinal cord in **Figure 11-10** shows the location of the two tracts, on the left and right sides. The fibers that

FIGURE 11-9 Left–Hemisphere Corticospinal Tract Nerve fibers descend from the left-hemisphere motor cortex to the brainstem, where the tract branches into the spinal cord. The lateral tract crosses the brainstem's midline, descending into the right side of the spinal cord to move limb and digit muscles on the body's right side. The anterior tract remains on the left side to move muscles at the body's midline.

cross to the opposite side of the brainstem descend the spinal cord in a lateral (side) position to form the *lateral corticospinal tract*. The fibers that remain on their original side continue from the brainstem down the spinal cord in an anterior (front) position, to form the *anterior corticospinal tract*.

Retracing the pathway, the corticospinal tracts originate in the neocortex and terminate in the spinal cord. Within the spinal cord, corticospinal fibers make synaptic connections with both interneurons and motor neurons, but the motor neurons carry all nervous system commands out to the muscles.

Motor Neurons

Spinal cord motor neurons are located in the anterior part of the spinal cord, the anterior horns, which jut out from the anterior part of the spinal cord. The anterior horns contain two kinds of neurons. Interneurons lie just medial to the motor neurons and project onto them. The motor neurons send their axons to the body muscles. The fibers from the corticospinal tracts make synaptic connections with both the interneurons and the motor neurons, but the motor neurons carry all nervous system commands to the muscles.

Figure 11-10 shows that a homunculus of the body is represented again in the spinal cord. The more lateral motor neurons project to muscles that control the fingers and hands, whereas intermediate motor neurons project to muscles that control the shoulders and arms. The most medial motor neurons project to muscles that control the body's trunk. Axons of the lateral corticospinal tract connect mainly with the lateral interneurons and motor neurons, and axons of the anterior corticospinal tract connect mainly to the medial interneurons and motor neurons.

To visualize how the cortical regions responsible for different movements relate to the motor neuron homunculus in the spinal cord, look again at Figure 11-9. Place your finger on the index finger region of the motor homunculus on the left side of the brain. If you trace the axons of the cortical neurons downward, your route takes you through the brainstem, across its midline, and down the right lateral corticospinal tract.

The journey ends at the interneurons and motor neurons in the most lateral region of the spinal cord's right anterior horn—the horn on the opposite (contralateral) side of the nervous system from which you began. Following the axons of these motor neurons, you find that they synapse on muscles that move the right index finger.

If you repeat the procedure by tracing the pathway from the trunk area of the motor homunculus, near the top on the left side of the brain, you follow the same route through the upper part of the brainstem. You do not cross over to the opposite side, however. Instead, you descend into the spinal cord on the left side, the same (ipsilateral) side of the nervous system on which you began, eventually ending up in the most medial interneurons and motor neurons of the left side's anterior horn. (At this point, some of these axons also cross over to the other side of the spinal cord.) Thus, if you follow these motor neuron axons, you end up at their synapses with the muscles that move the trunk on both sides of the body.

This visualization can help you remember the routes taken by motor system axons. The limb regions of the motor homunculus contribute most of their fibers to the lateral corticospinal tract, the fibers that cross over to the opposite side of the spinal cord. They activate motor circuits that move the arm, hand, leg, and foot on the opposite side of the body. In contrast, the trunk regions of the motor homunculus contribute their fibers to the anterior corticospinal tract. Only a few of these fibers cross, close to their termination in the spinal cord; most control the trunk and limbs on the same side of the body.

Anterior horn of spinal cord

Fingers
Arms
Shoulders
Trunk

Lateral corticospinal tract synapses with interneurons and motor neurons that innervate muscles of the limbs and digits.

Interneurons project to motor neurons.

Motor neurons project to muscles of the body.

Anterior corticospinal tract synapses with interneurons and motor neurons that innervate the trunk (midline of the body).

The interneurons and motor neurons of the spinal cord are envisioned as a homunculus representing the muscles that they innervate.

FIGURE 11-10 Motor Tract Organization Interneurons and motor neurons in the left and right anterior spinal cord tracts are topographically arranged: the more lateral neurons innervate more distal parts of the limbs (those farther from the midline), and the more medial neurons innervate more proximal body muscles (those closer to the midline).

If you are right-handed, the neurons your brain is using to carry out this task are the same neurons that you are tracing.

constraint-induced therapy Procedure in which restraint of a healthy limb forces a patient to use an impaired limb to enhance recovery of function.

corticospinal tract Bundle of nerve fibers directly connecting the cerebral cortex to the spinal cord, branching at the brainstem into an opposite-side lateral tract that informs movement of limbs and digits and a same-side anterior tract that informs movement of the trunk; also called *pyramidal tract*.

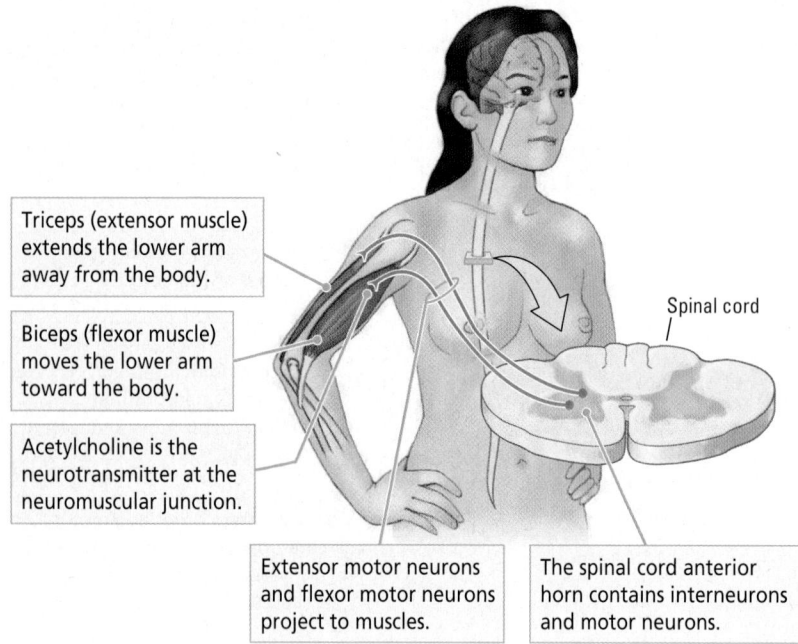

Triceps (extensor muscle) extends the lower arm away from the body.

Biceps (flexor muscle) moves the lower arm toward the body.

Acetylcholine is the neurotransmitter at the neuromuscular junction.

Spinal cord

Extensor motor neurons and flexor motor neurons project to muscles.

The spinal cord anterior horn contains interneurons and motor neurons.

FIGURE 11-11 Coordinating Muscle Movement

Figure 4-26 illustrates ACh action at a motor neuron–muscle junction.

Remember that the motor cortex is organized in terms of functional movement categories, such as reaching or climbing (see Figure 11-8). A similar template in the spinal cord ensures that instructions from the motor cortex are reproduced faithfully. Presumably, lateral interneurons produce acts of reaching or bringing the hand to the mouth, and the medial interneurons and motor neurons produce whole-body movements, including walking. Recall that a spinal cord isolated from the brain by a cut is capable of many kinds of movements, and it is able to do so because the movements are organized by its interneurons and motor neurons.

In addition to the corticospinal pathways, about 24 other pathways from the brainstem to the spinal cord carry instructions, such as information related to posture and balance (see Section 11-4), and they control the enteric nervous system as well as portions of the sympathetic division of the ANS. Remember that for all these functions, the motor neurons are the final common path.

Control of Muscles

Spinal cord motor neurons synapse on the muscles that control body movements. For example, the biceps and triceps of the upper arm control movement of the lower arm. Limb muscles are arranged in pairs, as shown in **Figure 11-11.** One member of a pair, the *extensor,* moves (extends) the limb away from the trunk. The other member of the pair, the *flexor,* moves (flexes) the limb in toward the trunk. Experiment 11-2 on page 368 demonstrates the on–off responses of cortical motor neurons, depending on whether the flexor or extensor muscle is being used.

Connections between spinal cord interneurons and motor neurons ensure that the muscles work together so that when one muscle contracts, the other relaxes. Thus, the spinal cord interneurons and motor neurons not only relay instructions from the brain but also, through their connections, cooperatively organize the movement of many muscles. As you know, the neurotransmitter at the motor neuron–muscle junction is acetylcholine.

(11-2) **REVIEW**

Motor System Organization

Before you continue, check your understanding.

1. The _____ organization of the motor cortex is represented by a _____, in which parts of the body that are capable of the most skilled movements (especially the mouth, fingers, and thumbs) are regulated by _____ cortical regions.

2. Change can take place in the cortical _____ to aid in recovery of function after motor cortex injury.

3. Instructions regarding movement travel out from the motor cortex through the _____ tracts to terminate on interneurons that project to motor neurons in the anterior horn of the spinal cord. Many corticospinal-tract fibers cross to the opposite side of the spinal cord to form the _____ tracts; some stay on the same side to form the _____ tracts.

4. The anterior corticospinal tracts carry instructions for _____ movements, whereas the lateral corticospinal tracts carry instructions for _____ and _____ movements.

5. Motor neuron axons in the spinal cord carry instructions to _____ that are arranged in pairs. One _____ a limb; the other _____ the limb.

6. What does the plan of movements in the motor cortex as revealed by electrical stimulation tell us about the brain's representation of movement?

Answers appear at the back of the book.

For additional study tools, visit 🅜 **LaunchPad**:
www.macmillanhighered.com/launchpad/kolb5e

11-3 Basal Ganglia, Cerebellum, and Movement

The main evidence that the basal ganglia and the cerebellum perform motor functions is that damage to either structure impairs movement. Both have extensive connections with the motor cortex, which further suggests their participation in movement. After an overview of each structure's anatomy, we look at some symptoms that arise after damage to the basal ganglia or the cerebellum. Then we consider the roles each structure plays in controlling movement.

Basal Ganglia and the Force of Movement

The neocortex connects extensively with the basal ganglia, a collection of nuclei lying just beneath the cortex, as illustrated in **Figure 11-12**. The basal ganglia do not produce movement directly, but rather modulate the activity of cortical motor systems. The nuclei participate in a wide range of functions, including association or habit learning, motivation, and emotion, as well as motor control.

Anatomy of the Basal Ganglia

Among the nuclei forming the basal ganglia are the *caudate nucleus* and the *putamen*, which together form the *striatum* (meaning striped body and named for the fibers, including corticospinal fibers, running through it), and the *subthalamic nucleus* and *globus pallidus*. As shown in Figure 11-12, the prominent striatum extends as a tail (*caudate* means *having a tail*) into the temporal lobe, ending in the amygdala. There are three main basal ganglia connections:

1. All areas of the neocortex and more primitive allocortex project to the basal ganglia.

2. The basal ganglia project to the motor cortex via relays in the thalamus.

3. The basal ganglia receive connections from the dopamine cells of the midbrain substantia nigra over the nigrostriatal pathway and also project to the substantia nigra.

Through these connections, the basal ganglia form reciprocal circuits, or loops, connecting all neocortical and allocortical regions to the motor cortex. Other loops connect the basal ganglia and substantia nigra, allowing the substantia nigra to modulate the subcortical–motor cortex loops. Separate loops likely participate in selecting and producing skilled movements for learned actions and emotional expression. Some of these loops' functions are revealed in behavioral deficits that follow damage to the basal ganglia.

How the Basal Ganglia Control Movement Force

Two types of movement disorders—in many ways opposites—result from basal ganglia damage. If cells of the caudate putamen are damaged, unwanted writhing and twitching movements called *dyskinesias* result. In Huntington disease, for example, characterized

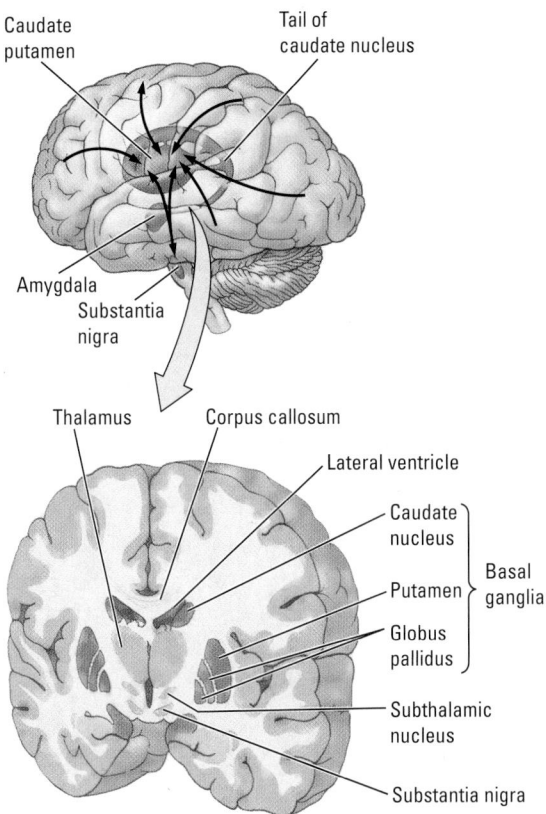

FIGURE 11-12 **Basal Ganglia Connections** The caudate putamen in the basal ganglia connects to the amygdala through the tail of the caudate nucleus. The lateral see-through view shows the basal ganglia relative to surrounding structures, including the substantia nigra, with which it shares reciprocal connections. The basal ganglia receive input from most regions of the cortex and send input into the frontal lobes through the subthalamic nucleus.

Figure 5-17 traces the nigrostriatal pathways in the dopaminergic activating system and highlights their importance for maintaining healthy motor behavior.

Focus 3-4 describes the genetic basis of Huntington disease.

Detailed coverage of Parkinson disease and its treatment appears in Chapters 5, 7, and 16.

hyperkinetic symptom Excessive involuntary movement, as seen in Tourette syndrome.

hypokinetic symptom Paucity of movement, as seen in Parkinson disease.

by involuntary, exaggerated, and disjointed movements, striatal cells are destroyed. Other involuntary movements related to striatal damage are the unwanted tics and vocalizations peculiar to the topic of Clinical Focus 11-4, Tourette Syndrome.

In addition to causing involuntary movements, or **hyperkinetic symptoms,** as just described, basal ganglia damage can result in a loss of motor ability, or **hypokinetic symptoms** that feature rigidity and difficulty initiating and producing movements. Parkinson disease is marked by hypokinetic symptoms caused by the loss of dopamine cells in the substantia nigra that project into the basal ganglia.

The fact that both hyperkinetic and hypokinetic symptoms arise subsequent to basal ganglia damage suggests that one function of these nuclei is regulating movement force. The idea is that hyperkinetic disorders such as Huntington disease result from errors of too much force and so result in excessive movement. Hypokinetic disorders such as Parkinson disease result from errors of too little force and so result in insufficient movement.

In support of these ideas, in a reaching task, Huntington subjects reached using too much force, thus seemingly flinging a limb. Parkinson subject reached with too little force, thus producing slowed movement (Moisello et al., 2011). An MRI study of basal ganglia

CLINICAL F◉CUS 11-4

Tourette Syndrome

The neurological disorder Tourette syndrome (TS) was first described in 1885 by Georges Gilles de la Tourette, a French neurologist, who described the symptoms as they appeared in Madame de D., one of his patients:

> Madame de D., presently age 26, at the age of 7 was afflicted by convulsive movements of the hands and arms. These abnormal movements occurred above all when the child tried to write, causing her to crudely reproduce the letters she was trying to trace. After each spasm, the movements of the hand became more regular and better controlled until another convulsive movement would again interrupt her work. She was felt to be suffering from over-excitement and mischief, and because the movements became more and more frequent, she was subject to reprimand and punishment. Soon it became clear that these movements were indeed involuntary and convulsive in nature. The movements involved the shoulders, the neck, and the face, and resulted in contortions and extraordinary grimaces. As the disease progressed, and the spasms spread to involve her voice and speech, the young lady made strange screams and said words that made no sense. (Friedhoff & Chase, 1982)

The statistical incidence of Tourette syndrome is about 1 in 1000 people. TS affects all racial groups and seems to be hereditary. The age range of onset is 2 to 25 years.

The most frequent symptoms of Tourette syndrome are involuntary tics and complex movements, such as hitting, lunging, or jumping. People with TS may also emit sudden cries and other vocalizations or inexplicably utter words that do not make sense in the context, including coprolalia and swearing.

Tourette syndrome is thought to reflect an abnormality of the basal ganglia, especially in the right hemisphere, because its symptoms can be controlled with haloperidol, an antipsychotic drug that blocks dopamine synapses in the basal ganglia. Using fMRI to correlate resting activity with brain regions, Church and colleagues (2009) documented cortical changes associated with TS. These include increased connectivity, mainly in the parietal cortex of Tourette patients, and decreased connectivity between parietal and frontal cortex. This finding, diagrammed in the illustration, suggests altered functioning in neural circuits that

connect the posterior sensory regions of the cortex to its anterior motor regions.

The urge to make involuntary movements and vocalizations may be similar to behaviors that have an urge-to-action feature, such as yawning and stretching (Tinaz et al., 2015). Using fMRI, the investigators suggest that an urge-to-action system in the brain involves the right dorsal *insula*, a multifunctional cortical area that integrates sensory and emotional awareness and is important for interoception (self-awareness). Why particular movements and vocalizations that characterize individuals with Tourette syndrome should be caught up by this urge-to-act system remains a mystery.

In fMRI analyses of young adults with Tourette syndrome, brain areas that show enhanced (green) or decreased (red) connectivity suggest abnormalities in dorsal stream structures linking the parietal cortex to the frontal cortex. Information from J. A. Church, D. A. Fair, N. U. Dosenbach, et al. (2009). Control networks in paediatric Tourette syndrome show immature and anomalous patterns of functional connectivity. *Brain*, 32, pp. 225–238.

activity in healthy participants who, for a small monetary reward, considered how much force to apply in a gripping task, showed more basal ganglia activity when they contemplated using a more forceful grip and less activity when contemplating a less forceful grip (Kurniawan et al., 2010). Together, these studies suggest that the basal ganglia play a role not just in producing force but also in computing the effortful costs of making movements.

What features of the reciprocal basal ganglia loops allow for selecting movements or modulating movement force? One theory holds that the basal ganglia can influence whether movement occurs (Friend & Kravitz, 2014). As illustrated in **Figure 11-13**, a pathway (green) from the thalamus to the cortex to the spinal cord produces movement. The globus pallidus (red) can inhibit this pathway at the level of the thalamus.

The globus pallidus is controlled by two basal ganglia pathways, one indirect and one direct. If the globus pallidus is excited, it in turn inhibits the thalamus and blocks movement. If it is inhibited, motor cortex circuits that include the thalamus are able to produce movement. The globus pallidus thus acts like a volume control. If it is turned down, movement can occur; if it is turned up, movement is blocked. This model proposes that diseases of the basal ganglia affecting its "volume control" function impair movement so that it is either excessive or slowed.

The idea that the globus pallidus acts like a volume control is the basis for several treatments for Parkinson disease. Consistent with the volume hypothesis, recordings made from globus pallidus cells show excessive activity, which inhibits movement in people with Parkinson disease. If the globus pallidus or the subthalamic nucleus (a relay in the indirect pathway) is partially surgically destroyed in Parkinson patients, muscular rigidity is reduced and normal movement is improved. Similarly, *deep brain stimulation* (DBS) of the globus pallidus inactivates it, freeing movement.

Interestingly, impairments in the application of force may underlie motor disorders of skilled movements such as writer's cramp, one of a number of impairments called *selective dystonias*. One such impairment, the yips, is distorted execution of skilled movements by professional athletes. For example, the yips have ended the career of many professional golfers by ruining the player's swing (Belton et al., 2014).

Another structure in the basal ganglia, the nucleus accumbens, is also called the ventral striatum, because it is the most ventral basal ganglia nucleus. The nucleus accumbens receives projections from dopamine cells of the ventral tegmental area, a nucleus just medial to the substantia nigra in the midbrain. Called the mesolimbic dopamine pathway, it is a part of a loop that aids our perception of cues signaling reward.

Cerebellum and Movement Skill

Musicians have a saying: "Miss a day of practice and you're OK, miss two days and you notice, miss three days and the world notices." Apparently, changes take place in the brain when we practice or neglect to practice a motor skill. The cerebellum may be the affected component of the motor system. Whether the skill is playing a musical instrument, pitching a baseball, or texting, the cerebellum is critical for acquiring and maintaining motor skills.

Anatomy of the Cerebellum

The cerebellum, a large and conspicuous part of the motor system, sits atop the brainstem, clearly visible just behind the cerebrum, and like the cerebrum, is divided into two hemispheres (**Figure 11-14**). A small lobe, the *flocculus*, projects from its ventral, or inferior, surface. Although smaller than the cerebrum, the cerebellum has many more gyri and sulci, and for all us primates, contains about four times as many neurons as does the cortex.

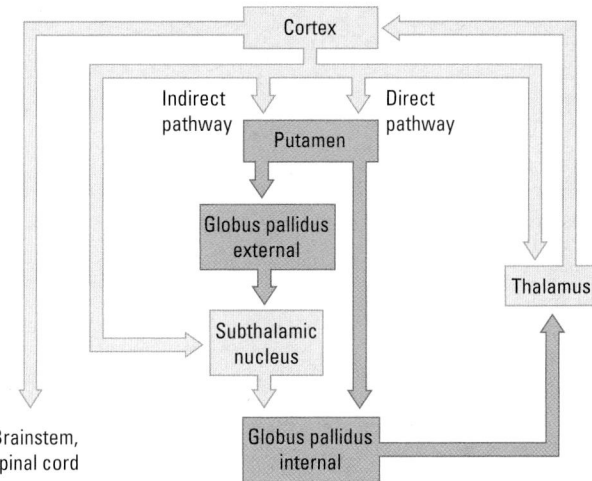

FIGURE 11-13 Regulating Movement Force Two pathways in the basal ganglia modulate movements produced in the cortex. Green pathways are excitatory; red are inhibitory. The indirect pathway excites the globus pallidus internal, whereas the direct pathway has an inhibitory effect. If activity in the indirect pathway dominates, the thalamus shuts down, and the cortex is unable to produce movement. If direct-pathway activity dominates, the thalamus can become overactive, amplifying movement. Information from R. E. Alexander & M. D. Crutcher (1990). Functional architecture of basal ganglia circuits: Neural Substrates of parallel processing. *Trends in Neuroscience, 13*, p. 269.

Figure 1-6 shows electrodes implanted in the brain for DBS.

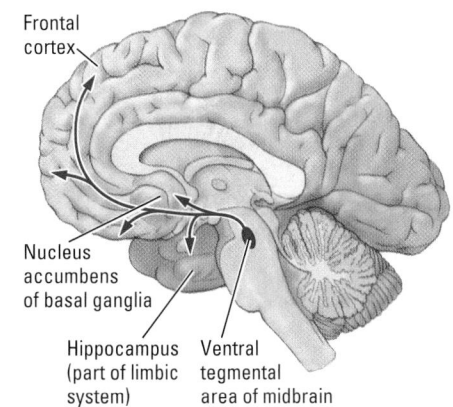

The mesolimbic DA pathway (purple projections from ventral tegmentum) is a substrate not only of reward but of addictive behavior as well. See Section 6-4.

The elephant's cerebellum, by contrast, contains 98.5% of its neurons. Details in Focus 1-3.

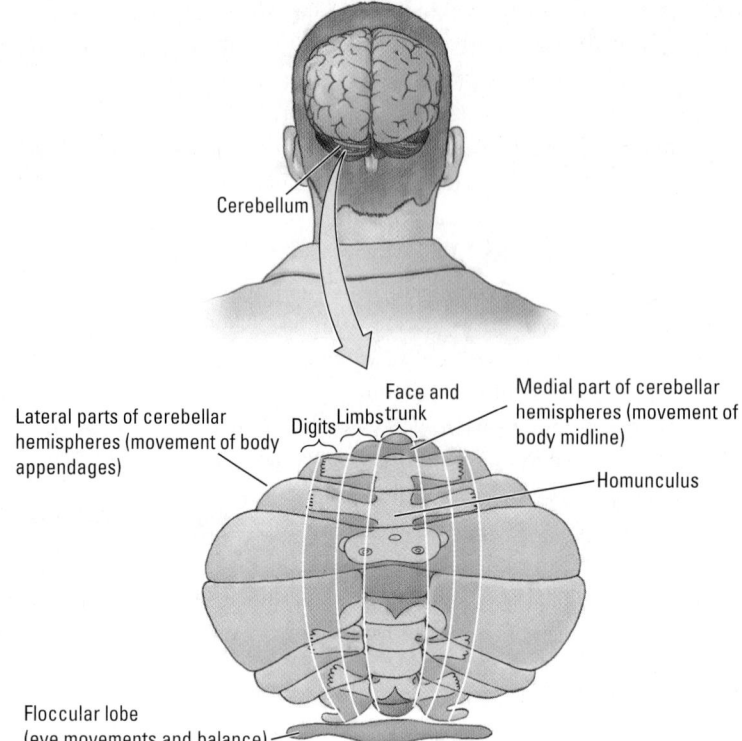

FIGURE 11-14 Cerebellar Homunculus The cerebellar hemispheres control body movements, and the flocculus controls eye movements and balance. In the cerebellum's topographical organization, relatively medial parts represent the body's midline and relatively lateral parts represent the limbs and digits.

Ramón y Cajal's drawing of a Purkinje cell, circa 1900.

As Figure 11-14 shows, the cerebellum can be divided into several regions, each specialized for an aspect of motor control. At its base, the flocculus receives projections from the middle ear vestibular system, described in Section 11-4, and takes part in controlling balance. Many projections from the flocculus go to the spinal cord and to the motor nuclei that control eye movements.

Just as the motor cortex has a homuncular organization and multiple homunculi, the cerebellar hemispheres have at least two, as shown in Figure 11-14. The medial part of each homunculus controls the face and the body's midline. The more lateral parts connect to motor cortex areas associated with movements of the limbs, hands, feet, and digits. Pathways from the cerebellar hemispheres project to nuclei at the interface of the cerebellum and spinal cord. These in turn project to other brain regions, including the motor cortex.

To summarize the cerebellum's topographic organization, the midline of the homunculus is represented in its central part; the limbs and digits are represented in the lateral parts. Tumors or damage to midline areas of the cerebellum disrupt balance, eye movement, upright posture, and walking but do not substantially disrupt other movements such as reaching, grasping, and using the fingers. A person with medial damage to the cerebellum may, when lying down, show few symptoms. Damage to lateral parts of the cerebellum disrupts arm, hand, and finger movements much more than movements of the body's trunk.

The arrangement and connections of the cerebellum are built to a common plan. The cerebellar cortex consists of three layers of cells, with the distinctive Purkinje cells forming the second layer. Purkinje cells are the output cells of the cerebellum. This plan suggests that the cerebellum has a common function with respect to its control over other motor system regions.

How the Cerebellum Improves Movement Control

Attempts to understand how the cerebellum controls movement have centered on two major ideas. Damage to the cerebellum (1) does not abolish any movement but (2) does disrupt the timing and execution of movement. Thus, the cerebellum must regulate the timing and flow of movement as required for the situation.

Tom Thach (2007), in an intriguing experiment, illustrates how the cerebellum helps make the adjustments needed to keep movements accurate. Control participants and subjects with cerebellar damage threw darts at a target, as shown in the Procedure section of **Experiment 11-4.** After a number of throws that allowed them to become reasonably accurate, both groups donned glasses containing wedge-shaped prisms that displaced the apparent location of the target to the left. Now when they threw a dart, it landed to the left of the intended target.

Both groups showed this initial distortion in aim. But then came an important difference, graphed in the Results section of Experiment 11-4. When controls saw the dart miss the mark, they adjusted each successive throw until reasonable accuracy was restored. In contrast, subjects with cerebellar damage could not correct for this error. Time after time, they missed the target far to the left.

Next, the controls removed the prism glasses and threw a few more darts. Again, a significant difference emerged. The first dart thrown by each participant was much too far to the right (owing to the previous adjustment they had learned to make), but soon each one adjusted once again until his or her former accuracy was regained.

▶ EXPERIMENT `11-4`

Question: Does the cerebellum help to make adjustments required to keep movements accurate?

Procedure

No prism

Prism

Prism glasses

No prism

Subject or healthy control throws dart at target

Subject or control participant wears prisms that divert gaze

Prisms removed, healthy control adapts; subject shows no change

Results

Control participant

Distance from target (to the right / to the left)

Initial throws | With prisms | Prisms removed

A control participant adapts when wearing the prisms and shows aftereffects when the prisms are removed.

Trials

Subject with damage to cerebellum

Initial throws | With prisms | Prisms removed

A subject with damage to the cerebellum fails to correct throws while wearing the prisms and shows no aftereffects when the prisms are removed.

Trials

Conclusion: Many movements we make depend on moment-to-moment learning and adjustments made by the cerebellum.

Information from W. T. Thach, H. P. Goodkin, & J. G. Keating (1992). The Cerebellum and the Adaptive Coordination of Movement. *Annual Review of Neuroscience, 15,* p. 429.

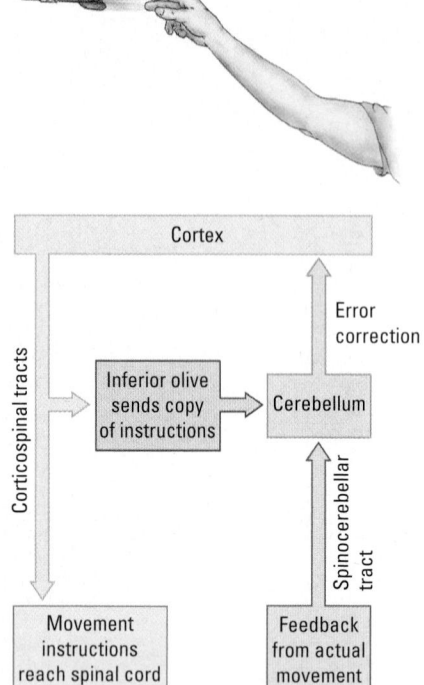

FIGURE 11-15 Intention, Action, and Feedback By comparing the message for the intended movement with the movement that was actually performed, the cerebellum sends an error message to the cortex to improve the accuracy of a subsequent movement.

In contrast, subjects with damage to the cerebellum showed no aftereffects of wearing the prisms; they had never compensated for the glasses to begin with. This experiment suggests that many movements we make—whether throwing a dart or organizing a movement sequence to shoot a basketball—depend on moment-to-moment learning and adjustments made by the cerebellum.

To examine the role of learning in this task, monkeys were trained on a similar task to point a finger to a target on a computer screen. Once they had mastered the task, they were required to perform it with prism glasses. The monkeys displayed a displacement of pointing and an aftereffect when the prism glasses were removed.

After 30 days of training with and without prisms, displacement and aftereffect disappeared, and the monkeys were immediately accurate when wearing the prisms and after they were removed. When the arm region of the cerebellar homunculus was then anesthetized with lidocaine, a local anesthetic agent, pointing without prisms was normal, but the learned adaptation to prisms was abolished. This experiment illustrates that the cerebellum is responsible not only for online adjustments of movement but also for learning relatively permanent movement skills (Norris et al., 2011). Using a somewhat similar task, Hashimoto and associates (2015) obtained similar results using humans who have cerebellar damage.

To better understand how the cerebellum improves motor skills by adjusting movements, consider the model charted in **Figure 11-15**. Imagine throwing a dart. You aim at the bull's-eye, throw the dart, and find that it misses the board completely. You aim again, this time adjusting your throw to correct for the original error. The model illustrates that there are actually two versions of your action: (1) the movement you intended to make and (2) the actual movement as recorded by sensory receptors in your arm and shoulder. If you carry out the intended movement successfully, you need make no correction on your next try. But if you miss, and you frequently will, an adjustment is called for.

The model illustrates that the cortex sends instructions to the spinal cord to throw a dart at the target. A copy of the same instructions is sent to the cerebellum through the inferior olive, a nucleus in the brainstem that projects to the cerebellum. Then, when you throw the dart, the sensory receptors in your arm and shoulder code the actual movement you make and send a message about it back to the cerebellum through the spinocerebellar tract. The cerebellum now has information about both versions of the movement—what you intended to do and what you actually did—and can calculate the error and inform the cortex how to correct the movement. When you next throw a dart, you incorporate the correction into your throw. If the cerebellum is damaged, the ability to correct errors by comparing intended and actual movements is impaired (Therrien & Bastian, 2015).

(11-3) **REVIEW**

Basal Ganglia, Cerebellum, and Movement

Before you continue, check your understanding.

1. The _____ contribute to motor control by adjusting the _____ associated with each movement.

2. Damage to the basal ganglia results either in unwanted involuntary _____ movements (too much force exerted) or in such _____ rigidity that movements are difficult to perform (too little force exerted).

3. The cerebellum contributes to motor control by improving movement _____ and the learning of motor _____ .

4. Describe how the cerebellum improves execution of motor skills.

Answers appear at the back of the book.

For additional study tools, visit 🐢 LaunchPad:
www.macmillanhighered.com/launchpad/kolb5e

11-4 Somatosensory System Receptors and Pathways

The motor system produces movement, but without sensation, movement would lack direction and quickly become impaired. The somatosensory system is indispensable for movement. The body senses tell us about the physical contact we make with the world as well as how successful our physical interactions with the world are.

Somatic sensation is unique among sensory systems. For the most part, it is distributed throughout the body, not localized in the head, as are vision, hearing, taste, and smell. Somatosensory receptors found in the skin, muscles, and internal organs, including the circulatory system, feature specialized dendritic attachments on sensory neurons, or the dendrites themselves are the sensory receptors. Somatosensory neurons convey information to the spinal cord and brain. One part of the system, however, is confined to a single organ. The inner ear houses the vestibular system, which contributes to our sensations of balance and head movement.

In considering the motor system, we started at the cortex and followed the motor pathways out to the spinal cord (review Figures 11-9 and 11-10). This efferent route follows the outward flow of neural instructions regarding movement. As we explore the somatosensory system, we proceed in the opposite direction, because afferent sensory information flows inward, from the body's sensory receptors through sensory pathways in the spinal cord to the cortex.

Somatosensory Receptors and Perception

Our body is covered with somatosensory receptors. Receptors include body hair, which is attached to the dendrites of sensory neurons. Many receptor types are embedded in surface skin, in deeper layers of the skin, and in muscles, tendons, and joints. Some receptors consist simply of a sensory neuron dendrite. Others are specialized capsules or connective tissue surrounding a dendrite, and still others include a dendrite attached to the base of a hair.

The density of somatosensory receptors, which varies greatly throughout the body, determines sensitivity to stimulation. Body parts that are highly sensitive to touch—including the hands, feet, lips, and tongue—have far more sensory receptors than less sensitive body parts—the arms, back, and legs.

Humans have two kinds of skin, hairy skin and **glabrous skin,** which includes the palms of the hands and feet, lips, and tongue. Glabrous skin is hairless and exquisitely sensitive to a wide range of stimuli. It covers the body parts that we use to explore objects—hence its heightened sensitivity.

The skin's touch sensitivity is often measured with a two-point sensitivity test. By touching the skin with two sharp points simultaneously, we can observe how close together the points can be placed while still being detected by the participant as two points rather than one. On glabrous skin, we can detect the two points when they are as close as 3 millimeters apart.

Two-point sensitivity test

On hairy skin, two-point sensitivity is weaker by a factor of about 10. The two points seem to merge into one below a separation distance ranging from 2 to 5 cm, depending on the exact body part tested. You can confirm these differences in sensitivity on your own body by touching two sharp pencil points to a palm and to a forearm, varying the distances that you hold the points apart. Be sure not to look as you touch each surface.

Classifying Somatosensory Receptors

The varied types of somatosensory receptors in the human body may total as many as 20 or more, but they can all be classified into the three functional groupings illustrated in **Figure 11-16** as perceptions of irritation, pressure, or movement.

glabrous skin Skin that does not have hair follicles but contains larger numbers of sensory receptors than do hairy skin areas.

Nociception (pain, temperature, itch)	Adaptation	Damage or irritation to the dendrite or to surrounding cells releases chemicals that stimulate the dendrite to produce action potentials.
Free nerve endings for pain (sharp pain and dull pain)	Slow	
Free nerve endings for temperature (heat or coldness)	Slow	

Hapsis (fine touch and pressure)	Adaptation	Pressure on the various types of tissue capsules mechanically stimulates the dendrites within them to produce action potentials.
Meissner's corpuscle (touch)	Rapid	
Pacinian corpuscle (flutter)	Rapid	
Ruffini corpuscle (indentation)	Slow	
Merkel's receptor (steady skin indentation)	Slow	
Hair receptors (flutter or steady skin indentation)	Slow	

Proprioception (body awareness)	Adaptation	Movements stretch the receptors to mechanically stimulate the dendrites within them to produce action potentials.
Muscle spindles (muscle stretch)	Rapid	
Golgi tendon organs (tendon stretch)	Rapid	
Joint receptors (joint movement)	Rapid	

FIGURE 11-16 Somatosensory Receptors Perceptions derived from the body senses of nociception, hapsis, and proprioception depend on various receptors in various parts of the skin, muscles, joints, and tendons.

Figure 4-25 illustrates the cellular processes at work in a sensory neuron dendrite when a touch receptor is activated.

IRRITATION Nociception is the perception of pain, temperature, or itch. Most nociceptors are free nerve endings, the tips of sensory neuron dendrites, as diagrammed at the top of Figure 11-16. When damaged or irritated, these endings secrete chemicals, usually peptides, that stimulate the nerve to produce an action potential. The action potential then conveys a message about pain, temperature, or itch to the central nervous system.

PRESSURE Hapsis (from the Greek for *touch*) is the ability to discriminate objects on the basis of touch. Haptic receptors enable us to perceive fine touch and pressure and to identify objects that we touch and grasp. Haptic receptors occupy both superficial and deep skin layers and are attached to body hairs as well.

As diagrammed in the center of Figure 11-16, haptic receptors consist of a dendrite attached to a hair, to connective tissue, or to a dendrite encased in a capsule of tissue. Mechanical stimulation of the hair, tissue, or capsule activates special ion channels on the dendrite, which in turn initiate an action potential. Differences in the tissue forming the capsule determine the kinds of mechanical energy transduced by the haptic receptor to the nerve. For example, pressure that squeezes the capsule of a Pacinian corpuscle is the necessary stimulus for initiating an action potential conveying pressure information. Displacement of a hair is a necessary stimulus for initiating action potentials conveying some other types of touch information.

MOVEMENT Proprioception, or body awareness, is the perception of body location and movement. Proprioceptors are encapsulated nerve endings sensitive to the stretch of muscles and tendons and the movement of joints. In the Golgi tendon organ shown at the bottom of Figure 11-16, for instance, an action potential is triggered when the tendon moves, stretching the receptor attached to it.

Duration of Receptor Response

Somatosensory receptors are specialized to tell us when a sensory event occurs and/or whether it is still occurring. Information about when a stimulus occurs is handled mainly by **rapidly adapting receptors**, which activate neurons when stimulation begins and when it ends. As shown in Figure 11-16, haptic receptors that respond to touch (Meissner corpuscles), to fluttering sensations (Pacinian corpuscles), and to vibration (Ruffini corpuscles) all are rapidly adapting receptors.

In contrast, **slowly adapting receptors** activate neurons as long as a sensory event is present: they detect whether a stimulus is still occurring. For instance, after you have put on an article of clothing and become accustomed to how it feels, only slowly adapting haptic receptors (such as Merkel receptors and hair receptors) remain active.

The difference between a rapidly adapting and a slowly adapting receptor rests on two factors: how the receptor is stimulated and how the ion channels in the membrane of its dendrite respond to mechanical stimulation. The stimulation may be sharp or cold, fluttery or deep, a stretch or a swerve.

Posterior Root Ganglion Neurons

The dendrites that carry somatosensory information into the CNS belong to neurons whose cell body is just outside the spinal cord in posterior root ganglia. Their axons enter the spinal cord. As illustrated in **Figure 11-17**, such a *posterior root ganglion neuron* contains a single long dendrite. Only the tip is responsive to sensory stimulation. This dendrite is continuous with the somatosensory neuron's axon, which enters the spinal cord. The somatosensory cell body sits to one side of this long pathway.

Every spinal cord segment is flanked by a posterior root ganglion that contains many types of neurons. Each type responds to a particular kind of somatosensory information. Within the spinal cord, the axons of posterior root ganglion neurons may synapse with other neurons or continue to the brain or do both.

The axons of posterior root ganglion neurons vary in diameter and myelination. These structural features are related to the kind of information the neurons carry. Proprioceptive information (location and movement) and haptic information (touch and pressure) are carried by posterior root ganglion neurons that have large, well-myelinated axons. Nociceptive information (pain, temperature, itch) is mainly carried by posterior root ganglion neurons that have smaller axons with little or no myelin.

Because of their size and myelination, the larger neurons carry information faster than the smaller neurons do. One possible reason proprioceptive and haptic neurons are designed to carry messages quickly is that their information requires rapid response. Imagine that

nociception Perception of pain, temperature, and itch.

hapsis Perceptual ability to discriminate objects on the basis of touch.

proprioception Perception of the position and movement of the body, limbs, and head.

rapidly adapting receptor Body sensory receptor that responds briefly to the onset of a stimulus on the body.

slowly adapting receptor Body sensory receptor that responds as long as a sensory stimulus is on the body.

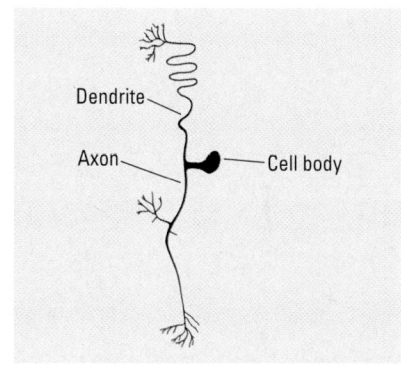

Somatosensory neuron

Myelin is the fatty coating around axons, formed by glial cells, that speeds neurotransmission. See Section 3-1.

1 Posterior-root ganglion neurons that carry fine-touch and pressure information...

2 ...have large, myelinated axons whose receptors are located in the skin, muscles, and tendons.

3 The cell body is located in a posterior-root ganglion.

4 Fine-touch and pressure axons ascend in the ipsilateral spinal cord, forming the posterior spinothalamic tract.

Somatosensory cortex

Somatosensory homunculus

Thalamus
Brainstem

Spinal cord

FIGURE 11-17 Haptic Neuron of the Posterior Root Ganglion The dendrite and axon of this neuron of the posterior root ganglion, which are contiguous, carry sensory information from the skin to the CNS. These large, myelinated ganglionic axons travel up the spinal cord to the brain in the posterior column, whereas the small axons synapse with neurons whose axons cross the spinal cord and ascend on the other side (shown in Figure 11-19).

you've touched a hot stove. A myelinated pain fiber activates and instructs the hand to withdraw quickly. A nonmyelinated pain fiber, less hurried, will let you know for some time afterward that your finger has been burned.

Disruption of Posterior Root Ganglion Function

We can support the claim that sensory information is essential for movement by describing what happens when posterior root ganglion cells do not function. A clue comes from a visit to the dentist. If you have ever had a tooth frozen for dental work, you have felt the strange effect of losing sensation on one side of your face. Not only do you lose pain perception but you also seem to lose the ability to move your facial muscles properly, making it awkward to talk and smile and downright dangerous to chew. Similarly, if your hands or mouth become terribly cold, disrupting receptor function, talking or making hand movements becomes difficult. So even though only the sensory nerves are blocked, movement is affected as well.

In much the same way, sensory nerve damage affects both sensory perceptions and motor abilities. John Rothwell and his coworkers (1982) described a patient, G. O., who was **deafferentated** (had lost afferent sensory fibers) by a disease that destroyed somatosensory posterior root ganglion neurons. G. O. received no sensory input from his hands. He could not, for example, feel when his hand was holding something.

However, G. O. could still accurately produce a range of finger movements, and he could outline figures in the air even with his eyes closed. He could also move his thumb accurately through different distances and at different speeds, judge weights, and match movement force. Nevertheless, his hands were relatively useless to him in daily life. Although G. O. could drive his old car, he was unable to learn to drive a new one. He was also unable to write, to fasten shirt buttons, and to hold a cup.

G. O. began movements quite normally, but as he proceeded, the movement patterns gradually fell apart, ending in failure. Part of G. O.'s difficulties lay in maintaining muscle force for any time. When he tried to carry a suitcase, he would quickly drop it unless he continually looked down to confirm that he was carrying it. Clearly, although only G. O.'s sensory neurons were damaged, he also had severe motor disability, including inability to learn new motor skills.

Disruption of Body Awareness

Oliver Sacks's research informed scientific understanding of conditions as diverse as Parkinson disease (Focus 5-3 and Section 16-3), ventral visual stream injury (Section 9-4), and thinking (Section 15-1).

Movement abnormalities also result from more selective damage to neurons that carry proprioceptive information about body location and movement. Neurologist Oliver Sacks (1998) gives a dramatic example in his description of a patient, Christina, whose proprioceptive sensory fibers throughout her body were damaged after she took megadoses of vitamin B_6. Christina was left with little ability to control her movements and spent most of each day lying prone. Here is how she describes what a loss of proprioception means:

> "What I must do then," she said slowly, "is use vision, use my eyes, in every situation where I used—what do you call it?—proprioception before. I've already noticed," she added, musingly, "that I may lose my arms. I think they are in one place, and I find they're in another. This proprioception is like the eyes of the body, the way the body sees itself. And if it goes, as it's gone with me, it's like the body's blind. My body can't see itself if it's lost its eyes, right? So I have to watch it—be its eyes." (Sacks, 1998, p. 46)

Clearly, Christina's motor system is intact, but with no sense of where in space her body is and what it is doing, she is almost completely immobilized. Jonathan Cole (1995) described the case of Ian Waterman, who lost proprioception after a presumed viral infection at age 19. He is the only person reported to have learned how to move again, and this relearning took years. He was even able to drive. All his regained movement was mediated by vision, however, without which he was as helpless as Christina.

Somatosensory Pathways to the Brain

As the axons of somatosensory neurons enter the CNS in the spinal cord, they divide, forming two pathways to the brain. The haptic-proprioceptive axons for touch and body awareness ascend the spinal cord ipsilaterally, whereas nociceptive (pain, temperature, itch)

Primary somatosensory cortex

6 Afferent somatosensory information arrives in the primary somatosensory cortex (areas 3-1-2).

5 The ventrolateral area of the thalamus relays sensory information to the primary somatosensory cortex.

4 In the brainstem, posterior spinothalamic neurons cross to the contralateral pathway, where axons of the medial lemniscus carry information from posterior and anterior tracts to the ventrolateral thalamus.

3 Posterior column nuclei that relay haptic–proprioceptive sensations ascend the dorsal spinothalamic tract ipsilaterally.

1 Posterior root ganglion neurons respond to fine touch and pressure; joint, tendon, and muscle change; pain, temperature, and itch.

2 After crossing to the contralateral side of the spinal cord, nociceptive nuclei form the anterior spinothalamic tract, which joins the medial lemniscus pathway.

Thalamus

Medial lemniscus

Brainstem

Posterior root ganglion

Spinal cord

FIGURE 11-18 Dual Somatosensory Pathways to the Brain As neurons from the posterior root ganglia enter the spinal cord, the two somatosensory pathways to the brain diverge.

Ipsilateral connections lie on the side of the body on which they enter; contralateral connections lie on the side opposite.

nerve fibers synapse with neurons whose axons cross to the contralateral side of the spinal cord before ascending to the brain. **Figure 11-18** shows these two routes through the spinal cord. The posterior haptic-proprioceptive pathway is shown as a solid red line, the anterior nociceptive pathway as a dashed red line.

The Posterior Spinothalamic Tract

Haptic-proprioceptive axons, which lie in the posterior portion of the spinal cord, form the **posterior spinothalamic tract.** These axons for fine touch and pressure synapse in the posterior column nuclei at the base of the brain. As shown in Figure 11-18, axons of neurons in the posterior column nuclei cross to the other side of the brainstem and ascend as part of a pathway called the *medial lemniscus.*

These posterior column axons synapse in the **ventrolateral thalamus,** the part of the thalamus that sends afferent information about body senses on to the somatosensory cortex. Although ventrolateral thalamic neurons send most of their axons to the somatosensory cortex, some do go to the motor cortex. Thus, three relay neurons are required to carry haptic-proprioceptive information to the cortex: posterior root ganglia neurons, posterior column nuclei neurons, and thalamic neurons. Because posterior column neurons cross to the opposite hemisphere, each hemisphere perceives the opposite side of the somatosensory world.

The Anterior Spinothalamic Tract

Most nociceptive axons take a different route to the brain. As shown in Figure 11-18, they first synapse with neurons in the anterior part of the spinal cord's gray matter, and in turn, these neurons send their axons across to the other side of the spinal cord. There they form the **anterior spinothalamic tract,** which carries afferent information about pain, temperature, and itch to the thalamus. This tract joins the medial lemniscus in the brainstem to continue on to the ventrolateral thalamus. The thalamic neurons project to the somatosensory cortex. So again, conveying information to the cortex requires three groups of relay neurons: posterior root neurons, spinal cord gray matter neurons, and ventrolateral thalamic neurons.

deafferentation Loss of incoming sensory input, usually due to damage to sensory fibers; also loss of any afferent input to a structure.

posterior spinothalamic tract Pathway that carries fine-touch and pressure fibers.

ventrolateral thalamus Part of the thalamus that carries information about body senses to the somatosensory cortex.

anterior spinothalamic tract Pathway from the spinal cord to the thalamus that carries information about pain and temperature.

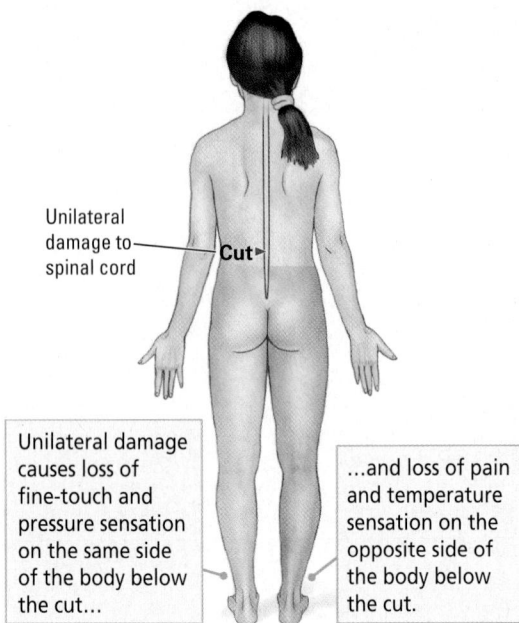

Unilateral damage to spinal cord

Cut▶

Unilateral damage causes loss of fine-touch and pressure sensation on the same side of the body below the cut...

...and loss of pain and temperature sensation on the opposite side of the body below the cut.

FIGURE 11-19 Effects of Unilateral Damage to the Somatosensory System

Effects of Unilateral Somatosensory System Damage

Unilateral damage dissociates the functions of the two somatosensory pathways—haptic-proprioceptive and nociceptive. Because they enter the spinal cord together, separate in the spinal cord, and finally join up again in the brainstem, unilateral damage to the system results in distinctive sensory losses, depending upon the site of injury.

Damage to the posterior roots produces global somatosensory deficits in a particular part of the body. In contrast, as illustrated in **Figure 11-19**, after unilateral spinal cord injury, loss of hapsis and proprioception occurs unilaterally, to the side of the body below where the damage occurred. Loss of nociception occurs contralaterally. This occurs because hapsis and proprioception take different routes through the spinal cord. Unilateral damage at the points where the pathways merge in the brainstem, thalamus, and cortex again affects hapsis, proprioception, and nociception together, because these parts of the pathways again lie in close proximity.

Spinal Reflexes

Not only do somatosensory nerve fibers convey information to the cortex, they also participate in behaviors mediated by the spinal cord and brainstem. Spinal cord somatosensory axons, even those ascending the posterior columns, give off axon collaterals that synapse with interneurons and motor neurons on both sides of the spinal cord. The circuits made between sensory neurons and muscles through these connections mediate spinal reflexes.

The simplest spinal reflex is formed by a single synapse between a sensory neuron and a motor neuron. **Figure 11-20** illustrates such a **monosynaptic reflex,** the knee jerk. It affects the quadriceps muscle of the thigh, which is anchored to the leg bone by the patellar tendon. When the lower leg hangs free and this tendon is tapped with a small hammer, the quadriceps muscle is stretched, activating the stretch-sensitive sensory receptors embedded in it.

The sensory receptors then send a signal to the spinal cord through sensory neurons that synapse with motor neurons projecting to the same thigh muscle. The discharge from the motor neurons stimulates the muscle, causing it to contract to resist the stretch.

1 A tap on the patellar tendon stretches the quadriceps muscle.

2 The sensory nerve responds to the muscle stretch...

3 ...by sending a signal to the spinal cord, where it connects to a motor neuron through a single synapse.

Spinal cord

Quadriceps muscle

4 The motor neuron stimulates the quadriceps muscle to contract and reduce the stretch.

5 The quadriceps contracts, extending the lower leg.

Extension

FIGURE 11-20 Monosynaptic Reflex

Because the tap is brief, the stimulation is over before the motor message arrives, and the muscle contracts even though it is no longer stretched. This contraction pulls the leg up, producing the knee jerk reflex.

This simplest of reflexes entails monosynaptic connections between single sensory neurons and single motor neurons. Somatosensory neurons receiving information from the skin make much more complex connections with both interneurons and motor neurons. These multisynaptic connections are responsible for more complex spinal movements, such as those involved in standing and walking, actions that include many muscles on both sides of the body.

Feeling and Treating Pain

As many as 30 percent of physician visits involve pain symptoms, as do 50 percent of emergency room visits. People have pain as a result of acute injuries such as broken bones, chronic conditions such as cancer and arthritis, and everyday conditions such as stiff muscles from exercising. Women have pain during menstruation, pregnancy, and childbirth. The incidence of living with pain increases as people age, and for many people, pain is a constant companion.

Perceiving Pain

People can experience *central pain* in a part of the body that is not obviously injured. One type of central pain is *phantom limb pain*. As described in Research Focus 11-5, Phantom Limb Pain on page 386, phantom sensations are felt in a limb that has been lost, hence the term.

People in pain would happily dispense with it. But pain is necessary: the rare person born without pain receptors has body deformities because of failure to adjust posture and acute injuries because of failure to avoid harm.

Pain perception results from synthesizing a plethora of sensory information. There may be as many as eight kinds of pain fibers, judging from the peptides and other chemicals released by these nerves when irritated or damaged. Some of these chemicals irritate surrounding tissue, stimulating it to release other chemicals to stimulate blood flow and to stimulate the pain fibers themselves. These reactions contribute to pain, redness, and swelling at the site of an injury.

Consider itch. We may feel itchy and consequently scratch a foreign object on our body. We also frequently feel itch in the absence of an obvious stimulus. Some drugs, including opioids, enhance itch sensations in the absence of a physical stimulus at the itchy body part.

Haptic information also contributes to pain perception. For example, people can accurately report the location and characteristics of various kinds of pain, but in the absence of fine-touch and pressure information, pain is more difficult to identify and localize.

The anterior spinothalamic tract, illustrated in Figure 11-18, is the main pain pathway to the brain, but as many as four other pathways may carry pain information from the spinal cord to the brain. These pathways are both crossed and uncrossed and project to the reticular formation of the midbrain, where they produce arousal; to the amygdala, where they produce emotional responses typically associated with pain; and to the hypothalamus, where they activate hormonal and cardiovascular responses.

The existence of multiple pain pathways in the spinal cord makes it difficult to treat chronic pain, even by selectively cutting the anterior spinothalamic tract—one radical procedure used to control chronic pain. It is likely that each pain pathway has its own function, whether for sensation, arousal, emotional responses, or other physiological responses.

Responding to Pain

Neuronal circuits in the spinal cord allow haptic-proprioceptive and nociceptive pathways to interact. Such interactions may be responsible for our puzzling and variable responses to pain. For example, people who are engaged in combat or intense athletic competition may receive a serious physical injury but start to feel the pain only much later.

monosynaptic reflex Reflex requiring one synapse between sensory input and movement.

RESEARCH F◉CUS 11-5

Phantom Limb Pain

Up to 80 percent of people who have had a limb amputated also endure phantom limb phenomena, including pain and other sensations and motor phantoms, such as phantom movement and cramps (Kern et al., 2009). Phantom sensations and movements are illusions that originate in the brain.

Various techniques used to minimize phantom limb pain include drug-based pain management with opioids and the injection of pain medications into the spinal cord. An innovative method devised by V. S. Ramachandran (1996) assists the patient in setting up a counter-illusion that the limb is intact and is providing normal sensory input to the brain.

Ramachandran devised a mirror box into which a person who has lost an arm inserts the intact arm and then observes its reflection in the mirror. The reflection suggests that the missing arm is present and can be controlled, as shown in the illustration. The perception of the limb as intact counteracts phantom pain and cramps.

Inspired by Ramachandran's mirror box, researchers have developed other illusions to suggest that a missing limb is present and can be controlled. One method uses virtual reality goggles. Another uses the so-called rubber limb phenomenon to produce the illusion that a missing limb is present. To induce this phenomenon, the stump of the amputated limb is stimulated tactually while the subject observes a prosthetic limb being touched.

All of the illusions lessen phantom limb pain and cramps by suggesting that a normal limb is present. Using similar logic, Hellman and associates (2015) suggest the possibility of developing neuroprosthetic limbs that provide their users sensory information to alleviate phantoms.

Alessandria and colleagues (2011) asked whether phantom limbs and their associated sensations also occur during dreaming. They awoke sleeping participants with amputations during rapid eye movement, or REM, sleep and asked them to recount their dreams. In none of the dreams did the participants remember having an amputated limb or phantom limb sensations.

This finding suggests that the integrity of brain regions associated with a limb is preserved even though the limb is absent. When awake, the loss of moment-to-moment sensory activity from the limb results in the opportunity for phantom perceptions.

Section 6-2 notes similarities between the brain's endogenous opioids and opioid analgesic drugs.

A friend of ours was attacked by a grizzly bear while hiking and received 200 stitches to bind his wounds. When friends asked if it hurt to be bitten by a grizzly bear, he surprisingly answered no, explaining, "I had read the week before about someone who was killed and eaten by a grizzly bear. So I was thinking that this bear was going to eat me unless I got away. I did not have time for pain. I was fighting for my life. It was not until the next day that I started feeling pain."

The primacy of our friend's fear over his pain is related to the stress he was under. Not feeling pain in a fight-or-flight situation is obviously adaptive, as this story illustrates, and may be related to the activation of endogenous opioid peptides. Treatments for pain include opioid drugs (such as morphine), acupuncture (which entails the rapid vibration of needles embedded in the skin), and simply rubbing the area surrounding the injury. Psychological factors interact with pain treatments, and most studies on pain management find that placebos can be as effective as actual treatments. Pain is puzzling in the variety of ways that lessen it.

To explain both the perception of pain and how it can be suppressed in so many ways, Ronald Melzack and Patrick Wall (1965) proposed a gate theory of pain. Its essence as applied to pain perception is that activities in different sensory pathways play off against each other and so determine whether and how much pain is perceived as a result of an injury. Melzack and Wall propose that haptic-proprioceptive stimulation can reduce pain perception, whereas the absence of such stimulation can increase pain perception through interactions at a pain gate.

FIGURE 11-21 Pain Gate A spinal cord interneuron receives excitatory input (plus signs) from the fine-touch and pressure pathway; and inhibitory input (minus signs) from the pain and temperature pathway. The interneuron's relative activity then determines whether pain and temperature information ascends to the brain. Information from R. Melzack (1973). *The Puzzle of Pain* (p. 154). New York: Basic Books.

A model of the **pain gate**, illustrated in **Figure 11-21,** consists of a haptic-proprioceptive fiber that conveys fine touch and pressure information and a nociceptive fiber that conducts pain information. Each fiber synapses with the same interneuron. Collaterals from the haptic-proprioceptive pathway excite the interneuron, whereas collaterals from the nociceptive pathway inhibit it. The interneuron, in turn, inhibits a neuron that relays pain information from the spinal cord to the brain. Consequently, when the haptic-proprioceptive pathway is active, the interneuron is stimulated, inhibiting the secondary pain neuron, and the interneuron acts as a gate, reducing the pain sensation.

Treating Pain

Gate theory helps to explain how so many pain treatments work (Foster et al., 2015). When you stub your toe, for instance, you feel pain because the pain pathway to the brain is open. Rubbing the toe activates the haptic-proprioceptive pathway and reduces the information flow in the pain pathway because the pain gate partly closes, relieving the pain by crowding it out.

Similarly, a variety of pain treatments, including massage, warm water immersion, and acupuncture, may produce pain-relieving effects by selectively activating haptic and proprioceptive fibers relative to pain fibers, thus closing the pain gate. For acupuncture, vibrating needles on different body points presumably activate fine-touch and pressure fibers. The pain gate model may also explain why opioid drugs influence pain. The interneuron that is the gate uses an endogenous opioid as an inhibitory neurotransmitter. Thus, opioids have one of their effects in relieving pain by mimicking the actions of the endogenous opioid neurotransmitter of the interneuron.

One of the most successful pain treatments is injecting small amounts of morphine under the dura mater, the outer layer of the meninges. This epidural anesthesia is mediated by the action of morphine on interneurons in the spinal cord. Although morphine is a highly useful pain treatment, its effects lessen with continued use. This form of habituation may be related to changes that take place on the postsynaptic receptors of pain neurons in the spinal cord and brain.

Gate theory also suggests an explanation for the pins and needles we feel after sitting too long in one position. Loss of oxygen from reduced blood flow first deactivates the large myelinated axons that carry touch and pressure information, leaving the small unmyelinated fibers that carry pain and temperature messages unaffected. As a result, ungated sensory information flows in the pain and temperature pathway, leading to the pins and needles.

Neural circuits resembling pain gates may be located in the brainstem and cortex as well as the spinal cord. These gates help to explain how cognition and emotion influence pain and how other approaches to pain relief work. For example, researchers have found that feelings of severe pain can be lessened when people can shift their attention from the pain to other stimuli. Dentists have long used this technique by giving their patients something soothing to watch or listen to during procedures.

Figure 2-4 diagrams the triple-layered meninges encasing the brain and spinal cord.

pain gate Hypothetical neural circuit in which activity in fine-touch and pressure pathways diminishes the activity in pain and temperature pathways.

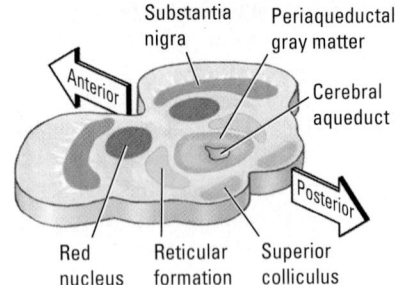

Substantia nigra   Periaqueductal gray matter

Anterior

Cerebral aqueduct

Posterior

Red nucleus   Reticular formation   Superior colliculus

The PAG is one nucleus in the midbrain's tegmentum (floor), shown here in cross section. DBS is pictured in Figure 1-6.

Area of referred pain

FIGURE 11-22 Referred Pain During a heart attack, pain from receptors in the heart is commonly felt in the left shoulder and upper arm, especially in men.

Vestibular hair cells work on the same principles as cochlear hair cells, which mediate hearing. See Section 10-2.

Cranial nerve 8 conveys both hearing and balance information to the brain. See Figure 2-27.

The brain can also influence the pain signal it receives from the spinal cord. The cell bodies of **periaqueductal gray matter** (PAG) neurons surround the cerebral aqueduct connecting the third and fourth ventricles. Electrical stimulation of the PAG is effective in suppressing pain. Neurons in the PAG produce their pain-suppressing effect by exciting pathways (including serotonergic and noradrenergic pathways) in the brainstem that project to the spinal cord. There they inhibit neurons that form the ascending pain pathways. Activation in these inhibitory circuits in part explains why pain sensation and perception ease during sleep. Deep brain stimulation of the PAG by implanted microelectrodes is one way of treating pain that proves resistant to all other therapies, including treatment with opioid drugs.

Many internal organs, including the heart, kidneys, and blood vessels, have pain receptors, but the ganglion neurons carrying information from these receptors do not have their own pathway to the brain. Instead, they synapse with spinal cord neurons that receive nociceptive information from the body's surface. Consequently, the spinal cord neurons that relay pain and temperature messages to the brain receive two sets of signals: one from the body's surface and the other from the internal organs.

These spinal cord neurons cannot distinguish the two sets of signals—nor can we. As a result, pain in body organs is felt as **referred pain** coming from the body surface. For example, pain in the heart associated with a heart attack is felt as pain in the left shoulder and upper arm (**Figure 11-22**). Pain in the stomach is felt as pain in the midline of the trunk; pain in the kidneys is felt as pain in the lower back. Pain in blood vessels in the head is felt as diffuse pain that we call a headache. (Remember, the brain has no pain receptors.)

Vestibular System and Balance

The only localized part of the somatosensory system, the **vestibular system,** consists of two organs, one in each inner ear. As **Figure 11-23**A shows, each vestibular organ consists of two groups of receptors: the three *semicircular canals* and the *otolith organs,* the *utricle* and the *saccule.* These vestibular receptors do two jobs: (1) they tell us the position of the body in relation to gravity and (2) they signal changes in direction and speed of head movement.

In Figure 11-23A the semicircular canals are oriented in three planes that correspond to the three dimensions in which we move through space. Each canal furnishes information about movement in its particular plane. The semicircular canals are filled with a fluid called *endolymph.* Immersed in the endolymph is a set of hair cells.

When the head moves, the endolymph also moves, pushing against the hair cells and bending the cilia at their tips. The force of the bending is converted into receptor potentials in the hair cells that send action potentials over auditory vestibular nerve axons to the brain. These axons are normally quite active: bending the cilia in one direction increases receptor potentials, consequently increasing vestibular nerve axon activity; bending them in the other direction decreases vestibular afferent axon activity. These responses are diagrammed in Figure 11-23B. Typically, when the head turns in one direction, the receptor message on that side of the body increases neuronal firing. The message on the body's opposite side leads to decreased firing.

The utricle and saccule lie stacked just beneath the semicircular canals, as shown at the right in Figure 11-23A. These organs also contain hair cells, but the receptors are embedded in a gelatinous substance that contains *otoconia* (sing. *otoconium*), small crystals of the salt calcium carbonate. When you tilt your head, the gelatin and otoconia press against the hair cells, bending them. The mechanical action of the hair bending modulates the rate of action potentials in vestibular afferent axons that convey messages about the head's position in three-dimensional space.

The receptors in the vestibular system tell us about our location relative to gravity, about acceleration and deceleration of our movements, and about changes in movement direction. They also allow us to ignore the otherwise destabilizing influence that our movements might

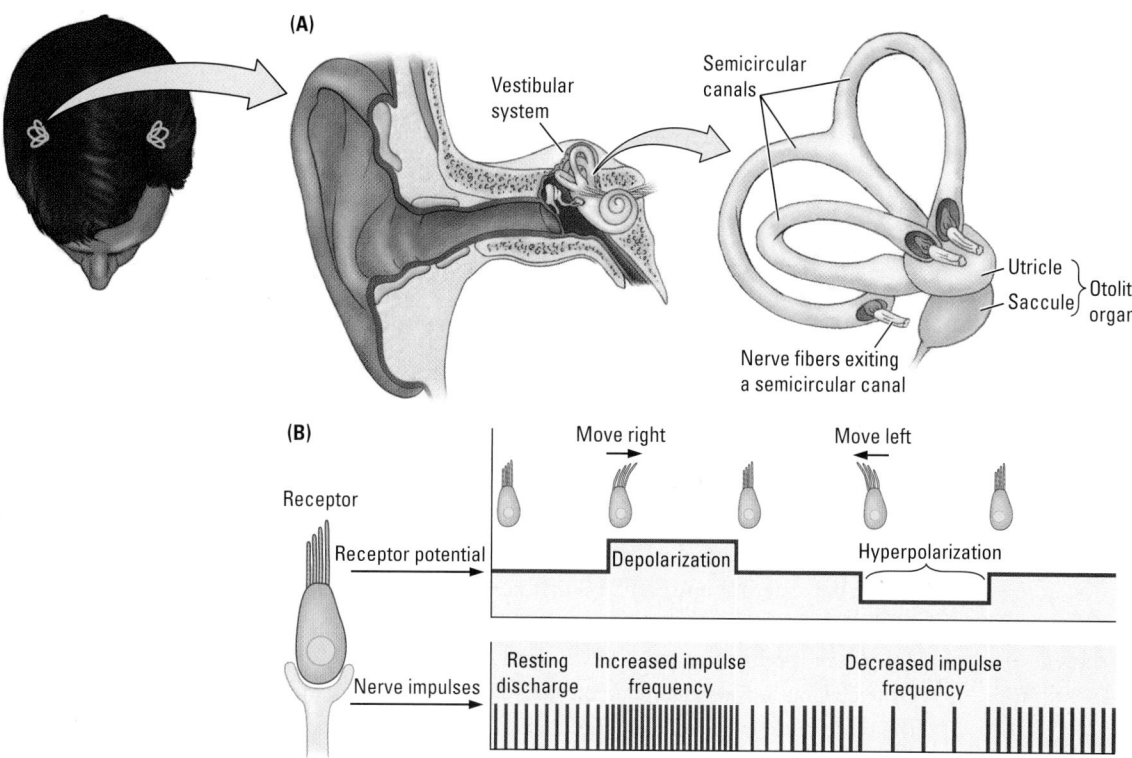

FIGURE 11-23 The Vestibular System **(A)** The vestibular organs in each inner ear contain hair cells sensitive to head movement and to gravity. **(B)** A vestibular neuron is normally active. Its activity increases if the cilia at the tips of its hair cell receptors bend in one direction but decreases if the receptors bend in the opposite direction.

have on us. When you are standing on a moving bus, for example, even slight movements of the vehicle could potentially throw you off balance, but they do not. Similarly, when you move, you easily avoid tipping over, despite the constant shifting of your body weight. Your vestibular system enables your stability.

To demonstrate vestibular receptors' role in helping you to compensate for your own movements, try this experiment. Hold your hand in front of you and shake it. Your hand appears blurry. Now shake your head instead of your hand, and the hand remains in focus. Compensatory signals from your vestibular system allow you to see the hand as stable even though you are moving around.

Vertigo (from the Latin for *spinning*), a sensation of spinning when one is not moving, a dysfunction of the inner ear, can be accompanied by nausea as well as difficulty maintaining balance while walking. A common way to induce vertigo is to spin, as children do when playing. Vertigo can also occur from looking down from a height or looking up at a tall object and as one is simply standing up or sitting down. One intoxicating effect of alcohol is vertigo. **Ménière disease,** named after a French physician, is a disorder of the inner ear resulting in vertigo and loss of balance (Lopez-Escamez et al., 2015).

periaqueductal gray matter (PAG) Nuclei in the midbrain that surround the cerebral aqueduct joining the third and fourth ventricles; PAG neurons contain circuits for species-typical behaviors (e.g., female sexual behavior) and play an important role in the modulation of pain.

referred pain Pain that arises in one of the internal organs but is felt on the surface of the body.

vestibular system Somatosensory system comprising a set of receptors in each inner ear that respond to body position and to movement of the head.

Ménière disease Disorder of the middle ear resulting in vertigo and loss of balance.

11-4 REVIEW

Somatosensory System Receptors and Pathways

Before you continue, check your understanding.

1. Body senses contribute to the perception of _____ (touch and pressure), _____ (location and movement), and _____ (temperature, pain, itch).

2. Haptic-proprioceptive information is carried into the CNS by the _____ spinothalamic tract; nociceptive information is carried in by the _____ spinothalamic tract.

3. The two tracts interact in the spinal cord to regulate pain perception via a _____.

4. In the midbrain, the _____ suppresses pain by activating neuromodulatory circuits that inhibit pain pathways.

5. The only localized somatosensory system is the _____ system, which helps us to maintain _____ by signaling information about the head's position and our movement through space.

6. Explain how proprioception acts as the "eyes of the body."

Answers appear at the back of the book.

For additional study tools, visit 🌐 LaunchPad:
www.macmillanhighered.com/launchpad/kolb5e

⟨11-5⟩ Exploring the Somatosensory Cortex

Somatosensory neurons do more than convey sensation to the brain: they enable us to perceive things that we describe as pleasant or unpleasant, the shape and texture of objects, the effort required to complete tasks, and even our spatial environment. They also play a central role in movement. **Figure 11-24** illustrates the two main somatosensory areas in the cortex.

The *primary somatosensory cortex* (S1), which receives projections from the thalamus, consists of Brodmann areas 3-1-2 (all appear red in Figure 11-24). The primary somatosensory cortex begins to construct perceptions from somatosensory information. It mainly consists of the postcentral gyrus in the parietal lobe, just behind the central fissure. Thus, S1 lies adjacent to the primary motor cortex, on the other side of the central fissure in the frontal lobe.

The *secondary somatosensory cortex* (Brodmann areas 5 and 7, shaded orange and yellow in Figure 11-24) is located in the parietal lobe just behind S1. The secondary somatosensory cortex (S2) refines perceptual constructions in relation to potential movement and sends information to the frontal cortex.

Korbinian Brodmann numbered these areas more than a century ago on his map of the cortex (see Figure 2-23).

FIGURE 11-24 Somatosensory Cortex Stimulation of the primary somatosensory cortex in the parietal lobe produces sensations that are referred to appropriate body parts. Information from the primary somatosensory cortex travels to the secondary somatosensory cortex for further perceptual analysis.

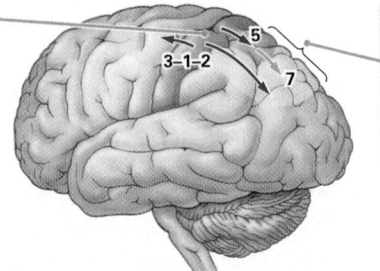

Primary somatosensory cortex receives sensory information from the body.

Secondary somatosensory cortex receives sensory information from the primary somatosensory cortex.

Somatosensory Homunculus

In his studies of human patients undergoing brain surgery, Wilder Penfield electrically stimulated the somatosensory cortex and recorded patients' responses. Stimulation at some sites elicited sensations in the foot; stimulation of other sites produced sensations in a hand, the trunk, or the face. By mapping these responses, Penfield was able to construct a somatosensory homunculus in the cortex, shown in **Figure 11-25A**. The sensory homunculus looks nearly identical to the motor homunculus shown in Figure 11-6 in that the most sensitive areas of the body are accorded relatively large cortical areas.

Using smaller electrodes and more precise recording techniques in monkeys, Jon Kaas (1987) found that Penfield's homunculus could be subdivided into a series of smaller homunculi. When Kaas stimulated sensory receptors on the body and recorded the activity of cells in the sensory cortex, he found that the somatosensory cortex comprises four representations of the body. Each is associated with a class of sensory receptors.

The progression of these representations across S1 from front to back is shown in Figure 11-25B. Area 3a cells are responsive to muscle receptors; area 3b cells are responsive

(A) Penfield's single-homunculus model

Primary somatosensory cortex

S1 is organized as a single homunculus with large areas representing body parts that are very sensitive to sensory stimulation.

FIGURE 11-25 Two Models of the Primary Somatosensory Cortex

(B) Four-homunculus model

Primary somatosensory cortex

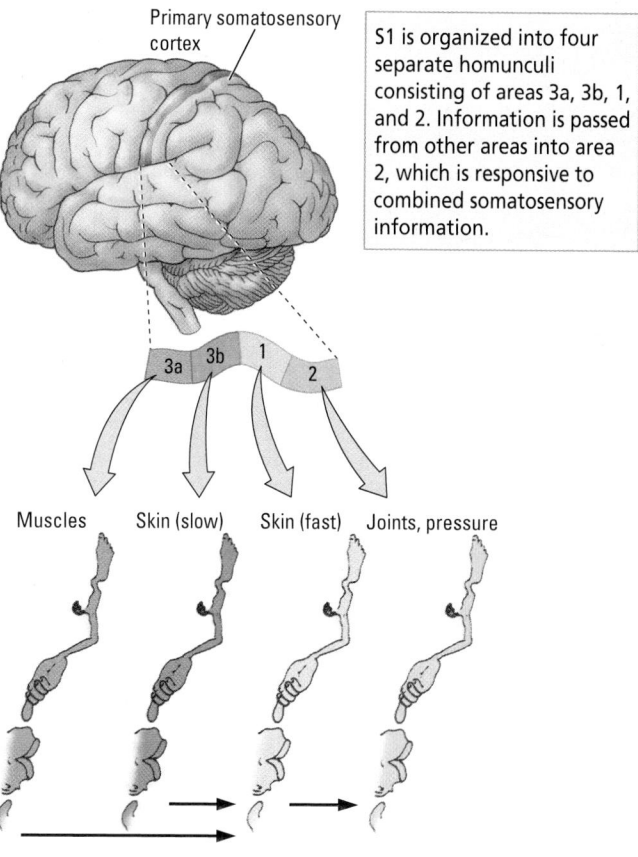

S1 is organized into four separate homunculi consisting of areas 3a, 3b, 1, and 2. Information is passed from other areas into area 2, which is responsive to combined somatosensory information.

3a 3b 1 2

Muscles   Skin (slow)   Skin (fast)   Joints, pressure

to slow-responding skin receptors. Area 1 cells are responsive to rapidly adapting skin receptors, and area 2 cells are responsive to deep tissue pressure and joint receptors. In another study, Hiroshi Asanuma (1989) and his coworkers found still another sensory representation in the motor cortex (area 4) in which cells respond to muscle and joint receptors.

Perceptions constructed from elementary sensations depend on combining the sensations. This combining takes place as areas 3a and 3b project onto area 1, which in turn projects onto area 2. Whereas a cell in area 3a or 3b may respond to activity in only a certain area on a certain finger, for example, cells in area 1 may respond to similar information from a number of fingers.

At the next level of synthesis, cells in area 2 respond to stimulation in a number of locations on a number of fingers as well as to stimulation from different kinds of somatosensory receptors. Thus, area 2 contains *multimodal neurons* responsive to force, orientation, and direction of movement. We perceive all these properties when we hold an object in our hands and manipulate it.

With each successive information relay, both the size of the pertinent receptive fields and the synthesis of somatosensory modalities increase. The segregation of sensory neuron types at the level of the cortex is likely the basis for our ability to distinguish among different kinds of sensory stimuli coming from different sources. For example, we distinguish between tactile stimulation on the surface of the skin, which is usually produced by some external agent, and stimulation coming from muscles, tendons, and joints, which is usually produced by our own movements.

At the same time, we perceive the combined sensory properties of a stimulus. For instance, when we manipulate an object, we know the object both by its sensory properties, such as temperature and texture, and by the movements we make as we handle it. Thus, the cortex provides for somatosensory synthesis too. The tickle sensation seems rooted in an other-versus-us somatosensory distinction, as described in Research Focus 11-6, Tickling, on page 392.

Research by Vernon Mountcastle (1978) shows that cells in the somatosensory cortex are arranged in functional columns running from layer I to layer VI, similar to the functional columns found in the visual cortex. Every cell in a functional somatosensory cortical column responds to a single class of receptors. Some columns are activated by rapidly adapting skin receptors, others by slowly adapting skin receptors, still others by pressure receptors, and so forth. All neurons in a functional column receive information from the same local skin area. In this way, neurons lying within a column seem to be an elementary functional unit of the somatosensory cortex.

See Section 9-1 for details on receptive fields.

Figure 9-33 shows functional column organization in V1.

Tickling

Everyone knows the effects and consequences of tickling. The perception is a curious mixture of pleasant and unpleasant sensations. The two kinds of tickling are *kinismesis*, the sensation from a light caress, and *gargalesis,* the pleasurable effect of hard rhythmic probing.

The tickle sensation is felt not only by humans but also by other primates and by cats, rats, and probably most mammals. Play in rats is associated with 50-kilohertz vocalizations, and tickling body regions that are targets of the rats' own play also elicits 50-kilohertz vocalizations (Panksepp, 2007).

Tickling is rewarding because people and animals solicit tickles from others. They even enjoy observing others being tickled. Using a robot and brain imaging techniques, Sarah Blakemore and her colleagues (1998) explained why we cannot tickle ourselves.

Blakemore had participants deliver two kinds of identical tactile stimuli to the palms of their hand. In one condition, the stimulus was predictable and in the other a robot introduced an unpredictable delay in the stimulus. Only the unpredictable stimulus was perceived as a tickle. Thus, it is not the stimulation itself but its unpredictability that accounts for the tickle perception. This is why we cannot tickle ourselves. Yet Windt and associates (2015), using a self-report method, find that during lucid dreams, the self–other distinction is absent: people do dream that they tickle themselves.

One interesting feature of tickling is the distinctive laughter it evokes. This laughter can be identified by sonograms (sound analysis), and people can distinguish tickle-related laughter from other forms of laughter.

Intrigued by findings that all apes appear to laugh during tickling, Ross and coworkers (2009) compared tickle-related laughter in apes and found that human laughter is more similar to chimpanzee laughter than to the laughter of gorillas and other apes. We humans thus have inherited from our common ape ancestors both a susceptibility to tickling and laughter as well.

LWA-Dann Tardif/CORBIS

Effects of Somatosensory Cortex Damage

Damage to S1 impairs the ability to make even simple sensory discriminations and movements. Suzanne Corkin and her coworkers (1970) demonstrated this effect by examining patients with cortical lesions that included most of areas 3-1-2 in one hemisphere. The researchers mapped the primary sensory cortex of these patients before they underwent elective surgery for removal of a carefully defined piece of that cortex, including the hand area. The patients' sensory and motor skills in both hands were tested on three occasions: before the surgery, shortly after the surgery, and almost a year afterward.

The tests included pressure sensitivity, two-point touch discrimination, position sense (reporting the direction in which a finger was being moved), and haptic sense (using touch to identify objects, such as a pencil, a coin, eyeglasses, and so forth). For all the sensory abilities tested, the surgical lesions produced a severe and seemingly permanent deficit in the contralateral hand. Sensory thresholds, proprioception, and hapsis—all were greatly impaired.

The results of other studies of both humans and other animals have shown that damage to the somatosensory cortex also impairs simple movements. For example, limb use in reaching for an object is impaired, as is the ability to shape the hand to hold an object (Leonard et al., 1991).

Nevertheless, like the motor cortex, the somatosensory cortex is plastic. Plasticity is illustrated by the reorganization of somatosensory cortex after deafferentation. In 1991, Tim Pons and his coworkers reported a dramatic change in the somatosensory maps of monkeys in which the ganglion cells for one arm had been cut, deafferentating the limb, a number of years earlier. The researchers had wanted to develop an animal model of damage to sensory nerves that could offer insight into human injuries, but they were interrupted by a legal dispute with an animal advocacy group. Years later, as the health of the animals declined, a court injunction allowed the mapping experiment to be conducted.

Section 7-7 considers debates over using laboratory animals in brain–behavior research.

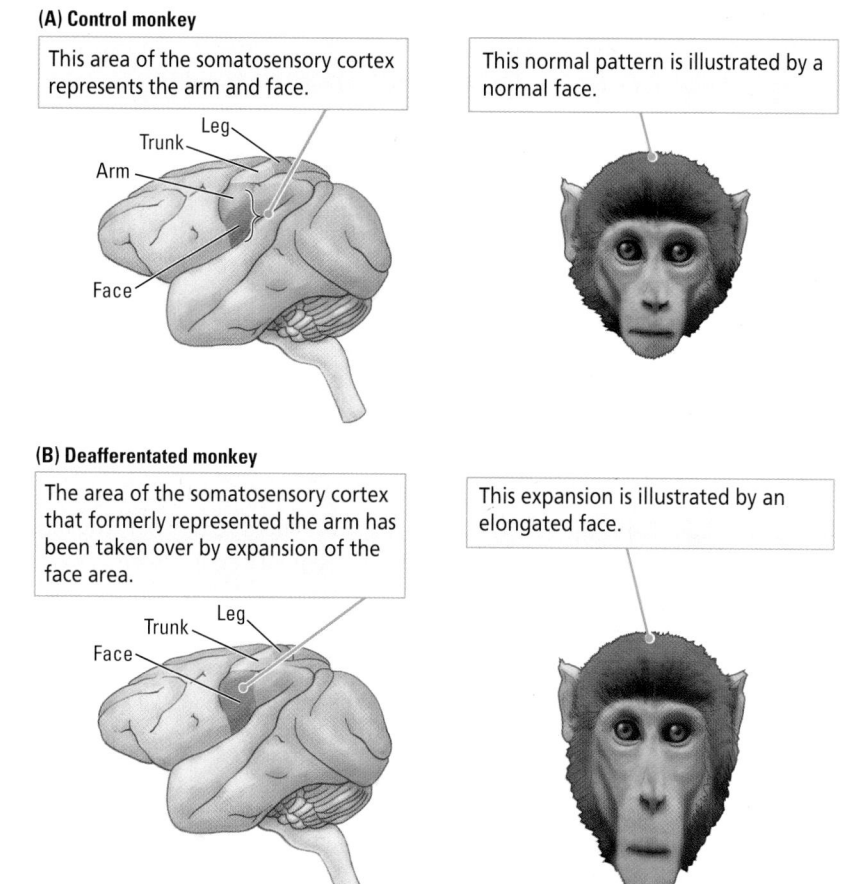

(A) Control monkey

This area of the somatosensory cortex represents the arm and face.

Leg
Trunk
Arm
Face

This normal pattern is illustrated by a normal face.

(B) Deafferentated monkey

The area of the somatosensory cortex that formerly represented the arm has been taken over by expansion of the face area.

Leg
Trunk
Face

This expansion is illustrated by an elongated face.

FIGURE 11-26 Somatosensory Plasticity Information from T. P. Pons, P. E. Garraghty, A. K. Ommaya, J. H. Kaas, & M. Mishkin (1991). Massive cortical reorganization after sensory deafferentation in adult macaques. *Science, 252*, p. 1858.

Pons and his coworkers discovered that the area of somatosensory cortex that had formerly represented the arm no longer did so. Light touches on a monkey's lower face now activated cells in what had formerly been the cortical arm region. As illustrated in **Figure 11-26,** the cortical facial area had expanded by as much as 10 to 14 millimeters, virtually doubling its original size by entering the arm area.

This massive change was completely unexpected. The stimulus–response patterns associated with the expanded facial area of the cortex appeared indistinguishable from those associated with the original facial area. Furthermore, the trunk area, which bounded the other side of the cortical arm area, did not expand into the vacated arm area.

What could account for this expansion of the face area into the arm area? There is evidence for preexisting axon collaterals that are not normally active, but these collaterals would probably not be able to extend far enough to account for all of the cortical reorganization. Another possibility is that within the thalamic and brainstem relay pathways, facial-area neurons project collaterals to arm-area neurons. These neurons are close together, so the collaterals need travel only a millimeter or so (Kambi et al., 2014). Whatever the mechanism, the dramatic cortical reorganizations observed in the Pons study are helpful in understanding other remarkable phenomena, including phantom limb sensations. In humans who have lost a forelimb, touches to the face can be felt as touches to the missing forearm.

Figure 14-23 diagrams this phenomenon.

Somatosensory Cortex and Complex Movement

How are our abilities to move and to interpret stimulation on the body related? Our somatosensory cortex actually makes an important contribution to movement. Damage to the secondary somatosensory cortex does not disrupt the plans for making movements,

Apraxia derives from the Greek words for *no* and *action*.

but it does disrupt how the movements are performed, leaving their execution fragmented and confused. This inability to complete a plan of action accurately—to make a voluntary movement—is called **apraxia.** The following case highlights its symptoms.

> A woman with a biparietal lesion [damage on the left- and right-hemisphere secondary somatosensory cortex] had worked for years as a fish-filleter. With the development of her symptoms, she began to experience difficulty in carrying on with her job. She did not seem to know what to do with her knife. She would stick the point in the head of a fish, start the first stroke, and then come to a stop. In her own mind she knew how to fillet fish, but yet she could not execute the maneuver. The foreman accused her of being drunk and sent her home for mutilating fish.
>
> The same patient also showed another unusual phenomenon that might possibly be apraxic in nature. She could never finish an undertaking. She would begin a job, drop it, start another, abandon that one, and within a short while would have four or five uncompleted tasks on her hands. This would cause her to do such inappropriate actions as putting the sugar bowl in the refrigerator, and the coffeepot inside the oven. (Critchley, 1953, pp. 158–159)

The somatosensory cortex contributes to movement by participating in both the dorsal and the ventral visual streams. The dorsal (how) stream, working without conscious awareness, provides vision for action, as when we automatically shape a hand as we reach to grasp a cup (recall Figure 11-1). Within this stream a number of channels specify the movements—reaching, manipulating, bringing a hand to the mouth, walking—that we should make in response not only to somatosensory information but also to visual and auditory information. The ventral (what) stream, in contrast, works with conscious awareness for perception—that an object is a cup.

As **Figure 11-27** illustrates, the dorsal visual stream projects to the secondary somatosensory cortex and then to the frontal cortex (Kaas et al., 2012). In this way, visual information is integrated with somatosensory information to produce unconscious movements appropriately shaped and directed to their targets, as in reaching for a cup. The secondary somatosensory area contributes perceptual information to the ventral stream by providing conscious haptic information about object identity and completed movements. From this information the frontal cortex can imagine the consequence of a movement and select the actions that appropriately follow from those already completed.

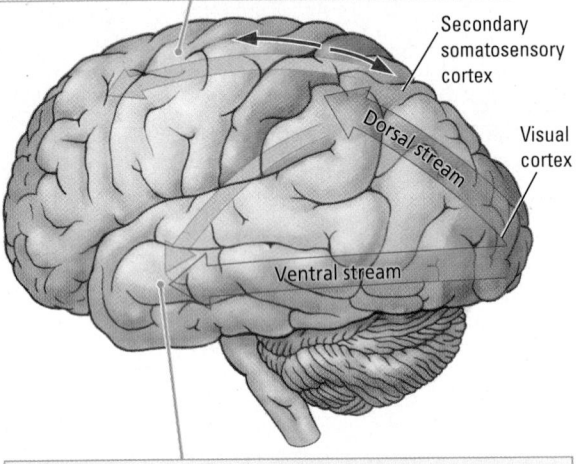

Information from the secondary somatosensory cortex contributes to the dorsal stream by specifying the movement used for grasping a target.

Secondary somatosensory cortex

Dorsal stream

Visual cortex

Ventral stream

Information from the secondary somatosensory cortex contributes to the ventral stream by providing information about objects' size, shape, and texture.

FIGURE 11-27 Visual Aid Section 9-4 explains how visual information from the dorsal and ventral streams contributes to movement.

11-5) **REVIEW**

Exploring the Somatosensory Cortex

Before you continue, check your understanding.

1. The _____ somatosensory cortex, arranged as a series of homunculi, feeds information to the _____ somatosensory cortex, which produces somatosensory perception.

2. Damage to the secondary somatosensory cortex produces _____, an inability to complete a series of movements.

3. The somatosensory cortex provides information to the _____ stream to produce unconscious movements and also provides information to the _____ stream for conscious recognition of objects.

4. Explain briefly what phantom limb pain tells us about the brain.

Answers appear at the back of the book.

apraxia Inability to make voluntary movements in the absence of paralysis or other motor or sensory impairment, especially an inability to make proper use of an object.

■ SUMMARY

In the nervous system, the somatosensory and motor systems are interrelated at all levels. At the level of the spinal cord, sensory information contributes to motor reflexes; in the brainstem, sensory information contributes to complex regulatory movements. At the level of the neocortex, sensory information represents the sizes, shapes, and positions of objects and records just-completed movements.

11-1 Hierarchy of Movement Control

Movement is organized hierarchically, using the entire nervous system (review Figure 11-1). The forebrain plans, organizes, and initiates movements, whereas the brainstem coordinates regulatory functions, such as eating and drinking, and controls neural mechanisms that maintain posture and produce locomotion. Many reflexes are organized at the level of the spinal cord and occur without the brain's involvement.

11-2 Motor System Organization

Maps produced by stimulating the primary motor cortex show that it is organized topographically as a homunculus with different cortical areas capable of producing different movements. Motor cortex neurons initiate movement, produce movement, control movement force, and indicate movement direction. Disuse of a limb, as might result from a motor cortex injury, results in shrinkage of the limb's cortical representation. This shrinkage can be prevented, however, if the limb can be somehow forced into use, as in constraint-induced therapy.

Two corticospinal pathways emerge from the motor cortex to the spinal cord. Lateral corticospinal axons project from cortical areas that control arm and hand movements. The lateral tract crosses from the contralateral brain hemisphere to form synapses with spinal interneurons and motor neurons located laterally in the spinal cord, and on the side opposite the brain hemisphere where the lateral tract formed. Anterior corticospinal tract axons project from the cortical motor regions that produce whole-body movements. The anterior tract synapses with interneurons and motor neurons located medially and ipsilaterally in the spinal cord.

Spinal cord interneurons and motor neurons also are topographically organized: lateral motor neurons project to digit, hand, and arm muscles to produce arm and hand movements, and medial motor neurons project to trunk muscles and mediate whole-body movements, including locomotion.

11-3 Basal Ganglia, Cerebellum, and Movement

Movement abnormalities result from damage to the basal ganglia or to the cerebellum. Both structures participate in movement control by modulating the movements initiated by the cortex. The basal ganglia regulate force; the cerebellum maintains accuracy and participates in learning.

11-4 Somatosensory System Receptors and Pathways

Distributed throughout the body, the somatosensory system consists of more than 20 types of specialized sensory neurons and receptors, each sensitive to a particular form of mechanical energy. Located in posterior dorsal root ganglia, each of these neurons carries sensory information into the spinal cord and the brain.

Neurons carrying proprioceptive (location and movement) information and haptic (touch and pressure) information have axons that ascend the spinal cord as the posterior spinothalamic tract. These fibers synapse in the posterior column nuclei at the base of the brain. From there axons cross to the other side of the brainstem to form the medial lemniscus, which ascends to the ventrolateral thalamus. Most of the ventrolateral thalamus cells project to the somatosensory cortex.

Nociceptive (pain, temperature, and itch) posterior root ganglion neurons synapse on entering the spinal cord. Their relay neurons cross the spinal cord to ascend to the thalamus as the anterior spinothalamic tract.

Because the two somatosensory pathways take somewhat different routes, unilateral spinal cord damage impairs proprioception and hapsis ipsilaterally below the site of injury and nociception contralaterally below the site.

11-5 Exploring the Somatosensory Cortex

The somatosensory system is represented topographically in parietal areas 3-1-2. The most sensitive body parts are accorded the largest somatosensory regions, as befits the body parts most capable of fine movements.

A number of sensory homunculi represent various sensory modalities, and these regions are hierarchically organized. If sensory input from anywhere in the body is cut off from the cortex by damage to sensory fibers, adjacent functional sensory cortex can expand into the now-unoccupied region.

Through the dorsal visual stream, the somatosensory cortex contributes to directing hand and body movements to visual targets. The somatosensory cortex also contributes to the ventral visual stream to produce perception of external objects, through which we can imagine the consequences of our movements.

KEY TERMS

anterior spinothalamic tract, p. 383

apraxia, p. 394

cerebral palsy, p. 363

connectome, p. 363

constraint-induced therapy, p. 371

corticospinal tract, p. 371

deafferentation, p. 383

glabrous skin, p. 379

hapsis, p. 381

homunculus, p. 367

hyperkinetic symptom, p. 374

hypokinetic symptom, p. 374

locked-in syndrome, p. 363

Ménière disease, p. 389

monosynaptic reflex, p. 385

motor sequence, p. 359

neuroprosthetics, p. 357

nociception, p. 381

pain gate, p. 387

paraplegia, p. 364

periaqueductal gray matter (PAG), p. 389

posterior spinothalamic tract, p. 383

proprioception, p. 381

quadriplegia, p. 364

rapidly adapting receptor, p. 381

referred pain, p. 389

scratch reflex, p. 364

slowly adapting receptor, p. 381

topographic organization, p. 367

ventrolateral thalamus, p. 383

vestibular system, p. 389

↪ Visit 🅜 LaunchPad to access the e-Book, videos, 🅜 LearningCurve adaptive quizzing, flashcards, and more.

www.macmillanhighered.com/launchpad/kolb5e

What Causes Emotional and Motivated Behavior?

Katherine Streeter

Streeter

397

The Pain of Rejection

We use words like *sorrow, grief,* and *heartbreak* to describe a loss. Loss evokes painful feelings, and the loss or absence of contact that comes with social rejection leads to hurt feelings. Several investigators have attempted to discover whether physically painful and emotionally hurtful feelings are manifested in the same neural regions.

Physical pain (say, hot or cold stimuli) is easy to inflict, but inducing equivalently severe emotional, or affective, pain is more difficult. Ethan Kross and colleagues (2011) performed an experiment that may have succeeded in balancing participants' degree of emotional and physical pain.

Using fMRI, they scanned 40 people who had recently gone through an unwanted breakup. To compare brain activation, the participants viewed two photographs: one of their ex-partner, to evoke negative emotion, or the photo of a same-gender friend with whom the participant shared a pleasant time at about the time of the breakup. The picture order was randomized across participants.

Emotional cue phrases associated with each photograph directed the participants to focus on a specific experience they shared with each person. The physical stimulus employed by the researchers, which was administered in a separate session, was either painfully hot or painless warm stimulation of participants' forearm.

The research question is, do physical pain and social pain have a common neuroanatomical basis? The results, shown in the illustration, reveal that four regions respond to both types of pain: the insula, dorsal anterior cingulate cortex (dACC), somatosensory thalamus, and secondary somatosensory cortex (S2). The conclusion: Social rejection hurts in much the same way physical pain hurts.

Previous studies, including Eisenberger and colleagues, 2003, 2006, showed anterior cingulate activity during the experience of both physical and emotional pain. But new results also showed activity in cortical somatosensory regions related to physical pain. The results imaged by Kross and colleagues suggest that the brain systems underlying emotional reactions to social rejection may have developed by co-opting brain circuits that support the affective component of physical pain. We hasten to point out, however, that the overlapping activity in brain regions does not rule out unique neural components of emotional experiences. Certainly our subjective experiences are unique (e.g., Woo et al., 2014).

Another insight from the Kross study is that normalizing the activity of these brain regions probably provides a basis for both physical and mental restorative processes. Seeing the similarity in brain activation during social pain and physical pain helps us understand why social support can reduce physical pain, much as it soothes emotional pain.

Overlapping Social Rejection and Physical Pain
These fMRIs result from averaging scans from 40 participants to image the brain's response to physical or emotional pain. We see activation in the insula, dorsal anterior cingulate cortex (dACC), somatosensory thalamus, and/or secondary somatosensory cortex (S2). Research from E. Kross, M.G. Berman, W. Mischel, E.E. Smith, & T.D. Water, "Social rejection shares somatosensory representations with physical pain," 2011, Proceedings of the National Academy of Sciences (USA), 108, 6270–6275.

Knowing that the brain makes emotional experience real—more than mere metaphors of *hurt* or *pain*—how do we incorporate our thoughts and reasons for behaving as we do? Clearly, our subjective feelings and thoughts influence our actions. The cognitive interpretations of subjective feelings are **emotions**—anger, fear, sadness, jealousy, embarrassment, joy. These feelings can operate outside our immediate awareness.

This chapter begins by exploring the causes of behavior. Sensory stimulation, neural circuits, hormones, and reward are primary factors in behavior. We focus both on emotion and on the underlying reasons for **motivation**—behavior that seems purposeful and goal-directed. Like emotion, motivated behavior is both inferred and subjective, and it can occur without awareness or intent. It includes both regulatory behaviors, such as eating, which are essential for survival, and nonregulatory behaviors, such as curiosity, which are not required to meet an animal's basic needs.

Research on the neuroanatomy responsible for emotional and motivated behavior focuses on a neural circuit formed by the hypothalamus, the limbic system, and the frontal lobes. But behavior is influenced as much by the interaction of our social and natural environments and by evolution as it is by biology. To explain how all these interactions affect the brain's control of behavior, we concentrate on two specific examples, feeding and sexual activity. Our exploration leads us to revisit the idea of reward, which is key to explaining emotional and motivated behaviors.

emotion Cognitive interpretation of subjective feelings.

motivation Behavior that seems purposeful and goal-directed.

(12-1) Identifying the Causes of Behavior

We may think that the most obvious explanation for our behavior is simply that that we act in a state of free will: we do what we want to, and we always have a choice. But free will is not a likely cause of behavior.

Consider Roger. We first met 25-year-old Roger in the admissions ward of a large mental hospital when Roger approached us and asked if we had any snacks. We had chewing gum, which he accepted eagerly. We thought little about this encounter until 10 minutes later, when we noticed Roger eating the flowers from the stems in a vase on a table. A nurse took the vase away but said little to Roger.

Later, as we wandered about the ward, we encountered a worker replacing linoleum floor tiles. Roger was watching the worker, and as he did, he dipped his finger into the pot of gluing compound and licked the glue from his finger, as if he were sampling honey from a jar. When we asked Roger what he was doing, he said that he was really hungry and that this stuff was not too bad. It reminded him of peanut butter.

One of us tasted the glue and concluded that it did not taste like peanut butter. It tasted awful. Roger was undeterred. We alerted a nurse, who quickly removed him from the glue. Later, we saw him eating flowers from another bouquet.

Neurological testing revealed that a tumor had invaded Roger's hypothalamus at the base of his brain. He was indeed hungry all of the time and in all likelihood could consume more than 20,000 calories a day if allowed to do so.

Would you say that Roger was exercising free will regarding his appetite and food preferences? Probably not. Roger seemed compelled to eat whatever he could find, driven by a ravenous hunger. The nervous system, not an act of free will, produced this behavior and undoubtedly produces many others.

If free will does not adequately explain why we act as we do, what does? One obvious answer is that we do things that we find rewarding. Rewarding experiences must activate brain circuits that make us feel good. Consider the example of prey killing by domestic cats.

One frustrating thing about being a cat owner is that even well-fed cats kill birds—often lots of birds. Most people are not much bothered when their cats kill mice: they view mice as a nuisance. But birds are different. People enjoy watching birds in their yard and garden. Many cat owners wonder why their pets keep killing birds.

To provide an answer, we look to the activities of neural circuits. Cats must have a brain circuit that controls prey killing. When this circuit is active, a cat makes an "appropriate" kill. Viewed in an evolutionary context, it makes sense for cats to have such a circuit: in the days when doting humans did not keep cats as pets, cats did not have food dishes that were regularly filled.

Why does this prey-killing circuit become active when a cat does not need food? One explanation is that, to secure survival, the activity of circuits like the prey-killing circuit are in some way rewarding—they make the cat feel good. As a result, the cat will engage often in the pleasure-producing behavior. This helps to guarantee that it will usually not go hungry.

In the wild, after all, a cat that did not like killing would probably be dead. In the early 1960s, Steve Glickman and Bernard Schiff (1967) first proposed the idea that behaviors such as prey killing are rewarding. We return to reward in Section 12-6 because it is important in understanding the causes of behavior.

Many people find watching and sharing cute cat videos rewarding: it makes them feel good, and they do it often.

FIGURE 12-1 Sensory Deprivation
Experimenters record the EEG of a participant lying on a bed in a dimly lit environmental cubicle 24 hours a day, with time out only for meals and bathroom breaks. A translucent plastic visor restricts the participant's vision; a U-shaped pillow and the noise of a fan and air conditioner limit hearing. Cotton gloves and long cardboard cuffs restrict the sense of touch. Information from W. Heron (1957). The Pathology of Boredom. *Scientific American*, 197(4), p. 52.

FIGURE 12-2 Brain Maintenance
Monkeys quickly learn to solve puzzles or perform other tricks to gain access to a door that looks out from their dimly lit quarters into an adjacent room. A toy train is a strong visual incentive for the monkey peeking through the door; a bowl of fruit is less rewarding. From R. A. Butler and H. F. Harlow (1954). Persistence of Visual Exploration in Monkeys. *Journal of Comparative and Physiological Psychology*, 47, p. 260.

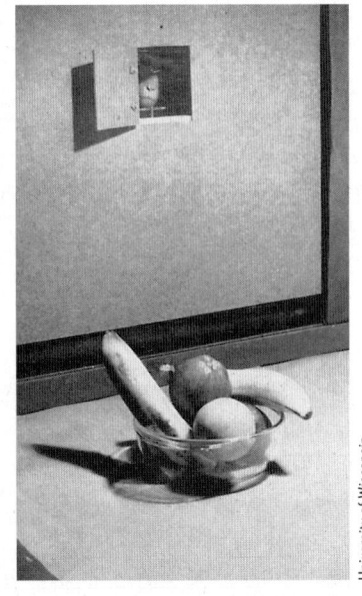

Behavior for Brain Maintenance

Some experiences are rewarding; others are aversive, again because brain circuits are activated to produce behaviors that reduce the aversive experience. One example is the brain's inherent need for stimulation.

Donald Hebb and his coworkers (Heron, 1957) studied the effects of **sensory deprivation**, depriving people of nearly all sensory input. They wanted to see how well-fed, physically comfortable college students who were paid handsomely for their time would react if they did nothing, saw nothing, and heard or touched very little 24 hours a day. **Figure 12-1** shows the experimental setup.

Each student lay on a bed in a small, soundproofed room with ears enveloped by a hollowed-out pillow that muffled the monotonous hums of a nearby fan and air conditioner. Cardboard tubes covered the hands and arms, cutting off the sense of touch, and a translucent visor covered the eyes, blurring the visual world. The participants were given food and access to bathroom facilities on request. Otherwise, they were asked simply to enjoy the peace and quiet. For doing so, they would receive $20 per day—about four times what a student could earn 60 years ago, even for a day's hard labor.

Wouldn't you think the participants would be ecstatic to contribute to scientific knowledge in such a painless way? In fact, they were far from happy. Most were content for perhaps 4 to 8 hours; then they became increasingly distressed. They craved stimulation of almost any kind. In one version of the experiment, the participants could listen, on request, to a talk for 6-year-old children on the dangers of alcohol. Some of them asked to hear it 20 times a day. Few lasted more than 24 hours in these conditions.

What caused their distress? Why did they find sensory deprivation so aversive? The answer, Hebb and colleagues concluded, must be that the brain has an inherent need for stimulation.

Psychologists Robert Butler and Harry Harlow (1954) came to a similar conclusion through a series of experiments they conducted at about the same time Hebb conducted his sensory deprivation studies. Butler placed rhesus monkeys in a dimly lit room with a small door that could be opened to view an adjoining room. As shown in **Figure 12-2**, the researchers could vary the stimuli in the adjoining room so that the monkeys could view different objects or animals each time they opened the door.

Monkeys in these conditions spent a lot of time opening the door and viewing whatever was on display, such as toy trains circling a track. The monkeys were even willing to perform various tasks just for an opportunity to look through the door. The longer they were deprived of a chance to look, the more time they spent looking when finally given the opportunity.

The Butler and Harlow experiments, together with Hebb and colleagues' research on sensory deprivation, show that in the absence of stimulation, the brain will seek it out.

Neural Circuits and Behavior

Researchers have identified brain circuits for "reward" and discovered that these circuits can modulate to increase or decrease activity. Researchers studying the rewarding properties of sexual activity in males, for example, found that a man's frequency of copulation correlates with his levels of **androgens** (male hormones). Unusually high androgen levels are related to ultrahigh sexual interest; abnormally low androgen levels are linked to low sexual interest or perhaps no interest at all. The brain circuits are more difficult to activate in the absence of androgens.

Another way to modulate reward circuits comes via our chemical senses, smell and taste. The odor of a mouse can stimulate hunting in cats, whereas the odor of a cat will drive mice into hiding. Similarly, the smell from a bakery can make us hungry, whereas foul odors can reduce the rewarding value of our favorite foods. Although we tend to view the chemical senses as relatively minor in our daily lives, they are central to motivated and emotional behavior, as discussed next, in Section 12-2.

Understanding the neural basis for motivated behavior has wide application. For instance, we can say that Roger had a voracious and indiscriminate appetite either because the brain circuits that initiate eating were excessively active or because the circuits that terminate eating were inactive. Similarly, we can say that Hebb's participants were highly upset by sensory deprivation because the neural circuits that respond to sensory inputs were forced into abnormal underactivity. So the main reason for a particular thought, feeling, or action lies in what is going on in brain circuits.

sensory deprivation Experimental setup in which a participant is allowed only restricted sensory input; participants generally have a low tolerance for deprivation and may even hallucinate.

androgen Male hormone related to level of sexual interest.

12-1 REVIEW

Identifying the Causes of Behavior

Before you continue, check your understanding.

1. One reason cats kill when they may not be hungry is that the killing behavior is _____.

2. A reason animals get bored and seek new things to do is to maintain a(n) _____.

3. Which senses strongly modulate neural circuits?

4. Why is free will inadequate to explain why we do the things we do?

Answers appear at the back of the book.

For additional study tools, visit **LaunchPad**:
www.macmillanhighered.com/launchpad/kolb5e

12-2 The Chemical Senses

Chemical reactions are central to nervous system activity, and *chemosignals* (chemical signals) play a central role in motivated and emotional behavior. Mammals identify group members by odor, mark their territory with urine and other odorants, identify favorite and forbidden foods by taste, and form associations among odors, tastes, and emotional events.

Olfaction

Olfaction is the most puzzling sensory system. We can discriminate thousands of odors, yet we have great difficulty finding words to describe what we smell. We may like or dislike smells or compare one smell to another, but we lack a vocabulary for olfactory perceptions.

Wine experts rely on olfaction to tell them about wines, but they must *learn* to use smell to do so. Training courses in wine sniffing typically run one full day per week for a year, and most participants still have great difficulty passing the final test. This degree of difficulty contrasts with that of vision and audition, senses designed to analyze the specific qualities of sensory input, such as pitch in audition or color in vision. In contrast, olfaction seems designed to discriminate whether information is safe or familiar—is the smell from an edible food? from a friend or a stranger?—or identifies a signal, perhaps from a receptive mate.

Receptors for Smell

Conceptually, identifying chemosignals is similar to identifying other sensory stimuli (light, sound, touch). But rather than converting physical energy such as light or sound waves into receptor potentials, scent interacts with chemical receptors. This constant chemical interaction must be tough on the receptors: in contrast with receptors for light, sound, and touch, chemical receptors are constantly being replaced. The life of an olfactory receptor neuron is about 60 days.

The receptor surface for olfaction, illustrated in **Figure 12-3**, is the *olfactory epithelium* in the nasal cavity. The epithelium is composed of receptor cells and support cells. Each receptor cell sends a process ending in 10 to 20 cilia into a mucous layer, the *olfactory mucosa*. Chemicals in the air we breathe dissolve in the mucosa to interact with the cilia. If an olfactory chemosignal affects the receptors, metabotropic activation of a specific G protein leads to an opening of sodium channels and a change in membrane potential.

Figure 5-15A illustrates activity in such a metabotropic receptor.

The epithelial receptor surface varies widely across species. In humans, this area is estimated to range from 2 to 4 square centimeters; in dogs, about 18 square centimeters; and in cats, about 21 square centimeters. No wonder our sensitivity to odors is less acute than that of dogs and cats: they have 10 times as much receptor area as humans have! Roughly analogous to the tuning characteristics of cells in the auditory system, olfactory receptor neurons in vertebrates do not respond to specific odors but rather to a range of odors.

How does a limited number of receptor types allow us to smell many different odors? The simplest explanation is that any given odorant stimulates a unique pattern of receptors, and the summed activity or pattern of activity produces our perception of a particular odor. Analogously, the visual system enables us to identify several million colors with only three receptor types in the retina: the summed activity of the three cones leads to our richly colored life.

FIGURE 12-3 Olfactory Epithelium

A fundamental difference, however, is that the olfactory system is estimated to contain about 400 kinds of receptors compared with 4 (rods plus the cones) in the visual system. Some researchers propose that humans can discriminate up to 1 trillion smells. At present the true number is unknown but likely more than commonly believed (Gerkin & Castro, 2015).

Olfactory Pathways

Olfactory receptor cells project to the olfactory bulb, ending in ball-like tufts of dendrites— the *glomeruli* shown in Figure 12-3—where they form synapses with the dendrites of *mitral cells*. Mitral cells send their axons from the olfactory bulb to the broad range of forebrain areas summarized in **Figure 12-4**. Many olfactory targets, such as the amygdala and pyriform cortex, have no connection *through* the thalamus, as do other sensory systems. However, a thalamic connection (to the dorsomedial nucleus) does project to the **orbitofrontal cortex** (OFC), the prefrontal area behind the eye sockets (the *orbits*) that receives projections from this thalamic nucleus. In Section 12-4 we explain the OFC's central role in emotional and social behaviors as well as in eating.

Accessory Olfactory System

A unique class of odorants is **pheromones**, biochemicals released by one animal that act as chemosignals and can affect the physiology or behavior of another animal of the same species. For example, Karen Stern and Martha McClintock (1998) found that when women reside together, their estrous cycles begin to synchronize. Furthermore, the researchers found that the synchronization of menstrual cycles, a phenomenon called the *Whitten effect*, is stimulated by the odor of male urine.

Pheromones appear able to affect more than sex-related behavior. A human chemosignal, androstadienone, has been shown to alter glucose utilization in the neocortex—that is, how the brain uses energy (Jacob et al., 2001). Thus, a chemosignal appears to affect cortical processes even though that signal was not consciously detected. The puzzle is why we would evolve such a mechanism and how it might actually affect cerebral functioning.

Pheromones are unique odors because they are detected by a special olfactory receptor system, the *vomeronasal organ*, which is made up of a small group of sensory receptors connected by a duct to the nasal passage. The receptor cells in the vomeronasal organ send their axons to the accessory olfactory bulb, which lies adjacent to the main olfactory bulb. The vomeronasal organ connects primarily with the amygdala and hypothalamus, via which it probably plays a role in reproductive and social behavior.

It is likely that the vomeronasal organ participates not in general olfactory behavior but rather in the analysis of pheromones, such as those in urine. You may have seen bulls or cats engage in a behavior known as *flehmen*, illustrated in **Figure 12-5**. When exposed to novel urine from a cat or human, cats raise their upper lip to close off the nasal passages and suck air into the mouth. The air flows through the duct on the roof of the mouth en route to the vomeronasal organ.

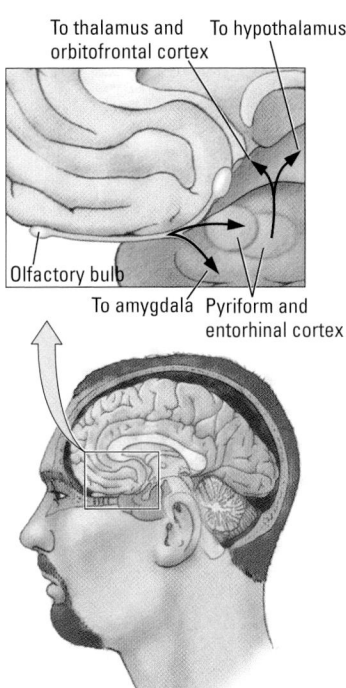

To thalamus and orbitofrontal cortex   To hypothalamus

Olfactory bulb

To amygdala   Pyriform and entorhinal cortex

FIGURE 12-4 Olfactory Pathways

Courtesy of Arthur Nonneman and Bryan Kolb

FIGURE 12-5 Response to Pheromones Left: A cat sniffs a urine-soaked cotton ball. Center: It raises its upper lip to close off the nasal passages. Right: It follows with the full gape response characteristic of flehmen, a behavior mediated by the accessory olfactory system.

orbitofrontal cortex (OFC) Prefrontal cortex behind the eye sockets (the *orbits*); receives projections from the dorsomedial nucleus of the thalamus; central to a variety of emotional and social behaviors, including eating; also called *orbital frontal cortex*.

pheromone Odorant biochemical released by one animal that acts as a chemosignal and can affect the physiology or behavior of another animal.

Human Olfactory Processing

Our ability to distinguish a surprisingly large number of odors upends the common misperception that people have a miserable sense of smell relative to other mammals. Still, our threshold for detecting many smells is certainly inferior to that of our pet dogs, cats, and horses. Yet humans have a surprisingly acute sensitivity to behaviorally significant smells.

Several studies show convincingly that people can identify their own odor, the odor of kin versus not-kin, and the odor of friends versus strangers with an accuracy well above chance (e.g., Olsson et al., 2006). Johan Lundstrom and colleagues (2008) used PET scans to identify the neural networks that process human body odors. They made two surprising findings.

First, the brain analyzes common odors and body odors differently. Although both activate primary olfactory regions, body odors also activate structures not previously believed to participate in olfactory processing, including the posterior cingulate cortex, occipital cortex, and anterior cingulate cortex—regions also activated by visually emotional stimuli. Considered in an evolutionary perspective, the ability to identify human odors probably is uniquely important to safety.

Second, smelling a stranger's odor activates the amygdala and insular cortex, similar to activation observed for fearsome visual stimuli such as masked or fearsome faces. The investigators also asked participants to rate the intensity and pleasantness of odors; they found that strangers' odors were rated as stronger and less pleasant than those of familiar persons.

Lundstrom and colleagues conclude that processing body odors is mostly unconscious. It represents an automatic process that matches odors to a learned library of smells. Similar unconscious processes seem to occur during visual and auditory information processing and to play an important role in our emotional reactions.

The insula contains regions related to language, taste perception, and social cognition.

Gustation

Research reveals significant differences in taste preferences both between and within species. Humans and rats like sucrose and saccharin solutions, but dogs reject saccharin and cats are indifferent to both, inasmuch as they do not detect sweetness at all. The failure of cats to taste sweet may not be surprising: they are pure carnivores, and nothing that they normally eat is sweet.

Within the human species, clear differences in taste thresholds and preferences are obvious. An example is the preference for or dislike of bitter tastes—the flavor of brussels sprouts, for instance. People tend to love them or hate them. Linda Bartoshuk (2000) showed absolute differences among adults: some perceive certain tastes as very bitter, whereas others are indifferent to them. Presumably, the latter group is more tolerant of brussels sprouts.

Sensitivity to bitterness is related to genetic differences in the ability to detect a specific bitter chemical (6-n-propylthiouracil, or PROP). PROP bitterness associates with allelic variation in the taste receptor gene *TAS2R38*. People able to detect minute quantities of PROP find the taste extremely bitter; they are sometimes called *supertasters*. Those who do not taste PROP as very bitter are *nontasters*. The advantage of being a supertaster is that many bitter "foods" are poisonous. The disadvantage is that supertasters avoid many nutritious fruits and vegetables that they find bitter.

Valerie Duffy and her colleagues (2010) investigated sensitivity to quinine (usually perceived as bitter) in participants who were assessed for the *TAS2R38* genotype. They estimated participants' taste bud density by counting the number of papillae (the little bumps on the tongue). Quinine was reported as more bitter to those who tasted PROP as very bitter or to those who had more taste buds. Thus, detection of bitterness is related both to *TAS2R38* and to tongue anatomy.

Nontasters, either by genotype or phenotype (for few taste buds), reported greater consumption of vegetables, both bitter and not. Nontasters with higher numbers of taste buds reported eating about 25% more vegetables than the other groups. These data suggest that genetic variation in taste can explain differences in overall consumption of all types of vegetables. It also suggests that persuading supertasters to eat more healthy foods—that is, vegetables—may prove difficult.

Differences in taste thresholds also emerge as we age. Children are much more responsive to taste than adults and are often intolerant of spicy foods because they have more taste receptors than adults have. It is estimated that by age 20, humans have lost at least 50 percent of their taste receptors. No wonder children and adults have different food preferences.

Receptors for Taste

Taste receptors are found in taste buds on the tongue, under the tongue, on the soft palate on the roof of the mouth, on the sides of the mouth, and at the back of the mouth on the nasopharynx. Each of the five taste receptor types responds to a different chemical component in food. The four most familiar are sweet, sour, salty, and bitter. The fifth type, called the *umami* receptor, is especially sensitive to glutamate, a neurotransmitter molecule, and perhaps to nucleotides. (Nucleotide bases are the structural units of nucleic acids such as DNA and RNA.)

Taste receptors are grouped into taste buds, each containing several receptor types, as illustrated in **Figure 12-6**. Gustatory stimuli interact with the receptor tips, the *microvilli*, to open ion channels, leading to changes in membrane potential. At its base, the taste bud contacts the branches of afferent cranial nerve 7 (facial), 9 (glossopharyngeal), or 10 (vagus).

Gustatory Pathways

Cranial nerves 7, 9, and 10 form the main gustatory nerve, the *solitary tract*. On entering the brainstem, the tract splits, as illustrated in **Figure 12-7**. One route (traced in red) travels through the posterior medulla to the ventroposterior medial nucleus of the thalamus. This nucleus in turn sends out two pathways, one to the primary somatosensory cortex (S1) and the other to the primary gustatory cortex of the insula, a region just rostral to the secondary somatosensory cortex (S2).

The gustatory region in the insula is dedicated to taste, whereas S1 is also responsive to tactile information and is probably responsible both for localizing tastes on the tongue and for our reactions to a food's texture. The gustatory cortex sends a projection to the orbital cortex in a region near the input from the olfactory cortex. Neuroimaging studies suggest that the mixture of olfactory and gustatory input in the orbital cortex gives rise to our perception of flavor. Ambience, including music and light, also affects this region of orbital cortex, increasing blood flow and so enhancing our experience of flavor.

A meta-analysis of noninvasive imaging studies that demonstrate taste-responsive brain regions, conducted by Maria Veldhuizen and colleagues (2011), also shows a brain asymmetry. The investigators conclude that areas in the right orbital cortex mediate the pleasantness of tastes, whereas the same region in the left hemisphere mediates the unpleasantness of tastes. Whereas the insula identifies the nature and intensity of flavors, the OFC evaluates the affective properties of tastes.

The second pathway from the gustatory nerve (shown in blue in Figure 12-7) projects via the nucleus of the solitary tract in the brainstem to the hypothalamus and amygdala. Researchers hypothesize that these inputs somehow participate in feeding behavior, possibly evaluating the pleasantness and strength of flavors.

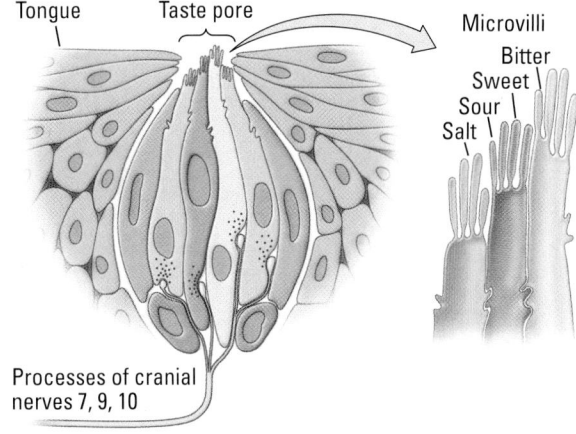

FIGURE 12-6 Anatomy of a Taste Bud
Information from D. V. Smith & G. M. Shepherd (2003). Chemical senses: Taste and olfaction. In L. R. Squire, F. E. Bloom, S. K. McConnell, J. L. Roberts, N. C. Spitzer, & M. J. Zigmond (Eds.), *Fundamental Neuroscience* (2nd ed., pp. 631–667), New York: Academic Press.

FIGURE 12-7 Gustatory Pathways

12-2 REVIEW

The Chemical Senses

Before you continue, check your understanding.

1. The receptor surface for olfaction is the _____.

2. Olfactory and gustatory pathways eventually merge in the orbitofrontal cortex, leading to the perception of _____.

3. Chemosignals that convey information about the sender are called _____.

4. The perception of bitterness is related to both the _____ and the _____.

5. How do a relatively limited number of receptor types allow us to smell a trillion different odors?

Answers appear at the back of the book.

For additional study tools, visit 🌐 **LaunchPad**
www.macmillanhighered.com/launchpad/kolb5e

(12-3) Evolution, Environment, and Behavior

Odor and taste play a fundamental role in the biology of emotional and motivated behavior. Why does the sight or smell of a bird or a mouse trigger stalking and killing in a cat? Why does the human body stimulate sexual interest? We can address such questions by investigating the evolutionary and environmental influences on brain circuit activity that contribute to behavior.

Evolutionary Influences on Behavior

One evolutionary explanation hinges on the concept of **innate releasing mechanisms** (IRMs), activators for inborn adaptive responses that aid an animal's survival. IRMs help an animal to feed, reproduce, and escape predators. The concept is best understood by analyzing its parts.

IRMs are present from birth rather than acquired through experience, as the term *innate* implies. These mechanisms have proved adaptive and therefore have been maintained in the genome of the species. The term *releasing* indicates that IRMs act as triggers for behaviors set in motion by internal programs.

Let us return to prey killing by cats. The cat's brain must have a built-in mechanism that triggers stalking and killing in response to such a stimulus as a bird or a mouse. A cat must also have a built-in mechanism that triggers mating behavior in the presence of a suitable cat of the opposite sex. Not all cat behaviors are due to IRMs, but you probably can think of other innate releasing mechanisms that cats possess—arching and hissing on encountering a threat, for example. For all these IRMs, the animal's brain must have a set of norms against which it can match stimuli to trigger an appropriate response.

The following experiment suggests the existence of such innate, internalized norms. Bryan Kolb and Arthur Nonneman allowed a litter of 6-week-old kittens to play in a room and become familiar with it. After this adjustment period, they introduced a two-dimensional image of an adult cat in a Halloween posture, as shown in **Figure 12-8A**.

The kittens responded with raised fur, arched backs, and bared teeth, all signs of being threatened by the image of the adult. Some even hissed at the model. These kittens had no experience with any adult cat except their mother, and there was no reason to believe that she had ever shown them this behavior. Some sort of template of this posture must be prewired in the kitten brain. Seeing the model that matched this preexisting template automatically triggered a threat response. This innate trigger is an IRM.

The IRM concept also applies to humans. In one study, Tiffany Field and her colleagues (1982) had an adult display to young infants various exaggerated facial expressions, such as happiness, sadness, and surprise. As **Figure 12-9** shows, the babies responded with very much the same expressions the adults displayed. These newborns were too young to be imitating the adult faces intentionally. Rather, babies must innately match these facial expressions to internal templates, in turn triggering some prewired program to reproduce the expressions in their own faces. Such an IRM would have adaptive value if these facial expressions serve as important social signals for humans.

---

innate releasing mechanism (IRM) Hypothetical mechanism that detects specific sensory stimuli and directs an organism to take a particular action.

evolutionary psychology Discipline that seeks to apply principles of natural selection to understand the causes of human behavior.

(A)

(B)

Courtesy of Arthur Nonneman and Bryan Kolb

FIGURE 12-8 Innate Releasing Mechanism in Cats **(A)** Displaying the Halloween cat image stimulates defensive responses in cats—raised fur, arched backs, and bared teeth. This behavior appears at about 6 weeks of age in kittens who have never seen such a posture before. **(B)** The scrambled "Picasso cat" evokes no response at all.

Evidence for a prewired motor program related to facial expressions also comes from study of congenitally blind children, who spontaneously produce the very same facial expressions that sighted people do, even though they have never seen them in others. IRMs are prewired into the brain, but experience can modify them. Our cat Hunter's stalking skills were not inherited fully developed at birth but rather matured functionally as she grew older. The same is true of many human IRMs, such as those for responding to sexually arousing stimuli.

Different cultures may emphasize different stimuli as arousing. Even within a single culture, what different people find sexually stimulating varies. Nonetheless, some human attributes are universally sexually arousing. For most human males, an example is the hip-to-waist ratio of human females. This ratio is probably part of an IRM.

The IRM concept can be related to the Darwinian view of nervous system evolution. Natural selection favors behaviors that prove adaptive for an organism, and these behaviors are passed on to future generations. Because behavior patterns are produced by the activity of neurons in the brain, the natural selection of specific behaviors is really the selection of particular brain circuits.

Animals that survive long enough to reproduce and have healthy offspring are more likely to pass on their brain circuit genes than are animals with traits that make them less likely to survive and successfully reproduce. Thus, feral cats adept at stalking prey or responding fiercely to threats are more likely to survive and produce many offspring, passing on their adaptive brain circuits and behaviors to their young. In this way, the behaviors become widespread in the species over time.

The Darwinian view seems straightforward when we consider how cats evolved brain circuits for stalking prey or responding to threats. It is less obvious when applied to complex human behaviors, however. Why, for instance, have humans evolved the behavior of killing other humans? At first glance, it seems counterproductive to the survival of the human species. Why has it endured? For an answer, we turn to **evolutionary psychology**, the field that applies principles of natural selection to explanations of human behavior.

Evolutionary psychologists assume that any behavior, including homicide, occurs because natural selection has favored the neural circuits that produce it. When two men fight a duel, one commonsense explanation might be that they are fighting over grievances. But evolutionary psychologists would instead ask, why is a behavior pattern that risks people's lives sustained in a population? Their answer: fights are about social status.

Men who fought and won duels passed on their genes to future generations. Through time, therefore, the traits associated with successful dueling—strength, aggression, agility—became more prevalent among humans, as did dueling. Martin Daly and Margot Wilson (1988) extended this evolutionary analysis to further account for homicide. In their view, homicide may endure in our society despite its severe punishment because it is related to behaviors that were adaptive in the human past.

Suppose that natural selection favored sexually jealous males who, to guarantee that they had fathered all offspring born of their mates, intimidated their rivals and bullied their mates. Male jealousy would be a prevalent motive for interpersonal violence, including homicide. Homicide itself does not help a man produce more children. But men who are apt to commit homicide are more likely to engage in other behaviors (bullying and intimidation) that improve their social status and therefore their reproductive fitness. Homicide therefore is related to adaptive traits that have been selected through millennia.

David Buss (2014) has examined patterns of mate selection across thousands of participants from 37 cultures, seeking to identify factors beyond culture that influence mate selection. His conclusions after nearly 30 years of study are that women around the world value dependability, stability, education, and intelligence in a long-term mate. Men, however, value good looks, health, and a desire for home and children more than women do.

FIGURE 12-9 Innate Releasing Mechanism in Humans Facial expressions made by young infants in response to expressions made by the experimenter. From M. Field, R. Woodson, R. Greenberg, D. Cohen, "Discrimination and imitation of facial expression by neonates," *Science* 8 October 1982: Vol. 218 no. 4568 pp. 179–181, Figure 1, permission conveyed through Copyright Clearance Center, Inc.

Section 15-5 posits a genetic explanation for the evolution of sex-related cognitive differences.

Older men and younger women are most likely to exhibit the mutually desired set of traits, which leads to a universal tendency for age differences between mates. Although the idea is controversial, Buss argues that these preferences are a product of natural selection in a Stone Age environment, when women and men would have faced different daily problems and thus would have developed separate adaptations related to mating.

Evolutionary theory cannot account for all human behavior, perhaps not even homicide or mate selection. By casting an evolutionary perspective on the neurological bases of behavior, though, evolutionary psychologists can generate intriguing hypotheses about how natural selection might have shaped the brain and behavior.

Environmental Influences on Behavior

Many psychologists have emphasized learning as a cause of behavior. No one would question that we modify our behavior as we learn, but the noted behaviorist B. F. Skinner (1938) went much further. He believed that behaviors are selected by environmental factors.

Skinner's argument is simple. Certain events function as rewards, or **reinforcers**. When a reinforcing event follows a particular response, similar responses are more likely to occur. Skinner argued that reinforcement can be manipulated to encourage the display of complex behaviors.

The power of experience to shape behavior by pairing stimuli and rewards is typified by one of Skinner's experiments. A pigeon is placed in a box that has a small disc on one wall (the stimulus). If the pigeon pecks at the disc (the response), a food tray opens, and the pigeon can feed (the reinforcement or reward). The pigeon quickly learns the association between the stimulus and the response, especially if the disc has a small spot on it. It pecks at the spot and within minutes it has mastered the response needed to receive a reward.

Now the response requirement can be made more complex. The pigeon might be required to turn 360 degrees before pecking the disc to gain the reward. The pigeon can learn this response too. Other contingencies might then be added, making the response requirements even more complex. For instance, the pigeon might be trained to turn in a clockwise circle if the disc is green, to turn in a counterclockwise circle if the disc is red, and to scratch at the floor if the disc is yellow.

If you suddenly came across this complex behavior in a pigeon, you would probably be astounded. But if you understood the experience that had shaped the bird's behavior, you would understand its cause. The rewards offered to the pigeon altered its behavior: its responses were controlled by the color of the disc on the wall.

Skinner extended behavioral analysis to include actions of all sorts—behaviors that at first do not appear easily explained. For instance, he argued that understanding a person's reinforcement history could account for various phobias. Someone who once was terrified by a turbulent plane ride thereafter avoids air travel and manifests a phobia of flying. The avoidance of flying is rewarding because it lowers the person's anxiety level, maintaining the phobic behavior.

Skinner also argued against the commonly held view that much of human behavior is under our own control. From Skinner's perspective, free will is an illusion, because behavior is controlled not by the organism but rather by the environment, through experience. But what is the experience actually doing? Increasing evidence suggests that epigenetic changes regulate changes in memory circuits. Skinner was not studying the brain directly, but it is becoming clear that epigenetics supports his perspective. We learn many complex behaviors through changes in memory-related genes that act to modify neural circuits (see the review by Day and Sweatt, 2011).

The environment does not always change the brain. A case in point can be seen again in pigeons. A pigeon in a Skinner box can quickly learn to peck a disc to receive a bit of food, but it cannot learn to peck a disc to escape from a mild electric shock to its feet. Why not? Although the same simple pecking behavior is being rewarded, apparently the pigeon's brain

Section 1-2 reviews Darwin's theory, materialism, and contemporary perspectives on brain and behavior.

Skinner box

Epigenetic mechanisms mediate synaptic plasticity, especially in learning and memory. See Section 14-4.

is not prewired for this second kind of association. The bird is prepared genetically to make the first association, for food, but not prepared for the second. This makes adaptive sense: typically, it flies away from noxious situations.

John Garcia and R. A. Koelling (1966) were the first psychologists to demonstrate the specific nature of this range of behavior–consequence associations that animals are able to learn. Garcia observed that farmers in the western United States are constantly shooting at coyotes for attacking lambs, yet despite the painful consequences, the coyotes never seem to learn to stop killing lambs in favor of safer prey. The reason, Garcia speculated, is that a coyote's brain is not prewired to make this kind of association.

So Garcia proposed an alternative to deter coyotes from killing lambs—an association that a coyote's brain *is* prepared to make: the connection between eating something that makes one sick and avoiding that food in the future. Garcia gave the coyotes a poisoned lamb carcass, which sickened but did not kill them. With only one pairing of lamb and illness, most coyotes learned not to eat sheep for the rest of their lives.

Many humans have similarly acquired food aversions because a certain food's taste—especially a novel taste—was subsequently paired with illness. This **learned taste aversion** is acquired even when the food eaten is in fact unrelated to the later illness. As long as the taste and the nausea are paired in time, the brain is prewired to connect them.

One of us ate his first Caesar salad the night before coming down with a stomach flu. A year later, he was offered another Caesar salad and, to his amazement, felt ill just at the smell of it. Even though he knew that the salad had not caused his earlier illness, he nonetheless had formed an association between the novel flavor and the illness. This strong and rapid *associative learning* makes adaptive sense. Having a brain that is prepared to make a connection between a novel taste and subsequent illness helps an animal avoid poisonous foods and so aids in its survival. A curious aspect of taste aversion learning is that we are unaware of having formed the association until we encounter the taste and/or smell again.

The fact that the nervous system is often prewired to make certain associations but not to make others has led to the concept of **preparedness** in learning theories. Preparedness can help account for some complex behaviors. For example, if two rats are paired in a small box and exposed to a mild electric shock, they will immediately fight with one another, even though neither was responsible for the shock. Apparently, the rat brain is predisposed to associate injury with nearby objects or other animals. The extent to which we might extend this idea to explain such human behaviors as bigotry and racism is an interesting topic to ponder.

Inferring Purpose in Behavior: *To Know a Fly*

We may tend to assume that behavior is intentional. A wonderful little book, *To Know a Fly*, by Vincent Dethier (1962), disabuses this assumption by illustrating the problems in inferring purpose from an organism's actions.

When a fly lands on a kitchen table, it wanders about, occasionally stomping its feet. Eventually, it finds a bit of food and sticks its proboscis (an extension like an elephant's trunk) into the food and eats. The fly may then walk to a nearby place and begin to groom by rubbing its legs together quickly. Finally, it spends a long period motionless.

If you observed a fly engaged in these behaviors, it might appear to have been searching for food because it was hungry. When it found food, you might assume that it gorged itself until it was satisfied, then it cleaned up and rested. In short, the fly's behavior might seem to you to be motivated—to have some purpose or intention.

Dethier studied flies for years to understand what a fly is actually doing when it engages in these behaviors. His findings have little to do with purpose or intention. When a fly wanders about a table, it is not deliberately searching. Rather, it is tasting what it walks on.

As **Figure 12-10** shows, a fly's taste receptors are on its feet. Tasting is automatic when a fly walks. An adult fly's nervous system has a built-in preference for sweet tastes and

reinforcer In operant conditioning, any event that strengthens the behavior it follows.

learned taste aversion Acquired association between a specific taste or odor and illness; leads to an aversion to foods that have the taste or odor.

preparedness Predisposition to respond to certain stimuli differently from other stimuli.

Section 14-4 has more on how our brains are wired to link unrelated stimuli.

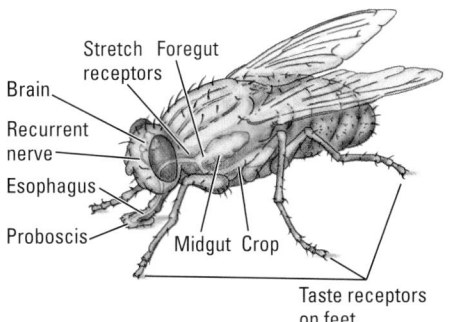

FIGURE 12-10 Feeding System of the Fly After the fly samples the surface using taste buds on its feet, it takes in food through the proboscis and passes it through the esophagus to the gut. Stretch receptors at the gut entrance determine when the esophagus is full. The recurrent nerve alerts the brain to signal cessation of eating.

an aversion to sour, salty, and bitter tastes. Therefore, when a fly encounters something sweet, it automatically lowers its proboscis and eats—or drinks if the sweet is liquid. The sweeter the food, the more a fly will consume. (Sweet foods attract us humans too, as Clinical Focus 12-4, Weight Loss Strategies, reports.)

Why does a fly stop eating? A logical possibility is that its blood sugar level rises to some threshold. If this were correct, injecting glucose into the circulatory system of a fly would prevent the fly from eating. But that does not happen. Blood glucose level has no effect on a fly's feeding. Furthermore, injecting food into the animal's stomach or intestine has no effect either. So what is left?

Flies have a nerve (the recurrent nerve) that extends from the neck to the brain and carries information about whether any food is present in the esophagus. If the recurrent nerve is cut, the fly is chronically hungry and never stops eating. Such flies become so full and fat that their feet no longer reach the ground, and they become so heavy that they cannot fly.

Even though a fly appears to act with a purpose in mind, a series of very simple mechanisms actually control its behavior—mechanisms not remotely related to our concept of thought or intent. Hunger is simply the activity of the nerve. Clearly, we should not assume simply from appearances that a behavior carries intent. Behavior can have very subtle causes that do not include conscious purpose. How do we know that any behavior is purposeful? That question turns out to be difficult to answer.

(12-3) **REVIEW**

Evolution, Environment, and Behavior

Before you continue, check your understanding.

1. B. F. Skinner argued that behaviors could be shaped by _____ in the environment.

2. John Garcia used the phenomenon of _____ to discourage coyotes from killing lambs.

3. The brain of a species is prewired to produce _____ to specific sensory stimuli selected by evolution to prompt certain associations between events.

4. When a fly wanders around on a table, it is not exploring so much as _____.

5. Explain briefly how the concept of preparedness accounts for puzzling human behaviors.

Answers appear at the back of the book.

For additional study tools, visit 🎧 **LaunchPad**
www.macmillanhighered.com/launchpad/kolb5e

(12-4) Neuroanatomy of Motivated and Emotional Behavior

The neural circuits that control behavior encompass regions at all levels of the brain, but the critical neural structures in emotional and motivated behavior are the hypothalamus and associated pituitary gland, the limbic system, and the frontal lobes. The expression of emotions includes physiological changes: in heart rate, blood pressure, and hormone secretions. It also includes motor responses, especially movements of the muscles that produce facial expressions (see Figure 12-9). So much of human life revolves around emotions that understanding them is central to understanding our humanness.

But emotions are not restricted to people. A horse that is expecting alfalfa for dinner will turn its nose up at grass hay and may stomp its front feet and toss its head. Two dogs that are in competition for attention may snap at one another. Charles Darwin interpreted such behaviors as emotions in his classic book *The Expression of the Emotions in Man and Animals*, published in 1872. We now know that emotional expression in all mammals is related to activity in the limbic system and frontal lobes.

Although the hypothalamus plays a central role in controlling motivated behavior, it takes its instructions from the limbic system and the frontal lobes. The limbic and frontal regions project to the hypothalamus, which houses many basic neural circuits for controlling behavior and for autonomic processes that maintain critical body functions within a narrow, fixed range—that is, **homeostatic mechanisms**.

Section 6-5 explores hormonal regulation of homeostatic mechanisms.

In **Figure 12-11**, the neck of a funnel represents the hypothalamus, and the limbic system and frontal lobes form the funnel's rim. To produce behavior, the hypothalamus sends axons to other brainstem circuits. But not all behavior is controlled via the funnel to the hypothalamus. Many other routes to the brainstem and spinal cord bypass the hypothalamus, among them projections from the motor cortex to the brainstem and spinal cord. Thus it is primarily motivated behaviors that require hypothalamic involvement.

Regulatory and Nonregulatory Behavior

We seek mates, food, or sensory stimulation because of brain activity, but we talk about such behavior as being motivated. Motivated behaviors are not something in the brain that we can point to, however. Rather, motivations are inferences we make about why someone, ourselves included, engages in a particular behavior. The two general classes of motivated behaviors are regulatory and nonregulatory. In this section we explore both categories before exploring the neuroanatomy of motivation and emotion.

FIGURE 12-11 Funneling Signals
In this model, many inputs from the frontal lobes and limbic system funnel through the hypothalamus, which sends its axons to control brainstem circuits that produce motivated behaviors.

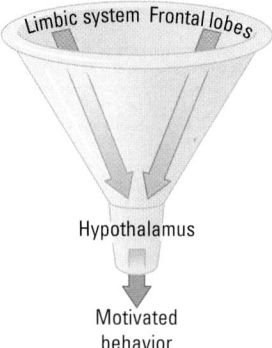

Regulatory Behaviors

Regulatory behaviors—behaviors motivated by an organism's survival—are controlled by homeostatic mechanisms. By analogy, consider a house whose thermostat is set at 18 degrees Celsius (°C). When the temperature falls below a certain tolerable range (say, to 16°C), the thermostat turns the furnace on. When the temperature rises above a certain tolerable level (say, 20°C), the thermostat turns on the air conditioner.

Human body temperature is controlled in a somewhat similar manner by a thermostat in the hypothalamus that holds internal temperature at about 37°C, a temperature referred to as a *set point*. Even slight variations cause us to engage in various behaviors to regain the set point. For example, when body temperature drops slightly, neural circuits that increase body temperature turn on. These neural circuits might induce an involuntary response such as shivering or a seemingly voluntary behavior such as moving closer to a heat source. Conversely, if body temperature rises slightly, we sweat or move to a cooler place.

Similar mechanisms control many other homeostatic processes, including the amount of water in the body, the balance of dietary nutrients, and the blood sugar level. Control of many such homeostatic systems is quite complex, requiring both neural and hormonal mechanisms. In some way, however, all of the body's homeostatic systems involve hypothalamic activity.

Imagine that specific cells are especially sensitive to temperature. When they are cool, they become very active; when they are warm, they become less active. These cells could function as a thermostat, telling the body when it is too cool or too warm. A similar set of cells could serve as a glucostat, controlling the level of sugar in the blood, or as a hydrostat, controlling the amount of water in the body. In fact, the body's real homeostatic mechanisms are slightly more complex than this imagined one, but they work on the same general principle.

Mechanisms to hold conditions such as temperature constant have evolved because the body, including the brain, is a chemical soup in which thousands of reactions are taking place all the time. Maintaining constant temperature is critical. When temperature changes, even by 2°C, the rates at which chemical reactions take place change.

Such changes might be tolerable, within certain limits, if all the reaction times changed to the same extent. But they do not. Consequently, an increase of 2°C might increase one

homeostatic mechanism Process that maintains critical body functions within a narrow, fixed range.

regulatory behavior Behavior motivated to meet the animal's survival needs.

reaction by 10 percent and another by only 2 percent. Such uneven changes would wreak havoc with finely tuned body processes such as metabolism and the workings of neurons.

A similar logic applies to maintaining homeostasis in other body systems. For instance, cells require certain concentrations of water, salt, and glucose to function properly. Wild fluctuations in the concentrations cause a gross disturbance of metabolic balance and eventually biological disaster.

Nonregulatory Behaviors

Unlike regulatory behaviors, such as eating or drinking, **nonregulatory behaviors** are neither required to meet the basic survival needs of an animal nor controlled by homeostatic mechanisms. Thus, nonregulatory behaviors include everything else we do—from sexual intercourse to parenting to such curiosity-driven activities as conducting psychology experiments.

Some nonregulatory behaviors, such as sexual intercourse, entail the hypothalamus, but most of them probably do not. Rather, such behaviors entail a variety of forebrain structures, especially the frontal lobes. Presumably, as the forebrain evolved and enlarged, so did our range of nonregulatory behaviors.

Most nonregulatory behaviors are strongly influenced by external stimuli. As a result, sensory systems must play some role in controlling them. For example, the sexual behavior of most male mammals is strongly influenced by the pheromone emitted by receptive females. If the olfactory system is not functioning properly, we can expect abnormalities in sexual behavior. We will return to sexual behavior in Section 12-5, as we investigate how a nonregulatory behavior is controlled. But first we explore the brain structures that take part in motivated behaviors—nonregulatory and regulatory.

Regulatory Function of the Hypothalamic Circuit

The hypothalamus maintains homeostasis by acting on both the endocrine system and the autonomic nervous system (ANS) to regulate our internal environment. The hypothalamus also influences the behaviors selected by the rest of the brain, especially by the limbic system. Although it constitutes less than 1 percent of the human brain's volume, the hypothalamus controls an amazing variety of motivated behaviors, ranging from heart rate to feeding and sexual activity.

Hypothalamic Involvement in Hormone Secretions

A principal function of the hypothalamus is to control the **pituitary gland**, which is attached to it by a stalk (**Figure 12-12**A). Figure 12-12B diagrams the anatomic location of the hypothalamus in each hemisphere, with the thalamus above and the optic tracts just lateral.

We can divide the hypothalamus into three regions, lateral, medial, and periventricular, illustrated in frontal view in Figure 12-12B. The lateral hypothalamus, composed both of nuclei and of nerve tracts running up and down the brain, connects the lower brainstem to the forebrain. The principal tract, shown in **Figure 12-13**, is the **medial forebrain bundle** (MFB).

The MFB connects brainstem structures with various parts of the limbic system and forms the activating projections that run from the brainstem to the basal ganglia and frontal cortex. Fibers that ascend from the dopamine- and noradrenaline-containing cells of the lower brainstem form a significant part of the MFB. The dopamine-containing MFB fibers contribute to the control of many motivated behaviors, including eating and sex. They also contribute to pathological behaviors, such as addiction and impulsivity.

Each hypothalamic nucleus is anatomically distinct, and most have multiple functions, in part because the cells in each nucleus contain a different mix of peptide neurotransmitters. Each peptide participates in different behaviors. For instance, transmitters in the cells in the paraventricular nucleus may be vasopressin, oxytocin, or various combinations of other peptides (such as enkephalin and neurotensin). When peptide neurotransmitters act, we may

Categories of Motivated Behavior

Some Regulatory Behaviors
Internal body temperature
Eating and drinking
Salt consumption
Waste elimination
Some Nonregulatory Behaviors
Sex
Parenting
Aggression
Food preference
Curiosity
Reading

Figure 2-30 diagrams ANS pathways and connections.

Section 6-4 elaborates on dopamine's importance in experiences related to drug use.

Section 5-2 reviews the structures and functions of peptide neurotransmitters.

(A)

Preoptic nucleus
Paraventricular nucleus
Dorsomedial hypothalamic nucleus
Posterior nucleus
Ventromedial hypothalamic nucleus
Hypothalamus
Pituitary gland
Pituitary stalk

(B)

Third ventricle
Periventricular region
Lateral hypothalamic region
Medial hypothalamic region
Ventromedial hypothalamic nucleus
Optic tract

FIGURE 12-12 Nuclei and Regions of the Hypothalamus **(A)** Medial view shows the relation between the hypothalamic nuclei and the rest of the brain. **(B)** Frontal view shows the relative positions of the hypothalamus, thalamus, and—in the midline between the left and right hemispheres—the third ventricle. Note the three principal hypothalamic regions: periventricular, lateral, and medial.

experience a range of feelings such as well-being (endorphins) or attachment (oxytocin and vasopressin). For example, oxytocin is released during intimate moments such as nurturing behavior, hugging, or sex, and thus is sometimes known as the bonding hormone.

The production of various neuropeptides hints at the special relation between the hypothalamus and the pituitary. The pituitary consists of distinct anterior and posterior glands, as shown in **Figure 12-14**. The posterior pituitary is composed of neural tissue and is essentially a continuation of the hypothalamus.

Neurons in the hypothalamus make peptides (e.g., oxytocin and vasopressin) that are transported down their axons to terminals lying in the posterior pituitary. If these neurons become active, they send action potentials to the terminals to release the peptides stored there. But rather than affecting another neuron, as occurs at most synapses, capillaries (tiny blood vessels) in the posterior pituitary's rich vascular bed pick up these peptides.

The peptides then enter the bloodstream, which carries them to distant targets where they exert their effects. Vasopressin, for example, affects water resorption by the kidneys, and oxytocin controls both uterine contractions and the ejection of milk by mammary glands in the breasts. Peptides can have multiple functions, depending on where their receptors are. Thus, oxytocin not only controls milk ejection in females but also performs a more general role in several forms of affiliative behavior, including parental care, grooming, and sexual behavior in both men and women (Insel & Fernald, 2004).

nonregulatory behavior Behavior unnecessary to the animal's basic survival needs.

pituitary gland Endocrine gland attached to the bottom of the hypothalamus; its secretions control the activities of many other endocrine glands; associated with biological rhythms.

medial forebrain bundle (MFB) Tract that connects brainstem structures with various parts of the limbic system; forms the activating projections that run from the brainstem to basal ganglia and frontal cortex.

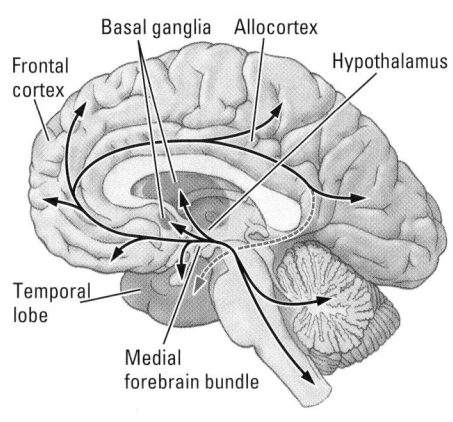

Basal ganglia Allocortex
Frontal cortex
Hypothalamus
Temporal lobe
Medial forebrain bundle

FIGURE 12-13 Medial Forebrain Bundle The activating projections that run from the brainstem to the basal ganglia and frontal cortex are major components of the MFB, a primary pathway for fibers connecting various parts of the limbic system with the brainstem.

FIGURE 12-14 Hypothalamus and Pituitary Gland The anterior pituitary is connected to the hypothalamus by a system of blood vessels that carry hormones from the hypothalamus to the pituitary. The posterior pituitary receives input from axons of hypothalamic neurons. Both regions respond to hypothalamic input by producing hormones that travel in the bloodstream to stimulate target organs.

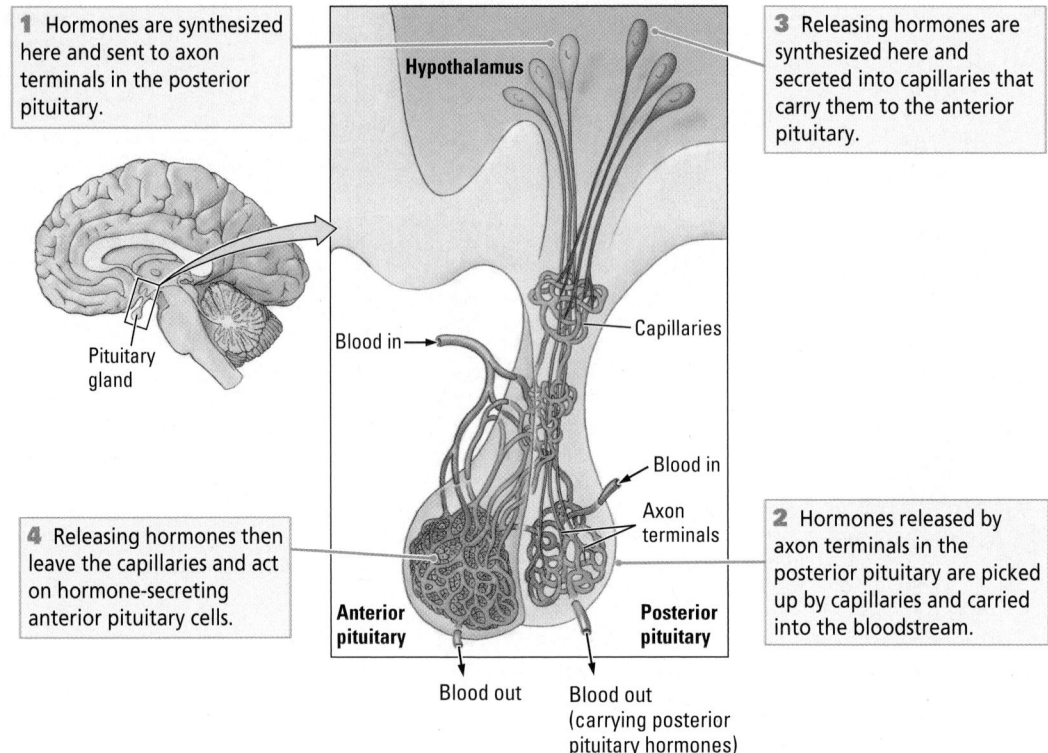

1 Hormones are synthesized here and sent to axon terminals in the posterior pituitary.

3 Releasing hormones are synthesized here and secreted into capillaries that carry them to the anterior pituitary.

4 Releasing hormones then leave the capillaries and act on hormone-secreting anterior pituitary cells.

2 Hormones released by axon terminals in the posterior pituitary are picked up by capillaries and carried into the bloodstream.

The glandular tissue of the anterior pituitary, by contrast, synthesizes various hormones. The major hormones and their functions are listed in **Table 12-1**. The hypothalamus controls the release of these anterior pituitary hormones by producing **releasing hormones**, peptides that act to increase or decrease hormone release. Produced by hypothalamic cell bodies, releasing hormones are secreted into capillaries that transport them to the anterior pituitary, as Figure 12-14 shows.

TABLE 12-1 Major Hormones Produced by the Anterior Pituitary

Hormone	Function
Adrenocorticotrophic hormone (ACTH)	Controls secretions of the adrenal cortex
Thyroid-stimulating hormone (TSH)	Controls secretions of the thyroid gland
Follicle-stimulating hormone (FSH)	Controls secretions of the gonads
Luteinizing hormone (LH)	Controls secretions of the gonads
Prolactin	Controls secretions of the mammary glands
Growth hormone (GH)	Promotes growth throughout the body

A releasing hormone can either stimulate or inhibit the release of an anterior pituitary hormone. For example, the anterior pituitary produces the hormone prolactin, but its release is controlled by a prolactin-releasing factor and a prolactin release–inhibiting factor, both synthesized in the hypothalamus. Hormone release by the anterior pituitary in turn provides the brain a means for controlling what is taking place in many other parts of the body. Three factors control hypothalamic hormone-related activity: feedback loops, neural regulation, and experience-based responses.

FEEDBACK LOOPS When the level of, say, thyroid hormone is low, the hypothalamus releases thyroid-stimulating hormone–releasing hormone (TSH-releasing hormone), which stimulates the anterior pituitary to release TSH. TSH then acts on the thyroid gland to secrete more thyroid hormone.

releasing hormone Peptide released by the hypothalamus that increases or decreases hormone release from the anterior pituitary.

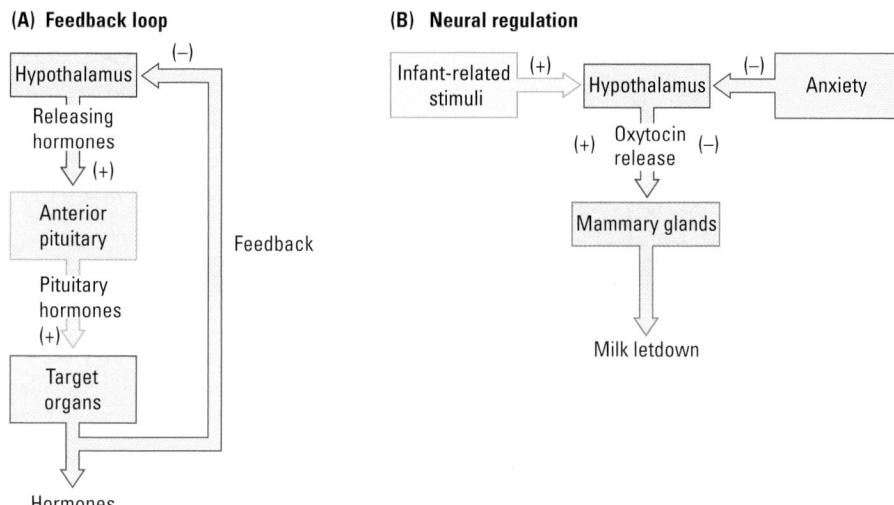

FIGURE 12-15 Hypothalamic Controls **(A)** Releasing hormones from the hypothalamus stimulate the anterior pituitary to release hormones. The pituitary hormones stimulate target organs, such as the thyroid and adrenal glands, to release their hormones. In the feedback loop, those hormones in turn influence the hypothalamus to decrease its secretion of the releasing hormones. **(B)** In the milk letdown response, oxytocin released from the hypothalamus stimulates the mammary glands to release milk. Milk letdown is enhanced by infant-related stimuli and inhibited by maternal anxiety.

Receptors in the hypothalamus detect the thyroid hormone level. When that level rises, the hypothalamus lessens its secretion of TSH-releasing hormone. This type of system is essentially a form of homeostatic control that works as a feedback mechanism, a system in which a neural or hormonal loop regulates the initiation of neural activity or hormone release, as illustrated in **Figure 12-15A**.

The hypothalamus initiates a cascade of events that culminates in hormone secretion, but it pays attention to how much hormone is released. When a certain level is reached, it stops its hormone-stimulating signals. Thus, the feedback mechanism in the hypothalamus maintains a fairly constant circulating level of certain hormones.

NEURAL CONTROL Hormonal activities of the hypothalamus necessitate regulation by other brain structures, such as the limbic system and the frontal lobes. Figure 12-15B diagrams this neural control in relation to the effects of oxytocin released from the hypothalamus by the paraventricular nucleus, which lies within the periventricular region illustrated in Figure 12-12. As stated earlier, one function of oxytocin is to stimulate cells of the mammary glands to release milk. As shown in Figure 12-15B, when an infant suckles the breast, the tactile stimulation causes hypothalamic cells to release oxytocin, which stimulates milk letdown. In this way, the oxytocin cells participate in a fairly simple reflex that is both neural and hormonal.

Other stimuli can influence oxytocin release, however, which is where control by other brain structures comes in. For example, the sight, sound, or even thought of her baby can trigger a lactating mother to eject milk. Conversely, as diagrammed in Figure 12-15B, feelings of anxiety in a lactating woman can inhibit milk ejection. These excitatory and inhibitory influences exerted by cognitive activity imply that the cortex can influence neurons in the periventricular region. It is likely that projections from the frontal lobes to the hypothalamus perform this role.

EXPERIENTIAL RESPONSES A third control on the hormonal activities of the hypothalamus is the brain's responses to experience: neurons in the hypothalamus undergo structural and biochemical changes just as cells in other brain regions do. In other words, hypothalamic neurons are like neurons elsewhere in the brain in that they can be changed by heavy demands on them.

Such changes in hypothalamic neurons can affect hormone output. For instance, when a woman is lactating, the cells producing oxytocin increase in size to promote oxytocin release and meet the increasing demands of a growing infant for more milk. Through this control, which is mediated by experience, a mother provides her baby with sufficient milk over time.

Recall the principle of neuroplasticity from Section 2-6.

FIGURE 12-16 Generating Behavior When rats receive electrical stimulation to the hypothalamus, they produce goal-directed behaviors. This rat is stimulated to dig when and only when the electricity is on. If the sawdust is removed (not shown), there is no digging.

hippocampus From the Greek word for *seahorse*; distinctive allocortical structure lying in the medial temporal lobe; participates in species-specific behaviors, memory, and spatial navigation and is vulnerable to the effects of stress.

Hypothalamic Involvement in Generating Behavior

Not only does the hypothalamus control hormone systems, it is also central in generating behavior. This function was first demonstrated by studies in which stimulating electrodes were placed in the hypothalamus of various animals, ranging from chickens to rats and cats. When a small electric current was delivered through a wire electrode, an animal suddenly engaged in some complex behavior—eating, drinking, or digging; displaying fear, attack, predatory, or reproductive behavior. Which behavior depended on which site was stimulated. All the behaviors were smooth, well integrated, and indistinguishable from typically occurring ones. Furthermore, all were goal directed.

The onset and termination of these behaviors depended entirely on hypothalamic stimulation. For example, if an electrode in a certain location elicited feeding behavior, the animal ate as soon as the stimulation was turned on and continued to eat until the stimulation was turned off. If the food was removed, however, the animal would not eat but might engage in other behaviors, such as drinking. Recall that Roger, profiled in Section 12-1, ate continuously if foodlike materials were present, corresponding to the continuous hypothalamic activity caused by a tumor.

Figure 12-16 illustrates the effect of stimulation at a site that elicits digging. When no current is delivered, the animal sits quietly. When the current is turned on, the animal vigorously digs in the sawdust; when the current is turned off, the animal stops digging. If the sawdust is removed, it does not dig.

Two more important characteristics of behaviors generated by hypothalamic stimulation are related to (1) survival and (2) reward. Animals apparently find the stimulation of these behaviors pleasant, as suggested by the fact that they willingly expend effort, such as pressing a bar, to trigger the stimulation. Recall that cats kill birds and mice because the act of stalking and killing prey is rewarding to them. Similarly, we can hypothesize that animals eat because eating is rewarding, drink because drinking is rewarding, and mate because mating is rewarding.

Organizing Function of the Limbic Circuit

We now turn our attention to parts of the brain that interact with the hypothalamus in generating motivated and emotional behaviors. These brain structures evolved as a ring around the brainstem in early amphibians and reptiles. Nearly 150 years ago, Paul Broca, impressed by this evolutionary development, called these structures the *limbic lobe*.

The limbic circuit derives its name from the Latin *limbus*, meaning *border*.

Allocortex is found in the brain of mammals and other chordates, especially birds and reptiles.

Known collectively as the *limbic system* today, these structures are formed from a primitive three-layered cortex known as allocortex, which lies adjacent to the six-layered neocortex. In mammals, the allocortex encompasses the cingulate (meaning *girdle*) gyrus and the hippocampal formation, as shown in **Figure 12-17**. The hippocampal formation includes the **hippocampus**—a cortical structure important in species-specific behaviors, memory, and spatial navigation and vulnerable to the effects of stress—and the *parahippocampal cortex* adjacent to it.

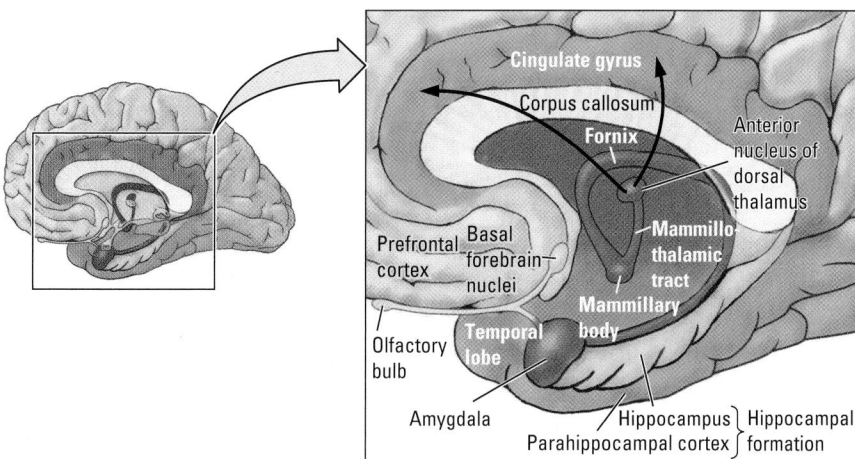

FIGURE 12-17 Limbic Lobe Encircling the brainstem, the limbic lobe as described by Broca consists of the cingulate gyrus and hippocampal formation (the hippocampus and parahippocampal cortex), the amygdala, the mammillothalamic tract, and the anterior thalamus.

Organization of the Limbic Circuit

As anatomists began to study the limbic structures, connections to the hypothalamus became evident. It also became apparent that the limbic system has a role in emotion. For instance, in the 1930s, James Papez observed that people with rabies display radically abnormal emotional behavior, and postmortem examinations showed that the rabies had selectively attacked the hippocampus. (Definitive proof of rabies remains postmortem hippocampal examination.)

Papez concluded from his observations that the limbic lobe and associated subcortical structures provide the neural basis of emotion. He proposed a neural circuit, traced in **Figure 12-18**A, now known as the *Papez circuit*, whereby emotion could reach consciousness, presumed at that time to reside in the cerebral cortex. In 1949, Paul MacLean expanded Papez's concept of the limbic circuit to include the amygdala and prefrontal cortex. Figures 12-17 and 12-18A show the amygdala lying adjacent to the hippocampus in the temporal lobe, with the prefrontal cortex lying just anterior.

Figure 12-18B charts the limbic circuit schematically. The hippocampus, amygdala, and prefrontal cortex all connect with the hypothalamus. The mammillary nucleus of the hypothalamus connects to the anterior thalamus, which in turn connects with the cingulate cortex. The cingulate cortex completes the circuit by connecting with the hippocampal formation, amygdala, and prefrontal cortex. This anatomical arrangement can be compared to the funnel in Figure 12-18C, which shows the hypothalamus as the spout leading to motivated and emotional behavior.

There is now little doubt that most limbic system structures, especially the amygdala and hypothalamus, take part in emotional behaviors, as detailed later in this section. But most limbic structures perform important roles in various motivated behaviors as well, especially in motivating species-typical behaviors such as feeding and sexual activity. The critical structures for such motivated behaviors, as well as for emotion, are the hypothalamus, which we have already considered, and the amygdala, to which we turn now.

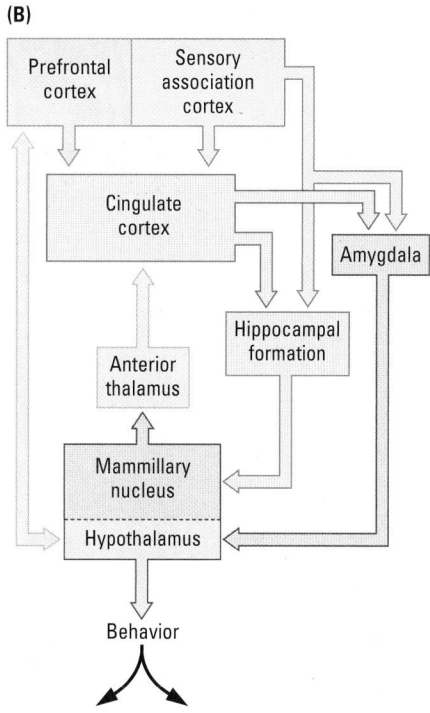

FIGURE 12-18 Limbic System (**A**) In this contemporary conception of the limbic system, an interconnected network of structures—the Papez circuit—controls emotional expression. (**B**) A schematic representation, coded to brain areas shown in part A by color, charts the limbic system's major connections. (**C**) A reminder that parts A and B can be conceptualized as part of a funnel rim of outputs that, through the hypothalamus, produce emotional and motivated behavior.

Amygdala

Named for the Greek word for *almond* because of its shape, the **amygdala** consists of three principal subdivisions, the corticomedial area, the basolateral area, and the central area. Like the hypothalamus, the amygdala receives inputs from all sensory systems. But in contrast with the hypothalamic neurons, more complex stimuli are necessary to excite amygdalar neurons. Indeed, many amygdalar neurons are *multimodal*: they respond to more than one sensory modality. In fact, some respond to the entire sensory array: sight, sound, touch, taste, and smell. These amygdalar cells must shape a rather complex image of the sensory world.

Section 15-3 elaborates on multisensory integration and the binding problem.

The amygdala sends connections primarily to the hypothalamus and the brainstem, where it influences neural activity associated with emotions and species-typical behavior. For example, when the amygdala of a person with epilepsy is electrically stimulated before brain surgery, the person becomes fearful and anxious. We observed a woman who responded with increased respiration and heart rate, saying that she felt as if something bad was going to happen, although she could not specify what.

Amygdala stimulation can also induce eating and drinking. We observed a man who drank water every time the stimulation was turned on. (There happened to be a pitcher of water on the table next to him.) Within 20 minutes, he had consumed about 2 liters of water. When asked if he was thirsty, he said, "No, not really. I just feel like drinking."

amygdala Almond-shaped collection of nuclei in the limbic system; plays a role in emotional and species-typical behaviors.

prefrontal cortex (PFC) Extensive frontal lobe area anterior to the motor and premotor cortex; key to controlling executive functions such as planning.

The amygdala's role in eating can be seen in patients with amygdalar lesions. Like Roger as a result of his tumor, many of these patients lose discrimination in their food choices, eating foods that were formerly unpalatable to them. Lesions of the amygdala may also give rise to hypersexuality.

Executive Function of the Frontal Lobes

The amygdala is intimately connected to the functioning of the frontal lobes that constitute all cortical tissue anterior to the central sulcus. This large area is made up of several functionally distinct regions mapped in **Figure 12-19**A.

Figure 11-2 charts the hierarchy of frontal lobe regions with regard to movement.

The motor cortex controls fine movements, especially of the fingers, hands, toes, feet, tongue, and face. The premotor cortex participates in selecting appropriate movement sequences. For instance, a resting dog may get up in response to its owner's call, which serves as an environmental cue for a series of movements processed by one region of the premotor cortex. Or a dog may get up for no apparent reason and wander about the yard, a sequence of actions in response to an internal cue processed by a different premotor region.

FIGURE 12-19 Gross Subdivisions of the Frontal Lobe and Prefrontal Cortex

(A) Lateral view

Dorsolateral prefrontal cortex Premotor cortex Motor cortex Central sulcus

Prefrontal cortex

Orbitofrontal cortex

(B) Ventral view

Ventromedial prefrontal cortex Orbitofrontal cortex

(C) Medial view

Dorsomedial prefrontal cortex

Anterior cingulate cortex

Ventromedial prefrontal cortex

Prefrontal Anatomy and Connections

As shown in Figure 12-19A, the **prefrontal cortex** (PFC) is anterior to the premotor cortex. The PFC is key to controlling executive functions such as planning movements. Its three primary areas are the dorsolateral region; the orbitofrontal cortex (OFC), also shown from a ventral aspect in Figure 12-19B; and the ventromedial PFC. The anterior cingulate cortex (ACC), shown in Figure 12-19C, is closely associated with the PFC, although not strictly part of it.

Prefrontal literally means *in front of the front.*

The prefrontal cortex contributes to specifying the goals toward which movement should be directed. It controls the processes by which we select movements appropriate to the particular time and context. This selection may be cued by internal information, such as memory and emotion, or it may be made in response to context (environmental information).

We focus here on the PFC and motivation and emotion. In Section 15-2 we turn to the PFC and cognition.

Like the amygdala, the frontal lobes receive highly processed information from all sensory areas, and many neurons in the prefrontal cortex, like those in the amygdala, are multimodal. As shown in **Figure 12-20**, the prefrontal cortex receives input via connections from the amygdala, dorsomedial thalamus, sensory association cortex, posterior parietal cortex, and the dopaminergic cells of the ventral tegmental area.

Dopaminergic input is important for regulating how prefrontal neurons react to stimuli, including emotional ones. Abnormalities in this dopaminergic projection may account for some disorders, including schizophrenia, in which people evince little emotional reaction to typically arousing stimuli.

Section 16-4 elaborates on the causes of and treatments for schizophrenia.

Figure 12-20 also shows the areas to which the prefrontal cortex sends connections—its output. The inferior prefrontal region projects axons to the amygdala and the hypothalamus in particular. These PFC axons provide a route for influencing the ANS and ENS, which control changes in blood pressure, respiration, and other internal processes. The dorsolateral prefrontal region sends its connections primarily to the sensory association cortex, posterior parietal cortex, cingulate cortex, basal ganglia, and premotor cortex.

PFC output influences movement (Section 11-1), memory (Section 14-3), and cognition (Section 15-2).

Prefrontal Functions

The prefrontal cortex takes part in selecting behaviors appropriate to the particular time and place. Selection may be cued by internal information or made in response to the environmental context. Disruption to this selection function can be seen in people with injury to the dorsolateral frontal lobe (see Figure 12-19A). They become overly dependent on environmental cues to determine their behavior. Like small children, they can be easily distracted by what they see or hear. We have all experienced a loss of concentration to some extent, but for a patient with frontal lobe damage, the problem is exaggerated and persistent. Because the person becomes so absorbed in irrelevant stimuli, he or she cannot act on internalized information most of the time.

Inputs to prefrontal cortex

Outputs from prefrontal cortex

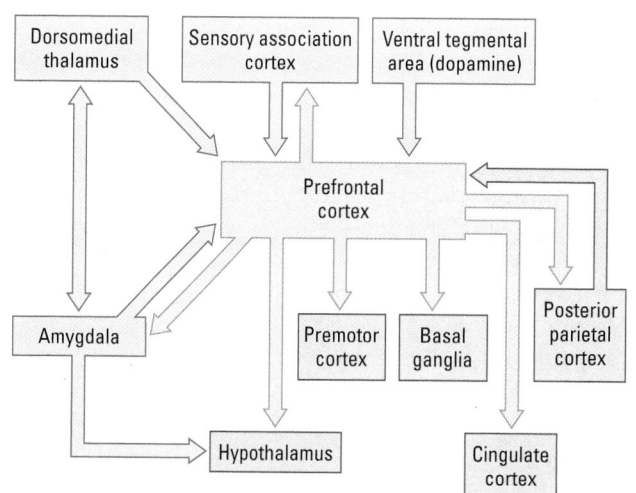

FIGURE 12-20 Prefrontal Connections At left, the PFC receives inputs (red arrows) and sends outputs (blue arrows) to the areas charted on the right.

A good example is J. C., in whom bilateral damage to the dorsolateral prefrontal cortex resulted from having a tumor removed. J. C. would lie in bed most of the day fixated on television programs. He was aware of his wife's opinion of this behavior, but only the sound of the garage door opening when she returned home from work in the evening would stimulate him into action. Getting out of bed was controlled by this specific environmental cue; without it, he seemed to lack motivation. Television completely distracted him from acting on internal knowledge of things that he could or should do.

Adapting behavior appropriately to the environmental context also is a PFC function. Most people readily change their behavior to match the situation at hand. We behave one way with our parents, another with our friends, another with our children, and yet another with our coworkers. Each set of people constitutes a different context, and we shift our behaviors accordingly. Our tone of voice, our use of slang or profanity, and the content of our conversations are quite different in different contexts.

Even among our peers we act differently, depending on who is present. We may be relaxed in the presence of some people and ill at ease with others. It is therefore no accident that the size of the frontal lobes is related to species' sociability. Social behavior is extremely rich in contextual information, and humans are highly social animals.

Controlling behavior in context requires detailed sensory information, which is conveyed from all sensory regions to the frontal lobes. This sensory input includes not only information from the external world but also internal information from the ANS. People with damage to the orbital prefrontal cortex, as is common in traumatic brain injuries, have difficulty adapting their behavior to the context, especially the social context. Consequently, they often make social gaffes.

In summary, the role of the frontal lobes in selecting behaviors is important for considering what causes behavior. The frontal lobes act much like a composer, but instead of selecting notes and instruments, they select our actions. Not surprisingly, the frontal lobes are sometimes described as housing the brain's executive functions. To grasp the full extent of frontal lobe control of behavior, see Clinical Focus 12-2, Agenesis of the Frontal Lobe.

Focus 1-1 and Section 1-2 recount behavioral effects of TBI; Section 14-5 details recovery; Section 16-3 explores TBI symptoms and treatments.

Section 15-2 considers the frontal lobes and the executive function of planning.

CLINICAL FOCUS 12-2

Agenesis of the Frontal Lobes

The role of the frontal lobes in motivated behavior is perhaps best understood by looking at J. P.'s case, described in detail by Stafford Ackerly (1964). Born in December 1914, J. P. was a problem child. Early on, he became a wanderer. Policemen would find him miles from home, as he had no fear of being lost. Severe whippings by his father did not deter him.

J. P.'s behavioral problems continued and expanded as he grew older, and by adolescence, he was constantly in trouble. Yet J. P. also had a good side. When he started school, his first-grade teacher was so impressed with his polite manners that she began writing a letter to his parents to compliment them on having such a well-mannered child who was such a good influence in the class.

As she was composing the letter, she looked up to find J. P. exposing himself to the class and masturbating. This juxtaposition of polite manners and odd behavior characterized J. P.'s conduct throughout his life. At one moment he was charming; at the next he was engaged in socially unacceptable behavior.

J. P. developed no close friendships with people of either sex, in large part because of his repeated incidents of public masturbation, stealing, excessive boastfulness, and wandering. He was a person of average intelligence who seemed unaffected by the consequences of his behavior. Police officers, teachers, and neighbors all ascribed intention to J. P.'s behavior: all believed that he was willfully misbehaving and blamed his parents for not enforcing sufficiently strict discipline.

Perhaps as a result, not until he was 19 years old was J. P.'s true condition detected. To prevent him from serving a prison term for repeated automobile theft, a lawyer suggested that J. P. undergo psychiatric evaluation. The psychiatrist who examined him ordered an X-ray (the only brain scan available at the time). The image revealed that J. P. lacked a right frontal lobe, and his left frontal lobe was about 50 percent of normal size. It is almost certain that his frontal lobes simply failed to develop.

Failure of a structure to develop is known as *agenesis*; J. P.'s condition was agenesis of the frontal lobes. His case offers an unusual opportunity to study the role of the frontal lobes in motivated behavior.

Clearly, J. P. lacked the bag of mental tricks that most people use to come to terms with the world. Normally behavior is affected both by its past consequences and by current environmental input. J. P. did not seem much influenced by either factor. As a result, the world was simply too much for him. He always acted childlike and was unable to formulate plans or to inhibit many of his behaviors. He acted on impulse. At home, he was prone to aggressive outbursts about small matters, especially with regard to his mother.

Curiously, J. P. seemed completely unaware of his life situation. Even though the rest of his brain was working fairly well—his IQ score was in the normal range, and his language skills were very good—the rest of his brain was unable to compensate for the absence of frontal lobes.

Stimulating and Expressing Emotion

Emotion, like motivation, is intangible: it is an inferred state. But the importance of emotion to our everyday lives is hard to exaggerate. Emotion can motivate us. It inspires artistic expression, for example, from poetry to filmmaking to painting. Many people enjoy the arts simply because they evoke emotions. And while people find certain emotions pleasant, severe and prolonged negative emotions, especially anxiety and depression, can cause clinical disorders.

To explore neural control of emotions, we must first specify the types of behavior we want to explain. Think of any significant emotional experience you've had recently. Perhaps you had a serious disagreement with a close friend. Maybe you just got engaged to be married.

A common characteristic of such experiences includes autonomic responses such as rapid breathing, sweating, and dry mouth. Emotions may also entail strong subjective feelings that we label as anger, fear, or love, among others. Finally, emotions typically entail thoughts or plans related to the experience itself and may take the form of replaying conversations and events in your mind, anticipating what you might say or do under similar circumstances in the future or in planning your married life.

These three forms of emotional experience suggest the influence of different neural systems. The autonomic component must include the hypothalamus and associated structures, as well as the enteric nervous system. The components of subjective feelings are more difficult to localize but clearly include the amygdala and probably parts of the frontal lobes. And thoughts and plans are likely to be cortical. What is the relation between our cognitive experience of an emotion and the associated physiological changes?

One view is that physiological changes (such as trembling and rapid heartbeat) come first, and the brain then interprets these changes as an emotion. This perspective implies that the brain (most likely the cortex) produces a cognitive response to autonomic information. That response varies with the context in which the autonomic arousal occurs, including the effects on the gut via the ENS. In cases of extreme autonomic activity, serotonin release surges in the gut, which can lead to diarrhea and cramping. If we are frightened by a movie, we feel a weaker, shorter-lived emotion than if we are frightened by a real-life encounter with a gang of muggers. Variations of this perspective have gone by many terms, beginning with the *James–Lange theory*, named for its originators, but all assume that the brain concocts a story to explain bodily reactions.

Two lines of evidence support the James–Lange theory and similar points of view. One is that the same autonomic responses can accompany different emotions. That is, particular emotions are not tied to unique autonomic changes. This line of evidence leaves room for interpreting what a particular pattern of arousal means, even though particular physiological changes may suggest only a limited range of possibilities. The physiological changes experienced during fear and happiness are unlikely to be confused.

The second line of evidence supporting the view that physiological changes are the starting point for emotions comes from people with reduced information about their own autonomic arousal, for example, owing to spinal cord injury. Spinal injury results in a decrease in perceived emotion, and its severity depends on how much sensory input is lost. **Figure 12-21** illustrates this relation. People with the greatest loss of sensory input, which occurs with injuries at the uppermost end of the spinal cord, also have the greatest loss of emotional intensity. In contrast, people with low spinal injuries retain most of their visceral input and have essentially typical emotional reactions.

Antonio Damasio (1999) emphasized an important additional aspect of the link between emotional and cognitive factors in his **somatic marker hypothesis**. When Damasio studied patients with frontal lobe injuries, he was struck by how they could be highly rational in analyzing the world yet still make decidedly irrational social and personal decisions. The explanation, he argued, is that the neural machinery underlying emotion no longer affects

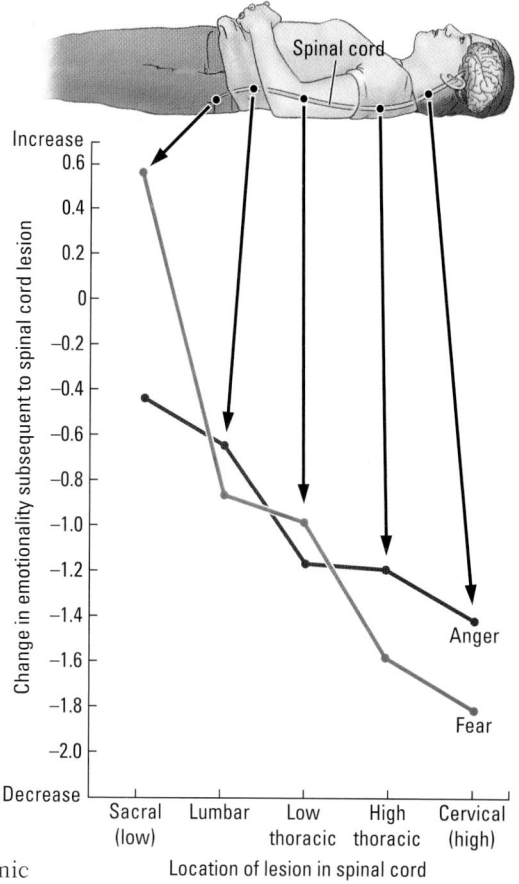

FIGURE 12-21 Losing Emotion Spinal cord injury blunts the emotional experience. Loss of emotionality is greatest when the lesion is high on the spine. Information from J. Beatty (1995). *Principles of Behavioral Neuroscience* (p. 339). Dubuque, IA: Brown & Benchmark.

After Christopher Reeve's spinal cord was severed at the cervical level (high), his emotions may have been blunted, but his motivation clearly remained intact. See Section 11-1.

somatic marker hypothesis Proposal that marker signals arising from emotions and feelings act to guide behavior and decision making, usually in an unconscious process.

the reasoning of people with frontal lobe injury, either consciously or unconsciously. Cut off from critical emotional input, many social and personal decisions suffer.

To account for these observations, Damasio proposed that emotions are responses induced by either internal or external stimuli not normally attended to consciously. For example, if you encounter a bear as you walk down the street (presuming that you live in a place where this event could take place), the stimulus is processed rapidly without conscious appraisal. In other words, a sensory representation of the bear in the visual cortex is transmitted directly to brain structures, such as the amygdala, that initiate an emotional response.

This emotional response includes actions on structures in the forebrain and brainstem and ultimately on the ANS. The amygdala has connections to the frontal lobes, so the emotional response can influence the frontal lobes' appraisal. But if the frontal lobes are injured, emotional information is excluded from cognitive processing, so the quality of emotion-related appraisals suffers, and the response to the bear might be inappropriate.

To summarize, Damasio's somatic marker hypothesis proposes how emotions are normally linked to a person's thoughts, decisions, and actions. In a typical emotional state, certain brain regions send messages to many other brain areas and to most of the rest of the body through hormones and the ANS. These messages produce a global change in the organism's state, and the altered state influences behavior, often unconsciously.

Amygdala and Emotional Behavior

In addition to controlling certain species-typical behaviors, described earlier, the amygdala influences emotion (Davis et al., 2003). Its role can be seen most clearly in monkeys whose amygdala has been removed. In 1939, Heinrich Klüver and Paul Bucy reported an extraordinary result, now known as **Klüver–Bucy syndrome**, that followed removal of the amygdala and anterior temporal cortex of monkeys. The principal symptoms included the following:

1. Tameness and loss of fear
2. Indiscriminate dietary behavior (eating many types of formerly rejected foods)
3. Greatly increased autoerotic, homosexual, and heterosexual activity with inappropriate object choice (e.g., the sexual mounting of chairs)
4. Tendency to attend to and react to every visual stimulus
5. Tendency to examine all objects by mouth
6. Visual agnosia, an inability to recognize objects or drawings of objects

Visual agnosia results from damage to the ventral visual stream in the temporal lobe, but the other symptoms are related to the amygdalectomy. Tameness and loss of fear are especially striking. Monkeys that normally show a strong aversion to stimuli such as snakes show no fear of them whatsoever. In fact, amygdalectomized monkeys may pick up live snakes and even put them in their mouth.

Although Klüver–Bucy syndrome is not common in humans—because bilateral temporal lobectomies are rare—its symptoms can be seen in people with certain forms of encephalitis, a brain infection. In some cases, encephalitis centered on the base of the brain can damage both temporal lobes and produce many Klüver–Bucy symptoms, including especially indiscriminate sexual behavior and the tendency to examine objects by mouth.

The amygdala's role in Klüver–Bucy syndrome points to its central role in emotion. So does its electrical stimulation, which produces an autonomic response (such as increased blood pressure and arousal) as well as a feeling of fear. Fear produced by the brain in the absence of an obvious threat may seem odd, but fear is basic to species' survival. To improve their chances of surviving, most organisms using fear as a stimulus minimize their contact with dangerous animals, objects, and places and maximize their contact with safe things.

Awareness of danger and of safety has both an innate and a learned component, as Joe LeDoux (1996) emphasized. The innate component, much as in the IRMs described in

The grizzly bear attack recounted in Section 11-4 confirms the primacy of emotion—fear—over other factors, including pain.

Section 9-4 describes varieties of visual form agnosia in a range of case studies.

Focus 2-2 examines some causes and symptoms of encephalitis.

Throughout human history, exploiting fear has proved especially effective in controlling group behavior.

Section 12-3, is the automatic processing of species-relevant sensory information—inputs from the visual, auditory, and olfactory systems. The importance of olfactory inputs is not obvious to us humans. Our senses are dominated by vision. But olfactory information connects directly to the amygdala in the human brain (see Figure 12-17). For many other animals, olfactory cues predominate.

A rat that has never encountered a ferret thus shows an immediate fear response to the odor of ferret. Other novel odors (such as peppermint or coffee) do not produce an innate fear reaction. The innate response triggers in the rat an autonomic activation that stimulates conscious awareness of danger.

In contrast, the learned component of fear consists of the avoidance of specific animals, places, and objects that the organism has come to associate with danger. The organism is not born with this avoidance behavior prewired. In a similar way, animals learn to increase contact with environmental stimuli that they associate with positive outcomes, such as food or sexual activity or, in the laboratory, drugs. Damage to the amygdala interferes with all these behaviors. The animal loses not only its innate fears but also its acquired fears of and preferences for certain environmental stimuli.

To summarize, a species' survival requires a functioning amygdala. It influences autonomic and hormonal responses through its connections to the hypothalamus. It influences our conscious awareness of the positive and negative consequences of events and objects through its connections to the prefrontal cortex.

Prefrontal Cortex and Emotional Behavior

At about the same time that Klüver and Bucy began studying their monkeys, Carlyle Jacobsen was studying the effects of frontal lobotomy on the cognitive capacities of two chimpanzees. A frontal lobotomy destroys substantial brain tissue as the result of inserting a sharp instrument into the frontal lobes and moving it back and forth.

In 1936, Jacobsen reported that one of the chimps was particularly neurotic before being subjected to this procedure. It became more relaxed afterward. Incredibly, a leading Portuguese neurologist of the time, Egas Moniz, seized on this observation as a treatment for behavioral disorders in humans, and the frontal lobotomy, illustrated in **Figure 12-22**, was initiated as the first technique of **psychosurgery**, or neurosurgery intended to alter behavior.

The use of psychosurgery grew rapidly in the 1950s. In North America alone, nearly 40,000 people received frontal lobotomies as a treatment for psychiatric disorders. Not until the 1960s was any systematic research conducted into the effects of frontal lesions on social and emotional behavior. By this time, the frontal lobotomy had virtually vanished as a "treatment." We now know that prefrontal lesions in various species, including humans, severely affect social and emotional behavior.

Agnes is a case in point. We met Agnes at the psychiatric hospital where we met Roger (whose indiscriminate eating we described in Section 12-1). At the time, Agnes, a 57-year-old woman, was visiting one of the nurses. She had, however, once been a patient.

The first thing we noticed about Agnes was that she exhibited no outward sign of emotion. She showed virtually no facial expression. Agnes had been subjected to a procedure known as a *frontal leukotomy* because her husband, an oil tycoon, felt that she was too gregarious. Evidently, he felt that her "loose lips" were a detriment to his business dealings. He convinced two psychiatrists that she would benefit from psychosurgery, and her life was changed forever.

To perform a leukotomy, as illustrated in Figure 12-22, a surgeon uses a special knife called a leukotome to sever the connections of a region of the orbitofrontal cortex (see Figure 12-19). In our conversations with Agnes, we quickly discovered her considerable insight into the changes brought about by the leukotomy. In particular, she indicated that she no longer had any feelings about things or most people, although, curiously, she was attached to her dog. She said that she often just felt empty and much like a zombie.

Klüver–Bucy syndrome Behavioral syndrome, characterized especially by hypersexuality, that results from bilateral injury to the temporal lobe.

psychosurgery Any neurosurgical technique intended to alter behavior.

FIGURE 12-22 Transorbital Leukotomy In this procedure, a leukotome is inserted through the bone of the eye socket to disconnect the orbitofrontal cortex from the rest of the brain.

Agnes's only moment of real happiness in the 30 years since her operation was the sudden death of her husband, whom she blamed for ruining her life. Unfortunately, Agnes had squandered her dead husband's considerable wealth as a consequence of her inability to plan or organize. This inability, we have seen, is another symptom of prefrontal injury.

The orbitofrontal area has direct connections with the amygdala and hypothalamus. Its stimulation can produce autonomic responses, and as we saw in Agnes, damage to the orbital region can produce severe personality change characterized by apathy and loss of initiative or drive. The orbital cortex is probably responsible for the conscious awareness of emotional states produced by the rest of the limbic system, especially the amygdala.

Agnes's loss of facial expression is also typical of frontal lobe damage. In fact, people with frontal lobe injuries and people who have schizophrenia or autism spectrum disorder are usually impaired at both producing and perceiving facial expressions, including a wide range of expressions found in all human cultures—happiness, sadness, fear, anger, disgust, and surprise. As with J. P.'s frontal lobe agenesis, described in Clinical Focus 12-2, it is difficult to imagine how such people can function effectively in our highly social world without being able to express their own emotions or to recognize others'.

Although facial expression is a key to recognizing emotion, so is tone of voice, or *prosody*. Patients with damage to the frontal lobe are devoid of prosody, both in their own conversations and in understanding the prosody of others. The lost ability to comprehend or produce emotional expression in both faces and language partly explains those patients' apathy. In some ways, they are similar to spinal cord patients who have lost autonomic feedback and so can no longer feel the arousal associated with emotion. These patients can no longer either read emotion in other people's faces and voices or express it in their own.

Some psychologists have proposed that our own facial expressions provide us with important clues to what we are feeling. This idea has been demonstrated in experiments reviewed by Pamela Adelmann and Robert Zajonc (1989). In one such study, people were required to contract their facial muscles by following instructions about which parts of the face to move. Unbeknown to the participants, the movements produced happy and angry expressions. Afterward, they viewed a series of slides and reported how the slides made them feel.

They said that they felt happier when they were inadvertently making a happy face and angrier when making the angry face. Patients with frontal lobe damage presumably have no such feedback from their own facial expressions, which could contribute to their emotional experiences being dampened.

Emotional Disorders

Major depression, a highly disruptive emotional disorder, is characterized by some or all the following: prolonged feelings of worthlessness and guilt, the disruption of normal eating habits, sleep disturbances, a general slowing of behavior, and frequent thoughts of suicide. A depressed person feels severely despondent for a long time. Major depression is common in our modern world, with a prevalence of about 6 percent of the population at any given time.

Depression has a genetic component. It not only runs in families but also frequently tends to occur in both members of a pair of identical twins. The genetic component in depression implies a biological abnormality, but the cause remains unknown. However, neuroscience researchers' interest in the role of epigenetic changes in depression is increasing. One hypothesis is that early life stress may produce epigenetic changes in the prefrontal cortex (see the review by Schroeder et al., 2010).

Excessive anxiety is an even more common emotional problem than depression. Anxiety disorders, including posttraumatic stress disorder (PTSD), phobias, generalized anxiety disorder, panic disorder, and obsessive-compulsive disorder (OCD), are estimated to affect 15 percent to 35 percent of the population. As described in Clinical Focus 12-3, Anxiety Disorders, symptoms include persistent fears and worries in the absence of any direct threat, usually accompanied by various physiological stress reactions, such as rapid heartbeat, nausea, and breathing difficulty.

ASD is the topic of Focus 8-2; schizophrenia, of Focus 8-5.

Major depression, detailed in Focus 6-3, is among the most treatable psychological disorders. Cognitive and intrapersonal therapies are as effective as drugs. See Section 16-4.

generalized anxiety disorder Persistently high levels of anxiety often accompanied by maladaptive behaviors to reduce anxiety; thought to be caused by chronic stress.

phobia Fear of a clearly defined object or situation.

panic disorder Recurrent attacks of intense terror that come on without warning and without any apparent relation to external circumstances.

Anxiety Disorders

Animals typically become anxious at times, especially when they are in obvious danger. But anxiety disorders are different. They are characterized by intense feelings of fear or anxiety inappropriate for the circumstances. People with an anxiety disorder have persistent and unrealistic worries about impending misfortune. They also tend to have multiple physical symptoms attributable to hyperactivity of the sympathetic nervous system.

G. B.'s case is a good example. He was a 36-year-old man with two college degrees who began to have severe spells initially diagnosed as a heart condition. He would begin to breathe heavily, sweat, develop heart palpitations, and sometimes feel pains in his chest and arms. During these attacks, he was unable to communicate coherently and would lie helpless on the floor until an ambulance arrived to take him to an emergency room.

Extensive medical testing and multiple attacks over about 2 years eventually led to the diagnosis of **generalized anxiety disorder**. Like most of the 5 percent of the U.S. population who have an anxiety disorder at some point in their life, G. B. was unaware that he was overly anxious. The cause of generalized anxiety is difficult to pinpoint, but one likely explanation is related to the cumulative effect of general stress.

Although G. B. appeared outwardly calm most of the time, he had been a prodemocracy activist in communist Poland, a dangerous position. Because of the dangers, he and his family eventually escaped from Poland to Turkey, and from there they went to Canada. G. B. may have had continuing worries about the repercussions of his political activities—worries (and stress) that eventually found expression in generalized anxiety attacks.

The most common and least disabling type of anxiety disorders are **phobias**. A phobia pertains to a clearly defined, dreaded object (such as spiders or snakes) or situation (such as enclosed spaces or crowds). Most people have a mild aversion to some types of stimuli. Such aversion becomes a phobia only when a person's feelings about a disliked stimulus lead to overwhelming fear and anxiety.

The incidence of disabling, that is, serious enough to interfere with living well, phobias is surprisingly high—estimated to affect at least 1 in 10 people. Most people with a phobia control the emotional reaction by avoiding what they dread. Others face their fears in controlled settings, with the goal of overcoming them.

Panic disorder has an estimated incidence on the order of 3 percent of the population. Symptoms include recurrent attacks of intense terror that begin without warning and without any apparent relation to external circumstances. Panic attacks usually last only a few minutes, but the experience is always terrifying. Sudden activation of the sympathetic nervous system leads to sweating, a wildly beating heart, and trembling.

Although panic attacks may occur only occasionally, the victim's dread of another episode may be continual. Consequently, many people with panic disorder also have *agoraphobia*, a fear of public places or situations in which help might not be available. This phobia makes some sense, because a person with a panic disorder may feel particularly vulnerable about the possibility of having an attack in a public place.

Freud believed that anxiety disorders are psychological in origin and treatable with talking therapies in which people confront their fears. Today, cognitive-behavioral therapies serve this purpose, as shown in the accompanying photo. More recently, a behavioral therapy called *mindfulness*, a form of meditation is proving effective in treating anxiety disorders. Its effectiveness is correlated with suppressed activity in the anterior cingulate region (Garrison et al., 2015). The effect is greater in trained as opposed to novice meditators, which supports the value of mindfulness training programs.

Pharmacologically, anxiety disorders are most effectively treated with benzodiazepines such as diazepam (Valium), the best known. Alprazolam (Xanax) is the most commonly prescribed drug for panic attacks. Benzodiazepines act by augmenting GABA's inhibitory effect and are believed to exert a major influence on neurons in the amygdala.

Whether treatments are behavioral, pharmacological, or both, the general goal is normalizing brain activity in the limbic system.

Lea Paterson/Science Source

Up to 90 percent of people with an animal phobia overcome their fears in a single exposure therapy session that lasts 2 or 3 hours.

As with depression, the root cause of anxiety disorders is unknown, but the effectiveness of the drug treatments described in Clinical Focus 12-3 implies a biological basis. The most widely prescribed anxiolytic (antianxiety) drugs are the benzodiazepines, such as Valium, Librium, and Xanax. Why would the brain have a mechanism for benzodiazepine action?

Figure 6-7 illustrates antianxiety agents'
action at the GABA_A receptor.

Section 16-4 further explores anxiety
disorders and reviews treatments.

It certainly did not evolve to allow us to take Valium. Probably this mechanism is part of a system that both increases and reduces anxiety levels. The mechanism for raising anxiety seems to entail a compound known as diazepam-binding inhibitor, which appears to bind antagonistically with the $GABA_A$ receptor, increasing anxiety.

Increased anxiety can be beneficial, especially if we are drowsy and need to be alert to deal with a crisis. Impairment of this survival mechanism or the one that reduces anxiety can cause serious emotional problems, even anxiety disorders.

12-4 REVIEW

Neuroanatomy of Motivated and Emotional Behavior

Before you continue, check your understanding.

1. The two types of motivated behaviors are _____ behaviors, which maintain homeostasis, and _____ behaviors, encompassing basically all other behaviors.

2. The brain's homeostat for many functions is found in the _____.

3. The three brain structures housing the major behavioral circuitry involved in motivation and emotion are _____, _____, and _____.

4. The prefrontal cortex has three main subdivisions: _____, _____, and _____.

5. Damage to the _____ is the primary cause of Klüver–Bucy syndrome.

6. The anterior pituitary gland produces _____.

7. Contrast the functions of the limbic system and the frontal lobes.

Answers appear at the back of the book.

For additional study tools, visit 🌐 **LaunchPad**
www.macmillanhighered.com/launchpad/kolb5e

12-5 Control of Regulatory and Nonregulatory Behavior

The two distinctly different types of motivated behaviors described in Section 12-4 are *regulatory* behaviors, which maintain vital body system balance, or homeostasis; and *nonregulatory* behaviors, those not controlled by a homeostatic mechanism—basically all other behaviors. In this section, we focus first on the control of two regulatory behaviors in humans—eating and fluid intake. Then we explore the control of human sexual behavior. While sexual behavior is nonregulatory; that is, not essential for an individual organism's survival, it is of enormous psychological significance to humans.

Controlling Eating

Feeding behavior entails far more than sustenance alone. We must eat and drink to live, but we also derive great pleasure from these acts. For many people, eating is a focus of daily life, if not for survival, for its centrality to social activities, from get-togethers with family and friends to business meetings and even to group identification. Are you a gourmet, a vegetarian, or a snack food junkie? Do you diet?

Control over eating is a source of frustration and even grief for many people in the developed world. In 2000, the World Health Organization identified **obesity**, the excessive accumulation of body fat, as a worldwide epidemic. The United States is a case in point. From 1990 to 2010, the proportion of overweight people increased from about 50 percent to 65 percent of the population. The proportion of people considered obese increased from about 12 percent in 1990 to 33 percent in 2014.

The increasing numbers of overweight and obese children and adults persist despite a substantial decrease in fat intake in American diets. What behaviors might cause persistent weight gain? One key to understanding weight gain in the developed world is evolutionary. Even 40 years ago, much of our food was only seasonally available. In a world with uncertain food availability, it makes sense to store excess body calories in the form of fat to be used later when food is scarce. Down through history and in many cultures today, plumpness was and is desirable as a standard of beauty and a sign of health and wealth.

In postindustrial societies, where food is continuously and easily available, overweight may not be the healthiest condition. People eat as though food will be scarce and fail to burn off the extra calories by exercising, and the result is apparent. About half of the U.S. population has dieted at some point in their life. At any given time, at least 25 percent report that they are currently on a diet. For a comparison of how some well-known dieting programs perform, see Clinical Focus 12-4, Weight Loss Strategies, on page 428.

Most Americans are overweight despite living in a culture obsessed with slimness. The human control system for feeding has multiple neurobiological inputs, including cognitive factors such as thinking about food and the association between environmental cues (e.g., watching television or studying) and the act of eating. The constant pairing of such cues with eating can result in the cues alone becoming a motivation—an incentive to eat. We return to this phenomenon in the discussion of reward and addiction in Section 12-6.

Eating disorders entail being either overweight or underweight. **Anorexia nervosa** is an eating disorder with a huge cognitive component: self-image. A person's body image is highly distorted in anorexia. This misperception leads to an exaggerated concern with being overweight. That concern spirals to excessive dieting, compulsive exercising, and severe, potentially life-threatening weight loss. Anorexia is especially prevalent among adolescent girls.

The neurobiological control of feeding behavior in humans is not as simple as it is in the fly described in Section 12-3. The multiple inputs to the human control system for feeding come from three major sources: the cognitive factors already introduced, the hypothalamus, and the digestive system.

Digestive System and Control of Eating

As illustrated in **Figure 12-23**, the digestive tract begins in the mouth and ends at the anus. Digestion is controlled by the enteric nervous system. As food travels through the tract, the digestive system extracts three types of nutrients: lipids (fats), amino acids (the building blocks of proteins), and glucose (sugar). Each nutrient is a specialized energy reserve. Because we require varying amounts of these reserves depending on what we are doing, the body has detector cells to keep track of the level of each nutrient in the bloodstream.

Glucose is the body's primary fuel and virtually the only energy source for the brain. Because the brain requires glucose even when the digestive tract is empty, the liver acts as a short-term reservoir of glycogen, a starch that acts as an inert form of glucose. When blood sugar levels fall, as when we are sleeping, detector cells tell the liver to convert glycogen into glucose for release into the bloodstream.

Thus the digestive system functions mainly to break down food, and the body needs to be apprised of how this breakdown is proceeding. Feedback mechanisms provide such information. When food reaches the intestines, it interacts with receptors in the ENS to trigger the release of at least 10 different peptide hormones, including cholecystokinin (CCK), glucagonlike peptide 1 (GLP-1), and peptide YY (PYY). Each, by virtue of its release as food, is absorbed and acts as a satiation or satiety signal that inhibits food intake. For example, when CCK is infused into an animal's hypothalamus, the animal's appetite diminishes.

obesity Excessive accumulation of body fat.

anorexia nervosa Exaggerated concern with being overweight that leads to inadequate food intake and often excessive exercising; can lead to severe weight loss and even starvation.

Figure 2-31 diagrams the inner workings of the ENS and Section 5-3 the main neurotransmitters it employs.

Weight Loss Strategies

Among the wide range of diets and weight loss strategies on the market, none has stopped the obesity epidemic facing the developed world. Diets range widely in their recommended allowed proportions and types of fats, carbohydrates, and proteins.

A study by Iris Shai and colleagues (2008) compared a low-fat diet, a low-carbohydrate diet, and the Mediterranean diet high in fruits, vegetables, legumes, and whole grains and including fish, nuts, and low-fat dairy products (Panagiotakos et al., 2004). The Shai study lasted 2 years and had relatively low dropout rates: 95.4 percent remained on their diet at 1 year and 84.6 percent at 2 years.

Figure A shows that all three diets led to weight loss. The low-carbohydrate diet produced the largest acute weight loss. Over the 2-year period subjects gained back some weight, and in the second year the low-carbohydrate and Mediterranean dieters achieved similar weight loss.

The low-carbohydrate diet had more favorable effects on lipid levels, whereas the Mediterranean diet provided better control of glucose and insulin levels. Those who followed the low-fat diet lost weight but fared less well than those on the other regimens.

The question of which foods are most likely to lead to weight gain was studied in a 20-year prospective study of three cohorts totaling about 120,000 U.S. women and men (Mozaffarian et al., 2011). None were obese when the study began. Participants gained an average of 3.4 pounds during every 4-year period.

Shown graphically in **Figure B**, weight gain was most strongly related to the intake of potato chips, potatoes, sugar-sweetened beverages, and red meat. Weight loss was related to the intake of vegetables, whole grains, fruits, nuts, and yogurt. Other lifestyle factors related to weight change included the amount of television watching (gain) and physical activity (loss).

Teresa Fung and her colleagues (2010) conducted a prospective study of mortality over a 26-year period in 85,000 women and 45,000 men. They found that a low-carbohydrate diet based on animal food sources was associated with higher mortality from all causes, whereas a vegetable-based, low-carbohydrate diet was associated with lower mortality from all causes.

Shai and her colleagues concluded that health care professionals might suggest more than one dietary approach based on individual preferences and metabolic needs, as long as the effort is sustained. At present, the only certain formula for weight loss appears to include (1) a permanent switch to a diet reduced in calories and fat and (2) increased ingestion of high-fiber foods (e.g., beans, whole grains, greens) combined with (3) increased physical activity. The results of the Mozaffarian study suggest cutting back on foods and beverages with high sugar content as well.

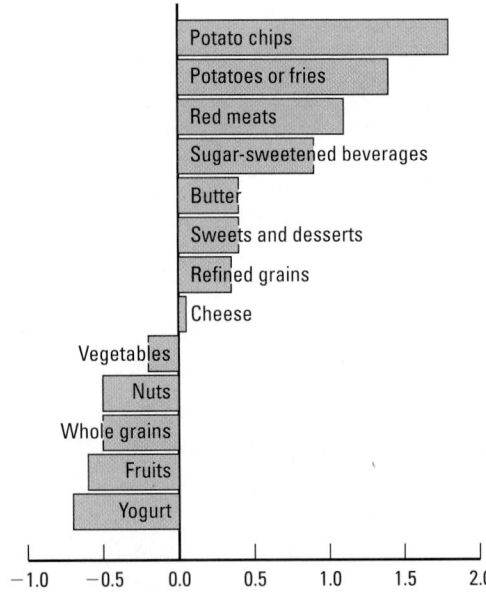

Average weight increase or decrease, in pounds per 4-year period, with each increase in daily serving

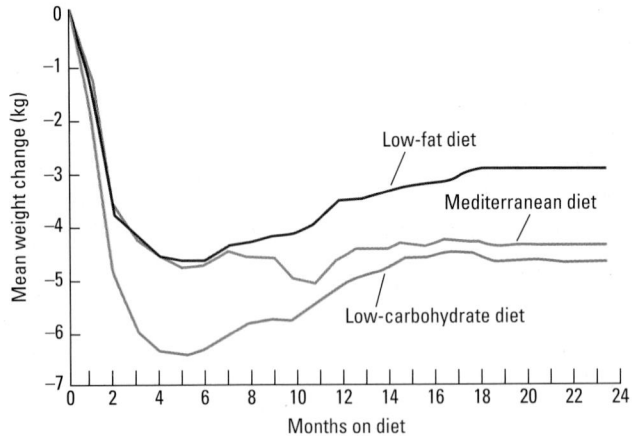

FIGURE A Benefits of Dieting Changes in body weight over a 2-year period on three diets. Low-carbohydrate and Mediterranean diets were equivalent after 1 year, and both led to more weight loss than did the low-fat diet. Information from I. Shai, D. Schwarzfuchs, Y. Henkin, et al. (2008). Weight loss with a low-carbohydrate, Mediterranean, or low-fat diet. *New England Journal of Medicine, 13*, pp. 229–241.

FIGURE B Foods Most Likely to Lead to Weight Gain or Loss Weight changes recorded for each increase in daily serving of a food per 4-year period, based on the diets and weights of nearly 125,000 people who were followed over 20 years. Information from D. Mozaffarian, M. P. H. Tao Hao, E. B. Rimm, W. C. Willett, & F. B. Hu (2011). Changes in diet and lifestyle and long-term weight gain in women and men. *New England Journal of Medicine, 3654*, pp. 2392–2404.

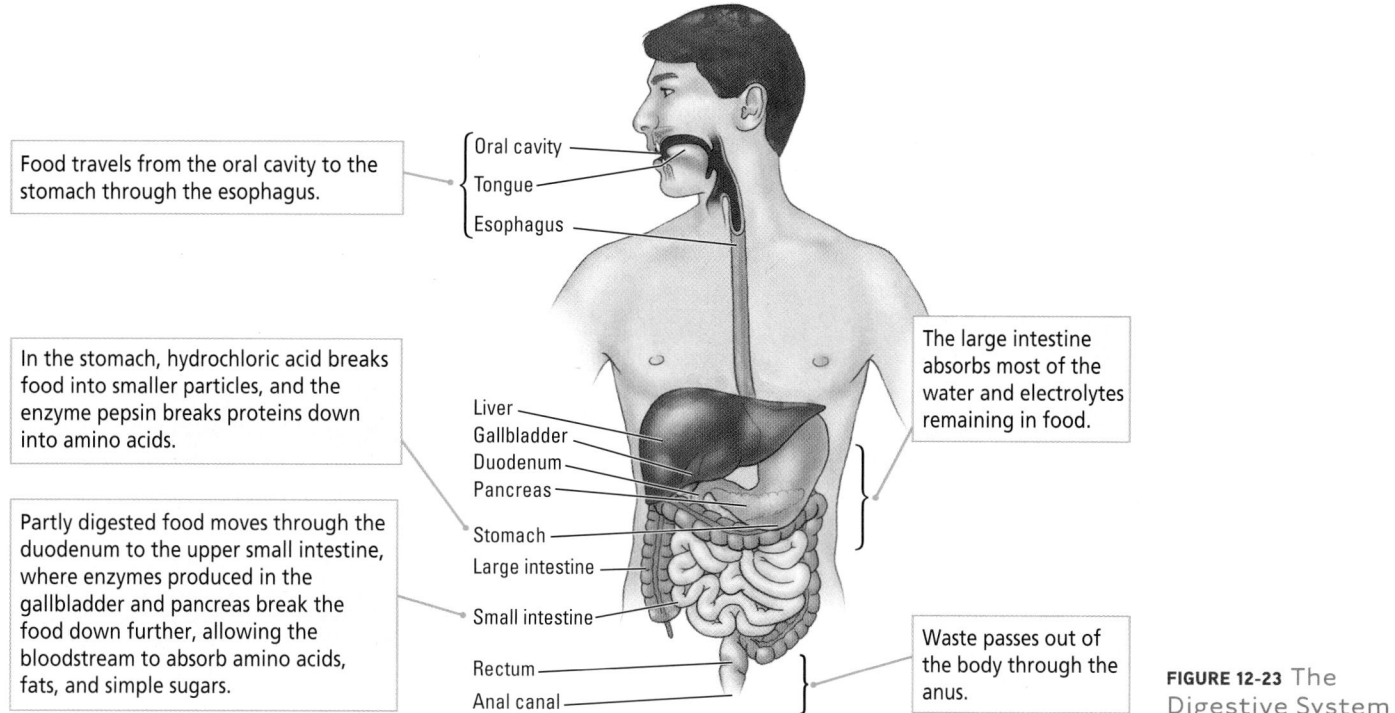

Food travels from the oral cavity to the stomach through the esophagus.

Oral cavity
Tongue
Esophagus

The large intestine absorbs most of the water and electrolytes remaining in food.

In the stomach, hydrochloric acid breaks food into smaller particles, and the enzyme pepsin breaks proteins down into amino acids.

Liver
Gallbladder
Duodenum
Pancreas

Partly digested food moves through the duodenum to the upper small intestine, where enzymes produced in the gallbladder and pancreas break the food down further, allowing the bloodstream to absorb amino acids, fats, and simple sugars.

Stomach
Large intestine
Small intestine
Rectum
Anal canal

Waste passes out of the body through the anus.

FIGURE 12-23 The Digestive System

Hypothalamus and Control of Eating

Feeding behavior is influenced by hormones, including insulin, growth hormone, and sex steroids, that stimulate and inhibit feeding and aid in converting nutrients into fat and fat into glucose. The hypothalamus, which controls hormone systems, is the key brain structure in feeding as well as in satiety.

Investigation into how the hypothalamus controls feeding began in the early 1950s, when researchers discovered that damage to the lateral hypothalamus in rats caused the animals to stop eating, a symptom known as **aphagia** (in Greek, *phagein* means *to eat*). In contrast, damage to the ventromedial hypothalamus (VMH) caused the animals to overeat—display **hyperphagia**. A VMH-lesioned rat that overate to the point of obesity is shown in the Procedure section of **Experiment 12-1** on page 430. The Results section reveals that the VMH-lesioned rat weighed more than 1 kilogram, three times the weight of her healthy sister, at 340 grams.

The researchers also found that electrical stimulation of the lateral hypothalamus elicits feeding, whereas stimulation of the ventromedial hypothalamus inhibits feeding. The opposing effects of injury and stimulation to these two regions led to the idea that the lateral hypothalamus signals turn eating on, whereas the VMH signals turn eating off. This model quickly proved too simple.

Not only does the lateral hypothalamus contain cell bodies; fiber bundles also pass through it. Damage to either the cell bodies or the fibers can produce aphagia. Similarly, damage to fibers passing through the VMH often causes injury as well to the paraventricular nucleus of the hypothalamus (review Figure 12-12A). But the role of the hypothalamus in controlling feeding involves more than the activities of its lateral and ventromedial structures alone.

In fact, another hypothalamic region, the arcuate nucleus, contains two major classes of neurons, one that initiates eating (e.g., neurons expressing genes for neuropeptide Y) and one that reduces eating behavior, the principal transmitter being α-melanocyte–stimulating hormone (α-MSH). Changes in hormone levels reflecting glucose (insulin) and lipid (leptin) levels in the blood act to stimulate either the first class, which initiates eating, or the second class,

Section 6-5 reviews the general categories of hormones and how they work.

aphagia Failure to eat; may be due to an unwillingness to eat or to motor difficulties, especially with swallowing.

hyperphagia Overeating that leads to significant weight gain.

▶ **EXPERIMENT 12-1**

Question: Does the hypothalamus play a role in eating?

Procedure

The ventromedial hypothalamus (VMH) of the rat on the right was damaged, and her body weight was monitored for a year. Her sister on the left is normal.

Intact brain of sister rat   Rat brain with lesion

Photos courtesy of Bryan Kolb and Ian Whishaw

Results

The VMH-lesioned rat showed a dramatic increase in food intake and body weight.

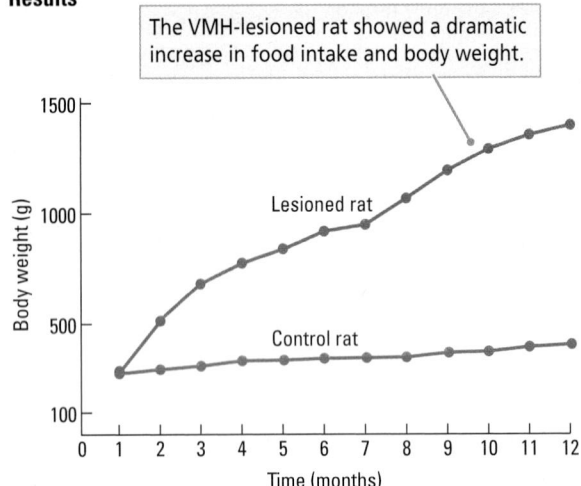

Conclusion: The VMH plays a role in controlling the cessation of eating. Damage to the VMH results in prolonged and dramatic weight gain.

FIGURE 12-24 Modeling Control of Feeding Behavior

which acts to inhibit eating. Neurons of the arcuate nucleus also connect to the paraventricular nucleus. Damage to this region produces hyperphagia.

The summed activity of all such hypothalamic neurons constitutes a complex homeostat that controls feeding. **Figure 12-24** shows that this homeostat receives inputs from three sources: the enteric nervous system (such as information about blood glucose levels), hormone systems (such as information about the level of appetite-diminishing CCK), and parts of the brain that process cognitive factors. We turn to these cognitive factors next.

Cognitive Control of Eating

Pleasure and its absence are cognitive factors in controlling eating. Just thinking about a favorite food can make many of us feel hungry. The cognitive aspect to feeding includes not only images of food that we pull from memory but also external sensations, especially food-related sights and smells. Learned associations, such as the taste aversions discussed in Section 12-3, are also related to feeding.

Neural control of the cognitive factors important for controlling eating in humans probably originates in multiple brain regions. Two structures are clearly important: the amygdala and the orbital prefrontal cortex. Damage to the amygdala alters food preferences and abolishes taste aversion learning. These effects are probably related to the amygdala's efferent connections to the hypothalamus.

The amygdala's role in regulating species-typical behaviors is well established, but the role of the orbital PFC is more difficult to pin down. Rats and monkeys with damage to the orbital cortex lose weight, in part because they eat less. Humans with orbital injuries are invariably slim, but we know of no formal studies on their eating habits. The orbital prefrontal cortex receives projections from the olfactory bulb, and cells in this region respond to smells. Because odors influence the taste of foods, it is likely that damage to the orbital cortex decreases eating, owing to diminished sensory responses to food odor and perhaps to taste.

An additional cognitive factor in control of eating is the pleasure we derive from it, especially from eating foods with certain tastes. Think chocolate. What pleasure is and how the brain produces it are discussed in Section 12-6 in the context of reward.

Randy Seeley and Stephen Woods (2003) noted that in spite of contemporary problems with weight gain, adult mammals do a masterful job of matching their caloric intake to caloric expenditure. Consider that a typical man eats 900,000 calories per year. To gain just one extra pound requires him to eat 4000 calories more than he burned in that year. This increase amounts to only 11 calories per day, equivalent to a single potato chip. But people rarely eat just one chip. As Figure B in Clinical Focus 12-4 illustrates, potato chips top the list of major food sources linked to weight gain over time.

Controlling Drinking

Dissolved in the water that is 70 percent of the human body are chemicals that participate in the hundreds of reactions necessary to bodily functions. Essential homeostatic mechanisms control water levels (and hence chemical concentrations) within rather narrow limits. The rate of a chemical reaction is partly determined by the concentration of the participating chemicals.

As with eating, we drink for many reasons. We consume some beverages, such as coffee, wine, beer, and juice, for an energy boost or to relax, as part of social activities, or just because they taste good. We drink water for its health benefits, to help wash down a meal or to intensify the flavor of dry foods. On a hot day, we drink water because we are thirsty, presumably because we become dehydrated through sweating and evaporation.

These examples illustrate the two kinds of thirst. **Osmotic thirst** results from increased concentrations of dissolved chemicals, known as *solutes*, in the body fluids. **Hypovolemic thirst** results from a loss of overall fluid volume from the body.

Osmotic Thirst

Solutes found inside and outside cells are ideally concentrated for the body's chemical reactions. Maintaining this concentration requires a kind of homeostat, much like the mechanism that controls body temperature. Deviations from the ideal solute concentration activate systems to reestablish it.

When we eat salty foods, such as potato chips, the salt (NaCl) spreads through the blood and enters the extracellular fluid between our cells. This shifts the solute concentration away from the ideal. Receptors in the hypothalamus along the third ventricle detect the altered solute concentration and relay the message *too salty* to various hypothalamic areas that in turn stimulate us to drink. Other messages are sent to the kidneys to reduce water excretion.

Water Intoxication

Eating too much leads to obesity. What happens when we drink too much water? Our kidneys are efficient at processing water, but if we drink a large volume all at once, the kidneys cannot keep up.

The result is a condition called water intoxication. Body tissues swell with the excess fluid, essentially drowning the cells in freshwater. At the same time, the relative concentration of sodium drops, leading to an electrolyte imbalance.

Water intoxication can produce widely ranging symptoms, from irregular heartbeat to headache. In severe cases, people may act as though they are drunk. The most likely way for an adult to develop water intoxication is to sweat heavily, by running a marathon in hot weather, for example, then drink too much water without added electrolytes.

Hypovolemic Thirst

Unlike osmotic thirst, hypovolemic thirst arises when the total volume of body fluids declines, motivating us to drink more and replenish them. In contrast with osmotic thirst, however, hypovolemic thirst encourages us to choose something other than water, because water would dilute the solute concentration in the blood. Rather, we prefer to drink flavored beverages that contain salts and other nutrients.

Hypovolemic thirst and its satiation are controlled by a hypothalamic circuit different from the one that controls osmotic thirst. When fluid volume drops, the kidneys send a hormone signal (angiotensin) that stimulates midline hypothalamic neurons. These neurons, in turn, stimulate drinking.

Controlling Sexual Behavior

Individuals must feed and drink continually to survive. This is the essence of regulatory behavior. But notwithstanding procreation, which is essential to the survival of the species, sexual behavior is nonregulatory: it is not essential for the individual organism's survival. That fact does nothing to convince most of us that sex is unimportant.

In Sigmund Freud's psychodynamic theory, sexual drives are central to human behavior. Sexual themes repeatedly appear in our art, literature, and films. They bombard us via advertising and other sales pitches. Such significance makes it all the more important to understand the control of human sexual behavior in terms of both gonadal hormones and brain circuits.

osmotic thirst Thirst that results from a high concentration of dissolved chemicals, or *solutes*, in body fluids.

hypovolemic thirst Thirst produced by a loss of overall fluid volume from the body.

Turning to sugar-sweetened beverages to quench thirst from eating salty foods increases the likelihood of weight gain.

Effects of Sex Hormones on the Brain

During the fetal stage of prenatal development, a male's Y chromosome controls the differentiation of embryonic gonad tissue into testes, which in turn secrete testosterone. This process is an organizing effect of gonadal hormones. Testosterone masculinizes both the sex organs and the brain during development. A major organizing effect of gonadal hormones on the brain is in the hypothalamus, especially the preoptic area of the medial hypothalamus. Organizing effects also operate in other nervous system regions, notably the amygdala, the prefrontal cortex, and the spinal cord.

Gonadal hormones produce enzymes necessary for epigenetic changes such as gene methylation. One action of steroid hormones is to methylate brain regions. For example, estrogen methylates the preoptic area of females, leading to the suppression of male characteristics. Growing evidence indicates that increased environmental levels of compounds, such as agricultural pesticides, can interfere with hormone activity, resulting in multigenerational epigenetic effects (e.g., McCarthy et al., 2009). These effects may be linked to anxiety levels and obesity and possibly to the organizational effects of gonadal hormones.

Sex-related differences in the nervous system make sense behaviorally. After all, animal courtship rituals differ between the sexes, as do copulatory behaviors, with females typically engaging in sexually receptive responses and males in mounting ones. Producing these sex differences in behaviors depends on the action of gonadal hormones on the brain during development and in adulthood.

Hormonal actions on the adult brain are referred to as *activating effects*, in contrast with developmental *organizing effects*. Next we consider both, separately.

ORGANIZING EFFECTS OF SEX HORMONES During fetal development, a male's testes produce male hormones, the androgens. In the developing rat, androgens are produced during the last week of fetal development and the first week after birth. The androgens produced at this time greatly alter both neural structures and later behavior. For example, a male rat's hypothalamus and prefrontal cortex differ structurally from those of both female rats and of males that were not exposed to androgens during development.

Males with little exposure to the androgen testosterone during development behave like genetically female rats in adulthood. If given estrogen and progesterone, they become sexually receptive and display typical female behaviors when mounted by males. Male rats castrated in adulthood do not act in this way.

Sexual dimorphism, the differential development of brain areas in the two sexes, arises from a complex series of steps. Cells in the brain produce aromatase, an enzyme that converts testosterone into estradiol, one of the class of female sex hormones called *estrogens*. That is, when males produce testosterone, the brain converts it to an estrogen. Thus a female hormone, estradiol, actually masculinizes the male brain.

Females are not masculinized by the presence of estrogens because fetuses of both sexes produce a liver enzyme (*alpha fetoprotein*) that binds to estrogen, rendering it incapable of entering neurons. Testosterone is unaffected by alpha fetoprotein: it enters neurons and is converted into estradiol.

The organizing effects of testosterone are clearly illustrated in the preoptic area of the hypothalamus (see Figure 12-12A), which plays a critical role in male rats' copulatory behavior. Comparing this area in males and females, Roger Gorski (1984) and his colleagues found a nucleus about five times as large in the males as in the females. Significantly, manipulating gonadal hormones during development can alter the sexual dimorphism of the preoptic area. Castrating male rats at birth leads to a smaller preoptic area; treating infant females with testosterone enlarges it.

The organizing effects of gonadal hormones are more difficult to study in humans. However, John Money and Anke Ehrhardt (1972) revealed an important role of these hormones in human development. Clinical Focus 12-5, Androgen Insensitivity Syndrome and Androgenital Syndrome, describes this role.

The case study in Section 3-3 describes such epigentic inheritance.

Section 8-4 explains organizing influences of gonadal hormones and critical periods in brain development.

Testosterone

Estradiol

CLINICAL FOCUS 12-5

Androgen Insensitivity Syndrome and the Androgenital Syndrome

After the testes have formed in a male fetus, sexual development depends on the actions of testicular hormones. Studying people with *androgen insensitivity syndrome* makes this dependence crystal clear. In this syndrome, an XY (genetic male) fetus produces androgens, but the body cannot to respond to them.

Because androgen insensitivity syndrome does not affect estrogen receptors, these people are still responsive to estrogen produced by both the adrenal glands and the testes. As a result, they develop female secondary sexual characteristics during puberty, even without additional hormone treatment. A person with androgen insensitivity syndrome is therefore a genetic male who develops a female phenotype, that is, appears to be female, as shown in the photograph on the left.

If no Y chromosome is present to induce the growth of testes, an XX (genetic female) fetus develops ovaries and becomes a female. If the adrenal glands of either the mother or the infant produces an excessive amount of androgens, however, exposure of the female fetus to them produces the *androgenital syndrome (congenital adrenal hyperplasia)*.

The effects vary, depending on when the androgens are produced and on the level of exposure. In extreme cases, the clitoris enlarges until it can be mistaken for a small penis, as shown in the photograph on the right.

In less severe cases, no gross change in genital structure develops, but there is a behavioral effect: these girls show a high degree of tomboyishness. In early childhood, they identify with boys and prefer boys' clothes, toys, and games. One explanation for this behavioral effect is that the developing brain is masculinized, which changes later behavior.

Left: In androgen insensitivity syndrome, a genetic male (XY) is insensitive to gonadal androgens but remains sensitive to estrogens, which leads to the development of a female phenotype. Right: In congenital adrenal hyperplasia, a genetic female (XX) is exposed to androgens produced by the adrenal gland embryonically, which leads to the partial development of male external genitalia.

Reprinted from J. Money & A. A. Ehrhardt (1972). *Man and Woman, Boy and Girl* (p. 116). Baltimore: Johns Hopkins University Press.

John Money and Anke A. Ehrhardt/John's Hopkins University Press

ACTIVATING EFFECTS OF SEX HORMONES The sexual behavior of both males and females also depends on the actions of gonadal hormones on the adult brain. In most vertebrate species, female sexual behavior varies in the course of an estrous cycle, during which the levels of ovarian hormones fluctuate. The rat's estrous cycle is about 4 days long, with sexual receptivity occurring only in the few hours during which the production of the ovarian hormones estrogen and progesterone peaks. These ovarian hormones alter brain activity, which in turn alters behavior. In female rats, various chemicals released after mating inhibit further mating behavior.

The activating effect of ovarian hormones can be seen clearly in hippocampal cells. **Figure 12-25** compares hippocampal pyramidal neurons taken from female rats at two points in the estrous cycle: one when estrogen levels are high and the other when they are low. When estrogen levels are high, more dendritic spines and presumably more synapses emerge. These neural differences during the estrous cycle are all the more remarkable when we consider that cells in the female hippocampus are continually changing their connections to other cells every 4 days throughout the animal's adulthood.

In males, testosterone activates sexual behavior in two distinct ways. First, testosterone's actions on the amygdala are related to the motivation to seek sexual activity. Second, the actions of testosterone on the hypothalamus are needed to produce copulatory behavior. We look at both processes next.

Section 6-5 details broader activating effects of sex hormones on male and female behavior.

sexual dimorphism Differential development of brain areas in the two sexes.

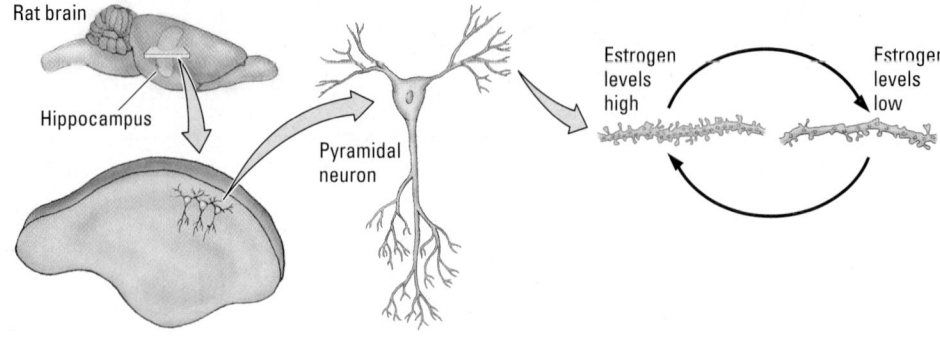

FIGURE 12-25 Hormonal Effects
A comparison of the dendrites of hippocampal pyramidal neurons at high and low levels of estrogen in the rat's (4-day) estrous cycle reveals far fewer dendritic spines in the low period. Information from C. S. Woolley, E. Gould, M. Frankfurt, & B. McEwen (1990). Naturally occurring fluctuation in dendritic spine density on adult hippocampal pyramidal neurons. *Journal of Neuroscience*, 10, p. 1289.

Typical posture

Lordosis

FIGURE 12-26 Studying Sexual Motivation and Mating In this experiment, a male rat must press the bar 10 times to gain access to a receptive female who drops in through a trapdoor. The copulatory behavior of the male rat illustrates mating behavior, whereas the bar pressing for access to a female rat illustrates sexual motivation. Barry J. Everitt, Department of Experimental Psychology and the MRC-Wellcome Behavioural and Clinical Neuroscience Institute, University of Cambridge.

Hypothalamus, Amygdala, and Sexual Behavior

The hypothalamus is the critical structure controlling copulatory behaviors in both male and female mammals. The ventromedial hypothalamus controls the female mating posture, which in quadrupedal animals is called *lordosis*: arching the back and elevating the rump while the female otherwise remains quite still. Damage to the VMH abolishes lordosis. The role of the VMH is probably twofold: it controls the neural circuit that produces lordosis, and it influences hormonal changes in the female during coitus.

In males, neural control of sexual behavior is somewhat more complex. The medial preoptic area, which is larger in males than in females, controls copulation. Damage to this area greatly disrupts mating performance, whereas its electrical stimulation activates mating, provided that testosterone is circulating in the bloodstream. Curiously, although destruction of the medial preoptic area stops male mammals from mating, they continue to show interest in receptive females. For instance, monkeys with lesions in the medial preoptic area will not mate with receptive females, but they will masturbate while watching them from across the room.

Barry Everitt (1990) designed an ingenious apparatus that allows male rats to press a bar to deliver receptive females. After males were trained to use this apparatus, shown in **Figure 12-26**, lesions were made in their medial preoptic areas. Immediately, their sexual behavior changed. They would still press the bar to obtain access to females but would no longer mate with them.

Apparently, the medial preoptic area controls mating but not sexual motivation. The brain structure responsible for motivation appears to be the amygdala. When Everitt trained male rats in the apparatus and then lesioned their amygdala, they would no longer press the bar to gain access to receptive females, but they would mate with receptive females provided to them.

It is not practical to discriminate small hypothalamic nuclei in fMRI studies of humans. Studies have shown a bilateral increase in hypothalamic activity when men view erotic video clips but not when they view sports video clips (**Figure 12-27**). The degree of sexual arousal is related to the increase in hypothalamic activity (e.g., Brunetti et al., 2008).

In summary, the hypothalamus controls copulatory behavior in both male and female mammals. In males, the amygdala influences sexual motivation and probably plays a key role in female sexual motivation as well, especially among females of species, such as humans, whose sexual activity is not tied to fluctuations in ovarian hormones.

Sexual Orientation, Sexual Identity, and Brain Organization

Does **sexual orientation**—a person's sexual attraction to the opposite sex or to the same sex or to both sexes—have a neural basis? Sexual orientation appears to be determined during early development, influenced by genetics and by epigenetic factors during prenatal brain development. No solid evidence points to any postnatal experience directing sexual orientation.

Indeed, it appears virtually impossible to change a person's sexual orientation. Lesbian couples commonly rear heterosexual children, and no evidence supports the notion that homosexuality is a lifestyle choice or that it is an effect of social learning (Bao & Swaab, 2011). The place to look for differences, therefore, is in the brain of people who identify themselves as heterosexual and homosexual.

Like rats, humans have sex-related differences in the structure of the hypothalamus and amygdala. Several hypothalamic nuclei are two to three times larger in males (for a review, see Becker and colleagues, 2008). Sexual differentiation of the brain results from the effect of testosterone and is complete by birth.

But sex differences in the brain are not simply a matter of hormones. Epigenetics plays a role too, beginning early in development. In females, for example, one of the two X chromosomes is largely silenced, but not all its genes are silenced, which provides a basis for sex differences. Furthermore, emerging evidence suggests that sex differences in the hypothalamus result from differences in gene methylation (for a review, see McCarthy and coworkers, 2009).

Among homosexuals, variations in epigenetic effects could lead to differences in the architecture and function of the hypothalamus. Differences in the hypothalamus of heterosexual and homosexual men suggest that homosexual men form, in effect, a third sex because their hypothalamus differs from that of both females and heterosexual males.

Architectural and functional differences in the hypothalamus may form a basis for the spectrum of **gender identity**—a person's degree of feeling male or female. People who view themselves as **transgender**, whose personal characteristics transcend traditional gender boundaries and corresponding sexual norms, believe they were born the wrong sex. Their desire to live as a member of the other sex can be so strong that they undergo sex change surgery.

Several biological factors appear to influence the likelihood of transgender identity—chromosomal abnormalities, polymorphisms of the genes for the estrogen and androgen receptors, atypical gonadal hormone levels, prenatal exposure to certain anticonvulsants, and immune system activity directed toward the Y chromosome. These factors are hypothesized to lead to changes in the architecture and function of brain structures, especially the hypothalamus, which match transgender peoples' identities even while their sex organs do not (Bao & Swaab, 2011).

In summary, differences in sexual orientation and gender identity appear to result from prenatal events that influence the organization and function of the brain, not from postnatal social or environmental experiences.

FIGURE 12-27 Hypothalamus and Sex in Males Red regions on the left and right represent bilateral activity in the hypothalamus of men viewing erotic film clips. This activity was absent as the men watched sports clips. Republished from "The Hypothalamus, Sexual Arousal and Psychosexual Identity in Human Males: A functional Magnetic Resonance Imaging Study," by M. Brunetti, C. Babiloni, A. Ferretti, C. Del Gratta, A. Merla, and M. Olivetti Belardino, 2008, *European Journal of Neuroscience, 27*, 2922–2927, Figure 2, permission conveyed through Copyright Clearance Center, Inc.

More evidence favoring a neural basis for gender identity, including transgender identity, in Section 15-5.

Before accepting the Arthur Ashe Courage Award at the 2015 ESPY ceremony, Caitlyn Jenner was known worldwide as Bruce Jenner. Bruce won Olympic Gold in the 1976 decathlon competition. Caitlyn began her physical transition nearly four decades later. At left, Bruce in 1984 and at center in 2003; at right, Caitlyn in 2015.

sexual orientation A person's pattern of sexual attraction—to the opposite sex or to the same sex or to both sexes.

gender identity The degree to which a person feels male or female.

transgender Possessing personal characteristics that transcend traditional gender boundaries and corresponding sexual norms; a person's belief that he or she was born the wrong sex.

Cognitive Influences on Sexual Behavior

People think about sex, dream about sex, make plans about sex. These behaviors may include activity in the amygdala or the hypothalamus, but they must certainly also include the cortex. This is not to say that the cortex is essential for sexual motivation and copulation.

In studies of rats whose entire cortex has been removed, both males and females still engage in sexual activity, although the males are somewhat clumsy. Nevertheless, the cortex must play a role in certain aspects of sexual behavior. For instance, imagery about sexual activity must include activity in the cortical ventral visual pathway. And thinking about sexual activity and planning for it must require frontal lobe participation.

As you might expect, these aspects of sexual behavior are not easily studied in rats, and they remain uncharted waters in research on humans. However, changes in the sexual behavior of people with frontal lobe injury are well documented. And recall J. P.'s case, described in Clinical Focus 12-2. Although J. P. was uninhibited in his sexual behavior, frontal lobe damage is just as likely to produce a loss of libido (sexual interest). The wife of a man who 5 years earlier had a small tumor removed from the medial frontal region complained that she and her husband had since had no sexual contact whatever. He was simply not interested, even though they were both still in their twenties.

The husband said that he no longer had sexual fantasies or sexual dreams, and although he still loved his wife, he did not have any sexual urges toward her or anyone else. Such cases clearly indicate that the human cortex is important in controlling sexual behaviors. The exact nature of its role remains poorly understood.

12-5 REVIEW

Control of Regulatory and Nonregulatory Behavior

Before you continue, check your understanding.

1. The three main hypothalamic regions that control feeding are _____, _____, and _____.

2. The key structures in the control of sexual behavior are the _____ and the _____.

3. The two types of effects that hormones exert on the brain are _____ and _____.

4. _____ thirst results from an increase in the concentration of dissolved chemicals; _____ thirst results from a decline in the total volume of body fluids.

5. Describe why sex differences in the brain are not simply a matter of hormones.

Answers appear at the back of the book.

For additional study tools, visit 🌀 LaunchPad
www.macmillanhighered.com/launchpad/kolb5e

12-6 Reward

Throughout this chapter we have concluded repeatedly that animals engage in a wide range of voluntary behaviors because those behaviors are rewarding. That is, they increase the activity in neural circuits that function to maintain an animal's contact with certain environmental stimuli, either in the present or in the future. Presumably, the animal perceives the activity of these circuits as pleasant. This would explain why reward can help maintain not only adaptive behaviors such as feeding and sexual activity but also potentially nonadaptive behaviors such as drug addiction. After all, evolution would not have prepared the brain specifically for the eventual development of psychoactive drugs.

The first clue to the presence of a reward system in the brain came with an accidental discovery by James Olds and Peter Milner in 1954. They found that rats would perform behaviors such as pressing a bar to administer a brief burst of electrical stimulation to specific sites in their brain. This phenomenon is called *intracranial self-stimulation* or *brain stimulation reward*.

Typically, rats will press a lever hundreds or even thousands of times per hour to obtain this brain stimulation, stopping only when they are exhausted. Why would animals engage in such behavior when it has absolutely no survival value to them or to their species? The simplest explanation is that the brain stimulation is activating the system underlying reward (Wise, 1996).

After more than a half-century of research on brain stimulation reward, investigators now know that dozens of brain sites maintain self-stimulation. Some especially effective regions are the lateral hypothalamus and medial forebrain bundle (see Figures 12-12 and 12-13). Stimulation along the MFB tract activates fibers that form the ascending pathways from dopamine-producing cells of the midbrain tegmentum, shown in **Figure 12-28**. This mesolimbic dopamine pathway sends terminals to sites that include especially the nucleus accumbens in the basal ganglia and the prefrontal cortex.

Neuroscientists have several reasons to believe that the mesolimbic dopamine system is central to circuits mediating reward:

1. Dopamine release shows a marked increase when animals are engaged in intracranial self-stimulation.

2. Drugs that enhance dopamine release increase self-stimulation, whereas drugs that decrease dopamine release also decrease self-stimulation. It seems that the amount of dopamine released somehow determines how rewarding an event is.

3. When animals engage in behaviors such as feeding or sexual activity, dopamine release rapidly increases in locations such as the nucleus accumbens.

4. Highly addictive drugs such as nicotine and cocaine increase the dopamine level in the nucleus accumbens.

Even opioids appear to affect at least some of an animal's actions through the dopamine system. Animals quickly learn to press a bar to obtain an opioid injection directly into the midbrain tegmentum or the nucleus accumbens. The same animals do not work to obtain the opioid if the dopaminergic neurons of the mesolimbic system are inactivated. Apparently, then, animals engage in behaviors that increase dopamine release.

Nor is dopamine the only rewarding compound in the brain. For example, opioid transmitters such as encephalin and dynorphin are also rewarding, as are benzodiazepines.

Robinson and Berridge (2008) propose that reward contains separable psychological components corresponding roughly to wanting, which is often called incentive, and liking, which is equivalent to an evaluation of pleasure. This idea can be applied to discovering why we increase contact with a stimulus such as chocolate.

Two independent factors are at work: our desire to eat the chocolate (wanting) and the pleasurable effect of eating the chocolate (liking). This distinction is important. If we maintain contact with a certain stimulus because dopamine is released, the question becomes whether the dopamine plays a role in the wanting or the liking aspect of the behavior. Robinson and Berridge propose that wanting and liking processes are mediated by separable neural systems and that dopamine is the transmitter for the wanting. Liking, they hypothesize, entails opioid and benzodiazepine–GABA systems.

According to Robinson and Berridge, wanting and liking are normally two aspects of the same process, so rewards are usually wanted and liked to the same degree. However, it is possible, under certain circumstances, for wanting and liking to change independently.

Consider rats with lesions of the ascending dopaminergic pathway to the forebrain. These rats do not eat. Is it simply that they do not desire to eat (a loss of wanting), or has

Section 7-1 describes how electrical stimulation works both as a treatment and as a research tool.

FIGURE 12-28 Mesolimbic Dopamine System Axons emanating from the ventral tegmentum (blue arrows) project diffusely through the brain. Dopamine release in these mesolimbic pathways has a role in feelings of reward and pleasure. The nucleus accumbens is a critical structure in this reward system.

Robinson and Berridge's wanting-and-liking theory of addiction includes a multipart reward system; see Section 6-4.

Positive reactions

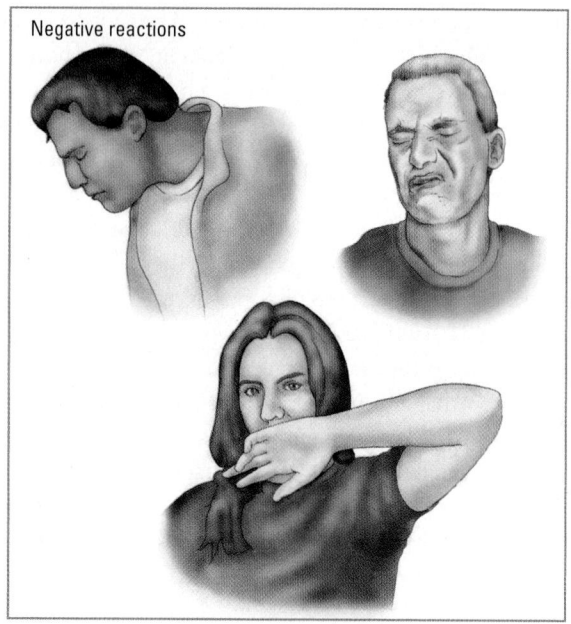

Negative reactions

FIGURE 12-29 Human Reactions to Taste Sucrose and other palatable tastes elicit positive (hedonic) reactions, including licking the fingers and the lips. Quinine and other unpleasant tastes elicit negative (aversive) reactions, including spitting, expressing distaste, and wiping the mouth with the back of the hand. Information from K. C. Berridge (1996). Food reward: Brain substrates of wanting and liking. *Neuroscience and Biobehavioral Reviews, 20,* p. 6.

food become aversive to them (a loss of liking)? To find out which factor is at work, the animals' facial expressions and body movements in response to food can be observed to see how liking is affected. After all, when animals are given various foods to taste, they produce different facial and body reactions, depending on whether they perceive the food as pleasant or aversive.

Among humans, typically when a person tastes something sweet, he or she responds by licking the fingers or the lips, as shown at the left of **Figure 12-29.** If the taste is unpleasantly salty, say, as shown in the right panel, the reaction is often spitting, grimacing, or wiping the mouth with the back of the hand. Rats, too, show distinctive positive and negative responses to pleasant and unpleasant tastes.

By watching the responses when food is squirted into the mouth of a rat that otherwise refuses to eat, we can tell to what extent a loss of liking is a factor in the animal's food rejection. Interestingly, rats that do not eat after receiving lesions to the dopamine pathway act as though they still like food.

Now consider a rat with a self-stimulation electrode in the lateral hypothalamus. This rat will often eat heartily while the stimulation is on. The obvious inference is that the food must taste good—presumably even better than usual. But what happens if we squirt food into the rat's mouth and observe its behavior when the stimulation is on versus when it is off?

If the brain stimulation primes eating by evoking pleasurable sensations, we would expect the animal to be more positive in its facial and body reactions to foods when the stimulation is turned on. In fact, the opposite occurs. During stimulation, rats react more aversively to tastes such as sugar and salt than when stimulation is off. Apparently, the stimulation increases wanting but not liking.

Such experiments show that what appears to be a single event—reward—is actually composed of at least two independent processes. Just as our visual system independently processes *what* and *how* information in separate streams, our reward system appears to process wanting and liking independently. Reward is not a single phenomenon any more than perception or memory is.

Like the networks underlying perception and memory, the prefrontal and limbic networks underlying reward are diffuse. Amy Janes and her colleagues (2012) used resting-state fMRI to identify a prefrontal–anterior cingulate network believed to support reward, illustrating the breadth of the reward system. They then compared these networks in nicotine

| Medial view | Frontal view | Dorsal view |

FIGURE 12-30 Craving Increases OMPFC Network Coupling Participants craving nicotine show an increase in the coupling of the orbital and medial prefrontal cortex (OMPFC, shown in green) with other regions including anterior cingulate cortex, other prefrontal regions, the striatum, right hippocampal region, ventral occipital cortex, and cerebellum (shown in shades of orange). An Increase in Tobacco Craving Is Associated with Enhanced Medial Prefrontal Cortex Network Coupling Amy C. Janes, Stacey Farmer, Blaise deB. Frederick, Lisa D. Nickerson, Scott E. Lukas, PLoS One. 2014 Feb 5;9(2):e88228. doi: 10.1371/journal. pone.0088228.eCollection 2014.

addicts and nonaddicts finding greater connectivity in the prefrontal–striatal connections in nicotine addicts. In a follow-up study the investigators also showed that craving in nicotine addicts is related to enhanced connectivity in this prefrontal network (**Figure 12-30**). (Janes et al., 2014).

The general conclusions from these studies and from related studies of gamblers are that neural reward pathways are diffuse and that the pathways' size and activity are related to the reward's intensity. The hope is that rs-fMRI can be used as a biomarker for both severity of addiction and efficacy of treatment. But the extent of addiction-related changes suggests that eliminating nicotine addiction is not easy—a conclusion many nicotine addicts would agree with.

12-6 REVIEW

Reward

Before you continue, check your understanding.

1. Animals engage in voluntary behaviors because the behaviors are _____.

2. Neural circuits maintain contact with rewarding environmental stimuli in the present or in the future through _____ and _____ subsystems.

3. The neurotransmitter systems hypothesized to be basic to reward are _____, _____, and _____ systems.

4. What is intracranial self-stimulation, and why is it rewarding?

Answers appear at the back of the book.

For additional study tools, visit 🧠 **LaunchPad**
www.macmillanhighered.com/launchpad/kolb5e

■SUMMARY

12-1 Identifying the Causes of Behavior

Our inner subjective feelings (emotions) and goal-directed thoughts (motivations) influence how we behave and adapt as individuals and as a species. Emotion and motivation are inferred states that can escape conscious awareness or intent and make the case for free will difficult to argue.

Biologically, reward motivates animals to engage in behavior. Aversive circumstances prompt brain circuits to produce behaviors that will reduce them. Such are the effects of sensory deprivation.

The brain inherently needs stimulation. In its absence, the brain will seek it out.

Sensory stimulation leads to hormone activity and to dopamine activity in the brainstem. Neural circuits organized in the brainstem control species-typical behaviors, such as mouse killing by cats and singing by birds. These brainstem circuits manifest their evolutionary advantage: they are rewarding. Rewarding behavior motivates living beings. When animals disengage from behaviors that motivate their species, they go extinct.

12-2 The Chemical Senses

In the olfactory and gustatory senses, chemical neuroreceptors in the nose and tongue interact with chemosignals, leading to neural activity in cranial nerve 1 for olfaction and cranial nerves 7, 9, and 10 for taste. The cranial nerves enter the brainstem, and through a series of synapses, pass into the forebrain. Smell and taste inputs merge in the orbitofrontal cortex to produce our perception of flavor.

12-3 Evolution, Environment, and Behavior

Behavior is controlled by its consequences as well as by its biology. Consequences may affect a species' evolution or an individual's behavior. Behaviors selected by evolution are often triggered by innate releasing mechanisms. Behaviors selected only in an individual animal are shaped by that animal's environment and are learned.

12-4 Neuroanatomy of Motivated and Emotional Behavior

The neural structures that initiate emotional and motivated behaviors are the hypothalamus, pituitary gland, amygdala, the dopaminergic and noradrenergic activating pathways from nuclei in the lower brainstem, and the frontal lobes.

The experience of both emotion and motivation is controlled by activity in the ANS, hypothalamus, and forebrain, especially the amygdala and frontal cortex. Emotional and motivated behavior may be unconscious responses to internal or external stimuli controlled either by the activity of innate releasing mechanisms or by cognitive responses to events or thoughts.

12-5 Control of Regulatory and Nonregulatory Behavior

The two distinctly different types of motivated behaviors are (1) regulatory (homeostatic) behaviors that maintain vital body system balance and (2) nonregulatory behaviors, basically all nonreflexive behaviors and behaviors not controlled by a homeostatic mechanism. Feeding is a regulatory behavior controlled by the interaction of the digestive and hormonal systems, the enteric nervous system, and the hypothalamic and cortical circuits. Sexual activity is a nonregulatory behavior motivated by the amygdala. Copulatory behavior is controlled by the hypothalamus (ventromedial hypothalamus in females and the preoptic area in males). Sexual orientation (a person's attraction to the opposite or same sex) and gender identity (a person's feeling of being male or female) are related to the organization of the hypothalamus. Differences in hypothalamic organization are likely related to epigenetic effects in early development.

12-6 Reward

Survival depends on maximizing contact with some environmental stimuli and minimizing contact with others. The reward mechanism controls this differential. Two independent features of reward are wanting and liking. The wanting component is thought to be controlled by dopaminergic activating systems, whereas the liking component is thought to be controlled by opioid and GABA–benzodiazepine systems.

■ KEY TERMS

amygdala, p. 418
androgen, p. 401
anorexia nervosa, p. 427
aphagia, p. 429
emotion, p. 399
evolutionary psychology, p. 406
gender identity, p. 435
generalized anxiety disorder, p. 424
hippocampus, p. 416

homeostatic mechanism, p. 411
hyperphagia, p. 429
hypovolemic thirst, p. 431
innate releasing mechanism (IRM), p. 406
Klüver–Bucy syndrome, p. 423
learned taste aversion, p. 409
medial forebrain bundle (MFB), p. 413
motivation, p. 399

nonregulatory behavior, p. 413
obesity, p. 427
orbitofrontal cortex (OFC), p. 403
osmotic thirst, p. 431
panic disorder, p. 424
pheromone, p. 403
phobia, p. 424
pituitary gland, p. 413
prefrontal cortex (PFC), p. 418
preparedness, p. 409

psychosurgery, p. 423
regulatory behavior, p. 411
reinforcer, p. 409
releasing hormone, p. 414
sensory deprivation, p. 401
sexual dimorphism, p. 433
sexual orientation, p. 435
somatic marker hypothesis, p. 421
transgender, p. 435

⤷ Visit 🔲 LaunchPad to access the e-Book, videos, 🅒 LearningCurve adaptive quizzing, flashcards, and more.

www.macmillanhighered.com/launchpad/kolb5e

Katherine Streeter

CHAPTER 13

Why Do We Sleep and Dream?

Doing the Right Thing at the Right Time

We have all heard this advice: Maintaining regular sleeping and eating habits contributes to good health. Scientific evidence supports this good advice.

We humans are **diurnal animals** (from the Latin *dies*, meaning *day*): we are active during daylight and we sleep when it is dark. This **circadian rhythm** is the day–night rhythm found in most animals. It evolved to maximize food acquisition during the day, when we see best, and to minimize expending our energy stores by sleeping during the night hours, when do not see well.

Today our environment allows us to intrude on our circadian rhythm in two ways. Artificial lighting allows us to extend our waking hours well into the night and into sleep time. Handy food sources—often easily metabolized high-calorie foods—allow us to eat whenever we want.

Together these intrusions into our natural circadian rhythm contribute to a combination of medical disorders known as **metabolic syndrome** that collectively increase the risk of developing sleep disorders, cardiovascular disease, and diabetes (Lajoie et al., 2015).

The roots of metabolic syndrome lie in disruptions of our **biological clock**, the neural system that times behavior. One clock controls sleep–waking. Another controls the functioning of body organs related to feeding, such as the liver, pancreas, and gut. The clock that controls sleep–waking responds to light, whereas the clock that controls feeding responds to eating. Their activity is reciprocal: disrupting one disrupts the other.

Irregular sleep and meal schedules thus change the synchrony of biological clocks. Metabolic rate, plasma glucose, and pancreatic insulin secretion can slow down or speed up at inappropriate times, contributing to obesity and diabetes. Prevention and treatment for obesity and diabetes can include doing the right thing at the right time when it comes to sleep schedules and mealtimes.

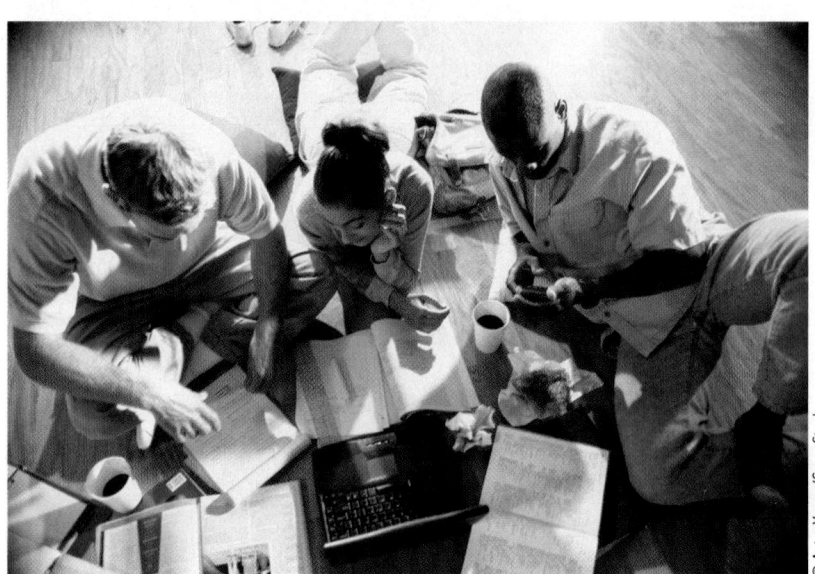

© AntonVengo/SuperStock

Humans and other animals perform a remarkable array of behaviors to adapt to daily and seasonal cycles. Our daily rhythms of sleeping and waking, feeding, exercising, and social interaction are rhythmical over days and years. Other animals share these daily activities and also migrate, hibernate, and shed or grow feathers or fur as the seasons change. In this chapter we answer questions related to these daily and seasonal rhythms, including how the brain produces biological rhythms, why sleep evolved, and what neural mechanisms regulate sleeping, waking, and sleep-related disorders.

13-1 A Clock for All Seasons

We first consider evidence that proved the existence of a biological clock: how the clock keeps time and how it regulates our behavior. Because environmental cues are not always consistent, we examine how biological clocks help us interpret environmental cues in an adaptive way.

Origins of Biological Rhythms

Biorhythms, the inherent timing mechanisms that control or initiate various biological processes, are linked to the cycles of days and seasons produced by Earth's rotation on its axis and by its progression in orbit around the sun (**Figure 13-1**). Earth rotates on its axis once

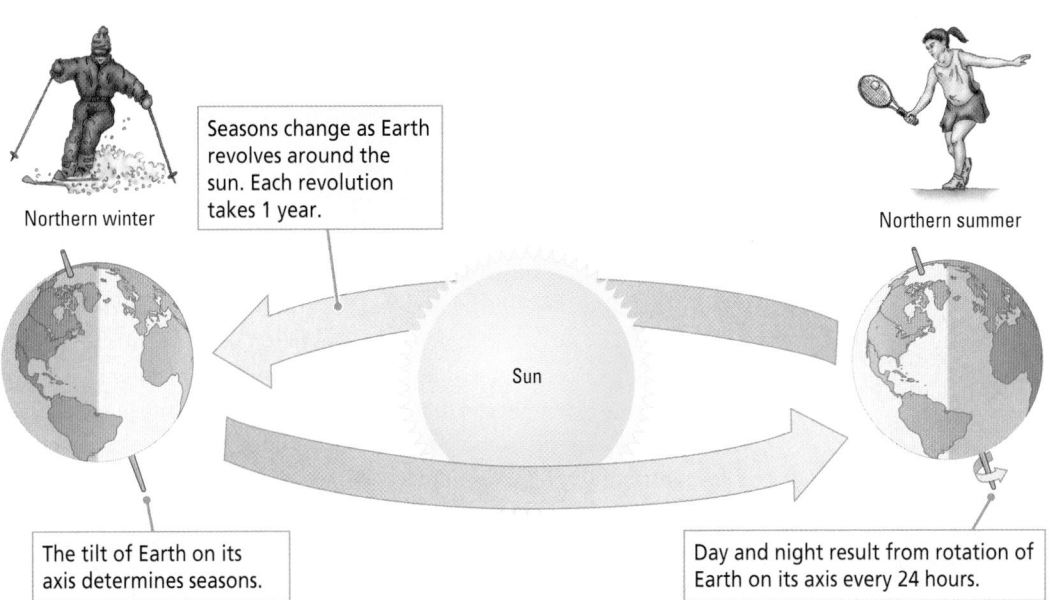

FIGURE 13-1 Origins of Biorhythms Each point on Earth between the Arctic and Antarctic circles faces the sun for part of its daily rotation cycle (daytime) and faces away from the sun for the other part (nighttime). Seasonal changes in temperature and in the amount of daylight result from the tilt of Earth's axis during its annual revolution around the sun.

every 24 hours, producing a 24-hour cycle of day and night. The day–night cycle changes across the seasons, however.

Earth's axis is tilted slightly, so as it orbits the sun once each year, the North and South Poles incline slightly toward the sun for part of the year and slightly away from it for the rest of the year. As the Southern Hemisphere inclines toward the sun, its inhabitants experience summer: more direct sunshine for more hours each day, and the weather is warmer. At the same time inhabitants of the Northern Hemisphere, inclined away from the sun, experience winter: less direct sunlight, making the days shorter and the weather colder. Over the year the polar inclinations reverse, as do the seasons. Tropical regions near the equator undergo little seasonal or day length change as Earth progresses around the sun.

Daily and seasonal changes have combined effects on organisms, inasmuch as the onset and duration of daily change depend on the season and latitude. Animals living in polar regions have to cope with greater seasonal fluctuations in daily temperature, light, and food availability than do animals living near the equator.

We humans largely evolved as equatorial animals, and our behavior is dominated by a circadian rhythm of daylight activity and nocturnal sleep. Nevertheless our daily cycles adapt to extreme latitudes. Not only does human waking and sleep behavior cycle daily; so also do pulse rate, blood pressure, body temperature, rate of cell division, blood cell count, alertness, urine composition, metabolic rate, sexual drive, feeding behavior, and responsiveness to medications. The activity of nearly every cell in our bodies shares a daily rhythm.

Biorhythms are not unique to animals. Plants display rhythmic behavior exemplified by species whose leaves or flowers open during the day and close at night. Even unicellular algae and fungi display rhythmic behaviors related to the passage of the day. Some animals, including lizards and crabs, change color in a rhythmic pattern. The Florida chameleon, for example, turns green at night, whereas its coloration matches its environment during the day. In short, almost every living organism and every living cell displays rhythms related to daily changes (Bosler et al., 2015).

Biological Clocks

If animal behavior were affected only by daily changes in external cues, the neural mechanisms that account for changes in behavior would be simple to study. An external cue—say, sunrise—could be isolated and the neural processes that respond to the cue identified.

diurnal animal Organism that is active chiefly during daylight.

circadian rhythm Day–night rhythm.

metabolic syndrome Combinations of medical disorders, including obesity and insulin abnormalities, that collectively increase the risk of developing cardiovascular disease and diabetes.

biological clock Neural system that times behavior.

biorhythm Inherent timing mechanism that controls or initiates biological processes.

▶ EXPERIMENT **13-1**

Question: Is plant movement exogenous or endogenous?

Procedure

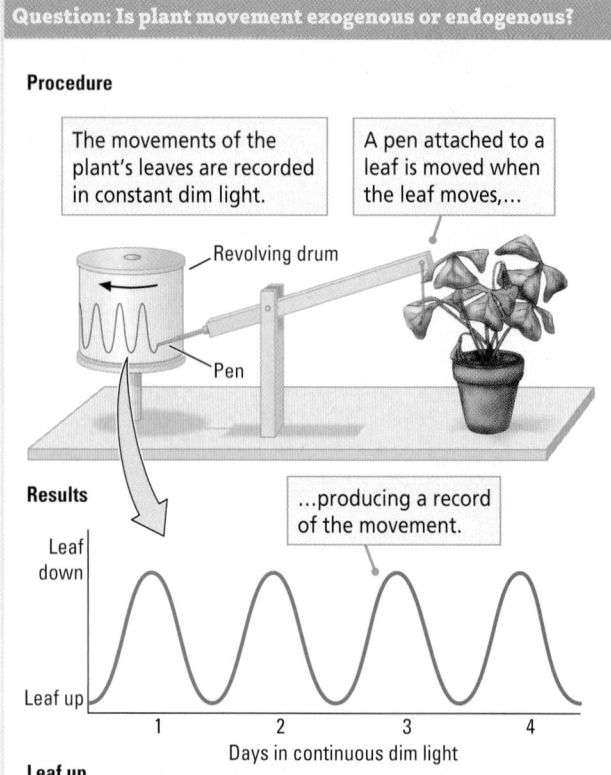

The movements of the plant's leaves are recorded in constant dim light.

A pen attached to a leaf is moved when the leaf moves,...

Revolving drum

Pen

Results

...producing a record of the movement.

Leaf down

Leaf up

1   2   3   4

Days in continuous dim light

Leaf up

Leaf down

Bryan Kolb/Ian Whishaw

Conclusion: Movement of the plant is endogenous. It is caused by an internal clock that matches the temporal passage of a real day.

In Latin *circa* means *about, annum* means *year*, and *dies* means *day*.

That behavior is not driven simply by external cues was first recognized in 1729 by the French geologist Jean Jacques d'Ortous de Mairan (see Raven et al., 1992). In an experiment similar to the one illustrated in the Procedure section of **Experiment 13-1**, de Mairan isolated a plant from daily light, dark, and temperature cues. He noted that the rhythmic movements of its leaves seen over a light–dark cycle continued when it was isolated as graphed in the Results section of the experiment.

What concerned investigators who came after de Mairan was the possibility that some undetected external cue stimulates the plant's rhythmic behavior. Such cues could include changes in temperature, in electromagnetic fields, and even in the intensity of cosmic rays from outer space. But further experiments showed that daily fluctuations are endogenous—they come from within the plant. Thus, the plant must have a biological clock. The contributions of endogenous rhythms to plants is important both to agriculture and to food storage (Bendix et al., 2015).

Similar experiments show that almost all organisms, including humans, have biological clocks that synchronize behavior to the temporal passage of a real day and make predictions about tomorrow. A biological clock signals that if daylight lasts for a given time today, it will last for about the same time tomorrow. A biological clock allows us to anticipate events and prepare for them both physiologically and cognitively. And unless external factors get in the way, a biological clock regulates feeding times, sleeping times, and metabolic activity as appropriate to day–night cycles. Biological clocks also produce epigenetic effects: they regulate gene expression in every cell in the body (Zhang et al., 2014).

Measuring Biological Rhythms

Although the existence of endogenous biological clocks was demonstrated nearly 300 years ago, detailed study of biorhythms had to await the development of electrical and computer-based timing devices. Behavioral analysis requires a method for counting behavioral events and a method for displaying those events in a meaningful way. For example, rodent behavior was first measured by giving the animal access to a running wheel for exercise (**Figure 13-2**A).

A computer records each turn of the wheel and displays the result (Figure 13-2B). Because most rodents are nocturnal, sleeping during light hours and becoming active during dark hours, their wheel running takes place in the dark. If each day's activity is plotted under the preceding day's activity in a column, we observe a pattern—a cycle of activity over time. A glance at the pattern reveals when and how active the animal is (Figure 13-2C).

The animal's activity cycle has a **period**, the time required to complete one cycle of activity. Most animals' activity period is about 24 hours in an environment in which the lights go on and off regularly. Our own sleep–wake period also is about 24 hours. The measurement of periods and the events that control them are central to understanding circadian rhythms.

Many behaviors have periods longer or shorter than this 24-hour circadian rhythm. *Circannual rhythms* last about a year. Many animals' migratory and mating cycles are circannual. Other biorhythms have monthly or seasonal periods greater than a day but less than a year. These are *infradian rhythms*. The menstrual cycle and associated hormonal changes of human females, with an average period of about 28 days, is an infradian biorhythm linked to the cycle of the moon and thus also referred to as a *circalunar cycle* (Amariei et al., 2014).

(A)

Rat has access to a running wheel.

(B)

Each wheel rotation is recorded as a tick on a chart. Each line represents one day's activity.

(C)

Animal's activity

12 noon 6 P.M.   Dark   6 A.M. 12 noon

When activity was plotted for a month under conditions of no light between 6:00 P.M. and 6:00 A.M., the rat was shown to be active during dark hours of the day–night cycle.

FIGURE 13-2 Recording the Daily Activity Cycle of a Rat Data from C. P. Richter (1965). Biological clocks in medicine and psychiatry (pp. 12–15). Springfield, IL: Charles C Thomas.

Ultradian rhythms have a period of less than one day. Our eating behavior, which takes place about every 90 minutes to 2 hours, including snacks, is one ultradian rhythm. Rodents, although active throughout the night, display an ultradian rhythm in being most active at the beginning and end of the dark period.

Biological rhythm	Time frame	Example
Circannual	Yearly	Migratory cycles of birds
Circadian	Daily	Human sleep–wake cycle
Infradian	More than a day	Human menstrual cycle
Ultradian	Less than a day	Human eating cycles

The fact that a behavior appears to be rhythmic does not mean that it is ruled only by a biological clock. Animals may postpone migrations as long as food supplies last. They adjust their circadian activities in response to the availability of food, the presence of predators, and competition from other members of their own species. We humans obviously change our daily activities in response to seasonal changes, work schedules, and play opportunities. Therefore, whether a rhythmic behavior is produced by a biological clock and the extent to which it is controlled by a clock must be demonstrated experimentally.

Free-Running Rhythms

To determine whether a rhythm is produced by a biological clock, researchers design three types of tests in which they manipulate relevant cues, especially light cues. A test is given (1) in continuous light, (2) in continuous darkness, or (3) by choice of the participant. Each treatment yields a slightly different insight into the periods of biological clocks.

Jurgen Aschoff and Rutger Weber first demonstrated that the human sleep–waking rhythm is governed by a biological clock. They allowed participants to select their light–dark cycle and studied them in an underground bunker, where no cues signaled when day began or ended. The participants selected the periods when they were active and when they slept, and they turned the lights on and off at will. In short they selected the length of their own day and night.

Measures of ongoing behavior and recording of sleep periods with sensors on the beds revealed that the participants continued to show daily sleep–activity rhythms. This finding demonstrates that humans have an endogenous biological clock that governs sleep–waking behavior. **Figure 13-3** shows, however, that the biorhythm is different when compared with biorhythms before and after isolation. Although the period of the participants' sleep–wake cycles approximated 24 hours before and after the test, during the test they lengthened to about 25 to 27 hours, depending on the person.

period Time required to complete an activity cycle.

FIGURE 13-3 Free-Running Rhythm in a Human   The record for days 1 through 3 shows the daily sleep period under typical day–night conditions. The record for days 4 through 20 shows the free-running rhythm that developed while this participant was isolated in a bunker and allowed to control day and night lengths. The daily activity period shifts from 24 hours to 25.9 hours. On days 21 through 25 the period returns to 24 hours as the participant is again exposed to a natural light–dark cycle. Data from J. A. Hobson (1989). *Sleep* (p. 33). New York: Scientific American Library.

The participants chose to go to bed 1 to 2 hours later every "night." Soon they were getting up at about the time the experimenters outside the bunker were going to bed. Clearly. the participants were displaying their own personal cycles. Such a **free-running rhythm** runs at a frequency of the body's own devising when environmental cues are absent. Humans' self-selected free-running rhythm is slightly longer than 24 hours.

The period of free-running rhythms also depends on the light-related biology of the species. When hamsters, a nocturnal species, are tested in constant darkness, their free-running periods are a little shorter than 24 hours; when they are tested in constant light, their free-running periods are a little longer than 24 hours. This test dependency is typical of nocturnal animals. As **Figure 13-4** shows, the opposite free-running periods are typical of diurnal animals (Binkley, 1990). When sparrows, diurnal birds, are tested in constant darkness, their free-running periods are a little longer than 24 hours; when they are tested in constant light, their free-running periods are a little shorter than 24 hours.

A rule of thumb to explain the period of free-running rhythms in light or dark is that animals expand and contract their sleep periods as the sleep-related period—light for hamsters and dark for sparrows—expands or contracts. Understanding this point enables us to predict how excess artificial lighting, which expands the light portion of our days, influences our circadian periods. Because we are diurnal, our sleep periods contract and we get less sleep each night.

Zeitgebers

Endogenous rhythmicity is not the only factor that contributes to circadian periods. A mechanism exists for setting rhythms to correspond to environmental events as well. To be useful, the biological clock must keep to a time that predicts actual changes in the day–night cycle. If a biological clock is like a slightly defective wristwatch, it will eventually provide times that are inaccurate by hours and so be useless.

If we reset an errant wristwatch each day, however—say, when we awaken—it provides useful information even though it is not perfectly accurate. Equivalent ways of resetting a free-running biological clock include sunrise and sunset, eating times, and many other activities that influence the period of the circadian clock.

Aschoff and Weber called a clock-setting cue a **Zeitgeber** (*time giver* in German). When a Zeitgeber resets a biorhythm, the rhythm is said to be **entrained**. Light is the most potent

---

free-running rhythm Rhythm of the body's own devising in the absence of all external cues.

Zeitgeber Environmental event that entrains biological rhythms: German for *time giver.*

entrain Determine or modify the period of a biorhythm.

light pollution Exposure to artificial light that changes activity patterns and so disrupts circadian rhythms.

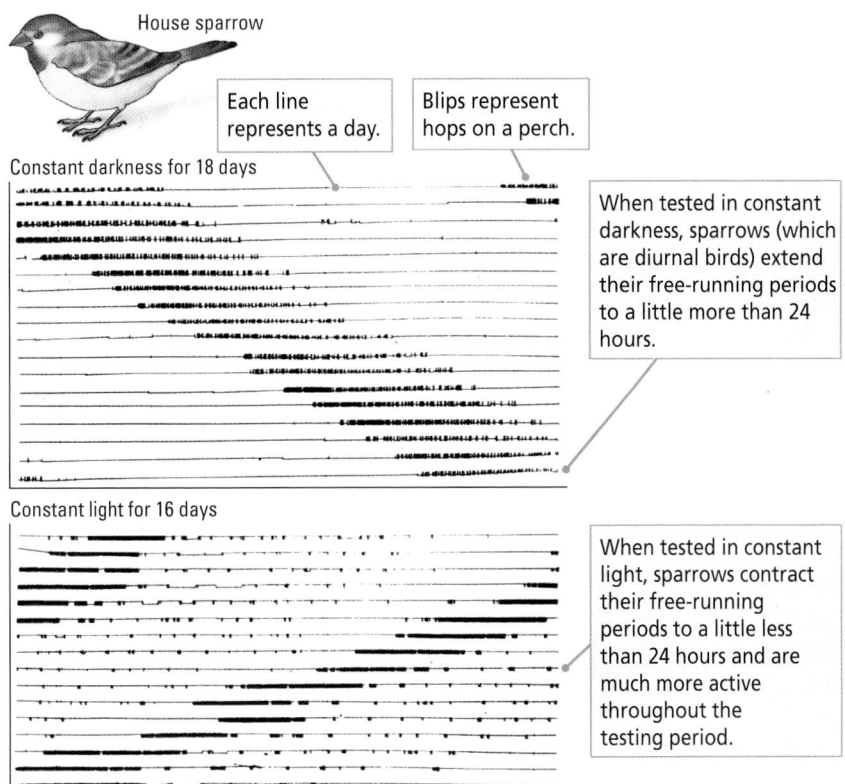

House sparrow

Each line represents a day.

Blips represent hops on a perch.

Constant darkness for 18 days

When tested in constant darkness, sparrows (which are diurnal birds) extend their free-running periods to a little more than 24 hours.

Constant light for 16 days

When tested in constant light, sparrows contract their free-running periods to a little less than 24 hours and are much more active throughout the testing period.

FIGURE 13-4 Free-Running Rhythms of a Diurnal Animal Data from S. Binkley (1990). *The Clockwork Sparrow* (p. 16). Englewood Cliffs NJ: Prentice Hall.

entraining stimulus. Clinical Focus 13-2, Seasonal Affective Disorder, explains its importance in entraining circadian rhythms.

The property that allows a biological clock to be entrained explains how circadian rhythms synchronize with seasonal changes in day–night duration. North and south of the equator the time of onset and the length of day and night change as the seasons progress. At extreme latitudes daylight begins very early in the morning in summer and very late in the morning in winter. An entrained biological clock allows an animal to synchronize its daily activity across these seasonal changes.

A biological clock that resets each day tells an animal that daylight will begin tomorrow at approximately the same time that it began today and that tomorrow will last approximately as long as today did. Current research finds that light Zeitgebers are effective at both sunrise and sunset: morning light sets the biological clock by advancing it, and evening darkness sets the clock by retarding it (Schmal et al., 2015).

The potent entraining effect of light Zeitgebers is illustrated by laboratory studies of Syrian hamsters, perhaps one of the most compulsive animal timekeepers. When given access to running wheels, hamsters exercise during the night segment of the laboratory day–night cycle. A single brief flash of light is an effective Zeitgeber for entraining their biological clocks.

Considering the less compulsive behavior that most of us display, we should shudder at the way we entrain our own clocks when we stay up late in artificial light, sleep late some days, and get up early by using an alarm clock on other days. **Light pollution,** the extent to which we are exposed to artificial lighting, disrupts circadian rhythms and accounts for a great deal of inconsistent behavior associated with accidents, daytime fatigue, alterations in emotional states, obesity, diabetes, and other disorders characteristic of metabolic syndrome described in Clinical Focus 13-1, Doing the Right Thing at the Right time (Gerhart-Hines & Lazar, 2015).

Entrainment works best if the adjustment made to the biological clock is not too large. People who work night shifts are often subject to huge adjustments, especially when they

If a hamster happens to blink during this Zeitgeber, the light will still penetrate its closed eyelids and entrain its biological clock.

Seasonal Affective Disorder

In *seasonal affective disorder* (SAD), a form of depression, low levels of sunlight in winter, do not entrain the circadian rhythm. Consequently, a person's biorhythm becomes a free-running rhythm. The perception of longer nights by the circadian pacemaker stimulates wanting more sleep. If the want is not satisfied, cumulative sleep deprivation can result.

Because people vary in the duration of their free-running rhythms, lack of entrainment affects individuals differently. Some are phase-retarded, with desired sleep time coming earlier each day; some are phase-delayed, with desired sleep time coming later each day.

The cumulative changes associated with altered circadian rhythms can promote depression. The finding that incidence of depressive symptoms increases as a function of the latitude at which a person lives supports this idea.

Because a class of retinal ganglion cells that express a photosensitive pigment called *melanopsin* are responsive to blue light (see Section 13-2), it has been proposed that exposure to bright white light that contains this blue frequency can reset the circadian clock and ameliorate depression. In this treatment, called *phototherapy*, the idea is to increase the short winter photoperiod by exposing a person to artificial bright light in the morning or both morning and evening (Mårtensson et al., 2015). Typical room lighting is not bright enough.

A word of caution, however. Decreased exposure to sunlight in winter can result in Vitamin D deficiency and is also suggested to contribute to depression (Kerr et al., 2015).

During the polar night in northern Norway schoolchildren take light treatment to combat SAD.

Bryan and Cherry Alexander/Science Source

work the graveyard shift (11:00 P.M. to 7:00 A.M.), the period when they would normally sleep. Study results show that adapting to such a change is difficult and stressful, and it increases susceptibility to disease by altering immune system rhythms (Labrecque & Cermakian, 2015). Compared with people who have a regular daytime work schedule, people who work night shifts have a higher incidence of metabolic syndrome. Thus, shift workers benefit from vigilance in maintaining good sleep habits and diet and in exercising to minimize other risk factors for metabolic syndrome. Adaptations to shift work fare better if people first work the swing shift (3:00 P.M. to 11:00 P.M.) for a time before beginning the graveyard shift.

Long-distance air travel—say from North America to Europe or Asia—also demands large and difficult time adjustments. For example, travelers flying east from New York to Paris begin their first day in Europe just when their biological clock is signaling that it is time for sleep (**Figure 13-5**). The difference between a person's circadian rhythm and the daylight cycle in a new environment can produce the disorientation and fatigue of **jet lag**.

The west-to-east traveler generally has a more difficult adjustment than does the east-to-west traveler, who needs to stay up only a little longer than usual. The occasional traveler may cope with jet lag quite well, but frequent travelers such as airline personnel face a substantial adaptive challenge. The occasional traveler can manage jet lag with sleep on arrival or shortly after. The brain's biological clock resets in a day and other body organs follow after about a week. For frequent travelers and flight crews, resetting is not so easy. Persistent asynchronous rhythms generated by jet lag are associated with altered sleep and temperature rhythms, fatigue, and stress, even reduced success by sports teams traveling more than 3 hours from west to east (Weingarten and Collop, 2013).

jet lag Fatigue and disorientation resulting from rapid travel through time zones and exposure to a changed light–dark cycle.

1 Traveler leaves New York at 9:00 P.M., when it's 3:00 A.M. in Paris.

2 Traveler arrives in Paris at 9:00 A.M., when it's 3:00 A.M. in New York. Because his biological clock is set for New York time, he is prepared for sleep, whereas residents of Paris are waking.

Paris (3:00 A.M.)

New York (3:00 A.M.) Paris (9:00 A.M.)

West-to-east travel (6-hour flight)

New York (9:00 P.M.)

Paris (3:00 A.M.)

East-to-west travel (6-hour flight)

Paris (9:00 P.M.) New York (3:00 P.M.)

New York (9:00 P.M.)

4 Traveler arrives in New York at 9:00 P.M. and needs to stay up only a little longer than normal for his biological clock to adjust.

3 Traveler leaves Paris at 9:00 P.M., when it's 3:00 P.M. in New York.

FIGURE 13-5 Jet Lag Disruption in the entrainment of a person's biological clock is undoubtedly more pronounced in west-to-east jet travel because the disruption in the person's circadian rhythm is dramatic. On the return journey the traveler's biological clock has a much easier adjustment to make.

13-1 REVIEW

A Clock for All Seasons

Before you continue, check your understanding.

1. Many behaviors occur in a rhythmic pattern in relation to time. These biorhythms may display a yearly, or _____, cycle or a daily, or _____, cycle.

2. Although biological clocks keep fairly good time, their _____ rhythms may be slightly shorter or longer than 24 hours unless they are reset each day by _____.

3. _____ and _____ can disrupt circadian rhythms.

4. Explain why the circadian rhythm is important.

Answers appear at the back of the book.

For additional study tools, visit LaunchPad:
www.macmillanhighered.com/launchpad/kolb5e

13-2 Neural Basis of the Biological Clock

Curt Richter (1965) was the first researcher who attempted to locate biological clocks in the brain. In the 1930s he captured wild rats and tested them in activity wheels. He found that the animals ran, ate, and drank when the lights were off and were relatively quiescent when the lights were on.

By ablating brain tissue with electric current, Richter found that animals lost their circadian rhythm after damage to the hypothalamus. Subsequently, by making much more discrete lesions, experimenters have shown that a region of the hypothalamus, the **suprachiasmatic nucleus** (SCN), acts as the master biological clock (Webb et al., 2014). The SCN is named for its location just above (*supra-*) the optic chiasm, where the optic tracts cross at the base of the hypothalamus.

Ian Whishaw

Optic chiasm   Suprachiasmatic nucleus   Hypothalamus

Suprachiasmatic Nucleus in a Rat Brain

Suprachiasmatic Rhythms

Evidence for the SCN's role in circadian rhythms now comes from additional lines of evidence:

1. If the suprachiasmatic nuclei are selectively damaged, animals still eat, drink, exercise, and sleep but at haphazard times.

2. If a form of glucose is tagged with a radioactive label, taken up by metabolically active cells, and trapped in them but not used by them, cells that are more active will subsequently emit more radioactivity. When this tracer is injected into rodents, more is found in the SCN after injections given in the light period of the light–dark cycle than in the dark period. This experiment demonstrates that suprachiasmatic cells are more active during the light period.

3. Recording electrodes placed in the SCN confirm that neurons in this region are more active during the light period of the cycle than during the dark period.

4. If all the pathways into and out of the suprachiasmatic nucleus are cut, SCN neurons maintain their rhythmic electrical activity.

5. SCN cells removed from the brain and cultured in a dish retain a periodic rhythm.

Clearly, suprachiasmatic neurons have an intrinsically rhythmic activity pattern. Although the SCN is the master biological clock, it is not the sole one. Two other neural structures, the intergeniculate leaflet and the pineal gland, also display clocklike activity. Further, nearly every cell in the body has its own clock.

After the SCN is destroyed, some behaviors retain a timed occurrence. One is feeding. Animals without an SCN can still display anticipatory behavior—becoming active in relation to scheduled mealtimes—and can organize related behaviors, including memory for food locations, in relation to mealtimes (Landgraf et al., 2015). How this anticipatory behavior is timed is not known, but whatever the mechanism, feeding-related activity can act as a Zeitgeber for the main SCN clock. That is, a regular feeding schedule can entrain the SCN clock and many other body organs, and cells and an irregular feeding schedule can be disruptive.

Keeping Time

If SCN neurons are isolated from one another, each remains rhythmic, but the period of some cells differs from that of other cells. Thus rhythmic activity is a property of SCN cells, but the timing of the rhythm must be set so that the cells can synchronize their activity in relation to each other. In the brain, SCN cells connect one to another through inhibitory GABA synapses, and these connections allow them to act in synchrony. Their entrainment depends upon external inputs, however.

suprachiasmatic nucleus (SCN) Master biological clock located in the hypothalamus just above the optic chiasm.

retinohypothalamic tract Neural route formed by axons of photosensitive retinal ganglion cells from the retina to the suprachiasmatic nucleus; allows light to entrain the rhythmic activity of the SCN.

chronotype Individual differences in circadian activity.

GABA is main inhibitory neurotransmitter in the CNS.

The SCN receives information about light through the **retinohypothalamic tract** (Figure 13-6). This pathway begins with specialized retinal ganglion cells (RGCs) that contain the photosensitive pigment *melanopsin*. These melanopsin-containing *photosensitive RGCs* receive light-related signals from the rods and cones and send that information to the brain's visual centers. Melanopsin-containing pRGCs also can be activated directly by certain wavelengths of blue light in the absence of rods and cones.

Melanopsin-containing photosensitive RGCs are distributed across the retina, and in humans they make up between 1 percent and 3 percent of all RGCs. Their axons project to various brain regions, including the SCN, which they innervate bilaterally. Melanopsin-containing ganglion cells use glutamate as their primary neurotransmitter but also contain two cotransmitters, substance P and pituitary adenylate cyclase–activating polypeptide (PACAP).

When stimulated by light, melanopsin-containing pRGCs are excited, and in turn they excite cells in the SCN. The existence of light-sensitive retinal ganglion cells that are involved in entraining the circadian rhythm explains the continued presence of an entrained rhythm in people who are blind as a result of retinal degeneration that destroys the rods and cones (Zaidi et al., 2007). Even so, melanopsin-containing pRGCs do receive inputs from cones and rods. Cones can influence their activity in bright daylight, and rods can influence their activity in dim light.

As illustrated in Figure 13-6, the SCN consists of two parts, a more ventrally located *core* and a more dorsally located *shell*. The retinohypothalamic tract activates the core cells. Core neurons are not rhythmic, but they entrain the shell neurons, which are rhythmic.

In addition to retinohypothalamic input, the SCN receives projections from other brain regions, including the intergeniculate leaflet in the thalamus and the raphe nucleus, which is the nonspecific serotonergic-activating system of the brainstem. The terminal regions of these inputs to the SCN display variations, suggesting that various portions of the shell and the core have somewhat different functions.

The SCN's circadian rhythm is usually entrained by morning and evening light, but it can also be entrained or disrupted by sudden changes in lighting, by arousal, by moving about, and by feeding. These influences differ from the light entrainment provided over the retinohypothalamic tract.

The intergeniculate leaflet and the raphe nucleus are pathways through which nonphotic events influence the SCN rhythm (Cain et al., 2007). The neural structures mediating these other entraining pathways explain why being aroused or eating during the sleep portion of the circadian cycle disrupts the cycle (Mistlberger & Antle, 2011).

It is likely that the regional variation in SCN shell anatomy provides the substrate for various rhythms of the circadian cycle. Findings from studies on the genes that control rhythms in fruit flies suggest two separate groups of circadian neurons. *M cells* control morning activity; they need morning light for entrainment. *E cells* control evening activity; they need onset of darkness for entrainment (Hughes et al., 2015).

Some people are early to bed and early to rise and are energetic in the morning. Other people are late to rise and late to bed and are energetic in the evening. Individual differences in circadian activity between these "lark" and "owl" **chronotypes** are due to differences in SCN shell neurons. The differences may be the equivalent of fruit fly M cells and E cells, When expressed

Section 9-2 traces three main routes from the retina to the visual brain. Figure 9-8 diagrams the retina's cellular structure.

Glutamate is the main excitatory neurotransmitter in the CNS.

FIGURE 13-6 The Retinohypothalamic Tract and the SCN

Healthy

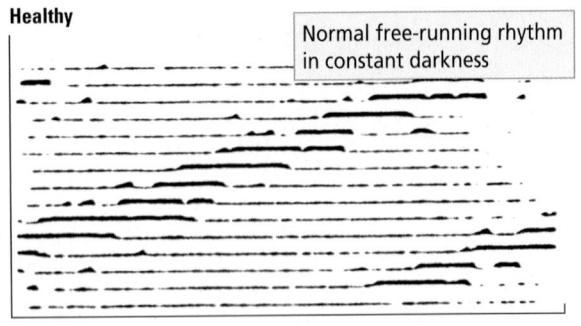

Normal free-running rhythm in constant darkness

Suprachiasmatic lesion

Absence of circadian rhythm in a light–dark environment

Suprachiasmatic transplant

Normal free-running rhythm in constant darkness restored by transplant

0   Time (hours)   24

FIGURE 13-7 Circadian Rhythms Restored by Neural Transplantation Information from M. R. Ralph & M. N. Lehman (1991). Transplantation: A new tool in the analysis of the mammalian hypothalamic circadian pacemaker. *Trends in Neurosciences, 14,* p. 363.

Figure 3-13 diagrams the process of protein synthesis.

differently in people, genes may account for differences in the amplitude of phases in the circadian period. (Pellegrino et al, 2015). Whether students are larks or owls does affect their performance on cognitive tasks, possibly by affecting memory for content (Smarr, 2015).

In hamsters and mice, mutant gene variations produce chronotypes with circadian periods as varied as 24, 20, or 17 hours (Monecke et al., 2011). As genetic analysis becomes less expensive, the study of the genes underlying human chronotypes is providing insights into individual differences in our biological clocks (Kang et al., 2015).

Immortal Time

How do suprachiasmatic cells develop rhythmic activity? Their endogenous rhythm is not learned. When animals are raised in constant darkness, their behavior still becomes rhythmic. In experiments in which animals have been maintained without entraining cues for a number of generations, each generation continues to display rhythmic behavior. Even if the mother has received an SCN lesion so that her behavior is not rhythmic, her offspring's behavior is rhythmic.

A line of evidence supporting the idea that suprachiasmatic cells are genetically programmed for rhythmicity comes from studies performed in Canada by Martin Ralph and his coworkers with the use of transplantation techniques (Ralph & Lehman, 1991). **Figure 13-7** illustrates the experiment.

As reflected in the top chart, hamsters are tested in constant dim light or in constant darkness to establish their free-running rhythms. They then receive a suprachiasmatic lesion followed by another test to show that the lesion has abolished their rhythmicity (center chart). Finally, the hamsters receive transplants of suprachiasmatic cells obtained from hamster embryos. About 60 days later the hamsters again show rhythmic activity, demonstrating that the transplanted cells have been integrated into the host brain and have reestablished rhythmic behavior (bottom chart). Follow-up studies show that the rhythms of many but not all body organs also show restored rhythmic activity.

What Ticks?

Molecular research is directed toward determining what genes control the ticking of the circadian clock. The timing device is in each SCN neuron and in most other cells of the body as well.

The circadian rhythm involves a feedback loop in which proteins are first made and then combine. The combined protein, called a *dimer,* for *two proteins,* inhibits production of its component proteins. Then the dimer degrades and the process begins anew. Research Focus 13-3, Synchronizing Biorhythms at the Molecular Level, describes the main feedback loop in mammals. Just as the back-and-forth swing of a pendulum makes a grandfather clock tick, the increase and decrease in protein synthesis once each day produce the cellular rhythm.

Pacemaking Circadian Rhythms

The SCN itself is not directly responsible for producing behavior. After it has been damaged, drinking and eating, sleeping and wakefulness still occur. They no longer occur at appropriate times, however.

An explanation for how the SCN controls biological rhythms is illustrated in **Figure 13-8**. In this model, light entrains the SCN, and the SCN in turn drives a number of slave oscillators. Each slave oscillator is responsible for the rhythmic occurrence of one activity. In other words, drinking, eating, body temperature, and sleeping are each produced by a separate slave oscillator.

dimer Two proteins combined into one.

Synchronizing Biorhythms at the Molecular Level

The retinohypothalamic tract carries information about light changes from the melanopsin-containing photosensitive retinal ganglion cells to the core of the SCN, the brain's main biological timekeeper (see Figure 13-6). Core cells synapse with SCN neurons in the shell and entrain the SCN shell cells to the light signal's 24-hour rhythm.

The timing mechanism in the shell cells is a pair of interlocking feedback loops that pace the SCN's function over a 24-hour period. The complete clockwork in the two feedback loops involves as many as 10 genes and their protein products. The secondary loop regulates functions for the main clockwork loop.

The main clock mechanism is the *transcription-translation-inhibition-feedback loop*. Its sequence, mapped in the illustration, follows:

STEP 1: TRANSCRIPTION In the cell nucleus three *Period* genes (*Per1,** *Per2, Per3*) and two *Cryptochrome* genes (*Cry1, Cry2*) are transcribed into *Per1, Per2,* and *Per3* messenger RNA and *Cry1* and *Cry2* mRNA.

STEP 2: TRANSLATION Ribosomes in the endoplasmic reticulum translate these mRNAs into the proteins PER1,† PER2, PER3, and CRY1, CRY2. In the intracellular fluid the proteins form various **dimers,** or two-protein combinations of PERCRY.

STEP 3: INHIBITION PERCRY dimers enter the cell nucleus, where they bind to and inhibit the CB dimer (formed by the CLOCK and BMAL proteins). The CB dimer turns on the Enhancer box (Ebox), a part of the DNA that activates transcription of the *Period* and *Cryptochrome* genes, so that when the CB dimer is inhibited, the *Per* and *Cry* genes are no longer expressed.

STEP 4: DECAY After they play their inhibitory role, the PERCRY proteins decay. Then the CB dimer resumes its activity, the *Per* and *Cry* genes resume expression, and the 24-hour cycle begins anew.

This sequence of gene turn-on followed by gene turn-off occurs in an inexorable daily loop.

Mutations in any circadian gene can lead to circadian alterations, including absence of a biorhythm or an altered biorhythm. For example, alleles of *Period 1* and *Period 2* genes determine chronotype—whether an individual will be early to bed and early to rise or late to bed and late to rise. The search for therapies for clock disorders includes looking for small molecules that can act as drugs to reset biorhythms disrupted by jet lag, shift work, and epigenetic and inherited gene irregularities.

*Gene and *mRNA* names are italicized.
†PROTEIN names are capitalized.

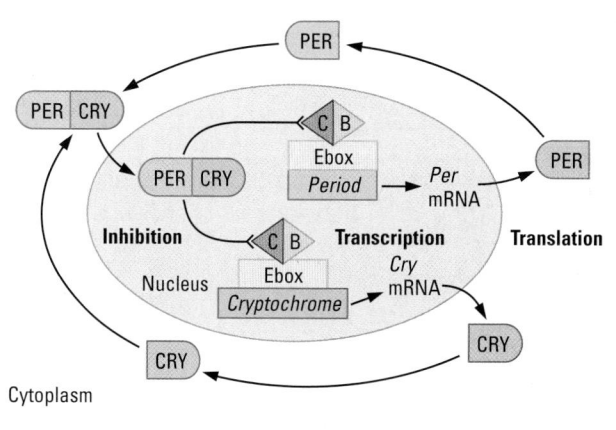

Main SCN Clock Mechanism

The SCN clock entrains slave oscillators through a remarkable array of pathways:

1. SCN neurons send axonal connections to nuclei close by in the hypothalamus and thalamus. These nuclei in turn connect extensively with other brain and body structures, to which they pass on the entraining signal.

2. The SCN connects with pituitary endocrine neurons to control hormone release. A wide range of hormones circulates through the body to entrain many body tissues and organs.

Figure 12-14 diagrams how the pituitary gland works.

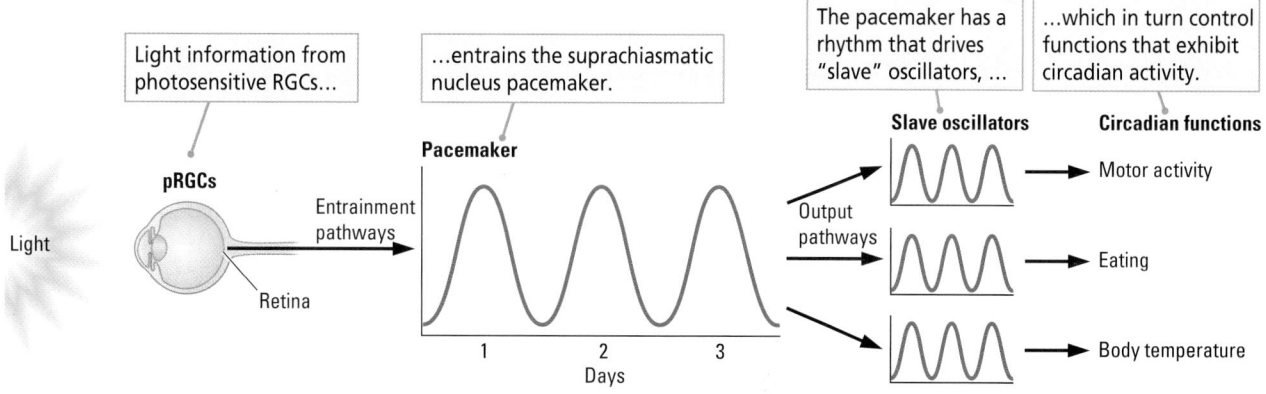

FIGURE 13-8 Circadian Timing System Organization

melatonin Hormone secreted by the pineal gland during the dark phase of the day–night cycle; influences daily and seasonal biorhythms.

Figure 2-30 diagrams the autonomic nervous system. Section 6-5 describes how glucocorticoids affect the body and brain.

3. The SCN also sends indirect messages to autonomic neurons in the spinal cord to inhibit the pineal gland from producing the hormone **melatonin**, which influences daily and seasonal biorhythms.

4. SCN cells themselves release hormones. Silver and colleagues (1996) used a transplantation technique in which encapsulated SCN cells were transplanted into hamsters that had received SCN lesions. Even though the transplanted cells did not make axonal connections, they restored many circadian behaviors, indicating that some SCN signals must be hormonal and travel through the bloodstream.

An illustration of the SCN's widespread effects is its control of two hormones, melatonin and glucocorticoids. The SCN controls melatonin release from the pineal gland so that melatonin circulates during the dark phase of the circadian cycle. It also controls the release of glucocorticoids from the adrenal glands so that they circulate during the light phase of the circadian cycle.

Melatonin promotes sleep and influences the parasympathetic rest-and-digest system as well as other physiological events in the body. Glucocorticoids mobilize glucose for cellular activity to support arousal responses in the sympathetic system. These two hormones will entrain any body organ that has receptors for them, and most organs do. Thus melatonin promotes rest activities, and glucocorticoids promote arousal activities during the dark and the light portions of the circadian cycle, respectively. Their actions explain in part why it is difficult to sleep during the day and stay awake to work at night. The role of melatonin as a slave oscillator in part explains its use as a drug for regulating sleep (Claustrat & Leston, 2015).

Pacemaking Circannual Rhythms

The suprachiasmatic nucleus controls not only daily rhythms but circannual rhythms as well. Russel Reiter (1980) first illustrated this form of pacemaking in hamsters. Hamsters are summertime (long-day) breeders. As the days lengthen in springtime, the gonads of male hamsters grow and release hormones that stimulate sexual behavior. As the days shorten in the winter, the gonads shrink, the amount of the hormones they produce decreases, and the males lose interest in sex.

During the dark phase of the day–night cycle the pineal gland secretes melatonin; during the light phase it does not. **Figure 13-9** shows that when a male hamster's melatonin level is low, the gonads enlarge, and when the level is high, the gonads shrink. The SCN thus

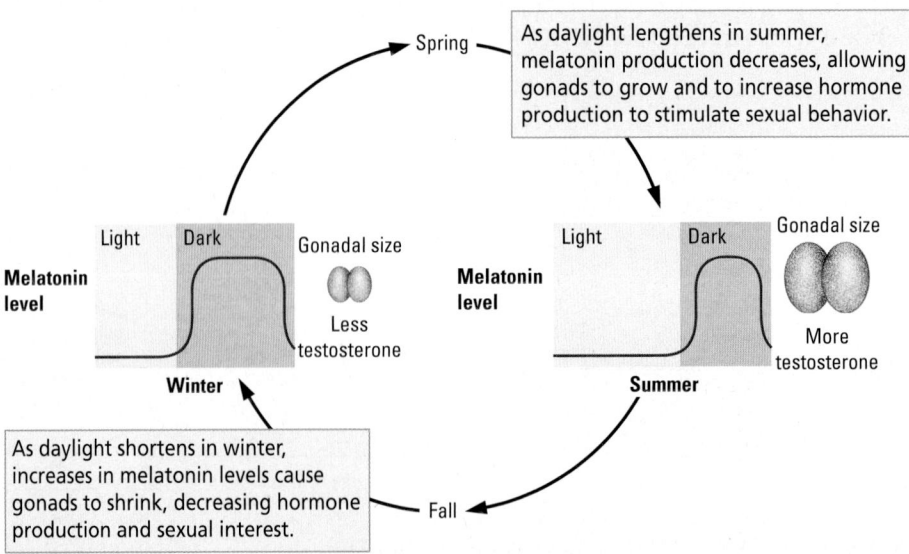

FIGURE 13-9 Hamster's Circannual Pacemaker Information from R. J. Reiter (1980). The pineal and its hormones in the control of reproduction in mammals. *Endocrinology Review, 1,* p. 120.

controls the pineal gland's sway over the gonads. Through connections in the autonomic nervous system the SCN drives the pineal gland as a slave oscillator.

During the long daylight period of the circadian cycle the SCN inhibits melatonin secretion by the pineal gland. As the days become shorter, the melatonin inhibition period shortens and the release period lengthens. When the daylight period is shorter than 12 hours, melatonin release time becomes sufficient to inhibit the hamster's gonads, and they shrink. Melatonin also influences the testes of short-day breeders, such as sheep and deer, that mate in the fall and early winter. Melatonin's effect on reproductive behavior in these species is the reverse of that in the hamster: reproductive activities begin as melatonin release increases.

The SCN's influence on circadian and circannual cycles is proposed to contribute to obesity in humans (Gangwisch, 2014). The idea is that long daylight hours involve fueling high-energy demanding activities during summer and thus extra food consumption. If a person is exposed to light pollution during winter, increased food consumption continues throughout the year, leading to weight gain. Light exposure can come from surprising sources. Some street lamps, reading lights, and e-readers emit blue-light wavelengths that activate pRGCs and through the SCN suppress melatonin (Chang et al., 2015). Thus, incidental light pollution can contribute to obesity.

In his classic book *Biological Clocks in Medicine and Psychiatry*, Curt Richter (1965) hypothesized that many physical and behavioral disorders might be caused by shocks, either physical or environmental, that upset the timing of biological clocks. For example, the record of psychotic episodes of the English writer Mary Lamb illustrated in **Figure 13-10** is one of many rhythmic records that Richter thought represented the action of an abnormally functioning biological clock.

FIGURE 13-10 Dysfunctional Clock? Attacks of mental illness displayed by the English writer Mary Lamb through her adult life appear to have had a cyclical component. Such observations would be difficult to obtain today because the drugs used to treat psychiatric disorders can mask disordered biorhythms. Information from C. P. Richter (1965). Biological clocks in medicine and psychiatry (p. 92). Springfield IL: Charles C Thomas.

29 31 33 35 37 39 41 43 45 47 49 51 53 55 57 59 61 63 65 67 69 71 73 75 77 79 81 83
Age

Cognitive and Emotional Rhythms

Circadian rhythms are synchronized in many parts of the body. In a phasic manner they influence cognitive and emotional functions, including emotional experience, learning and retention, decision making, and motivation. The extent to which a process depends on the expenditure of metabolic energy dictates optimal times for its activity during the circadian cycle: time of day can serve as a good index for the time and place at which things should happen. Studies suggest that as much as 10 percent of the genome is under the epigenetic control of circadian rhythms.

Many cognitive events require changes in gene expression. Animals remember previous events better if they are tested at the time of the circadian period when the initial event occurred. Donald Cain and his colleagues (2008) used a conditional place response to test rats' memories for a location at which they had previously received a small foot shock. The rats receive the noxious stimulation in a test box, then are returned to their home cage.

The following day groups of rats are tested at the time of training or a different time. Rats trained at time 1 and tested at time 1 show better retention as measured by the time they spent immobile (freezing) than rats trained at time 1 and tested at time 2, six hours later in the day. Similarly, rats trained at time 2 and tested at time 2 show better retention than rats trained at time 2 and tested at time 1, six hours earlier in the day. The results show that the circadian cycle puts a time stamp on the memory that allows it to be better recalled at the same time of the period that the initial event occurred.

Cognitive behaviors also synchronize with circadian periods. Animals have a variety of needs for food, water, and sleep, and it is adaptive for them to know when these resources become available. If food is available on a schedule, animals display anticipatory behaviors, becoming active as the feeding time arrives, for example. Other anticipatory events include salivation, intestinal activity, and sensations of hunger. Anticipatory activity might also include recalling events related to the timing of feeding and food location. Many cognitive activities can occur in the absence of the SCN, but it is adaptive for them to occur at the right time and place. SCN activity enables this. As animals age, their ability to associate appropriate activity with appropriate time declines, impairing their daily schedule, an effect that might in part account for poor scheduling and sleep in some older humans (Mulder et al., 2015).

Studies also find that the circadian period influences emotional behavior. A time of day effect may account for some of our emotional responses to daily events independent of the events themselves (Li et al., 2015). Nighttime fear is common, but is it the dark or the nighttime circadian rhythm that accounts for heightened emotion? By independently varying lighting conditions and test times during the circadian cycle, Li and colleagues found heightened emotional responses to stimuli at night independent of ambient lighting. Thus the cycle, not just darkness, contributes to emotional responding. Apparently at least two factors explain why horror movies watched at night are scarier: the movie's content and the time of day effect.

13-2 REVIEW

Neural Basis of the Biological Clock

Before you continue, check your understanding.

1. Biological rhythms are timed by internal biological clocks. The master clock is the _____.

2. Light cues entrain the suprachiasmatic nucleus to control daily rhythms via the _____ tract, which receives information via _____ cells.

3. Pacemaking produced by the SCN is a product of its _____ cells, which activate slave oscillators via both _____ signals and _____ connections.

4. Why should studying for an exam and taking the exam occur at the same time of day?

Answers appear at the back of the book.

For additional study tools, visit 🌏 **LaunchPad**:
www.macmillanhighered.com/launchpad/kolb5e

13-3 Sleep Stages and Dreaming

Waking behavior encompasses periods when we are physically active or inactive, and so does sleep. Our sleeping behavior consists of periods of rest, napping, long bouts of sleep, and sleep-related events, including snoring, dreaming, thrashing about, even sleepwalking. In this section we describe some sleeping and dreaming behaviors and the neural processes underlying them.

Measuring How Long We Sleep

A crude measure of sleeping and waking behavior is the *self-report*: people record in a diary when they wake and when they retire to sleep. The diaries show both optimal average sleep durations and considerable variation in sleep–waking behavior. An optimal sleep time of 7 to 8 hours per night is a popular adage, but many exceptions exist. People sleep more when they are young, after engaging in physical activity, or when pregnant. Some people are long sleepers; some are short sleepers. Numerous genetic mutations have been identified in people displaying very short sleep durations—as short as 1 hour.

Some people nap for a brief period in the daytime; others never nap. Benjamin Franklin is credited with the aphorism "early to bed and early to rise makes a man healthy wealthy and wise," but measures of sleep behavior indicate that the correlation Franklin proposed

Recommended Sleep Duration by Age

Age	Sleep time (hours)
Newborn up to 3 months	14–17
Infant under 1 year	12–15
Toddler up to 3 years	11–14
Preschool	10–13
Elementary-school age	9–11
Adolescent	8–10
Adult	7–9
Adult 65 years and older	7–8

Source: Information from National Sleep Foundation

(A) Electroencephalogram (EEG)

(B) Electromyogram (EMG)

(C) Electrooculogram (EOG)

Hank Morgan/Getty Images

FIGURE 13-11 Sleep Laboratory Setup Electronic equipment records readouts from electrodes attached to the sleeper. **(A)** EEG made from a point on the skull relative to a neutral point on the ear. **(B)** EMG made between two muscles, such as those on the chin and throat. **(C)** EOG made between the eye and a neutral point on the ear.

does not actually exist. Variations in sleeping times are normal, and napping normally is good.

Measuring Sleep in the Laboratory

Laboratory sleep studies allow researchers to measure sleep accurately and to record physiological changes associated with sleep. Miniaturized sleep-measuring technology and data compression now allow laboratory methods to be extended into the home (Lan et al., 2015). Measuring sleep requires recording at least three electrical body signals; the brain activity, muscle activity, and the eye movement. **Figure 13-11** illustrates a typical polygraph setup in a sleep laboratory and these commonly used measures that define sleep.

Electrodes pasted onto standard locations on the skull's surface yield an electroencephalogram (EEG), a record of brain wave activity. Electrodes placed on neck muscles provide an electromyogram (EMG), a record of muscle activity. Electrodes located near the eyes provide an electrooculogram (EOG), a record of eye movements. Body temperature, circulating hormones, and blood glucose levels provide additional measures of sleep.

Stages of Waking and Sleeping

Biological measurements show that sleep, like waking, is not a unitary state but encompasses several stages. For example, the EEG recording shows distinct patterns of brain wave activity as the neocortex generates distinct rhythmic patterns for states categorized as awake, relaxed, drowsy, sleep, deep sleep, and dreaming.

Figure 7-9 diagrams EEG patterns that reflect a range of conscious states in humans.

Waking State

When a person is awake, the EEG pattern consists of small-amplitude (height) waves with a fast frequency (repetition period). This pattern, the **beta (β) rhythm**, is defined by a frequency of 15 to 30 Hz (times per second). The pattern is also called fast-wave activity-activated

beta (β) rhythm Fast brain wave activity pattern associated with a waking EEG.

Excited

Relaxed, eyes closed

Deep sleep

EEG, or waking EEG. Also associated with waking, the EMG is active and the EOG indicates that the eyes move.

Relaxed State

When participants relax and close their eyes, they may produce the *alpha* (α) *rhythm*—large, extremely regular brain waves with a frequency ranging from 7 to 11 Hz. Humans generate alpha rhythms in the region of the visual cortex at the back of the brain, and the rhythms abruptly stop if a relaxed person is disturbed or opens his or her eyes. Not everyone displays alpha rhythms, and some people display them much better than others.

Drowsy State

When a person grows drowsy, the EEG indicates that beta wave activity in the neocortex gives way to slower EEG wave activity. The amplitude of the EEG waves increases and their frequency becomes a slower *theta* (θ) *rhythm* of 4- to 7-Hz waves. Concurrently the EMG remains active, as the muscles have tone, and the EOG indicates that the eyes are not moving.

Sleeping State

As participants enter deeper sleep, they produce yet slower, larger EEG waves called **delta (δ) rhythms**. Delta rhythm has a frequency of 1 to 3 Hz and is associated with the loss of consciousness that characterizes sleep. This stage is sometimes called **slow-wave sleep**. Still, the EMG indicates muscle activity, signifying that the muscles retain tone, although the EOG indicates that the eyes do not move.

REM and NREM Sleep Phases

Sleep consists of periods when a sleeper is relatively still and periods when the mouth, fingers, and toes twitch. This behavior is readily observed in household pets and bed partners. In 1955 Eugene Aserinsky and Nathaniel Kleitman (Lamberg, 2003), working at the University of Chicago, observed that the twitching is periodic and is also associated with rapid eye movements (REM). Other than twitches and eye movements, the EMG indicates that muscles are inactive, a condition termed **atonia** (Greek via Latin, "without tone").

By accumulating and analyzing REM recorded on EEGs, the Chicago investigators were the first to identify **REM sleep**, a fast-wave sleep period whose pattern is reminiscent of a waking EEG (see Dement, 1972). This discovery led to the contemporary naming of two sleep states, REM and NREM. The delta rhythm sleep period, during which the EEG pattern is slow and large and the EOG is inactive, is called **NREM** (for non-REM) **sleep** to distinguish it from REM sleep.

Other Sleep- and Waking-Related Activities

Although electrophysiological measures define the sleep stages, many other bodily and physiological events are associated with waking and sleep stages. Measures of metabolic activity, such as body temperature, generally decline during sleep. Breathing and heart rate provide further insights into waking and sleeping. The sleeper's behavior—tossing and turning, moaning and laughing—also occur during specific sleep stages. Taken together, these measures yield insights into the many causes and symptoms of normal sleep and disturbed sleep.

A Typical Night's Sleep

Figure 13-12A displays the EEG patterns associated with waking, NREM sleep, and REM sleep from a typical night's sleep. NREM sleep is divided into four stages on the basis of EEG recordings. The main change in the progression from stage 1 sleep through stage 4 sleep is the increased size and slowing speed of brain waves.

The designation of these stages assumes that the sleeper moves from relatively shallow sleep in stage 1 to deep sleep in stage 4. Self-reports from participants who are awakened from sleep at different times suggest that stage 4 is the deepest sleep: participants act groggy

delta (δ) rhythm Slow brain wave activity pattern associated with deep sleep.

slow-wave sleep NREM sleep.

atonia Lacking tone; condition of complete muscle inactivity produced by motor neuron inhibition.

REM sleep Fast brain wave pattern displayed by the neocortical EEG record during sleep.

NREM (non-REM) sleep Slow-wave sleep associated with delta rhythms.

(A) EEG

Awake

Stage 1

Stage 2

Stage 3

Stage 4

REM

(B) Sleep

NREM dominant

Time (hr)

1
2
3
4
5
6
7

REM

REM

REM

REM

REM

REM dominant

Typical sleep cycles

FIGURE 13-12 Sleep Recording and Revelations **(A)** EEG patterns associated with waking with the four NREM sleep stages and with REM sleep. **(B)** Over a typical night's sleep, a person undergoes several sleep state changes in roughly 90-minute periods. NREM sleep dominates the early sleep periods, and REM sleep dominates later sleep. The duration of each sleep stage is reflected in the thickness of each bar, which is color-coded to the corresponding stage in part A. The depth of each stage is graphed as the relative length of the bar. Information from D. D. Kelley (1991). Sleep and Dreaming (p. 794). In E. R. Kandel, J. H. Schwartz, & T. M. Jessell (Eds.). *Principles of Neuroscience.* New York: Elsevier.

when awakened from it. As described earlier, REM sleep is distinctive because although a participant is asleep, EEG activity shows a waking pattern.

Figure 13-12B graphs one participant cycling through these stages in the course of a night's sleep. Notice that the depth of sleep changes several times through the four stages of NREM sleep, then entry into REM sleep. This NREM–REM sequence lasts approximately 90 minutes and occurs five times in the course of the participant's sleep period.

The labels indicating REM sleep in Figure 13-12B tell us that the sleep stage durations roughly divide sleep into two parts, the first dominated by NREM sleep, the second dominated by REM sleep. Separate measures of body temperature record that it is lowest (about 1.5°C below a normal temperature of 37.7°C) during the earlier NREM-dominated part of the sleep period and rises during the later REM-dominated part.

Findings from sleep laboratory studies confirm that individuals tend to conform to this sleep pattern with some variability. Studies also confirm that REM sleep takes up substantial time: adults who typically sleep about 8 hours spend about 2 of those hours in REM. A person's duration of REM sleep varies at different times of life and changes dramatically over the life span. Periods of REM sleep are high in infancy; they increase during growth spurts, in conjunction with physical exertion, and during pregnancy. **Figure 13-13** shows that most people sleep less as they grow older. In the first 2 years of life REM sleep makes up nearly half of sleep time, but it declines proportionately until in middle age it constitutes little more than 10 percent of sleep time.

Contrasting NREM Sleep and REM Sleep

Although it seems an inactive period, a remarkable range of activity takes place during sleep. Events associated with NREM sleep and REM sleep, for example, are dramatically different, not only in physiological measures but also in such behavioral events as cognition, memory storage, and sleep disorders.

During NREM sleep body temperature declines, heart rate and blood flow decrease, body weight decreases from water loss in perspiration, and growth hormone levels increase. NREM sleep is also the time when we toss and turn in bed, pull on the covers, and engage in other movements. (For an extreme example see Clinical Focus 13-4, Restless Legs Syndrome.) If we talk in our sleep or grind our teeth, we do so during NREM sleep. If we flail, banging an arm or kicking a foot, we usually do so in NREM sleep. Some people even get up and walk around, and this sleepwalking takes place during NREM sleep. All this activity during our so-called resting state is remarkable! We maintain muscle tone during NREM

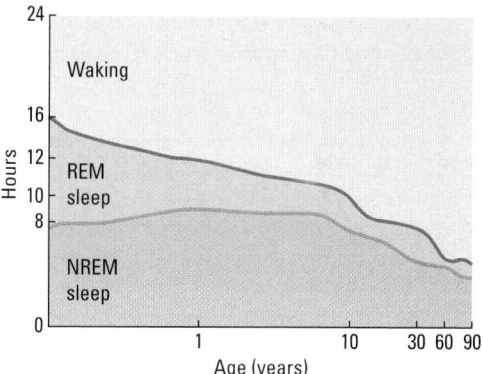

Waking

REM sleep

NREM sleep

Hours

24
16
12
10
8
0

1   10   30 60 90
Age (years)

FIGURE 13-13 Sleeping and Waking over the Life Span The amount of time humans spend sleeping decreases with age. The proportion of REM sleep is especially high in the first few years of life. Information from H. P. Roffward, J. Muzio, & W. C. Dement (1966). Ontogenetic development of the human sleep–dream cycle. *Science, 152,* 604–619.

Restless Legs Syndrome

I've always been a fairly untalented sleeper. Even as a child, it would take me some time to fall asleep, and I would often roll around searching for a comfortable position before going under. But my real difficulties with sleeping did not manifest themselves until early adulthood. . . .

Initially, my symptoms consisted of a mild tingling in my legs. It caused me to be fidgety and made it hard to fall asleep. Eventually, I went through a number of days without much sleep and reached a point where I simply could not function. I went to a doctor who prescribed a small course of sleeping medication (a benzodiazepine). I was able to get good sleep and my sleep cycle seemed to get back on track. Over the next decade I had periodic bouts of tingling in my legs which caused me to be fidgety and interfered with sleep. As time passed, the bouts occurred with increasing frequency and the symptoms became more noticeable and uncomfortable. I would simply suffer through these bouts, sleeping poorly and paying the consequences. . . .

Being a student, I did not have a regular doctor. Unfortunately, most physicians I met did not know about restless legs syndrome, or RLS, and thought I was "drug seeking" or merely stressed out. I received a variety of patronizing responses and found these experiences insulting and demeaning. . . .

When I took my current position, I started seeing a doctor on a regular basis, and experimented with better medications. By this time, my sleep was being seriously affected by RLS. The sensations in my legs were something like a combination of an ache in my muscles (much like one gets after exercising) and an electrical, tingling sensation. They would be briefly relieved with movement, such as stretching, rubbing, contracting my muscles, or changing position, but would return within seconds. In fact, my wife says my cycle is about 13 to 15 seconds between movements. I do this either when awake or during sleep. Trying not to move greatly increases the discomfort—much like trying to not scratch a very bad itch. The symptoms get worse in the evening and at night. Most nights, I have trouble falling asleep. Other nights, I wake up after an hour or so and then have trouble going back under. . . .

I am very up front about the fact that I have RLS. In fact, whenever I teach the topic of sleep and sleep disorders in my brain and behavior classes, I always make some time to talk about my experiences with RLS. Occasionally, students approach me with their own difficulties, and I try to provide them with information and resources. (Stuart Hall, Ph.D., University of Montana)

People with the sleep disorder *restless legs syndrome* (RLS) experience unpleasant sensations in the legs—usually in the calf area but anywhere from thigh to ankle—described as creeping, crawling, tingling, pulling, or pain. One or both legs may be affected; some people also feel the sensations in their arms.

B. W. Hoffmann, U of WI Hospital, Sleep Study Program, Madison, WI/Envision

Many people who display RLS have a related sleep disorder, *periodic limb movement in sleep* (PLMS), characterized by involuntary jerking or bending leg movements that typically occur every 10 to 60 seconds during sleep. Some people make hundreds of such movements per night; they disturb their sleep, can wake themselves, and assuredly annoy bed partners.

RLS may affect as much as 10 percent of the population, more commonly women than men. In mild cases massage, exercise, stretching, and hot baths may be helpful. For more severe cases, patients can restrict their intake of caffeine and take benzodiazepines to help them get to sleep.

RLS is difficult to treat (Wijemanne & Jankovic, 2015). L-Dopa, a drug used to treat Parkinson disease, is a frequent treatment, but no evidence confirms that RLS occurs more frequently in Parkinson patients, whose condition is related to low dopamine function. RLS has been associated with poor iron uptake, especially in the substantia nigra, and some people have been helped by iron supplements. One focus of research into RLS is to improve iron absorption by the brain.

sleep and can sleep in a variety of postures, including standing up, sitting (as might occur in a lecture), or in any of several reclining positions.

REM sleep is no less eventful than NREM sleep. During REM sleep our eyes move; our toes, fingers, and mouths twitch; and males have penile erections. Still, we are paralyzed, as indicated by atonia. This absence of muscle tone stems from motor neuron inhibition by sleep regions of our brainstem. In the sleep lab atonia is recorded on an electromyogram as the absence of muscle activity (see Figure 13-11B).

Posture is not completely lost during NREM sleep. You can get an idea of NREM sleep posture by observing a cat or dog sleeping. During NREM they may be lying down but still have some posture, with the head partly supported in a partially upright position. At the onset of REM sleep the animal usually subsides into a sprawled position as muscle paralysis sets in. **Figure 13-14** illustrates the sleep postures of a horse. Horses can sleep while standing up by locking their knee joints, and they can sleep while lying down with their head held slightly up. At these times they are in NREM sleep. When they are completely sprawled out, they are in REM sleep.

During REM sleep mammals' limbs twitch visibly, and if you look carefully at the face of a dog or cat, you will also see the skin of the snout twitch and the eyes move behind the eyelids. It might seem strange that an animal that is paralyzed can make small twitching movements, but the neural pathways that mediate these twitches obviously are spared the paralysis.

One explanation for the twitching of eyes, face, and distal parts of the limbs is that such movements help to maintain blood flow in those parts of the body. Another explanation is that the brain is developing coordinated movements and tuning the neural circuits that support those movements—an activity especially important to infants, who have not yet developed full motor control (Blumberg, 2015).

An additional change resulting from atonia during REM sleep is that mechanisms that regulate body temperature stop working and body temperature moves toward room temperature. You may wake up from REM sleep feeling cold or hot (or because you are cold or hot), depending on the temperature of the room, because your body has drifted toward room temperature during a REM period.

Dreaming

The most remarkable aspect of REM sleep—dreaming—was discovered by William Dement and Nathaniel Kleitman in 1957 (Dement, 1972). When participants were awakened from REM sleep, they reported that they had been having vivid dreams. In contrast, participants aroused from NREM sleep were much less likely to report that they had been dreaming, and the dreams they did report were much less vivid. The technique of electrical recording from a sleeping participant in a sleep laboratory made it possible to subject dreams and dreaming to experimental analysis. Such studies provided objective answers to interesting questions concerning dreaming. They also raised many more questions, because the electrical events of sleep are complex and difficult to associate with the content of specific dreams (Nir & Tononi, 2010).

How often do we dream? Reports by people on their dreaming behavior once suggested that dreaming was quite variable: some reported that they dreamed frequently and others that they never dreamed. Waking participants up during REM periods showed that everyone dreams, that they dream several times each night, and that dreams last longer as a sleep session progresses. Those who claimed not to dream presumably forgot their dreams. Perhaps people forget their dreams because they do not wake up during a dream or immediately afterward, which allows subsequent NREM sleep activity to erase the memory of the dream. Perhaps, too, the neural systems that store our daily memories are inactive during NREM sleep.

How long do dreams last? Common wisdom once suggested that dreams last but an instant. By waking people up at different intervals after the onset of REM sleep and matching the reported dream content to the previous duration of REM sleep, however, researchers demonstrated that dreams appear to take place in real time. An action that a person performs in a dream lasts about as long as it would take to perform while awake. It is likely that time shrinking is a product of remembering a dream, just as time shrinking is a feature of our recall of other memories.

What We Dream About

Studying dreaming in a sleep laboratory allows researchers to study other questions that have always intrigued people: Why do we dream? What do we dream about? What do dreams mean?

FIGURE 13-14 Nap Time Horses usually seek open, sunny areas for a brief sleep. I. Q. W.'s horse Lady Jones illustrates three sleep postures. Top: NREM sleep, standing with legs locked and head down. Center: NREM sleep, lying down with head up. Bottom: REM sleep, in which all postural and muscle tone is lost.

Courtesy of Ian Whishaw

Figure 16-1 presents a contemporary take on Freud's model of the mind.

Past explanations of dreaming have ranged from messages from the gods to indigestion. The first modern treatment of dreams was described by the founder of psychoanalysis, Sigmund Freud, in *The Interpretation of Dreams*, published in 1900. Freud reviewed the early literature on dreams, described a methodology for studying them, and provided a theory to explain their meaning. We briefly consider Freud's theory because it remains popular in psychoanalysis and in the arts and is representative of other psychoanalytical theories of dreams.

Freud suggested that the function of dreams is the symbolic fulfillment of unconscious wishes. His theory of personality is that people have both a conscious and an unconscious. Freud proposed that the unconscious contains unacknowledged desires and wishes that are sexual. He further proposed that dreams have two levels of meaning. The *manifest content* of a dream is a series of often-bizarre, loosely connected images and actions. The *latent content* of the dream contains its true meaning. Freud's images called *phallic symbols* reflect sexual events. As interpreted by a psychoanalyst, the symbolic events of a dream provide a coherent account of the dreamer's unconscious wishes—for Freud, the wishes were related to sex.

Freud provided a method for interpreting manifest symbols and reconstructing the latent content of dreams. For example, he pointed out that a dream usually begins with an incident from the previous day, incorporates childhood experiences, and includes ongoing unfulfilled wishes. He also identified several types of dreams, such as those that deal with childhood events, anxiety, and wish fulfillment. The latent content of the dream was important to Freud and other psychoanalysts in clinical practice because interpretation of dreams was proposed to offer insight into a patient's problems.

Other psychoanalysts, unhappy with Freud's emphasis on sex, developed their own methods of interpretation. The psychoanalyst Carl Jung, a contemporary of Freud, proposed that dream symbolism signifies distant human memories encoded in the brain but long since lost to conscious awareness. Jung proposed that dreams allow the dreamer to relive the history of the human race—our "collective unconscious." As more theories of dream interpretation developed, their central weakness became apparent: it was impossible to know which interpretation was correct.

The dream research of Freud and his contemporaries was also impeded by their reliance on a subject's memory of a dream and by the fact that many subjects were patients. This situation unquestionably resulted in the selection of the unusual by both the patient and the analyst. Now researchers study dreams more objectively by waking participants and questioning them.

Experimental analysis indicates that most dreams are related to events that happened quite recently and concern ongoing problems. Colors of objects, symbols, and emotional content most often relate to events taking place in a person's recent waking period. Calvin Hall and his colleagues (1982) documented more than 10,000 dreams of healthy people and found that more than 64 percent are associated with sadness, anxiety, or anger. Only about 18 percent are happy. Hostile acts against the dreamer outnumber friendly acts by more than two to one. Surprisingly, in regard to Freud's theory, only about 1 percent of dreams include sexual feelings or acts.

Contemporary researchers continue to attempt to interpret dream content. The two approaches that follow are polar: one sees no meaning in dreams, and the other sees the content of dreams as reflecting biologically adaptive coping mechanisms. The first approach is bottom-up: the person has a dream, and then either the dreamer or a dream interpreter analyzes it. The second approach is top-down: the dreamer creates the dream (Foulkes & Domhoff, 2014).

Dreams as Meaningless Brain Activity

In his bottom-up approach, J. Allan Hobson (2004) proposed the *activation–synthesis hypothesis*. During a dream the cortex is bombarded by signals from the brainstem, and these signals produce the pattern of waking (or activated) EEG. The cortex in response to this excitation generates images, actions, and emotion from personal memory stores. In the absence of external verification these dream events are fragmented and bizarre and reveal nothing more than that the cortex has been activated.

Furthermore, Hobson proposes, on the basis of PET imaging, that part of the frontal cortex is less active in dreaming than in waking. The frontal cortex controls working memory for recent events and attention. The dreamer thus cannot remember and link dream events as they take place, because monitoring by the frontal cortex is required for these functions. On waking, the dreamer may attempt to come up with a story line for these fragmented meaningless images.

In Hobson's hypothesis dreams are personal in that memories and experiences are activated but have no meaning. So the following dream, for example, with its bizarre delusional and fragmented elements, represents images synthesized to accompany brain activation. Any apparent meaning is invented after the fact, in this case by the middle-aged dreamer recounting it.

> I found myself walking in a jungle. Everything was green and fresh and I felt refreshed and content. After some time I encountered a girl whom I did not know. The most remarkable thing about her was her eyes, which had an almost gold color. I was really struck by her eyes not only because of their unique color but also because of their expression. I tried to make out other details of her face and body but her eyes were so dominating that was all I could see. Eventually, however, I noticed that she was dressed in a white robe and was standing very still with her hands at her side. I then noticed that she was in a compound with wire around it. I became concerned that she was a prisoner. Soon, I noticed other people dressed in white robes and they were also standing still or walking slowly without swinging their arms. It was really apparent that they were all prisoners. At this time I was standing by the fence that enclosed them, and I was starting to feel more concerned. Suddenly it dawned on me that I was in the compound and when I looked down at myself I found that I was dressed in a white robe as well. I remember that I suddenly became quite frightened and woke up when I realized that I was exactly like everyone else. The reason that I remembered this dream is the very striking way in which my emotions seemed to be going from contentment, to concern, to fear as the dream progressed. I think that this dream reflected my desire in the 1970s to maintain my individuality. (Recounted by A. W.)

Dreams as a Coping Strategy

Anttio Revonsuo of Finland uses content analysis to argue that dreams are biologically adaptive in that they lead to enhanced coping strategies for threatening life events (Valli & Revonsuo, 2009). The evolutionary aspect of this top-down approach, or *coping hypothesis*, is that enhanced performance is especially important for people whose environment typically includes dangerous events that constitute extreme threats to reproductive success. Revonsuo notes that dreams are highly organized and significantly biased toward threatening images, as was A. W.'s dream. People seldom dream about reading, writing, and calculating even if these behaviors occupy much of their day.

Dream threats are the same events that are threatening in waking life (**Figure 13-15**). For example, animals and strange men who could be characterized as enemies figure

Chapter 14 describes the extent of frontal cortex involvement in memory. Attention is the topic of Section 15-2.

FIGURE 13-15 Dream Content
Terrifying visions that may persist even after awakening from a frightening dream as represented in *The Night,* by Swiss painter Ferdinand Hodler. *The Night,* by Ferdinand Hodler (1853–1918). Oil on canvas 116 × 299 cm. Kunstmuseum, Bern, Switzerland.

prominently in dreams. Dream content incorporates the current emotional problems of the dreamer and leads to improvements in and adjustments to life problems.

In contrast with the threat interpretation of dreams and from their own analysis of dream content, Malcolm-Smith and her coworkers (2012) report that approach behavior occurs more frequently in dreams than does avoidance behavior. They therefore suggest that reward-seeking behavior is as likely to represent a dream's latent content as avoidance behavior is.

An extension of the top-down approach to dream interpretation contends that people are problem solvers when awake, and problem solving continues during sleep (Edwards et al., 2013). Have you ever been advised to sleep on it? Did that prove to be good advice?

Part of the challenge in studying dreams is that they occur throughout our sleep–waking behavior. Dreams occur during NREM sleep but not as vividly as in REM sleep. We can have dreamlike experiences just as we drop off to sleep, as our ongoing thoughts seem to disintegrate into hallucinations. Sometimes we are aware of our dreams as we dream, a phenomenon called *lucid dreaming*. People who have vivid dreamlike experiences when awake are said to be hallucinating. And of course we daydream when awake. Eric Klinger (1990) suggests that daydreams are ordinary and often fun, with little of the turmoil of REM dreams, and so seem the true opposite of night dreams.

Much about dreams is not understood. Very young children spend a lot of time in REM sleep yet do not report complex dreams filled with emotion and conflict. Children may experience brief frightening dreams called *night terrors* during NREM sleep. Night terrors can be so vivid that the child continues to experience the dream and the fear after awaking. A 4-year-old child suddenly woke up screaming that she was covered in ants. It took hours for her father to convince her that her experience was not real and that she could go back to bed. Only reassurance from a sleep expert later convinced the father that nothing was amiss with his daughter and that night terrors are common among young children (Carter et al., 2014).

(13-3) REVIEW

Sleep Stages and Dreaming

Before you continue, check your understanding.

1. Sleep consists of two phases: _____, which stands for _____, and _____, which stands for _____.

2. REM sleep is characterized by eye movement, as recorded by the _____; atonia, recorded by the _____; and waking activity, recorded by the _____.

3. Sleepers experience about _____ REM sleep periods each night, with each period _____ as sleep progresses.

4. Evidence from sleep lab analysis suggests that _____ dreams and that dreams take place in _____.

5. What major factor makes interpreting dreams difficult?

Answers appear at the back of the book.

For additional study tools, visit 🧠 **LaunchPad:**
www.macmillanhighered.com/launchpad/kolb5e

(13-4) What Does Sleep Accomplish?

basic rest–activity cycle (BRAC)
Recurring cycle of temporal packets, about 90-minute periods in humans, during which an animal's level of arousal waxes and wanes.

Sleep is not a passive process that results from a decrease in sensory stimulation. Findings from sensory deprivation research reveal that when participants are isolated in quiet bedrooms, they spend less time asleep, not more. These results do not support the idea that sleep sets in for lack of anything else to do. Here we consider three contemporary explanations for sleep: as adaptive, as restorative, and as supportive of memory.

Sleep As a Biological Adaptation

Many lines of evidence argue that sleep is a biologically adaptive behavior influenced by the ways a species has evolved to interact with its environment:

- Sleep serves as an energy-conserving strategy for coping with times when food is scarce. Each animal species gathers food at optimal times and conserves energy the rest of the time. If the food that a species eats has a high nutrient value, the species can spend less time foraging and more time sleeping.

- Whether a species is predator or prey influences its sleep behavior. A predator can sleep at its ease; the prey's sleep time is reduced because it must remain alert and ready to fight or flee at unpredictable times (**Figure 13-16**).

- Strictly nocturnal or diurnal animals are likely to sleep when they cannot travel easily. Dement proposed this colloquially: "We sleep to keep from bumping into things in the dark."

Much about animals' sleep patterns are consistent with the adaptive explanation. **Figure 13-17** charts the average sleep time of some common mammals. Herbivores, including donkeys, horses, and cows, spend a long time collecting enough food to sustain themselves. Relatively short sleep time for them is adaptive. Because they are also prey, not sleeping much is adaptive, as they watch for predators. Carnivores, including domestic cats and dogs, eat nutrient-rich foods and usually consume most of a day's or even a week's food at a single meal. Because they do not need to eat constantly and because by resting they can conserve energy, and because they are not at great risk of predation, a great deal of sleep is adaptive.

The behavior of some animals does appear odd, so understanding any animal's sleep behavior requires understanding its natural history. Opossums, which spend much of their time asleep, may have specialized in energy conservation as a survival strategy. We humans are average among species in our sleep time. As we are omnivores, not subject to overwhelming predation, our sleep is intermediate between that of herbivores and carnivores.

Sleep can contribute to energy conservation. During sleep, energy is not being expended in moving the body or supporting its posture. The brain is a major energy user, so switching off the brain during sleep, especially NREM sleep, conserves energy. The decline in body temperature during sleep is an adaptive energy-conserving mechanism: it decreases the body's metabolism, as exemplified by animals that display extreme decreases in body temperature characteristic of hibernation.

A good explanation of sleep must account not only for sleep but also for NREM and REM sleep. Before the discovery of REM sleep, Kleitman suggested that animals have a **basic rest–activity cycle** (BRAC) that for humans lasts about 90 minutes (see Dement, 1972). Kleitman based his hypothesis on the observation that human infants have frequent feeding periods between which they sleep.

As illustrated in **Figure 13-18**, the behavior of adult humans does suggest that activity and rest are organized into 90-minute temporal packets. School classes, work periods, exercise sessions, mealtimes, coffee breaks, and snack times appear to be divided into intervals of 90 minutes or so. The later discovery that REM sleep occurs at intervals of about 90 minutes suggests that it too can be considered a continuation into sleep of the 90-minute BRAC cycle. This hypothesis assumes that periods of eating are periods of high brain activity, just as are periods of REM.

Kleitman proposed that the BRAC rhythm is so fundamental that it cannot be turned off. Accordingly, for a night's sleep to be uninterrupted by periodic waking (and perhaps snacking), the body is paralyzed and only the brain is active. An analogy: rather than turning off your car's engine when you're stopped at a red light, you apply the brakes to keep the idling car from moving. For REM sleep the atonia that paralyzes movement is the brake.

FIGURE 13-16 Do Not Disturb Biological theories of sleep suggest that it is an energy-conserving strategy that serves other functions as well, such as staying safe through the night.

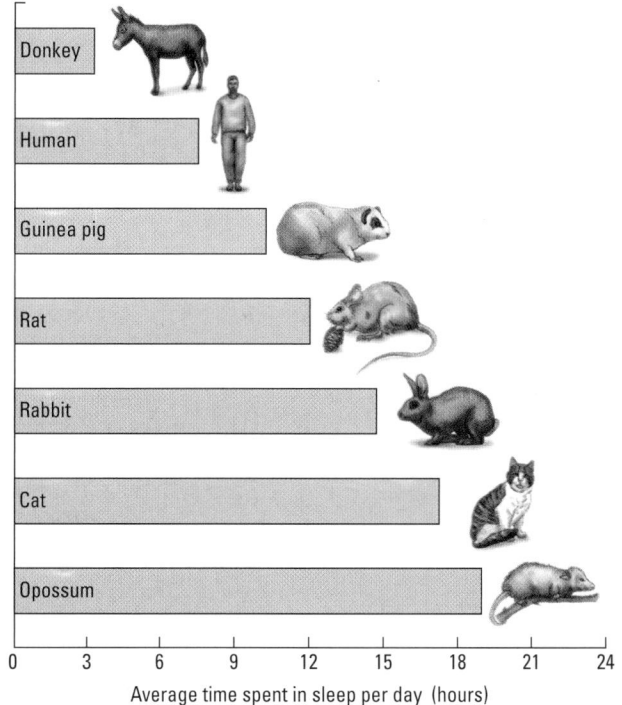

FIGURE 13-17 Average Sleep Time Sleep time is affected both by the amount of time species require to obtain food and by the risk of predation.

FIGURE 13-18 Behavioral Rhythms Our behavior is dominated by a basic rest-activity cycle (red) through which our activity levels change in the course of the day and by an NREM–REM sleep cycle (purple) during the night.

Sleep   Breakfast   Coffee   Lunch   Snack   Dinner   Snack   Sleep
         8:00 A.M.   10:00 A.M.   12:00 P.M.   3:00 P.M.   5:00 P.M.   7:00 P.M.

Sleep as a Restorative Process

In Macbeth's description of sleep Shakespeare illustrates in words the idea that sleep has restorative properties:

> Sleep that knits up the ravell'd sleave of care,
> The death of each day's life, sore labour's bath,
> Balm of hurt minds, great nature's second course,
> Chief nourisher in life's feast. —Act II, scene 2

Sleep Deprivation Studies

We can understand the idea of sleep as a restorative from our personal perspective. Toward the end of the day we grow tired, and when we awaken from sleep, we are refreshed. If we do not get enough sleep, we become irritable. One hypothesis of sleep as restorative proposes that the chemical events that provide energy to cells are reduced during waking and replenished during sleep.

Even so, fatigue and alertness may simply be aspects of the circadian rhythm and have nothing at all to do with wear and tear on the body or depletion of its essential resources. To evaluate whether sleep is essential for bodily processes, investigators have conducted sleep deprivation studies. These studies have not clearly identified any essential function for sleep but rather point to multiple physiological and cognitive functions altered by various degrees of sleep deprivation (Elliott et al., 2014).

Dement participated as an observer in one case study on sleep deprivation that illustrates this point. In 1965, as part of a science fair project, a high school student named Randy Gardner planned to break the world record of 260 hours (almost 11 days) of consecutive wakefulness with the help of two classmates who would keep him awake. Gardner did break the record, then slept for 14 hours and reported no ill effects. Given concerns about the deleterious effects that sleep deprivation has on health, *Guinness World Records* no longer records wakefulness records.

Dement reported that Gardner hallucinated and had cognitive and memory lapses during his period of sleep deprivation. These negative effects did not last. Reviews of sleep deprivation research are consistent in concluding that at least limited periods of sleep deprivation produce no marked physiological alterations.

Sleep deprivation does not seem to have adverse physiological consequences, but it is associated with poor cognitive performance. Performance on tasks that require attention declines as a function of hours of sleep deprivation. Irregular sleep can contribute to metabolic syndrome, described in Clinical Focus 13-1. Finally, sleep deprivation figures in accidents at work and on the road. The sleep deprivation deficit does not manifest itself in an inability to do a task, because sleep-deprived participants can perform even very complex tasks; rather the deficit is in maintaining sustained attention.

A confounding factor in evaluating sleep-deprived participants is that they take **microsleeps**, brief sleep periods lasting up to a few seconds. During microsleep, participants may remain sitting or standing, but their eyelids droop briefly and they become less responsive to external stimuli. If you have driven a car while tired, you may have had a microsleep and awakened just in time to prevent yourself from driving off the road—or worse.

microsleep Brief sleep period lasting a second or so.

REM Sleep Deprivation

Some studies have focused on the selective benefits of REM sleep. To deprive a participant of REM sleep, researchers allow participants to sleep but awaken them as REM sleep begins. REM-sleep deprivation has two effects:

1. Participants show an increased tendency to enter REM sleep in subsequent sleep sessions, so awakenings must become more and more frequent.

2. After REM deprivation, participants experience REM rebound, showing more than the usual amount of REM sleep in the first available sleep session.

Because most sleep studies are of relatively brief duration, capturing potential long-term physiological changes that may take place during or after sleep deprivation remains elusive. The consequences of sleep deprivation may become apparent only some time after an experimental manipulation has taken place. Furthermore, gross assessment of behavior may be less adequate for documenting sleep deprivation's effects than more focal physiological and behavioral assessments. For example, some evidence suggests that REM sleep deprivation weakens the immune system, decreasing resistance to infections and other disease (Lungato et al., 2015). Other evidence suggests that REM sleep deprivation reduces neurogenesis, especially in the hippocampus, thus impairing memory processes and weakening resistance to stress (Kreutzmann et al., 2015).

Two kinds of observations, however, argue against effects of prolonged or even complete REM sleep deprivation. Virtually all antidepressant drugs, including MAO inhibitors, tricyclic antidepressants, and SSRIs, suppress REM sleep either partly or completely. The clinical effectiveness of these drugs may in fact derive from their REM-suppressant effects (Wilson & Argyropoulos, 2005). Nevertheless, about 6 percent of people on antidepressants display *REM sleep behavioral disorder*, characterized by agitated movements, as if the sleeper were acting out dreams (see Section 13-6). This disorder argues against the idea that REM suppression by antidepressant drugs is complete (Postuma et al., 2013).

Section 6-2 reviews the full spectrum of antidepressant drugs.

In several reported cases lower-brainstem damage has resulted in a complete loss of REM sleep. For example, patients with brainstem lesions reportedly remained ambulatory and verbally communicative, but their REM was abolished. They were reported to live quite satisfactorily without REM sleep (Osorio & Daroff, 1980).

Sleep and Memory Storage

The suggestion that sleep plays a role in memory dates back over a century, and in the interval a lot has changed with respect to our understanding of memory and of sleep. Investigators now know of two general categories of memory. *Episodic memory* includes conscious information such as our autobiographical memories and knowledge of facts. *Implicit memory* includes unconscious processes such as motor skills learning. Within these categories specific types of memory include spatial, emotional, verbal, even immune system memory. Investigators also know that during the various stages of sleep many EEG and neuronal events, biochemical events, and genetic events take place. Thus the central challenge for sleep-related memory research lies in associating the complexity of memory with the complexity of brain metabolic and genetic events (Rasch and Born, 2013).

Section 14-1 expands on the workings of explicit and implicit memory systems.

Investigators also know that storing memories takes time. Memory is proposed to have at least three phases: labile, consolidation (storage), and recall. During the initial *labile phase*, as a memory is encoded, it is fragile and must compete with existing memories and the addition of new memories. The *consolidation phase* forges a relatively permanent representation of the memory; it depends upon biochemical and genetic activity that underlie structural changes in the nervous system. The *recall phase* puts the memory to work at some future time and also integrates it into existing memory stores.

Research on the role of sleep in memory focuses on the latter two processes, consolidation and recall, and is conducted within the framework of three theories: multiple process,

place cell Hippocampal neuron maximally responsive to specific locations in the world.

Figure 7-8 shows the classes of place cells and their directional selectivity.

sequential process, and storage process. *Multiple process* theories propose that different kinds of memory are stored during different sleep states. *Sequential process* theories propose that memory is manipulated in different ways during different sleep states. For example, one sleep state erases older competing memories, while another sleep state stores the new memories. *Storage process* theories propose that brain regions that handle different kinds of memory during waking continue to do so during sleep. The advantage is that sleep offers a state relatively free from the competition of new waking experiences.

Each theory of memory and sleep has generated volumes, but the remainder of this section focuses on experimental demonstrations of sleep's role in the general memory categories of explicit and implicit memory storage during sleep.

NREM Sleep and Explicit Memory

Gerrard and colleagues (2008) used a method which had found that many hippocampal cells fire when a rat is in a certain location in an environment. These **place cells** are relatively inactive until the rat passes through that place again. Recordings from as many as 100 cells at the same time in three conditions—during NREM sleep, during a food search task, and during NREM sleep after a food search—show that during the food search the activity of some place cells correlates. During the rats' subsequent periods of NREM sleep the correlations recur (**Figure 13-19**).

This result suggests that the memory of the previous food-searching experience is being replayed and thus stored during NREM sleep. In pursuing the idea that memory for places is stored during sleep, one research group identified neuronal firing of hippocampal cells in awake animals in relation to a specific location in a maze. Then during sleep they provided rewarding brain stimulation whenever that neuronal firing pattern occurred. In a subsequent test in the maze, the reinforced animals showed a preference for the target location. The experiments had produced an episodic memory for that place as the animals slept (de Lavilléon et al., 2015).

REM Sleep and Implicit Memory

To determine whether humans' dreams are related to memory, Pierre Maquet and his coworkers in Belgium (2000) trained participants on a serial reaction task. The investigators observed regional blood flow in the brain with PET scans during training and during REM sleep on the subsequent night. The participants faced a computer screen displaying six positional markers and were instructed to push one of six keys when a corresponding positional marker was illuminated. They did not know that the illumination sequence was predetermined. This exemplifies an implicit memory task in which a motor skill is mastered.

Consequently, as training progressed, the participants indicated that they were learning by the fact that their reaction time improved during trials in which one positional marker was correlated with a preceding marker. On PET scan measures of brain activation, a similar pattern of neocortical activation appeared during task acquisition and during REM sleep (**Figure 13-20**). On the basis of this result Maquet and coworkers suggest first that the participants were dreaming about their learning experience and second that replay during REM

FIGURE 13-19 Neural Replay? Hippocampal cell activity suggests that rats dream about their experiences. Dots on the periphery of the circles represent the activity of 42 hippocampal cells recorded at the same time during (left) NREM sleep before a food-searching task, (center) the food-searching task, and (right) NREM sleep after the task. No strong correlations among cells emerged during the NREM sleep that preceded the food search, but correlations were strong among cells during the food search and during the subsequent slow-wave sleep.

Information from M. A. Wilson & B. L. McNaughton (1994). Reactivation of hippocampal ensemble memories during sleep. *Science, 165,* p. 678.

Dots represent individual hippocampal cells.

Red lines connecting dots represent cells that fire at the same time. The thicker the line, the higher the correlation of cell activity.

NREM sleep before food search

Search for food

NREM sleep after food search

The correlation of cell activity during sleep is similar to that during searches for food when previously awake.

Reaction-time task

Participants are trained on a reaction-time task, and brain activity is recorded with PET.

REM sleep that night

Participants display a similar pattern of brain activity during subsequent REM sleep.

FIGURE 13-20 Do We Store Implicit Memories During REM Sleep? Information from P. Maquet, S. Laureys, P. Peigneux, S. Fuchs, C. Petiau, et al. (2000). Experience-dependent changes in cerebral activation during human REM sleep. *Nature Neuroscience, 3,* p. 832.

strengthened the task memory. Research in which participants are given a language task that contains hidden rules finds that sleep also strengthens this implicit rule learning (Batterink et al., 2014). Thus, much rule learning in both motor and cognitive domains likely is strengthened during sleep, including REM sleep.

Storing Memories During Sleep

Although evidence shows that memory strengthens during sleep, less clear is whether the neural and molecular changes that support sleep memory storage are similar or different from those that store memory during wakefulness. Researchers are addressing this question in innovative animal models of sleep. Nelini and coworkers (2012) studied spatial memory formation in chicks, a species in which such memories are stored mainly in the right hemisphere. Chickens, like many bird species, alternate sleep in each hemisphere, and the researchers showed that after a learning experience, the right hemisphere displayed more sleep than did the left hemisphere. Birds' selectivity in hemispheric sleep opens up the possibility of comparing plastic changes between the hemispheres as a way of understanding genetic, biochemical, and plastic changes associated with memory formation.

The fruit fly *Drosophila* also offers insights into the effects of sleep on memory and on plasticity (Dissel et al., 2015). These researchers identified a variety of mutations that disrupt memory formation and plasticity and found that the memory disruptions decrease after sleep. Slight increases in ambient temperature put one mutant strain of fly to sleep, which greatly aided the research. For this strain a learning task can be followed by various sleep doses induced by manipulating room temperature. A finding of this research is that the same group of neurons that enhance memory are those that induce sleep. This finding suggests a causal link between memory and sleep: *Drosophila* sleeps to remember! Generalizing this finding to us humans suggests that learning will make us tired.

13-4 REVIEW

What Does Sleep Accomplish?

Before you continue, check your understanding.

1. Sleep is proposed to occur as a(n) _____ adaption, as a(n) _____ process, or as an aid in storing _____.

2. _____ memory is associated with NREM sleep, and _____ memory is associated with REM sleep.

3. In rats performing a spatial task, correlations develop between _____ firing in the hippocampus that is then replayed in _____ sleep.

4. When you are sleep-deprived, you are more likely to slip into a _____ for a few seconds.

5. Describe a difficulty in relating memory formation to sleep.

Answers appear at the back of the book.

For additional study tools, visit 🌐 LaunchPad:
www.macmillanhighered.com/launchpad/kolb5e

<u>13-5</u> Neural Bases of Sleep

The idea that the brain contains a sleep-inducing substance has long been popular and is reinforced by the fact that a variety of chemical agents induce sleep. Such substances include sedative-hypnotics and morphine. Our understanding of circadian rhythms suggests, however, that changes in many neurochemicals and hormones and the metabolic activity of most of the body's cells produce our sleep–waking cycles.

The hormone melatonin, secreted from the pineal gland during the dark phase of the light–dark cycle, causes sleepiness. A synthetic form can be taken as a sleep aid, so melatonin might be thought to be the sleep-producing substance. But sleep survives the removal of the pineal gland. Thus melatonin and many other chemical substances may only contribute to sleep, not cause it (see Research Focus 13-3).

Some observations suggest that it is not a circulating bloodstream compound that produces sleep. In dolphins and birds only one brain hemisphere sleeps at a time. This ability presumably allows an animal's other hemisphere to remain behaviorally alert. More important, it suggests that sleep is produced by the action of some brain region, and in these species, within each hemisphere.

In this section we consider the neural mechanisms that regulate sleep. First we examine evidence that the activity of a slave oscillator of the suprachiasmatic nucleus produces sleep (see Figure 13-8). Second we look at evidence that a number of brainstem nuclei control the various events associated with sleep, including those associated with REM and NREM sleep.

Reticular Activating System and Sleep

A pioneering experiment by Giuseppe Moruzzi and Horace Magoun (1949) began to answer the question of which brain areas regulate sleep. The experimenters were recording the cortical EEG from anesthetized cats while electrically stimulating the cats' brainstem. They were surprised to find that, in response to the electrical stimulation the large, slow delta EEG typical of anesthesia is replaced by the low-voltage fast-wave beta EEG typical of waking.

The beta EEG activity outlasted the stimulation period, demonstrating that the effect was not simply due to the online activity of neurons in the region of the stimulating electrode but could be maintained by these neurons independent of the stimulation. During the "waking period" the anesthetized cat did not become behaviorally aroused, but its cortical EEG appeared to indicate that it was awake. In a sleeping cat the same stimulation did lead to waking.

Subsequent experiments show that a waking EEG and waking behavior can be induced from a large neural area running through the center of the brainstem. Anatomically this area is composed of a mixture of cell nuclei and nerve fibers that form a *reticulum*. Moruzzi and Magoun named this brainstem area the **reticular activating system** (RAS) and proposed that it is responsible for sleep–waking behavior. **Figure 13-21** diagrams the location of the RAS.

If someone disturbs you when you are asleep, you usually wake up. To explain that their experimentally induced effect did not result simply from sensory stimulation, Moruzzi and Magoun cut the brainstem just behind the RAS, severing its incoming sensory pathways. RAS stimulation still produced a desynchronized EEG. Thus, the RAS is the source of waking, and sensory stimulation produces waking because it activates RAS neurons.

The idea that the brainstem participates in waking behavior helps to explain why brainstem damage can result in **coma**, a prolonged state of deep unconsciousness resembling sleep. In one well-publicized case, after taking a minor tranquilizer and having a few drinks at a birthday party, a 21-year-old woman named Karen Ann Quinlan sustained RAS damage that left her comatose (Quinlan & Quinlan, 1977). She was hospitalized, placed on a respirator to support breathing, and fed by tubes. Her family fought a protracted legal battle to have her removed from life support, a battle they finally won before the Supreme Court of New Jersey. Even after she was removed from life support, however, Karen Ann lived for 10 more years in a perpetual coma.

---

reticular activating system (RAS) Large reticulum (mixture of cell nuclei and nerve fibers) that runs through the center of the brainstem; associated with sleep–wake behavior and behavioral arousal; also called the *reticular formation.*

coma Prolonged state of deep unconsciousness resembling sleep.

peribrachial area Cholinergic nucleus in the dorsal brainstem having a role in REM sleep behaviors; projects to medial pontine reticular formation.

medial pontine reticular formation (MPRF) Nucleus in the pons participating in REM sleep.

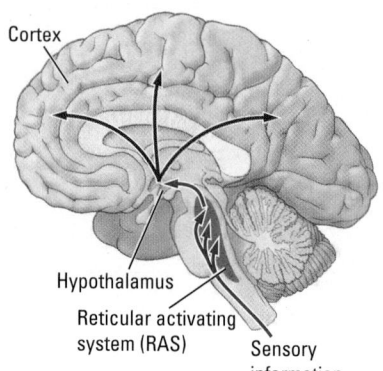

FIGURE 13-21 Sleep—Wake Controller The reticular activating system, a region at the center of the brainstem, contains a mixture of cell bodies and fiber pathways. RAS stimulation produces a waking EEG, whereas damaging it produces a slow-wave sleeplike EEG.

Neural Basis of EEG Changes Associated with Waking

Research built on those pioneering studies of the RAS has since revealed that many neural systems in the brainstem play a role in sleeping and waking behavior. Case Vanderwolf and his coworkers (Vanderwolf, 2002) showed that at least two brainstem systems influence waking EEG. **Figure 13-22** illustrates their locations in the rat brain.

The basal forebrain contains large cholinergic cells. These neurons secrete acetylcholine (ACh) from their terminals onto cortical neurons to stimulate a waking EEG (beta rhythm). The midbrain structure the median raphe contains serotonin (5-HT) neurons whose axons also project diffusely to the cortex, where they also stimulate cortical cells to produce a waking EEG.

Although the two pathways produce similar patterns of waking EEG activity, their relations to behavior differ. If the activity of the cholinergic projection is blocked by drugs or by lesions to the cells of the basal forebrain, the waking EEG normally recorded from an immobile rat is replaced by EEG activity resembling that of NREM sleep. Only if the rat walks or is otherwise active is a waking EEG obtained from the cortex. These findings, graphed in Figure 13-22, suggest that the cholinergic EEG is responsible for waking associated with being alert yet still, whereas the serotonergic activation is responsible for the waking EEG associated with movement.

Neither the basal forebrain system nor the median raphe system is responsible for behavior. In fact, if both structures are pharmacologically or surgically destroyed, a rat can still stand and walk around. Its EEG, however, permanently resembles that of a sleeping animal.

As long as one activating system is producing a waking EEG, rats can learn simple tasks. If both systems are destroyed, an animal, although still able to walk around, is no longer able to learn or display intelligent behavior. In a sense the cortex is like a house in which the lights are powered by two separate sources: both must fail for the house to be left in darkness, but if at least one source is operating, the lights stay on.

These experimental results suggest that the RAS produces its arousal effects by influencing activity in these two pathways, which then produce EEG events associated with waking. In humans the basal forebrain and median raphe likely produce the same two desynchronized EEG patterns that they produce in rats. Consequently, when we are alert and still, cholinergic neurons are active; when we move, serotonin neurons also are active.

Perhaps when you have felt sleepy, say in a class or behind the wheel of a car, you may have been able to wake yourself up by moving—shaking your head or stretching. Presumably, while sitting still, your arousal level decreased as your cholinergic neurons became inactive. When you moved, activating your serotonergic neurons restored your arousal level. When we enter sleep, both cholinergic and serotonergic neurons become less active, allowing slow waves to emanate from the cortex.

Neural Basis of REM Sleep

Barbara Jones (1993) and her colleagues described a group of cholinergic neurons known as the **peribrachial area** that contributes to REM sleep. This area is located in the dorsal brainstem just anterior to the cerebellum (**Figure 13-23**). Jones selectively destroyed peribrachial cells by spraying them with the neurotoxin kainic acid. She found that REM sleep was drastically reduced. This result suggests that the peribrachial area contributes to REM sleep and REM-related behaviors.

The peribrachial area extends into a more ventrally located nucleus called the **medial pontine reticular formation** (MPRF), shown in Figure 13-23. Lesions of the MPRF also abolish REM sleep, and injections of cholinergic agonists (drugs that act like ACh) into

Figure 5-17 summarizes the major neural activating systems and their functions.

FIGURE 13-22 Brain Activators Basal forebrain ACh neurons produce an activated EEG pattern when a rat is alert but immobile. The 5-HT raphe neurons of the midbrain produce an activated EEG pattern when the rat moves.

FIGURE 13-23 Brainstem Nuclei Responsible for REM Sleep Damage to either the peribrachial area or the medial pontine formation reduces or abolishes REM sleep.

Figure 6-5 shows agonist action at the ACh synapse.

FIGURE 13-24 Neural Control of REM Sleep

this region induce REM sleep. If both the peribrachial area and the MPRF take part in producing REM sleep, how do other events related to REM sleep, including a waking EEG, rapid eye movements (REM), and atonia, take place in the absence of muscle tone? **Figure 13-24** charts an explanation showing how other REM-related activities are induced:

- The peribrachial area initiates REM sleep by activating the medial pontine reticular formation.

- The MPRF sends projections to excite basal forebrain cholinergic neurons, resulting in an activated EEG recorded from the cortex.

- The MPRF also excites brainstem motor nuclei to produce rapid eye movements and other twitches.

- The atonia of REM sleep is produced by the MPRF through a pathway that sends input to the subcoerulear nucleus located just behind it.

- The subcoerulear nucleus excites the magnocellular nucleus of the medulla, which sends projections to the spinal motor neurons to inhibit them so that paralysis is achieved during the REM sleep period.

In support of such a neural arrangement French researcher Michel Jouvet (1972) observed that cats with lesions in the subcoerulear nucleus display a remarkable behavior when they enter REM sleep. Rather than stretching out in the atonia that typically accompanies REM sleep, the cats he was studying stood up, looked around, and made movements of catching an imaginary mouse or running from an imaginary threat. Apparently if cats with damage to this brain region dream about catching mice or escaping from a threat, they are now acting out their dreams. We revisit Jouvet's phenomenon in the next section, describing sleep disorders.

13-5 REVIEW

Neural Bases of Sleep

Before you continue, check your understanding.

1. The _____ in the central region of the brainstem is responsible for producing _____ sleep.

2. Loss of the RAS produces _____.

3. The peribrachial area and the MPRF, through activating pathways to the neocortex and spinal cord, are responsible for producing events associated with _____.

4. Cats with lesions to the _____ nucleus act out their dreams.

5. If you nod off to sleep at an inconvenient time, why does moving awaken you?

Answers appear at the back of the book.

For additional study tools, visit 🅼 **LaunchPad**:
www.macmillanhighered.com/launchpad/kolb5e

13-6 Sleep Disorders

Occasional sleep disturbances are annoying and may impair performance the following day. About 15 percent of people complain of ongoing sleep problems; an additional 20 percent complain of occasional sleep problems. As people age, the incidence of complaints increases.

In the extreme, a rare genetic condition, *fatal familial insomnia*, causes individuals to stop sleeping altogether. Their insomnia contributes to death after a number of months without sleep. *Prions* (misfolded proteins) are proposed to cause the condition. A proposed treatment is doxycycline, an antibiotic with antiprion activity (Forloni et al., 2015). In this section we consider more common dysfunctions of NREM sleep and REM sleep (for more about prion disorders, see Chapter 16).

Disorders of NREM Sleep

The two most common sleep disorders occur during NREM sleep are **insomnia**, prolonged inability to sleep, and **narcolepsy**, uncontrollably falling asleep at inappropriate times. Insomnia and narcolepsy are related, as anyone who has stayed up late at night can confirm: a night without sleep is often accompanied by a tendency to fall asleep at inconvenient times the next day.

Insomnia

Our understanding of insomnia is complicated by the wide variation among people in how much time they spend asleep. Some short sleepers may think they should sleep more, and some long sleepers may think they should sleep less. Yet the sleeping pattern may be appropriate for each.

People's sleep is disrupted by lifestyle choices such as those described in Clinical Focus 13-1. Staying up late, for example, may set a person's circadian rhythm forward, encouraging a cascade of late sleep followed by staying up still later. Indoor and outdoor light pollution contributes to sleep disorders by disrupting circadian rhythms. Some sleep problems are brought on by shift work or by jet lag, as described in Section 13-1. Other common causes of sleep disorders are stress, long work hours, and an irregular lifestyle. Just worrying about insomnia is estimated to play a major role in 15 percent of cases.

Depressed people may sleep too much or too little. Anxiety and depression account for about 35 percent of insomnias. Quantitative differences also exist in depressed patients' sleep because they enter REM sleep very quickly, as do people who are sleep-deprived.

Insomnia is brought on by sedative-hypnotic drugs, including Seconal, sodium amytal, and many minor tranquilizers. These sleeping pills do help people get to sleep, but the person is likely to feel groggy and tired the next day, which defeats the purpose of taking the drug. Although sleeping pills promote NREM sleep, they deprive the user of REM sleep. In addition, people develop tolerance to these medications, become dependent on them, and display rebound insomnia when they stop taking them. A person then may increase the dose each time the drug fails to produce the desired effect. The syndrome in which patients unsuccessfully attempt to sleep by increasing their drug dosage is called **drug dependence insomnia**.

Narcolepsy

Like many people, you may suddenly have been overcome by an urge to sleep at an inconvenient time, perhaps while attending a lecture. For some people such experiences with narcolepsy are common and disruptive. J. S., a junior in college, sat in the front row for his course on the brain. Within a few minutes after each class began, he dropped off to sleep. The instructor became concerned and asked J. S. to stay after class to discuss his sleeping behavior.

J. S. reported that sleeping in classes was a chronic problem. Not only did he sleep in class, he fell asleep whenever he tried to study. He even fell asleep at the dinner table and in other inappropriate locations. His sleeping problem had made getting through high school a challenge and was making it difficult for J. S. to pass his college courses.

About 1 percent of people have narcolepsy, which takes surprisingly varied forms. J. S. fell asleep while sitting still, and his sleeping bouts consisted of brief spurts of NREM sleep lasting 5 to 10 minutes. This pattern is similar to napping and to dropping off to sleep in class after a late night but is distinguishable as narcolepsy by its frequency and disruptive effect. J. S. eventually discussed his problem with his physician and received a prescription for Ritalin, an amphetaminelike drug that stimulates dopamine transmission. The treatment proved helpful.

Studies of narcoleptic people in sleep clinics resulted in a surprising discovery concerning one cause of narcolepsy: **sleep apnea**, an inability to breathe during sleep. Clinical Focus 13-5,

Narcolepsy derives from the Greek words for numbness and to be seized.

insomnia Disorder of slow-wave sleep resulting in prolonged inability to sleep.

narcolepsy Slow-wave sleep disorder in which a person uncontrollably falls asleep at inappropriate times.

drug dependence insomnia Condition resulting from continuous use of sleeping pills; drug tolerance also results in deprivation of either REM or NREM sleep, leading the user to increase the drug dosage.

sleep apnea Inability to breathe during sleep, causing a sleeper to wake up to breathe.

Section 6-4 presents theories of drug tolerance and dependence.

Focus 6-1 explores amphetamine use for cognitive enhancement. Focus 7-4 describes how Ritalin mitigates symptoms of ADHD.

Apnea from Latin a, not, and pnea, breathing.

Sleep Apnea

The first time I went to a doctor for my insomnia, I was twenty-five—that was about thirty years ago. I explained to the doctor that I couldn't sleep; I had trouble falling asleep, I woke up many, many times during the night, and I was tired and sleepy all day long. As I explained my problem to him, he smiled and nodded. Inwardly, this attitude infuriated me—he couldn't possibly understand what I was going through. He asked me one or two questions: Had any close friend or relative died recently? Was I having any trouble in my job or at home? When I answered no, he shrugged his shoulders and reached for his prescription pad. Since that first occasion I have seen I don't know how many doctors, but none could help me. I've been given hundreds of different pills—to put me to sleep at night, to keep me awake in the daytime, to calm me down, to pep me up—have even been psychoanalyzed. But still I cannot sleep at night. (In Dement, 1972, p. 73)

When this patient entered the Stanford University Sleep Disorders Clinic in 1972, recording electrodes monitored his brain, muscle, eye, and breathing activity while he slept (see Figure 13-11). The attending researchers were amazed to find that he had to wake up to breathe. They observed that he would go more than a minute without breathing before he woke up, gasped for breath, and returned to sleep. Then the sequence began again.

Sleep apnea may be produced by a CNS problem, such as weak neural command to the respiratory muscles, or it may be obstructive, caused by collapse of the upper airway. When people with sleep apnea stop breathing, they either wake up completely and have difficulty getting back to sleep or they partially awaken repeatedly throughout the night to gasp for breath.

Sleep apnea affects people of all ages and both sexes, and 30 percent of those older than 65 may have some form of it. Sleep apnea can

Breathing rate and blood oxygen level recorded during REM sleep from a person with sleep apnea. Blood oxygen increased after each breath, then continued to fall until another breath was taken. This person inhaled only 4 times in the 6-minute period; a healthy sleeper would breathe more than 60 times in the same interval.

even occur in children; it may be related to some cases of *sudden infant death syndrome* (SIDS), or crib death, in which otherwise healthy infants inexplicably die in their sleep. Sleep apnea is thought to be more common among overweight people and those who snore, two conditions in which airflow is restricted.

Treatments for sleep apnea include surgery or an appliance to expand the upper airway, weight loss, and a face mask to deliver negative pressure to open the airway. Untreated sleep apnea can cause high blood pressure and other cardiovascular disease, memory problems, weight gain, impotence, headaches, and brain damage due to oxygen insufficiency (Corrêa Cde et al., 2015).

Sleep Apnea, describes a person who spent all night every night waking up to breathe. This nighttime behavior left him extremely tired and caused him to nod off in the daytime. Being overweight contributes to sleep apnea as well as to metabolic syndrome. Clearly the relationship between sleep and health is both complex and interconnected.

Disorders of REM Sleep

Several sleep disorders are associated with the unexpected onset of atonia and dreams, two main features of REM sleep. We describe three: sleep paralysis, cataplexy, and REM sleep behavioral disorder.

Sleep Paralysis

In **sleep paralysis** both atonia and dreaming can occur when a person is awake, usually just falling asleep or waking up. L. M., a college senior, recounted the following experience.

She had just gone to sleep when her roommate came into their room. L. M. woke up and intended to ask her roommate if she wanted to go skating the next morning but found herself unable to speak. She tried to turn her head to follow her roommate's movements across the room but found that she was paralyzed. She had the terrifying feeling that some creature was hiding in the bathroom waiting for her roommate. She tried to cry out but produced only harsh gurgling noises. In response to these peculiar noises the roommate knocked her out of her paralysis by hitting her with a pillow.

Sleep paralysis is common. In informal class surveys almost a third of students report having had such an experience, as do some war veterans during group therapy sessions.

sleep paralysis Atonia and dreaming occurring when a person is awake, usually just falling asleep or waking up.

cataplexy State of atonia, as in REM sleep, occurring while a person is awake and active; linked to strong emotional stimulation.

hypnogogic hallucination Dreamlike event as sleep begins or while a person is in a state of cataplexy.

The atonia is typically accompanied by dread or fear. It seems likely that in sleep paralysis a person has entered REM sleep partially. He or she is dreaming, atonia has occurred, but the sleeper remains "awake." When sleep paralysis occurs as a person wakes up, the paralysis and dreaming characteristic of a REM episode continue.

Cataplexy

The atonia of REM sleep can also occur while a person is awake and active, a condition called **cataplexy**. The person loses muscle tone and gradually or even quickly falls to the floor, atonic. The collapse can be so sudden that injury is a real risk. Cataplexy can be triggered by excitement or laughing. While in an atonic condition, the person sees imaginary creatures or hears imaginary voices. People who fall into a state of cataplexy with these **hypnogogic hallucinations** give every appearance of having fallen into REM sleep while remaining "awake."

Cataplexy can have a genetic basis. In 1970 William Dement was given a litter of Doberman pinscher dogs and later a litter of Labrador retrievers. These dogs displayed cataplexy. The disease is transmitted as a recessive trait: to develop it, a dog must inherit the gene from both its mother and its father. The descendants of those dogs continue to provide animal models for investigating the neural basis of the disease as well as its treatment.

Jerome Siegel (2004) investigated the cause of narcolepsy in dogs. He found that neurons in the subcoerulear nucleus become inactive and neurons in the magnocellular nucleus of the medulla become active during attacks of cataplexy, just as they do during REM sleep. On the basis of anatomical examinations of the brains of narcoleptic dogs, Siegel suggested that the death of neurons in the amygdala and adjacent forebrain areas is a one-time event that occurs just before the onset of the disease early in life.

A remarkable discovery that came from this line of investigation is that a subset of these affected neurons produces a peptide called *orexin* (also called *hypocretin*) that serves as a signaling molecule to maintain wakefulness. Orexin cells, which are located in the hypothalamus, send projections to many other brain regions, as do the nonspecific activating systems using acetylcholine and serotonin. This suggests that orexin plays a role in maintaining activity during waking.

To test the idea that orexin loss is related to cataplexy, investigators have bred knockout mice that lack orexin. When these mice become active, such as at feeding time, they collapse into cataplexy, supporting the idea that an orexin system contributes to healthy waking behavior. Research with mice also suggests that lifestyle may contribute to orexin cell loss. Mice fed a high-fat diet display a reduction in orexin cells and symptoms of cataplexy (Nobunaga et al., 2014). Another proposed cause of narcolepsy in humans is an autoimmune reaction: the immune system attacks and kills orexin cells.

REM Sleep Behavioral Disorder

In Section 13-4 we described REM sleep behavioral disorder (REM without atonia), a symptom displayed by some people who take antidepressant drugs. They wake up seemingly acting out dream activity. In Section 13-5 we described Jouvet's experiment: he reported that cats with lesions to the subcoerulear region of the brainstem entered REM sleep without accompanying atonia and so apparently acted out their dreams.

A similar condition reported in people may have either a genetic basis or a neurological cause associated with aging. People who display REM sleep behavioral disorder behave as though they are acting out their dreams (Mahowald & Schenck, 2015). Following is the account of a 67-year-old patient (Schenck et al., 1986):

> I had a dream where someone was shooting at me with a rifle and it was in a field that had ridges in it, so I decided to crawl behind a ridge—and I then had a gun too—and I look over the ridge so when he showed up I would shoot back at him and when I came to [i.e., awakened] I was kneeling alongside the bed with my arms extended like I was holding the rifle up and ready to shoot.

In the dream the patient saw vivid images but heard nothing and felt afraid. Although many patients have described such experiences, most are elderly and suffer from brain injury

The word *cataplexy* comes from the Greek word *kataplessein,* meaning *to strike down. Hypnogogic* comes from the Greek *hypnos, sleep* and *agogos, leading into.*

Figure 3-21 explains inheritance patterns for genetic disorders.

View a researcher working with narcoleptic dogs at https://www.youtube.com/watch?v=R6_hwbp97eU.

Section 3-3 investigates knockout technology and other genetic engineering techniques.

View a dancer experiencing narcolepsy with cataplexy at https://www.youtube.com/watch?v=1PuvXpv0yDM.

or other brain-related disorders. REM sleep behavioral disorder can be treated with benzo-diazepines, antianxiety drugs that block REM sleep.

13-6 REVIEW

Sleep Disorders

Before you continue, check your understanding.

1. Disorders of NREM sleep include _____, in which a person has difficulty falling asleep at night, and _____, in which a person falls asleep involuntarily in the daytime.

2. Treating insomnia with sleeping pills, usually sedative-hypnotics, may cause _____: progressively higher doses must be taken to achieve sleep.

3. Disorders of REM sleep include _____, in which a person awakens but cannot move and is afraid, and _____, in which a person may lose all muscle tone and collapse while awake.

4. The people who act out their dreams, a condition termed _____, may have damage to the _____ nucleus.

5. Is orexin the substance that produces waking?

Answers appear at the back of the book.

For additional study tools, visit 🅜 **LaunchPad**:
www.macmillanhighered.com/launchpad/kolb5e

13-7 What Does Sleep Tell Us about Consciousness?

René Descartes conceived his idea of a mind through a lucid dream. He dreamed that he was interpreting the dream as it occurred. Later, when awake, he reasoned that if he could think and analyze a dream while asleep, his mind must function during both waking and sleeping. He proposed therefore that the mind must be independent of the body that undergoes sleeping and waking transitions. Contemporary fMRI studies suggest that lucid dreaming is especially common in people who display high levels of prefrontal cortex activity in Brodmann's areas 9 and 10 (Filevich et al., 2015).

Section 1-2 recounts how Descartes chose the pineal gland as the seat of the mind.

As described in preceding sections, what we colloquially refer to as waking comprises at least three states. First, alert consciousness without accompanying movement is associated with cholinergic system activity. Second, consciousness with movement is associated with serotonergic system activity. Third, the peptide orexin also plays a role in maintaining waking activity.

Similarly, sleep consists of NREM and REM phases. NREM sleep consists of the four stages indicated by the EEG (see Figure 13-12A). REM sleep periods consist of at least two stages, one in which small twitching movements occur and one in which such motion twitching is absent.

REM neurobehavioral events can occur relatively independently. Sleepers may awake to find themselves in a condition of sleep paralysis, during which they experience the hallucinations and fear common in dreams. People who are awake may fall into a state of cataplexy: they are conscious of being awake during the atonia and visual and emotional features of dreams.

Sleep researcher J. Allan Hobson reported his peculiar symptoms after a brainstem stroke (Hobson, 2002). For the first 10 days after the lesion, he had complete insomnia, neither REM nor NREM sleep. Whenever he closed his eyes, however, he did have visual hallucinations that had a dreamlike quality. This experience suggested that eye closure is sufficient to produce the visual components of REM sleep but with neither loss of consciousness nor atonia. Hobson eventually recovered typical sleeping patterns, and the hallucinations stopped.

Beyond teaching us that the neural basis of consciousness is extremely complex, the study of sleep states and dreaming may help to explain some psychiatric and drug-induced conditions. For example visual and auditory hallucinations are among the symptoms of schizophrenia. Are these hallucinations dream events that occur unexpectedly during waking? Many people who take hallucinogenic drugs such as LSD report visual hallucinations. Does the drug initiate the visual features of dreams? People who have panic attacks suffer from very real fright that has no obvious cause. Are they experiencing the fear attacks that commonly occur during sleep paralysis and cataplexy?

What the study of sleep tells us about consciousness is that a remarkable number of variations of conscious states exist. Some are associated with waking and some with sleeping, and the two can mix together to produce a variety of odd conditions. When it comes to consciousness, there is far more to sleeping and waking than just sleeping and waking.

Section 15-7 explores the neural basis of consciousness and ideas about why humans are conscious.

SUMMARY

(13-1) A Clock for All Seasons

Biorhythms are cyclic behavior patterns of varying length displayed by animals, plants, even single-celled organisms. Biorhythms displayed by mammals include, among others, circadian (daily) rhythms and circannual (yearly) rhythms. In the absence of environmental cues circadian rhythms are free-running, lasting a little more or a little less than their usual period of about 24 hours depending on the individual organism or the environmental conditions. Cues called Zeitgebers reset biological clocks to a 24-hour rhythm. Circadian rhythms allow us to synchronize our behavior with our body's metabolic processes—so that we are hungry, and at optimal times. Environmental intrusions into our natural circadian rhythm, from artificial lighting to jet lag, contribute to metabolic syndrome. Biological clocks produce epigenetic effects: they regulate gene expression in every cell in the body.

(13-2) Neural Basis of the Biological Clock

A biological clock is a neural structure responsible for producing rhythmic behavior. Our master biological clock is the suprachiasmatic nucleus. The SCN is responsible for circadian rhythms; it has its own free-running rhythm with a period of a little more or a little less than 24 hours. Stimuli from the environment, such as sunrise and sunset, meals, or exercise, entrain the free-running rhythm so that its period approximates 24 hours.

SCN neurons are active in the daytime and inactive at night. These neurons retain their rhythmicity when disconnected from other brain structures, when removed from the brain and cultured in a dish, and after culture in a dish for many generations. When reimplanted in a brain without an SCN, they restore the animal's circadian rhythms. Aspects of neuronal circadian rhythms, including their period, are under genetic and epigenetic control.

(13-3) Sleep Stages and Dreaming

Sleep events are measured by recording the brain's activity to produce an electroencephalogram (EEG), muscular activity to produce an electromyogram (EMG), and eye movements to produce an electrooculogram (EOG).

A typical night's sleep, as indicated by physiological measures, consists of stages that take place in cycles over the course of the night. During REM sleep the EEG displays a waking pattern and the sleeper displays rapid eye movements. Sleep stages in which the EEG has a slower rhythm are called non-REM (NREM) sleep.

Intervals of NREM sleep and REM sleep alternate four or five times each night. The duration of NREM sleep periods is longer earlier in sleep, whereas the duration of REM sleep periods is longer in the later part of sleep. These intervals also vary with age.

A sleeper in NREM has muscle tone, may toss and turn, and has dreams that are not especially vivid. A sleeper in REM sleep has vivid dreams in real time but has no muscle tone and so is paralyzed. Dream duration coincides with the duration of the REM period.

The activation–synthesis hypothesis proposes that dreams are not meaningful, merely a by-product of the brain's state of excitation during REM. The coping hypothesis suggests that dreaming evolved as a mechanism to deal with challenges and fears posed by life.

(13-4) What Does Sleep Accomplish?

Several theories of sleep have been advanced, but the main proposition is that sleep is a biological adaptation that conserves energy. Sleep is suggested as a restorative process that fixes wear and tear in the brain and body. Sleep also organizes and stores memories.

(13-5) Neural Bases of Sleep

Separate neural regions are responsible for NREM and REM sleep. The reticular activating system, located in the central brainstem, is responsible for NREM sleep. If the RAS is stimulated, a sleeper awakes; if it is damaged, a person may enter a coma.

The peribrachial area and the medial pontine reticular formation in the brainstem are responsible for REM sleep. If these areas are damaged, REM sleep may no longer occur. Pathways projecting from these areas to the cortex produce the cortical activation of REM, and those projecting to the brainstem produce the muscular paralysis of REM.

13-6 Sleep Disorders

Disorders of NREM sleep include insomnia, the inability to sleep at night, and narcolepsy, inconveniently falling asleep in the daytime. Sedative-hypnotics used to induce sleep may induce drug dependence insomnia, a sleep disorder in which progressively larger doses are required to produce sleep.

Disorders of REM sleep include sleep paralysis, in which a person awakens but remains unable to move and sometimes feels fear and dread. In cataplexy, caused by a loss of orexin cells in the brain, a person collapses into a state of paralysis while awake. At the same time the person may have hypnogogic hallucinations similar to dreaming. In REM sleep behavioral disorder a sleeping person acts out dreams.

13-7 What Does Sleep Tell Us about Consciousness?

Sleep research provides insight into consciousness by revealing many kinds of waking and sleeping. Just as the events of wakefulness intrude into sleep, the events of sleep can intrude into wakefulness. The array of conditions thus produced demonstrates that consciousness is not a unitary state.

■ KEY TERMS

atonia, p. 458

basic rest–activity cycle (BRAC), p. 464

beta (β) rhythm, p. 457

biological clock, p. 443

biorhythm, p. 443

cataplexy, p. 474

chronotype, p. 450

circadian rhythm, p. 443

coma, p. 470

delta (δ) rhythm, p. 458

dimer, p. 452

diurnal animal, p. 443

drug dependence insomnia, p. 473

entrain, p. 446

free-running rhythm, p. 446

hypnogogic hallucination, p. 474

insomnia, p. 473

jet lag, p. 448

light pollution, p. 446

medial pontine reticular formation (MPRF), p. 470

melatonin, p. 454

metabolic syndrome, p. 443

microsleep, p. 466

narcolepsy, p. 473

NREM (non-REM) sleep, p. 458

peribrachial area, p. 470

period, p. 445

place cell, p. 468

REM sleep, p. 458

reticular activating system (RAS), p. 470

retinohypothalamic tract, p. 450

sleep apnea, p. 473

sleep paralysis, p. 474

slow-wave sleep, p. 458

suprachiasmatic nucleus (SCN), p. 450

Zeitgeber, p. 446

➔ Visit 🔳 **LaunchPad** to access the e-Book, videos, 🔳 **LearningCurve** adaptive quizzing, flashcards, and more.

www.macmillanhighered.com/launchpad/kolb5e

CHAPTER

14

How Do We Learn and Remember?

Streeter

Katherine Streeter

479

Remediating Dyslexia

As children absorb their society's culture, acquiring language skills seems virtually automatic. Yet some people face lifelong challenges in mastering language-related tasks. Educators classify these difficulties under the umbrella of *learning disabilities.*

Dyslexia, impairment in learning to read, may be the most common learning disability. Children with dyslexia (from Greek words suggesting *bad* and *reading*) have difficulty learning to write as well as to read.

In 1895, James Hinshelwood, an eye surgeon, examined some schoolchildren who were having reading problems, but he could find nothing wrong with their vision. Hinshelwood was the first to suggest that children with reading problems were impaired in brain areas associated with language use. Norman Geshwind and Albert Galaburda (1985) proposed how such impairment might come about.

Struck by the finding that dyslexia is far more common in boys than in girls, they reasoned that hormones influence early brain development. They examined postmortem the brains of a small sample of people who had dyslexia and found abnormal collections of neurons, or warts, in and around the brain's language areas.

This relation between structural abnormalities in the brain and learning disabilities is further evidence that an intact brain is necessary for healthy human functioning. Geshwind and Galaburda also found abnormalities in the auditory thalamus, suggesting a deficit in auditory processing. More recently, brain imaging has determined that, relative to the brains of healthy participants, activity is reduced in the left temporoparietal cortex of people with dyslexia.

Michael Merzenich and his colleagues designed a remedial treatment program based on the assumption that the fundamental problem in learning disabilities lies in auditory processing, specifically of language sounds (e.g., Temple et al., 2003). Remediation involves learning to make increasingly difficult sound discriminations, for example, discriminating *ba* and *da.*

When the sounds are spoken slowly, discriminating between them is easy, but as they grow briefer and occur faster, discrimination becomes more difficult. Previous studies using rats and monkeys showed that discrimination training stimulates neural plasticity in the auditory system, making it capable of discrimination of sounds that previously was not possible.

The representative fMRIs shown here reveal decreased activation in many brain regions in untreated dyslexic children compared with typical children. With training, dyslexic readers can normalize their brain activity and presumably its connectivity.

The extent of increased brain activation in the language-related regions (circled in the images) correlates to the amount of increased brain activation overall. The results suggest that the remedial treatment both improves brain function in regions associated with phonological processing and produces compensatory activation in related brain regions.

Typical-reading children while rhyming | Dyslexic-reading children while rhyming (before remediation)

Regions of the frontal and temporoparietal cortex that showed decreased activation in children with untreated dyslexia. "Neural Deficits in Children with Dyslexia Ameliorated by Behavioral Remediation: Evidence from Functional MRI," by E. Temple, G. K. Deutsch, R. A. Poldrack, S. L. Miller, P. Tallal, M. M. Merzenich, and J. D. E. Gabrieli, 2003, *Proceedings of the National Academy of Sciences (USA) 100*, pp. 2860–2865.

Neuroplasticity is the nervous system's potential for physical or chemical change that enhances adaptability.

The brain is plastic. It changes throughout life, allowing us to modify our behavior, to adapt and learn, and to remember. If we reflect on our own lives, we can easily compile a list of experiences that must change the brain:

- Profound changes during development

- Acquisition of culture

- Preferences among foods and beverages, art and music, and other activities and experiences

- Ability to cope with the neurodegeneration of aging and to accommodate neurological injury or disease at any age

Learning is common to all these experiences. Understanding how the brain supports learning is fundamental in neuroscience. At the level of the neuron, synapses change with experience—learning new information, for example. Such changes can take place anywhere in the brain.

We can investigate neuronal changes that support learning specific types of information by describing changes in cells exposed to specific sensory experiences. Or we can look at the neural changes that mediate brain plasticity—recovery from brain injury, addiction to drugs, or conquering a learning disability. This chapter's goal is to move beyond the general concept of neuroplasticity toward understanding what stimulates plastic change in the brain. We inspect changes related to environment and experience, learning and memory, electrical stimulation, chemical influences, and brain injury.

14-1 Connecting Learning and Memory

Learning is a relatively permanent change in an organism's behavior as a result of experience. **Memory** is the ability to recall or recognize previous experience. Memory thus implies a mental representation of a previous experience, sometimes termed a *memory trace*. Neuroscientists presume that this hypothetical memory trace corresponds to a physical change in the brain, most likely involving synapses.

At the macro level, we infer what we know about learning and memory formation from behavioral changes, not by observing the brain directly. Studying learning and memory therefore requires behavioral measures that evaluate how these changes come about. We begin here by reviewing how learning and memory researchers study animals in the laboratory. The results suggest, in a general way, how the brain organizes its learning and memory systems.

The memory trace is a *psychological construct*, an abstract mental process inferred only from behavior (see Section 15-1). Others include learning, language, emotion, motivation, and thinking.

Studying Learning and Memory in the Laboratory

A challenge for psychologists studying memory in laboratory animals (or people) is to get subjects to reveal what they remember. Because laboratory animals do not speak, investigators must devise ways for a subject to show its knowledge. Different species "talk" to us in different ways, so the test choice must match each species' capabilities.

Mazes or swimming pools are typically used to study rats because rats live in tunnels and near water. Monkey studies take advantage of their sharp vision and avid curiosity by requiring them to look under objects for food or watch television monitors. With birds, natural behaviors such as singing are used. And for humans, investigators tend to use paper-and-pencil tests.

Psychologists have devised hundreds of tests over the past century, and the test results reveal many types of learning and memory. Each appears to have its own neural circuitry. Two classic traditions for training animals to talk to investigators emerged a century ago. These diverse approaches are based on the work of Edward Thorndike (1898) in the United States and on experiments conducted by Ivan Pavlov in Russia.

Figure 7-4 samples swimming pool tests for rats, Experiment 15-1, monkeys' perceptual threshold, and Focus 15-4, the effects of brain injuries on humans' cognitive performance.

Pavlovian Conditioning

Early in the twentieth century, Ivan Pavlov, a Russian physiologist, discovered that when a food reward accompanies some stimulus, such as a tone, dogs learn to associate the stimulus with the food. Then whenever they hear the tone, they salivate even though no food is present. This type of learning has many names, including **Pavlovian conditioning**, *respondent conditioning*, and *classical conditioning*, and many studies document its characteristics.

A key feature of Pavlovian conditioning is that animals learn to associate two stimuli (the presentation of the food and the tone) and to communicate to us that they have learned it by giving the same response (salivation) to both stimuli. Pet owners know that to a cat or dog, the sound of a can being opened is a clear stimulus for food. Two forms of Pavlovian conditioning are common in experiments today: eyeblink conditioning and fear conditioning. Each is

dyslexia Impairment in learning to read and write; probably the most common learning disability.

learning Relatively permanent change in an organism's behavior as a result of experience.

memory Ability to recall or recognize previous experience.

Pavlovian conditioning Learning achieved when neutral stimulus (such as a tone) comes to elicit a response after its repeated pairing with some event (such as delivery of food); also called *classical conditioning* or *respondent conditioning*.

FIGURE 14-1 Eyeblink Conditioning
Neural circuits in the cerebellum mediate
this form of stimulus–response learning.

1 Headgear is arranged
for eyeblink conditioning.

Electrodes

2 Puff of air to
eye causes eye
to blink.

Air jet
tube

Audio
speaker

3 After pairing air puff with tone,
tone alone comes to elicit a blink.

In the cerebellum, the flocculus controls eye
movements; see Figure 11-14.

The shock approximates a spark of static
electricity.

associated with neural circuits in discrete brain
regions; thus both are especially useful.

Eyeblink conditioning has been used to
study Pavlovian learning in rabbits and people
(**Figure 14-1**). In these studies, a tone (or some
other stimulus) is associated with a painless puff
of air to the participant's eye. The tone is the
conditioned stimulus (CS) that comes to elicit
a blink produced initially by the air puff. The
air puff is the **unconditioned stimulus (UCS)**,
because blinking is the normal reaction—the
unconditioned response (UCR)—to a puff
of air. The participant communicates having learned that the signal stimulus predicts
the puff by blinking in response to the signal
(the CS) alone—a **conditioned response (CR)**.
The circuits in the cerebellum that mediate such Pavlovian learning are designed to pair
motor responses with environmental events. Eyeblink conditioning experiments take advantage of this biological predisposition.

In **fear conditioning,** an unpleasant but harmless stimulus is used to elicit an emotional
response: fear. A rat or other animal is placed in a box. A mild but unpleasant electric current can be passed through the grid floor. As shown in **Experiment 14-1,** a tone (the CS) is
presented just before a brief, unexpected mild electric shock. When the tone is presented
later without the shock, the animal acts afraid, becoming motionless and perhaps urinating
in anticipation of the shock. A novel stimulus, say, a light, presented in the same environment has little effect. Thus, the animal communicates that it has learned the association
between the tone and the shock.

Because the CR is emotional, circuits of the amygdala rather than the cerebellum mediate fear conditioning. Although both eyeblink and fear conditioning are Pavlovian, different
brain areas mediate the learning.

Operant Conditioning

In the United States, Edward Thorndike (1898) began a second tradition for studying learning and memory. Thorndike was interested in how animals solve problems. In one series of
experiments, he placed cats in a box with a plate of fish outside it (**Figure 14-2**). The only way
for a hungry cat to get to the fish was to figure out how to get out of the box.

The solution was to press on a lever to activate a system of pulleys that opened the box
door. The cat gradually learned that its actions had consequences: on the initial trial, the cat

▶ EXPERIMENT **14-1**

Question: Does an animal learn the association between emotional experience and environmental stimuli?

Procedure and results

Rat receives mild electrical shock
in combination with tone.

**Tone
plus shock**

Later →

If a light is presented alone
later, rat ignores it.

**Light only—
no tone**

Later →

Rat freezes in fear when tone
alone sounds.

Tone only

Conclusion: The rat has learned an association between the tone and the shock, which
produces a fear response. Circuits that include the amygdala take part in this learning process.

The cat is placed in the box with the food reward outside.

Pulley system

The hungry cat eventually learns that pressing on the lever will result in getting out of the box and getting to the food.

Lever

Food reward

FIGURE 14-2 Thorndike's Puzzle Box

touched the releasing mechanism only by chance as it restlessly paced inside the box. The cat apparently learned that something it had done opened the door, and it tended to repeat its behaviors from just before the door opened. After a few trials, the cat took just seconds to get the door open to devour the fish.

Later studies by B. F. Skinner (e.g., 1938) used a similar strategy of *reinforcement* to train rats to press bars or pigeons to peck keys to obtain food. Just as Thorndike's cats learned to escape his puzzle boxes, many animals learn to press the bar or peck the key simply if they are placed in the apparatus and allowed to discover the response that obtains the reward. This type of learning is **operant conditioning,** or *instrumental conditioning,* as Thorndike called it. The animal demonstrates that it has learned the association between its actions and the consequences by performing the task faster.

The variety of operant associations is staggering: we learn constantly to associate our behavior with its consequences. No surprise, then, that operant learning is not localized to any particular brain circuit. The circuits needed vary with the task requirements. For example, olfactory tasks involve olfactory-related structures like the orbitofrontal cortex and amygdala, spatial tasks recruit the hippocampus, and motor tasks require the basal ganglia.

Two Categories of Memory

Humans present a distinct challenge to researchers studying memory because so much of our learning is verbal. Psychologists have studied human memory since the mid-1800s. More recently, cognitive psychologists have developed sophisticated measures of learning and memory for neuropsychological investigations. Two such measures help to distinguish between two categories of memory in humans.

In one kind of task, a group of participants reads a list of words, such as *spring, winter, car,* and *boat*. Another group reads a list consisting of *trip, tumble, run,* and *sun*. All the participants are then asked to define a series of words. One is *fall*.

The word *fall* has multiple meanings, including the season and a tumble. People who have just read the word list containing names of seasons are likely to give the meaning as *autumn*; those who have read the second list, containing action words, typically give the meaning as *tumble*. Some form of unconscious (and unintentional) learning takes place as the participants read the word lists.

This task measures **implicit memory:** participants demonstrate knowledge—a skill, conditioned response, or recall of events on prompting—but cannot explicitly retrieve the information. People with **amnesia,** a partial or total loss of memory, perform at normal on tests of implicit memory. The amnesic person has no recollection of having read the word list yet acts as though some neural circuit has been influenced by it. In amnesia, a *dissociation*—a

eyeblink conditioning Experimental technique in which subjects learn to pair a formerly neutral stimulus with a defensive blinking response.

conditioned stimulus (CS) In Pavlovian conditioning, an originally neutral stimulus that after association with an unconditioned stimulus (UCS) triggers a conditioned response (CR).

unconditioned stimulus (UCS) A stimulus that naturally and automatically (unconditionally) triggers an unconditioned response (UCR).

unconditioned response (UCR) Unlearned, naturally occurring response to the unconditioned stimulus (UCS), such as salivation when food is in the mouth.

conditioned response (CR) In Pavlovian conditioning, the learned response to a formerly neutral conditioned stimulus (CS).

fear conditioning Conditioned emotional response between a neutral stimulus and an unpleasant event, such as a shock, that results in a learned association.

operant conditioning Learning procedure in which the consequences (such as obtaining a reward) of a particular behavior (such as pressing a bar) increase or decrease the probability of the behavior occurring again; also called *instrumental conditioning*.

implicit memory Unconscious memory: subjects can demonstrate knowledge, such as a skill, conditioned response, or recall of events on prompting but cannot explicitly retrieve the information.

amnesia Partial or total loss of memory.

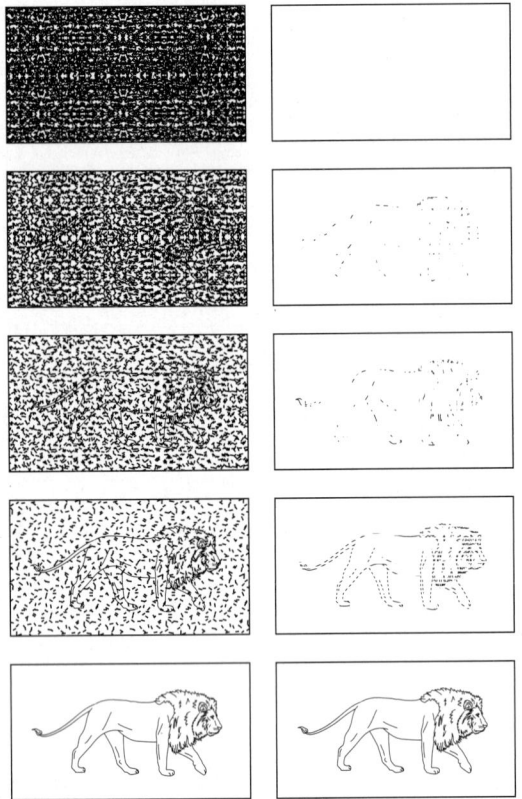

FIGURE 14-3 Gollin Figure Test
Participants are shown a series of drawings in sequence, from least to most clear, and asked to identify the image. Most people must see several panels before they can identify it. On a retention test some time later, however, participants identify the image sooner than they did on the first test, indicating some form of memory for the image. Amnesic subjects also show improvement on this test, even though they do not recall taking it.

disconnect—occurs between the memory of the unconscious (or implicit) learning and **explicit memory,** conscious recollection of training. Nonamnesic people can retrieve an explicit memory and indicate that they know the retrieved item is correct.

This implicit–explicit distinction is not restricted to verbal learning; it is true of visual learning and motor learning as well. For example, when people are shown the top panel of the Gollin figure test in **Figure 14-3** and asked what it shows, they are unlikely to identify an image. They are then presented with a succession of more nearly complete sketches until they can identify the picture. When control participants and amnesics are later shown the same sketch, both groups identify the figure sooner than they could the first time. Even though the amnesic subjects may not recall seeing the sketches before, they behave as though they had.

To measure implicit motor skills learning, a person learns a skill, such as the pursuit rotor task shown in **Figure 14-4.** A small metal disc moves in a circular pattern on a turntable that also is moving. The task is to hold a stylus on the small disc as it spins. This task is not as easy as it looks, especially when the turntable is moving quickly. Nonetheless, with an hour's practice most people become reasonably proficient. Presented with the same task a week later, both controls and amnesics take less time to perform it. Here, too, the amnesics fail to recall performing the task before.

The distinction between tests of implicit and explicit memory is consistent and therefore must offer a key to how the brain stores information. Some theorists make subtle distinctions between the implicit–explicit dichotomy we use and other terminologies for categorizing unconscious and conscious memory. Many researchers prefer to distinguish between **declarative memory,** the specific contents of specific experiences that can be verbally recalled (times, places, or circumstances), and **procedural memory,** the ability to perform a task. As applied to humans there is little practical difference.

Table 14-1 lists commonly used dichotomies, the general distinction being that one memory category requires recalling specific information, whereas the other refers to knowledge of which we are not consciously aware. We can include Pavlovian conditioning and Thorndike's and Skinner's operant learning in this analysis too: all are forms of implicit learning.

Nonspeaking animals can display explicit memory. One of us owned a cat that loved to play with a little ball. One day, as the cat watched, the ball was temporarily put on a high shelf to keep it away from an inquisitive toddler. For weeks afterward, the cat sat and stared at the shelf where the ball had been placed, even though the ball was not visible—an example of explicit memory.

Animals also display explicit memory when they learn psychological tasks. Rats can be trained to find highly palatable food in a new location in a large compound each day.

FIGURE 14-4 Pursuit-Rotor Task The participant must keep the stylus in contact with a metal disc moving in a circular pattern on a turntable while also rotating in a circular pattern. Although the task is difficult, most people show significant improvement after brief training. Given a second test at some later time, both participants and amnesics show task retention, but typically the amnesics do not recall learning it before.

The task is to go to the most recent location. This piece of information is explicit and demonstrably can be forgotten.

Suppose a rat trained to find food in a particular location in a small arena is given several trials with the food at a new location and then retested an hour, a day, 3 days, or a week later. The rat has no difficulty with an hour's delay or perhaps even a day's. Some rats are flawless at 3 days, but most have forgotten the location by the time a week has elapsed. Instead, they wander around looking for the food. This behavior illustrates their implicit memory of the **learning set,** the rules of the game—an implicit understanding of how a problem can be solved with a rule that can be applied in many situations—namely, here, that a desired food can be found with a certain search strategy.

What Makes Explicit and Implicit Memory Different?

One reason explicit and implicit memories differ is that the set of neural structures that houses each is different. Another reason they differ is that the brain processes explicit and implicit information differently.

Encoding Memories

Implicit information is encoded in much the same way it is perceived: it can be described as data-driven, or bottom-up, processing. The idea is that information enters the brain through sensory receptors, then is processed in a series of subcortical and cortical regions. For example, visual information about an object moves from the photoreceptors (the bottom) to the thalamus, occipital cortex, then through the ventral stream to the temporal lobe (the top), where the object is recognized.

Explicit memory, in contrast, depends on conceptually driven, or top-down, processing: the person reorganizes the data. If you were searching for a particular object, your keys, for example, you would ignore other objects. This process is top-down because circuits in the temporal lobe (the top) form an image (keys) that influences how incoming visual information (the bottom) is processed and in turn greatly influences information recall later.

Because a person has a relatively passive role in encoding implicit memory, he or she has difficulty recalling the memory spontaneously but recalls it more easily with **priming** by the original stimulus or some feature of it. Because a person plays an active role in processing information explicitly, internal cues used in processing can also be used to initiate spontaneous recall.

Findings from studies of eyewitness testimony demonstrate the active nature of explicit memory recall—and its fallibility (e.g., Loftus, 1997). In a typical experiment, participants view a video clip of an accident in which a car collides with another car stopped at an intersection. One group is asked to estimate how fast the moving car was going when it "smashed" into the other car. A second group is asked how fast the car was going when it "bumped" into the other car.

Later questioning indicates that the memory of how fast the moving car was going is biased by the instruction: participants looking at "smashing" cars estimate faster speeds than those estimated by participants looking at "bumping" cars. The instruction actually causes the information to be processed differently. In both cases, participants were certain their memories were accurate.

Other experiments show that implicit memory also is fallible. For example, participants are read the following list of words: *sweet, chocolate, shoe, table, candy, horse, car, cake, coffee, wall, book, cookie, hat.* After a few minutes' delay, they hear another list of words that includes some from the first list and some that are new. Participants are asked to identify which words were present on the first list and to indicate how certain they are of the identification.

One of the words on the second list is *sugar.* Most participants indicate not just that *sugar* was on the first list but that they are certain it was. Although other sweet things were, *sugar* was not. This demonstration is intriguing, because it shows how easily we can form false memories and defend their veracity with certainty.

TABLE 14-1 Differentiating Two Memory Categories

Terms that describe conscious memory	Terms that describe unconscious memory
Explicit	Implicit
Declarative	Nondeclarative
Fact	Skill
Memory	Habit
Knowing that	Knowing how
Locale	Taxon
Conscious recollection	Skills
Elaboration	Integration
Memory with record	Memory without record
Autobiographical	Perceptual
Representational	Dispositional
Episodic	Procedural
Semantic	Nonassociative
Working	Reference

Note: This paired list of terms differentiates conscious from unconscious forms of memory. It will help you relate other memory discussions to the one in this book, which favors the explicit–implicit distinction.

explicit memory Conscious memory: subjects can retrieve an item and indicate that they know the retrieved item is the correct one.

declarative memory Ability to recount what one knows, to detail the time, place, and circumstances of events; often lost in amnesia.

procedural memory Ability to recall a movement sequence or how to perform some act or behavior.

learning set Rules of the game; implicit understanding of how a problem can be solved with a rule that can be applied in many different situations.

priming Using a stimulus to sensitize the nervous system to a later presentation of the same or a similar stimulus.

Processing Memories

Although we can distinguish memories generally as implicit or explicit, the brain does not process all implicit or all explicit memories in the same way. Memories can be divided according to categories that differ from those listed in Table 14-1. For example, we can make a distinction between memories for different types of sensory information.

Different neural areas process visual and auditory information, so it is reasonable to assume that auditory memories are stored in brain regions different from the regions that store visual memories. We can also make a distinction between information stored in so-called *short-term memory* and information held in *long-term memory*. In short-term memory, information—the final score of a playoff game or the combination of your friend's bike lock, for instance—is held in memory only briefly, for a few minutes at most, and then discarded. In long-term memory, information—such as a close friend's name—is held in memory indefinitely, perhaps for a lifetime.

The frontal lobes are central in short-term memory, whereas the temporal lobe is central in long-term storage of verbal information. The crucial point is that no single place in the nervous system can be identified as *the* location for memory or learning. Virtually the entire nervous system can be changed by experience, but different parts of an experience change different parts of the nervous system. One challenge for the experimenter is to devise ways of manipulating experience to demonstrate change in different parts of the brain.

Storing Memories

Understanding that every part of the brain can learn influences how we view the neural circuits that mediate memory. We could expect areas that process information to also house the memory of that information. Areas that process visual information, for example, probably house visual memory. Since the temporal lobe has specialized regions for processing color, shape, and other visual characteristics, we can predict that the memory for various visual attributes of objects is stored separately.

A series of PET studies by Alex Martin and colleagues (1995) at the U.S. National Institute of Mental Health confirmed this prediction. In one study, participants were shown black-and-white line drawings of objects and asked to generate words denoting either their colors or actions. The idea is that processing color and motion are carried out in different temporal lobe locations, and thus the activity linked with the memories of color and motion also might be dissociated.

Just such dissociation was demonstrated. **Figure 14-5** shows that color recall activates a region in the ventral temporal lobe, just anterior to the area controlling color perception, whereas recall of action words activates a region in the middle temporal gyrus, just anterior to the area controlling motion perception. This distribution of neural activation shows not only that object memory is at least partly located in the temporal lobes but also that it is found in regions associated with the original perception of the objects.

FIGURE 14-5 Memory Distribution Blood flow in left-hemisphere regions increases when participants generate color words (red) and action words (blue) to describe static black-and-white drawings of objects. Purple areas indicate overlap. The red region extends into the ventral temporal lobe, suggesting that object memory is organized as a distributed system. Objects' attributes are stored close to the cortical regions that mediate their perceptions. Parietal lobe activation likely is related to movements associated with action words, and frontal lobe activation, to the spontaneously generated behavior. Information from A. Martin, J. V. Haxby, F. M. Lalonde, C. L. Wiggs, & L. G. Ungerleider (1995). Discrete cortical regions associated with knowledge of color and knowledge of action. *Science, 270,* p. 104.

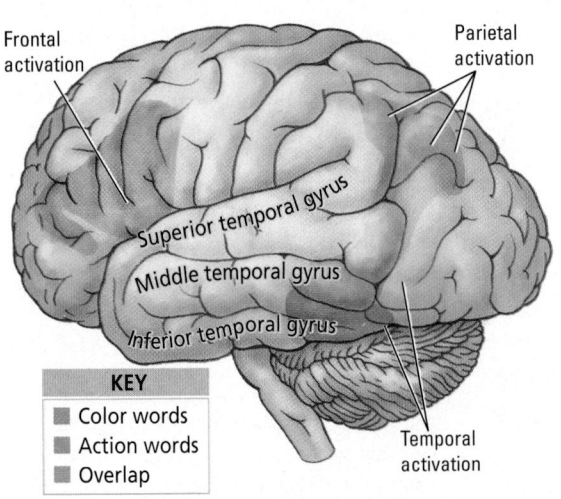

What Is Special about Personal Memories?

One aspect of memory unique to each of us is our personal, or *autobiographical*, memory. This **episodic memory** includes not only a record of events (episodes) that took place but also a record of our presence and role in the events. Our personal experiences form the basis of who we are and the rules by which we live. That is, we have memories not only for events but also for their context at a particular time in a particular place. We thus gain a concept of time and a sense of our personal role in a changing world.

Imagine what would happen if we lost our personal memories. We would still recall events but we would be unable to see our role in them. People with frontal lobe injuries sometimes exhibit such symptoms, as illustrated in a case described by Endel Tulving (2002).

K. C. suffered a serious traumatic brain injury in a motorcycle accident that produced multiple cortical and subcortical lesions. Remarkably, K. C.'s cognitive abilities were intact and indistinguishable from those of most typical healthy adults. He played chess and the organ, and his short-term memory was intact. He knew who he was and when his birthday was, the names of schools he had attended, and the location of the family cottage. Recalling facts, figures, dates and times posed no difficulty for K. C.

What K. C. could not do was to recall any personally experienced events. This episodic amnesia covered his entire life, from birth. He knew facts about himself but had no memory for events that included him personally. For example, K. C. could not describe an event that took place in school that specifically included him, while at the same time recalling going to school and the knowledge he had gained there.

Findings from neuroimaging studies of people with episodic amnesia suggest that they consistently have frontal lobe injuries (Lepage et al., 2001), but exactly why these lesions produce episodic amnesia remains unclear. Nonetheless, Tulving made the interesting proposal that episodic memory is a marvel of nature: it transforms the brain into a kind of time machine that allows us to dwell on the past and make plans for the future. He goes further, suggesting that this ability may be unique to humans and is presumably due to some novel evolutionary development of the frontal lobe.

Not all people with episodic amnesia have brain injury, however. Many case reports describe patients with massive memory disturbances resulting from some "psychiatric" or "psychogenic" disorder. Such cases have been fodder for numerous movie plots. Hans Markowitsch (2003) noted that the amnesia reported in some of these cases is remarkably similar to episodic amnesia seen in neurological patients. Neuroimaging of patients with *psychogenic amnesia* shows a massive reduction in brain activity in frontal regions, a reduction remarkably similar to that seen in neurological patients with episodic amnesia **(Figure 14-6)**. Therefore, we can assume that patients with psychogenic amnesias have a dysfunction of frontal brain activity that blocks the retrieval of autobiographical memory.

Just as some people exhibit poor autobiographical memory, a rare group displays *highly superior autobiographical memory* (HSAM) (LePort et al., 2012). These people display virtually complete recall for events in their lives, usually beginning around age 10, and can often describe any episode, including the day of the week that it occurred and the date. They can even recall the weather that day, as well as social and public events. Brain imaging of those who display HSAM shows increased gray matter in the temporal and parietal lobes and increased size in the fiber projection between the temporal and frontal lobes.

Lawrence Pathihis and colleagues (2013) wondered if HSAM individuals might also be immune to memory distortion, such as the false memories described earlier. The investigators found that HSAM individuals are as likely to develop false memories as are other participants. Whatever the source of their extraordinary autobiographical memory, it does not prevent the sort of memory distortions the rest of us experience. Possibly that is because the research paradigms employed are not strictly autobiographical.

episodic memory Autobiographical memory for events pegged to specific place and time contexts.

FIGURE 14-6 Lost Episodes Left to right: Horizontal, frontal, and sagittal sections imaged in a patient with impaired autobiographical memory. White arrows point to areas of reduced glucose metabolism in frontal and temporal regions as she attempts to retrieve remote personal memories. Her MRI scan was normal. Republished with permission of Elsevier Science and Technology Journals from "The impairment of recollection in functional amnesic states" Hans J. Markowitsch and Angelica Staniloiu, *Cortex 49* (2013) 1494–1510. Permission conveyed through Copyright Clearance Center, Inc.

Connecting Learning and Memory

Before you continue, check your understanding.

1. An organism learns that some stimulus is paired with a reward. This is _____ conditioning.

2. After learning that consequences follow its behavior, an organism modifies its behavior. This is _____ conditioning.

3. Information that is unconsciously learned forms _____ memory, whereas specific factual information forms _____ memory.

4. _____ memory is autobiographical and unique to each person.

5. Where is memory stored in the brain?

Answers appear at the back of the book.

For additional study tools, visit 🌀 LaunchPad:
www.macmillanhighered.com/launchpad/kolb5e

14-2 Dissociating Memory Circuits

Beginning in the 1920s and continuing until the early 1950s, American psychologist Karl Lashley searched in vain for the neural circuits underlying memories. Lashley's working hypothesis was that memories must be represented in the perceptual and motor circuitry used to learn to solve problems. To find that circuitry, he investigated the ways laboratory rats and monkeys learn specific tasks for food reward. He believed that if he removed bits of this circuitry or disconnected it, amnesia should result.

Brain lesions are an ablation technique—the first and simplest brain manipulation; see Section 7-1.

In fact, neither ablation procedure produced amnesia. Lashley found instead that the severity of memory disturbance was related to the size of the lesion rather than to its location. After searching for 30 years, Lashley concluded that he had failed to find the location of a memory trace, although he believed that he knew where it was *not* located (Lashley, 1960).

Just two years later, neurosurgeon William Scoville discovered serendipitously what Lashley's studies had not predicted. Scoville was attempting to rid people of seizures by removing the abnormal brain tissue that caused them. In August 1953, Scoville performed a bilateral medial temporal lobe resection on a young man, Henry Molaison (H. M.), whose severe epilepsy was not controlled by medication. H. M.'s seizures originated in the medial temporal lobe region, so Scoville bilaterally removed much of the hippocampal formation, along with some of the amygdala and adjacent neocortical structures. The procedure left the more lateral temporal lobe tissue intact. As shown in **Figure 14-7**, removal specifically included the anterior part of the hippocampus, the amygdala, and adjacent cortex.

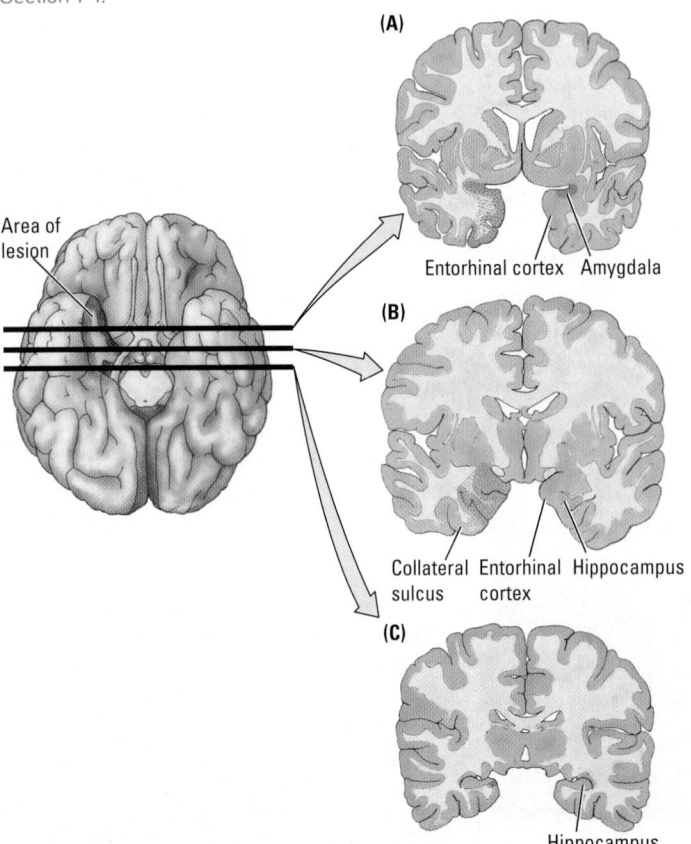

FIGURE 14-7 Extent of H. M.'s Surgery H. M.'s right-hemisphere lesion is highlighted in the brain viewed ventrally. The lesion runs along the wall of the medial temporal lobe. The left side of the brain has been left intact to show the relative location of the medial temporal structures. Parts A, B, and C, based on MRI scans, depict a series of coronal sections of H. M.'s brain. Research from S. Corkin, D. G. Amaral, R. G. Gonzalez , K. A. Johnson, & B. T. Hyman (1997). H. M.'s medial temporal lobe lesion: findings from magnetic resonance imaging. by *Journal of Neuroscience, 17,* p. 3966.

Disconnecting Explicit Memory

The behavioral symptoms Scoville noted after the surgery were completely unexpected. He invited Brenda Milner (Milner et al., 1968) to study H. M. Milner had been studying memory difficulties in patients with unilateral temporal lobe removals for the treatment of epilepsy. She and her colleagues worked with H. M. for more than 50 years, making his the most studied case in neuroscience (e.g., Corkin, 2002). H. M. died in 2008.

His most remarkable symptom was severe amnesia: he was unable to recall anything that had happened since his surgery in 1953. H. M. retained an above-average I.Q. score (118 on the Wechsler Adult Intelligence Scale; 100 is average), and he performed at normal on perceptual tests. His recall of events from his childhood and school days was intact. Socially, H. M. was well mannered, and he engaged in sophisticated conversations. However, he had no recall for recent events. H. M. lacked any explicit memory.

In one study by Suzanne Corkin (2002), H. M. was given a tray of hospital food, which he ate. A few minutes later, he was given another tray. He did not recall having eaten the first meal and proceeded to eat another. A third tray was brought, and this time he ate only the dessert, explaining that he did not seem to be very hungry.

To understand the implications and severity of H. M.'s condition, one need only consider a few events in his postsurgical life. His father died, but H. M. continued to ask where his father was, only to experience anew the grief of learning that his father had passed away. (Eventually H. M. stopped asking about his father, suggesting that some type of learning had taken place.)

Similarly, in the hospital, he typically asked the nurses, with many apologies, to tell him where he was and how he came to be there. He remarked on one occasion, "Every day is alone in itself, whatever enjoyment I've had and whatever sorrow I've had." He perceived his surroundings but could not comprehend his situation because he did not remember what had gone before.

Formal tests of H. M.'s memory showed, as you would expect, no recall for specific information just presented. In contrast, his implicit memory performance was nearly intact. He performed at normal on tests such as the incomplete figure and pursuit rotor tasks, illustrated in Figures 14-3 and 14-4, respectively. So while his implicit memory system must have been intact, the systems crucial to explicit memory were missing or dysfunctional. Yet H. M. recognized faces, including his own, and he recognized that he aged. Face recognition depends on the parahippocampal gyrus, which was partly intact on H. M.'s right side. Clinical Focus 14-2, Patient Boswell's Amnesia, describes a case similar to H. M.'s.

Prosopagnosia, an inability to recognize faces, and other visual form agnosias are topics in Chapter 9.

Disconnecting Implicit Memory

Among the reasons Lashley's research did not find a syndrome like that shown by H. M., the two most important are that Lashley did not damage the medial temporal regions. Nor did he use tests of explicit memory, so his animal subjects would not have shown H. M.'s deficits. Rather, Lashley's tests were mostly measures of implicit memory, with which H. M. had no problems.

The following case illustrates that Lashley probably should have been looking in the basal ganglia for the deficits that his implicit memory tests revealed. The basal ganglia play a central role in motor control. Among the compelling examples of implicit memory is motor learning—driving and playing musical instruments or online games, to name a few.

J. K. was above average in intelligence and worked as a petroleum engineer for 45 years. In his mid-70s, he began to show symptoms of Parkinson disease, in which the projections from the dopaminergic cells of the brainstem to the basal ganglia die. At about age 78, J. K.'s memory difficulties started.

Focus features 5-2, 5-3, and 5-4 and Section 7-1 detail aspects of Parkinson disease. Section 16-3 reviews treatments.

Curiously, his memory disturbance was related to tasks J. K. had performed his whole life. On one occasion, he stood at his bedroom door, frustrated by his inability to recall how to turn on the lights. "I must be crazy," he remarked. "I've done this all my life and now I can't remember how to do it!" On another occasion, he was seen trying to turn the radio off with the television remote control. This time he explained, "I don't recall how to turn off the radio so I thought I would try this thing!"

Patient Boswell's Amnesia

At the age of 48, Boswell developed herpes simplex encephalitis, a brain infection. He had completed 13 years of schooling and had worked for nearly 30 years in newspaper advertising. By all accounts a normal, well-adjusted person, Boswell was successful in his profession.

Boswell recovered from the acute symptoms, including seizures and a 3-day coma. His intelligence post disease was low average, probably owing to neurological damage caused by the infection. Nonetheless, his speech and language remained typical in every respect, and he showed no perceptual or movement deficits.

But Boswell was left with a severe amnesic syndrome. If he hears a short paragraph and is asked to describe its main points, he routinely scores zero. He can only guess the day's date and is unable even to guess the year. When asked what city he is in, he simply guesses.

Boswell does know his place of birth and can correctly recall his birth date about half the time. In sum, Boswell has severe amnesia for events both before and since his encephalitis. Like H. M., he does show implicit memory on tests such as the pursuit rotor task.

Antonio Damasio and his colleagues (1989) have investigated Boswell's amnesia extensively, and his brain pathology is now well documented. The critical damage, diagrammed in the adjoining illustration, is bilateral destruction of the medial temporal regions and a loss of the basal forebrain and the posterior part of the orbitofrontal cortex. In addition, Boswell has lost the insular cortex from the lateral fissure (not visible in the illustration).

Boswell's sensory and motor cortices are intact, as are his basal ganglia, but his injury is more extensive than H. M.'s. Like H. M., he has no new memories. Unlike H. M., he also has a severe loss of access to

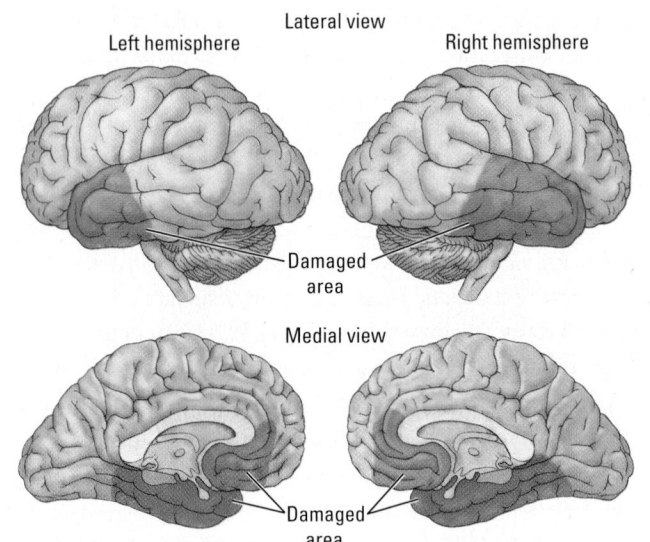

After recovering from a herpes simplex encephalitis infection, patient Boswell has great difficulty remembering events before and after his illness. Areas of damage in the medial temporal region, basal forebrain, and posterior orbitofrontal cortex are highlighted in red. Compare Figure 14-6.

old information, probably owing to his insular and prefrontal injuries. Nonetheless, again like H. M.'s, Boswell's procedural memory is intact, illustrating the dissociation between neural circuits underlying explicit and implicit forms of memory.

J. K.'s clear implicit memory deficit contrasts sharply with his awareness of daily events. He recalled explicit events as well as most men his age and spoke intelligently on issues of the day that he had just read about. Once when two of us visited him, one of us entered the room first and he immediately asked where the other was, even though it had been 2 weeks since we told him that we would be coming to visit.

This intact long-term memory is vastly different from H. M.'s situation: he would not have remembered that anybody was coming even 5 minutes after being told. Because Parkinson disease primarily affects the basal ganglia, J. K.'s deficit in implicit memory was probably related to his basal ganglia dysfunction.

14-2 REVIEW

Dissociating Memory Circuits

Before you continue, check your understanding.

1. Based on the case of H. M., we can conclude that the structures involved in explicit memory include the _____, the _____, and adjacent cortex.

2. Implicit memory deficits in patients with Parkinson disease demonstrate that a major structure in implicit memory is the _____.

3. What is the main difference between the Lashley and Milner studies?

Answers appear at the back of the book.

14-3 Neural Systems Underlying Explicit and Implicit Memories

Findings from laboratory studies, largely on rats and monkeys, have reproduced the symptoms of patients such as H. M. and J. K. by injuring the animals' medial temporal regions and basal ganglia, respectively. Other structures, most notably in the frontal and temporal lobes, also participate in certain types of explicit memory. We now consider the systems for explicit and implicit memory separately.

Neural Circuit for Explicit Memories

The dramatic amnesic syndrome discovered in H. M. in the 1950s led investigators to focus on the hippocampus, at the time regarded as a large brain structure in search of a function. But H. M. had other damaged structures, too, and the initial focus on the hippocampus as the location of explicit memory processing turned out to be misguided.

After decades of anatomical and behavioral studies sorted out the complexities, consensus on the anatomy of explicit memory had coalesced by the mid-1990s. The primary structures for explicit memory include the medial temporal region, the frontal cortex, and structures closely related to them.

Before considering the model, we first revisit medial temporal anatomy. Review Figure 14-5's summary of findings, which show that memories for objects' colors and motion characteristics reside in separate temporal lobe locations. Thus the medial temporal region receives multiple sensory inputs.

The macaque monkey's medial temporal region shares many anatomical similarities with the region in the human brain. In addition to the hippocampus and amygdala, three medial temporal areas illustrated in **Figure 14-8** take part in explicit memory: lying adjacent to the hippocampus are the **entorhinal cortex**, the **parahippocampal cortex**, and the **perirhinal cortex**. A sequential arrangement of two-way connections, charted in **Figure 14-9**, projects from the major cortical regions into the perirhinal and parahippocampal cortices, which in turn project to the entorhinal cortex, then to the hippocampus.

The prominent cortical input to the perirhinal region is from the visual ventral stream coursing through the temporal lobe. The perirhinal region is thus a prime candidate location for visual object memory. Similarly, the parahippocampal cortex receives strong input from parietal regions believed to take part in visuospatial processing and likely

entorhinal cortex Located on the medial temporal lobe surface; provides a major route for neocortical input to the hippocampal formation; often degenerates in Alzheimer disease.

parahippocampal cortex Cortex located along the dorsal medial temporal lobe surface.

perirhinal cortex Cortex lying next to the rhinal fissure on the ventral surface of the brain.

Turns out, the hippocampus participates in species-specific behaviors, spatial navigation, and memory, and it is vulnerable to stress.

Consult sources published before 1995, and you may find explanations for memory far different from this chapter's (see Gazzaniga, 2000).

In Greek, *para* means *beside*; *rhino* means *nose*. The perirhinal cortex lies beside the rhinal sulcus on the bottom of the brain.

FIGURE 14-8 Medial Temporal Structures Ventral view of the rhesus macaque monkey brain. Left side: The medial temporal regions. Each plays a distinct role in processing sensory information for memory storage. Right side: The hippocampus and amygdala are not directly visible from the brain surface; they lie within the cortical regions illustrated on the left. All these structures are present on both sides of the brain.

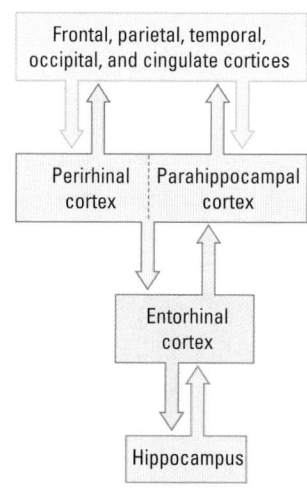

FIGURE 14-9 Reciprocal Medial Temporal Connections Flow of input from the sensory cortices: first to the parahippocampal and perirhinal regions, then to the entorhinal cortex, and finally to the hippocampus. The hippocampus feeds back to the medial temporal regions and then to the neocortical sensory regions.

Alzheimer Disease

In the 1880s it was noted that the brain may undergo atrophy with aging, but the reason was not really understood until the German physician Alois Alzheimer published a landmark study in 1906. Alzheimer described a set of behavioral symptoms and associated neuropathology in a 51-year-old woman who was demented. The cellular structure of her neocortex and allocortex showed various abnormalities.

An estimated 5.4 million people in the United States have Alzheimer disease, although the only certain diagnostic test remains postmortem examination of cerebral tissue. The disease progresses slowly, and many people with Alzheimer disease probably die of other causes before the cognitive symptoms incapacitate them.

We knew of a physics professor who continued to work until, when he was nearly 80, he died of a heart attack. Postmortem examination of his brain revealed significant Alzheimer pathology. His colleagues had attributed the professor's slipping memory to the old-timer's disease.

The cause of Alzheimer disease remains unknown, although it has been variously attributed to genetic predisposition, abnormal levels of trace elements (e.g., aluminum), immune reactions, slow viruses, and *prions* (abnormal, infectious forms of proteins). Two principal neuronal changes take place in Alzheimer disease:

1. *Loss of cholinergic cells in the basal forebrain.* One treatment for Alzheimer disease, therefore, is medication that increases acetylcholine levels in the forebrain. An example is Exelon, which is the trade name for rivastigmine, a cholinergic agonist that appears to provide temporary relief from the progression of the disease and is available both orally and as a skin patch.

2. *Development of neuritic plaques in the cerebral cortex.* A **neuritic plaque** consists of a central core of homogeneous protein material (*amyloid*) surrounded by degenerative cellular fragments. The plaques are not distributed evenly throughout the cortex but are concentrated especially in temporal lobe areas related to memory. Neuritic plaques are often associated with another abnormality, neurofibrillary tangles, paired helical filaments found in both the cerebral cortex and the hippocampus. The prion paradigm holds that misfolded tau proteins, illustrated here, which have the ability to self-propagate, cause many

age-related neurodegenerative diseases (Walker & Jucker, 2015). Researchers are conducting clinical trials on new drugs that act either to find and neutralize misfolded proteins or as immunizing agents, to prevent protein misfolding (Wisniewski & Goni, 2015).

Cortical neurons begin to deteriorate as the cholinergic loss, plaques, and tangles develop. The first cells to die are in the entorhinal cortex (see Figure 14-8). Significant memory disturbance ensues.

A controversial idea emerging from stroke neurologists is that dementia may reflect a chronic cerebrovascular condition, marginal high blood pressure. Marginal elevations in blood pressure can lead to cerebral microbleeds, especially in white matter. The cumulative effect of years or even decades of tiny bleeds would eventually lead to increasingly disturbed cognition. This may first appear as *mild cognitive impairment* (MCI) that slowly progresses with cumulative microbleeds.

Thomas Deerinck, MCMIR/Science Source

The red area near the cell nucleus in this false-color brain cell from a person with Alzheimer disease represents a neurofibrillary tangle of misfolded tau proteins.

Section 9-2 traces visual pathways in detail.

Section 16-3 elaborates on Alzheimer and other dementias and on prion theory.

participates in **visuospatial memory**—using visual information to recall an object's location in space.

Because both the perirhinal and the parahippocampal regions project to the entorhinal cortex, this region probably participates in more integrative memory functions. The entorhinal cortex is in fact the first area to show cell death in Alzheimer disease, a dementia characterized by severe deficits in explicit memory (see Clinical Focus 14-3, Alzheimer Disease).

The Hippocampus and Spatial Memory

We are left with a conundrum. If the hippocampus is not the key structure in explicit memory even as it receives the entorhinal connections, what does it do? John O'Keefe and

Lynn Nadel were the first to advance the idea, in 1978, that the hippocampus is probably engaged in visuospatial memory processes required for places, such as recalling an object's location.

Certainly both laboratory animals and human patients with selective hippocampal injury have severe deficits in various forms of spatial memory. Similarly, monkeys with hippocampal lesions have difficulty learning the location of objects (*visuospatial learning*), as can be demonstrated in tasks such as the ones illustrated in **Figure 14-10.**

Monkeys are trained to displace objects to obtain a food reward (Figure 14-10A), then given one of two tasks. In the *visual recognition task* (Figure 14-10B), the animal displaces a sample object for the food reward. After a short delay, the animal is presented with two objects. One is novel. The task is to learn to displace the novel object for the food reward. This task tests explicit visual object memory. Monkeys with perirhinal lesions are impaired at the task.

In the *object position task* in Figure 14-10C, the monkey is shown one object to be displaced for a food reward. Then the monkey is shown the same object along with a second identical one. The task is to learn to displace the object that is in the same position as it was in the initial presentation. Monkeys with hippocampal lesions are selectively impaired at this task.

From these results, we would predict that a species with an especially good spatial memory should have bigger hippocampi than do species with a poorer spatial memory. David Sherry and his colleagues (1992) tested this hypothesis in birds.

Many birds are cachers: they harvest sunflower seeds and other favored foods and hide (cache) them to eat later. Some birds can find hundreds of items they have cached. To evaluate whether the hippocampus plays a role in this activity, Sherry and his coworkers measured hippocampal size in closely related bird species, only one of which is a food cacher. As shown in **Figure 14-11,** the hippocampal formation is larger in birds that cache food than in birds that do not. In fact, the hippocampi of food-storing birds are more than twice as large as expected for birds of their brain size and body weight.

Sherry found a similar relation when he compared different species of food-storing rodents. Merriam's kangaroo rats, rodents that store food throughout their territory, have larger

neuritic plaque Area of incomplete necrosis (dead tissue) consisting of a central protein core (amyloid) surrounded by degenerative cellular fragments; often seen in the cortex of people with dementias such as Alzheimer disease.

visuospatial memory Use of visual information to recall an object's location in space.

Section 1-4 explains the encephalization quotient, an index of ratios of brain to body size. EQs allow comparisons of the relative brain sizes of different species.

FIGURE 14-10 Two Memory Tasks for Monkeys **(A)** In "basic training," a monkey learns to displace an object to obtain a food reward. In **(B)** and **(C)** the plus and minus signs indicate whether the object (1) is or (2) is not associated with food.

(A) Basic training

A monkey is shown an object,...

...which it then displaces to obtain a food reward.

(B) Visual-recognition task

A monkey is trained to displace an object to obtain a food reward...

...then shown two objects. The task is to displace the *new* object to obtain the reward.

(C) Object-position task

The monkey is shown one object to displace for a food reward.

On the next trial, the monkey is shown two identical objects and must choose the one at the same location as in the initial presentation.

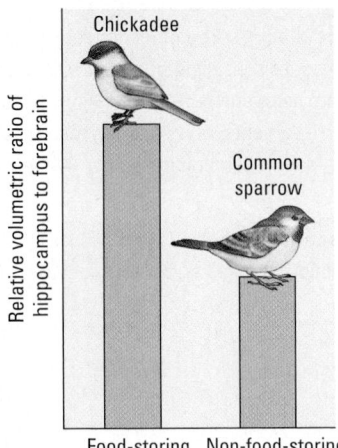

FIGURE 14-11 Inferring Spatial Memory This graph relates hippocampal volume to forebrain volume in food-storing (left) and non-food-storing (right) families of songbirds. Birds that cache food, such as the black-capped chickadee, have hippocampi about twice as large as those of birds, such as the sparrow, that are not cachers. Data from D. F. Sherry, L. F. Jacobs, & S. J. C. Gaulin (1992). Spatial memory and adaptive specialization of the hippocampus. *Trends in Neuroscience, 15*, pp. 298–303.

hippocampi than bannertail kangaroo rats, which store food only in their burrow. Hippocampal size, both in birds and in mammals, appears to be related to the cognitive demands of two highly spatial activities, foraging for and storing food.

One prediction we might make based on the Sherry experiments is that people who have a job with high spatial demands have large hippocampi. Taxi drivers in London fit this category. Successful candidates for a cab driver's license in London must demonstrate that they know the location of every street in that huge and ancient city. Using MRI, Eleanor Maguire and her colleagues (2000) found the posterior region of the hippocampus in London taxi drivers to be significantly larger than the same region in the control participants. This finding presumably explains why a select few pass a spatial memory test that most of us would fail miserably.

Spatial Cells in the Hippocampal Formation

Given the role of the hippocampus in spatial behavior, we might predict that individual cells would code spatial information. They do. Three classes of spatially related cells have been identified in the rat and mouse hippocampus (**Figure 14-12**). Together they form an internal GPS, a neural global positioning system. That is, neurons vigorously fire when an animal is in a specific place in the environment. In 2014, John O'Keefe, Edvard Moser, and May-Britt Moser were awarded the Nobel Prize in Physiology or Medicine for this discovery.

Place cells, shown in Figure 14-12A and B, discharge when rats are in a spatial location, irrespective of its orientation. *Head direction cells* (Figure 14-12C) discharge whenever a rat's head points in a particular direction. *Grid cells* (Figure 14-12D) discharge at many locations, forming a virtual grid invariant to changes in the rat's direction, movement, or speed.

These cells are not localized to the hippocampus but are found within a network that includes the hippocampus as its central structure. Place cells and head direction cells are located in the hippocampus and closely related structures. Grid cells are found in the entorhinal cortex, a major afferent route into the hippocampus (see Figure 14-9). Taken together, we can envision the place cell system as indicating where things are in the world, the grid system indicating how big our present navigating environment is, and the head direction and grid systems telling us where we ourselves are in the environment.

Reciprocal Connections for Explicit Memory

Explicit memory's temporal pathway is reciprocal: connections from the neocortex run to the entorhinal cortex, then back to the neocortex (see Figure 14-9). Reciprocal connections have two benefits:

1. Signals from the medial temporal regions back to the cortical sensory regions keep the sensory experience alive in the brain: the neural record of an experience outlasts the actual experience.

FIGURE 14-12 Classes of Spatially Related Cells in the Hippocampal Formation At right in each part, X–Y coordinates indicate the directional selectivity of the cell recorded at left. **(A and B)** Place cells discharge when a rat is at a spatial location, irrespective of its orientation. **(C)** Head direction cells discharge when the rat's head points in a given direction, irrespective of its location. **(D)** Grid cells discharge at many locations, forming a virtual grid that is invariant in the face of changes in the rat's direction, movement, or speed. Research from O'Keefe, 2006, Fig. 11-21.

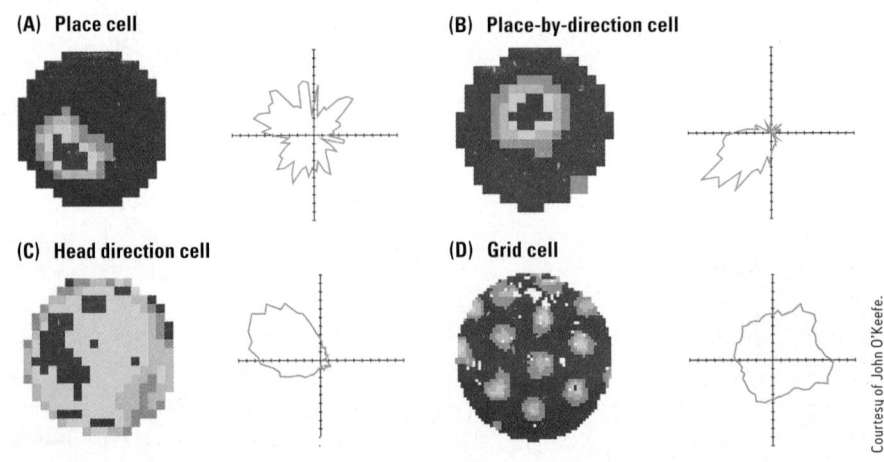

(A) Place cell

(B) Place-by-direction cell

(C) Head direction cell

(D) Grid cell

Courtesy of John O'Keefe.

2. The pathway back to the neocortex keeps it appraised of information being processed in the medial temporal regions.

Although we have focused on the medial temporal regions, other structures also are important in explicit memory. People with frontal lobe injuries are not amnesic like H. M. or J. K., but they do have difficulties with memory for the temporal (time) order of events. Imagine being shown a series of photographs and asked to remember them. A few minutes later, you are asked whether you recognize two photographs and if so, to indicate which one you saw first.

H. M. would not remember the photographs. People with frontal lobe injuries would recall seeing the photographs but would have difficulty recalling which one they had seen more recently. The frontal lobe's role in explicit memory clearly is subtler than that of the medial temporal lobe.

THE FRONTAL LOBE AND SHORT-TERM MEMORY All sensory systems in the brain send information to the frontal lobe, as do the medial temporal regions. This information is not used for direct sensory analysis, so it must have another purpose. In general, the frontal lobe appears to participate in many forms of short-term memory.

Joaquin Fuster (e.g., Fuster, Bodner, & Kroger, 2000) studied single-cell activity in the frontal lobe during short-term memory tasks. For example, if monkeys are shown an object that they must remember for a short time before being allowed to make a response, neurons in the prefrontal cortex show sustained firing during the delay. Consider the tests illustrated in **Figure 14-13**:

• In the general design for each test, a monkey is shown a light (the cue), and after a delay it must make a response to get a reward.

• In the *delayed-response task*, the monkey is shown two lights in the choice test and must choose the one that is in the same location as the cue.

• In the *delayed-alternation task*, the monkey is again shown two lights in the choice tests but now must choose the light that is *not* in the same location as the cue.

• In the *delayed matching-to-sample task*, the monkey is shown, say, a red light, then, after a delay, a red and a green light. The task is to choose the red light regardless of its new location.

Fuster found that in each task certain cells in the prefrontal cortex fire throughout the delay. Animals that have not learned the task show no such cell activity. Curiously, if a trained animal makes an error, its cellular activity corresponds: the cells stop responding before the error occurs. They have "forgotten" the cue.

TRACING THE EXPLICIT MEMORY CIRCUIT People who have chronically abused alcohol can develop an explicit memory disturbance known as **Korsakoff syndrome.** In some cases, severe deficits in explicit memory extend to implicit memory as well. Korsakoff syndrome is caused by a thiamine (vitamin B_1) deficiency that kills cells in the medial part of the diencephalon—the between brain at the top of the brainstem—including the medial thalamus and mammillary bodies in the hypothalamus. In 80 percent of Korsakoff patients, the frontal lobes show atrophy (loss of cells). The memory disturbance is probably so severe because the damage includes not only forebrain but also brainstem structures (see Clinical Focus 14-4, Korsakoff Syndrome).

Mortimer Mishkin and his colleagues (Mishkin, 1982; Murray, 2000) proposed a neural circuit for explicit memory that incorporates the evidence from both humans and laboratory animals with injuries to the temporal and frontal lobes. **Figure 14-14** presents a modified version of the Mishkin model. Anatomically (Figure 14-4A), it includes not only the frontal and temporal

The basal ganglia systems that take part in implicit memory do not feed back to the cortex, which helps explain its unconscious nature.

In the following tests, a monkey is shown a light, which is the cue, and then it makes a response after a delay.

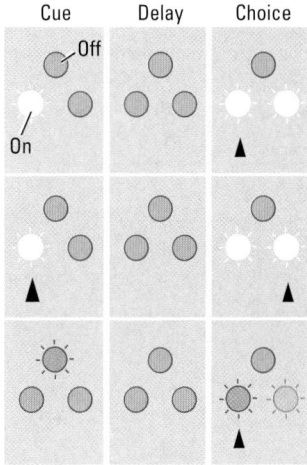

Delayed-response task: The monkey must choose the light that is in the same location as the cue.

Delayed-alternation task: The monkey must choose the light that is not in the same location as the cue.

Delayed matching-to-sample task: The monkey must choose the light that is the same color as the cue.

Cue   Delay   Choice

Time ⟶

FIGURE 14-13 Testing Short-Term Memory A monkey performing a short-term memory task responds by pressing the disc to get a fruit juice reward (top). The correct disc varies, depending on the task requirements (bottom). (For each task, an arrowhead shows the correct choice.)
Information from J. Fuster (1995). *Memory in the cerebral cortex* (p. 178). Cambridge, MA: MIT Press.

Korsakoff syndrome Permanent loss of the ability to learn new information (anterograde amnesia) and to retrieve old information (retrograde amnesia) caused by diencephalic damage resulting from chronic alcoholism or malnutrition that produces a vitamin B_1 deficiency.

Korsakoff Syndrome

Over the long term, alcoholism, especially when accompanied by malnutrition, obliterates memory. When 62-year-old Joe R. was hospitalized, his family complained that his memory had become abysmal. His intelligence was in the average range, and he had no obvious sensory or motor difficulties. Nevertheless, he could not say why he was in the hospital and usually stated that he was actually in a hotel.

When asked what he had done the previous night, Joe R. typically said that he "went to the Legion for a few beers with the boys." Although he had, in fact, been in the hospital, it was a sensible response because going to the Legion is what he had done on most nights in the preceding 30 years.

Joe R. was not certain what he had done for a living but believed he had been a butcher. In fact, he had been a truck driver for a local delivery firm. His son was a butcher, however, so once again his story related to something in his life.

Joe's memory for immediate events was little better. On one occasion, we asked him to remember having met us; then we left the room. On our return 2 or 3 minutes later, he had no recollection of ever having met us or of having taken psychological tests that we had administered.

Joe R. had Korsakoff syndrome. Sergei Korsakoff was a Russian physician who in the 1880s first called attention to a syndrome that accompanies chronic alcoholism. The most obvious symptom is severe memory loss, including amnesia for both information learned in the past (**retrograde amnesia**) and information learned since the onset of the memory disturbance (**anterograde amnesia**).

One unique characteristic of the amnesic syndrome in Korsakoff patients is that they tend to make up stories about past events rather than admit that they do not remember. These stories are generally plausible, like those Joe R. told, because they are based on actual experiences.

Curiously, Korsakoff patients have little insight into their memory disturbance and are generally indifferent to suggestions that they have a memory problem. Such patients are generally apathetic to what's going on around them too. Joe R. was often seen watching television when the set was turned off.

The cause of Korsakoff syndrome is a thiamine (vitamin B₁) deficiency resulting from poor diet and prolonged intake of large quantities of alcohol. (In addition to a "few beers with the boys," Joe R. had a long history of drinking a 26-ounce bottle of rum every day.) The thiamine deficiency results in the death of cells in the midline diencephalon, including especially the medial regions of the thalamus and the mammillary bodies of the hypothalamus.

Most Korsakoff patients also show cortical atrophy, especially in the frontal lobe. With the appearance of Korsakoff symptoms, which can happen suddenly, prognosis is poor. Only about 20 percent of patients show much recovery after a year on a vitamin B₁–enriched diet. Joe R. has shown no recovery after several years and will spend the rest of his life in a hospital setting.

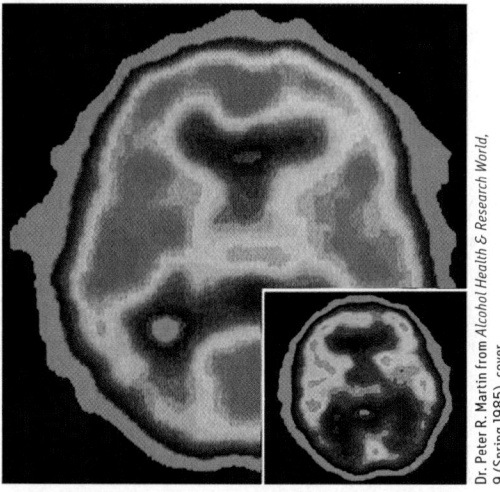

Dr. Peter R. Martin from *Alcohol Health & Research World*, 9 (Spring 1985), cover

PET scans from a healthy patient (larger image) and a Korsakoff patient (inset) reveal reduced activity in the frontal lobes of the diseased brain. (The frontal lobes are at the bottom center of each scan.) Red and yellow represent areas of high metabolic activity; activity is lower in the darker areas.

lobes but also the medial thalamus, implicated in Korsakoff syndrome, and the basal forebrain–activating systems implicated in Alzheimer disease. Figure 14-4B charts the information flow:

- Sensory and motor neocortical areas send their connections to the medial temporal regions, which are in turn connected to the medial thalamus and prefrontal cortex.

- Basal forebrain structures are hypothesized to play a role in maintaining appropriate activity levels in other forebrain structures so that they can process information.

(A)

Basal forebrain
Thalamus
Neocortex
Prefrontal cortex
Amygdala
Rhinal cortex
Hippocampus

(B)

Prefrontal cortex → Temporal-lobe structures → Rest of neocortex ← Sensory and motor information

Medial thalamus

Brainstem-to-cortex activating systems
Acetylcholine
Serotonin
Noradrenaline

- The temporal lobe structures are hypothesized to be central to long-term explicit memory formation.

- The prefrontal cortex is central to maintaining temporary (short-term) explicit memories as well as memory for the recency (chronological order) of explicit events.

Consolidation of Explicit Memories

Amnesia often appears to be time-dependent. H. M. could not form new explicit memories but appeared to have good recall of facts and events from periods long before his surgery, including his childhood. Such findings led to the idea that the medial temporal region could *not* be the ultimate storage site for long-term memories; more likely that site was the neocortex (for a review, see Squire et al., 2015).

This idea led to the hypothesis that the hippocampus *consolidates* new memories, a process that makes them permanent. In **consolidation,** or stabilizing a memory trace after learning, memories move from the hippocampus to diffuse neocortical regions. Once they move, hippocampal involvement is no longer needed.

It is not clear how memories are moved, however, or how long it takes. Robert Sutherland and his colleagues (2010) propose a model of consolidation, the *distributed reinstatement theory*. In their model, a learning episode rapidly produces a stored memory representation that is strong in the hippocampus but weak elsewhere. The memory is replayed on the time scale of hours or days after the learning, leading to enhanced representations outside the hippocampus. Each repetition of the learning—that is, each practice—progressively enhances the nonhippocampal memory representation. Then if the hippocampus is extensively damaged, the memory remains.

Memory is not constant over time. When people get misleading information about events they have experienced, for example, their later recall of those events often is modified. Indeed, this contributes to the notorious unreliability of eyewitness testimony. (Do you remember the "smashing" and "bumping" car collisions from Section 14-1?) The fact that memories appear changeable seems to fly in the face of the consolidation concept, which presumes that once consolidated, memories are fixed.

One solution to this conundrum suggests that whenever a memory is replayed in the mind, it is open to further consolidation, or **reconsolidation,** the process of restabilizing a memory trace after the memory is revisited. Interest in this idea has been intense, and although the final story is yet to be written, it appears that reconsolidation does occur, at least for some types of memories.

One way to think of the process is to see memory consolidation as never-ending: new information is constantly being integrated into existing memory networks (for a review, see McKenzie and Eichenbaum, 2011). After all, we frequently recall memories, rehash them,

FIGURE 14-14 Reciprocal Neural Circuit Proposed for Explicit Memory **(A)** General neuroanatomical areas controlling explicit memory. **(B)** The information flow begins on the right with inputs from the sensory and motor systems, which are not considered part of the explicit memory circuit.

retrograde amnesia Inability to remember events that took place before the onset of amnesia.

anterograde amnesia Inability to remember events subsequent to a disturbance of the brain such as head trauma, electroconvulsive shock, or neurodegenerative disease.

consolidation Process of stabilizing a memory trace after learning.

reconsolidation Process of restabilizing a memory trace after the memory is revisited.

and integrate them with new events. Our memories are not laid on a tabula rasa but must be interwoven into a lifetime of memories.

One implication of reconsolidation is that it ought to be possible to erase negative memories by using amnesic agents when the memory is revisited. This idea has important implications for reducing or eliminating the effects of strong emotional experiences, such as those seen in posttraumatic stress disorder (PTSD). One promising agent is the inert gas xenon, which has been used in humans as a fast-acting anesthetic and has been shown to erase memories during reconsolidation in a rat model of PTSD (Meloni et al., 2014).

Neural Circuit for Implicit Memories

Hypothesizing that the basal ganglia are central to implicit memory, Mishkin and his colleagues proposed a neural circuit for implicit memories (Mishkin, 1982; Mishkin et al., 1997). As **Figure 14-15** shows, the basal ganglia receive input from the entire neocortex and send projections first to the ventral thalamus and then to the premotor cortex. The basal ganglia also receive widely and densely distributed projections from dopamine-producing cells in the substantia nigra. Dopamine appears necessary for basal ganglia circuits to function and may indirectly participate in implicit memory formation.

The connection from the cortex to the basal ganglia in the implicit memory system flows only in one direction. Most of the neocortex receives no direct information regarding activities in the basal ganglia. Mishkin believes that this unidirectional flow accounts for the unconscious nature of implicit memories. For memories to be conscious, the neocortical regions involved must receive feedback, as they do in the explicit memory system Mishkin and colleagues proposed (see Figure 14-14).

Mishkin's models show why people with basal ganglia dysfunction, as occurs in Parkinson disease, have implicit memory deficits. People with frontal or temporal lobe injuries, by contrast, have relatively good implicit memories even as they may have profound explicit memory disturbances. Some people with Alzheimer disease can play games expertly, even with no recollection of having played them before.

Daniel Schacter (1983) wrote of a golfer with Alzheimer disease whose medial temporal system was severely compromised by the disease, but his basal ganglia were unaffected. Despite his explicit knowledge impairment, as indexed by his inability to find balls he had shot or to remember how many strokes he made on each hole, the man retained his ability to play the game.

Neural Circuit for Emotional Memories

Whether **emotional memory** for the affective properties of stimuli or events is implicit or explicit is not altogether clear. It could be both. Certainly people can react with fear to specific stimuli they can identify, and we have seen that they can also fear situations for which they do not seem to have specific memories. Panic disorder is a common pathology of emotional memory. People show marked anxiety but cannot identify a specific cause. Emotional memory has a unique anatomical component—the amygdala, which mediates fear conditioning (see Experiment 14-1) and seems to evoke our feelings of anxiety toward stimuli that by themselves would not typically produce fear.

Emotional memory has been studied most thoroughly in fear conditioning by pairing unpleasant stimuli, such as foot shock, with a tone. Michael Davis (1992) and Joseph LeDoux (1995) used fear conditioning to demonstrate that the amygdala is critical to emotional memory. Damage to the amygdala abolishes emotional memory but has little effect on implicit or explicit memory.

The amygdala has close connections with medial temporal cortical structures as well as with the rest of the cortex. It also sends projections to brainstem structures that control autonomic responses such as blood pressure and heart rate; to the hypothalamus, which controls hormonal systems; to the periaqueductal gray matter (PAG), which affects pain perception;

Section 5-4 links sensitization to PTSD. Sections 6-5 and 12-4 document how stress fosters and prolongs its effects, and Focus 16-1 covers treatments.

(A)

Premotor cortex Thalamus
Basal ganglia
Amygdala
Substantia nigra

(B)

Rest of neocortex → Basal ganglia → Ventral thalamus → Premotor cortex

Sensory and motor information

Substantia nigra Dopamine

FIGURE 14-15 Unidirectional Neural Circuit Proposed for Implicit Memory **(A)** Anatomical areas controlling implicit memory. **(B)** Circuit diagram showing the one-way flow of implicit information, beginning with inputs from the sensory and motor systems not considered part of the memory circuit.

Section 12-4 details the amygdala's influence on emotional behavior. Focus 12-3 describes panic and other anxiety disorders.

emotional memory Memory for the affective properties of stimuli or events.

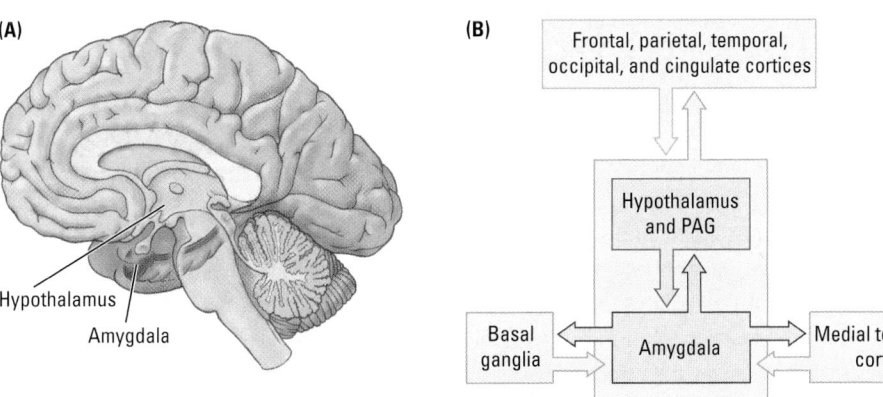

(A)

Hypothalamus

Amygdala

(B)

Frontal, parietal, temporal, occipital, and cingulate cortices

Hypothalamus and PAG

Basal ganglia

Amygdala

Medial temporal cortex

FIGURE 14-16 Neural Circuit Proposed for Emotional Memory **(A)** The amygdala is the key structure in emotional memory. **(B)** Circuit diagram showing information flow in emotional memory.

and to the enteric nervous system. The amygdala hooks in to the implicit memory system through its connections with the basal ganglia (**Figure 14-16**).

Fear is not the only aspect of emotional memory the amygdala codes, as a study of severely demented patients by Bob Sainsbury and Marjorie Coristine (1986) nicely illustrates. The patients were believed to have severe cortical abnormalities but intact amygdalar functioning. The researchers first established that the patients' ability to recognize photographs of close relatives was severely impaired.

The patients were then shown four photographs, one depicting a relative (either a sibling or a child) who had visited in the past 2 weeks. The task was to identify the person whom they liked better than the other three. Although the subjects were unaware they knew anyone depicted in the photographs, they consistently preferred pictures of their relatives. This result suggests that although the explicit, and probably the implicit, memory of the relative was gone, each patient's emotional memory guided his or her preference.

We tend to remember emotionally arousing experiences vividly, a fact confirmed by findings from both animal and human studies. James McGaugh (2004) concluded that emotionally significant experiences, pleasant and unpleasant, must activate hormonal and brain systems that act to stamp in these vivid memories.

McGaugh noted that many neural systems probably take part, but the basolateral part of the amygdala is critical. The general idea is that emotionally driven hormonal and neurochemical activating systems (probably cholinergic and noradrenergic) stimulate the amygdala. The amygdala in turn modulates the laying down of emotional memory circuits in the rest of the brain, especially in the medial temporal and prefrontal regions and in the basal ganglia. We would not expect people with amygdala damage to have enhanced memory for emotion-laden events, and they do not (Cahill et al., 1995).

The ANS monitors and controls life support functions (Figure 2-30); the ENS controls the gut (Figure 2-31). Section 11-4 reviews the PAG's role in pain perception.

Figure 5-17 traces neural activating system connections. Section 6-5 explains how hormones work.

14-3 REVIEW

Neural Systems Underlying Explicit and Implicit Memories

Before you continue, check your understanding.

1. The two key structures for explicit memory are _____ and _____.

2. A system consisting of the basal ganglia and neocortex forms the neural basis of the _____ memory system.

3. The _____ and associated structures form the neural basis for emotional memory.

4. The progressive stabilization of memories is known as _____.

5. Why do we remember emotionally arousing experiences so vividly?

Answers appear at the back of the book.

14-4 Structural Basis of Brain Plasticity

We have encountered three categories of memory—explicit, implicit, and emotional—and their underlying brain circuits. Next we consider how the neurons in these circuits change to allow us to consolidate and store memories. The consensus among neuroscientists is that the changes take place at the synapse, in part simply because that is where neurons influence one another. This idea dates to 1928, when the Spanish anatomist Santiago Ramón y Cajal suggested that learning might produce prolonged morphological (structural) changes in the efficiency of synapses activated in the learning process. Cajal's idea turned out to be easier to propose than to study.

Researchers still encounter a major challenge as they investigate Cajal's suggestion because where in the brain to look for synaptic changes that might correlate with memory for a specific stimulus is unclear. The task is formidable. Imagine trying to find the exact location of the neurons responsible for storing your grandmother's name. You would face a similar challenge in trying to pinpoint the neurons responsible for the memory of an object in a monkey's brain as the monkey performs the visual recognition task illustrated in Figure 14-10B.

One approach to finding memory's neuronal correlates aims first to determine that synaptic changes do correlate with memory in the mammalian brain; second, to localize the synaptic changes to specific neural pathways; and third, to analyze the synaptic changes themselves. This section reviews studies that begin to show how experience correlates with synaptic changes related to memory. We first consider a strategy based on neuronal physiology and experience. We then look at gross neural changes that correlate with select experiences. These range from potentially good—living in enriched environments and learning specific tasks—to probably bad—chronic administration of trophic factors, hormones, and addictive drugs. Each diverse experience modifies the brain's general synaptic organization in a strikingly similar manner.

Long-Term Potentiation

Findings from studies of behavioral *habituation* (a weakened response to a stimulus) and *sensitization* (a strengthened response) in the sea slug *Aplysia* show that physical changes in synapses do underlie learning. Adaptive synapses in the mammalian brain participate in **associative learning,** a response elicited by linking unrelated stimuli together—by learning that A goes with B.

Learned associations are a common type of explicit memory. Associating a face with a person, an odor with a food, a sound with a musical instrument are everyday examples. Learning that learning takes place at synapses is another. The phenomenon underlying associative learning entails an enduring neural change in a postsynaptic cell after an excitatory signal, or EPSP, from the presynaptic cell crosses the synaptic gap.

Both the relatively simple circuitry of the hippocampus and the ease of recording postsynaptic potentials there make it ideal for studying the neural basis of associative learning. In 1973, Timothy Bliss and Terje Lømo demonstrated that repeated electrical stimulation of the pathway entering the hippocampus progressively increases EPSP size as recorded from hippocampal cells. The enhancement in the size of these graded field potentials lasts several hours to weeks or even longer. Bliss and Lømo called it **long-term potentiation** (LTP), a long-lasting increase in synaptic effectiveness after high-frequency stimulation.

Figure 14-17A illustrates the experimental procedure for obtaining LTP. The presynaptic neuron is stimulated electrically while the electrical activity the stimulation produces is recorded from the postsynaptic neuron. The readout in Figure 14-17A shows the EPSP produced by a single pulse of electrical stimulation. In a typical experiment, many test stimuli are given to estimate the size of the induced EPSP. Then a strong burst of stimulation, consisting

---

Cajal's neuron theory—that it is the nervous system's functional unit—is now universally accepted, including the idea that these discrete cells' interactions enable behavior.

associative learning Linkage of two or more unrelated stimuli to elicit a behavioral response.

long-term potentiation (LTP) Long-lasting increase in synaptic effectiveness after high-frequency stimulation.

long-term depression (LTD) Long-lasting decrease in synaptic effectiveness after low-frequency electrical stimulation.

Experiment 5-2 explains habituation at the neuronal level, Experiment 5-3, sensitization.

Postsynaptic potentials increase (excitatory/EPSP) or decrease (inhibitory/IPSP) the probability that an action potential will occur. See Experiment 4-1.

(A)

(B)

Each dot represents EPSP amplitude in response to one weak test stimulation.

FIGURE 14-17 Recording Long-Term Potentiation **(A)** Experimenters stimulate the presynaptic neuron with a test pulse and record the EPSP from the postsynaptic neuron. **(B)** After an intense stimulation period, the amplitude of the EPSP produced by the test pulse increases: LTP has taken place.

of a few hundred pulses of electrical current per second, is administered (Figure 14-17B). The test pulse is then given again. The increased amplitude of the EPSP endures for as long as 90 minutes after the high-frequency burst: LTP has taken place. For the EPSP to increase in size, more neurotransmitter must be released from the presynaptic membrane, or the postsynaptic membrane must become more sensitive to the same amount of transmitter, or both changes must take place.

The discovery of LTP led to a revolution in thinking about how memories are stored. As investigators varied the stimulation that produced LTP, they discovered its opposite. Instead of using high-frequency stimulation (e.g., 100 Hz), they used low-frequency stimulation (e.g., 5 Hz) and recorded a *decrease* in EPSP size, termed **long-term depression** (LTD). If LTP is a mechanism for creating memories, perhaps LTD is a mechanism for clearing out old memories.

If LTP and LTD form a basis for understanding synaptic changes underlying memory, two predictions follow. First, when animals learn problems, we should see enhanced LTP in the recruited pathways. Second, LTP should produce enduring changes in synaptic morphology that resemble those seen in memory. Both predictions appear to be true.

The original studies of LTP concentrated on excitatory glutamate synapses. Glutamate is released from the presynaptic neuron and acts on two different types of receptors on the postsynaptic membrane, the NMDA and AMPA receptors, as shown in **Figure 14-18A**. AMPA receptors ordinarily mediate responses produced when glutamate is released from a presynaptic membrane. They allow sodium ions (Na$^+$) to enter, depolarizing and thus

Deep brain stimulation used for severely depressed subjects induces a change, similar to LTP, which appears to increase brain plasticity; see Section 16-1.

FIGURE 14-18 Lasting Effects of Glutamate Enhanced glutamate prompts a neurochemical cascade that underlies synaptic change and LTP.

(A) Weak electrical stimulation

Because the NMDA receptor pore is blocked by a magnesium ion, release of glutamate by a weak electrical stimulation activates only the AMPA receptor.

Presynaptic neuron **Postsynaptic neuron**

(B) Strong electrical stimulation (depolarizing EPSP)

A strong electrical stimulation can depolarize the postsynaptic membrane sufficiently that the magnesium ion is removed from the NMDA receptor pore.

(C) Weak electrical stimulation

Now glutamate, released by weak stimulation, can activate the NMDA receptor to allow Ca^{2+} influx, which, through a second messenger, increases the function or number of AMPA receptors or both.

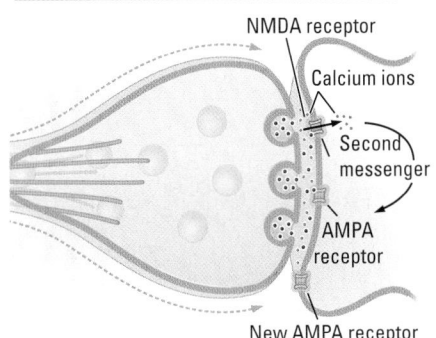

NMDA is shorthand for *N*-methyl-D-aspartate; AMPA stands for alpha-amino-3-hydroxy-5-methylisoazole-4-proprionic acid.

exciting the postsynaptic membrane. The initial amplitude of the EPSP in Figure 14-17A is produced by this AMPA receptor action.

NMDA receptors do not usually respond to glutamate, because their pores are blocked by magnesium ions (Mg^{2+}). NMDA receptors are doubly gated ion channels that can open to allow the passage of calcium ions if two events take place at approximately the same time:

1. The postsynaptic membrane is depolarized, displacing the magnesium ion from the NMDA pore (Figure 14-18B). The strong electrical stimulation delivered by the experimenter serves as a way of displacing magnesium.

2. NMDA receptors are activated by glutamate from the presynaptic membrane (Figure 14-18C).

With the doubly gated NMDA channels open, calcium ions enter the postsynaptic neuron and act through second messengers to initiate the cascade of events associated with LTP. These events include increased responsiveness of AMPA receptors to glutamate, formation of new AMPA receptors, and even retrograde messages to the presynaptic terminal to enhance glutamate release. One or more of these actions produce the final EPSP amplitude in Figure 14-17B.

Although the studies generated by the Bliss and Lømø discoveries have focused on excitatory synapses, experiments on inhibitory GABA interneurons demonstrate phenomena similar to LTP and LTD, labeled *LTPi* and *LTDi*. This discovery was a surprise. At the time it was generally believed that inhibitory neurons were not plastic, but they definitely are. It appears that plasticity of GABAergic (inhibitory) synapses plays some fundamental role in modulating networks of excitatory neurons.

Studying LTP mechanisms highlights neuroscientists' uncertainty over where plastic changes are located. Our discussion emphasizes postsynaptic changes, but a strong case can be made that key presynaptic changes are at work too (e.g., MacDougall & Fine, 2014). In general, plasticity likely requires change on both sides of the synapse. The presynaptic side, by virtue of being activated first, may prove key in the early phases of synaptic changes.

Measuring Synaptic Change

In principle, experience could change the brain in either of two ways: by modifying existing circuitry or by creating novel circuitry. In actuality, the plastic brain uses both strategies.

Modifying Existing Circuits

The simplest way to find synaptic change is to look for gross changes in the morphology of dendrites. Essentially, dendritic spines are extensions of the neuron membrane that allow more space for synapses. Cells that have few or no dendrites have limited space for inputs, whereas cells with complex dendritic protrusions may have space for tens of thousands of inputs.

So more dendrites mean more connections. Change in dendritic structure, therefore, implies change in synaptic organization. In complex neurons, such as pyramidal cells, 95 percent of synapses are on the dendrites. Measuring the extent of dendritic changes allows us to infer synaptic change.

Figure 3-5 shows how dendrites branch from three types of neurons.

Dendritic shape is highly changeable. Dale Purves and his colleagues (Purves & Voyvodic, 1987) labeled cells in the dorsal root ganglia of living mice with a dye that allowed them to visualize the cells' dendrites. When they examined the same cells at intervals ranging from a few days to weeks, they identified obvious qualitative changes in dendritic extent (**Figure 14-19**). We can assume that new dendritic branches have new synapses and that lost branches mean lost synapses.

An obvious lesson from the Purves studies is that neuronal morphology is not static: neurons change their structure in response to changing experiences. As they search for neural correlates of memory, researchers can take advantage of this changeability by studying variations in dendritic morphology that are correlated with specific experiences, such as learning some task.

Focus 5-5 diagrams how dendritic spines form and explains why they provide the structural basis for behavior.

What do changes in dendritic morphology reveal? Let us consider a given neuron that generates more synaptic space. The new synapses can provide either additional contacts between neurons that were already connected with that neuron or contacts between neurons not formerly connected. **Figure 14-20** illustrates examples of these distinct synapse types.

New synapses can result either from the growth of new axon terminals or from the formation of synapses along axons as they pass by dendrites (Figure 14-20A and B). In both cases, new synapses correspond to changes in local or regional circuitry rather than to the development of new connections between distant parts of the brain. Forming new connections between widely separated brain regions would be difficult in a fully grown brain: the dense plexus of cells, fibers, and blood vessels blocks the way.

Thus, the growth of new synapses indicates modifications to basic circuits already in the brain. This strategy has an important implication for the location of synaptic changes underlying memory. During development, the brain forms circuits to process sensory information and to produce movement (behavior). These are the circuits most likely to be modified to form memories (see Figure 14-5).

Creating Novel Circuits

Only 25 years ago, the general assumption was that the mammalian brain did not generate new neurons in adulthood. The unexpected discovery in the 1970s that the brains of songbirds such as canaries grow new neurons to produce songs in the mating season led researchers to reconsider this assumption. They found that the adult mammalian brain, too, is capable of generating new neurons.

This discovery emerged from directly injecting animals with a compound—bromodeoxyuridine (BrdU)—taken up by cells when they divide to produce new cells, including neurons. When the compound is injected into adult rats, dividing cells incorporate it into their DNA. In later analysis, a specific stain can identify the new neurons.

The BrdU technique yielded considerable evidence that the mammalian brain, including the primate brain, can generate neurons destined for the olfactory bulb, the hippocampal formation, and possibly even the frontal and temporal lobe neocortex (Eriksson et al., 1998; Gould et al., 1999). The reason is not yet clear, but adult neurogenesis may enhance brain plasticity, particularly in processes underlying learning and memory. Elizabeth Gould and her colleagues (1999) showed, for example, that generation of new neurons in the hippocampus is enhanced when animals learn explicit memory tasks.

Experience appears to increase the generation of these new neurons. A fascinating demonstration of experience driving neurogenesis comes from a study by Katherine Woollett and Eleanor Maguire (2011). We noted in Section 14-3 that London taxi drivers, who must learn the locations of and pass an exam on central London's roughly 25,000 irregular streets, have larger-than-normal volume in their hippocampal posterior region. The investigators asked whether the increase resulted from taking a 4-year course to pass the exam or was already present when the candidate drivers started the course.

FIGURE 14-19 Dendritic Plasticity Reconstructions of parts of the dendrites from three mouse spinal ganglion cells after 3 months evince changes in both the extension and the retraction of particular dendritic branches. Information from D. Purves & J. T. Voyvodic (1987). Imaging mammalian nerve cells and their connections over time in living animals. *Trends in Neuroscience, 10,* p. 400.

Experiment 7-1 confirms the hypothesis that hippocampal neurons contribute to memory formation.

(A) Before experience

Single synapse on dendritic spine

Axon 1
Axon 2
Axon 3

(B) After experience

New axon
Axon 1
New axon
Axon 2
New axon collateral
Axon 3

Formation of new synapses from new axon terminals

Formation of new synapses from original terminals

(C) Various observed shapes of new dendritic spines

FIGURE 14-20 Effects of Experience on Dendrites **(A)** Three inputs to a pyramidal cell dendrite. Each axon forms a synapse with a different dendritic spine. **(B)** In forming multiple spine heads, either the original axons can divide and innervate two spine heads or new axons or axon collaterals (dotted outlines) can innervate the new spine heads. **(C)** Single dendritic spines may sprout multiple synapses.

FIGURE 14-21 Learning Effects on Hippocampal Volume After a 4-year course devoted to learning London's street layout, trainees who qualified as licensed taxi drivers show increased gray matter volume in the most posterior part of the hippocampus (orange and yellow areas). Republished with permission of Elsevier Science and Technology Journals, from Woollett, K. and Maguire, E.A. (2011) Acquiring "the knowledge" of London's layout drives structural brain changes. *Current Biology, 21,* 2109–2114. Permission conveyed through Copyright Clearance Center, Inc.

Section 8-4 details Hebb's first enrichment exercise—and his wife's reaction.

Enriched Enclosure for Rats

Mitochondria power the cell. Figure 3-10 diagrams these organelles in the context of the neuron's other internal components.

Woollett and Maguire recorded structural MRIs from the would-be taxi drivers before and after training, then compared the trainees who qualified ($n = 39$) to those who failed ($n = 20$). The images in **Figure 14-21** show that hippocampal volume increased in the qualifiers. Those who failed showed no changes. The trainees' average age was about 40 years, leading Woollett and Maguire to conclude that the capacity for memory improvement and correlated structural changes in the hippocampus extends well into adulthood.

Enriched Experience and Plasticity

One way to stimulate animals' brains is to house the animals in environments that provide sensory or motor experience. Donald Hebb (1947) took laboratory rats home and gave them the run of his kitchen. After an interval, Hebb compared these "enriched" rats with a group that had remained caged in his laboratory at McGill University: he trained both groups to solve various mazes. The enriched animals performed better, and Hebb concluded that one effect of the enriched experience is to enhance later learning. This important conclusion laid the foundation for the U.S. Head Start programs, which provide academic experience for preschool-aged children living in under-resourced environments.

Subsequent investigators have opted for a more constrained enriched enclosure. For example, in our own studies, we place groups of about six rats in enclosures. The enclosures give animals a rich social experience as well as extensive sensory and motor experience. The most obvious consequence is increased brain weight—on the order of 10 percent relative to cage-reared animals—even though the "enriched" rats typically weigh less, in part because they get more exercise.

The key question is: What is responsible for the increased brain weight? A comprehensive series of studies by Anita Sirevaag and William Greenough (1988) used light- and electron-microscopic techniques to analyze 36 aspects of cortical synaptic, cellular, and vascular morphology in rats raised either in a cage or in a complex environment. The simple conclusion: in response to differential experiences a coordinated change occurs not only in dendritic extent but also in glial, vascular, and metabolic processes (**Figure 14-22**).

Animals with enriched experience have more synapses per neuron and also more astrocytes, more blood capillaries, and higher mitochondrial volumes. Clearly, when the brain changes in response to experience, the expected neural changes take place, and adjustments in the metabolic requirements of the now larger neurons take place as well.

Gerd Kempermann and his colleagues (1998) sought to determine whether experience actually alters the number of neurons in the brain. To test this idea, they compared neuronal generation in the hippocampi of mice housed in a complex environment with that of mice reared in a laboratory cage. They located the number of new neurons by injecting the animals with BrdU several times while they were living in complex housing.

The new neurons generated in the brain during the experiment incorporated the BrdU. When the researchers later looked at the hippocampi, they found more new neurons in the complex-housed rats than in the caged rats. Although the investigators did not look in other parts of the brain, such as the olfactory bulb, we can reasonably expect that similar changes took place in other neural structures. This result is exciting because it implies that experience not only can alter existing circuitry but also can influence neurogenesis and thus new circuitry.

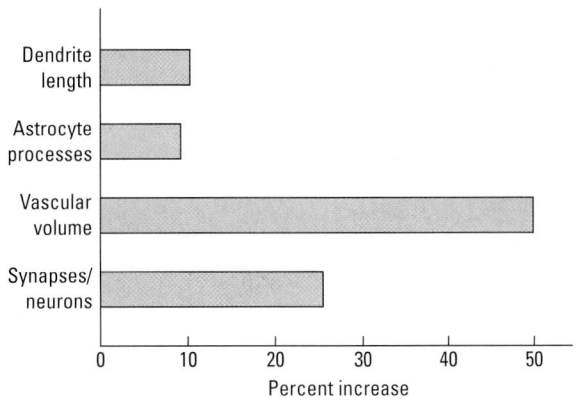

FIGURE 14-22 **Consequences of Enrichment** Cortical changes that occur in response to experience are found not only in neurons but also in astrocytes and vasculature. Data from A. Turner & W. T. Greenough (1985). Differential rearing effects on rat visual cortex synapses. I. Synaptic and neuronal density and synapses per neuron. *Brain Research, 329*, pp. 195–203 No ref.3; A. M. Sirevaag & W. T. Greenough (1987). Differential rearing effects on rat visual cortex synapses. III. Neuronal and glial nuclei. *Brain Research, 424*, pp. 320–332; and B. Kolb, R. Gibb, & G. Gorny (2003). Experience-dependent changes in dendritic arbor and spine density in neocortex vary with age and sex *Neurobiology of Learning and Memory, 79*, pp. 1–10.

Sensory or Motor Training and Plasticity

Studies showing neuronal change in animals housed in a complex environment demonstrate that large areas of the brain can change with such experience. This finding leads us to ask whether specific experiences produce synaptic changes in localized cerebral regions. One way to approach this question is to give animals specific experiences, then see how their brain has changed. Another way is to look at the brain of people who have had a lifetime of some particular experience. We consider each research strategy separately.

Manipulating Experience Experimentally

Fen-Lei Chang and William Greenough (1982) conducted perhaps the most convincing manipulated-experience study. They took advantage of the fact that the laboratory rat's visual pathways are about 90 percent crossed. That is, about 90 percent of connections from the left eye to the cortex project through the right thalamus to the right hemisphere and vice versa for the right eye.

Chang and Greenough placed a patch over one eye of each rat, then trained the animals in a maze. The visual cortex of only one eye received input about the maze, but their two hemispheres' auditory, olfactory, tactile, and motor regions were equally active as the animals explored. A comparison of the neurons in each hemisphere revealed that those in the visual cortex of the trained hemisphere had more extensive dendrites. Because the hemispheres did not differ in other respects, the researchers concluded that some feature associated with encoding, processing, or storage of visual input from training was responsible for forming new synapses.

Randy Nudo and his colleagues (1997) conducted complementary studies, mapping the motor cortex of monkeys. They noted striking individual differences in topography. The investigators speculated that individual variability might be due to each monkey's experiences up to the time at which the cortical map was derived. To test this idea directly, Nudo and colleagues trained two groups of squirrel monkeys to retrieve banana-flavored food pellets from either a small or a large food well. A monkey was able to insert its entire hand into the large well but only one or two fingers into the small well, as illustrated in the Procedures section of **Experiment 14-2.**

Monkeys in the two groups were matched for number of finger flexions, which totaled about 12,000 for the entire study. The monkeys trained on the small well improved with practice, making fewer finger flexions per food retrieval as training proceeded. Maps of forelimb movements, shown in the Results section, were produced by microelectrode stimulation of the cortex. The maps show systematic changes in the animals trained on the small but not on the large well. Presumably, these changes result from the more demanding motor requirements of the small-well condition. The results demonstrate that learning new motor skills, not simply repetitive motor use, shapes the functional topography of the motor cortex.

Most studies demonstrating plasticity in the motor cortex have been performed with laboratory animals whose cortex was mapped by microelectrode stimulation. Today, imaging

In humans, only about half the optic fibers cross. Figure 9-10 diagrams the pathways.

▶ **EXPERIMENT 14-2**

Question: Does the learning of a fine motor skill alter the cortical motor map?

Procedures

Difficult task	Simple task
One group of monkeys was trained to retrieve food from a small well.	Another group of monkeys was trained to retrieve food from a large well.

Both groups were allowed 12,000 finger flexions. The small-well task was more difficult and required the learning of a fine motor skill in order to match performance of the simpler task.

Results

The motor representation of digit, wrist, and arm was mapped.

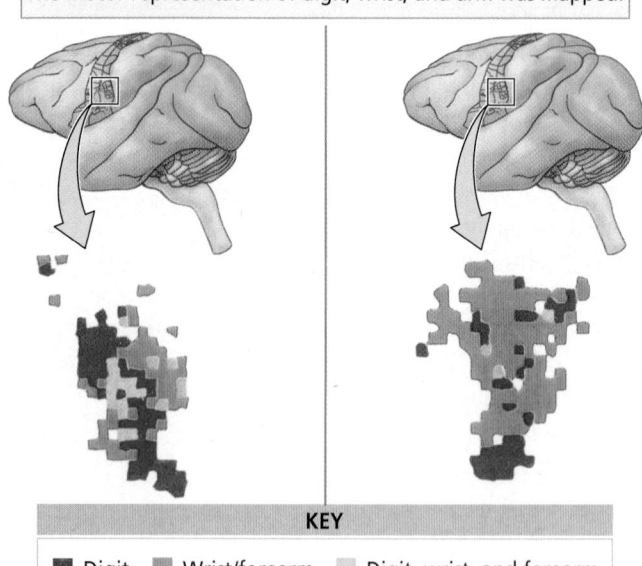

KEY

■ Digit   ■ Wrist/forearm   ▪ Digit, wrist, and forearm

Conclusion: The digit representation in the brain of the animal with the more difficult task is larger, corresponding to the neuronal changes necessary for the acquired skill.

Information from R. J. Nudo, E. J. Plautz, & G. W. Miliken (1997). Adaptive plasticity in primate motor cortex as a consequence of behavioral experience and neuronal injury. *Seminars in Neuroscience, 9*, p. 20.

techniques such as transcranial magnetic stimulation (TMS) and functional magnetic resonance imaging (fMRI) make it possible to show parallel results in humans who have special motor skills. For example, right-handed musicians who play stringed instruments show an increased cortical representation of the fingers of the left hand and Braille readers an increased cortical representation of the reading finger.

Thus, the functional organization of the motor cortex is altered by skilled use in humans. It can also be altered by chronic injury in humans and laboratory animals. Jon Kaas (2000) showed that when the sensory nerves in one limb are severed in monkeys, large-scale changes in somatosensory maps ensue. In particular, in the absence of input, the relevant part of the cortex no longer responds to limb stimulation, which is not surprising. But this cortex does not remain inactive. Rather, the deafferented cortex begins to respond to input from other body parts. The region that formerly responded to hand stimulation now responds to stimulation on the face, a cortical area normally adjacent to the hand area.

Similar results can be found in the cortical maps of people whose limb has been amputated. For example, Vilayanur Ramachandran (1993) found that when a hand amputee's face is brushed lightly with a cotton swab, the person has a sensation of the amputated hand being touched. **Figure 14-23** illustrates the rough map of the hand that Ramachandran was actually able to chart on the face. The likely explanation is that the face area in the motor cortex has expanded to occupy

FIGURE 14-23 Cortical Reorganization When a hand amputee's face is stroked lightly with a cotton swab **(A)**, the person experiences the stroke as a light touch on the missing hand **(B)** as well as a touch to the face. The deafferented cortex forms a representation of the amputated hand on the face. As in the normal somatosensory homunculus, the thumb is disproportionately large. Information from V. S. Ramachandran (1993). Behavioral and magnetoencephalographic correlates of plasticity in the adult human brain. *Proceedings of the National Academy of Sciences USA, 90*, p. 10418.

the deafferented limb cortex, but the brain circuitry still responds to the cortical activity as representing input from the limb. This response may explain the phantom limb pain often experienced by amputees.

Focus 11-5 recounts Ramachandran's therapy for minimizing phantom limb pain.

The idea that experience can alter cortical maps can be demonstrated with other experiences. For example, if animals are trained to make certain digit movements over and over again, the cortical representation of those digits expands at the expense of the remaining motor areas. Similarly, if animals are trained extensively to discriminate among different sensory stimuli such as tones, the auditory cortical areas responding to those stimuli increase in size.

As described in Research Focus 14-5, Movement, Learning, and Neuroplasticity, one effect of musical training is to alter the motor representations of the digits used to play different instruments. We can speculate that musical training probably alters the auditory representations of specific sound frequencies as well. Both changes are essentially forms of memory, and the underlying synaptic changes likely take place on the appropriate sensory or motor cortical maps.

Sections 10-4 and 15-4 discuss music's benefits for the brain.

RESEARCH FOCUS 14-5

Movement, Learning, and Neuroplasticity

Many lines of research show that practicing a motor skill—playing a musical instrument, for instance—induces changes in the cortical somatosensory and motor maps. The mental maps generally become larger, at least the finger and hand representations.

Presumably, musical skill improves with practice, but are other abilities enhanced too? Patrick Ragert and colleagues (2003) showed that professional pianists not only have better motor skills in their fingers but enhanced somatosensory perception as well.

When the researchers measured the ability to detect subtle sensory stimulation of the fingertips, they found that the pianists were more sensitive than controls. They also found that the enhanced tactile sensitivity was related to the hours per day that the musicians spent practicing.

The investigators then asked whether the enhanced perceptual ability precluded further improvement in the musicians. Surprisingly, when both the musicians and controls were given a 3-hour training session designed to improve tactile sensitivity, the musicians showed more improvement than did the controls. Again the extent of improvement correlated with daily practice time.

© Michel Garnier/Lebrecht Music & Arts/Corbis

This result implies that well-practiced musicians not only learn to play music but also develop a greater capacity for learning. Rather than using up all the available synapses, they gain the capacity to make even more.

Not all motor learning is good, however. Many musicians develop *focal hand dystonia*—abnormal finger and hand positions, cramps, and

difficulty in coordinating hand and finger movements. Dystonia can be so disabling that some musicians must give up their occupation.

Typically, dystonia afflicts musicians who practice trying to make perfect finger movements on their instruments. Musicians at high risk include string players, who receive vibratory stimulation at their fingertips. The constant practice has been suggested to lead not only to improved musical ability but also to distorted or disordered cortical motor maps. Synchronous activation of the digits by the vibration leads to this unwanted side effect.

Victor Candia and colleagues (2003) reasoned that musicians' dystonia was probably an example of disordered learning and could be treated by retuning the motor map. The investigators used magnetoencephalography (MEG) to measure changes in sensory-evoked magnetic fields in the cortex.

At the beginning of the study, the musicians with dystonia had a disordered motor map: the finger areas overlapped one another. In training, each subject used a hand splint tailored to his or her hand. The splint allowed for immobilizing different fingers while the subjects independently moved the others.

After 8 days of training for about 2 hours per day, the subjects showed marked alleviation in the dystonic symptoms, and the neuroimaging showed a normalization of the cortical map, with distinct finger areas. Thus, training reversed the learned changes in the motor map and treated the dystonia. The musicians had actually learned a disorder, and they were able to unlearn it.

Experience-Dependent Change in the Human Brain

According to Ramachandran's amputee study, the human brain appears to change with altered experience. But this study did not examine neuronal change directly; it inferred neuronal change from behavior. The only way to examine synaptic change directly is to look directly at brain tissue. In living humans, this is not an option, but the brain of people who died of something other than neurological causes can be examined and the structure of their cortical neurons related to their experiences.

One way to approach this idea is to look for a relation between neuronal structure and education. Arnold Scheibel and his colleagues conducted many such studies in the 1990s (e.g., Jacobs and Scheibel, 1993; Jacobs, Scholl, and Scheibel, 1993). In one, they found a relation between dendrite size in Wernicke's area and level of education. In the brain of deceased people with a college education, the cortical neurons from this language area had more dendritic branches than did those from people with a high-school education, which in turn, had more dendritic material than did those from people with less education. People who have more dendrites may be more likely to go to college, but that hypothesis is not easy to test.

Another way to look at the relation between neurons in Wernicke's area and behavior is to take advantage of the now well-documented observation that on average females' verbal abilities are superior to those of males. When Scheibel and his colleagues examined the structure of neurons in Wernicke's area, they found that females do have more extensive dendritic branching there than males do.

Finally, these investigators took a slightly different approach to the link between experience and neuronal morphology. They began with two hypotheses. First, they suggested a relation between the complexity of dendritic branching and the nature of the computational tasks performed by a brain area.

To test this hypothesis, they examined the dendritic structure of neurons in different cortical regions that handle different computational tasks. For example, when they compared the structure of neurons corresponding to the somatosensory representation of the trunk with those for the fingers, they found the latter to have more complex cells (**Figure 14-24**). They reasoned that the somatosensory inputs from receptive fields on the chest wall would constitute less of a computational challenge to cortical neurons than would those from the fingers and that the neurons representing the chest would therefore be less complex.

The group's second hypothesis was that dendritic branching in all regions is subject to experience-dependent change. The researchers hypothesized that predominant life experience (e.g., occupation) should, as a result, alter dendritic structure. Although they did not test this hypothesis directly, they did make an interesting observation. In their study comparing cells in the trunk area, in the finger area, and in the supramarginal gyrus—a parietal lobe region associated with higher cognitive processes (thinking)—they found curious individual differences.

For example, especially large differences in trunk and finger neurons appeared in the brain of people who had a high level of finger dexterity maintained over long periods (say, career word processors). In contrast, no difference between trunk and finger neurons was found in sales representatives. Remember, Scheibel and colleagues conducted their research before portable electronic devices entered the workplace. We would not expect a good deal of specialized finger use among sales reps of that time and thus less complex demands on their finger neurons.

In summary, although the studies showing a relation between experience and neuronal structure in humans depend on correlations rather than actual experiments, the findings are consistent with those observed in experimental studies of other species. We are thus led to the general conclusion that specific experiences can produce localized changes in the synaptic organization of the brain and that such changes form the structural basis of memory.

Wernicke's area contributes to speech and to language comprehension; see Figure 10-18.

Figure 15-16 diagrams tasks that consistently show, on average, that females' verbal fluency surpasses males' and that males outperform females on spatial reasoning tasks.

FIGURE 14-24 Experience and Neuronal Complexity Confirmation of Scheibel's hypothesis that cell complexity is related to the computational demands required of the cell. Neurons that represent the body's trunk area have relatively less computational demand than do cells representing the finger region. In turn, cells engaged in higher cognitive functions (such as language, as in Wernicke's area) have greater computational demand than do those engaged in finger functions.

Epigenetics of Memory

An enigma in the search for neural mechanisms underlying memory is the fact that whereas memories remain stable over time, all cells are constantly undergoing molecular turnover. The simplest explanation for this is epigenetic: specific sites in the DNA of neurons involved in specific memories might exist in either a methylated or a nonmethylated state.

Courtney Miller and colleagues (2010) tested this idea directly by measuring methylation in the hippocampi of rats that underwent contextual fear conditioning (see Experiment 14-1). They showed that fear conditioning is associated with rapid methylation, but if they blocked methylation, there was no memory. The investigators conclude that epigenetic mechanisms mediate synaptic plasticity broadly, but especially in learning and memory. One implication of these results is that cognitive disorders, including memory defects, could result from aberrant epigenetic modifications (for a review, see Day et al., 2015).

Figure 3-25 illustrates two aspects of methylation: histone and DNA modification.

Plasticity, Hormones, Trophic Factors, and Drugs

The news media often report that psychoactive drugs can damage your brain. Some drugs certainly do act as toxins and can selectively kill brain regions, but a more realistic mode of drug action is to *change* the brain. Although not many studies have looked at drug-induced morphological changes, evidence reveals that some compounds can greatly change the brain's synaptic organization. These compounds include hormones, neurotrophic factors, and psychoactive drugs. We briefly consider each category.

Hormones and Plasticity

Levels of circulating hormones are critical both in determining brain structure and in eliciting certain behaviors in adulthood. Although the structural effects of hormones were once believed to be expressed only in the course of development, current belief is that adult neurons also can respond to hormonal manipulations with dramatic structural changes. We consider the actions of gonadal hormones and stress hormones here.

Section 6-5 explains the classes, functions, and control that hormones exert; Section 8-4, their organizing effects during development; Section 12-5, their activating effects in adulthood.

Research findings have established that structural differences in cortical neurons of male and female rats depend on gonadal hormones. More surprising, perhaps, is that gonadal hormones continue to influence cell structure and behavior in adulthood. Elizabeth Hampson and Doreen Kimura (1988) showed that women's performance on various cognitive tasks changes throughout the menstrual cycle as their estrogen levels fluctuate.

Changes in estrogen level appear to alter the structure of neurons and astrocytes in the neocortex and hippocampus, which probably accounts for at least part of the performance fluctuation. **Figure 14-25** illustrates changes in dendritic spines in the hippocampal cells of female rats at different phases of their 4-day estrous cycle. As the estrogen level rises, the number of synapses rises; as the estrogen level drops, the number of synapses declines.

Curiously, estrogen's influence on cell structure may differ in the hippocampus and neocortex. Jane Stewart found, for example, that when the ovaries of middle-aged female rats are removed, estrogen levels drop sharply, producing increased numbers of spines on pyramidal cells throughout the neocortex but decreased spine density in the hippocampus (Stewart & Kolb, 1994). How these synaptic changes might influence processes such as memory is not immediately obvious, but the question is reasonable, especially because menopausal women also experience sharp drops in estrogen levels and a corresponding decline in verbal memory ability.

This question is also relevant to middle-aged men, who show a slow decline in testosterone levels that correlates with a drop in spatial ability. Rats that are gonadectomized in adulthood show increased cortical spine density, much like the ovariectomized females. Although we do not know how this change relates to spatial behavior, a reasonable supposition is that testosterone levels might influence spatial memory throughout life.

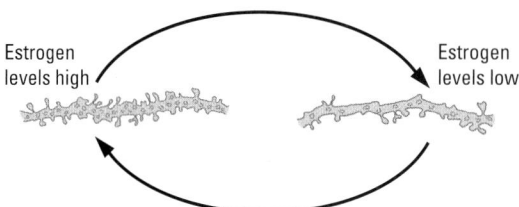

FIGURE 14-25 Hormones and Neuroplasticity Sections of dendrites from hippocampal cells during times of high and low estrogen levels during the rat's 4-day estrous cycle reveal many more dendritic spines when estrogen levels are high. Information from C. S. Woolley, E. Gould, M. Frankfurt, & B. S. McEwen (1990). Naturally occurring fluctuation in dendritic spine density on adult hippocampal pyramidal neurons. *Journal of Neuroscience, 10*, p. 4038.

When the body is stressed, the pituitary gland produces adrenocorticotrophic hormone (ACTH), which stimulates the adrenal cortex to produce steroid hormones, the *glucocorticoids*. Important in protein and carbohydrate metabolism, controlling sugar levels in the blood, and the absorption of sugar by cells, glucocorticoids have many actions on the body, including the brain. Robert Sapolsky (1992) proposed that glucocorticoids can sometimes be neurotoxic.

In particular, he found that with prolonged stress, glucocorticoids appear to kill hippocampal cells. Elizabeth Gould and her colleagues (1998) showed that even brief periods of stress can reduce the number of new granule cells produced in the hippocampi of monkeys, presumably through the actions of stress hormones. Evidence of neuron death and reduced neuron generation in the hippocampus has obvious implications for animal behavior, especially for processes such as spatial memory. Finally, Richelle Mychasiuk and her colleagues (2015) showed that stress has contrasting epigenetic effects in the hippocampus and prefrontal cortex, with virtually no overlap between males and females.

In sum, hormones can alter the brain's synaptic organization and even the number of neurons in the brain. Little is known today about the behavioral consequences of such changes. It is likely that hormones can alter the course of plastic changes in the brain, possibly through epigenetic mechanisms.

Neurotrophic Factors and Plasticity

Neurotrophic factors, chemical compounds listed in **Table 14-2** that signal stem cells to develop into neurons or glia, also act to reorganize neural circuits. The first, **nerve growth factor** (NGF), was discovered in the peripheral nervous system more than a generation ago. NGF is trophic (nourishing) in the sense that it stimulates neurons to grow dendrites and synapses and in some cases promotes neuronal survival.

Trophic factors produced in the brain by neurons and glia can affect neurons both through cell membrane receptors and by actually entering the neuron to act internally on its operation. Trophic factors may be released postsynaptically, for example, to act as signals that can influence the presynaptic cell. Experience stimulates their production, so neurotrophic factors have been proposed as agents of synaptic change. For example, brain-derived neurotrophic factor (BDNF) increases when animals solve specific problems such as mazes. This finding has led to speculation that BDNF release may enhance such plastic changes as the growth of dendrites and synapses.

Although many researchers would like to conclude that BDNF has a role in learning, this conclusion does not necessarily follow. When animals solve mazes, their behavior differs from their behavior when they remain in cages. So we must first demonstrate that changes in BDNF, NGF, or any trophic factor are actually related to forming new synapses. Nevertheless, if we assume that trophic factors do act as synaptic change agents, then we should be able to use increased trophic factor activity during learning as a marker for where to look for changed synapses associated with learning and memory.

Psychoactive Drugs and Plasticity

Many people regularly use the stimulant caffeine, and some use more stimulating psychoactive drugs such as nicotine, amphetamine, or cocaine. The long-term consequences of abusing psychoactive drugs are now well documented, but the question of why these drugs cause problems remains to be answered. One explanation for the behavioral changes associated with chronic psychoactive drug abuse is that the drugs change the brain.

One experimental demonstration of these changes is *drug-induced behavioral sensitization*, often referred to simply as **behavioral sensitization,** the progressive increase in behavioral actions in response to repeated administration of a drug. Behaviors increase even when the amount given in each dose does not change. Behavioral sensitization occurs with most psychoactive drugs, including amphetamine, cocaine, morphine, and nicotine.

The sea slug *Aplysia* becomes more sensitive to a stimulus after repeated exposure. Psychoactive drugs appear to have a parallel action: they lead to increased behavioral sensitivity

---

Figure 6-23 illustrates the body's stress response.

Section 8-2 explains how neurotrophic factors send these signals.

A Hebb synapse—one that changes with use so that learning takes place—hypothetically employs just such a mechanism; see Section 5-4.

TABLE 14-2 Molecules Exhibiting Neurotrophic Activities

Proteins initially characterized as neurotrophic factors
Nerve growth factor (NGF)
Brain-derived neurotrophic factor (BDNF)
Neurotrophin 3 (NT-3)
Ciliary neurotrophic factor (CNTF)
Growth factors with neurotrophic activity
Fibroblast growth factor, acidic (aFGF *or* FGF-1)
Fibroblast growth factor, basic (bFGF *or* FGF-2)
Epidermal growth factor (EGF)
Insulinlike growth factor (ILGF)
Transforming growth factor (TGF)
Lymphokines (interleukin 1, 3, 6 or IL-1, IL-3, IL-6)
Protease nexin I, II
Cholinergic neuronal differentiation factor

to their actions. For example, a rat given a small dose of amphetamine may show increased activity. When the rat is given the same dose of amphetamine on subsequent occasions, the increase in activity is progressively larger. If no drug is given for weeks or even months and then amphetamine is given in the same dose as before, behavioral sensitization picks up where it left off and continues to progress. Some long-lasting change must have taken place in the brain in response to the drug. Drug-induced behavioral sensitization can therefore be viewed as a memory for a particular drug.

The parallel between drug-induced behavioral sensitization and other forms of memory leads us to ask if the changes in the brain after behavioral sensitization are similar to those found after other forms of learning. They are. For example, there is evidence of increased numbers of receptors at synapses and of more synapses in sensitized animals.

In a series of studies, Terry Robinson and his colleagues found dramatic increases in dendritic growth and spine density in rats sensitized to amphetamine, cocaine, or nicotine relative to rats that received injections of a saline solution (Robinson & Kolb, 2004). **Experiment 14-3** compares the effects of amphetamine and saline treatments on cells in the nucleus accumbens in the basal ganglia. Neurons in amphetamine-treated brains have more dendritic branches and increased spine density. Repeated exposure to psychoactive stimulants thus alters the structure of brain cells. These changes in turn may be related to learned addictions.

These plastic changes were not found throughout the brain. Rather, they were localized to regions such as the

▶ EXPERIMENT 14-3

Question: What effect do repeated doses of amphetamine, a psychomotor stimulant, have on neurons?

Procedure

Animals received multiple doses of amphetamine. Neurons were drawn from nucleus accumbens.

Results

Amphetamine   Saline

Nucleus accumbens

Rats that show sensitization to amphetamine have increased dendritic growth and spine density...

...relative to saline-treated rats that served as controls.

Conclusion: The sensitization induced by repeated exposure to amphetamine changes the structure of neurons in certain brain areas.

Information from T. E. Robinson & B. Kolb (1997). Persistent structural adaptations in nucleus accumbens and prefrontal cortex neurons produced by prior experience with amphetamine. *Journal of Neuroscience, 17*, p. 8496.

prefrontal cortex and nucleus accumbens that receive a large dopamine projection. Dopamine is believed to factor significantly in the rewarding properties of drugs (Wise, 2004). Other psychoactive drugs also appear to alter neuronal structure. Marijuana, morphine, and certain antidepressants change dendritic length and spine density, although in ways different from those of stimulants. Morphine, for example, reduces dendritic length and spine density in the nucleus accumbens and prefrontal cortex (Robinson & Kolb, 2004).

What do drug-induced changes in synaptic organization mean for later experience-dependent plasticity? If rats are given amphetamine, cocaine, or nicotine for 2 weeks before being placed in a complex environment, the expected increases in dendritic length and spine density in the cortex do not happen (Kolb et al., 2003). This is not because the brain can no longer change: giving the animals additional drug doses can still produce change. Rather, something about prior drug exposure alters the way in which the brain later responds to experience.

Why prior drug exposure has this effect is as yet unknown, but obviously drug taking can have long-term effects on brain plasticity. One possible explanation is epigenetic. Giving animals repeated doses of amphetamine or nicotine decreases methylation in both the prefrontal cortex and the nucleus accumbens, and decreased methylation is related to drug- and region-specific increases in gene expression (Mychasiuk et al., 2013). These epigenetic changes may render the synapses less able to change in response to later experiences.

nerve growth factor (NGF) Neurotrophic factor that stimulates neurons to grow dendrites and synapses and in some cases promotes the survival of neurons.

behavioral sensitization Escalating behavioral response to the repeated administration of a psychomotor stimulant such as amphetamine, cocaine, or nicotine; also called *drug-induced behavioral sensitization.*

Figure 12-30 shows enhanced connectivity in prefrontal and limbic circuits in nicotine-dependent smokers.

Some Guiding Principles of Brain Plasticity

Brain plasticity will continue as a fundamental concept underlying research into brain–behavior relationships through the coming decades. Some basic rules have emerged to guide this research (see Kolb and Gibb, 2014, for more details). Here we list seven.

1. Behavioral Change Reflects Brain Change

The brain's primary function is to produce behavior, but behavior is not static. We learn and remember, we think new thoughts or visualize new images, and we change throughout life. All these processes require changes in neural networks. Whenever neural networks change, behavior, including mental behavior, also changes. A corollary is especially important as neuroscientists search for treatments for brain injuries or behavioral disorders: *To change behavior, we must change the brain.*

2. All Nervous Systems Are Plastic in the Same General Way

Investigators study neuroplasticity in species ranging from worms and insects to fish, birds, and mammals.

Even the simplest animals, such as the roundworm *C. elegans,* can show simple learning that correlates with neuronal plasticity. The molecular details may differ between simple and complex systems, but the principles of neuroplasticity appear to be conserved across both simple and complex animals. This conservation allows more studies of neural plasticity among a wider range of animal species than in most areas of neuroscience.

3. Plastic Changes Are Age-Specific

Section 8-4 traces how brain organization details change rapidly—and sometimes critically—during development.

The brain responds to the same experiences differently at different ages—and especially during development. The prefrontal cortex is late to mature, for example, so the same experience affects this region differently in infancy than it does in adolescence and on throughout life.

4. Prenatal Events Can Influence Brain Plasticity Throughout Life

Section 8-4 recounts benefits of tactile stimulation; Focus 8-2, epigenetic factors in the autism spectrum; Focus 6-2, the tragedy of fetal alcohol spectrum disorder.

Prenatal experiences can alter brain organization. Potentially negative experiences, such as prenatal exposure to recreational or prescription drugs, and positive experiences, such as tactile stimulation of the mother's skin, may alter gene expression or induce other epigenetic effects that produce enduring effects on brain organization. Even paternal or maternal experiences before conception can alter later offsprings' brain development and organization.

5. Plastic Changes Are Brain Region Dependent

Figure 12-19 diagrams these prefrontal regions.

Although we are tempted to expect plastic changes in neuronal networks to be fairly general, it is becoming clear that many experience-dependent changes are highly specific. We saw this specificity in the effects of psychoactive drugs on the prefrontal cortex but not on other cortical regions. Not only do drugs selectively change the prefrontal cortex but the dorsolateral and orbital prefrontal areas also show opposite changes—the precise changes varying with the particular drug. For example, stimulants such as amphetamine increase spine density in the dorsolateral region but decrease it in the orbital region.

6. Experience-Dependent Changes Interact

Metaplasticity is a property of a lifetime's interaction among different plastic changes in the brain. As an animal travels through life, infinite experiences can alter its brain organization. A lifetime's experiences might interact. Housing animals in complex environments produces profound changes in their neural network organization, but prior exposure to psychoactive drugs completely blocks the enrichment effect. Conversely, although complex housing does not block drug effects, enrichment markedly attenuates them. Prenatal events can affect later drug effects: prenatal tactile stimulation of the mother, for example, reduces the later effects of psychoactive drugs on the child.

7. Plasticity Has Pros and Cons

We have mainly emphasized the neuroplastic changes that can support improved motor and cognitive function. But as noted for the effects of psychoactive drugs, plastic changes in neural networks can also interfere with behavior. Drug addicts whose prefrontal cortex has been altered are prone to poor judgment in their personal life. People who have posttraumatic

metaplasticity Interaction among different plastic changes in the brain.

stress disorder show altered blood flow in the amygdala and cingulate cortex. That's the bad news.

Encouraging plastic changes that reverse these prefrontal alterations is the good news, and it is associated with a loss of the prefrontal disorder. Age-related dementia is related to synaptic loss that various forms of cognitive therapy can reverse (e.g., Mahncke, Bronstone, & Merzenich, 2006).

(14-4) REVIEW

Structural Basis of Brain Plasticity

Before you continue, check your understanding.

1. Repeated high-frequency stimulation of excitatory neurons leads to the phenomenon of _____, whereas repeated low-frequency stimulation leads to _____.

2. LTPi and LTDi are found in _____ neurons.

3. Structural changes underlying memory include changes in both _____ and _____.

4. Learning complex spatial information has been linked to increased gray matter in the _____.

5. The progressive increase in behavioral actions in response to repeated administration of a drug is called _____.

6. How can plastic changes in the brain produce adverse effects?

Answers appear at the back of the book.

For additional study tools, visit 🌐 **LaunchPad**:
www.macmillanhighered.com/launchpad/kolb5e

(14-5) Recovery from Brain Injury

The nervous system appears conservative in its use of mechanisms related to behavioral change. If neuroscientists wish to change the brain, as after injury or disease, then they should look for treatments that will produce plastic changes related to learning, memory, and other behaviors.

Recall that H. M. failed to recover his lost memory capacities, even after 55 years of practice in trying to remember information. Relearning simply was not possible for H. M. He had lost the requisite neural structures. But other people do show some recovery.

An average person would probably say that the recovery process after brain trauma requires the injured person to relearn lost skills, whether walking, talking, or using the fingers. But what exactly does recovery entail? Partial recovery of function is common after brain injury, but a person with brain trauma or brain disease has lost neurons. The brain may be missing structures critical for relearning or remembering.

Donna's Experience with Traumatic Brain Injury

Donna started dancing when she was 4 years old, and she was a natural. By the time she finished high school, she had the training and skill necessary to apprentice with and later join a major dance company. Donna remembers vividly the day she was chosen to dance a leading role in *The Nutcracker*. She had marveled at the costumes as she watched the popular Christmas ballet as a child, and now she would dance in those costumes!

The births of two children interrupted her career as a dancer, but Donna never lost the interest. In 1968, when both her children were in school, she began dancing again with a local company. To her amazement, she could still perform most of the movements, although

Focus 1-1 and Section 1-2 introduce consequences of and treatments for TBI, which we elaborate here and in Section 16-3.

she was rusty on the choreography of the classical dances that she had once memorized so meticulously. Nonetheless, she quickly relearned. In retrospect, she should not have been so surprised, because she had always had an excellent memory.

One evening in 1990, while on a bicycle ride, a drunk driver struck Donna. She was wearing a helmet but received a brain-damaging blow to the head—a **traumatic brain injury,** or TBI. She was comatose for several weeks. As she regained consciousness, she was confused and had difficulty talking to and understanding others. Her memory was very poor; spatial disorientation meant she often got lost; she endured various motor disturbances; and she had difficulty recognizing anyone but her family and closest friends.

Over the ensuing 10 months, Donna regained most of her motor abilities and language skills, and her spatial abilities improved significantly. Nonetheless, she was short-tempered and easily frustrated by the slowness of her recovery, symptoms typical of people with brain trauma. She had periods of depression.

Donna also found herself prone to inexplicable surges of panic when doing simple things. On one occasion early in her rehabilitation, she was shopping in a large supermarket and became overwhelmed by the number of salad dressing choices. She ran from the store, and only after she sat outside and calmed herself could she go back inside to continue shopping.

Two years later, Donna was dancing once again, but now she found learning and remembering new steps difficult. Her emotions were still unstable, which put a strain on her family, but her episodes of frustration and temper outbursts grew far less frequent. A year later, they were gone, and her life was not obviously different from that of other middle-aged women.

Even so, some cognitive changes persisted. Donna seemed unable to remember the names or faces of new people she met. She lost concentration if background distractions such as a television or a radio playing intruded. She could not dance as she had before her injury, but she did work at it diligently. Her balance on sudden turns gave her the most difficulty. Rather than risk falling, she retired from her life's first love.

Donna's case demonstrates the human brain's capacity for continuously changing its structure and ultimately its function throughout a lifetime. From what we have learned in this chapter, we can identify three ways in which Donna could recover from her brain injury: she could learn new ways to solve problems, she could reorganize the brain to do more with less, and she could generate new neurons to produce new neural circuits. We briefly examine each possibility.

Dean Berry/Getty Images

The brain changes in response to these dancers' new experiences and new abilities. After her accident, Donna's brain had to change to allow her to regain her lost abilities, but she never recovered the ability these young women have to learn new dances.

Three-Legged Cat Solution

Cats that lose a leg quickly learn to compensate for the missing limb and once again become mobile. They show recovery of function: the limb is gone, but behavior has changed to compensate. This simplest solution to recovery from brain injury we call the three-legged cat solution.

A similar explanation can account for many instances of apparent recovery of function after TBI. Imagine that a right-handed person has a stroke that costs her the use of her right hand and arm. Unable to write with the affected limb, she switches to her left hand. Such behavioral compensation presupposes that some nervous system changes underlie this new skill.

New-Circuit Solution

A second way to recover from brain damage is for the brain to form new connections that allow it to do more with less. This change is most easily accomplished by processes similar to those we considered for other forms of plasticity. The brain changes its neural connections to overcome the loss.

Without some intervention, recovery from most brain injuries is relatively modest. Recovery can increase significantly if the person engages in behavioral, pharmacological, or brain-stimulation therapy that encourages the brain to make new connections.

traumatic brain injury (TBI) Damage to the brain that results from a blow to the head.

▶ EXPERIMENT 14-4

Question: Does nerve growth factor stimulate recovery from stroke, influence neural structure, or both?

Procedure

Animals received a cortical stroke. Some were treated with NGF; others were not. Skilled reaching was assessed.

Results

Motor cortex

Control

NGF increases dendrites and spines.

NGF

Remaining motor cortex

Lesion reduces dendrites and spines.

Lesion

Stroke

NGF after a stroke reverses loss of dendrites and spines.

NGF + lesion

Bryan Kolb

Conclusion: Nerve growth factor stimulates dendritic growth and increased spine density in both healthy and injured brains. These neuronal changes correlate with improved motor function after stroke.

Information from B. Kolb, S. Cote, A. Ribeiro-da-Silva, & A. C. Cuello (1997). Nerve growth factor treatment prevents dendritic atrophy and promotes recovery of function after cortical injury. *Neuroscience, 76,* p. 1146.

Behavioral therapy—speech therapy, physiotherapy, and music therapy are examples—presumably increases brain activity, which facilitates neural changes. In a pharmacological intervention, the patient takes a drug, such as nerve growth factor, known to influence brain plasticity. When NGF is given to animals with strokes that damaged the motor cortex, their motor functions improve (**Experiment 14-4**). The behavioral changes correlate with a dramatic increase in dendritic branching and spine density in the remaining intact motor regions. The morphological changes correlate with improved motor functions, such as reaching with the forelimb to obtain food, as illustrated in Experiment 14-2 (Kolb, Cote, et al., 1997). But because brain tissue is still missing, recovery is by no means complete.

epidermal growth factor (EGF)
Neurotrophic factor; stimulates the subventricular zone to generate cells that migrate into the striatum and eventually differentiate into neurons and glia.

Focus 5-4 recounts a successful case of fetal stem cell transplantation. Section 13-2 describes SCN cell replacement.

The striatum, a region in the basal ganglia, includes the caudate nucleus and putamen.

Even in adults, neural stem cells line the subventricular zone, diagrammed in Figure 8-10A.

In principle, we might expect that any drug that stimulates the growth of new connections would help people recover from brain injury. However, that neural growth must occur in brain regions that can influence a lost function. A drug that stimulates synaptic growth on cells in the visual cortex, for example, would not enhance recovery of hand use. The visual neurons play no direct role in moving the hand.

A third strategy to generate new neural circuits uses either deep brain stimulation (DBS) or direct electrical stimulation of perilesional regions. The goal of electrical stimulation is to directly increase activity in remaining parts of specific damaged neural networks. In DBS, it is to put the brain into a more plastic (trainable) state so that rehabilitation therapies work better. Both strategies are in preliminary clinical trials.

Lost Neuron Replacement Solution

The third strategy a patient like Donna could pursue is to generate new neurons to produce new neural circuits. The idea that brain tissue could be transplanted from one animal to another goes back a century. The evidence is good that tissue transplanted from fetal brains will grow and form some connections in the new brain.

Unfortunately, in contrast with transplanted hearts or livers, transplanted brain tissue functions poorly. The procedure seems most suited to conditions in which a small number of functional cells are required, as in the replacement of dopamine-producing cells in Parkinson disease or in the replacement of suprachiasmatic cells to restore circadian rhythms.

By 2004, dopamine-producing cells had been surgically transplanted into the striata of many Parkinson patients. Although the disease has not been reversed, some patients, especially the younger ones, have shown functional gains that justify the procedure. Nonetheless, ethical issues will remain as long as the tissue is taken from aborted human fetuses.

Adult stem cells offer a second way to replace lost neurons. Investigators know that the brain is capable of making neurons in adulthood. The challenge is to get the brain to do so after an injury. Brent Reynolds and Sam Weiss (1992) made the first breakthrough in this research.

Cells lining the ventricles of adult mice were removed and placed in a culture medium. The researchers demonstrated that if the correct trophic factors are added, the cells begin to divide and can produce new neurons and glia. Furthermore, if the trophic factors—particularly **epidermal growth factor** (EGF)—are infused into the ventricle of a living animal, the subventricular zone generates cells that migrate into the striatum and eventually differentiate into neurons and glia.

In principle, it ought to be possible to use trophic factors to stimulate the subventricular zone to generate new cells in the injured brain. If these new cells were to migrate to the site of injury and essentially regenerate the lost area, as shown in **Figure 14-26,** then it might be possible to restore at least some lost function. Not all lost behaviors could be restored, however, because the new neurons would have to establish the same connections with the rest of the brain that the lost neurons once had.

This task would be daunting: connections would have to be formed in an adult brain that already has billions of connections. Nonetheless, such a treatment might someday be feasible. Cocktails of trophic factors are effective in stimulating neurogenesis in the subventricular zone after

FIGURE 14-26 Stem Cells Do the Trick Left: After cortical stroke—damage is visible at upper right—infusion of epidermal growth factor into a rat's lateral ventricle induced neurogenesis in the subventricular zone. Right: The stem cells migrated to the site of injury and filled in the damaged area. But the cytological organization is abnormal.

Bryan Kolb

brain injury. For example, in Figure 14-26 at left, animals first received ischemic injuries (strokes), then received intraventricular infusions of trophic factors for 14 days. New cells migrated to the site of injury, as shown at right in Figure 14-26, and many differentiated into immature neurons.

Although they did not integrate well into the existing brain, the new cells influenced behavior and led to functional improvement (Kolb et al., 2007). The mechanism of influence is poorly understood. The new neurons apparently had some trophic influence on the surrounding uninjured cortex. Preliminary clinical trials with humans are under way and so far show no ill effects in volunteers.

14-5 REVIEW

Recovery from Brain Injury

Before you continue, check your understanding.

1. Three ways to compensate for the loss of neurons are (1) _____, (2) _____, and (3) _____.

2. Two ways of using electrical stimulation to enhance postinjury recovery are _____ and _____.

3. Endogenous stem cells can be recruited to enhance functional improvement by using _____ factors.

4. What is the lesson of the three-legged cat?

Answers appear at the back of the book.

For additional study tools, visit 🔊 **LaunchPad**:
www.macmillanhighered.com/launchpad/kolb5e

■ SUMMARY

14-1 Connecting Learning and Memory

Learning is a change in an organism's behavior as a result of experience. Memory is the ability to recall or recognize previous experience. For more than a century, laboratory studies using animals have uncovered two diverse types of learning: Pavlovian (or classical) and operant (or instrumental).

The two basic types of memory are implicit (unconscious) and explicit (conscious). Episodic memory includes not only a record of events (episodes) that occurred but also our presence there and our role in the events. The frontal lobe likely plays a unique role in this autobiographical memory.

14-2 Dissociating Memory Circuits

Multiple subsystems control different aspects of memory within the explicit and implicit systems. People with damaged explicit memory circuits have impaired recall for facts and events. People with damaged implicit memory circuits are impaired in their recall and/or performance of skills and habits.

14-3 Neural Systems Underlying Explicit and Implicit Memories

The neural circuits underlying implicit and explicit memory are distinctly different: the reciprocal system for explicit memory includes medial temporal structures; the unidirectional system for implicit memory includes the basal ganglia. Emotional memory has characteristics of both implicit and explicit memory. Neural circuits for emotional memory also are unique in that they include the amygdala. The chart summarizes broad categories within these multiple memory systems.

For memories to become established in the brain—the process of consolidation—experiences must change neural connections, and these changes must become relatively permanent. When memories are revisited, neural connectivity can become less fixed, allowing for the neural networks and thus the memory to be modified, a process called reconsolidation.

Multiple Memory Systems

14-4 Structural Basis of Brain Plasticity

The brain has the capacity for structural change, and structural change presumably underlies functional change. The brain changes structure in two fundamental ways in response to experience.

Some Guiding Principles of Brain Plasticity

1. Behavioral change reflects brain change.
2. All nervous systems are plastic in the same general way.
3. Plastic changes are age-specific.
4. Prenatal events can influence brain plasticity throughout life.
5. Plastic changes are brain region dependent.
6. Experience-dependent changes interact.
7. Plasticity has pros and cons.

First, existing neural circuits change largely by modifying synaptic connections. One proposed mechanism of synaptic change is long-term potentiation (LTP), reflected in modification of EPSPs following learning.

Second, novel neural circuits form both by forging new connections among existing neurons and by generating new neurons. Generating new neurons in the hippocampus is one mechanism for establishing novel circuits. A likely mechanism for maintaining synaptic changes is epigenetic: specific sites in the neuronal DNA in modified circuits can exist in either methylated or unmethylated states.

Neuronal activity is key to brain plasticity: through it, synapses form and change. Neuronal activity can be induced by general or specific experience as well as by electrical or chemical stimulation. Chemical stimulation may range from hormones and neurotrophic compounds to psychoactive drugs.

Much of the brain is capable of plastic change with experience. Different experiences lead to changes in different neural systems. The table summarizes seven principles that guide research about brain plasticity and behavior.

14-5 Recovery from Brain Injury

Plastic changes after brain injury parallel those seen when the brain changes with experience. Changes related to recovery do not always occur spontaneously, however, but must be stimulated by behavioral training, by the effects of psychoactive drugs or neurotrophic factors, or by electrical brain stimulation. The key to stimulating recovery from brain injury is to increase the plastic changes underlying the recovery.

■ KEY TERMS

amnesia, p. 483

anterograde amnesia, p. 497

associative learning, p. 500

behavioral sensitization, p. 511

conditioned response (CR), p. 483

conditioned stimulus (CS), p. 483

consolidation, p. 497

declarative memory, p. 485

dyslexia, p. 481

emotional memory, p. 498

entorhinal cortex, p. 491

epidermal growth factor (EGF), p. 516

episodic memory, p. 487

explicit memory, p. 485

eyeblink conditioning, p. 483

fear conditioning, p. 483

implicit memory, p. 483

Korsakoff syndrome, p. 495

learning, p. 481

learning set, p. 485

long-term depression (LTD), p. 500

long-term potentiation (LTP), p. 500

memory, p. 481

metaplasticity, p. 512

nerve growth factor (NGF), p. 511

neuritic plaque, p. 493

operant conditioning, p. 483

parahippocampal cortex, p. 491

Pavlovian conditioning, p. 481

perirhinal cortex, p. 491

priming, p. 485

procedural memory, p. 485

reconsolidation, p. 497

retrograde amnesia, p. 497

traumatic brain injury (TBI), p. 514

unconditioned response (UCR), p. 483

unconditioned stimulus (UCS), p. 483

visuospatial memory, p. 493

➡ Visit LaunchPad to access the e-Book, videos, LearningCurve adaptive quizzing, flashcards, and more.

www.macmillanhighered.com/launchpad/kolb5e

CHAPTER

15

How Does the Brain Think?

Streeter

Katherine Streeter

519

Split Brain

Epileptic seizures may begin in a restricted region of one brain hemisphere and spread through the fibers of the corpus callosum to the corresponding location in the opposite hemisphere. To prevent the spread of seizures that cannot be controlled through medication, neurosurgeons sometimes sever the 200 million nerve fibers of the corpus callosum.

The procedure is medically beneficial for many people with epilepsy, leaving them virtually seizure free, with only minimal effects on their everyday behavior. In special circumstances, however, the aftereffects of a severed corpus callosum become more readily apparent, as extensive psychological testing by Roger Sperry, Michael Gazzaniga, and their colleagues (Sperry, 1968; Gazzaniga, 1970) has demonstrated.

On close inspection, such **split-brain** patients reveal a unique behavioral syndrome that offers insight into the nature of cerebral asymmetry. Cortical asymmetry is essential for such integrative tasks as language and body control.

One split-brain subject was presented with several blocks. Each block had two red sides, two white sides, and two half-red and half-white sides, as illustrated. The task was to arrange the blocks to form patterns identical with those shown on cards.

When the subject used his right hand to perform the task, he had great difficulty. His movements were slow and hesitant. In contrast, when he performed the task with his left hand, his solutions were not only accurate but also quick and decisive.

Sample card

Blocks

Using his right hand, the subject is unable to duplicate the pattern...

...but with his left hand, the split-brain patient performs the task correctly.

In this experiment, a split-brain patient's task is to arrange a set of blocks to match the pattern shown on a card. Information from M. S. Gazzaniga, R. B. Ivry, and G. R. Mangun (1999). *Cognitive Science: The Biology of the Mind* (p. 323). New York: Norton.

Findings from studies of other split-brain patients have shown that, as tasks of this sort become more difficult, left-hand superiority increases. Participants whose brain is intact perform equally well with either hand, indicating the intact connection between the two hemispheres. But in split-brain subjects, each hemisphere works on its own.

Apparently, the right hemisphere, which controls the left hand, has visuospatial capabilities that the left hemisphere does not.

Studies of split-brain patients reveal that the left and right cerebral hemispheres engage in fundamentally different types of thinking. Yet typically we are unaware of these brain asymmetries. In this chapter we examine the neural systems and subsystems that control thinking. In the mammalian brain these systems are in the cortex.

Our first task is to define the mental processes we wish to study—to ask, what is the nature of thought? Then we consider the cortical regions—for vision, audition, movement, and associative function—that play major roles in thinking. We examine how these cortical connections are organized into such systems and subsystems as the dorsal and ventral visual streams and how neuroscientists study them.

Next we explore the brain's asymmetrical organization and delve deeper into split-brain phenomena. Another distinguishing feature of human thought is the different ways that individual people think. We consider several sources of these differences, including those related to gender and to what we call intelligence. Finally, we address consciousness and how it may relate to the neural control of thought.

15-1 The Nature of Thought

Studying abstract mental processes such as thought, language, memory, emotion, and motivation is tricky. They cannot be seen but can only be inferred from behavior and are best thought of as **psychological constructs,** ideas that result from a set of impressions. The mind constructs the idea as being real, even though it is not tangible.

We run into trouble when we try to locate constructs such as thought or memory in the brain. That we have words for these constructs does not mean that the brain is organized around them. Indeed, it is not. For instance, although people talk about memory as a unitary thing, the brain neither treats memory as unitary nor localizes it in one particular place. The many forms of memory are each treated differently by widely distributed brain circuits. The psychological construct of memory that we think of as being a single thing turns out not to be unitary at all.

Assuming a neurological basis for psychological constructs such as memory and thought is risky, but we certainly should not give up searching for where and how the brain produces them. After all, thought, memory, emotion, motivation, and other such constructs are the most interesting activities the brain performs.

Psychologists typically use the term **cognition** (knowing) to describe thought processes, that is, how we come to know about the world. For behavioral neuroscientists, cognition usually entails the ability to pay attention to stimuli, whether external or internal, to identify stimuli, and to plan meaningful responses to them. External stimuli cue neural activity in our sensory receptors. Internal stimuli can spring from the autonomic nervous system (ANS) as well as from neural processes—from constructs such as memory and motivation.

split brain Surgical disconnection of the hemispheres by severing the corpus callosum.

psychological construct Idea or set of impressions that some mental ability exists as an entity; memory, language, and emotion are examples.

cognition Act or process of knowing or coming to know; in psychology, refers to thought processes.

syntax Ways in which words are put together; proposed to be unique to human language.

Section 14-1 details types of memory, Section 14-4 how neuroplasticity contributes to memory processing and storage.

Characteristics of Human Thought

Human cognition is widely believed to have unique characteristics. One is that human thought is verbal, whereas the thought of other animals is nonverbal. Language is presumed to give humans an edge in thinking, and in some ways it does:

- Language provides the brain a means of categorizing information. It allows us easily to group together objects, actions, and events that have common factors.

- Language provides a means of organizing time, especially future time. It enables us to plan our behavior around time (say, Monday at 3:00 P.M.) in ways that nonverbal animals cannot.

- Perhaps most important, human language has **syntax**—sets of rules for putting words together to create meaningful utterances.

The appearance of human language correlates with a dramatic brain size increase; see Section 2-3. Section 10-4 explains foundations underlying all languages.

Linguists argue that although other animals, such as chimpanzees, can use and recognize vocalizations (about three dozen for chimps), they do not rearrange these sounds to produce new meanings. This lack of syntax, linguists maintain, makes chimpanzee language literal and inflexible. Human language, in contrast, has enormous flexibility that enables us to talk about virtually any topic, even highly abstract ones like psychological constructs. In this way, our thinking is carried beyond a rigid here and now.

Before you accept the linguists' position, review Focus 1-2, featuring the chimp Kanzi.

Neurologist Oliver Sacks illustrated the importance of syntax to human thinking in his description of Joseph, an 11-year-old deaf boy who was raised without sign language for his first 10 years and so was never exposed to syntax. According to Sacks:

> Joseph saw, distinguished, used; he had no problems with perceptual categorization or generalization, but he could not, it seemed, go much beyond this, hold abstract ideas in mind, reflect, play, plan. He seemed completely literal—unable to juggle images or hypotheses or possibilities, unable to enter an imaginative or figurative realm. . . . He seemed, like an animal, or an infant, to be stuck in the present, to be confined to literal and immediate perception. (Sacks, 1989, p. 40)

Language, including syntax, develops innately in children because the human brain is programmed to use words in a form of universal grammar. But in the absence of words—either spoken or signed—no grammar can develop. Without the linguistic flexibility that grammar allows, no "higher-level" thought can emerge. Without syntactical language, thought is stuck in the world of concrete, here-and-now perceptions. Syntax, in other words, influences the very nature of our thinking.

In addition to arranging words in syntactical patterns, the human brain has a passion for stringing together events, movements, and thoughts. We combine musical notes into melodies, movements into dance, images into videos. We design elaborate rules for games and governments. To conclude that the human brain is organized to chain together events, movements, and thoughts seems reasonable. Syntax is merely one example of this innate human way of thinking about the world.

We do not know how this propensity to string things together evolved, but one possibility is natural selection: stringing movements together into sequences is highly adaptive. It would allow for building houses or weaving threads into cloth, for instance.

William Calvin (1996) proposed that the motor sequences most important to ancient humans were those used in hunting. Throwing a rock or a spear at a moving target is a complex act that requires much planning. Sudden ballistic movements, such as throwing, last less than an eighth of a second and cannot be corrected by feedback. The brain has to plan every detail and then spit them out as a smooth-flowing sequence.

Today, a football quarterback does just this when he throws a football to a receiver running a zigzag pattern to elude a defender. A skilled quarterback can hit the target on virtually every throw, stringing movements together rapidly in a continuous sequence with no pauses or gaps. This skill is uniquely human. Chimpanzees can throw, but their throws are inaccurate. No chimpanzee could learn to throw a ball to hit a moving target.

The human predisposition to sequence movements may have encouraged language development. Spoken language, after all, is a sequence of movements involving the throat, tongue, and mouth muscles. Viewed in this way, language is the by-product of a brain that was already predisposed to operate by stringing movements, events, or even ideas, together.

A critical characteristic of human motor sequencing is our ability to create novel sequences with ease. We constantly produce new sentences. Composers and choreographers earn their living making new music and dance sequences. Novel movement or thought sequences are a product of the frontal lobe.

People with frontal lobe damage have difficulty generating novel solutions to problems. They are described as lacking imagination. The frontal lobes are critical not only for organizing behavior but also for organizing thinking. One major difference between the human brain and other primates' brains is the size of the frontal lobes.

Neural Unit of Thought

What exactly goes on within the brain to produce what we call thinking? Is thought an attribute exclusive to humans? Before you answer, consider the mental feats of Alex the parrot, profiled in Comparative Focus 15-2, Animal Intelligence.

Alex's cognitive abilities are unexpected in a bird. In the past 40 years, the intellectual capacities of chimpanzees and dolphins have provoked great interest, but Alex's mental life appears to have been just as rich as the mental life of those two large-brained mammals.

The fact that birds are capable of thought is a clue to the neural basis of thought. A logical presumption may be that thinking, which humans are so good at, must be due to some special property of the massive human neocortex. But birds do not possess a neocortex. Rather, they evolved specific brain nuclei that function much as the layers of the human cortex do. This organizational difference in the forebrain of birds and mammals implies that thinking must be an activity of complex neural circuits, not of some particular brain region.

The idea of neural circuits is the essence of Donald Hebb's (1949) concept that **cell assemblies** (networks of neurons) represent objects or ideas, and the interplay among the networks results in complex mental activity such as cognition. Connections among neurons are not random but rather are organized into systems and subsystems. Thinking must result from the activity of these complex neural circuits. One way to identify their role is to consider how individual neurons respond during cognitive activity.

William Newsome and his colleagues (1995) took this approach in training monkeys to identify apparent motion in a set of moving dots on a television screen. The Procedure

Figure 11-2 diagrams the frontal lobe hierarchy that initiates motor sequences.

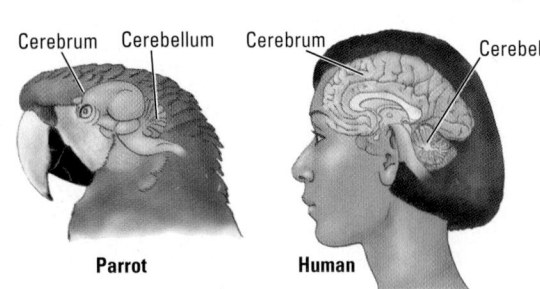

Cerebrum   Cerebellum   Cerebrum   Cerebellum

Parrot   **Human**

cell assembly Hypothetical group of neurons that become functionally connected via common sensory inputs; proposed by Hebb as the basis of perception, memory, and thought.

Animal Intelligence

Intelligent animals think. We all know that parrots can talk, but most of us assume that no real thought lies behind their words. An African grey parrot named Alex proved otherwise. Irene Pepperberg, pictured here with Alex, studied his ability to think and use language for more than three decades (Pepperberg, 1990, 1999, 2006).

A typical session with Alex and Pepperberg proceeded roughly as follows (Mukerjee, 1996): Pepperberg would show Alex a tray with four corks. "How many?" she would ask. "Four," Alex would reply. She then might show him a metal key and a green plastic one.

"What toy?"
"Key."
"How many?"
"Two."
"What's different?"
"Color."

Alex did not just have a vocabulary: words had meaning to him. He correctly applied English labels to numerous colors (red, green, blue, yellow, gray, purple, orange), shapes (two-, three-, four-, five-, six-cornered), and materials (cork, wood, rawhide, rock, paper, chalk, wool). He also labeled various items made of metal (chain, key, grate, tray, toy truck), wood (clothespin, block), and plastic or paper (cup, box).

Most surprisingly, Alex used words to identify, request, and refuse items. He responded to questions about abstract ideas, such as the color, shape, material, relative size, and quantity of more than 100 objects.

Alex's thinking was often quite complex. Presented with a tray that contained seven items—a circular rose-colored piece of rawhide, a piece of purple wool, a three-cornered purple key, a four-cornered yellow piece of rawhide, a five-cornered orange piece of rawhide, a six-cornered purple piece of rawhide, and a purple metal box—and then asked, "What shape is the purple hide?" Alex would answer correctly, "Six-corner."

To come up with this answer, Alex had to comprehend the question, locate the correct object of the correct color, determine the answer to the question about the object's shape, and encode his answer into an appropriate verbal response. This task was not easy. After all, four objects were pieces of rawhide and three objects were purple.

Wm. Munoz

The African grey parrot Alex, shown here with Irene Pepperberg and a sampling of the items he could count, describe, and answer questions about. Alex died in 2007 at the age of 31.

Alex could not respond just to one attribute. Rather, he had to combine the concepts of rawhide and purple and find the object that possessed them both. Then he had to figure out the object's shape. Clearly, considerable mental processing was required, but Alex succeeded at such tasks time and again.

Alex also demonstrated that he understood what he said. If he requested one object and was presented with another, he was likely to say no and repeat his original request. In fact, when given incorrect objects on numerous occasions in formal testing, he said no and repeated his request 72 percent of the time, said no without repeating his request 18 percent of the time, and made a new request the other 10 percent of the time.

These responses suggest that Alex's requests led to an expectation in his mind. He knew what he was asking for, and he expected to get it.

---

section of **Experiment 15-1** on page 524 shows how the researchers varied the difficulty of the task by manipulating the number of dots that moved in the same direction. If all the dots move in the same direction, perceiving the whole array as moving is very easy. If only a small percentage of the dots move in the same direction, however, perceiving apparent motion in that direction is much more difficult.

In fact, a threshold number of dots moving together is required to make directional motion apparent. If too few dots are moving in the same direction, the viewer gets an impression of random movement. Apparently, on the basis of the proportion of dots moving in the same direction, the brain decides whether dots are moving in a consistent direction.

After the monkeys were trained in the task, the investigators recorded from single neurons in visual area V5. V5 contains cells sensitive to movement in a preferred direction. When vertical movement crosses its receptive field, a neuron that is sensitive to vertical motion responds with a vigorous burst of action potentials. But just as the observer has a threshold

Figure 9-16 locates visual regions V1 through V5 in the occipital lobe.

▶ EXPERIMENT 15-1

Question: How do individual neurons mediate cognitive activity?

Procedure

Monkeys were trained to identify apparent motion in a set of moving dots on a TV screen.

Random dot movement (no apparent motion perceived)

Semirandom dot movement (still no apparent motion perceived)

Semicoordinated dot movement (threshold level needed to perceive apparent motion)

Coordinated dot movement (apparent motion strongly perceived)

Results

After the monkeys were trained in the task, investigators recorded from single neurons in visual area V5, which contains cells that are sensitive to motion in a preferred direction. The neural responses to the four different patterns of movement are shown below.

Baseline response

Baseline response

Moderate response

Strong response

Conclusion: The increase in neuronal firing rate correlates with the monkey's perception of motion, suggesting that individual neurons, not the summed activity of many neurons, influence perception.

for perceiving coherent motion in one direction, so too does the neuron. If at some point the random activity of the dots increases to a level that obscures movement in a neuron's preferred direction, the neuron will stop responding because it does not detect any consistent pattern.

So how does the activity of any given neuron correlate with the perceptual threshold for apparent motion? On the one hand, if our perception of apparent motion results from the summed activity of many dozens or even thousands of neurons, little correlation would exist between the activity of any one neuron and the perception. On the other hand, if individual neurons influence our perception of apparent motion, then a strong correlation would exist between the activity of a single cell and the perception.

The results of Experiment 15-1 are unequivocal: the sensitivity of individual neurons is very similar to the perceptual sensitivity of the monkeys to apparent motion. As shown in the Results section, if individual neurons failed to respond to the stimulus, the monkeys behaved as if they did not perceive any apparent motion.

This finding is curious. Given the large number of V5 neurons, it seems logical that perceptual decisions are based on the responses of a large pool of neurons. But Newsome's results show that the activity of individual cortical neurons is correlated with perception rather than perception being the property of a particular brain region.

Still, Hebb's idea of a cell assembly—an ensemble of neurons that represents a complex concept—suggests some way of converging the inputs of individual neurons to arrive at a consensus. Here, the neuronal ensemble represents a sensory event (apparent motion) that the activity of the ensemble detects. Cell assemblies could be distributed over fairly large regions of the brain, or they could be confined to smaller areas, such as cortical columns.

Figures 9-33 to 9-35 diagram functional columns in occipital and temporal cortices.

Via computer modeling, cognitive scientists have demonstrated the capacity of cell assembly circuits to perform sophisticated statistical computations. Other complex tasks, such as Alex the parrot's detecting an object's color, also are believed to entail neuronal ensembles. Cell assemblies provide the basis for cognition. Different ensembles come together, much like words in language, to produce coherent thoughts.

What do individual neurons contribute to a cell assembly? Each acts as a computational unit. As Experiment 15-1 shows, even one solitary neuron can decide on its own when to fire if its summed inputs indicate that movement is taking place. Neurons are the only elements in the brain that combine evidence and make decisions. Neurons are the foundation of cognitive processes and of thought. The combination of individual neurons into novel neural networks produces complex mental representations—ideas, for instance.

Hebb's Cell Assembly "Cells that fire together wire together." Image from D. O. Hebb (1949). *The Organization of Behavior* (Figure 9, p. 71). New York: McGraw-Hill.

15-1 REVIEW

The Nature of Thought

Before you continue, check your understanding.

1. Cognition, or thought, entails the abilities of _____, _____, and _____ stimuli.

2. Unlike thought in other animals, humans have the added advantage of _____, which adds _____ to thought.

3. The _____ is the basic unit of thought production.

4. Describe the most important way in which human thought differs from thinking in other animals.

Answers appear at the back of the book.

For additional study tools, visit LaunchPad: 🧠 **LaunchPad**
www.macmillanhighered.com/launchpad/kolb5e

15-2 Cognition and the Association Cortex

Altogether, the primary sensory and motor cortical regions occupy about a third of the neocortex (**Figure 15-1**). The remaining two-thirds, located in the frontal, temporal, parietal, and occipital lobes, is referred to generally as the **association cortex**. It functions to produce cognition.

A fundamental difference between association cortex and primary sensory and motor areas is that the association cortex has a distinctive pattern of connections. A major source of input to all cortical areas is the thalamus, which rests atop the brainstem. The primary sensory cortex receives inputs from thalamic nuclei that receive information from the body's sense organs. But inputs to the association cortex come from thalamic areas that receive their inputs from other cortical regions. As a result, inputs to the association cortex are already highly processed. So this information must be fundamentally different from the raw information reaching the primary sensory and motor cortex. The association regions contain knowledge either about our external or internal world or about movements.

Owing to its close relationship to the visual and auditory sensory regions, the temporal association regions tend to produce cognition related to visual and auditory processing.

KEY (cortical areas)		
Primary motor	Primary visual	Primary olfactory and taste
Primary sensory	Primary auditory	

FIGURE 15-1 Cortical Functions Lateral view of the left hemisphere and medial view of the right hemisphere, showing the primary motor and sensory areas. All remaining cortical areas are collectively referred to as the association cortex, which functions in thinking.

association cortex Neocortex outside primary sensory and motor cortices; functions to produce cognition.

FIGURE 15-2 Prefrontal Association Cortex Lateral view of the brain's left hemisphere (A) and medial view of the right hemisphere (B) represent regions of the prefrontal cortex (PFC) in relation to the associated anterior cingulate allocortex, shown in (B). Figure 12-19 illustrates how these areas function in producing emotional behavior.

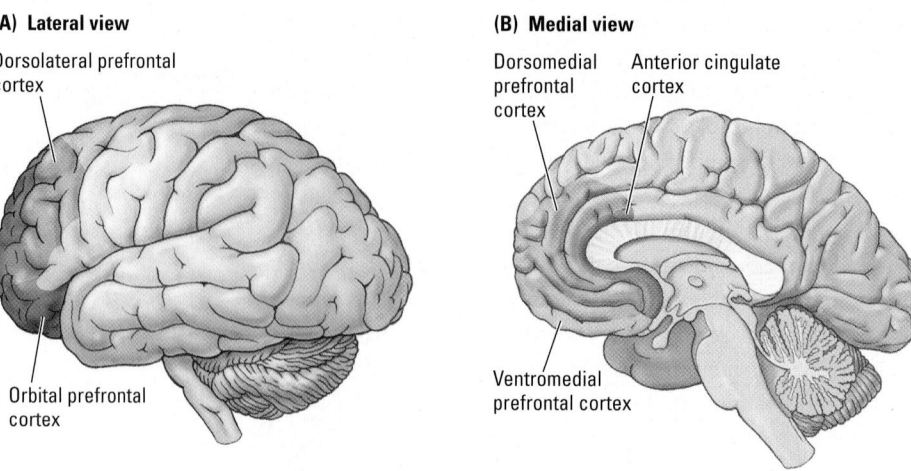

(A) Lateral view
Dorsolateral prefrontal cortex
Orbital prefrontal cortex

(B) Medial view
Dorsomedial prefrontal cortex
Anterior cingulate cortex
Ventromedial prefrontal cortex

Similarly, the parietal cortex is closely related to somatosensation and movement control. In contrast, the frontal cortex coordinates information coming from the parietal and temporal association regions with information coming from subcortical regions.

As diagrammed in **Figure 15-2,** the multiple subdivisions of the *prefrontal cortex* (PFC) encompass its dorsal, lateral, orbital, and medial regions. Activity in each prefrontal region is associated with the types of cognitive processing that we describe throughout this chapter. An additional frontal lobe region shown in Figure 15-2 is the anterior cingulate cortex (ACC). Although the ACC was once believed only to play a role in emotion, it is becoming clear that it functions as an interface between emotion and cognition.

To understand the types of knowledge that the association areas contain, we next consider discrete cognitive behaviors, then trace these behaviors to different parts of the association cortex.

Knowledge about Objects

Visualize a milk carton sitting on a counter directly in front of you. What do you see? Now imagine moving the carton a few inches off to one side as you continue to stare directly ahead. What do you see now? Next, imagine that you tilt the carton toward you at a 45° angle. Again, what do you see? Probably you answered that you saw the same thing in each situation: a rectangular box with lettering on it.

Intuitively, you feel that the brain must see the object much as you have perceived it. The brain's seeing, however, is more compartmentalized than are your perceptions. Compartmentalization is revealed in people with damage to various regions of the occipital cortex, many of whom lose one particular aspect of visual perception. For instance, those with damage to visual area V4 can no longer perceive color, whereas those with damage to area V5 can no longer see movement (when the milk carton moves, it becomes invisible to them).

Moreover, your perception of the milk carton's consistently rectangular shape does not always match the forms your visual system is processing. When you tip the carton toward you, you still perceive it as rectangular, even though it is no longer presenting a rectangular shape to your eyes. Your brain has somehow ignored the change in information about shape that your retinas have sent it and concluded that this object, no matter its apparent shape, remains the same milk carton.

There is more to your conception of the milk carton than merely perceiving and processing its physical characteristics. You also know what a milk carton is, what it contains, and where you can get one. The knowledge about milk cartons that you have acquired is represented in the temporal association cortex, which forms the ventral stream of visual processing. If the temporal association regions are destroyed, a person loses visual knowledge not only about milk cartons but also about all other objects. The person becomes *agnosic* (unknowing).

Section 9-4 recounts cases illustrative of various visual-form agnosias.

Knowledge about objects includes even more than how they look and what they are used for. It depends on what will be done with the information—how to pick up the milk carton, for example. Knowledge of *what* things are is temporal; knowledge of *how* to grasp the object is parietal (**Figure 15-3**).

Multisensory Integration

Our knowledge about the world comes through multisensory channels. When we see and hear a barking dog, the visual information and auditory information fit together seamlessly. How do all our neural systems and functional levels combine to afford us a unified conscious experience?

Philosophers, impressed with this integrative capacity, identified the **binding problem**, which asks how the brain ties its single and varied sensory and motor events together into a unified perception or behavior. It is gradually becoming clear how the brain binds up our perceptions and how this ability is gradually acquired in postnatal life (see the review by Stein & Rowland, 2011).

One solution to the sensory integration aspect of the binding problem lies in *multimodal* regions of the association cortex, that is, regions populated by neurons that respond to information from more than one sensory modality, as illustrated in **Figure 15-4**. Investigators presume that multimodal regions combine characteristics of stimuli across different senses when we encounter them separately or together. For example, the fact that we can visually identify objects that we have only touched implies a common perceptual system linking the visual and somatic circuits. In Section 15-5, Clinical Focus 15-6 profiles a man in whom stimulation from one sensory modality (taste) concurrently induces the experience of a different modality (touch).

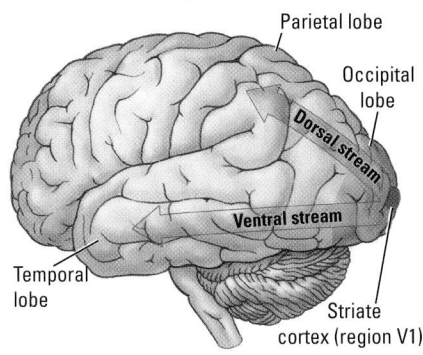

FIGURE 15-3 Streaming Visual Information The dorsal visual stream mediates vision for action. The ventral stream mediates vision for object recognition.

binding problem Philosophical question focused on how the brain ties single and varied sensory and motor events together into a unified perception or behavior.

The senses of smell and taste combine to produce the experience of flavor; see Section 12-2.

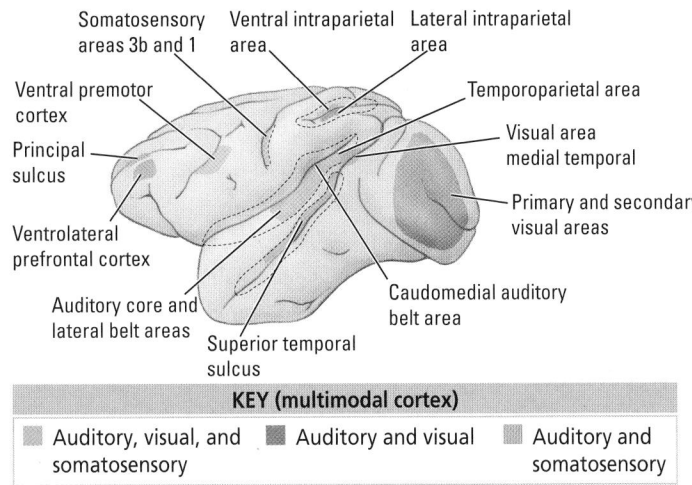

Somatosensory areas 3b and 1
Ventral intraparietal area
Lateral intraparietal area
Ventral premotor cortex
Temporoparietal area
Principal sulcus
Visual area medial temporal
Ventrolateral prefrontal cortex
Primary and secondary visual areas
Caudomedial auditory belt area
Auditory core and lateral belt areas
Superior temporal sulcus

KEY (multimodal cortex)

| Auditory, visual, and somatosensory | Auditory and visual | Auditory and somatosensory |

FIGURE 15-4 Multisensory Areas in the Monkey Cortex Color-coded areas represent regions where anatomical data and/or electrical stimulation demonstrate multisensory interactions. Dashed lines represent multimodal areas revealed when sulci are opened. Information from A. A. Ghanzanfar & C. E. Schroeder (2006). Is neocortex essentially multisensory? *Trends in Cognitive Science*, 10, pp. 278–285.

Spatial Cognition

The location of objects is just one aspect of what we know about space. *Spatial cognition* encompasses a whole range of mental functions that vary from navigational ability (getting from point A to point B) to mentally manipulating complex visual arrays like those shown in **Figure 15-5**.

Imagine going for a walk in an unfamiliar park. You do not go around and around in circles. Rather, you proceed in an organized, systematic way. You also need to find your way back. These abilities require a representation of the physical environment in your mind's eye.

At some time during the walk, let's assume you are uncertain where you are—a common problem. One solution is to make a mental image of your route, complete with various landmarks and turns. It is a small step from mentally manipulating these kinds of navigational

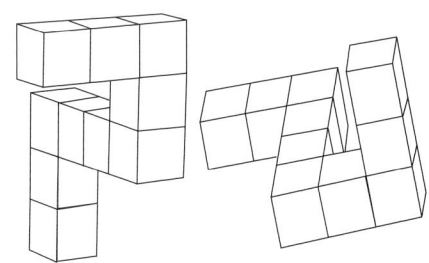

FIGURE 15-5 Spatial Cognition These two figures are the same but are oriented differently in space. Researchers test spatial cognition by giving subjects pairs of stimuli like this and asking if the shapes are the same or different.

The Basics, Section 1-3, traces nervous system evolution across the animal kingdom.

Alex the parrot manipulated objects with his beak.

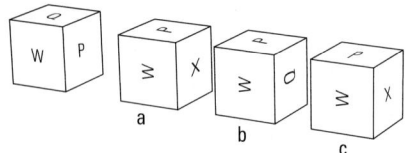

FIGURE 15-6 Mental Manipulation Try this sample test item used to measure spatial orientation. Compare the three cubes on the right with the one on the left. No letter appears on more than one face of a given cube. Which cube—a, b, or c—could be a different view of the cube on the left? The correct answer is at the bottom of the page.

attention Narrowing or focusing awareness to a part of the sensory environment or to a class of stimuli.

contralateral neglect Ignoring a part of the body or world on the side opposite (contralateral to) that of a brain injury.

extinction In neurology, neglect of information on one side of the body when presented simultaneously with similar information on the other side of the body.

The answer to the mental manipulation in Figure 15-6 is *a*.

landmarks and movements to manipulating other kinds of images in your mind. Thus the ability to mentally manipulate visual images seems likely to have arisen in parallel with the ability to navigate in space.

The evolution of skill in mental manipulation is also closely tied to the evolution of physical movements. It is likely that animals first moved using whole-body movements (the swimming motion of a fish), then developed coordinated limb movements (quadrupedal walking), and finally mastered discrete limb movements, such as a human arm reaching out. As the guidance strategies for controlling movements became more sophisticated, cognitive abilities evolved to support the guidance systems.

It seems unlikely that more sophisticated cognitive abilities evolved on their own. Why would a fish, say, be able to manipulate an object in its mind that it could not manipulate in the real world? But a human, who *can* manipulate objects by hand, should be able to imagine such manipulations. After all, we are constantly observing our hands or feet manipulating things: we must have many mental representations of such activities.

Once the brain can manipulate objects that are physically present, it seems a small step to manipulating imagined objects—to solve problems like the one depicted in **Figure 15-6.** The ability to manipulate an object in the mind's eye probably flows from the ability to manipulate tangible objects with the hands.

Research findings provide clues to the brain regions participating in various aspects of spatial cognition. For instance, the dorsal stream in the parietal lobes is central in controlling vision for action. Humans make discrete limb movements to points in space, so a reasonable supposition is that the dorsal stream's evolutionary development provided a neural basis for such spatial cognitive skills as mentally rotating objects. In fact, people with damaged parietal association regions, especially in the right hemisphere, have deficits in processing complex spatial information, both in the real world and in their imagination.

By tracing the evolutionary development of the human brain, we find that the parietal association regions expanded considerably more in humans than in other primates. This expanded brain region functions in part to perform the complex spatial operations just discussed. Humans have a capacity for building that far exceeds that of our nearest relative, the chimpanzee. You may consider it a long leap of logic, but perhaps our increased capacity for building and manipulating objects played heavily into our developing cognitive spatial abilities.

Attention

Imagine you're meeting some friends at a football game. You search for them as you meander through the crowd in the stadium. Suddenly you hear one friend's distinctive laugh and turn to scan in that direction. You see your group and rush to join them.

This everyday experience demonstrates the nature of **attention**, selective narrowing or focusing of awareness to part of the sensory environment or to a class of stimuli. Even as sounds, smells, feelings, and sights bombard you, you still can detect a familiar laugh or spot a familiar face: you can direct your attention.

More than 100 years ago, William James (1890) defined attention: "It is the taking possession by the mind in clear and vivid form of one out of what seem several simultaneous objects or trains of thought." James's definition goes beyond our example of locating friends in a crowd, inasmuch as he notes that we can attend selectively to thoughts as well as to sensory stimuli. Who hasn't at some time been so preoccupied with a thought as to exclude all else from mind? So attention can be directed inward as well as outward.

Selective Attention

As with many other inferred mental processes, studying the neural basis of attention is challenging. Research with monkeys trained to attend to particular locations or visual stimuli, however, has identified neurons in the cortex and midbrain that show enhanced firing rates to particular locations or visual stimuli. Significantly, the same stimulus can activate a neuron at one time but not at another, depending on the monkey's learned focus of attention.

In the study shown in **Experiment 15-2**, James Moran and Robert Desimone (1985) trained monkeys to hold a bar while gazing at a fixation point on a screen. A sample stimulus (e.g., a vertical red bar) appeared briefly at one location in the visual field, followed about 500 milliseconds later by a test stimulus at the same location. When the test stimulus was identical with the initial sample stimulus, an animal was rewarded if it immediately released the bar.

Each animal was trained to attend to stimuli presented in one particular area of the visual field and to ignore stimuli in any other area. In this way, the same visual stimulus could be presented to different regions of a neuron's receptive field to test whether the cell's response varied with stimulus location.

As the animals performed the task, the researchers recorded neurons firing in visual area V4. Neurons in V4 are sensitive to color and form, and different neurons respond to different combinations of the two variables (e.g,, a red vertical bar or a green horizontal bar). Visual stimuli were presented either in the correct location for a reward or in an incorrect location for no reward.

As diagrammed in the Results section of Experiment 15-2, neurons responded only when a visual stimulus was in the reward location, even though the same stimulus was presented in a no-reward location. Before training, the neurons responded to all stimuli in both locations. This finding tells us that attending to specific parts of the sensory world is a property of single neurons: more evidence that the neuron is the computational unit of cognition.

Deficits of Attention

Attention is probably a property of neurons throughout the brain, with some regions playing more prominent roles than others. The frontal lobes, for instance, are central in attention. People with frontal lobe injuries tend to become overly focused on environmental stimuli. They seem to selectively direct attention to an excessive degree or to have difficulty shifting attention. Studies of these people suggest that the frontal association cortex controls the ability to direct attention flexibly to where it is needed. Indeed, planning, a key frontal lobe function, requires this ability.

That the parietal association cortex is key in other aspects of attention is perhaps best illustrated by the attention deficit referred to as *neglect*. Neglect occurs when a brain-injured person ignores sensory information that should be considered important. Usually the condition affects only one side of the body and is called **contralateral neglect**. We observed a dog that had developed a right-hemisphere tumor and ate only the food on the right side of its dish, ignoring the food on the left side. Neglect is a fascinating symptom because often no damage to sensory pathways accompanies it. Rather, neglect is a failure of attention.

People with damage to the parietal association cortex of the right hemisphere may have particularly severe neglect of objects or events in the left side of their world. For example, one man dressed only the right side of his body, shaved only the right side of his face, and read only the right side of a page (if you can call that reading). He could move his left limbs spontaneously, but when asked to raise both arms, he would raise only the right. When pressed, he could be induced to raise the left arm, but he quickly dropped it to his side again.

As people with contralateral neglect begin to recover, they show another interesting symptom. They neglect information on one side of the body when it is simultaneously presented with similar information on the other side of the body. **Figure 15-7** shows a common clinical test for this symptom, called **extinction**.

► EXPERIMENT **15-2**

Question: Can neurons learn to respond selectively to stimuli?

Procedure

Monkeys were trained to release a bar when a certain stimulus was presented in a certain location. The monkeys learned to ignore stimuli in all other locations.

Fixation point Stimulus

Results

During performance of this task, researchers recorded the firing of neurons in visual area V4, which are sensitive to color and form. Stimuli were presented in either rewarded or unrewarded locations.

Pretraining recordings:

Rewarded location | Unrewarded location

Strong response | Strong response

Before training, neurons responded to stimuli in all locations.

Posttraining recordings:

Rewarded location | Unrewarded location

Strong response | Baseline response

After training, neurons responded only when the visual stimuli were in the rewarded location.

Conclusion: Neurons can learn to respond selectively to information in their receptive field.

When shown two identical objects

Patient's right
visual field

Patient's left
visual field

Patient
sees only
the object
in his right
visual field.

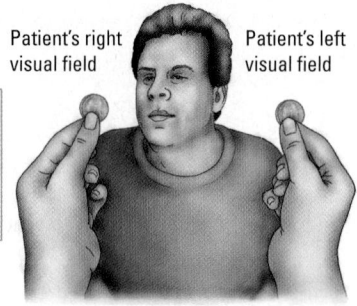

When shown two different objects

Patient sees
the object
in both
visual fields.

When shown two kinds of an object

Patient
sees only
the object
in his right
visual
field.

FIGURE 15-7 Testing for Extinction
A stroke patient who shows neglect for
information presented to his left responds
differently depending on whether objects
in the left and right visual fields are similar
or different.

In an extinction test, the patient is asked to keep his or her eyes fixed on the examiner's face and to report objects presented in one or both sides of the visual field. When presented with a single object (a fork) to one side or the other, the patient orients himself or herself toward the appropriate side of the visual field, so we know that he or she cannot be blind on either side. But now suppose that two forks are presented, one on the left and one on the right. The patient ignores the fork on the left and reports the one on the right. When asked about the left side, the patient is quite certain that nothing appeared there and that only one fork was presented, on the right.

Perhaps the most curious aspect of neglect is that people who have it fail to pay attention not only to one side of the physical world around them but also to one side of the world represented in their mind. We studied one woman who had complete neglect for everything on her left side. She complained that she could not use her kitchen because she could never remember the location of anything on her left.

We asked her to imagine standing at the kitchen door and to describe what was in the various drawers on her right and left. She could not recall anything on her left. We then asked her to imagine walking to the end of the kitchen and turning around. We again asked her what was on her right, the side of the kitchen that had previously been on her left. She broke into a big smile and tears ran down her face as she realized that she now knew what was on that side of the room. All she had to do was reorient her body in her mind's eye. She later wrote and thanked us for changing her life, because she was now able to cook again. Clearly, neglect can exist in the mind as well as in the physical world.

Although complete contralateral neglect is usually associated with parietal lobe injury, specific forms of neglect can arise from other injuries. Ralph Adolphs and his colleagues (2005) describe the case of S. M., a woman with bilateral amygdala damage who could not recognize fear in faces. On further study, the reason was discovered: S. M. failed to look at the eyes when she looked at faces; instead, she looked at other facial features such as the nose. Because fear is most clearly identified in the eyes, not the nose, she did not identify the emotion. When she was specifically instructed to look at the eyes, her recognition of fear became entirely normal. Thus, the amygdala plays a role in directing attention to the eyes to identify facial expressions.

Planning

At noon on a Friday, a friend proposes that she and you go to a nearby city for the weekend to attend a concert. She will pick you up at 6:00 P.M. and you will drive there together.

Because you are completely unprepared for this invitation and because you are going to be busy until 4:00, you must rush home and get organized. En route you stop at a fast food restaurant so that you won't be hungry on the 2-hour drive. You also need cash, so you head to the nearest ATM. When you get home, you grab various pieces of clothing appropriate for the concert and the trip. You also pack your toiletries. You somehow manage to get ready by 6:00, when your friend arrives.

Although the task of getting ready in a hurry may make us a bit harried, most of us can manage it. People with frontal lobe injury cannot. To learn why, let's consider what the task requires.

1. To plan your behavior, you must select from many options. What do you need to take with you? Cash? Then which ATM is closest, and what is the quickest route to it? Are you hungry? Then what is the fastest way to get food on a Friday afternoon?

2. In view of your time constraint, you have to ignore irrelevant stimuli. If you pass a sign advertising a sale in your favorite store, for instance, you have to ignore it and persist with the task at hand.

3. You have to keep track of what you have done already, a requirement especially important while you are packing. You do not want to forget anything or pack duplicates. You do not want to take four pairs of shoes but no toothbrush.

The task's general requirements can be described as the temporal (time) organization of behavior. You are planning what you need to do and when you need to do it. Temporal planning is the general function of the frontal lobes, especially the prefrontal cortex.

But to plan, you also need to recognize objects (an occipital and temporal lobe function) and to make appropriate movements with respect to them (a parietal lobe function). You can therefore think of the frontal lobes as acting like an orchestra conductor. The frontal lobes make and read a motor plan to organize behavior in space and time—a kind of score, analogous to the musical score a conductor uses. People with frontal lobe injuries are simply unable to organize their behavior.

Performance on the Wisconsin Card Sorting Test exemplifies the deficits frontal lobe injury causes. **Figure 15-8** shows the testing materials. The subject is presented with four stimulus cards bearing designs that differ in color, form, and number of elements, thus setting up three possible sorting categories. The subject must sort a deck of cards into piles in front of the various stimulus cards, depending on the sorting category called for. But the correct sorting category is never stated. The subject is simply told after placing each card whether the choice is correct or incorrect.

In one trial, for example, the first correct sorting category is color. After the subject has sorted a number of cards by color, the correct solution switches, without warning, to form. When the subject has started to sort by form, the correct solution again changes unexpectedly, this time to the number of items on each card. The sorting rule later becomes color again, and so on, with each change in rule coming unannounced.

Shifting response strategies is particularly difficult for people with frontal lobe lesions: they may continue responding to the original stimulus (color) for as many as 100 cards until the test ends. This pattern, known as **perseveration,** is the tendency to emit repeatedly the same verbal or motor response to varied stimuli.

Frontal lobe subjects may even comment that they know that color is no longer the correct category, but they continue to sort by color. One stated: "Form is probably the correct solution now so this [sorting by color] will be wrong, and this will be wrong, and wrong again." Despite knowing the correct sorting category, the frontal lobe patient cannot shift behavior in response to the new external information.

Imitation and Understanding

In all communication—verbal and nonverbal—the sender and receiver must share an understanding of what counts. If a person speaks a word or makes a gesture, another person will understand only if he or she interprets it correctly. To accomplish this coordination in communication, the processes of producing and perceiving a message must share a common representation in the sender's and the receiver's brains.

How do both sender and receiver of a potentially ambiguous gesture, such as a raised hand or a faint smile, achieve a common understanding? Giacomo Rizzolatti and his colleagues (Rizzolatti, 2007; Rizzolatti & Craighero, 2004) proposed an answer. In monkeys' frontal lobes they identified neurons that discharge during active movements of the hand or mouth or both. These neural discharges do not precede the movements but instead occur in synchrony with them. But it takes time for a neural message to go from a frontal lobe to a hand, so we would predict that, if these cells are controlling the movements, they will discharge *before* the movements take place. The cells must therefore be recording a movement that is taking place.

In the course of his studies, Rizzolatti also found that many "movement" neurons located in the inferior frontal and posterior parietal cortex discharge when a monkey sees other monkeys make the same movements. They also discharge when the monkey sees the

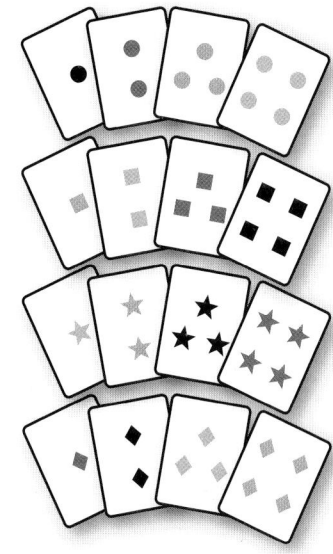

FIGURE 15-8 Wisconsin Card Sorting Test The subject receives a deck of cards containing multiple copies of those represented here and is presented with a row of four cards selected from among them. The task is to place each card in the pile under the appropriate card in the row, sorting by one of three possible categories. Subjects are never explicitly told what the correct sorting category is—color, number, or form; they are told only whether their responses are correct or incorrect. After subjects have begun sorting by one category, the tester unexpectedly changes to another category.

perseveration Tendency to emit repeatedly the same verbal or motor response to varied stimuli.

mirror neuron Cell in the primate premotor and parietal cortex that fires when an individual observes an action taken by another individual.

experimenter make the movements. Rizzolatti called them **mirror neurons.** The researchers proposed that mirror neurons represent actions, one's own or those of others. Such neural representations could be used both for imitating others' actions and for understanding their meanings, thus enabling appropriate responses. Mirror neurons therefore could provide the link between the sender and the receiver of a communication.

Rizzolatti and his colleagues used PET to look for these same neuron populations in humans. Participants were asked to watch a movement, to make the same movement, or to imagine the movement. Each condition activated a region of the lateral frontal lobe in the left hemisphere, including Broca's area. Taken together with the results of the monkey studies, this finding suggests that primates have a fundamental mechanism for recognizing action. People apparently recognize others' actions, because the neural patterns produced when they observe those actions are similar to those produced when they themselves make those same actions. Research Focus 15-3, The Rise and Fall of Mirror Neurons, frames the debate on mirror neuron function.

RESEARCH FOCUS 15-3

The Rise and Fall of Mirror Neurons

Rizzolatti and colleagues' discovery of mirror neurons in the 1990s was serendipitous (e.g., Rizzolatti, 2007). The group was investigating how neurons in the premotor cortex of macaque monkeys control grasping actions. The monkeys were trained to make different grasping movements to retrieve bits of food. When the animals reached for the food, cells in the premotor cortex were highly active, revealing their role in movement control.

Between reaching trials the monkeys could observe an investigator making reaching movements similar to those the monkey had made. Unexpectedly, many of the same neurons fired in response to the monkeys observing the experimenter's reaching: the cells appeared to mirror others' behavior. The name *mirror neurons* stuck. Studies using noninvasive imaging demonstrated similar neuronal populations, although apparently more widespread, in humans.

Over the ensuing decade, mirror neurons were hypothesized to be the basis of *understanding* actions rather than merely recognizing them. This possibility had profound implications and led to propositions that mirror neurons were the basis of speech and language, empathy, social cognition, theory of mind—even civilization! Dysfunction of the mirror neuron system was proposed as a basis for disorders such as the broken mirror hypothesis of autism (Ramachandran & Oberman, 2006).

The lure of mirror neurons spread well beyond neuroscience and into the popular media. All the hype resulted in mirror neurons being widely perceived as among the most important discoveries in neuroscience in the past generation.

But by the early 2000s, cracks began to show in the mirror. Gregory Hickok (2014) has argued that mirror neurons do not make actions understandable, but they do refine movement control. Hickok and others suggest that mirror neurons do not "understand" action, but rather their function arises from an association between executing an action and the self-observation of the action.

Thus, the neurons learn to mirror. But why? What is the benefit? One possibility is that because the actions of others are relevant to one's own actions, having a system to link others' perceived actions with one's own appropriate actions is adaptive. An extension of this idea is that mirror neurons are activated after an action is understood by other brain regions as a way to make predictions about future actions (Hickok, 2013). In this view, mirror neurons simply reflect the fact that the brain understands actions (Csibra, 2007). The advantage of this type of mirror system is that with this knowledge we can make movements faster and more accurately.

The lessons from the rise and fall of mirror neurons: First, although the mirror neuron theory of functioning to *understand* action may be wrong, it has served the field well by stimulating new research. That research has led to better understanding of how the brain thinks. A second lesson is vigilance: some scientists and media can push scientific theories well beyond the data.

15-2 REVIEW

Cognition and the Association Cortex

Before you continue, check your understanding.

1. The association cortex contains _____ and functions to produce _____.

2. As a general rule, the _____ lobes generate knowledge about objects, whereas the _____ lobes produce various forms of spatial cognition.

3. The frontal lobes function not only to make movements but also to _____ and to _____.

4. _____ neurons in the frontal and parietal lobes represent actions, one's own or those of others.

5. Describe the function of multimodal cortex.

Answers appear at the back of the book.

For additional study tools, visit LaunchPad: **LaunchPad**
www.macmillanhighered.com/launchpad/kolb5e

15-3 Expanding Frontiers of Cognitive Neuroscience

Sophisticated noninvasive stimulation and recording techniques for measuring the brain's electrical activity and noninvasive brain imaging methods led to a major shift in studying brain and behavior: **cognitive neuroscience**, the field that studies the neural bases of cognition. Cognitive neuroscience focuses on high-tech research methods but continues to rely on the decidedly low-tech tools of neuropsychological assessment—behavioral tests that compare the effects of brain injuries on performing particular tasks. Clinical Focus 15-4, Neuropsychological Assessment, illustrates its benefits.

cognitive neuroscience Study of the neural bases of cognition.

CLINICAL FOCUS 15-4

Neuropsychological Assessment

In this high-tech age of PET, fMRI, and ERP, low-tech behavioral assessment endures as among the best, simplest, most economical ways to measure cognitive function.

To illustrate the nature and power of neuropsychological assessment, we compare three patients' test performance on an array of tests selected from among those used in a complete neuropsychological assessment. The five tests presented here measure verbal and visual memory, verbal fluency, abstract reasoning, and reading. Performance was compared with that of a healthy control participant.

In the delayed memory tests—one verbal, the other visual—the patients and the control were read a list of words and two short stories. They were also shown a series of simple drawings. Their task: repeat the words and stories immediately after hearing them and draw the simple figures.

Half an hour later, without warning, they were asked to perform the tasks again. Their performance on these tests yielded the delayed verbal and visual memory scores listed in the table.

In the delayed verbal fluency test, patients and control had 5 minutes to write down as many words as they could think of that start with the letter *s*, excluding numbers and people's names. Then came the Wisconsin Card Sorting Test, which assesses abstract reasoning (see Figure 15-8). Finally, all were given a reading test.

The first patient, J. N., was a 28-year-old man who had developed a tumor in the anterior and medial left temporal lobe. His preoperative psychological tests showed superior intelligence scores. His only significant deficits appeared on tests of verbal memory.

When we saw J. N. a year after surgery that successfully removed the tumor, he had returned to his job as a personnel manager. His intelligence was still superior, but as the score summary shows, he was impaired on the delayed verbal memory test, recalling only about 50 percent as much as the control and other subjects.

The second patient, E. B., was a college senior majoring in psychology. An aneurysm in her right temporal lobe had burst due to a bulge in the artery. The anterior part of that lobe had been removed. E. B. was of above-average intelligence and completed her undergraduate degree with good grades. Her score on the delayed visual memory test, just over half the scores of the other test-takers, clearly showed her residual deficit.

The third patient, also of above-average intelligence, was J. W., a 42-year-old police detective who had a college degree. A benign tumor had been removed from his left frontal lobe.

We saw J. W. 10 years after his surgery. He was still on the police force but working a desk job. His verbal fluency was markedly reduced, as was his ability to solve the card-sorting task. His reading skill, however, was unimpaired. This was also true of the other patients.

Two principles emerge from the results of these three neuropsychological assessments:

1. *Brain functions are localized.* Damage to different brain regions produces different symptoms.

2. *Brain organization is asymmetrical.* Left-hemisphere damage preferentially affects verbal functions; right-hemisphere damage preferentially affects nonverbal functions.

Subjects' Scores

Test	Control	J. N.	E. B.	J. W.
Delayed verbal memory	17	9*	16	16
Delayed visual memory	12	14	8*	12
Verbal fluency	62	62	66	35*
Card-sorting errors	9	10	12	56*
Reading	15	21	22	17

*Atypically poor score.

Sophisticated imaging techniques are helping cognitive neuroscientists map the human brain. Its methods assist social psychologists in discovering how the brain mediates social interactions and economists in discovering how the brain makes decisions.

Mapping the Brain

Among the great scientific challenges of the twenty-first century, mapping the human **brain connectome** may be the most intriguing. Toward this end, the U.S. National Institutes of Health (NIH) awarded grants totaling $40 million to map the complete structural and functional fiber pathway connections of the human brain in vivo. Researchers participating in the Human Connectome Project (HCP) are combining diffusion tensor imaging (DTI) and functional connectivity magnetic resonance imaging (fcMRI) to plot these connections in the living human brain. By the end of 2015 HCP investigators had completed scanning 1200 healthy adults' brains, including 300 twin pairs.

The HCP's goal is to provide a reference atlas for those seeking to understand human brain function and dysfunction. It has attracted considerable public interest, and an explosion of studies outside the HCP also seeks to map the human brain. For example, in a review, Roser Sala-Llonch and colleagues (2015) report that as people age, they show reduced functional connectivity compared to young adults. The investigators hypothesize that this finding could explain age-related cognitive changes.

Using fMRI in Brain Mapping

The fcMRI technique uses resting-state fMRI (rs-fMRI) to measure functional correlations between brain regions. Pooling rs-fMRI data across thousands of healthy young adults makes it possible to identify consistent patterns of connectivity, or nerve tracts, in the brain. Utilizing rs-fMRI data from 1000 participants, Thomas Yeo and colleagues (2011) parcellated the human cerebral cortex into the 17 networks illustrated in **Figure 15-9**.

The cerebral cortex is made up of primary sensory and motor networks as well as the multiple, large-scale networks that form the association cortex. The sensory and motor networks are largely local: adjacent areas tend to show strong functional coupling with one another. In Figure 15-9, the turquoise and blue/gray regions in somatosensory and motor cortex and the purple region in visual cortex illustrate these couplings.

In contrast, the association networks include areas distributed throughout the prefrontal, parietal, anterior temporal, and midline regions. In Figure 15-9, the distributed yellow regions show prefrontal–posterior parietal connectivity. Some distributed networks, shown in light red, include temporal, posterior parietal, and prefrontal regions.

Unlike DTI, fcMRI does not measure static anatomical connectivity but rather uses temporal (time-based) correlations between neurophysiological activities in different regions to infer functional connectivity. One obvious direction of investigations based on fcMRI is searching for individual phenotypic variations. Such mapping will allow examination of

For more on the HCP, including connectome images, go to www.humanconnectomeproject.org. *National Geographic* published an accessible article in February 2014.

FIGURE 15-9 Parcellation of Cerebral Cortical Networks An estimate of 17 cortical networks based on fcMRI data from 1000 participants. Each color represents a network. Some, such as the blue auditory areas in temporal lobe, are localized; others are widely distributed, such as the yellow regions, which reveal prefrontal–posterior parietal connectivity.

Republished with permission of the American Physiological Society from B. T. T. Yeo, F. M. Fienen, J. Sepulcre, M. R. Sabuncu, D. Lashkari, et al., "The Organization of the Human Cerebral Cortex Estimated by Intrinsic Functional Connectivity," 2011, *Journal of Neurophysiology, 106*, pp. 1125–1165. Permission conveyed through Copyright Clearance Center, Inc.

Left hemisphere, lateral view

Left hemisphere, Medial view

specific traits (e.g., musical ability) or psychiatric diagnoses (see the review by Kelly and colleagues, 2012).

Tractography Using Diffusion Tensor Imaging

DTI studies provide results, often called *tractography*, that complement the networks mapped by fcMRI. Tractography measures actual neuroanatomical pathways that can be related to specific traits. Traditional postmortem tract tracing was performed on single brains. Today, tractography can be performed quickly on many living brains, and measurements can be made simultaneously in the entire brain. This advance allows researchers to correlate specific behavioral traits with specific patterns of connectivity.

Psyche Loui and her colleagues (2011) were interested in the neural basis of perfect (or absolute) pitch, the ability not only to discriminate among musical notes but also to name any note heard. Perfect pitch is rare among humans but shared by people with remarkable musical talents. Think Mozart. Development of perfect pitch is sensitive to early experiences, including musical training and exposure to tonal languages such as Japanese.

Loui's team studied musicians, with and without absolute pitch, who were matched in gender, age, handedness, ethnicity, IQ score, and years of musical training. Participants were given a test of pitch-labeling that allowed the researchers to place the musicians with absolute pitch into two categories: more accurate and less accurate. The less accurate group was superior to participants without absolute pitch, who could not accurately identify the note.

The investigators hypothesized that absolute pitch could be related to increased connectivity in brain regions that process sounds. They used DTI to reconstruct white-matter tracts connecting two temporal cortex regions involved in auditory processing, the superior and middle temporal gyri, and regions not involved in auditory processing (corticospinal tract). The results, reproduced in **Figure 15-10,** show that people with absolute pitch have greater connectivity in temporal lobe regions responsible for pitch perception than do people without it. The effect is largest in people in the more accurate group.

Although enhanced connectivity appears in both hemispheres of the musicians, when the investigators correlated performance on a test of absolute pitch with tract volume, only left-hemisphere tract volume predicted performance. It appears that having more local connections, or **hyperconnectivity,** in the left hemisphere is responsible for absolute pitch.

It is tempting to speculate that other exceptional talents, such as creativity, might be related to hyperconnectivity in cerebral regions. Conversely, we can speculate that reduced structural and functional connectivity is related to cognitive impairments after acquired brain injuries and/or neurodevelopmental and psychiatric disorders.

Cognition and the Cerebellum

So far we have emphasized the role of the neocortex in cognitive functions, in part because of its marked expansion in size and neuron numbers in primate brains. Yet the human

brain connectome Map of the complete structural and functional fiber pathways of the human brain in vivo.

hyperconnectivity Increased local connections between two related brain regions.

(A) More accurate perfect pitch

Left hemisphere   Right hemisphere

(B) Less accurate perfect pitch

Left hemisphere   Right hemisphere

(C) Lacking perfect pitch

Left hemisphere   Right hemisphere

FIGURE 15-10 Tractography of Temporal Lobe Auditory Circuits Color overlaid on DTI images demonstrates tracts between the superior temporal gyrus and middle temporal gyrus in three individuals. Participants A and B had more accurate and less accurate perfect pitch, respectively; Case C did not. The tracts that connect the regions in the left hemisphere (orange) are larger in participants A and B than in C. Tracts colored purple connect the regions in the right hemisphere. Copyright © 2011, Massachusetts Institute of Technology. Loui, P., Li, H. C., Hohmann, A., & Schlaug, G. (2011). Enhanced Connectivity in Absolute Pitch Musicians: A Model of Hyperconnectivity. Journal of Cognitive Neuroscience 23(4), 1015-1026. Permission conveyed through Copyright Clearance Center, Inc.

Research Focus 2-1 describes the effects of cerebellar agenesis.

cerebellum accounts for 80 percent of the brain's neurons. The cerebellum has long been known to play a central role in motor control and motor learning, but the concurrent evolution of neocortex, cerebellum, and cognitive complexity in primates suggests that the cerebellum may play a larger role in cognitive processes than investigators have appreciated (e.g., Barton, 2012).

The extensive neocortex–cerebellum interconnections include prefrontal cortex, Broca's area, and neocortical regions that have sensory or perceptual functions. Thus, the cerebellum appears to be critical in producing fine movements and perception, but some executive function also may be associated with working memory, attention, language, music, and decision-making processes (Bauman et al., 2015). No single coherent model of cerebellar activity in cognition has emerged, partly because researchers interested in cognitive functions have neglected the cerebellum for decades. Undoubtedly, the coming decade will deliver an abundance of new information, allowing for a better- informed model of cerebellar functions in cognition.

Social Neuroscience

social neuroscience Interdisciplinary field that seeks to understand how the brain mediates social interactions.

theory of mind Ability to attribute mental states to others.

By combining cognitive neuroscience tools, especially functional neuroimaging, with abstract constructs from social psychology, **social neuroscience** seeks to understand how the brain mediates social interactions. Matthew Lieberman (2007) identified broad themes that attempt to encompass all cognitive processes involved in understanding and interacting with others and in understanding ourselves.

Understanding Others

Animals' mind and experiences are not open to direct inspection. We infer animals' mind in part by observing their behaviors and peoples' mind by listening to their words. In doing so, we may develop a **theory of mind**, the attribution of mental states to others. Theory of mind includes an understanding that others may have feelings and beliefs different from our own. This broader understanding has led some investigators to conclude that theory of mind may be uniquely human. But many researchers who study apes strongly believe that other apes, too, possess a theory of mind.

Many fMRI studies over the past decade suggest that the brain region believed most closely associated with theory of mind is the dorsolateral prefrontal cortex (see Figure 15-2). Human prefrontal regions are disproportionately large as corrected for brain size, but other apes also have large prefrontal regions. The anatomy supports the likelihood that they also possess a theory of mind.

The capacity to understand others can also be inferred from the presence of empathy. For example, when participants watch videos of others smelling disgusting odors, they report a feeling of disgust. Lieberman and his colleagues (Rameson et al., 2012) used fMRI to assess the neural correlates of empathy by asking participants to empathize with sad images. Empathy correlated with increased activity in the medial prefrontal region, suggesting that the area is critical for empathic experience.

Understanding Oneself

Not only are we humans aware of others' intentions, we also have a sense of self. Humans and apes have the ability to recognize themselves in a mirror, an ability that human infants demonstrate by about 21 months of age. Studies using fMRI show that when we recognize our own face versus the face of

The Povinelli Group LLC

Looking at its reflection and pointing to a dot placed on its forehead, this chimpanzee displays self-recognition, a cognitive ability possessed by higher primates.

familiar others, brain activity increases in the right lateral prefrontal cortex and in the lateral parietal cortex. The parietal cortex activation is thought to reflect the body's recognition of what itself feels like.

But self-recognition is only the beginning of understanding oneself. People also have a self-concept that includes beliefs about their own personal traits (e.g., kind, intelligent). When participants are asked to determine whether trait words or sentences are self-descriptive, brain activity in medial prefrontal regions increases.

Self-Regulation

Self-regulation is the ability to control emotions and impulses as a means of achieving long-term goals. We may wish to yell at the professor because an exam was unfair, but most of us recognize that this course will not be productive. Dynamic imaging studies again reveal that prefrontal regions are critical in social cognition, in this case in self-regulation.

Children are often poor self-regulators, which probably reflects slow development of the prefrontal regions responsible for impulse control. A uniquely human ability to self-regulate is by putting feelings into words, a strategy that allows us to control emotional outbursts. Curiously, such verbal labeling is associated with increased activity in the right lateral prefrontal regions but *not* in the left.

Not only can humans control their emotions; they also have expectations about how a stimulus might feel (e.g., an injection by syringe). Our expectations can alter the actual feeling of an event. It is common for people to say ouch when they do something like stub a toe, even if they actually feel no pain. Nobukatsu Sawamoto and colleagues (2000) found that when participants expect pain, activity increases in the anterior cingulate cortex (see Figure 15-2B), a region associated with pain perception, even if the stimulus turns out not to be painful.

Section 8-2 describes unique aspects of frontal lobe development that extend beyond childhood—up to age 30.

Feeling and treating physical pain is a topic in Section 11-4. Focus 12-1 reports on emotional pain.

Living in a Social World

We spend much of our waking time interacting with others socially. In a sense, our understanding of our self and our social interactions link together into a single mental action. One important aspect of this behavior includes forming attitudes and beliefs about ourselves and about others. When we express attitudes (including prejudices) toward ideas or human groups, brain imaging shows activation in prefrontal, anterior cingulate, and lateral parietal regions.

Samuel McLure and colleagues (2004) took advantage of the fact that many people have strong attitudes toward cola-flavored sodas. Coca-Cola and Pepsi Cola are nearly identical in chemical composition, yet subjectively, people routinely prefer one to the other. The researchers ran blind taste tests among people who stated a cola brand preference.

As a group, participants failed to discriminate the drinks accurately when they were presented in a blind taste test. Brain activity was also equivalent for each cola in the blind condition. However, when participants believed that they were drinking Coca-Cola, significant changes in brain activity were recorded in many regions, including the hippocampus and dorsolateral prefrontal cortex. The investigators concluded that cultural information biases brain systems, which in turn biases attitudes.

Social Cognition and Brain Activity

Social cognitions running the gamut from understanding ourselves to understanding others clearly are associated with activation of specific brain regions, especially prefrontal regions. The obvious conclusion is that prefrontal activity produces our social cognitions, just as activity in visual regions produces our visual perceptions. But this conclusion has proved controversial. Ed Vul and colleagues (2009, 2012) go so far as to suggest that "correlations in social neuroscience are voodoo." Their assertion has led to strong disputations (e.g., Lieberman et al., 2012). The arguments are complex, focus on the nature of the analysis of fMRI data, and will certainly continue. In our view, the debate does not impugn the general conclusion that brain states produce behavioral states.

Neuroeconomics

Leonard Mlodinow's wonderful 2009 book, *The Drunkard's Walk: How Randomness Rules Our Lives*, offers many everyday examples.

Historically, economics was a discipline based on the "rational actor," the belief that people make rational decisions. In the real world, people often make decisions based on assumption or intuition, as is common in gambling. Why don't people always make rational decisions?

The cerebral processes underlying human decision making are not easily inferred from behavioral studies. But investigators in the field of **neuroeconomics**, which combines ideas from economics, psychology, and neuroscience, attempt to explain those processes by studying patterns of brain activity as people make decisions in real time. The general assumption among neuroeconomists is that two neural decision pathways influence our choices. One is deliberate, slow, rule-driven, and emotionally neutral; it acts as a *reflective system*. The other pathway—fast, automatic, emotionally biased—forms a *reflexive system*.

Figure 6-17 maps the dopaminergic pathways associated with reward.

If people must make quick decisions they believe will provide immediate gain, widespread activity appears in the dopaminergic reward system. This includes the ventromedial prefrontal cortex and ventral striatum (nucleus accumbens): the reflexive pathway. If slower, deliberative decisions are possible, activity is greater in the lateral prefrontal, medial temporal, and posterior parietal cortex, the areas that form the reflective pathway.

Neuroeconomists are looking to identify patterns of neural activity in everyday decision making, patterns that may help account for how people make decisions about their finances, social relations, and other personal choices. Although most neuroeconomic studies to date have used fMRI, in principle these studies could also use other noninvasive imaging technologies. Epigenetic factors probably contribute to developing the balance between the reflective and reflexive systems in individuals. Epigenetic studies therefore may help explain why many people make decisions that are not in their long-term best interest.

neuroeconomics Interdisciplinary field that seeks to understand how the brain makes decisions.

Because of predictions that all mammals will have similar reflective and reflexive decision systems and because all animals make decisions, the neural bases of decision processes in nonhumans undoubtedly will receive more study in the future.

(15-3) REVIEW

Expanding Frontiers of Cognitive Neuroscience

Before you continue, check your understanding.

1. Noninvasive imaging techniques enable cognitive psychologists to investigate the neural bases of thought in the "normal" brain, leading to the field called _____.

2. Imaging methods such as DTI and fcMRI are allowing researchers to develop a _____, a map of the complete structural and functional fiber pathway connections in the living human brain.

3. The role of the _____ in cognition, formerly unappreciated, is now attracting researchers' attention.

4. Social neuroscience is an interdisciplinary field that seeks to understand how the brain mediates _____.

5. Our attribution of mental states to others is known as _____.

6. Neuroeconomics seeks to understand the neural bases of _____.

7. List four general themes of social neuroscience research.

Answers appear at the back of the book.

15-4 Cerebral Asymmetry in Thinking

Fundamental to behavioral neuroscience was the finding by Paul Broca and his contemporaries in the mid-1800s that language is lateralized to the brain's left hemisphere. But the implications of lateralized brain functions were not really understood until the 1960s, when Roger Sperry (1968) and his colleagues began to study people who, as described in Research Focus 15-1, had undergone surgical separation of the two hemispheres as a treatment for intractable epilepsy. It soon became apparent that the cerebral hemispheres are more functionally specialized than researchers had previously realized. Before considering how the brain's two sides cooperate in generating cognitive activity, we look at the anatomical differences between the left and right hemispheres.

Seizing on Sperry's findings, the 1980s saw an avalanche of self-help books about "left-brained" and "right-brained" people. The novelty wore off, but cerebral asymmetry remains important to understanding how the human brain thinks.

Anatomical Asymmetry

Building on Broca's findings, investigators have learned how the language- and music-related areas of the left and right temporal lobes differ anatomically. In particular, the primary auditory area is larger on the right, whereas the secondary auditory areas are larger on the left in most people. Other brain regions also are asymmetrical.

Figure 15-11 shows that the lateral fissure, which partly separates the temporal and parietal lobes, has a sharper upward course in the right hemisphere relative to the left. As a result, the posterior right temporal lobe is larger than the same region on the left, as is the left parietal lobe relative to the right.

Among the anatomical asymmetries in the frontal lobes, the region of sensorimotor cortex representing the face is larger in the left hemisphere than in the right, a difference that presumably corresponds to the left hemisphere's special role in talking. Broca's area is organized differently on the left and the right. The area visible on the brain's surface is about one-third larger on the right than on the left, whereas the cortical area buried in the sulci of Broca's area is greater on the left than on the right.

Not only do these gross anatomical differences exist but so too do hemispheric differences in the details of their cellular and neurochemical structures. For example, neurons in Broca's area on the left have larger dendritic fields than do corresponding neurons on the right. The discovery of structural asymmetries told us little about the reasons for such differences, but ongoing research is revealing that they result from underlying differences in cognitive processing by the brain's two sides.

Although many anatomical asymmetries in the human brain are related to language, brain asymmetries are not unique to humans. Most if not all mammals have asymmetries, as do many bird species. The functions of cerebral asymmetry therefore cannot be limited to language processing. Rather, human language likely evolved after the brain became asymmetrical. Language simply took advantage of processes, including the development of mirror neurons, that had already been lateralized by natural selection in earlier members of the human lineage.

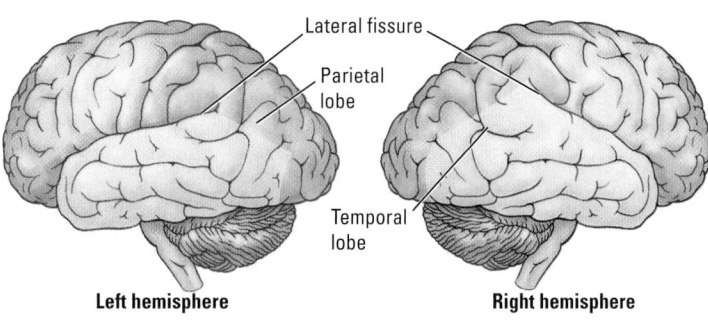

Left hemisphere   **Right hemisphere**

FIGURE 15-11 Cerebral Asymmetry The lateral fissure takes a flatter course in the left hemisphere than in the right. As a result, the posterior right temporal lobe is larger than the same region on the left side, and the inferior parietal region is larger on the left than on the right.

Functional Asymmetry in Neurological Patients

The specialized functions of the cerebral hemispheres become obvious in people with damage to the left or right side of the brain. To see these functional differences clearly, compare the cases of G. H. and M. M.

Right Parietal Damage

When G. H. was 5 years old, as he was hiking with his family, a large rock rolled off an embankment and hit him on the head. He was unconscious for a few minutes and had a severe headache for a few days but quickly recovered. Around age 18, however, he started having seizures. Neurosurgical investigation revealed that G. H. had had a right posterior parietal injury from the rock accident. **Figure 15-12**A shows the area affected. After surgery to remove this area, G. H. had weakness on the left side of his body and showed contralateral neglect. But these symptoms lessened fairly quickly, and a month after the surgery, they had completely cleared.

Nevertheless, G. H. had chronic difficulties in copying drawings; 4 years later, he still performed this task at about the level of a 6-year-old. He also had trouble assembling puzzles, a pastime he enjoyed before his surgery. When asked to perform mental manipulations like the one in Figure 15-6, he became very frustrated and refused to continue. G. H. also had difficulty finding his way around familiar places. The landmarks he had used to guide his travels before the surgery no longer worked for him. G. H. now has to learn street names and use a verbal strategy to go from one place to another.

FIGURE 15-12 Contrasting Parietal Lobe Injuries

(A) Participant G. H.

Injury to this area of the right hemisphere caused difficulties in copying drawings, assembling puzzles, and finding the way around a familiar city.

(B) Participant M. M.

Injury to this area of the left hemisphere caused difficulties in language, copying movements, reading, and generating names of objects or animals.

Left Parietal Damage

Meningioma is imaged in Focus 3-3.

M. M.'s difficulties were quite different. A meningioma had placed considerable pressure on the left parietal region. The tumor was surgically removed when M. M. was 16 years old. It had damaged the area shown in Figure 15-12B.

After the surgery, M. M. had various problems, including *aphasia*, impaired language use. The condition lessened over time: a year after the surgery, M. M. spoke fluently. Unfortunately, other difficulties persisted. In solving arithmetic problems, in reading, and even in simply calling objects or animals by name, M. M. performed at about a 6-year-old level. She had no difficulty making movements spontaneously, but when asked to copy a series of arm movements, such as those diagrammed in **Figure 15-13**, she had great difficulty. She could not figure out how to make her arm move to match the example. A general impairment in making voluntary movements in the absence of paralysis or a muscular disorder is a symptom of *apraxia*, the inability to complete a plan of action accurately.

Section 10-4 describes how left-hemisphere damage causes aphasias. Section 11-5 explains how somatosensory cortex damage contributes to apraxia.

Series 1

Series 2

FIGURE 15-13 Two Arm Movement Series Subjects observe the tester perform each sequence, then copy it as accurately as they can. People with left-hemisphere injury, especially in the posterior parietal region, are impaired at copying such movements.

Lessons from Patients G. H. and M. M.

What can we learn about brain function by comparing G. H. and M. M.? Their lesions were in approximately the same location but in opposite hemispheres, and their symptoms were very different.

Judging from G. H.'s difficulties, the right hemisphere contributes to controlling spatial skills, such as drawing, assembling puzzles, and navigating in space. In contrast, M. M.'s condition reveals that the left hemisphere seems to contribute to controlling language functions and cognitive tasks related to schoolwork—namely, reading and arithmetic. In addition, the left hemisphere's role in controlling voluntary movement sequences differs from the right hemisphere's role.

To some extent, then, the left and right hemispheres think about different types of information. The question is whether these functional differences can be observed in a healthy brain.

Functional Asymmetry in the Healthy Brain

In the course of studying the auditory capacity of people with a temporal lobe lesion, Doreen Kimura (1967) found something unexpected. She presented her control participants with two strings of digits, one played into each ear, a procedure known as **dichotic listening.** The task was to recall as many digits as possible.

Kimura found that the controls recalled more digits presented to the right ear than to the left. This result is surprising because the auditory system crosses repeatedly, beginning in the midbrain. Nonetheless, information coming from the right ear seems to have preferential access to the left (speaking) hemisphere.

In a later study, Kimura (1973) played two pieces of music for participants, one to each ear. She then gave the participants a multiple-choice test, playing four bits from musical selections and asking the participants to pick out the bits they had heard before. In this test, she found that participants were more likely to recall the music played to the left ear than to the right. This result implies that the left ear has preferential access to the right (musical) hemisphere.

The demonstration of this functional asymmetry in the healthy brain provoked much interest in the 1970s, leading to demonstrations of functional asymmetries in the visual and tactile systems as well. Consider the visual system. If we fixate on a target, such as a dot positioned straight ahead, all the information to the left of the dot goes to the right

dichotic listening Experimental procedure for simultaneously presenting a different auditory input to each ear through stereophonic earphones.

hemisphere and all the information to the right of the dot goes to the left hemisphere, as shown in **Figure 15-14.**

If information is presented for a relatively long time—say, 1 second—we can easily report what was in each visual field. If, however, the presentation is brief—say, only 40 milliseconds—then the task is considerably harder. This situation reveals a brain asymmetry.

Words presented briefly to the right visual field and hence sent to the left hemisphere are more easily reported than are words presented briefly to the left visual field. Similarly, if complex geometric patterns or faces are shown briefly, those presented to the left visual field and hence sent to the right hemisphere are more accurately reported than are those presented to the right visual field.

Apparently, the hemispheres not only think about different types of information, they also process information differently. The left hemisphere seems biased toward processing language-related information, whereas the right hemisphere seems biased toward processing nonverbal, and especially spatial, information.

A word of caution: Although asymmetry studies are fascinating, what they tell us about the differences between the hemispheres is not entirely clear. They tell us *something* is different, but it is a broad leap to conclude that the hemispheres house entirely different skill sets.

The hemispheres have many common functions, such as controlling movement in the contralateral hand and processing sensory information through the thalamus. Still, differences in the hemispheres' cognitive operations do exist. We can better understand these differences by studying split-brain patients, whose cerebral hemispheres have been surgically separated for medical treatment.

Functional Asymmetry in the Split Brain

Before considering the details of split-brain studies, let us review what we already know about cerebral asymmetry. First, the left hemisphere has speech; the right hemisphere does not. Second, as demonstrated in Research Focus 15-1, on page 520, the right hemisphere performs better than the left on certain nonverbal tasks, especially those that engage visuospatial skills.

But how does a severed corpus callosum affect how the brain thinks? After the corpus callosum has been cut, the hemispheres have no way of communicating with one another. The left and right hemispheres are therefore free to think about different things. In a sense, a split-brain patient has two brains.

One way to test the hemispheres' cognitive functions in a split-brain patient takes advantage of the fact that information in the left visual field goes to the right hemisphere and information in the right field goes to the left hemisphere (see Figure 15-14). With the corpus callosum cut, however, information presented to one side of the brain has no way of traveling to the other side. It can be processed only in the hemisphere that receives it.

Experiments 15-3 and **15-4** show some basic testing procedures based on this dichotomy. The split-brain subject fixates on the dot in the center of the screen while information is presented to the left or right visual field. The person must respond with the left hand (controlled by the right hemisphere), with the right hand (controlled by the left hemisphere), or verbally (also a left-hemisphere function). In this way, researchers can observe what each hemisphere knows and what it is capable of doing.

As illustrated in Experiment 15-3, for instance, a picture—say, of a spoon—might be flashed and the subject asked to state what he or she sees. If the picture is presented to the right visual field, the person will answer, "Spoon." If the picture is presented to the left visual field, however, the person will say, "I see nothing." The subject responds in this way for two reasons:

1. The right hemisphere (which receives the visual input) does not talk, so it cannot respond verbally, even though it sees the spoon in the left visual field.

Those popular left brain–right brain accounts of the 1980s ignored the many functions the hemispheres have in common.

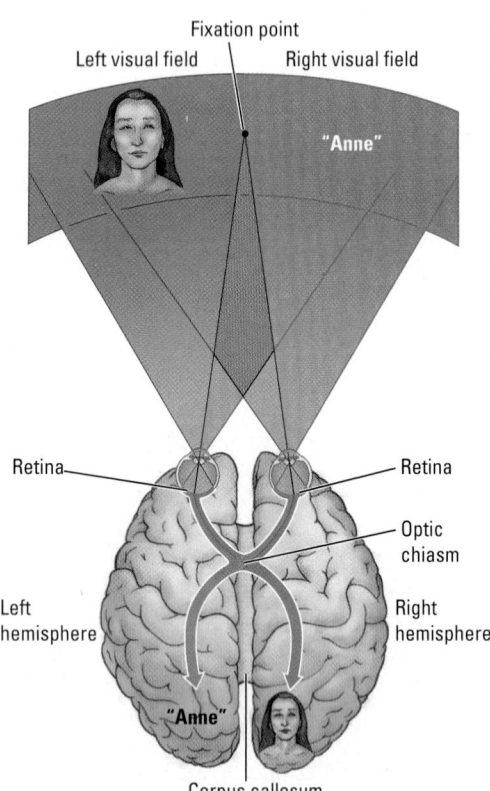

FIGURE 15-14 Visual Pathways to the Hemispheres When fixating at a point, each eye sees both visual fields but sends information about the right visual field only to the left hemisphere. Information about the left visual field proceeds only to the right hemisphere. In healthy participants given short exposures to stimuli (well under 1 second), the left hemisphere is more accurate at perceiving words, whereas the right hemisphere is more accurate at perceiving objects, including faces.

2. The left hemisphere does talk, but it does not see the spoon, so it answers—quite correctly, from its own perspective—that nothing was presented.

Now suppose the task changes. In Experiment 15-4A, the picture of a spoon is still presented to the left visual field, but the subject is asked to use the left hand to pick out the object shown on the screen. In this case, the left hand, controlled by the right hemisphere, which sees the spoon, readily picks out the correct object. Can the right hand also choose correctly? No, because it is controlled by the left hemisphere, which cannot see the spoon. If the person in this situation is forced to select an object with the right hand, the left hemisphere does so at random.

Now let's consider an interesting twist. In the Procedure for Experiment 15-4B, each hemisphere is shown a different object—say, a spoon to the right hemisphere and a pencil to the left. The subject is asked to use both hands to pick out "the object." The problem here is that the right and left hands do not agree. While the left hand tries to pick up the spoon, the right hand tries to pick up the pencil or tries to prevent the left hand from picking up the spoon.

This conflict between the hemispheres can be seen in the everyday behavior of some split-brain subjects. One woman, P. O. V., reported frequent interhemispheric competition for at least 3 years after her surgery. "I open the closet door. I know what I want to wear. But as I reach for something with my right hand, my left comes up and takes something different. I can't put it down if it's in my left hand. I have to call my daughter."

We know from Experiment 15-3 that the left hemisphere is capable of using language, and Research Focus 15-1 reveals that the right hemisphere has visuospatial capabilities that the left hemisphere does not. Although findings from half a century of studying split-brain patients show that the hemispheres process information differently, another word of caution is needed. There is more functional overlap between the hemispheres than was at first suspected. The right hemisphere, for instance, does have some language functions, and the left hemisphere does have some spatial abilities. Nonetheless, the two undoubtedly are different.

Explaining Cerebral Asymmetry

Various hypotheses propose to explain hemispheric differences. One idea, that the left hemisphere is important in controlling fine movements, dates back a century. Recall M. M., the meningioma patient with left parietal lobe damage and apraxia (see Figure 15-12B). Although the apraxia subsided, she was left with chronic trouble in copying movements.

Perhaps one reason that the left hemisphere has a role in language is that speaking requires fine motor movements of the mouth and tongue. Significantly, damage to the language-related areas of the left hemisphere almost always interferes with both language and movement, whether the person speaks or signs. Reading Braille, however, may not be so affected by left-hemisphere lesions. Most people prefer to use the left hand to read Braille, which essentially consists of spatial patterns, so processes related to reading Braille may reside in the right hemisphere.

That said, another clue that the left hemisphere's specialization for language may be related to its special role in controlling fine movements comes from investigating where the brain processes certain parts of speech. Recall that cognitive systems for representing abstract concepts likely are related to systems that produce more concrete behaviors.

▶ EXPERIMENT 15-3

Question: Will severing the corpus callosum affect the way in which the brain responds?

Procedure

The split-brain subject fixates on the dot in the center of the screen while an image is projected to the left or right visual field. He is asked to identify verbally what he sees.

Screen   Projector

Results

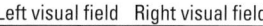

| If the spoon is presented to the right visual field, the subject answers, "Spoon." | If the spoon is presented to the left visual field, the subject answers, "I see nothing." |

Left visual field   Right visual field   Left visual field   Right visual field

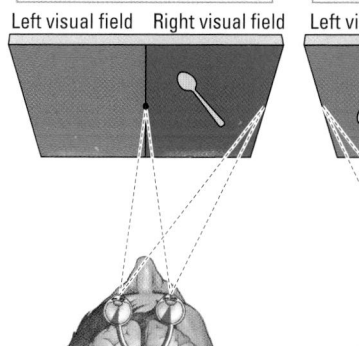

Severed corpus callosum

Conclusion: When the left hemisphere, which can speak, sees the spoon in the right visual field, the subject responds correctly. When the right hemisphere, which cannot speak, sees the spoon in the left visual field, the subject does not respond.

h   ou   s   e

Braille

(A) Question: How can the right hemisphere of a split-brain subject show that it knows information?

(B) Question: What happens if both hemispheres are asked to respond to competing information?

Procedure

The split-brain participant is asked to use his left hand to pick out the object shown on the screen to the left visual field (right hemisphere).

Procedure

Each visual field is shown a different object—a spoon to the left and a pencil to the right. The split-brain participant is asked to use both hands to pick up the object seen.

Results

The participant chooses the spoon with his left hand because the right hemisphere sees the spoon and controls the left hand. If the right hand is forced to choose, it will do so by chance because no stimulus is shown to the left hemisphere.

Results

In this case, the right and left hands do not agree. They may each pick up a different object, or the right hand may prevent the left hand from performing the task.

Left visual field Right visual field

Severed
corpus callosum

Left visual field Right visual field

Severed
corpus callosum

Conclusion: Each hemisphere is capable of responding independently. The left hemisphere may dominate in a competition, even if the response is not verbal.

Consequently, we might expect that the left hemisphere would participate in forming concepts related to fine movements.

Concepts that describe movements are the parts of speech we call verbs. A fundamental difference between left- and right-hemisphere language abilities is that verbs seem to be processed only in the left hemisphere, whereas nouns are processed in both hemispheres.

In other words, not only does the left hemisphere specialize in producing actions, it also produces mental representations of actions in the form of words.

If the left hemisphere excels at language because it is better at controlling fine movements, what is the basis of the right hemisphere's abilities? One idea is that the right hemisphere specializes in controlling movements in space. In a sense, this role elaborates the functions of the dorsal visual stream (diagrammed in Figure 15-3).

Once again, we can propose a link between movement at a concrete level and movement at a more abstract level. If the right hemisphere is producing movements in space, then it is also likely to produce mental images of such movements. We would therefore predict impairment of right-hemisphere patients' ability both to think about and to make spatially guided movements. And they are thus impaired.

Bear in mind that theories about the reasons for hemispheric asymmetry are highly speculative. The brain has evolved to produce movement and to construct a sensory reality, so the observed asymmetry must somehow relate to these overriding functions. That is, more recently evolved functions, such as language, likely are extensions of preexisting functions. So the fact that language is represented asymmetrically does not mean that the brain is asymmetrical because of language. After all, other species that do not talk have an asymmetrical brain.

The nervous system produces movement within a perceptual world the brain constructs.

Left Hemisphere, Language, and Thought

As we end our examination of brain asymmetry, consider one more provocative idea. Michael Gazzaniga (1992) proposed that the left hemisphere's superior language skills are important for understanding the differences between humans' and other animals' thinking. He called the speaking hemisphere the interpreter. The following experiment, using split-brain patients as subjects, illustrates what Gazzaniga meant.

Each hemisphere is shown a picture of a match followed by a picture of a piece of wood, for example. Another set of pictures is then shown. The task is to pick from this set a third picture that has an inferred relation to the first two. In this example, the third related picture might be a bonfire. The right hemisphere is incapable of making the inference that a match struck and held to a piece of wood could start a bonfire, whereas the left hemisphere easily arrives at this interpretation.

An analogous task uses words. One or the other hemisphere might be shown the words *pin* and *finger* then be asked to pick out a third word related to the other two. In this case, the correct answer might be *bleed*.

The right hemisphere cannot make this connection. Although it has enough language ability to pick out close synonyms for *pin* and *finger* (*needle* and *thumb*, respectively), it cannot make the inference that pricking a finger with a pin will result in bleeding.

Again, the left hemisphere has no difficulty with this task. Apparently, the left hemisphere's language capability gives it a capacity for interpretation that the right hemisphere lacks. One reason may be that language serves to label and express the computations of other cognitive systems.

Gazzaniga goes even further. He suggests that the evolution of left-hemisphere language abilities makes humans a "believing" species: humans can make inferences and have beliefs about sensory events. By contrast, Alex, the African grey parrot profiled in Comparative Focus 15-2, would not have been able to make inferences or hold beliefs because he did not have a system analogous to our left-hemisphere language system. Alex could use language but could not make inferences about sensory events with language.

Gazzaniga's idea is intriguing. It implies a fundamental difference in the nature of cerebral asymmetry—and therefore in the nature of cognition—that exists between humans and other animals because of the nature of human language. We return to this idea in Section 15-7.

┌─────────┐
│ **15-5** │ # Variations in Cognitive Organization
└─────────┘

No two brains are identical. Some differences are genetically determined; others result from plastic changes caused, for example, by experience and learning or epigenetic factors. Some brain differences are idiosyncratic (unique to a particular person); many others are systematic and common to whole categories of people. In this section, we consider two systematic variations in brain organization, those related to sex and handedness, and one idiosyncratic variation, the fascinating sensory phenomenon *synesthesia*.

Sex Differences in Cognitive Organization

The idea that men and women think differently probably originated with the first men and women. Science backs it up. Books, including one by Doreen Kimura (1999), present persuasive evidence for marked differences between men's and women's performance on many cognitive tests. As illustrated in **Figure 15-15**, paper-and-pencil tests consistently show that on average females have better verbal fluency than males do, whereas males do better on tests of spatial reasoning. Our focus here is on how such differences relate to the brain.

Neural Bases of Sex Differences

Considerable evidence points to sex differences, both in the brain's gross cerebral structure and at a neuronal level. Jill Goldstein and her colleagues (2001) conducted a large MRI study of sexual dimorphism in the human brain. They found that women have larger volumes of dorsal prefrontal and associated paralimbic regions, whereas men have larger volumes of more ventral prefrontal regions (**Figure 15-16**). (Brain size is related to body size, and on average, male brains are bigger than female brains, so the investigators corrected for size.)

Another way to measure sex differences is cortical thickness independent of volume. **Figure 15-17** shows that relative to men, women have increased cortical gray matter concentration in many cortical regions. Men's gray matter concentration, by contrast, is more uniform across the cortex. The MRI studies represented in Figures 15-16 and 15-17 thus point to differences between men's and women's cortical organization.

Sex differences in neuronal structure also exist. Gonadal hormones influence the structure of neurons in the prefrontal cortices of rats (Kolb & Stewart, 1991). The cells in one prefrontal region, located along the midline, have larger dendritic fields (and presumably more synapses) in males than in females, as shown in the top row of **Figure 15-18** on page 548. In contrast, the cells in the orbitofrontal region have larger dendritic fields (and presumably more synapses) in females than in males, as shown in the bottom row. These sex differences

(A) Spatial relation–type task

Participants were asked to draw a line to indicate waterline in tipped glass.

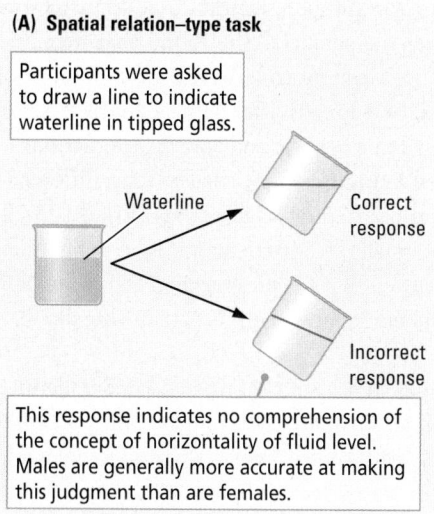

Waterline → Correct response

→ Incorrect response

This response indicates no comprehension of the concept of horizontality of fluid level. Males are generally more accurate at making this judgment than are females.

(B) Mental rotation–type task

Participants were asked to choose the block that could be made from a plan.

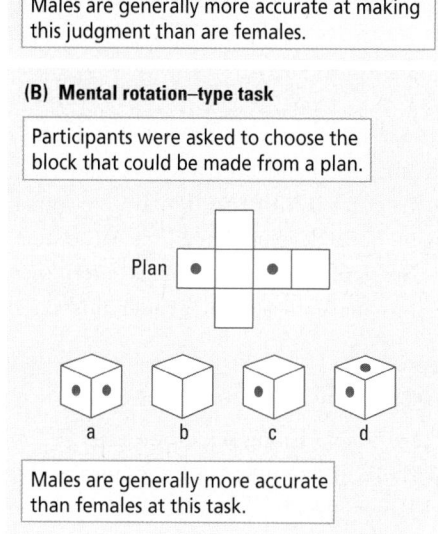

Plan

a   b   c   d

Males are generally more accurate than females at this task.

(C) Short-term-memory–type task

Participants were asked to fill in the empty boxes with the appropriate symbols from the top row.

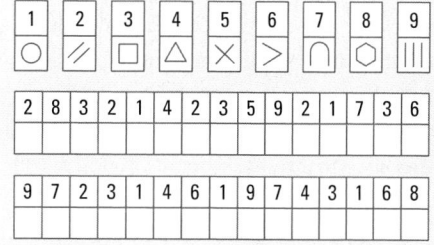

1	2	3	4	5	6	7	8	9
○	∕∕	□	△	✕	＞	∩	⬡	∥∥∥

| 2 | 8 | 3 | 2 | 1 | 4 | 2 | 3 | 5 | 9 | 2 | 1 | 7 | 3 | 6 |

| 9 | 7 | 2 | 3 | 1 | 4 | 6 | 1 | 9 | 7 | 4 | 3 | 1 | 6 | 8 |

When given a larger number of boxes to fill in and a time limit, females complete from 10 to 20 percent more items than males do.

(D) Verbal fluency–type task

Participants were asked to fill in each blank to form words that make a sentence.

1. F_____ M_____ A_____ J_____

2. C_____ B_____ E_____ S_____

3. D_____ I_____ J_____ K_____

Females are generally faster at this type of test than males are.

FIGURE 15-15 Tasks That Reliably Show Sex-Related Cognitive Differences

Lateral view

Medial view

FIGURE 15-16 Sex Differences in Brain Volume Women's brain volume in prefrontal and medial paralimbic regions (orange) is significantly higher than men's. Men have larger relative volumes in the medial and orbitofrontal cortex and the angular gyrus (green). Orange areas correspond to regions that have high levels of estrogen receptors during development, green to regions high in androgen receptors during development. Information from J. M. Goldstein, L. J. Seidman, N. J. Horton, N. Makris, D. N. Kennedy, et al. (2001). Normal sexual dimorphism of the adult human brain assessed by in vivo magnetic resonance imaging. *Cerebral Cortex 11*, pp. 490–497.

are not found in rats that have had their testes or ovaries removed at birth. Presumably, sex hormones somehow change the brain's organization and ultimately its cognitive processing.

Stewart and Kolb (1994) found that the presence or absence of gonadal hormones affects the brain in adulthood as well as in early development. In this study, which focused on how hormones affect recovery from brain damage, middle-aged female rats' ovaries were removed. On examining the brains of these rats and those of control rats some months later, researchers observed that the cortical neurons of the rats whose ovaries had been removed—especially the prefrontal neurons—had undergone structural changes. The cells had grown 30 percent more dendrites, and their spine density increased compared with the control rats' cells. Clearly, gonadal hormones can affect the brain's neuronal structure at any point in an animal's life.

An additional way to consider the neural basis of sex differences is to look at the effects of cortical injury in men and women. If sex differences exist in the neural organization of cognitive processing, differences in the effects of cortical injury in the two sexes should appear. Doreen Kimura (1999) conducted this kind of study and showed that the pattern of cerebral organization within each hemisphere may in fact differ between the sexes.

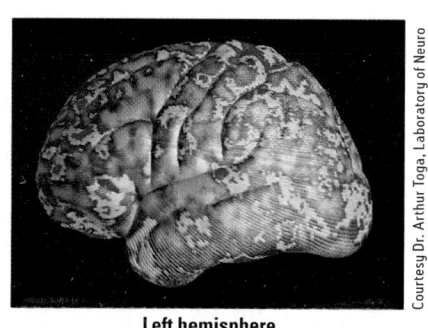

Courtesy Dr. Arthur Toga, Laboratory of Neuro Imaging at USC

Left hemisphere

FIGURE 15-17 Sex Differences in Gray Matter Concentration Women show increased gray matter concentration in the cortical regions, shown in color on this MRI. Gray-shaded regions are not statistically different in males and females.

Investigating people who had a cortical stroke in adulthood, Kimura tried to match the location and extent of injury in her male and female subjects. She found that men and women were almost equally likely to be aphasic subsequent to left-hemisphere lesions of some kind. But men were more likely to be aphasic and apraxic after damage to the left posterior cortex, whereas women were far more likely to be aphasic and apraxic after lesions to the left frontal cortex. These results, summarized in **Figure 15-19,** suggest a sex difference in intrahemispheric organization, a conclusion supported by a later study (**Figure 15-20**) using diffusion tensor analysis of brain networks in over 900 participants. The population, comprising nearly equal numbers of each sex, showed that females have greater *inter*hemispheric connectivity, whereas males' *intra*hemispheric connectivity is greater (Ingalhalikar et al., 2013).

Section 12-5 describes the gender identity spectrum.

Evidence strongly favors a neural basis for gender identity, including transgender identity. Georg Krantz and colleagues (2014) used diffusion tensor analysis to compare brain networks of female-to-male and male-to-female transsexuals with those of gender-typical females and males. The imaging replicated the distinctly different pattern of hemispheric connectivity in gender-typical females and males. The pattern of connectivity in transsexuals, however, falls halfway between those of females and males.

That is, DTIs of the white matter microstructure of transgender females and males falls halfway between that of gender-typical females and males. The investigators take these patterns as evidence that neural white matter microstructure is influenced by the hormonal environment during late prenatal and early postnatal brain development. This is the time, they hypothesize, that determines gender identity. But genital differentiation is determined earlier in development. The timing difference thus makes a genital–gender mismatch possible.

Evolution of Sex-Related Cognitive Differences

Although gonadal hormones have taken center stage in explaining sex differences in cognitive function, we are still left to question how these differences arose. To answer this question, we must look back at human evolution. Mothers pass their genes to both sons and daughters, and fathers do the same. Ultimately then, males and females of a species have virtually all their genes in common.

Male rat **Female rat**

Cells from medial frontal cortex

Cells from orbito-frontal region

The only way a gene can affect one sex preferentially is for the animal's gonadal hormones to influence the gene's activities. Gonadal hormones are in turn determined by the presence or absence of the Y chromosome, which carries a gene called the *testes-determining factor. TDF* stimulates the body to produce testes, which then manufacture androgens, which in turn influence other genes' activities.

Like other body organs, the brain is a potential target of natural selection. We should therefore expect to find sex-related differences in the brain whenever the sexes differ in the adaptive problems they have faced in their species' evolution. Aggressive behavior is a good example. Males in most mammalian species typically are more physically aggressive than females. This trait presumably improved males' reproductive success by selecting against individuals with lesser aggressiveness. Producing higher levels of aggression entails male hormones. We know from studies of nonhuman species that aggression is related directly to the presence of androgens and to their effects on gene expression, both during brain development and later in life. In this case, therefore, natural selection has worked on gonadal hormone levels to favor aggressiveness in males.

FIGURE 15-18 Sex Differences in Neuronal Architecture In the frontal cortices of male and female rats, cells in the midline frontal region (top two drawings) are more complex in males than in females, whereas the opposite is true of the orbitofrontal region (bottom two drawings).

FIGURE 15-19 Evidence for Sex Differences in Cortical Organization Apraxia and aphasia are associated with frontal damage to the left hemisphere in women and with posterior damage in men. Information from D. Kimura (1999). *Sex and Cognition*, Cambridge, MA: MIT Press.

Explaining sex-related differences in cognitive processes, such as language or spatial skills, is more speculative than explaining sex-related differences in aggressive behavior. Nevertheless, some hypotheses come to mind. We can imagine, for instance, that in the history of mammalian evolution, males have tended to range over larger territories than have females. This behavior requires spatial abilities, so evolution would have favored these skills in males.

Support for this hypothesis comes from comparing spatial problem solving in males of closely related mammalian species—species in which the males range over large territories versus species in which the males' range is not extensive. Pine voles, for example, have a restricted range and no sex-related difference in range, whereas meadow voles have a range about 20 times as large as pine voles', and male meadow voles range more widely than the females.

Meadow voles display far superior spatial skills to those of pine voles. A sex difference in spatial ability among meadow voles favors males, but pine voles have no such sex difference. The hippocampus is implicated in spatial navigation skills. Significantly, the hippocampus is larger in meadow voles than in pine voles, and it is larger in male meadow voles than in females (Gaulin, 1992). A similar logic could help explain sex-related differences in spatial abilities between human males and females (see Figure 15-15).

Explaining sex-related differences in language skills also is speculative. One hypothesis holds that if males were hunters and often away from home, home-based females formed social groups selectively favored to develop tools, one of which is language, for social interactions. We might also argue that females with superior fine motor skills (such as foraging for food and making clothing and baskets) had a selective advantage. The relation between language and fine motor skills may have favored enhanced language capacities in females.

Although such speculations are interesting, they are not testable. We will probably never know with certainty why sex-related differences in brain organization developed.

Handedness and Cognitive Organization

Nearly everyone prefers one hand to the other for writing or throwing a ball. Most people prefer the right hand. In fact, left-handedness has historically been viewed as odd. But it is not rare. An estimated 10 percent of the human population worldwide is left-handed. This proportion represents only the number of people who write with the left hand. When broader criteria are used to determine left-handedness, estimates range from 10 percent to 30 percent of the population.

(A) Male brain

(B) Female brain

FIGURE 15-20 Sex Differences in the Connectome DTI analysis of brain networks in these dorsal views reveals greater intrahemispheric connections in males (A) and greater interhemispheric connections in females (B). Image from M. Ingalhalikar, A. Smith, D. Parker, P. D. Satterthwaite, M. A. Elliott, K. Ruparel, et al. (2013). Sex differences in the structural connectome of the human brain. *Proceedings of the National Academy of Sciences U S A*, 111, 823–828, Fig. 2.

Sodium Amobarbital Test

Guy, a 32-year-old lawyer, had a vascular malformation over the region corresponding to the posterior speech zone. The malformation was beginning to cause neurological symptoms, including seizures. The ideal surgical treatment was removal of the abnormal vessels.

The complication with this surgery is that removing vessels sitting over the posterior speech zone poses a serious risk of permanent aphasia. Because Guy was left-handed, his speech areas could be in the right hemisphere. If so, the surgical risk would be much lower.

To achieve certainty in such doubtful cases, Jun Wada and Ted Rasmussen (1960) pioneered the technique of injecting sodium amobarbital, a barbiturate, into the carotid artery to briefly anesthetize the ipsilateral hemisphere. (Injections are now usually made through a catheter inserted into the femoral artery.) The procedure enables an unequivocal localization of speech because injection into the speech hemisphere results in speech arrest lasting as long as several minutes. As speech returns, it is characterized by aphasic errors.

Injection into the nonspeaking hemisphere may produce no or only brief speech arrest. The amobarbital procedure has the advantage of allowing each hemisphere to be studied separately in the functional absence of the other (anesthetized) hemisphere. Because the period of anesthesia lasts several minutes, a variety of functions, including memory and movement, can be studied to determine a hemisphere's capabilities.

The sodium amobarbital test is always performed bilaterally, with the second cerebral hemisphere being injected several days after the first

Left carotid artery

Sodium amobarbital

To avoid damaging speech zones in patients about to undergo brain surgery, surgeons inject sodium amobarbital into the carotid artery. The drug anesthetizes the hemisphere where it is injected (here, the left), allowing the surgeon to determine whether that hemisphere is dominant for speech.

one to make sure that no residual drug effect lingers. In the brief period of drug action, the patient is given a series of simple tasks requiring the use of language, memory, and object recognition. To test speech, the patient is asked to name some common objects presented in quick succession, to count, to recite the days of the week forward and backward, and to spell simple words.

If the injected hemisphere is nondominant for speech, the patient may continue to carry out the verbal tasks, although there is often a period as long as 30 seconds during which he or she appears confused and is silent but can resume speech with urging. When the injected hemisphere is dominant for speech, the patient typically stops talking and remains completely aphasic until recovery from the anesthesia is well along, somewhere in the range of 4 to 10 minutes.

Guy was found to have speech in the left hemisphere. During the test of his left hemisphere, he could not talk. Later, he said that when he was asked about a particular object, he wondered just what the question meant. When he finally had some vague idea, he had no idea of what the answer was or how to say anything. By then he realized that he had been asked all sorts of other questions to which he had also not responded.

When asked which objects he had been shown, he said he had no idea. However, when given an array of objects and asked to choose with his left hand, he identified the objects by pointing because his nonspeaking right hemisphere controlled that hand. In contrast, his speaking left hemisphere had no memory of the objects: it had been asleep.

Because the left hemisphere controls the right hand, the general assumption is that right-handedness is somehow related to the presence of speech in the left hemisphere. If this were so, language would be located in the right hemisphere of left-handed people. This hypothesis is easily tested, and it turns out to be false.

In the course of preparing patients with epilepsy for surgery to remove the abnormal tissue causing their seizures, Ted Rasmussen and Brenda Milner (1977) injected the left or right hemisphere with sodium amobarbital. This drug produces a short-acting anesthesia of the entire hemisphere, making it possible to determine where speech originates. As described in Clinical Focus 15-5, Sodium Amobarbital Test, if a person becomes aphasic when the drug is injected into the left hemisphere but not when the drug is injected into the right, then speech must reside in that person's left hemisphere.

Rasmussen and Milner found that in virtually all right-handed people, speech was localized in the left hemisphere, but the reverse was not true for left-handed people. About 70 percent of left-handers also had speech in the left hemisphere. Of the remaining 30 percent, about half had speech in the right hemisphere and half had speech in both hemispheres.

Findings from neuroanatomical studies have subsequently shown that left-handers with speech in the left hemisphere have asymmetries similar to those of right-handers. By contrast, in left-handers with speech originating in the right hemisphere or in both hemispheres—known as **anomalous speech representation**—the anatomical symmetry is reversed or absent.

Sandra Witelson and Charlie Goldsmith (1991) asked whether any other gross differences in the brain structure of right- and left-handers might exist. One possibility is that the connectivity of the cerebral hemispheres may differ. To test this idea, the investigators studied the hand preference of terminally ill subjects on a variety of one-handed tasks. They later performed postmortem studies of these patients' brains, paying particular attention to the size of the corpus callosum. They found that the callosal cross-sectional area was 11 percent greater in left-handed and ambidextrous (little or no hand preference) people than in right-handed people.

Whether this enlarged callosum is due to a greater number of fibers, to thicker fibers, or to more myelin remains to be seen. If the larger corpus callosum is due to more fibers, the difference would be on the order of 25 million more fibers. Presumably, such a difference would have major implications for the organization of cognitive processing in left- and right-handers.

Synesthesia

Some variations in brain organization are idiosyncratic rather than systematic. **Synesthesia** is an individual's capacity to join sensory experiences across sensory modalities, as discussed in Clinical Focus 15-6, A Case of Synesthesia. Examples include the ability to hear colors or taste shapes. Edward Hubbard (2007) estimated the incidence of synesthesia at about 1 in 23 people, although for most it likely is limited in scope.

Synesthesia runs in families—the family of Russian novelist Vladimir Nabokov, for example. As a toddler, Nabokov complained to his mother that the letter colors on his

anomalous speech representation
Condition in which a person's speech zones are located in the right hemisphere or in both hemispheres.

synesthesia Ability to perceive a stimulus of one sense as the sensation of a different sense, as when sound produces a sensation of color; literally, *feeling together*.

CLINICAL FOCUS 15-6

A Case of Synesthesia

Michael Watson tastes shapes. His sensory joining first came to the attention of neurologist Richard Cytowic over dinner. After tasting a sauce he was making for roast chicken, Watson blurted out, "There aren't enough points on the chicken."

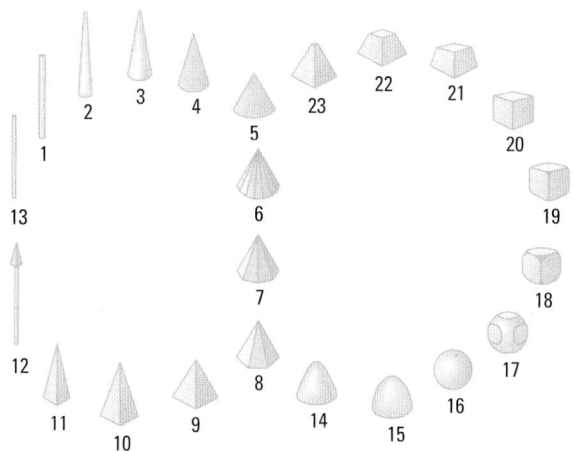

Neurologist Richard Cytowic devised this set of figures to help Michael Watson communicate the shapes he senses when he tastes food.

When Cytowic quizzed him about this strange remark, Watson said that all flavors had shape for him. "I wanted the taste of this chicken to be a pointed shape, but it came out all round. Well, I mean it's nearly spherical. I can't serve this if it doesn't have points" (Cytowic, 1998, p. 4).

Watson has synesthesia, which literally means *feeling together*. All his life Watson has experienced the feeling of shape when he tastes or smells food. When he tastes intense flavors, he reports an experience of shape that sweeps down his arms to his fingertips. He experiences the feeling of weight, texture, warmth or cold, and shape, just as though he were grasping something.

The feelings are not confined to his hands, however. Watson experiences some taste shapes, such as points, over his whole body. He experiences others only on the face, back, or shoulders. These impressions are not metaphors, as other people might use when they say that a cheese is sharp or a wine is textured. Such descriptions make no sense to Watson. He actually feels the shapes.

Cytowic systematically studied Watson to determine whether his feelings of shape were always associated with particular flavors and found that they were. Cytowic devised the set of geometric figures shown here to allow Watson to communicate which shapes he associated with various flavors.

Musician–composer Stevie Wonder is a synesthete, as were music legends Duke Ellington and Franz Liszt and Nobel Prize–winning physicist Richard Feynman.

wooden alphabet blocks were all wrong. His mother understood what he meant, because she too perceived letters and words in particular colors. Nabokov's son is synesthetic in the same way.

If you've shivered on hearing a particular piece of music or the noise of fingernails scratching across a chalkboard, you have felt sound. Even so, other sensory blendings may be difficult to imagine. How can sounds or letters possibly produce colors? Studies of synesthetes show that the same stimuli always elicit the same experiences for them.

The most common form of synesthesia is colored hearing. For many synesthetes, this means hearing both speech and music in color—perceiving a visual mélange of colored shapes, movement, and scintillation. The fact that colored hearing is more common than other types of synesthesia is curious.

The five primary senses (vision, hearing, touch, taste, and smell) all generate synesthetic pairings. Most, however, are in one direction. For instance, whereas synesthetes may see colors when they hear, they do not hear sounds in colors. Furthermore, some sensory combinations occur rarely, if at all. In particular, taste or smell rarely triggers a synesthetic response like Michael Watson's.

Because each case is idiosyncratic, synesthesia's neurological basis is difficult to investigate. Few studies have related it directly to brain function or brain organization, and different people may experience it for different reasons. Various hypotheses have been advanced to account for synesthesia:

- Extraordinary neural connections between the sensory regions are related in a particular synesthete.

- Activity is increased in the frontal lobe multimodal cortex, which receives inputs from more than one sensory area.

- Particular sensory inputs elicit unusual patterns of cerebral activation.

Whatever the explanation, when it comes to certain sensory inputs, the brain of a synesthete certainly works differently from other people's brains.

(15-5) **REVIEW**

Variations in Cognitive Organization

Before you continue, check your understanding.

1. The two major contributors to organizational differences in individual brains are _____ and _____.

2. Differences in the cerebral organization of thinking are probably related to differences in the _____ that underlie different types of cognitive processing.

3. People who experience certain sensations in more than one sensory modality are said to have _____.

4. What roles do gonadal hormones play in brain organization and function?

Answers appear at the back of the book.

For additional study tools, visit LaunchPad: 🌐 **LaunchPad**
www.macmillanhighered.com/launchpad/kolb5e

(15-6) # Intelligence

Intelligence exerts a major influence on anyone's thinking ability. It is easy to identify in people and even easy to observe in other animals. Yet intelligence is not at all easy to define. Despite a century of study, researchers have not yet reached agreement on what intelligence entails. We therefore begin this section by reviewing some hypotheses of intelligence.

Concept of General Intelligence

In the 1920s, Charles Spearman proposed that although different kinds of intelligence may exist, there is also an underlying general intelligence, which he called the *g* factor. Consider for a moment what a general intelligence factor might mean for the brain. Presumably, brains with high or low *g* would have some general difference in brain architecture—perhaps in gyral patterns, cytoarchitectonics, vascular patterns, or neurochemistry, for example.

This difference could not be something as simple as size, because human brain size (which varies from about 1000 to 2000 grams) correlates poorly with intelligence. Another possibility is that *g* is related to special cerebral connectivity or even to the ratio of neurons to glia. Still another possibility is that *g* is related to the activation of specific brain regions, possibly in the frontal lobe (Duncan et al., 2000; Gray & Thompson, 2004).

The results of preliminary studies of Albert Einstein's brain implied that cerebral connectivity and ratio of glia to neuron may be important. Sandra Witelson and her colleagues (Witelson et al., 1999) found that although Einstein's brain is the same size and weight as the average male brain, its lateral fissure is short, and both the left and the right lateral fissures take a particularly striking upward deflection (**Figure 15-21**; compare Figure 15-11). This arrangement essentially fuses the inferior parietal area with the posterior temporal area.

The inferior parietal cortex has a role in mathematical reasoning, so it is tempting to speculate that Einstein's mathematical abilities were related to neural rearrangements in this area. But another important difference may distinguish Einstein's brain. Marion Diamond and her colleagues (1985) looked at its glia-to-neuron ratio versus the mean for a control population. They found that Einstein's ratio in the inferior parietal cortex was higher than average: each neuron in this region had an unusually high number of glial cells supporting it.

The glia-to-neuron ratio was not unusually high in any other cortical areas of Einstein's brain measured by these researchers. Possibly, then, certain types of intelligence could be related to differences in cell structure in localized brain regions. But even if this hypothesis proves correct, it offers little neural evidence in favor of a general intelligence factor.

One possibility is that *g* is related to the brain's language processes, because language ability qualitatively changes the nature of cognitive processing in humans. So perhaps people with very good language skills also have an advantage in general thinking ability.

Cytoarchitectonics refers to brain cell organization, structure, and distribution.

Section 1-5 reveals fallacies inherent in correlating human brain size with intelligence.

FIGURE 15-21 Einstein's Brain The lateral fissure of Einstein's brain takes an exaggerated upward course relative to its course in typical brains, essentially fusing the posterior temporal regions with the inferior parietal regions. The arrow in each hemisphere indicates Einstein's ascending lateral fissure as it runs into the postcentral sulcus. Republished with permission of Elsevier Science and Technology Journals from The Exceptional Brain of Albert Einstein, S. Witelson, D. Kigar, T. Harvey, *The Lancet*, June 19, 1999, Vol. 353, p. 2151. Permission conveyed through Copyright Clearance Center, Inc.

Multiple Intelligences

Many other hypotheses on intelligence have been set forth since Spearman's, but few have considered the brain directly. One exception, proposed by Howard Gardner (1983), a neuropsychologist at Harvard, considers the effects of neurological injury on people's behavior. Gardner concludes that seven distinct forms of intelligence exist and that brain injury can selectively damage any form. The idea of multiple human intelligences should not be surprising given the varied cognitive operations the human brain can perform.

Gardner's seven categories of intelligence are linguistic, musical, logical-mathematical, spatial, bodily-kinesthetic, intrapersonal, and interpersonal. Linguistic and musical intelligence are straightforward concepts, as is logical-mathematical intelligence. Spatial intelligence refers to abilities discussed in this chapter, especially navigating in space, and to the ability to draw and paint. Bodily-kinesthetic intelligence refers to superior motor abilities, such as those exemplified by skilled athletes and dancers.

The two types of "personal" intelligence are less obvious. They refer to the frontal and temporal lobe operations required for success in a highly social environment. The intrapersonal aspect is awareness of one's own feelings, whereas the interpersonal aspect entails recognizing others' feelings and responding appropriately. Gardner's definition of intelligence has the advantage not only of being inclusive but also of acknowledging forms of intelligence not typically recognized by standard intelligence tests, abilities such as theory of mind, described in Section 15-3.

One prediction stemming from Gardner's analysis of intelligence is that brains ought to differ in some way when people have more of one form of intelligence and less of another. Logically, we could imagine that if a person were higher in musical intelligence and lower in interpersonal intelligence, then the brain regions for music (especially the temporal lobe) would differ in some fundamental way from the "less efficient" regions for interpersonal intelligence. One way to examine such differences is to use fcMRI or DTI to identify differences in pathways, as in the example of absolute pitch (see Figure 15-10).

Divergent and Convergent Intelligence

One clear difference between lesions in the parietal and temporal lobes and lesions in the frontal lobes is in the way they affect performance on standardized intelligence tests. Posterior lesions produce reliable and often large decreases in intelligence test scores, whereas frontal lesions do not. This is puzzling. If frontal lobe damage does not diminish a person's intelligence test score, why do people with this kind of damage often do stupid things? The answer lies in the difference between two kinds of intelligence.

According to J. P. Guilford (1967), traditional intelligence tests measure **convergent thinking**—applying knowledge and reasoning skills to narrow the range of possible solutions to a problem, then zeroing in on one correct answer. Typical intelligence test items using vocabulary words, arithmetic problems, puzzles, block designs, and so forth all require convergent thinking. They demand a single correct answer that can be easily scored.

In contrast, **divergent thinking** reaches outward from conventional knowledge and reasoning skills to explore new, more unconventional solutions to problems. Divergent thinking assumes a variety of possible approaches and answers to a question rather than a single "correct" solution. A task that requires divergent thinking is to list all the possible uses you can imagine for a coat hanger.

Clearly, a person who is very good at divergent thinking might not necessarily be good at convergent thinking and vice versa. The distinction is useful because it helps us to understand the effects of brain injury on thought. Frontal lobe injury is believed to interfere with divergent thinking. The convergent thinking measured by standardized IQ tests is often impaired in people with damage to the temporal and parietal lobes.

Injury to the left parietal lobe in particular causes devastating impairment in the ability to perform cognitive processes related to academic work. People with this kind of injury may be aphasic, alexic, and apraxic. Many have severe deficits in arithmetic ability. All such impairments would interfere with school performance and performance at most jobs.

Patient M. M., discussed in Section 15-4, had left parietal lobe injury and was unable to return to school. In contrast with people like M. M., those with frontal lobe injuries seldom have deficits in reading, writing, or arithmetic. And they show no decrement in standardized IQ tests. C. C.'s case provides a good example.

C. C. had a meningioma along the midline between the frontal lobes. Extracting it required removing brain tissue from both hemispheres. Before his surgery C. C. was a prominent lawyer. Afterward, although he still had a superior IQ and superior memory, he was unable to work, in part because he no longer had any imagination. He could not generate the novel solutions to legal problems that had characterized his career before the surgery. Thus, both M. M. and C. C. had problems that prevented them from working, but their problems differed because their injuries affected different kinds of thinking.

Intelligence, Heredity, Epigenetics, and the Synapse

Donald Hebb proposed another way to categorize human intelligence. Like Guilford, Hebb thought of people as having two forms, which he called intelligence A and intelligence B. Unlike Guilford's convergent–divergent dichotomy, Hebb's **intelligence A** refers to innate intellectual potential, which is highly heritable: it has a strong genetic component. **Intelligence B** is observed intelligence, which is influenced by experience as well as other factors, such as disease, injury, or exposure to environmental toxins, especially during development.

Hebb (1980) understood that experience can influence brain cell structure significantly. In his view, experiences influence brain development, and thus observed intelligence, because they alter the brain's synaptic organization. It follows that appropriate postnatal experiences can enhance development of intelligence B in people with lower than average intelligence A, whereas a poor or underresourced environment can hinder the development of intelligence B in people with higher than average intelligence A. The task is to identify a good and a bad environment so as to stimulate people to reach their highest potential intelligence.

One implication of Hebb's view of intelligence: the brain's synaptic organization is key. Synaptic organization is partly directed by a person's genes but is also affected by epigenetic factors. Variations in the experiences to which people are exposed, coupled with variations in genetic patterns, undoubtedly contribute to the individual differences in intelligence that we observe—both quantitative differences (as measured by IQ tests) and qualitative differences (as in Gardner's view).

Hikaru Takeuchi and colleagues (2012) used fMRI to characterize brain activation while participants performed working memory tasks of varied complexity. Performance on IQ tests and memory are highly correlated, so the investigators reasoned that brain activity during memory tests might reflect brain differences related to IQ score.

Performance speed correlated with increased activation in the right dorsolateral prefrontal cortex as well as an increase in the interaction between the prefrontal cortex and right posterior parietal cortex. Gray matter volume in the right dorsolateral prefrontal region correlated with the participant's accuracy in working memory tasks, which in turn correlated with psychometric intelligence measures.

Others have obtained parallel results using event-related potentials (e.g., Langer et al., 2009). The general conclusion from ERP studies is that general intelligence is related to the efficiency of cortical networks linking prefrontal and parietal regions. We can speculate that the efficiency of different neural networks, as might be seen in fcMRI studies, will underlie the variation in each of Gardner's seven forms of intelligence.

Finally, neuropsychological studies using tests of executive (frontal lobe) function show an advantage for bilingual speakers relative to monolinguals. The difference is hypothesized to reflect bilinguals' consistent need to select language-appropriate words and to inhibit language-inappropriate words. Further, learning two languages early in life appears to confer an even greater advantage than acquiring a second language later in life.

Olulade and colleagues (2015) found that, versus monolinguals, increased gray matter volume in the frontal lobe of adults who learned two languages before age 6 reflects this behavioral advantage. No such difference appeared when the investigators compared individuals who acquired an oral language and American Sign Language. The finding is consistent with the idea that the challenge of selecting language-appropriate words is critical. How the increased gray matter volume correlates with other measures of intelligence is unknown, but the results are consistent with evidence showing long-term cognitive advantages in elderly bilinguals. This suggests a broader advantage for bilinguals than in executive functions alone.

Review Focus 8-1. Section 8-4 recounts Hebb's pioneering work on enriched environments' importance in early childhood education.

convergent thinking Form of thinking that searches for a single answer to a question (such as 2 + 2 = ?); contrasts with divergent thinking.

divergent thinking Form of thinking that searches for multiple solutions to a problem (how many ways can a pen be used?); contrasts with convergent thinking.

intelligence A Hebb's term for innate intellectual potential, which is highly heritable and cannot be measured directly.

intelligence B Hebb's term for observed intelligence, influenced by experience and other factors in the course of development; measured by intelligence tests.

Section 7-2 describes ERP's use in mapping brain function.

Focus 8-3 backs up these ideas about bilingual speakers.

15-6 REVIEW

Intelligence

Before you continue, check your understanding.

1. Different concepts of intelligence include Spearman's _____, Gardner's _____, Guilford's concepts of _____ and _____ thinking, and Hebb's _____ and _____.

2. Each form of intelligence that humans possess is probably related to the brain's _____ organization as well as to its _____ efficiency.

3. No two brains are alike. They differ, for example, in _____, _____, and _____.

4. Evidence that Hebb's intelligence A and intelligence B can be altered by experience is evidence of _____ influences on brain organization.

5. How might intelligence be related to brain activity?

Answers appear at the back of the book.

For additional study tools, visit LaunchPad: LaunchPad
www.macmillanhighered.com/launchpad/kolb5e

15-7 Consciousness

Our conscious experience is familiar and intimate yet remains largely a mysterious product of the brain. Everyone has an idea of what it means to be conscious, but like thinking and intelligence, consciousness is easier to identify than to define. Definitions range from a mere manifestation of complex thought processes to more slippery notions that see it as the subjective experience of awareness or the "inner self."

Despite the difficulty of defining consciousness, scientists generally agree that it is a process, not a thing. And consciousness is probably not a single process but several, such as are associated with seeing, talking, thinking, emotion, and so on.

Consciousness is not unitary but can take various forms. A person is not necessarily equally conscious at all stages of life. We don't think of a newborn baby as being conscious in the same way that a healthy older child or adult is. Indeed, we might say that part of the maturation process is becoming fully conscious. The level of consciousness even changes across the span of a day as we pass through various states of drowsiness, sleep, and waking. One trait that characterizes consciousness, then, is its constant variability.

Section 13-3 explores sleep stages and dream states.

Why Are We Conscious?

Countless people, including neuroscience researchers, have wondered why we experience **consciousness**, the mind's level of responsiveness to impressions made by the senses. The simplest explanation is that consciousness provides an adaptive advantage. Either our construct of the sensory world or our selection of behavior is enhanced by being conscious. Consider visual consciousness.

Investigators' conclusions from sensory deprivation experiments: the brain inherently needs stimulation; see Figure 12-1.

According to Francis Crick and Christof Koch (1998), an animal such as a frog acts a bit like a zombie when it responds to visual input. Frogs respond to small, preylike objects by snapping and to large, looming objects by jumping. These responses are controlled by different visual systems and are best thought of as reflexive rather than conscious. And these visual systems work well for the frog. So why would humans need to add consciousness?

Crick and Koch suggest that reflexive systems are fine when their number is limited, but as their numbers grow, reflexive arrangements become inefficient, especially when two or more systems conflict. As the amount of information about an event increases,

consciousness The mind's level of responsiveness to impressions made by the senses.

it becomes advantageous to produce a single complex representation and make it available for a sufficient time to the parts of the brain—such as the frontal lobes—that choose among many possible action plans. This sustained, complex representation is consciousness.

Of course, to survive we must retain the ability to respond quickly and unconsciously when we need to. This reflexive ability exists alongside our ability to process information consciously. The ventral visual stream is conscious, but the dorsal stream, which acts more rapidly, is not. Athletes model the unconscious action of the online dorsal stream. To hit a baseball or tennis ball traveling at more than 100 miles per hour requires athletes to swing before they are consciously aware of actually seeing the ball. Conscious awareness of the ball comes just after hitting it.

In a series of experiments, Marc Jeannerod and his colleagues (Castiello et al., 1991) found a similar dissociation between behavior and awareness in healthy volunteers as they make grasping movements. **Experiment 15-5** illustrates a representative experiment. Participants were required to grasp one of three rods as quickly as possible. A light on a rod indicated it to be the correct target rod on any given trial.

On some trials, unknown to the participants, the light jumped from one target to another. Participants were asked to report whether such a jump had occurred. As shown in the Results section of the experiment, although participants were able to make the trajectory correction, they were sometimes actually grasping the correct target before they were aware it had changed.

On some trials, the extent of dissociation between motor and vocal responses was so great that, to their surprise, participants grasped the target some 300 milliseconds before they emitted the vocal response. As with baseball players, their conscious awareness of the stimulus event occurred only after their movements took place. No thought was required to make the movement, just as frogs catch flies without having to think about it.

Unconscious movements are different from those consciously directed toward a specific object, as when we reach into a bowl of jellybeans to select a candy of a certain color. In this case, we must be aware of all the different colors surrounding the color we want. Here the conscious ventral stream is needed to discriminate among particular stimuli and respond differentially to them. Consciousness, then, allows us to select behaviors that correspond to an understanding of the nuances of sensory inputs.

What Is the Neural Basis of Consciousness?

Consciousness must be related in some way to neural system activity, particularly in the forebrain. One way to investigate these systems is to contrast two kinds of neurological conditions.

In the first condition, a person lacks conscious awareness of some subset of information, even though he or she processes that information unconsciously. Examples include blindsight, visual form agnosia, implicit learning in amnesia, and visual neglect (discussed in Section 15-2). Another example is obsessive-compulsive disorder, in which people persist in some checking behavior—to see that the stove is off or the door is locked—even though they have already checked many times.

All these phenomena show that stimuli can be highly processed by the brain without entering conscious awareness. This is quite different from the second neurological condition, in which people are consciously aware of stimuli that are not actually there. Examples include phantom limbs and the hallucinations of schizophrenia. In both, consciousness of specific events, such as pain in a missing limb or hearing voices, exists even though these events clearly are not "real."

▶ EXPERIMENT **15-5**

Question: Can people alter their movements without conscious awareness?

Procedure

Volunteers were required to move their hands and grasp the illuminated rod as quickly as possible.

In this trial, the volunteer reaches for illuminated rod 3.

Results

On some trials, the light jumps from one target to another,…

… causing the volunteer to correct his trajectory. Most participants found that they were actually grasping the new target before they were aware that it had

Conclusion: It is possible to dissociate behavior and conscious awareness.

Research from C. Frith, R. Perry, & E. Lumer (1999). The neural correlates of conscious experience. *Trends in Cognitive Sciences, 3*, pp. 105–114.

Focus 9-1 describes blindsight, Section 9-4 visual agnosias, Section 14-2 implicit learning in amnesia, and Section 16-4, OCD.

Focus 11-5 outlines phantom limb pain, Figure 14-20 how amputation remaps the cortex, Focus 8-5 brain abnormalities in schizophrenia.

We can draw two conclusions from these contrasting conditions. First, the representation of a visual object or event is likely to be distributed over many parts of the visual system and probably over parts of the frontal lobes as well. Damage to different areas not only produces different specific symptoms, such as agnosia or neglect, but can also produce a specific loss of visual consciousness. Disordered functioning can induce faulty consciousness, such as hallucinations. Second, because visual consciousness can be lost, it follows that parts of the neural circuit must produce this awareness.

In Section 15-1, we appointed the neuron the unit of thinking. It is unlikely, however, that the neuron can be the unit of conscious experience. Instead, consciousness presumably is a process that emerges from neural circuits, with greater degrees of consciousness associated with increasingly complex circuitry.

For this reason, humans, with their highly complex brain circuits, are often credited with a greater degree of consciousness than other animals have. Simple animals such as worms are assumed to have less consciousness (if any) than dogs, which in turn are assumed to have less consciousness than humans. Brain injury may alter self-awareness in humans, as happens in contralateral neglect, but unless a person is in a coma, he or she retains some conscious experience.

Some people argue that language fundamentally changes the nature of consciousness. Gazzaniga, for one, believes that the left hemisphere, with its language capabilities, acts as an interpreter of stimuli (see Section 15-4). He maintains that this ability is an important difference between the functions of the two hemispheres.

Yet people who are aphasic have not lost consciousness. Although language may alter the nature of our conscious experience, equating any one brain structure with consciousness seems an unlikely hypothesis. Rather, viewing consciousness as a product of all cortical areas, their connections, and their cognitive operations holds more promise.

We end our discussion of thinking on an interesting, if speculative, note. David Chalmers (1995) proposed that consciousness includes not only the information the brain receives through its sensory systems but also the information the brain has stored and presumably the information the brain can imagine. In his view, consciousness is the end product of all the brain's cognitive processes.

An interesting implication of Chalmers's notion is that as the brain changes with experience, so does the state of consciousness. As our sensory experiences become richer and our store of information greater, our consciousness may become more complex. From this perspective, some advantage may attend growing old.

The Glasgow Coma Scale, described in Section 1-2, objectively scores degrees of consciousness in brain-injured people.

15-7 REVIEW

Consciousness

Before you continue, check your understanding.

1. Over the course of human evolution, one characteristic of sensory processing is that it has become more _____.

2. _____ is the mind's level of responsiveness to impressions made by the senses.

3. As relative human brain size and complexity have increased, so too has our degree of _____.

4. Not all behavior is under conscious control. What types of behaviors are not conscious?

Answers appear at the back of the book.

For additional study tools, visit LaunchPad: LaunchPad
www.macmillanhighered.com/launchpad/kolb5e

■ SUMMARY

15-1 The Nature of Thought

The complex processes we call thinking, or cognition, are products of both human and nonhuman brain activity. We use such words as *language* and *memory* to describe cognitive operations, but these concepts are abstract psychological constructs—merely inferred and not found in discrete places in the brain. They exist but have no physical form.

The brain carries out multiple cognitive operations—perception, action for perception, imagery, planning, spatial cognition, and attention. Each requires widespread activity in many cortical areas. The unit of cognition, however, is the neuron.

15-2 Cognition and the Association Cortex

The brain's association cortex includes medial, dorsal, and orbital subdivisions of the prefrontal cortex, the posterior parietal cortex, and anterior regions of the temporal lobe. Cell assemblies in the association cortex specifically take part in most forms of cognition.

The frontal lobes not only plan, organize, and initiate movements but also organize our behavior over time (temporally). As a general rule, the temporal lobes generate knowledge about objects, whereas the parietal lobes produce varied forms of spatial cognition. Neurons in both the temporal and the parietal lobes contribute to our ability to selectively attend to sensory information.

Regions in the frontal and parietal lobes contain mirror neurons that represent actions—one's own or those of others. Such neural representations could be used both for imitating others' actions and for moving faster and more accurately. A significant area of the cortex is multisensory, allowing the brain to combine characteristics of stimuli across sensory modalities, whether we encounter the stimuli together or separately.

15-3 Expanding Frontiers of Cognitive Neuroscience

Neuropsychological studies that began in the late 1800s to examine the behavioral capacities of people and laboratory animals with localized brain injuries did not allow investigators to study "normal" brains. Today, noninvasive brain recording systems and imaging techniques further the field of cognitive neuroscience, which studies the neural basis of cognition by measuring brain activity while healthy participants engage in cognitive tasks.

An important step in identifying the neural bases of cognition is mapping cortical connections for the brain connectome. Two promising imaging tools are functional connectivity magnetic resonance imaging (fcMRI) and tractography using diffusion tensor imaging.

The cerebellum, which houses 80 percent of the human brain's neurons, was long believed primarily to have motor functions. Emerging data, however, reveal cerebellar involvement in a wide range of cognitive functions as well.

Social neuroscience, a field that combines cognitive neuroscience with social psychology, explores how we understand others' intentions by constructing a theory of mind. Social neuroscience also investigates how we develop attitudes, beliefs, and a sense of self.

Using noninvasive imaging techniques such as fMRI, researchers have shown that social cognition primarily involves activity in the prefrontal cortex.

Neuroeconomics combines psychology, neuroscience, and economics in seeking to understand human decision making. fMRI studies reveal two decision-making pathways. One is slow and reflective, involving diffuse regions of association cortex. The other is quick and reflexive, involving the dopaminergic reward system.

15-4 Cerebral Asymmetry in Thinking

Cognitive operations are organized asymmetrically in the left and right cerebral hemispheres: each carries out complementary functions. The most obvious functional difference is language, typically housed in the left hemisphere.

Cerebral asymmetry, manifested in anatomical differences between the two hemispheres, can be inferred from the differential effects of injury to opposite sides of the brain. Asymmetry can also be seen in the healthy brain and in the brain that is surgically split to relieve intractable epilepsy. Various syndromes result from association cortex injury, among them agnosia, apraxia, aphasia, and amnesia. Each includes the loss or disturbance of some cognitive function.

15-5 Variations in Cognitive Organization

Unique brains produce unique thought patterns. Marked variations in brain organization among individuals are exhibited in idiosyncratic capacities such as synesthesia. Systematic differences in cognition exist as well, manifested in the performance of females and males on cognitive tests, especially on tests of spatial and verbal behavior.

Sex differences in cognition result from gonadal hormones' actions on cortical organization, possibly on the architecture of cortical neurons, and ultimately on neural networks. Female and male cerebral hemispheres exhibit marked differences in anatomical organization.

Right- and left-handers also differ in hemispheric organization. Left-handers constitute at least three distinct groups. In one, speech appears to reside in the left hemisphere, as it does in right-handers. The other two groups have anomalous speech representation, either in the right hemisphere or in both hemispheres. The reasons for these organizational differences remain unknown.

15-6 Intelligence

Intelligence is easy to spot but difficult to define. Obvious differences exist across, as well as within, species, and we find varied forms of intelligence among humans within our own culture and in other cultures. Intelligence is unrelated to differences in brain size within a species or to any obvious gross structural differences among members of the species. Intelligence may be related to synaptic organization and processing efficiency.

15-7 Consciousness

The larger a species' brain is relative to its body size, the more knowledge the brain acquires. Consciousness, the mind's level of responsiveness to impressions made by the senses, emerges from the nervous system's complexity.

■ KEY TERMS

anomalous speech
   representation, p. 551

association cortex, p. 525

attention, p. 528

binding problem, p. 527

brain connectome, p. 535

cell assembly, p. 522

cognition, p. 521

cognitive neuroscience, p. 533

consciousness, p. 556

contralateral neglect, p. 528

convergent thinking, p. 555

dichotic listening, p. 541

divergent thinking, p. 555

extinction, p. 528

hyperconnectivity, p. 535

intelligence A, p. 555

intelligence B, p. 555

mirror neuron, p. 532

neuroeconomics, p. 538

perseveration, p. 531

psychological construct, p. 521

social neuroscience, p. 536

split brain, p. 521

synesthesia, p. 551

syntax, p. 521

theory of mind, p. 536

➡ Visit 🅜 LaunchPad**LaunchPad** to access the e-Book, videos, 🅜 LearningCurve**LearningCurve** adaptive quizzing, flashcards, and more: **www.macmillanhighered.com/launchpad/kolb5e**

CHAPTER 16

What Happens When the Brain Misbehaves?

Katherine Streeter

Posttraumatic Stress Disorder

Life is filled with stress. Routinely, we cope. But some events are so physically threatening and often emotionally shattering that long-term consequences ensue. Flashbacks and nightmares persist long after any physical danger has passed. These symptoms can lead to emotional numbness and a diagnosis of **posttraumatic stress disorder**, or PTSD (Jorge, 2015).

Traumatic events that may trigger PTSD include violent assault, natural or human-caused disaster, accident, and war. An estimated 1 in 6 veterans of the conflicts in Iraq and Afghanistan, many not directly exposed to combat, developed symptoms of PTSD, including intrusive, unwanted thoughts; avoiding thoughts related to stressful events; negative cognitions and moods; and altered arousal and reactivity responses. Understanding the neural basis and identifying new PTSD treatments has spurred intense interest. Nevertheless, treatment is often difficult, and most sufferers receive no or little treatment.

That a beneficial therapy is to relive a traumatic event is counterintuitive. Yet in **virtual reality (VR) exposure therapy**, a controlled virtual immersion environment combines realistic street scenes, sounds, and odors that allow people to relive traumatic events (Gonçalves et al., 2012). The Virtual Iraq and Afghanistan Simulation is customized for war veterans to start with benign events—such as children playing—and gradually add increasingly stressful components, culminating in such traumatic events as a roadside bomb exploding in the virtual space around an armored personnel carrier, illustrated here.

To make Virtual Iraq realistic, the system pumps in smells, stepping up from the scent of bread baking to body odor to the reek of gunpowder and burning rubber. Speakers provide sounds while off-the-shelf subwoofers mounted under the subject's chair re-create movements. VR exposure therapy is now used prior to stress exposure for soldiers, police, firefighters, and other first responders, as a means of preventing PTSD (Rizzo et al., 2012).

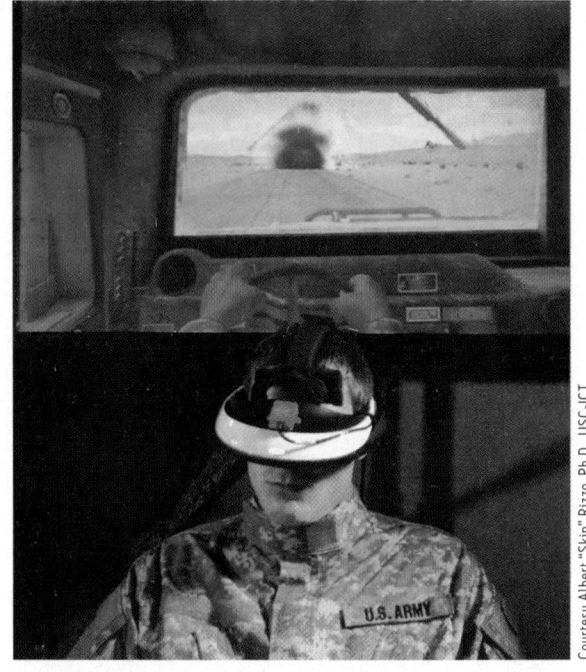

Courtesy Albert "Skip" Rizzo, Ph.D., USC-ICT

Many unknowns related to PTSD remain, including how stress injures the brain, especially the frontal lobes and hippocampus (Wingenfeld & Wolf, 2014); why some people do not develop PTSD following extremely stressful events; and the extent to which PTSD is associated with other health events, including previous stressors, diabetes, and head trauma (Costanzo et al., 2014). That said, assessment and treatment options for most of those who endure PTSD are poor: over half of all war veterans, for example, receive no assessment or treatment.

posttraumatic stress disorder (PTSD)
Syndrome characterized by physiological arousal brought on by recurring memories and dreams related to a traumatic event for months or years after the event.

virtual reality (VR) exposure therapy
Controlled virtual immersion environment that, by allowing individuals to relive traumatic events, gradually desensitizes them to stress.

Current understanding of PTSD illustrates how thinking on the brain's role in health can shift. Largely as a result of symptoms displayed by returning Vietnam War veterans, in 1980 the DSM-III introduced PTSD as a mental disorder. Lynda Holmstrom and Ann Burgess (1978) as well pointed out similarities in symptoms between war veterans and rape victims.

A prominent feature of PTSD diagnosis is that a traumatic external agent, rather than internal causes, is prominent in producing the characteristic set of behavioral symptoms described in Research Focus 16-1, Posttraumatic Stress Disorder. Neuroscientists now recognize that the brain contributes to PTSD development and that traumatic experiences related to policing, firefighting, and accidental events can contribute to the condition.

The many discussions of behavioral disorders and organic disease presented throughout this book serve both to illustrate the brain's organization and functioning and to exemplify how knowledge about brain function contributes to understanding and treating brain disorder and disease. Classifying and treating organic and behavioral conditions is our focus in this chapter.

We know that the brain is complex. We do not yet understand all its parts and their functions, nor is it clear how the brain produces mind, a sense of well-being, and a sense of self. Still, significant advances have led to the realization that while under some circumstances the brain copes competently with life's challenges, under other circumstances, it is not up to the job.

To illustrate progress in studying brain and behavior over the past century, we can contrast the theories of Sigmund Freud with present-day views. Freud's theories were based on his observations of patients while not having the help of the anatomical or imaging data available today. The underlying tenet of Freud's theory is that our motivations are largely hidden away in our unconscious mind. Freud posited that a mysterious, repressive force actively withholds our sexual and aggressive motivations from conscious awareness. He believed that mental illness resulted from the failure of these repressive processes.

Freud proposed the three components of mind illustrated in **Figure 16-1A**:

1. Primitive functions, including the "instinctual drives" of sex and aggression, arise from the *id*, the part of the mind that Freud thought operated on an unconscious level.

2. The rational part of the mind he called the *ego*. Freud also believed, much of the ego's activity to be unconscious, although experience (to him, perceptions of the world) is conscious.

3. The *superego* aspect of mind acts to repress the id and to mediate ongoing interactions between the ego and the id.

For Freudians, abnormal behaviors result from the emergence of unconscious drives into voluntary conscious behavior. The aim of *psychoanalysis*, the original talk therapy, is to trace symptoms to their unconscious roots and thus expose them to rational judgment.

By the 1970s, scientific studies of the brain made the whole notion of id, ego, and superego seem antiquated. Nevertheless, some resemblance between Freud's theory and brain theory is apparent (Figure 16-1B). The limbic system and brainstem have properties akin to those of the id: they produce emotional and motivated behavior, including the will to survive and to reproduce. The posterior and the dorsolateral frontal cortices have properties akin to those of the ego: they allow us to learn and to solve everyday problems. The prefrontal neocortex has properties akin to those of the superego, enabling us to be aware of others and to learn to follow social norms. Furthermore, as abundantly displayed in earlier chapters, many processes underlying these functions are unconscious: they operate outside our awareness.

Three differences between Freud's view and present-day neuroscience are apparent. First, we now recognize that the brain is composed of hundreds of interacting structures, not just three. Second, we know that the functions of these brain parts is complicated and depends upon ongoing expression of genes, interactions of myriad chemicals, and functioning and connections of glia and neurons. Third, we understand that behavioral disorders have

FIGURE 16-1 Mind Models **(A)** Freud based his model of the mind, drawn in 1933, solely on clinical observations (color added). **(B)** In a contemporary brain imaging and lesioning studies map, the brainstem and limbic system correlate with Freud's depiction of the id, the ventral frontal and posterior cortex with the ego, and the dorsal frontal cortex with the superego. Information from a drawing by Mark Solms and Oliver Turnbull.

complex causes, including genetic abnormalities, abnormalities in nervous system development over the life-span, and environmental and epigenetic effects that modulate genetic and developmental expression.

Investigating the origins and treatment of disordered behavior is perhaps the most fascinating pursuit in studying the brain and behavior. Once, neurologists treated *organic disorders* of the nervous system—conditions such as Parkinson disease and stroke—medically. Psychiatrists treated *mental disorders* such as schizophrenia and PTSD pharmacologically. Psychological disorders were treated with counseling and other behavioral therapies. Increasingly, practitioners are synthesizing their insights into a unified understanding of mind and brain, a **neuropyschoanalysis** that views the brain as the ultimate source of behavior. When loved ones develop brain disorders, family members usually become the primary caregivers and as such join practitioners as participants, because they and their loved ones are those most affected.

With this synthesis of understanding about brain and behavior in mind, we first survey how researchers investigate the neurobiology of organic and behavioral disorders. We then examine how disorders are classified, treated, and distributed in the population and review established and emerging treatments both for neurological and for psychiatric disorders.

16-1 Multidisciplinary Research on Brain and Behavioral Disorders

Brain research is multidisciplinary. One way to summarize methods of studying links between brain and behavior is to consider them from the macro level of the whole organism down to the molecular level of neuronal excitation and inhibition. Behavioral studies by their nature investigate the whole organism, but understanding the whole organism requires understanding its parts—its cells, its chemistry, and its genes.

Chapter 7 surveys research methods ranging from single-cell recordings to functional brain imaging.

Molecular biology offers neuroscientists varied approaches to studying behavior. Scientists can breed strains of animals, such as fruit flies, fish, or mice, with either a gene knocked out (deleted or inactivated) or a gene inserted. Knockout technology is used both to create animal models of human disorders and to generate treatments for neurobehavioral disorders. Variations on this technology include methods for turning genes on or off for periods of time. What is clear from this research is that the genes related to disordered behavior in fruit flies, fish, and mice are largely the same as those related to similar disordered behavior in people.

Section 3-3 reviews genetics, genetic engineering, and epigenetic mechanisms; Section 7-5 explores techniques for measuring genetic and epigenetic influences.

Freud was limited to probing the brain with conversation. Today, brain imaging techniques allow behavioral neuroscientists to describe structures and pathways in an individual brain and the changes it undergoes during development, learning, and after damage, all without directly accessing the brain. Understanding the brain's structure and function leads to understanding that individual brains differ—why, for example, one person may have PTSD or any other disorder, whereas another person in similar circumstances does not.

Causes of Disordered Behavior

Neuroscientists presume that abnormal brain functioning results in disordered behavior. Evidence for brain abnormalities is relatively straightforward in neurological disorders, and at least in a general sense, the causes are largely known:

1. *Genetic errors*, as in Huntington disease

2. *Epigenetic mechanisms* at work prenatally, later in life, even in succeeding generations

3. *Progressive cell death* resulting from neurodegenerative causes, as in Parkinson or Alzheimer disease

Focus 3-4 describes Huntington disease's genetic basis; Focus 5-2, neural degeneration in Parkinson disease; Focus 2-3, symptoms and aftereffects of stroke; and Focus 4-2, myelin breakdown in MS.

4. *Rapid cell death*, as in stroke or traumatic brain injury

5. *Loss of neural function and connections* seen in disorders such as multiple sclerosis and myasthenia gravis

In contrast to these organic neurological disorders, far less is known about neurobiological causes of behavioral and psychiatric disorders. But results of neurobiological studies of pathology and newer research methods are revealing clues to causation: changes in the brain's structure or activity are implicated. **Table 16-1** lists the most likely causal categories underlying behavioral disorders, micro to macro.

At the microscopic level is genetic error, such as that responsible for Tay-Sachs disease and Huntington disease. Intermediate categories include one-time events, such as infections, injuries, and toxins. At the macro level, nutrition, stress, and negative experience are prominent actors. Of course, many of these factors interact. Genetic error is probably linked to more macro causes, such as hormonal or developmental anomalies. Genetic vulnerability to stress, infection, or pollution may be the immediate cause of some disorders. In other cases, no direct genetic predisposition is needed: disordered behavior arises strictly from epigenetic factors, such as stress and negative experiences, which influence gene expression and function.

TABLE 16-1 Causes of Selected Behavioral Disorders

Cause	Disorder
Genetic error	Tay-Sachs disease
Hormonal anomaly	Androgenital syndrome
Developmental anomaly	Schizophrenia
Infection	Encephalitis
Injury	Traumatic brain injury
Toxins	MPTP poisoning
Poor nutrition	Korsakoff syndrome
Stress	Anxiety disorders
Negative experience	Developmental delays among Romanian orphans

Investigating the Neurobiology of Behavioral Disorders

A single brain abnormality can cause a behavioral disorder, explaining everything about it and its treatment. **Phenylketonuria** (PKU) is an example. PKU results from a defect in the gene for phenylalanine hydroxylase (PHA), an enzyme that breaks down the amino acid phenylalanine. Babies with PKU have elevated blood levels of phenylalanine, leading to intellectual impairments, seizures, and other physiological conditions. To inherit PKU, both parents must carry a defective PHA gene. This recessive condition confers resistance to certain fungal toxins. About 400 mutations of the PHA gene are known (Foroozani et al., 2015).

Left untreated, PKU causes severe intellectual disability, but PKU can be treated just by restricting dietary intake of phenylalanine—foods high in protein, including beef, fish, cheese, and soy. A strict diet in infancy prevents brain damage by PKU, and controlled diet throughout life ensures protection. Expectant mothers who have had PKU might provide an in utero environment with high PHA levels, and this too can be controlled if the mother restricts her dietary intake of phenylalanine. Several drugs to reduce phenylalanine levels are in development.

If other behavioral disorders were as simple and well understood as PKU, neuroscience research could quickly yield cures for them. Many disorders do not result from a single genetic abnormality, however, and the causes of most disorders remain conjectural. The major problem: diagnosis of a disability is based mainly on behavioral symptoms, and behavioral symptoms give few clues to specific neurochemical or neurostructural causes.

This problem also appears in treating PKU. **Table 16-2** lists what is known about PKU at different levels of analysis: genetic, biochemical, histological, neurological, behavioral, and social. The underlying problem becomes less apparent with the procession of entries in the table. In fact, it is not possible to predict the specific biochemical abnormality from information at the neurological, behavioral, or social level, exactly where the most accessible information resides.

For most psychiatric diseases, the underlying pathology is unknown. For PKU, the distinctive smell of her baby's urine detected by one mother was the first link in a chain of discoveries that identified elevated PHA. The task for future study and treatment of most behavioral disorders is to identify biological markers that will lead to similar understandings.

Challenges to Diagnosis

Knowledge about behavioral disorders is hampered by its subjective nature. Most diagnostic information gathered about a patient's behavior comes both from patients and their families. Unfortunately, people seldom are objective observers of their own behavior or that of a loved one. We tend to be selective in noticing and reporting symptoms. If we believe someone has a memory problem, for example, we often notice memory lapses that we might ordinarily ignore.

The Index of Disorders inside the book's front cover lists where each condition in Table 16-1 is discussed.

neuropsychoanalysis Movement within neuroscience and psychoanalysis to combine the insights of both to yield a unified understanding of mind and brain.

phenylketonuria (PKU) Behavioral disorder caused by elevated levels of the amino acid phenylalanine in the blood and resulting from a defect in the gene for the enzyme phenylalanine hydroxylase; the major symptom is severe developmental disability.

TABLE 16-2 PKU: Neurobiological Pathogenesis of a Behavioral Disorder

Level of analysis*	Known information
Genetic	Inborn metabolism error Recessive defective gene (autosomal)
Biochemical	Conversion of phenylalanine to tyrosine impaired, elevating levels of phenylalanine and its metabolites in the blood
Abnormal tissue	Abnormal cortical lamination Decrease in neuron size and dendritic length Lowered spine density
Neurological	Severe intellectual impairment Slow growth Seizure Abnormal EEG
Behavioral	IQ score below 50 (in 95 percent of patients)
Social, economic	Significant loss of meaningful life and productivity
Treatment	Dietary intake of phenylalanine restricted

*From most to least specific

Source: Information from "Special Challenges in the Investigation of the *Neurobiology of Mental Illness*," by G. R. Heninger, 1999, in *The Neurobiology of Mental Illness* (p. 90), edited by D. S. Charney, E. J. Nestler, and B. S. Bunney. New York: Oxford University Press.

Nor are we often specific in identifying symptoms. Simply identifying a memory problem is not sufficient. Treatment requires knowing exactly what type of memory deficit underlies the problem. Losses of memory for words, places, or habits—each has different underlying pathologies and brain systems.

Just as patients and their loved ones make diagnosis difficult, so too do diagnosticians. Behavioral information about patients may be interpreted differently by general physicians, psychiatrists, neurologists, psychologists, social workers, and others. Evaluators with different conceptual biases shape and filter the questions they ask and the information they gather.

One evaluator believes that a behavioral disorder is genetic; another believes it results from a virus; and a third, that it can be traced to repressed sexual experiences during childhood. Each makes different types of observations and administers different kinds of diagnostic tests. In contrast, diagnosing organic disorders is less dependent on subjective observations than on objective experimental methods—but these too have limitations.

Research Challenges

Even if the problems of diagnosis were solved, major obstacles to investigating behavioral disorders would still exist. Following is a partial list.

ORGANIZATIONAL COMPLEXITY The nervous system far outstrips other body systems in complexity. The brain has a wider variety of cell types than does any other body organ, and nervous system cells and their connections are plastic: they change with experience. These features add a whole new dimension to understanding healthy and disordered functioning.

SYSTEMIC COMPLEXITY As our understanding of brain and behavior has progressed, so it has become apparent that multiple receptor systems serve widely varied functions. For example, the brain's major activating systems, those that employ acetylcholine, dopamine, norepinephrine, serotonin, and GABA are diffuse, with little specificity between biochemistry and behavior. The neurotransmitter GABA affects some 30 percent of the brain's synapses. When people ingest a GABA agonist, such as a benzodiazepine, multiple effects on behavior become apparent. So it is with most drug treatments, which may improve a target behavior but at the same time produce varied side effects.

NEURONAL PLASTICITY The nervous system can adapt to extreme stress or injury. Even the nigrostriatal dopaminergic system's close relation to Parkinson disease is enigmatic. It is impossible to tie dopamine depletion to a consistent behavioral syndrome. Two people with

Sections 14-2 and 14-3 explain a range of memory deficits.

Figure 5-17 summarizes major neural activating systems; Figure 6-7, how psychoactive drugs affect the GABA$_A$ receptor.

Parkinson disease can exhibit vastly different symptoms, even though the common basis of the disease is a loss of neurons from the substantia nigra (Fereshtehnejad et al., 2015). Further, only when the loss of dopamine neurons exceeds about 60 percent to 80 percent do investigators see clinical signs of Parkinson disease. Are those cells not all needed? That is unlikely, but the result shows that the brain's compensatory plasticity is considerable. When a disease progresses slowly, the brain has a remarkable capacity for adapting.

COMPENSATORY PLASTICITY Even the best technology produces uncertain relationships. Magnetic resonance imaging may show that a person with multiple sclerosis has many nervous system lesions yet displays few outward symptoms. Just as brain lesions do not always produce behavioral symptoms, behavioral symptoms are not always linked to obvious neuropathology. Clearly, people display compensatory plasticity: they can change their behavior to adapt to neural change just as they can display disordered behavior without obvious brain pathology.

TECHNOLOGICAL RESOLUTION Some people have notable behavioral problems after a brain trauma, yet no obvious signs of brain damage appear on an MRI. An infant's brain may seem healthy only to display severe cerebral palsy later. The resolution of a technology may lack sufficient detail to detect subtle neuronal change, such as a drop in dendritic spine density or injury so diffuse that it is hard to identify. Given the current diagnostic methods for both behavioral disorders and neuropathology, identifying disorders and their causes is seldom easy.

MODELING SIMPLICITY A major avenue for investigating the causes of disorders is to develop and study animal models. Rats with specific lesions of the nigrostriatal dopamine system are used to model Parkinson disease. Animal models lead to significant advances in understanding neural conditions and their treatment. But the view they provide of the neurobiology behind behavioral disorders can be oversimplified.

The fact that a drug reduces symptoms does not necessarily mean that it is acting on a key biochemical aspect of the pathology. Aspirin can get rid of a headache, but that does not mean that the headache is caused by the receptors on which aspirin acts. Similarly, antipsychotic drugs block dopamine D_2 receptors, but that does not mean that schizophrenia is caused by abnormal D_2 receptors. Schizophrenia quite possibly results from a disturbance in glutamatergic systems, and for some reason dopamine antagonists can rectify the abnormality.

MODELING LIMITATIONS Modeling human disorders is complex, and critical thinking is imperative when you encounter media reports about studies using animal models that point toward possible cures for human behavioral diseases. Caution applies especially to psychiatric disorders whose causes remain unknown. Further, many symptoms of disorders such as schizophrenia and anxiety are largely cognitive. Objectively identifying any cognitive processes mimicked by a laboratory model is a difficult task.

Nigrostriatal Dopamine Pathways
Axons of neurons in the midbrain substantia nigra project to the basal ganglia, supplying dopamine to maintain healthy motor behavior. Dopamine loss contributes to muscle rigidity and dyskinesia in Parkinson disease.

Section 7-7 reviews the benefits of creating animal models of disorders.

(16-1) REVIEW

Multidisciplinary Research on Brain and Behavioral Disorders

Before you continue, check your understanding.

1. Neural correlates of Freud's id, ego, and superego could be, respectively, the _____, _____, and _____.

2. Causes of disordered behavior include _____, _____, _____, _____, and _____.

3. For most psychiatric disorders, the causes are unknown, but _____ is an exception.

4. A major challenge in diagnosing disorders is that diagnosis tends to be _____.

5. Describe a research conundrum for understanding brain injury.

Answers appear at the back of the book.

16-2 Classifying and Treating Brain and Behavioral Disorders

Behavioral disorders afflict millions every year. The National Institute for Mental Disorders estimates that in a given year about one in four people in the United States has a diagnosable behavioral disorder, and nearly half of the population does over their lifetime. Only a minority receive treatment of any kind, and even fewer receive treatment from a mental health specialist. Large-scale surveys of neurological disorders show a similar pattern of prevalence. Together, behavioral, psychiatric, and neurological disorders are the leading cause of disability after age 15. Behavioral disorders, traditionally classified as social, psychological, psychiatric, and neurological, reflect the assessment and treatment roles different professional groups play. As understanding of brain function increases, the lines between behavioral disorders are blurring.

Figure 8-31 pegs the peak age of onset for mental disorders at 14 years.

Identifying and Classifying Behavioral Disorders

Epidemiologists study disease distribution and causes in human populations and help define and assess behavioral disorders of three general types—psychoses, mood, and affect. Various professional organizations classify disorders differently, for example, as in **Table 16-3**.

TABLE 16-3 Summary of DSM-5 Diagnostic Classification of Disorders

Diagnostic category	Core features and examples of specific disorders
Neurodevelopmental disorders	Disorders typically manifest early; characterized by developmental deficits that produce impairments of personal, social, or academic functioning, including ASD, ADHD, Tourette disorder.
Schizophrenia spectrum and other psychotic disorders	Functioning deteriorates toward psychosis or loss of contact with reality defined by delusions, hallucinations, disorganized thinking, grossly disorganized or disordered motor behavior, and negative symptoms.
Bipolar and related disorders	Disorders placed between schizophrenia and depressive disorders, bridging two diagnostic classes, and characterized by periods of extreme elation and/or significant depressive symptoms.
Depressive disorders	All feature sad, empty, or irritable mood, accompanied by physical and cognitive changes that significantly affect the individual's capacity to function. Includes major depressive disorder, dysthymia, premenstrual dysphoric disorder.
Anxiety disorders	All feature excessive fear and anxiety but differ in objects or situations that induce fear, anxiety, or avoidance and associated cognitive ideation. Includes generalized anxiety disorder (GAD), specific phobia, agoraphobia, panic disorder, separation anxiety disorder.
Obsessive-compulsive and related disorders	Differ from developmentally normative preoccupations and rituals by excessiveness or persistence beyond developmentally appropriate periods.
Trauma- and stressor-related disorders	Exposure to a traumatic or stressful event, as in PTSD, is an explicit diagnostic criterion.
Dissociative disorders	Disruption of and/or discontinuity of consciousness, memory, identity, emotion, perception, body representation, motor control, and behavior, including dissociative identity disorder (multiple personality disorder), dissociative amnesia.
Somatic symptom disorder and related disorders	Physical symptoms apparently caused primarily by psychological rather than physiological factors; commonly encountered in medical rather than mental health settings. Includes somatic symptom disorder, illness anxiety disorder, conversion disorder.
Feeding and eating disorders	Abnormal patterns of eating that significantly impair physical health and/or psychosocial functioning, including pica, anorexia nervosa, bulimia nervosa, and binge-eating disorder.
Elimination disorders	Inappropriate elimination of urine or feces, usually first diagnosed in childhood or adolescence.
Sleep–wake disorders	Characterized by chronic sleep problems, including insomnia disorder, narcolepsy, sleep apneas, circadian rhythm sleep–wake disorders, restless legs syndrome.

The first set of criteria for diagnoses in psychiatry was developed in 1972. Since that time, three parallel sets of criteria have gained prominence, and new versions appear periodically. One is the most recent edition of the World Health Organization's International Classification of Diseases (ICD-10); another, the American Psychiatric Association's **Diagnostic and Statistical Manual of Mental Disorders** (DSM). The newest, launched by the National Institutes of Mental Health, is the Research Domain Criteria (RDoC). With this new classification system, NIMH is looking to transform behavioral diagnoses by incorporating genetics, imaging, and cognitive science, among other levels of information.

In addition, the Society for Clinical Psychology provides a list of psychological disorders, their symptoms, and a summary of psychological treatments. The National Institute of Neurological Disorders and Stroke provides a list of neurological disorders, including their symptoms, treatments, and any clinical trials that are investigating treatments. Classification systems organize knowledge about disorders and their treatments and are useful for decision making in such institutions as insurance companies, courts, and schools.

Table 16-3 summarizes the classification scheme used currently in the DSM-5. As with any attempt to classify psychiatric disorders, the DSM is to some extent arbitrary and unavoidably depends on prevailing cultural views. A good example is the social definition of sexual behavior viewed as abnormal. At its inception, the DSM listed homosexual behavior as pathological but has omitted it since 1980. With evidence solidifying around a neural basis for the spectrum of gender identity, a similar fate will likely befall the DSM category gender dysphoria.

Diagnostic and Statistical Manual of Mental Disorders **(DSM)** The American Psychiatric Association's classification system for psychiatric disorders.

Section 12-5 explores the relationship among sexual orientation, sexual identity, and brain organization; and Section 15-5, sex differences in cognitive organization.

TABLE 16-3 (Continued)

Diagnostic category	Core features and examples of specific disorders
Sexual dysfunctions	Characterized by a clinically significant disturbance in a person's ability to respond sexually or to experience sexual pleasure. Includes premature or delayed ejaculation and erectile disorder in males; female orgasmic or sexual interest/arousal disorder.
Gender dysphoria	Distress accompanying the incongruence between experienced or expressed gender and assigned gender.
Disruptive, impulse-control, and conduct disorders	Problems in self-control of emotions and behaviors, manifested in behaviors that violate others' rights, such as aggression, and/or conflict with societal norms and authority figures. Includes oppositional defiant disorder, intermittent explosive disorder, pyromania, kleptomania.
Substance-related and addictive disorders	Encompasses 10 separate drug classes that affect the central nervous system, and gambling disorder.
Neurocognitive disorders	Disorders dominated by impaired cognitive functioning of determinable underlying pathology and etiology, including TBI and Alzheimer, Huntington, or Parkinson disease.
Personality disorders	Enduring pattern of pervasive and inflexible inner experience and behavior that deviates markedly from cultural expectations; onset occurs in adolescence or early adulthood and is stable over time. Includes paranoid personality disorder, schizoid personality disorder, antisocial personality disorder, borderline personality disorder, histrionic personality disorder, narcissistic personality disorder, dependent personality disorder, obsessive-compulsive personality disorder.
Paraphilic disorders	Disorders that cause distress or impairment to the individual; a paraphilia whose satisfaction entails harm or risk of harm to others, including voyeuristic disorder, exhibitionistic disorder, frotteuristic disorder, sexual masochism disorder, sexual sadism disorder, pedophilic disorder, fetishistic disorder.
Other mental disorders	Symptoms characteristic of a mental disorder predominate but do not meet the full criteria for any other DSM mental disorder.
Medication-induced movement disorders and other adverse effects of medication	Determining causal relationships between medication exposure and development of movement disorders is difficult. Some may occur in the absence of the medication. Notably, *not* categorized as mental disorders are medication-induced parkinsonism, acute dystonia, acute akathisia, tardive dyskinesia, antidepressant discontinuation syndrome.
Other conditions that may be a focus of clinical attention	Conditions or problems that cause significant impairment, including relational problems, problems related to abuse or neglect, educational and occupational problems, housing and economic problems, problems related to crime or interaction with the legal system.

Source: Information from *Diagnostic and Statistical Manual of Mental Disorders* (5th ed.), 2013. Washington, DC: American Psychiatric Association.

Focus 8-2 describes the autism spectrum.

Each revision of any classification system reflects new perspectives. For example, the DSM-5 labels all forms of autism as autism spectrum disorder (ASD) and most forms of schizophrenia as schizophrenia spectrum disorder. Classifying broad ranges of conditions as one simplifies diagnosis but draws criticism for its associated loss of descriptive power and a perceived difficulty in obtaining treatment sensitive to the severity of particular symptoms.

Among the continually emerging means of searching for indicators of behavioral disorders, genetics and brain imaging, including MRI and PET, stand out. Although these tools are not currently used clinically, they are increasingly used both to classify disorders and to monitor treatment effectiveness. But to be useful, imaging test resolution, for example, must be sensitive enough to detect unique features of brain disorders and specific enough to rule out similar conditions. This sets a high bar, because many behavioral disorders display similar abnormalities. Enlarged ventricles, indicating a loss of brain cells, may appear in schizophrenia, Alzheimer disease, alcoholism, or head trauma, for example.

FIGURE 16-2 Early-Onset Schizophrenia Comparison of three-dimensional maps derived from MRI scans reveals that, compared with healthy teenagers aged 13 to 18 (left), patients with childhood-onset schizophrenia (right) have widespread loss of gray matter across the cerebral hemispheres. Courtesy of Paul Thompson and Arthur W. Toga, Laboratory of Neuro Imaging, Keck School of Medicine of USC and Judith L. Rapoport, National Institute of Mental Health.

Nonetheless, imaging technology is shedding new light on behavioral disturbances. Imaging the brain structure, connections, and chemistry of subjects with childhood-onset schizophrenia, for example, suggests that the condition begins in utero and is characterized by excessive pruning of short-distance cortical connections (Rao et al., 2015). Cortical maps derived by Judith Rapoport and coworkers (2012) reveal that between the ages of 13 and 18, children who developed schizophrenia showed a remarkable loss of gray matter in the cerebral cortex (**Figure 16-2**). An earlier study by the same group found changes in the quantity of growth factors that influence brain development and a delayed growth rate in white matter—on the order of 2 percent per year—in children with schizophrenia compared with healthy children (Gogtay et al., 2008).

Abnormalities found throughout the brain vary by functional region and correlate with the onset of behavioral disturbances characteristic of schizophrenia. Not all disorders show such obvious loss of tissue but may show abnormal blood flow or metabolism that can be detected by either fMRI or PET. The PET images in **Figure 16-3** illustrate metabolic changes in adult-onset schizophrenia. The scan on the left reveals an obvious abnormality in prefrontal cortex activity compared with the scan on the right, from an adult who does not have schizophrenia. Note that the prefrontal area does not show loss of gray matter in the MRI study of early-onset schizophrenia reproduced in Figure 16-2. Therefore, it is likely that the two diseases have different origins.

Combining behavioral diagnoses with genetic analysis and neuroimaging will move practitioners beyond symptom checklists to objective medical diagnoses. Imaging analyses will help target treatments to reduce the severity of such serious disorders as schizophrenia and Alzheimer disease. Current imaging techniques do not detect all brain pathology. It is not

FIGURE 16-3 Adult-Onset Schizophrenia Note the abnormally low blood flow in the prefrontal cortex at the top of the PET scan in the brain (left) of an adult schizophrenia patient compared (right) with that of an adult who does not have schizophrenia.

Hank Morgan/Science Source

whether a gene is present or absent but whether that gene is or is not expressed that is relevant to its effects. The challenge lies in improving current techniques and in developing others that can identify subtler nervous system abnormalities.

Classification systems such as taxonomy, the branch of biology that groups organisms according to their common characteristics and relationships, have advanced our knowledge of brain structure and function. Likewise, classifications of behavioral disorders produced by the behavioral sciences have advanced understanding. Yet classification systems have their critics. One criticism is that "just because you name a disorder does not mean it exists." Another is that changing societal views result in the inclusion or exclusion of disorders, as with sexual relationships other than heterosexuality.

Naming disorders becomes problematic as well. The term *idiot* once designated a person with a low IQ score. When the term became pejorative, it was replaced with the term *retarded*. That term then became pejorative, and the DSM-5 now uses the term *intellectual disability*. Nevertheless, just as genetics has clarified taxonomic relationships among animals, our growing understanding of brain function and genetics likely will clarify the taxonomy of behavioral disorders. The NIMH's Research Domain Criteria project, for example, is one response to criticisms of broad behavioral classifications such as those used in the DSM-5.

The Basics in Section 1-3 overviews taxonomy.

Treatments for Disorders

An inclusive list of brain and behavioral disorders would number in the thousands, including, on the organic side, genetic and developmental disorders, infectious diseases, nervous system injuries, and degenerative dementias. Behavioral disorders would include PTSD among the anxiety-related disorders. Abnormalities may also appear via imbalances in biochemical organization or nervous system operation. Biochemical abnormalities include disordered proteins in cell membrane channels, low or high neuroreceptor numbers, and low or high numbers of molecules, especially neurotransmitters or hormones. Each disorder may be associated with various structural changes, congenital abnormality of neurons or glia, and neuronal death.

The conditions listed in the Index of Disorders constitute a mere fraction of the total.

The ultimate goal for behavioral neuroscientists lies in applying their knowledge to generate treatments that can restore a disordered brain to a range of healthy functioning. This goal is daunting because the first task is so difficult: learning what causes a particular behavioral disturbance. Few behavioral disorders have a cause as simple as PKU does. Most, like schizophrenia, are complex. A more achievable goal is to make small advances by improving current treatments, to develop new treatments, and to analyze disease causes. Available treatments, while extensive, fall into four general categories:

1. *Neurosurgical.* The skull is opened and some intervention is performed on the brain.

2. *Electrophysiological.* Brain function is modified by stimulation through the skull.

3. *Pharmacological.* A chemical that affects the brain is either ingested or injected.

4. *Behavioral.* Treatment manipulates the body or the experience, which in turn influences the brain.

Neurosurgical Treatments

Neurosurgical manipulation of the nervous system is largely reparative, as when tumors are removed or arteriovenous (AV) malformations corrected. Typically, such neurosurgical interventions are successful. Advances include improved imaging of a target for surgery—as the surgery takes place—and methods that allow diseased tissue to be destroyed without opening the skull. For example, *radiosurgery* uses energy, such as X-rays directed from different sources to converge on a target and destroy abnormal cells. The x-rays lack the energy to damage healthy cells through which they pass: tissue is destroyed only where multiple beams converge.

Brain tumors are the topic of Focus 3-2. AV malformation, or angioma, is imaged on page 582.

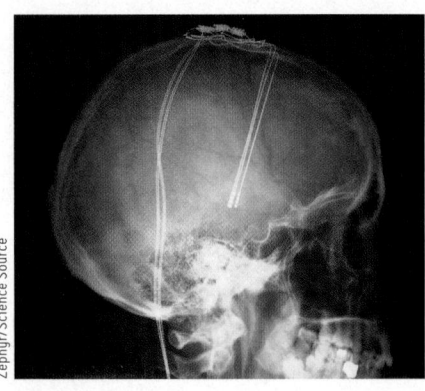

FIGURE 16-4 Deep Brain Stimulation X-ray of a human brain showing electrodes implanted in the thalamus for DBS.

deep brain stimulation (DBS) Neurosurgery in which electrodes permanently implanted in the brain stimulate a targeted area with a low-voltage electrical current to facilitate behavior.

Figure 14-26 shows neurogenesis induced in a rat brain to repair a cortical stroke.

Figure 8-8 diagrams the origins of specialized brain cells from multipotent neural stem cells.

Neurotrophic factors, nourishing chemical compounds, support neuronal growth, development, and viability.

Figure 7-7 diagrams how TMS works.

Treatment for Parkinson disease entails inactivating brain regions that produce tremors and regions participating in the production of muscular rigidity that impairs movement. An electrode is placed in the motor thalamus and an electric current used to damage neurons responsible for producing the unwanted effects. Alternatively, in **deep brain stimulation** (DBS), an electrode fixed in place in the globus pallidus or subthalamic nucleus is connected to an external electrical stimulator that the patient can activate (**Figure 16-4**). The stimulation can inactivate cells responsible for unwanted effects and so restore more normal movement (Knight et al., 2015).

DBS is also used experimentally to treat traumatic brain injury (TBI) and behavioral dysfunctions such as obsessive-compulsive disorder (OCD) and major depression (Cleary et al., 2015). Electrodes implanted in the brain are well tolerated and remain effective for several years. Electrical stimulation can have an activating effect and so relieve depression or compulsive behaviors. Stimulation may also make brain tissue more plastic and receptive to other treatments. During stimulation, patients can learn more effective thought and behavioral patterns. For many conditions, DBS remains an experimental option of last resort. It is not a permanent cure: when the stimulation stops, beneficial effects are reduced; hence the importance of coupling DBS with cognitive-behavioral therapy.

Another highly experimental neurosurgical strategy draws on the fixed sequence of prenatal brain development from cell division and cell differentiation to cell migration and synaptogenesis. If a brain region is functioning abnormally or if it is diseased or dead, as occurs in TBI or after a stroke, it should be possible to return this region to the embryonic state and regrow a healthy region. The use of so-called induced neurogenesis has a science fiction ring but may someday be feasible. In laboratory rats, for example, stem cells can be induced by *neurotrophic factors* to generate new cells that can migrate to the site of an injury.

In the 1980s, neurosurgeons experimented with implanting fetal stem cells in adult brains. Success was limited due to difficulties in cell placement and connections and rejection by the patient's immune system. Another restorative idea comes from the discovery that multipotent stem cells in other body regions, such as bone marrow and skin, appear capable of manufacturing neural stem cells. Indeed, using appropriate manipulations, any cell can potentially be returned to a stem cell state. The advantage is that the patient's own cells are not rejected by the immune system.

If people's own multipotent stem cells prove practical for generating neural stem cells, it should be possible to extract stem cells, place them in a special culture medium to generate thousands or millions of cells, and place these stem cells in the damaged brain. The cells would be instructed to differentiate appropriately and develop the correct connections. Stem cell transplantation is taken seriously today as a potential treatment for disorders such as TBI and stroke, but it remains largely at an investigative stage (Savitz, 2015).

Electrophysiological Treatments

Treating the mind by treating the body is an ancient notion. In the 1930s, researchers used insulin to lower blood sugar and produce seizures as a treatment for depression. By the 1950s, insulin therapy had been replaced by electroconvulsive therapy (ECT), the first electrical brain stimulation treatment.

ECT was developed as a treatment for otherwise untreatable depression, and although its mode of action was not understood, it did prove useful. Although rarely used today, ECT sometimes remains the only treatment that works for people with severe depression. One reason may be that it stimulates the production of a variety of neurotrophic factors, especially BDNF (brain-derived neurotrophic factor), that in turn restore inactive cells to a more active mode.

Problems with ECT include the massive convulsions electrical stimulation causes. Large doses of medication are normally required to prevent them. ECT also leads to memory loss, a symptom that can be troublesome with repeated treatments. A noninvasive technique, transcranial magnetic stimulation (TMS), uses magnetic rather than electrical stimulation.

Treating Behavioral Disorders with Transcranial Magnetic Stimulation

In transcranial magnetic stimulation (TMS) a magnetic coil placed over the scalp induces an electrical current in underlying brain regions. TMS can be applied to localized brain regions (focal areas) thought to be implicated in specific disorders. Manipulation of the magnetic field can stimulate an area of cortex as small as a quarter—the cortical surface only or deeper layers of brain tissue.

The primary clinical use of TMS, which the U.S. Food and Drug Administration formally approved in 2008, is for depression. Numerous studies report positive effects using TMS, but the required duration of treatment and the duration of beneficial effects remains under investigation.

The effects of brief pulses of TMS do not outlive the stimulation. *Repetitive TMS* (rTMS), however, which involves continuous stimulation for up to several minutes, produces longer-lasting effects. What is needed to fully evaluate TMS effects in alleviating depression is a double-blind study, in which both therapists and patients are unaware of whether real or sham stimulation is administered (Serafini et al., 2015).

In addition to treating depression, small but promising studies have extended the possible benefits of TMS to schizophrenic auditory hallucinations, anxiety disorders, neurodegenerative diseases, hemiparesis, and pain syndrome (Wassermann & Zimmerman, 2012).

Among the problems in all studies of TMS are questions related to the duration and intensity of stimulation and also to the area stimulated. Each person's brain is slightly different, so to ensure that appropriate structures are stimulated, MRI must be performed on each subject.

Does TMS stimulation make the brain more plastic? If so, can learning be enhanced? The idea is, when a train of TMS is delivered, it produces a change in cortical excitability. This change in turn facilitates learning. Indeed, combined TMS and training can improve the therapeutic effects of motor or cognitive training given alone (Nevler & Ash, 2015).

Marcello Massimini/University of Milan

In clinical therapy for depression, TMS influences neural activity in a localized brain area.

Magnetic stimulation can be applied to a localized brain region. Anesthesia is not necessary. TMS is an FDA-approved treatment for depression. Clinical applications, reviewed in Research Focus 16-2, Treating Behavioral Disorders with Transcranial Magnetic Stimulation, are growing.

Pharmacological Treatments

Several accidental discoveries, beginning in the 1950s, led to a pharmacological revolution in the treatment of behavioral disorders:

1. The development of phenothiazines (neuroleptics) to treat schizophrenia stemmed from a drug used to premedicate surgical patients. In the following decades, neuroleptic drugs became increasingly more selective, and they remain effective.

2. A new class of antianxiety drugs was invented: the anxiolytics. Medications such as Valium quickly became—and remain—the most widely prescribed drugs in the United States.

3. L-Dopa provided the first drug treatment for serious motor dysfunction in Parkinson disease. Once taken, L-dopa is converted into and replaces dopamine lost due to Parkinson disease.

The power of psychoactive drugs to change disordered behavior revolutionized the pharmaceutical industry. The central goal is developing drugs that can act as magic bullets to correct the chemical imbalances found in various disorders. Research is directed toward making drugs more selective in targeting specific disorders while producing fewer side effects. Both goals have proved difficult to achieve.

Section 6-2 classifies psychoactive drugs and their therapeutic effects.

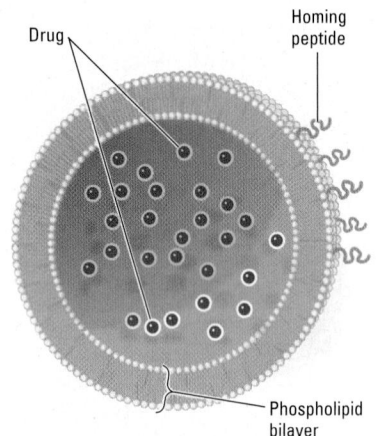

Liposome for Drug Delivery
Biosynthetic vesicles can deliver microscopic drugs or DNA to the body's cells. Synthetic biology is a topic in Section 7-1.

Focus 12-3 recounts a case of generalized anxiety disorder.

Pharmacological treatments have significant downsides. Acute and chronic side effects top the list, and long-term use may cause new problems. Consider a person who receives antidepressant medication. The drug may ease the depression but it may also produce unwanted side effects, including decreased sexual desire, fatigue, and sleep disturbance. The last two effects may also interfere with cognitive functioning.

Thus, although a medication may be useful for getting a person out of a depressed state, it may produce other symptoms that are themselves disturbing and may complicate recovery. Furthermore, in depression related to a person's life events, a drug does not provide the behavioral tools needed to cope with an adverse situation. Some psychologists say, "A pill is not a skill."

Negative side effects of drug treatments are evident in many people whose schizophrenia is being treated with neuroleptics. Antipsychotic drugs act on the mesolimbic dopamine system, which affects motivation, among other functions. The side effect emerges because the drugs also act on the nigrostriatal dopaminergic system, which controls movement. Patients who take neuroleptics also eventually develop motor disturbances. **Tardive dyskinesia**, an inability to stop the tongue, hands, or other body parts from moving, is a motor symptom of long-term neuroleptic administration. Side effects of movement disorders can persist after the psychoactive medication has been stopped. Taking drugs for behavioral disorders, then, does carry risk. Rather than magic bullets, these medications often act like shotguns.

Despite their drawbacks, drugs do prove beneficial for many people. Improved drug chemistry will reduce side effects, as will improved delivery modes that bring a drug to a target system with minimal effects on other systems. One improved delivery system uses nanoparticles called *liposomes*, biosynthetic molecules 1 to 100 nm (nanometers, or billionths of a meter) in size. One natural biological nanoparticle, with a radius of about 40 nm, is the synaptic vesicle that houses a neurotransmitter for delivery into the cell's extracellular space. Liposomes consisting of a synthetic vesicle with a homing peptide on the surface can, in principle, be constructed to carry a drug across the blood–brain barrier and deliver it to specified types of neuron or glial cells within the nervous system.

Behavioral Treatments

Treatments for behavioral disorders need not be direct biological or medical interventions. Just as the brain can alter behavior, behavior can alter the brain. Behavioral treatments focus on key environmental factors that influence how a person acts. As behavior changes in response to treatment, the brain is affected as well.

An example is treatment for *generalized anxiety disorders* attributed to chronic stress. People who endure a persistently high anxiety level often engage in maladaptive behaviors to reduce it. While they require immediate treatment with antianxiety medication, long-term treatment entails changing their behavior. Generalized anxiety disorder is not simply a problem of abnormal brain activity but also of experiential and social factors that fundamentally alter the person's perception of the world.

Perhaps you are thinking that behavioral treatments may help somewhat in treating brain dysfunction, but the real solution must lie in altering brain activity. Since every aspect of behavior is the product of brain activity, behavioral treatments *do* act by changing brain function. If people can change how they think and feel about themselves or some aspect of their lives, this change has taken place because talking about their problems or resolving a problem alters how their brain functions. In a sense then, a behavioral treatment is a biological intervention. Behavioral treatments may sometimes be helped along by drug treatments that make the brain more receptive to change through behavioral therapy. In this way, drug treatments and behavioral treatments have synergistic effects, each helping the other to be more effective.

Your behavior is a product of all your learning and social experiences. An obvious approach to developing a treatment is to re-create a learning environment that replaces a maladaptive behavior with an adaptive behavior. Thus, the various approaches to behavioral treatment use principles derived from experiment-based learning theory. Following is a sampling of these approaches.

BEHAVIOR MODIFICATION **Behavioral therapies** apply well-established learning principles to eliminate unwanted behaviors. Therapists apply principles developed in studying learning by reinforcement in laboratory settings, including operant and classical conditioning. For example, if a person is debilitated by a fear of insects, rather than looking for inner causes, the behavioral therapist tries to replace the maladaptive behaviors with more constructive ways of behaving. These might include training the patient to relax while systematically exposing him to unthreatening insects (butterflies) followed by gradual exposure to more threatening insects (bees). This form of habituation (adaption to a repeatedly presented stimulus) is called *systematic desensitization.*

COGNITIVE THERAPY **Cognitive therapy** operates from the perspective that thoughts intervene between events and emotions. Consider responses to losing a job. One thought could be, *I'm a loser, life is hopeless.* An alternative thought is, *The job was a dead end. The boss did me a favor.* The former cognition might lead to depression, whereas the latter would not. Cognitive therapies challenge a person's self-defeating attitudes and assumptions and are important for people with brain injury too, because it is easy for people to think that they are crazy or stupid after brain injury. Equally if not more powerful is cognitive-behavioral therapy, discussed in Section 16-4.

NEUROPSYCHOLOGICAL THERAPY If a relative or friend had a stroke and became aphasic, you would expect him or her to attend speech therapy—a behavioral treatment for an injured brain. The logic in speech therapy is that by practicing (relearning) the basic components of speech and language, the patient should be able to regain at least some lost function. The same logic can apply to other types of behavioral disorders, whether motor or cognitive.

Therapies for cognitive disorders resulting from brain trauma or dysfunction aim to retrain people in the fundamental cognitive processes they have lost. Although cognitive therapy seems as logical as speech therapy after a stroke, cognitive therapy assumes that we know what fundamental elements of cognitive activity are meaningful to the brain. Cognitive scientists are far from understanding these elements well enough to generate optimal therapies. Still, neuropsychologists are developing neurocognitive programs that can improve functional outcomes following TBI and stroke (Mateer & Sira, 2006; Sohlberg & Mateer, 1989). Treatment effectiveness can be improved with computer-based tools and follow-up therapy.

EMOTIONAL THERAPY In the 1920s, Sigmund Freud developed the idea that talking about emotional problems enables people to gain insights into the causes of the problems and serves as treatment too. Talk cures and other forms of psychological intervention may be broadly categorized as psychotherapies.

Since Freud's time, many ideas have been put forth about the best type of therapy for emotional disorders. Key here is that for many disorders, whether neurological or psychiatric, medical treatments are not effective unless patients also receive **psychotherapy**. Indeed, the only effective treatment in many cases lies in addressing the unwanted behaviors directly—in acquiring the skill rather than taking the pill.

Consider a 25-year-old woman pursuing a promising career as a musician who suffered a traumatic brain injury in an automobile accident. After the accident, she found that she was unable to read music. Not surprisingly, she soon became depressed. Part of her therapy required her to confront her disabling cognitive loss by talking about it rather than by simply stewing over it. Only when she pursued psychotherapy did she begin to recover from her intense depression.

For many people with emotional impairments resulting from brain disease or trauma, the most effective treatment for depression or anxiety is helping them adjust by encouraging them to talk about their difficulties. Group therapy provides such encouragement and is standard treatment in brain injury rehabilitation units.

Systematic desensitization for a phobia, the most common among anxiety disorders, as Focus 12-3 reports.

Lea Paterson/Science Source

tardive dyskinesia Inability to stop the tongue or other body parts from moving; motor side effect of neuroleptic drugs.

behavioral therapy Treatment that applies learning principles, such as conditioning, to eliminate unwanted behaviors.

cognitive therapy Psychotherapy based on the perspective that thoughts intervene between events and emotions, and thus the treatment of emotional disorders requires changing maladaptive patterns of thinking.

psychotherapy Talk therapy derived from Freudian psychoanalysis and other psychological interventions.

Exercise boosts your mood because it boosts your dopamine levels. Section 10-4 observes that practitioners have only begun to tap music's power as a therapeutic tool.

Focus 11-5 describes an effective low-tech strategy for controlling phantom limb pain.

real-time fMRI (rt-fMRI) Behavior-modification technique in which individuals learn to change their behavior by controlling their own patterns of brain activation.

PHYSICAL ACTIVITY AND MUSIC AS THERAPY Exercise and music have positive effects on peoples' attitudes, emotional well-being, and brain function. Physical exercise demands visual control of movement. Music affects arousal and activates the motor and premotor cortex. Listening to music can improve gait in Parkinson and stroke patients and reduce pain post surgery. Learning to play a musical instrument likewise is beneficial therapy (François et al., 2015). Singing, a useful adjunct to rehabilitative speech therapy, enhances the ability to enunciate. Physical activity, including dancing and playing sports, combined with other therapies, improves well-being and counteracts the effects of depression.

REAL-TIME FMRI Using this behavior-modification technique, individuals learn to change their behavior by controlling their own brain activation patterns. Real-time fMRI was first used to treat intractable pain, which produces a characteristic brain activity pattern (deCharms, 2008). The researchers proposed that if subjects could see their brain activity via fMRI in real time as they felt pain, they could be trained to reduce the neural activity and lessen their pain. **Real-time fMRI** (rt-fMRI) uses a form of operant conditioning in which the gradual modification of a participant's behavior increases the probability of reward.

Think of rt-fMRI as a form of neural plasticity in which the individual learns new strategies, guided by brain activation information. When subjects decrease brain activation in regions associated with pain, they report decreased pain perception. Conversely, through learning to increase brain activation in these regions, they would be able to increase their pain—although it seems unlikely that this ability would be much cultivated! An actual potential application of rt-fMRI is in monitoring brain activation when treatment for disorders occurs in the context of behavioral therapy. Patients need not be consciously aware of the therapy's objectives: induced brain changes, whether conscious or unconscious, can prove beneficial (Birbaumer et al., 2013).

VIRTUAL REALITY THERAPY The principle behind VR therapy is that patients enter or interact with a virtual world displayed on a computer screen or through goggles. One example is the Virtual Iraq and Afghanistan Simulation described in Research Focus 16-1. The participant can experience sights, sounds, even smells that mimic situations related to acquiring the behavioral disorder, in this case PTSD. In modified VR therapy a patient interacts as a character in a computer game. Winning the game necessitates making adaptive choices; maladaptive choices result in losing the game (Shin et al., 2015).

(16-2) REVIEW

Classifying and Treating Brain and Behavioral Disorders

Before you continue, check your understanding.

1. Three classifications of behavioral disorders are _____, _____, and _____.

2. _____ is the study of the distribution and causes of diseases in human populations.

3. Developments in _____ and _____ have enabled their use in identifying brain and behavior disorders.

4. Four treatment categories for behavioral disorders are _____, _____, _____, and _____.

5. A therapy in which an electrode delivers stimulation directly to the brain is called _____.

6. An effective replacement for electroconvulsive therapy (ECT) is _____.

7. Why are classification systems useful even though they are inexact?

Answers appear at the back of the book.

16-3 Understanding and Treating Neurological Disorders

In everyone's lifetime, at least one close friend or relative will develop a neurological disorder, even if we ourselves escape them. Disorder causes are understood in a general sense, and for most, rehabilitative treatment is emerging. In this section we review some common neurological disorders: traumatic brain injury, stroke, epilepsy, multiple sclerosis, and neurodegenerative disorders.

Traumatic Brain Injury

Traumatic brain injury (TBI), a wound to the brain that usually results from a blow to the head, is the most common form of brain damage in people under age 40. TBI commonly results from the head making impact with other objects—as can occur in automobile and industrial accidents and in sports injuries. TBI can also follow blows to the chest that result in a rapid increase in blood pressure, which can damage the brain indirectly. The incidence of TBI is about eight times that of breast cancer, AIDS, spinal cord injury, and multiple sclerosis combined.

The two most important factors in the incidence of head trauma are age and sex. Children and elderly people are more likely to injure their head in a fall than are others, and males between 15 and 30 incur brain injury especially in automobile and motorcycle accidents **(Figure 16-5)**. A child's chance of having significant traumatic brain injury before he or she is old enough to drive is 1 in 30.

Section 14-5 details a dancer's recovery from TBI.

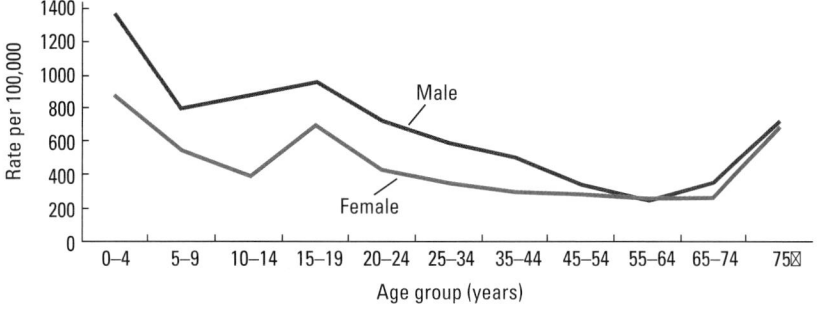

FIGURE 16-5 Incidence Rates of Head Trauma Based on combined reports of emergency room visits, hospitalizations, and deaths, this chart graphs the estimated frequency of TBI in males and females across the life span. Information from the Centers for Disease Control. *TBI in the United States: Emergency department visits, hospitalizations, and deaths, 2004* (report).

Concussion is a critical concern for both professional and amateur athletes, especially those who play football, ice hockey, lacrosse, soccer, and no less for those on active military duty. Sports account for about 20 percent of TBIs, and the U.S. Army Institute of Surgical Research reports that traumatic brain injury affects more than 1 in 5 U.S. soldiers wounded in war.

A large-scale longitudinal study is under way in cooperation with football and ice hockey players who have a history of concussion and who have agreed to donate their brain for postmortem analysis. Preliminary examination of the brains of deceased professional football players who had a history of concussion and severe postconcussion symptoms, described in Clinical Focus 16-3, Concussion, reveal extensive, diffuse loss of cerebral tissue.

In longitudinal research, over time investigators repeatedly observe or examine subjects with respect to the study's variable(s).

Symptoms and Outcome of Brain Trauma

TBI can cause direct damage to the brain. Trauma can disrupt the brain's blood supply, induce bleeding (leading to increased intracranial pressure), cause swelling (leading to increased intracranial pressure), expose the brain to infection, and scar brain tissue (the scar

Concussion

Early in 2011, 50-year-old former Chicago Bears defensive back Dave Duerson shot himself in the chest and died. He left a note asking that his brain be studied. Duerson had played 11 years in the National Football League, won two Super Bowls, and received numerous awards.

As a pro player he endured at least 10 concussions, but they did not seem serious enough to cause him to leave the game. After retiring from football, he went to Harvard and obtained a business degree. He pursued a successful business career until he began to have trouble making decisions and controlling his temper.

Eventually, Duerson's business and marriage failed. After his suicide, the Center for the Study of Traumatic Encephalopathy in Boston did study his brain. The Center is conducting postmortem anatomical analyses of the brains of former athletes as part of a long-term longitudinal study.

Duerson's diagnosis, **chronic traumatic encephalopathy** (CTE), is a progressive degenerative disease found in individuals with a history of multiple concussions and other closed-head injuries. (A variant long associated with boxing is *dementia pugilistica*, or DP.)

Concussion, the common term for mild traumatic brain injury (MTBI), is common in sports, especially contact sports, including American football, ice hockey, and rugby. Concussion also results from falls in many other sports and from vehicular accidents. It is likely that the incidence of concussion is higher than 6 per 1000 individuals.

Concussion often goes unrecognized. For those that are diagnosed, little apparent pathology appears after relatively short periods of rest, the usual treatment. Nevertheless, the relationship is well established between concussion and a range of degenerative diseases that occur later in life—dementias, including Alzheimer disease, as well as Parkinson disease, motor neuron disease, and CTE.

Dave Duerson's Brain Staining for tau protein highlights degenerating brain tissue (dark brown areas) in the frontal cortex and medial temporal lobe of these coronal sections through Duerson's anterior right hemisphere. Damage to the subcortical basal ganglia in the sections' central portions (yellowish areas) is sparse by comparison.

Ann C McKee MD VA Boston/ Boston University School of Medicine

The relationship between concussion in early life and later degenerative brain disease suggests that concussion can initiate a cascade of pathological events that over years develop into CTE. CTE is characterized by neurofibrillary tangles, plaques, and neuronal death. Cerebral atrophy and expanded ventricles due to cell loss are typical in advanced cases. As shown in the illustration, researchers test for cell death by staining for accumulation of the tau protein, which is associated with neuronal death and so is a sensitive marker for brain trauma.

The unknowns about CTE are many. Is just one or are many concussions required to initiate a cascade that results in CTE? Are individuals who get CTE especially susceptible? What constitutes a concussion? Should blows to the head that result in no pronounced symptoms be distinguished from blows that result in loss of consciousness?

What we do know is that many well-known athletes, especially football and ice hockey players, have developed CTE. Clearly, much more care needs to be taken, beginning in childhood, to prevent concussion and to ensure that concussion is treated, even though what constitutes adequate treatment remains uncertain (Rose et al., 2015).

---

being a focus for later epileptic seizures). The disruption in blood supply tends to be brief, but a parallel disruption of energy production by neuronal mitochondria, which can persist for weeks, is related to many postconcussion behavioral symptoms.

Traumatic brain injury is commonly accompanied by a loss of consciousness that may be brief (minutes) or prolonged (coma). Duration of unconsciousness can serve as a measure of the severity of damage, because it correlates directly with mortality, intellectual impairment, and deficits in social skills. The longer coma lasts, the greater the possibility of serious impairment or death.

Two kinds of behavioral effects result from TBI: (1) impairment of specific functions mediated by the cortex at the coup (the site of impact) or contrecoup (opposite side) lesion,

Section 1-2 presents a case study on recovering consciousness following TBI.

A variety of mechanical forces cause traumatic brain injuries as a result of a blow to the head.

Damage at the site of impact is called a coup (shown in pink).

◄— **Direction of blow**   **Direction of blow** —►

Pressure resulting from a coup produces a contrecoup on the opposite end or side of the brain (shown in blue).

Movement of the brain may shear nerve fibers, causing microscopic lesions, especially in frontal and temporal lobes. Blood trapped in the skull (hematoma) and swelling (edema) cause pressure on the brain.

FIGURE 16-6 Mechanics of TBI Pink and blue shading mark brain regions most frequently damaged in closed-head injury. A blow can produce a contusion both at the site of impact and on the opposite side of the brain, owing to rebound compression.

as illustrated in **Figure 16-6,** and (2) more generalized impairments from widespread trauma throughout the brain. Discrete impairment is most commonly associated with damage to the frontal and temporal lobes, the brain areas most susceptible to TBI. (See tissue samples in Focus 16-3.)

More generalized impairment results from minute lesions and lacerations scattered throughout the brain. Movement of the hemispheres in relation to one another causes tearing characterized by a loss of complex cognitive functions, including mental speed, concentration, and overall cognitive efficiency.

TBI patients generally complain of poor concentration or lack of ability. They fail to do things as well as they could before the injury, even though their intelligence is unimpaired. In fact, in our experience, people with high skill levels seem to be the most affected by TBI, in large part because they are acutely aware of loss of a skill that prevents them from returning to their former competence level.

Traumatic brain injury that damages the frontal and temporal lobes also tends to significantly affect personality and social behavior. Few victims of traffic accidents who have sustained severe head injuries ever resume their studies or return to gainful employment. If they do reenter the work force, they do so at a lower level than before their accident.

One frustrating problem with traumatic brain injury is misdiagnosis: chronic effects of injuries often are unaccompanied by any obvious neurological signs or abnormalities in CT or MRI scans. Patients may therefore be referred for psychiatric or neuropsychological evaluation. MRI-based imaging techniques such as **magnetic resonance spectroscopy** (MRS), however, are useful for accurate TBI diagnosis (Reis et al., 2015).

MRS, a modification of MRI, can identify changes in specific markers of neuronal function. One such marker is N-acetylaspartate (NAA), the second most abundant amino acid in the human brain. Assessing the level of NAA expression provides a measure of neuronal integrity, and deviations from normal levels (up or down) can be taken as a marker of abnormal brain function. People with traumatic brain injury show a chronic decrease in NAA that correlates with the severity of the injury. Although not yet in wide clinical use, MRS is a promising tool, not only for identifying brain abnormalities but also for monitoring cellular response to therapeutic interventions.

chronic traumatic encephalopathy (CTE) Progressive degenerative disease caused by multiple concussions and other closed-head injuries, characterized by neurofibrillary tangles, plaques, cerebral atrophy, and expanded ventricles due to cell loss.

magnetic resonance spectroscopy (MRS) Modification of MRI to identify changes in specific markers of neuronal function; promising for accurate diagnosis of traumatic brain injuries.

Section 7-3 introduces the MRS technique.

Recovery from Traumatic Brain Injury

Recovery from head trauma may continue for 2 to 3 years and longer, but most cognitive recovery occurs in the first 6 to 9 months. Recovery of memory functions appears to be slower than recovery of general intelligence, and the final level of memory performance is lower than for other cognitive functions. People with brainstem damage, as inferred from oculomotor disturbance, have a poorer cognitive outcome, and a poorer outcome is probably true of people with initial dysphasias or hemiparesis as well.

Although the prognosis for significant recovery of cognitive functions is good, optimism about the recovery of social skills or personality traits, areas that often show significant change, is less rosy. Findings from numerous studies support the conclusions that quality of life—in social interactions, perceived stress levels, and enjoyment of leisure—is significantly reduced after TBI and that this reduction is chronic. Attempts to develop tools to measure changes in psychosocial adjustment in brain-injured people are few, so we must rely largely on subjective descriptions and self-reports. Neither provides much information about the specific causes of these problems (Block et al., 2015).

Stroke

Focus 2-3 describes the symptoms and aftereffects of stroke.

Diagnosticians may be able to point to a specific immediate cause of *stroke,* an interruption of blood flow from either blockage of a vessel or bleeding from a vessel. This initial event, however, merely sets off a sequence of damage that progresses, even if the blood flow is restored. Stroke results in a lack of blood, called **ischemia,** followed by a cascade of cellular events that wreak the real damage. Changes at the cellular level can seriously compromise not only the injured part of the brain but other brain regions as well.

Effects of Stroke

Consider what happens after a stroke interrupts the blood supply to a cerebral artery. In the first seconds to minutes after ischemia, as illustrated in **Figure 16-7,** changes begin in the affected regions' ionic balance, including changes in pH and in the properties of the cell membrane. These ionic changes result in several pathological events.

1. Release of massive amounts of glutamate results in prolonged opening of calcium channels in cell membranes.

2. Open calcium channels in turn allow toxic levels of calcium to enter the cell, not only producing direct toxic effects but also instigating various second-messenger pathways that can harm neurons. In the ensuing minutes to hours, mRNA is stimulated, altering protein production in the neurons and possibly proving toxic to the cells.

Figure 5-4 shows how calcium affects neurotransmitter release; Figure 5-15, how metabotropic receptors can activate second messengers.

3. Brain tissues become inflamed and swollen, threatening the integrity of cells that may be far removed from the stroke site. As in TBI, an energy crisis ensues as mitochondria reduce their production of ATP, resulting in less cerebral energy.

4. A form of neural shock occurs. During this **diaschisis,** areas distant from the damage are functionally depressed. Thus, not only are local neural tissue and its function lost but areas related to the damaged region also undergo a sudden withdrawal of excitation or inhibition.

5. Stroke may also be followed by changes in the injured hemisphere's metabolism, its glucose utilization, or both. These changes may persist for days. As with diaschisis, the metabolic changes can severely affect the functioning of otherwise healthy tissue. For example, after a cortical stroke, metabolic rate has been shown to decrease about 25 percent throughout the hemisphere.

Treatments for Stroke

The ideal treatment is to restore blood flow in blocked vessels before the cascade of nasty events begins. One clot-busting drug is tissue plasminogen activator (t-PA), but t-PA must be

ischemia Lack of blood to the brain, usually as a result of a stroke.

diaschisis Neural shock that follows brain damage in which areas connected to the site of damage show a temporary arrest of function.

neuroprotectant Drug used to try to block the cascade of poststroke neural events.

administered within 3 to 5 hours to be effective. Currently, only a small percentage of stroke patients arrive at the hospital soon enough, in large part because stroke is not quickly identified, transportation is slow, or the stroke is not considered an emergency.

Other drugs called **neuroprotectants** can be used to try to block the cascade of postinjury events, but to date we have no truly effective drugs. Clinical trials based on animal studies have generally failed, in part because understanding what the appropriate brain targets should be is limited.

When the course of the stroke leads to dead brain tissue, the only treatments that can be beneficial are those that facilitate plastic changes in the remaining brain. Examples are speech therapy and physical therapy. Revolutionary approaches to stroke rehabilitation use virtual reality, computer games, and robotic machines (Laver et al., 2015).

Still, some simple treatments are surprisingly effective. One is *constraint-induced therapy,* pioneered by Edward Taub in the 1990s (Kawakkel et al., 2015). Its logic confronts a problem in poststroke recovery related to learned nonuse. Stroke patients with motor deficits in a limb often compensate by overusing the intact limb, which in turn leads to increased loss of use in the impaired limb.

In constraint-induced therapy, the intact limb is held in a sling for several hours per day, forcing the patient to use the impaired limb. Nothing about the procedure is magical: virtually any treatment that forces patients to practice behaviors extensively is successful. An important component of these treatments, however, is a posttreatment contract in which the patients continue to practice after the formal therapy is over. If they fail to do so, the chances for learned nonuse and a return of symptoms are high.

Another common effect of stroke is loss of speech. Specific speech therapy programs can aid in the recovery of speech. Music and singing, mediated in part by the right hemisphere, can augment speech therapy after left hemisphere stroke.

Therapies using pharmacological interventions (e.g., noradrenergic, dopaminergic, cholinergic agonists) combined with behavioral therapies provide equivocal gains in stroke patients. The bulk of evidence suggests that patients with small gray matter strokes are most likely to show benefits from these treatments, whereas those with large strokes that include white matter show little benefit.

Finally, there have been many attempts to use either direct cortical stimulation or TMS in combination with behavioral therapy as a stroke treatment. The idea is to induce plasticity in regions adjacent to the dead tissue with the goal of enhancing the efficiency of the residual parts of the neuronal networks. These treatments have proved beneficial in patients with good residual motor control, but again, those with larger injuries show much less benefit, presumably because the residual neuronal network is insufficient.

Epilepsy

Epilepsy is characterized by recurrent seizures, which register on an electroencephalogram (EEG) as highly synchronized neuronal firing indicated by a variety of abnormal waves. About 1 person in 20 has at least one seizure in his or her lifetime, usually associated with an infection, temperature, and hyperventilation during childhood (6 months to 5 years of age). Most children who experience a seizure do not develop epilepsy, which affects between 0.2 percent and 4.1 percent of the population. Developed nations record a lower prevalence and incidence of epilepsy compared with developing nations.

Classifying Seizures

Causes of epileptic seizures are categorized as genetic, structural/metabolic, or unknown. *Genetic epilepsy* results directly from a known genetic defect. Causes of *structural/metabolic epilepsy* include brain malformations and tumors, acquired disorders such as stroke and

Use the F.A.S.T. Test to Spot Stroke

Face Ask for a smile to check both understanding and muscle control.
Arms Check if one arm is weak by asking the person to raise both arms.
Speech Listen for slurred speech.
Time If you see any symptom, call 911 or the local emergency services number right away.

Experiment 11-3 describes research with monkeys that contributed to developing constraint-induced therapy for people.

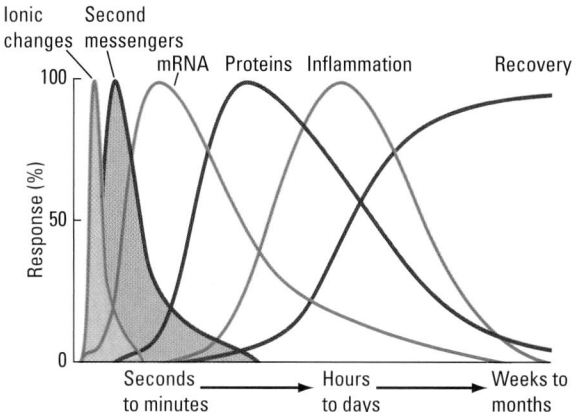

FIGURE 16-7 Results of Ischemia A cascade of events takes place after blood flow is blocked as a result of stroke. Within seconds, ionic changes at the cellular level spur changes in second-messenger molecules and RNA production. Changes in protein production and inflammation follow and resolve slowly, in hours to days. Recovery begins within hours to days and continues for weeks to months or years.

Focus 4-1 describes a diagnosis of epilepsy and shows an EEG being recorded.

Structural or metabolic epilepsy may result from brain malformations such as angioma, or AV malformation, shown on this dorsal view MRI. Abnormal cerebral blood vessels (in white) form a balloonlike structure (blue area at lower right) that caused the death of brain tissue around it in the right occipital cortex.

Simon Fraser/Royal Victoria Infirmary/Newcastle Upon Tyne/Science Photo Library/Science Source

TABLE 16-4 Factors That May Precipitate Seizures in Susceptible Persons

Drugs
Alcohol
Analeptics
Excessive anticonvulsants
Phenothiazines
Tricyclic antidepressants
Emotional stress
Fever
Hormonal changes
Adrenal steroids
Adrenocorticotrophic hormone (ACTH)
Menses
Puberty
Hyperventilation
Sensory stimuli
Flashing lights
Laughing
Reading, speaking, coughing
Sounds: music, bells
Sleep
Sleep deprivation
Trauma

Source: Information from J. H. Pincus & G. J. Tucker (1974). *Behavioral Neurobiology* (p. 5). New York: Oxford University Press.

trauma, and infections. The *unknown* category encompasses causes yet to be identified. **Table 16-4** summarizes the great variety of circumstances that appear to precipitate a seizure. The range of circumstances is striking, but seizures do have a consistent feature: they are most likely to occur when a person is sleeping.

Seizures are classified by the way participating neural networks are distributed. **Focal seizures** arise from a synchronous, hyperactive local brain region. Thus, focal seizures may have motor, sensory, autonomic, and/or psychogenic features. Focal seizures are further classified as to whether awareness is retained or altered (dyscognitive seizure). **Generalized seizures** may start at a focal location, then spread rapidly and bilaterally to distributed networks in both hemispheres. In *primary generalized epilepsy*, seizures begin in more widespread neural networks. Seizure diagnosis is improved by the use of a wearable device that records them (Gubbi et al., 2015).

People having a seizure may cycle through the four stages charted in **Figure 16-8**: (1) normal EEG record before onset; (2) onset and tonic phase, in which the body stiffens; (3) clonic phase, in which the person makes rhythmic movements in time with the large, highly synchronized discharges; and (4) a period of depressed EEG activity after the seizure ends.

For the most part, seizures self-terminate. In some cases, termed *status epilepticus*, the seizure's driving force does not abate, often due to a brain insult or to drug withdrawal. In this life-threatening condition, drug intervention with a fast-acting GABA agonist or glutamate antagonist is required to end the seizure. Death due to status epilepticus is much more common in adults than in children (26 percent vs. 3 percent, respectively), and survivors often live with significant brain damage. The recommended time limit before intervention is 5 minutes. Longer-lasting seizures are unlikely to self-terminate.

People with epilepsy die unexpectedly at a rate 24 times that of the general population. *Sudden unexpected death in epilepsy* (SUDEP) has no identifiable cause (such as status epilepticus, drowning, or falling). Most evidence suggests that SUDEP occurs during or more often after a seizure. Respiratory and cardiac failure may be common causes, but events leading up to SUDEP have yet to be characterized.

Treating Epilepsy

The first-line treatment for epilepsy is drugs to inhibit seizure development and propagation. Among the diverse range of mechanisms drugs employ to raise seizure thresholds are enhancing the action of the inhibitory neurotransmitter GABA and stabilizing the inactive state of sodium channels. Most people with epilepsy work with their physician to find a drug and dosage that cause few side effects. In 30 percent to 40 percent of people with epilepsy, however, antiseizure drugs fail to completely control the condition—intractable epilepsy. The most common treatment for intractable epilepsy in adults is surgical resection of epileptogenic tissue, which has a success rate of about 70 percent. Deep-brain stimulation

Left   Right

FIGURE 16-8 Generalized Seizure Patterns Examples of EEG patterns recorded during a generalized seizure. Dots on the hemispheres below indicate the approximate recording sites. Column numbers mark the seizure's stages: (1) normal record before the attack; (2) onset of seizure and tonic phase; (3) clonic phase; and (4) a period of depressed EEG activity after the seizure ends. Abbreviations: LT and RT, left and right temporal; LF and RF, left and right frontal; LO and RO, left and right occipital.

may prove useful for intractable epilepsy: bilateral stimulation of the anterior thalamus has been successful in reducing seizure frequency. While DBS shows promise, more research is needed (Ostergard & Miller, 2014).

Multiple Sclerosis

In multiple sclerosis (MS), the myelin that encases axons is damaged and neuronal functions are disrupted. MS is characterized by myelin loss in both motor and sensory tracts and nerves. The oligodendroglia that form the myelin sheath, and in some cases the axons, are destroyed. Brain imaging with MRI, as shown in **Figure 16-9,** identifies areas of sclerosis in the brain as well as in the spinal cord.

Remission followed by relapse is a striking feature of MS: in many cases, early symptoms initially are followed by improvement. The course varies, running from a few years to as long as 50 years. Paraplegia, the classic feature of MS, may eventually confine the affected person to bed.

Worldwide, about 1 million people have MS; women outnumber men about two to one. Multiple sclerosis is most prevalent in northern Europe and northern North America, rare in Japan and in more southerly or tropical countries. Depending on region, incidence of MS ranges from 2 to 150 per 100,000 people, making it one of the most common structural nervous system diseases.

The cause or causes of MS are unknown. Proposed causes include bacterial infection, a virus, environmental factors including pesticides, an immune response of the central nervous system, misfolded proteins, and lack of vitamin D. Often, multiple cases occur in a

focal seizure Seizure that arises at a synchronous, hyperactive, localized brain region (at a focus).

generalized seizure Seizure that may start at a focal location then spread rapidly and bilaterally to distributed networks in both hemispheres.

Plane of MRI section

Lateral ventricles

White matter

Lesions

FIGURE 16-9 Diagnosing MS Imaged by MRI, discrete multiple sclerosis lesions appear as dark patches all around the lateral ventricles and in the brain's white matter.

Living Art Enterprises, LLC/Science Source

Section 4-4 describes another autoimmune disease, myasthenia gravis.

Normal myelinated nerve fiber

Nerve affected by MS

Exposed fiber

Damaged myelin

MS destroys the myelin sheath. *Sclerosis* comes from the Greek word for *hardness*.

autoimmune disease Illness resulting from the loss of the immune system's ability to discriminate between foreign pathogens in the body and the body itself.

dementia Acquired and persistent syndrome of intellectual impairment characterized by memory and other cognitive deficits and impairment in social and occupational functioning.

single family. Many genes have been associated with MS, but no clear evidence indicates as yet that MS is inherited or transmitted from one person to another.

Research has focused on the immune system's relation to MS and the possibility that MS is an **autoimmune disease.** The ability to discriminate between a foreign pathogen in the body and the body itself is central to immune system functioning. If this discrimination fails, the immune system makes antibodies to a person's own body, in this case, to myelin.

As various organisms' genomes have been sequenced, it has become apparent that all have many genes in common. Thus the proteins found in different organisms are surprisingly similar. And here is the problem for the human immune system: a foreign microbe may contain proteins that are nearly identical to the body's own proteins. If microbe and human have a common gene sequence, the immune system can mistakenly attack itself, a process known as *horror autotoxicus*.

Many microbial protein sequences are homologous with structures found in myelin, which leads to an attack against the microbe and a person's own myelin. Research showing the important role of the immune system in MS has intensified work on developing new treatments (Kornek, 2015). One strategy is to build up immune system tolerance by injecting DNA-encoding myelin antigens and DNA-encoding specific molecules in the cascade of steps that leads to oligodendroglial cell death.

That MS is more common in extreme northern and southern latitudes has raised the possibility that inadequate direct sunlight, which is necessary for the body to synthesize vitamin D, factors into precipitating the condition (Sundström & Salzer, 2015). Lack of understanding whether an acute or a longstanding deficiency is relevant complicates identifying a possible relationship. Possibly a vitamin D deficiency interacts with other factors to increase susceptibility to MS. For example, a number of genes are involved in the transport and absorption of vitamin D and variants of these genes are related to low levels of vitamin D.

Some research has suggested that MS might originate from insufficient blood drainage from the brain, which can be improved by cleaning or expanding veins from the brain, including the jugular, to improve drainage. The treatment has been called liberation therapy for its potential relief from a condition of chronic cerebrospinal venous insufficiency (CCSVI). Internet discussion worldwide has led to Web sites advertising treatment using vascular surgery for patients with MS. Numerous studies are examining a plethora of questions related to CCSVI. Primary among them: Is venous flow restricted in people with MS? Optimism about an outcome has far outpaced the science, which questions the treatment (Tsivgoulis et al., 2015).

Neurodegenerative Disorders

Human societies have never before undergone the age-related demographic shifts now developing in North America and Europe. Since 1900, the percentage of older people has increased steadily. In 1900, about 4 percent of the population had attained 65 years of age. By 2030, about 20 percent will be older than 65—about 50 million people in the United States alone.

Dementias affect 1 percent to 6 percent of the population older than age 65 and 10 percent to 20 percent of those older than age 80. For every person diagnosed with dementia, it is estimated that several others endure undiagnosed cognitive impairments that affect their quality of life. Currently, more than 6 million people in the United States have a dementia diagnosis, a number projected to rise to about 15 million by 2050. By then, 1 million new U.S. cases per year will be emerging. Extending these projections across the rest of the developed world portends staggering social and economic costs (Khachaturian & Khachaturian, 2015). The World Health Organization estimates that by 2050, the incidence of dementia will balloon to 135.5 million people worldwide.

Types of Dementia

Dementia is an acquired and persistent syndrome of intellectual impairment. Its two essential features are (1) loss of memory and other cognitive deficits and (2) impairment in social and occupational functioning. Dementia is not a singular disorder, but there is no clear agreement on how to split up subtypes. Daniel Kaufer and Steven DeKosky (1999) divide dementias into the broad categories of degenerative and nondegenerative (**Table 16-5**).

Nondegenerative dementias, a heterogeneous group of disorders with diverse causes, including diseases of the vascular or endocrine systems, inflammation, nutritional deficiency, and toxins, are summarized on the right in Table 16-5. The most prevalent cause is vascular. The most significant risk factors for nondegenerative dementias are chronic hypertension, obesity, sedentary lifestyle, smoking, and diabetes. All are as well risk factors for cardiovascular disease. *Degenerative dementias,* listed on the left in the table, presumably have a degree of genetic transmission.

We now review two degenerative dementias, Parkinson and Alzheimer diseases. Both pathological processes are primarily intrinsic to the nervous system, and both tend to affect certain neural systems selectively.

TABLE 16-5 Degenerative and Nondegenerative Dementias

Degenerative	Nondegenerative
Alzheimer disease	Vascular dementias (e.g., multi-infarct dementia)
Extrapyramidal syndromes (e.g., progressive supernuclear palsy)	Infectious dementia (e.g., AIDS dementia)
Wilson disease	Neurosyphilis
Huntington disease	Posttraumatic dementia
Parkinson disease	Demyelinating dementia (e.g., multiple sclerosis)
Frontal temporal dementia	Toxic or metabolic disorders (e.g., vitamin B_{12} and niacin deficiencies)
Corticobasal degeneration	Chronic alcohol or drug abuse (e.g., Korsakoff syndrome)
Leukodystrophies (e.g., adrenoleukodystrophy)	
Prion-related dementias (e.g., Creutzfeldt-Jakob disease)	

Source: Information from D. I. Kaufer & S. T. DeKosky (1999). Diagnostic Classifications: Relationship to the Neurobiology of Dementia. In D. S. Charney, E. J. Nestler, & B. S. Bunney (eds). *The Neurobiology of Mental Illness* (p. 642). New York: Oxford University Press

Parkinson Disease

Parkinson disease is common. Estimates of its incidence vary up to 1.0 percent of the population, rise sharply in old age, and are certain to grow in coming decades. The disease seems related to degeneration of the substantia nigra and attendant loss of the neurotransmitter dopamine produced there and released in the striatum. The disease therefore offers insight into the roles played by the substantia nigra and dopamine in movement control.

That Parkinson symptoms vary enormously illustrates the complexity inherent in understanding a neurological disorder. A well-defined set of cells degenerates, yet the symptoms are not the same in every patient. Many symptoms strikingly resemble changes in motor activity that occurs as a consequence of aging. Thus Parkinson disease offers indirect insight into more general problems of neural changes in aging.

Symptoms begin insidiously, often with a tremor in one hand and slight stiffness in distal parts of the limbs. Movements may become slower, the face becoming masklike with loss of eye blinking and poverty of emotional expression. Thereafter the body may stoop and the gait become a shuffle, with arms hanging motionless at the sides. Speech may slow and become monotonous, and difficulty swallowing may cause drooling.

Although the disease is progressive, the rate at which symptoms worsen varies; only rarely is progression so rapid that a person becomes disabled within 5 years. Usually 10 to 20 years elapse before symptoms cause incapacity. A distinctive aspect of Parkinson disease is its on-again–off-again quality: symptoms may appear suddenly and just as suddenly disappear.

Partial remission may also occur in response to interesting or stimulating situations. Neurologist Oliver Sacks (1998) recounted an incident in which a stationary Parkinson patient leaped from his wheelchair at the seaside and rushed into the breakers to save a drowning man, only to fall back into his chair immediately afterward and become inactive again. Remission of some symptoms in activating situations is common but usually not as dramatic as this case. Simply listening to familiar music can help an otherwise inactive patient get up and dance, for example. Or a patient who has difficulty walking may ride a bicycle or skate effortlessly. Such activities can be used as physical therapy, and physical therapy is important because it may slow disease progression.

Figure 7-5 diagrams degeneration in the substantia nigra associated with Parkinson symptoms.

Sacks, whose writings enriched the neurological literature beyond measure, died in 2015.

Positive symptoms are behaviors not typically seen in people. *Negative symptoms* are the absence of typical behaviors or inability to engage in an activity.

The four major symptoms of Parkinson disease are tremor, rigidity, loss of spontaneous movement (*hypokinesia*), and postural disturbances. Each symptom may manifest in different body parts in different combinations. Because some symptoms entail the appearance of abnormal behaviors (positive symptoms) and others the loss of normal behaviors (negative symptoms), we consider both major categories.

POSITIVE SYMPTOMS Because positive symptoms are common in Parkinson disease, they are thought to be inhibited, or held in check, in unaffected people but released from inhibition in the process of the disease. Following are the three most common:

1. *Tremor at rest*. Alternating movements of the limbs occur when they are at rest and stop during voluntary movements or sleep. Hand tremors often have a pill-rolling quality, as if a pill were being rolled between the thumb and forefinger.

2. *Muscular rigidity*. Increased muscle tone simultaneously in both extensor and flexor muscles is particularly evident when the limbs are moved passively at a joint. Movement is resisted, but with sufficient force the muscles yield for a short distance then resist movement again. Thus, complete passive flexion or extension of a joint occurs in a series of steps, giving rise to the term *cogwheel rigidity*. Rigidity may be severe enough to make all movements difficult—like moving in slow motion and being unable to speed up the process.

3. *Involuntary movements*. Small movements or changes in posture, sometimes referred to as **akathesia**, or *cruel restlessness*, may accompany general inactivity to relieve tremor and sometimes to relieve stiffness but often occurs for no apparent reason. Other involuntary movements are distortions of posture, such as occur during *oculogyric crisis* (involuntary turns of the head and eyes to one side), which last minutes to hours.

NEGATIVE SYMPTOMS After detailed analysis of negative symptoms, Jean Prudin Martin (1967) divided patients severely affected with Parkinson disease into five groups:

1. *Disorders of posture*. A *disorder of fixation* presents as an inability or difficulty in maintaining a part of the body in its normal position in relation to other parts. A person's head may droop forward or a standing person may gradually bend forward, ending up on the knees. *Disorders of equilibrium*. These disorders cause difficulties in standing or even sitting unsupported. In less severe cases, people may have difficulty standing on one leg, or if pushed lightly on the shoulders, they may fall passively without taking corrective steps or attempting to catch themselves.

2. *Disorders of righting*. A person in a supine position has difficulty standing. Many advanced patients have difficulty in even rolling over.

3. *Disorders of locomotion*. Normal locomotion requires support of the body against gravity, stepping, balancing while the weight of the body is transferred from one leg to the other, and pushing forward. Parkinson patients have difficulty initiating stepping. When they do walk, they shuffle with short footsteps on a fairly wide base of support because they have trouble maintaining equilibrium when shifting weight from one leg to the other. On beginning to walk, Parkinson patients often demonstrate **festination:** they take faster and faster steps and end up running forward.

4. *Speech disturbances*. One symptom most noticeable to relatives is the almost complete absence of prosody (rhythm and pitch) in the speaker's voice.

5. *Hypokinesia*. Poverty or slowness of movement may also manifest itself in a blankness of facial expression, a lack of blinking or of swinging the arms when walking, a lack of spontaneous speech, or an absence of normal fidgeting. Akinesia also manifests in difficulty making repetitive movements, such as tapping, even in the absence of rigidity. People who sit motionless for hours show hypokinesia in its most striking manifestation.

akathesia Small, involuntary movements or changes in posture; motor restlessness.

festination Tendency to engage in a behavior, such as walking, faster and faster.

COGNITIVE SYMPTOMS Although Parkinson disease is usually viewed as a motor disorder, changes in cognition occur as well. Psychological symptoms in Parkinson patients are as variable as the motor symptoms. Nonetheless, a significant percentage of patients show cognitive symptoms that mirror their motor symptoms.

Oliver Sacks (1998) reported impoverishment of feeling, libido, motive, and attention: people may sit for hours, apparently lacking the will to begin or continue any activity. Thinking seems generally to be slowed and is easily confused with dementia because patients do not appear to be processing the content of conversations. In fact, they may be simply processing very slowly.

Cognitive slowing in Parkinson patients has some parallels to Alzheimer disease.

CAUSES OF PARKINSONISM The ultimate cause of Parkinson disease—loss of cells in the substantia nigra—may result from disease, such as encephalitis or syphilis, from drugs such as MPTP, or from unknown causes. *Idiopathic* causes—those related to the individual—may include environmental pollutants, insecticides, and herbicides. Demographic studies of patient admissions in the cities of Vancouver, Canada, and Helsinki, Finland, show an increased incidence of patients contracting the disease at ages younger than 40. This finding has prompted the suggestion that water and air might contain environmental toxins that work in a fashion similar to MPTP (1-methyl-4-phenylpyridinium), a contaminant that has been found in synthetic heroin and causes Parkinson disease.

Actor Michael J. Fox, a native of Canada pictured in Focus 5-2, was diagnosed with young-onset Parkinson disease at age 30.

TREATING PARKINSON DISEASE The cure for Parkinson disease is either to stop degeneration in the substantia nigra or to replace it. Neither goal is achievable at present. Thus, current treatment is pharmacological and directed toward support and comfort.

Psychological factors influence Parkinsonism's major symptoms: outcome is affected by how well a person copes. Patients should seek behaviorally oriented treatment early—counseling on the meaning of symptoms, the nature of the disease, and the potential for most patients to lead long, productive lives. Physical therapy consists of simple measures, such as heat and massage, to alleviate painful muscle cramps as well as training and exercise to cope with debilitating movement changes. Used therapeutically, music and exercise can improve other aspects of behavior, including balance and walking, and may actually slow the course of the disease.

Copyright Katsuyoshi Tanaka, courtesy of the Mark Morris Dance Group

The prime objective of pharmacological treatment is increasing the activity in whatever dopamine synapses remain. L-Dopa, a precursor of dopamine, is converted into dopamine in the brain and enhances effective dopamine transmission, as do drugs such as amantadine, amphetamine, monoamine oxidase inhibitors, and tricyclic antidepressants. Anticholinergic drugs, such as atropine, scopolamine, benztropine (Cogentin), and trihexyphenidyl (Artane), block the brain cholinergic systems that seem to show heightened activity in the absence of adequate dopamine activity. As the disease progresses, drug therapies become less effective, and the incidence of side effects increases. Some drug treatments that directly stimulate dopamine receptors have been reported to result in increased sexuality and an increased incidence of compulsive gambling.

Two surgical treatments described in Section 16-2 are based on the idea that increased activity of globus pallidus neurons inhibits motor function. A lesion of the internal part of the globus pallidus (GPi) can reduce rigidity and tremor. Hyperactivity of GPi neurons can also be reduced neurosurgically by electrically stimulating the neurons via deep brain stimulation (see Figure 16-4). A stimulating electrode is permanently implanted in the GPi or an adjacent area, the subthalamic nucleus. Patients carry a small electric stimulator that they can turn on to induce DBS and so reduce rigidity and tremor. These two treatments may be used sequentially: when DBS becomes less effective as the disease progresses, a GPi lesion may be induced.

A promising prospective Parkinson treatment involves increasing the population of dopamine-producing cells. The simplest way is to transplant embryonic dopamine cells into

Rhythmic movement helps Parkinson patients restore the balance between positive and negative symptoms. Patients who participate in a specially designed Dance for PD (http://danceforparkinsons.org/) class for people with Parkinson (PwP) like the one at the Mark Morris Dance Center, pictured here, report that moving to music helps them regain muscle control. Exercise, including tai chi and boxing, also reinforces treatments directed toward replacing depleted dopamine.

Figure 11-13 charts how the GP$_i$, a structure in the basal ganglia, regulates movement force.

the basal ganglia. In the 1980s and 1990s, this treatment reported varying degrees of success marked by poorly conducted studies with inadequate preassessment and postassessment procedures. A newer treatment course proposes either transplanting stem cells that could then be induced to take a dopaminergic phenotype or stimulating endogenous stem cells to migrate to the basal ganglia. The advantage is that these stem cells need not be derived from embryonic tissue but can come from a variety of sources, including the person's own body.

All these treatments are experimental (Politis & Lindvall, 2012). Before cell replacement will become a useful therapy, many questions must be resolved, including which cell source is best, where in the brain to put grafts, and how new cells can be integrated into existing brain circuits. Stem cells are not a quick fix for Parkinson disease, but the pioneering work on this disease will be instrumental in applying such technology to other diseases.

Anatomical Correlates of Alzheimer Disease

Given the increasing population of elderly people and thus of Alzheimer disease, which accounts for about 65 percent of all dementias, research is directed toward potential causes. Personal lifestyle, environmental toxins, high levels of trace elements such as aluminum in the blood, an autoimmune response, a slow-acting virus, reduced blood flow to the cerebral hemispheres, and genetic predisposition are targets of ongoing research.

Incidence of Alzheimer disease is high in some families, making genetic causes pertinent to understanding disease progression. Risk factors include the presence of the *Apoe4* gene, below-average IQ score, poor education, and TBI. Presumably, better educated and/or more intelligent people and those who carry the *Apoe2* gene are better able to compensate for cell death in degenerative dementia.

A decade ago, the only way to identify and study Alzheimer disease was postmortem pathology examination. This approach was less than ideal because determining which brain changes came early in the disease and which resulted from those early changes was impossible. Nonetheless, it became clear that widespread changes take place in neocortex and allocortex and that associated changes take place in many neurotransmitter systems. Most of the brainstem, cerebellum, and spinal cord are relatively spared from Alzheimer's major ravages.

The principal neuroanatomical change in Alzheimer disease is the emergence of amyloid plaques (clumps of protein from dead neurons and astrocytes), chiefly in allocortex and neocortex. Increased plaque concentration in the cortex has been correlated with the magnitude of cognitive deterioration. Plaques are generally considered nonspecific phenomena in that they can be found in non-Alzheimer patients and in dementias caused by other known events.

Another anatomical correlate of Alzheimer disease is neurofibrillary tangles (accumulations of microtubules from dead cells) found in both neocortex and allocortex, where the posterior half of the hippocampus is affected more severely than the anterior half. Neurofibrillary tangles have been described mainly in human tissue and have also been observed in patients with Down syndrome and Parkinson disease and other dementias.

Finally, neocortical changes that correlate with Alzheimer disease are not uniform. As **Figure 16-10** shows plainly, the cortex atrophies and can lose as much as one-third of its

Focus 14-3, on Alzheimer etiology, includes a micrograph of an amyloid plaque.

Neurofilaments are a type of *tubule* that reinforces cell structure, aids its movement, and transports proteins.

(A) Healthy brain

(B) Brain characteristic of Alzheimer disease

FIGURE 16-10 Cortical Degeneration in Alzheimer Disease Brain of **(A)** a healthy elderly adult contrasted with **(B)** an elderly adult's brain that shows shriveling due to cell shrinkage characteristic of Alzheimer disease.

Brain images were provided courtesy of the Nun Study, University of Minnesota

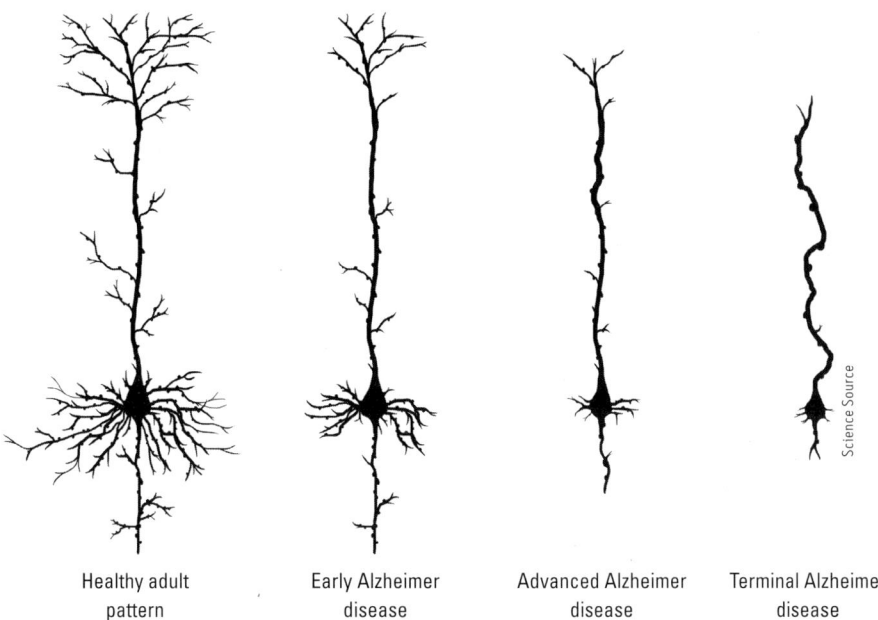

Healthy adult
pattern

Early Alzheimer
disease

Advanced Alzheimer
disease

Terminal Alzheimer
disease

FIGURE 16-11 Stripped Branches
Alzheimer patients' dendritic trees
degenerate and their neurons atrophy,
worsening their symptoms, including
memory loss and personality changes.

volume as the disease progresses. But cellular analyses at the microscopic level reveal that some areas, including the primary sensory and motor cortices, especially the visual and sensorimotor cortex, are relatively spared. The frontal lobes are less affected than is the posterior cortex.

Areas of most extensive change are the neocortical association areas and the allocortex. The entorhinal cortex is affected earliest and most severely. Entorhinal cortex is the major information relay from the neocortex traveling to the hippocampus and related structures, then back to the neocortex. Entorhinal damage is associated with memory loss, an early and enduring symptom of Alzheimer disease, and is most likely caused by degenerative changes that take place in this area.

Many studies describe cell loss in the cortices of Alzheimer patients, but this finding is disputed. There seems to be a substantial reduction in large neurons, but these cells may shrink rather than disappear. The more widespread cause of cortical atrophy appears to be a loss of dendritic arborization (**Figure 16-11**).

In addition to cell loss and shrinkage, changes take place in the remaining cells' neurotransmitters. In the 1970s, researchers believed that a treatment paralleling L-dopa treatment of Parkinson disease could be found for Alzheimer disease. The prime candidate neurotransmitter was acetylcholine, and one treatment developed for Alzheimer disease is medication that increases acetylcholine levels in the forebrain. An example, available both orally and as a skin patch, is Exelon, the brand name for rivastigmine, a cholinergic agonist that appears to provide temporary relief from disease progression. Unfortunately, Alzheimer has proved far more complex, because transmitters other than ACh clearly are changed as well. Noradrenaline, dopamine, and serotonin are reduced, as are the NMDA and AMPA receptors for glutamate.

Figure 14-17 shows how glutamate can affect NMDA and AMPA receptors to promote learning by association.

Are All Degenerative Dementias Aspects of a Single Disease?

Neither Parkinson nor Alzheimer disease is related to a single brain structure or region, although dopamine in the case of the former and acetylcholine in the case of the latter seem more affected. Other similarities in their pathology suggest some common neurodegenerative processes. Donald Calne (Calne & Mizuno, 2004) noted that when scientists traveled to

FIGURE 16-12 Midbrain Lewy Body
Lewy bodies (arrow) characteristic of
Parkinson disease are found in the brain of
patients with other disorders as well.

Infection as referred to in the definition is not
one caused by casual contact.

Lewy body Circular fibrous structure found
in several neurodegenerative disorders;
forms within the cytoplasm of neurons
and is thought to result from abnormal
neurofilament metabolism.

prion From *protein* and *infection,* an
abnormally folded protein that causes
progressive neurodegenerative disorders.

Guam at the end of World War II to investigate a reportedly widespread dementia described
as similar to Alzheimer disease, they did indeed report a high incidence of Alzheimer. Many
years later, Calne and his colleagues, also experts in Parkinson disease, examined the same
general group of people and found that they had Parkinson disease. Calne noted that, if
you look for Alzheimer symptoms in these people, you find them and miss the Parkinson
symptoms. And vice versa.

The best-studied similarity between the two diseases is the **Lewy body** (**Figure 16-12**), a
fibrous ring that forms within neuronal cytoplasm and is thought to correspond to abnormal
neurofilament metabolism. Until recently, the Lewy body was most often found in the region
of the midbrain substantia nigra and believed to be a hallmark of Parkinson disease, as amyloid plaques were viewed as a marker of Alzheimer disease. In fact, Lewy bodies appear in
several neurodegenerative disorders, including Alzheimer disease. There are even reports of
people with Alzheimerlike dementias who have no plaques and tangles but do have extensive
Lewy bodies in the cortex.

Alzheimer and Parkinson symptoms may be similar because both diseases have similar
origins. Indeed, the idea that several diseases marked by brain degeneration—including Huntington disease, MS, and ALS—may have a similar origin is central to *prion theory*, advanced
in 1982 by Stanley B. Prusiner, who received the Noble Prize for his work in 1997. Its name
derived from the terms *protein* and *infection*, a **prion** is an abnormally folded protein that
causes progressive neurodegeneration.

Prions were identified during investigation of various degenerative brain diseases in humans and other animals. Creutzfeldt-Jakob disease, a rare human degenerative disease that
progresses rapidly, gained public prominence in the 1990s. People were contracting a similar
condition after eating beef from cattle that had displayed symptoms of *bovine spongiform
encephalopathy* (BSE), a degenerative brain condition accompanied by muscle wasting. BSE
in turn is similar to a condition in sheep called *scrapies* (the animals scrape or scratch themselves) that also features wasting of brain and body. *Chronic wasting disease* is a similar condition found in deer and elk.

The infectious nature of such conditions was observed in the Fore tribe of Papua New
Guinea in the 1950s. A large number of Fore were dying of a muscle-wasting condition called
kuru (meaning *to shake* in Fore). The Fore contracted kuru by practicing ritual cannibalism:
they ate the brains of dead relatives, which the Fore believed preserves their spirits. In an
experiment to investigate the condition, body parts from kuru victims were fed to a chimp
that contracted the disease.

The infectious agent in these conditions is a prion. Prion proteins are found in healthy
cell membranes and may play a role in attaching one cell to another. Prion proteins also bind
to metallic ions, for example, copper. The proteins typically fold in a normal configuration
but can also misfold (**Figure 16-13**). The altered configuration causes disease.

A misfolded prion protein will attach to a healthy prion protein and cause it to misfold.
Misfolded prions tend to clump together, forming protein aggregates that eventually result
in cell death. Misfolded prions can also infect neighboring brain and body cells, resulting
in general brain degeneration
and muscle wasting. An infectious prion can pass from
one individual to another,
and even from one species to
another, but only if the normal prion proteins in the two
individuals are similar. Investigations show that among
several alleles of the gene
that produces normal prion

FIGURE 16-13 Disease Process
Left: Prion proteins typically fold into
helixes and pleated sheets. Right: In
misfolding, part of the protein helix
changes into a sheet. The result is an
infectious disease–causing prion.

Normal   **Diseased prion**

Amino
acids in
alpha helix

Amino acids
in beta helix

Amino acids
in sheet form

proteins, some are more susceptible to misfolding than are others. Individuals with alleles that are not susceptible to misfolding, as are those Fore tribespeople who did not contract kuru, are resistant to prion disease.

In Parkinson disease, the misfolded protein is proposed to be *alpha synuclein*. Its accumulation, largely in substantia nigra cells, is a Lewy body (Olanow & Brundin, 2013). In Alzheimer disease, the accumulating protein forms amyloid plaques and mainly affects cortical cells (Kumar et al., 2015). Misfolded proteins in oligodendroglia may be responsible for the cell demyelination characteristic of MS and ALS (Shi et al., 2015).

The prion theory opens new avenues for investigating degenerative disease treatments, including drugs that remove prions, block prion misfolding, or alter prion forms prone to misfolding (Asante et al., 2015). Selective cattle breeding for prion alleles that do not produce misfolding prevents BSE. Inserting a misfolding-resistant human prion allele into mice renders them resistant to prion disease. Any treatment developed for humans could potentially treat BSE in cattle, scrapie in sheep, and wasting disease in deer and elk. Preventing prion misfolding could even arrest, in part, degenerative consequences of traumatic brain injury and concussion.

Age-Related Cognitive Loss

Most people who grow old do not become demented, but virtually everyone acquires age-related cognitive loss, even while living an active, healthy, productive life. Aging is associated with declines in perceptual functions, especially vision, hearing, and olfaction, and declining motor, cognitive, and executive (planning) functions as well. Older people tend to learn at a slower pace and typically do not attain the same mastery of new skills as do younger adults.

Noninvasive imaging studies reveal that aging is correlated with decreased white matter volume, probably related to myelin loss. This condition is reparable. There is little evidence of neuronal loss in typical aging, although a reduction in neurogenesis in the hippocampus does occur. Compared with younger people, older people tend to activate larger regions of their attentional and executive networks (parietal and prefrontal cortex) when they perform complex cognitive and executive tasks. This increased activation correlates with reduced performance on tests of working memory as well as tests of attentional and executive tasks.

Brain Workout Engaging in cognitively stimulating activities can keep neural networks and general cognitive function from declining with age.

Two lines of evidence suggest that that age-related declines in function can be slowed. The first is aerobic exercise to enhance general health and improve the brain's plasticity via increased neurogenesis, gliogenesis, and trophic factor support. The second treatment is brain exercise employing training strategies that enhance neural plasticity and reverse learned nonuse. Most of us know the frustration of losing a skill—whether it's trigonometry or tennis—after getting out of practice. Skill loss does not reflect dementia but simply a use-it-or-lose-it effect. Training programs designed to stimulate plasticity in the appropriate cerebral circuitry include motor, auditory, or visual system–based cognitive and/or attentional training. Brain training is designed to stimulate plasticity rather than to rehabilitate specific losses.

William Milberg and his colleagues (e.g., Kuo et al., 2005; Leritz et al., 2011) have explored the idea that aging changes in the brain take place in the context of the entire body's aging. For example, dementia may reflect a chronic cerebrovascular disorder, marginal high blood pressure. Marginal elevations in blood pressure can lead to cerebral microbleeds, especially in white matter. The cumulative effect of years or even decades of tiny bleeds would lead eventually to increasingly disturbed cognition. The condition may first appear as a *mild cognitive impairment* (MCI) that slowly progresses, with cumulative microbleeds, toward dementia.

View the progression of these microbleeds, or silent strokes, at https://www.youtube.com/watch?v=J3fb0CaDpEk.

16-3) REVIEW

Understanding and Treating Neurological Disorders

Before you continue, check your understanding.

1. As the developed world's population ages, _____ disease will become more common than _____ disease.

2. Even imaging techniques may miss pathology produced by _____.

3. Interruption of blood to the brain is called _____ and if prolonged can result in _____.

4. Although superficially appearing to be very different diseases, Parkinson and Alzheimer have similarities such as _____ and _____ that suggest that they may be part of a common disease spectrum.

5. Name two strategies that can reduce or reverse neurological and cognitive decline with aging.

Answers appear at the back of the book.

For additional study tools, visit 🌀 LaunchPad:
www.macmillanhighered.com/launchpad/kolb5e

16-4) Understanding and Treating Psychiatric Disorders

The DSM-5 summarizes a wide range of mental disorders. We focus on the three general behavioral categories—psychoses, mood disorders, and anxiety disorders—that are the best studied and understood. **Figure 16-14** summarizes their prevalence. Personal, family, and social costs are not reflected in these statistics. Schizophrenia, bipolar disorder, and major depression affect a smaller number of people, but their costs, in loss of social relationships, productivity, and medical care, are disproportionate.

Schizophrenia Spectrum and Other Psychotic Disorders

Psychoses are psychological disorders in which a person loses contact with reality, subject to irrational ideas and distorted perceptions. Among the varieties of psychosis, schizophrenia is the most common and best understood. Although it takes many forms, whether schizophrenia is a single disorder or several disorders that share some symptoms is uncertain. The complexity of behavioral and neurobiological factors that characterize schizophrenia makes it especially difficult to diagnose and classify. Understanding schizophrenia is an evolving process and far from complete.

Diagnosing Schizophrenia

The DSM lists six diagnostic symptoms of schizophrenia:

1. Delusions—beliefs that distort reality

2. Hallucinations—distorted perceptions, such as hearing voices

3. Disorganized speech, such as incoherent statements or senselessly rhyming talk

4. Disorganized behavior or excessive agitation

5. The opposite extreme of agitation: catatonic behavior

6. Negative symptoms, such as blunted emotions or loss of interest and drive, all characterized by the absence of some healthy response

The DSM criteria are subjective and more helpful in clinical diagnoses than in relating schizophrenia to objective, measurable brain abnormalities.

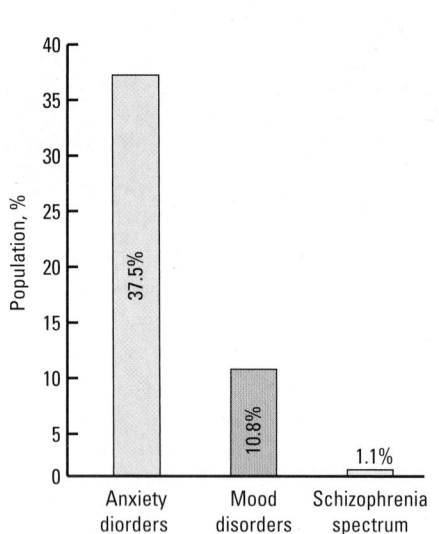

FIGURE 16-14 Prevalence of Some Psychiatric Illnesses Data from National Institutes of Mental Health, http://www.nimh.nih.gov/health/statistics/index.shtml

Neurobiology of Schizophrenia

Although schizophrenia may produce a wide range of symptoms, individual differences in behavioral effects exist as well. Voluminous research related to the origins and causes of schizophrenia has emerged, but the three lines of research summarized in this section have transformed ideas about its genetics, its development, and its associated brain correlates.

GENETICS It has long been recognized that genetics figures in schizophrenia, as does environment. The more closely related an individual is to someone diagnosed with schizophrenia, the more likely he or she is to develop the condition. The concordance of schizophrenia in identical twins is high: 50 percent is often cited. That the concordance for schizophrenia is not 100 percent means that environmental factors also play a role (Shorter & Miller, 2015).

It is also likely that many genes are associated with schizophrenia. Mutations on a number of chromosomes (candidates are 1, 6, 8, 13, and 22) predispose an individual to schizophrenia. It is also likely that many mutations in candidate genes on those chromosomes are involved. Genetic studies suggest that schizophrenia is probably a family of disorders and that the family may include other conditions, such as major depression and bipolar disorder (Claes et al., 2012). What may be common to the genes involved is that they contribute to brain development and so may contribute to various abnormalities in brain development.

DEVELOPMENT Typically, schizophrenia is diagnosed in young adulthood, but a body of evidence suggests that it originates much earlier, even prenatally. Its expression in adulthood must therefore await the conclusion of a host of developmental processes that ultimately shape the adult human brain. That schizophrenia has developmental origins has many implications.

First, environmental factors acting through epigenetic mechanisms are likely to influence brain development such that a subset of at-risk individuals develops adult schizophrenia. Second, identifying developmental factors that contribute to schizophrenia provides the best opportunity for intervention to reduce the risks of developing it. Any potential "cure" for schizophrenia will depend on early detection and remediation through epigenetic mechanisms (Gebicke-Haerter, 2012).

BRAIN CORRELATES Many studies show anatomical changes in the brain associated with schizophrenia, especially in the temporal and frontal lobes.

1. Suggesting cell loss in these areas, the schizophrenic brain generally has large ventricles and thinner cortex in the medial temporal regions and frontal cortex.

2. Some aspects of neuronal and fiber composition of the temporal lobes and the frontal lobes are changed, as indicated by changes in their density imaged by MRI (Kong et al., 2012).

3. Alterations in neuronal structure show abnormal dendritic fields in cells in the dorsal prefrontal regions; as shown in **Figure 16-15,** in the hippocampus (Cho et al., 2004); and in the entorhinal cortex (Arnold et al., 1997).

In sum, this evidence seems almost definitive in identifying schizophrenia as a developmental brain disorder associated in the main with alteration in the temporal and the frontal cortex. These brain regions are associated with memory, language, and decision making.

Hippocampus

(A)

Organized (healthy) pyramidal neurons

(B)

Disorganized (schizophrenic) pyramidal neurons

FIGURE 16-15 Organic Dysfunction **(A)** Rather than the consistently parallel orientation of hippocampal neurons typical in healthy brains, **(B)** the orientation of hippocampal neurons in the brain of a person with schizophrenia is haphazard. Information from J. A. Kovelman & A. B. Scheibel (1984). A neurohistologic correlate of schizophrenia. *Biological Psychiatry, 19,* p. 1613.

Neurochemical Correlates of Schizophrenia

Neuroscientists also consider the neurochemical correlates of brain–behavior relations in schizophrenia. Dopamine abnormalities were the first to be linked to schizophrenia, through two lines of evidence. First, most neuroleptic drugs act on the dopamine synapse was taken as evidence that schizophrenia is a disease of heightened activity in the ventral tegmental dopamine system. Second, drugs that enhance dopaminergic activity, such as amphetamine, can produce psychotic symptoms reminiscent of schizophrenia.

This dopamine theory of schizophrenia appears too simple, however, because many other neurochemical abnormalities, summarized in **Table 16-6,** are also associated with schizophrenia—in particular, abnormalities in dopamine and dopamine receptors and in GABA and GABA-binding sites. Recent evidence also suggests changes in the NMDA receptor in schizophrenia, a finding that is leading to the development of new classes of glutamate drug therapy (Pannese et al., 2012). Patients vary widely in the extent of each abnormality, however. How these neurochemical variations might relate to the presence or absence of specific symptoms is not yet known.

To summarize, schizophrenia is a complex disorder associated with abnormalities in brain structure and metabolism, especially in prefrontal and temporal cortex, and with neurochemical abnormalities in dopamine, glutamate, and GABA. Given the complexity of all these factors, it comes as no surprise that schizophrenia is so difficult to characterize and to treat.

Neuroleptics are antipsychotic drugs described in Section 6-2.

GABA is the brain's main inhibitory neurotransmitter.

TABLE 16-6 Biochemical Changes Associated with Schizophrenia

Decreased dopamine metabolites in cerebrospinal fluid
Increased striatal D_2 receptors
Decreased expression of D_3 and D_4 mRNA in specific cortical regions
Decreased cortical glutamate
Increased cortical glutamate receptors
Decreased glutamate uptake sites in cingulate cortex
Decreased mRNA for synthesizing GABA in prefrontal cortex
Increased $GABA_A$-binding sites in cingulate cortex

Source: Information from W. Byne, E. Kemegther, L. Jones, V. Harouthunian, and K. L. Davis (1999). The neurochemistry of schizophrenia. In D. S. Charney, E. J. Nestler, & B. S. Bunney. *The Neurobiology of Mental Illness* (p. 242). New York: Oxford University Press.

Mood Disorders

The DSM-5 identifies a continuum of affective disorders, separating bipolar and related disorders from depressive disorders (see Table 16-3). The bipolar category is positioned between schizophrenia and depressive disorders, forming a bridge between the diagnostic classes that takes into account symptoms, family history, and genetics. Depression and mania—our principal interests here—represent the extremes of affect. The main symptoms of *major depression* are prolonged feelings of worthlessness and guilt, disruption of normal eating habits, sleep disturbances, a general slowing of behavior, and frequent thoughts of suicide.

Focus 6-3 explains the threat of suicide attendant to untreated major depression.

Mania, the opposite affective extreme from depression, is characterized by excessive euphoria, which the subject perceives as typical. The affected person often formulates grandiose plans and is uncontrollably hyperactive. Periods of mania often change, sometimes abruptly, to depression and back again to mania, a condition designated as **bipolar disorder.**

Neurobiology of Depression

Brain and environment both contribute to the complex neurobiology of depression. Predisposing factors related to brain anatomy and chemistry thus may contribute more to affective changes in some people, whereas life experiences contribute mainly to affective changes in other people. As a result, a bewildering number of life, health, and brain factors have been related to depression. These factors include economic or social failure, circadian rhythm disruption, vitamin D and other nutrient deficiency, pregnancy, brain injury, diabetes, cardiovascular events, and childhood abuse, among many others.

A major approach in neurobiological studies of depression is to ask whether a common brain substrate exists for depression. Antidepressant drugs acutely increase the synaptic levels of norepinephrine and serotonin, a finding that led to the idea that depression results from decreased availability of one or both neurotransmitters. Lowering their levels in healthy participants does not produce depression, however. And while antidepressant medications increase the level of norepinephrine and serotonin within days, it takes weeks for drugs to start relieving depression.

Among the various explanations suggested for these confounding results, none is completely satisfactory. Ronald Duman (2004) reviewed evidence to suggest that antidepressants act, at least in part, on signaling pathways, such as on cAMP, in the postsynaptic cell. Neurotrophic factors appear to affect antidepressant action and may underlie the neurobiology of depression. Investigators know, for example, that brain-derived neurotrophic factor (BDNF) is down-regulated by stress and up-regulated by antidepressant medication (Wang et al., 2012).

Given that BDNF acts to enhance the growth and survival of cortical neurons and synapses, BDNF dysfunction may adversely affect norepinephrine and serotonin systems through the loss of either neurons or synapses. Antidepressant medication may increase BDNF release through its actions on cAMP. Key here is that the cause of depression probably is not merely a simple decrease in transmitter levels. Many brain changes are related to depression.

Mood and Reactivity to Stress

A significant psychological factor in understanding depression is reactivity to stress. Monoamines—the noradrenergic and serotoninergic activating systems diagrammed in **Figure 16-16**A—modulate hormone secretion by the hypothalamic–pituitary–adrenal system—the **HPA axis**—illustrated in Figure 16-16B. When we are stressed, the HPA axis is stimulated to secrete corticotropin-releasing hormone, which stimulates the pituitary to produce adrenocorticotropic hormone (ACTH). ACTH circulates through the blood and stimulates the adrenal medulla to produce cortisol. Normally, cortisol helps us deal with stress. If we cannot cope, or if stress is intense, excessive cortisol can wield a negative influence on the brain, damaging the feedback loops the brain uses to turn off the stress response.

Excessive stress early in life may be especially detrimental. During critical periods in early childhood, abuse or other severe environmental stress can permanently disrupt HPA axis reactivity: it becomes constantly overactive. Overactivity in the HPA axis results in oversecretion of cortisol, an imbalance associated with depression in adulthood. Patrick McGowan and colleagues (2010) wondered if early experiences could alter gene expression related to cortisol activity in the HPA axis. They compared, postmortem, hippocampi obtained from suicide victims with a history of childhood abuse and hippocampi from other suicide victims

Section 14-4 explores the relation of hormones, trophic factors, and psychoactive drugs to neuroplasticity.

Section 6-5 explains the neurobiology of the stress response—how it begins and ends.

mania Disordered mental state of extreme excitement.

bipolar disorder Mood disorder characterized by periods of depression alternating with normal periods and periods of intense excitation, or *mania*.

HPA axis Hypothalamic–pituitary–adrenal circuit that controls the production and release of hormones related to stress.

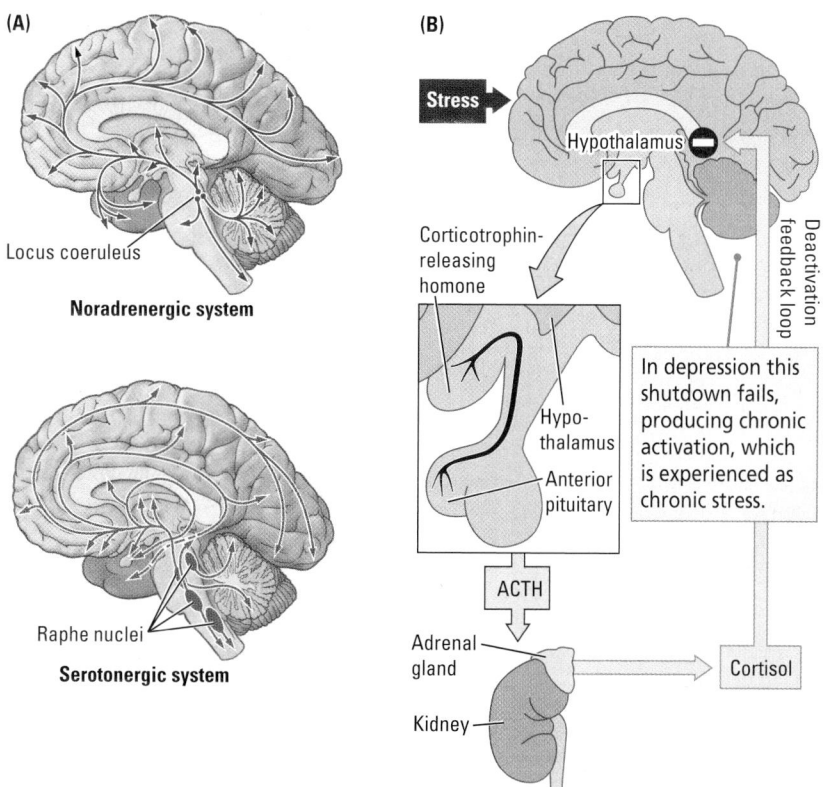

FIGURE 16-16 Stress-Activating System **(A)** Medial view showing that in the brainstem, cell bodies of noradrenergic (norepinephrine) neurons emanate from the locus coeruleus (top) and cell bodies of the serotonergic activating system emanate from the raphe nuclei (bottom). **(B)** When activated, the HPA axis affects mood, thinking, and indirectly, cortisol secretion by the adrenal glands. HPA deactivation begins when cortisol binds to hypothalamic receptors.

This research confirms studies on the effects of stress on hippocampal function reported in Sections 6-5, 7-5, and 8-4.

with no childhood abuse or from controls. Abused suicide victims showed decreased gene expression for cortisol receptors relative to the controls. These results, derived from epigenetics, confirm that early neglect or abuse alters the HPA axis for life.

To summarize, the diffuse distribution of the norepinephrine- and serotonin-activating systems makes relating depression to a single brain structure impossible. Findings from neuroimaging studies show that depression is accompanied by increased blood flow and glucose metabolism in the orbitofrontal cortex, anterior cingulate cortex, and amygdala. Blood flow drops as the symptoms of depression remit when a patient takes antidepressant medication (Drevets, Kishore, & Krishman, 2004). Antidepressants effectively increase the amount of serotonin in the cortex and may also stimulate brain repair. For example, fluoxetine (Prozac) stimulates both BDNF production and neurogenesis in the hippocampus, resulting in a net increase in granule cells, described in Research Focus 16-4, Antidepressant Action and Brain Repair.

cognitive-behavioral therapy (CBT)
Problem-focused, action-oriented, structured treatment for eliminating dysfunctional thoughts and maladaptive behaviors.

Although we have emphasized biological correlates of depression, the best treatment need not be a direct biological intervention. **Cognitive-behavioral therapy** (CBT) is an excellent—arguably the best—therapy for depression. It focuses on challenging the patient's beliefs and perceptions. The objective is to identify dysfunctional thoughts and beliefs that accompany negative emotions and to replace them with more realistic ones.

Simply pointing out that a person's beliefs are faulty is not likely to be effective, however, because it probably took months or years to develop those beliefs. The neural circuits underlying faulty beliefs must change, just as the strategies for developing new ones must change. In a real sense then, CBT is effective if it induces neural plasticity and changes brain activity.

RESEARCH FOCUS 16-4

Antidepressant Action and Brain Repair

Excessive stress, poor coping skills, or both contribute to excessive cortisol levels in the brain and to depression and anxiety. Granule cells in the hippocampus, which are especially sensitive to cortisol, can die when cortisol levels either are reduced, as shown in the figure, or increased excessively.

These hippocampal cells may play a role in regulating cortisol levels and switching off the brain's stress response. Their absence leaves the HPA axis unchecked. Then increased cortisol levels contribute to more neuron death and to depression and anxiety. It's a vicious circle.

A remarkable finding emerged from studying how antidepressants such as fluoxetine (Prozac) and other selective serotonin reuptake inhibitors affect the hippocampus. The SSRIs increased neurogenesis in the subgranular zone, cell migration into the dentate gyrus, and the number of functioning cells there (Malberg et al., 2000).

That antidepressants take some weeks to produce their positive effects on behavior and that new neurons take some weeks to migrate and incorporate into the hippocampus suggest that the antidepressants' mechanism of action is to enhance hippocampal function—in essence, to replace the neural switch that turns off the stress response.

Luca Santarelli and colleagues (2003) used knockout mice that lacked a specific serotonin receptor (5-HT-1A) sensitive to fluoxetine. They exposed these mice along with mice with intact 5-HT-1A receptors to chronic, unpredictable stress. Both groups developed a general deterioration in their fur coat.

Chronic antidepressant treatment affected only the mice with intact serotonin receptors, and only these mice displayed enhanced neurogenesis. Thus, because antidepressants activate serotonin receptors, serotonin must participate in enhancing neurogenesis.

The literature on hippocampal neurogenesis is the most prolific in neuroscience, represented by over 3000 papers reporting mainly on animal models. To summarize their findings, phenomena we perceive as bad (deprivation in infancy, conflict, stress, poor diet, most drugs) depress neurogenesis, and phenomena we perceive as good (exercise, enriched environment, sufficient sleep, good diet) enhance neurogenesis. Finding the signaling pathways that enhance neurogenesis may reveal the relationships among altered cognition, memory, depression, and the effects of antidepressant drugs (Costa et al., 2015).

Healthy rat hippocampus

Neuronal degeneration

Hippocampus

Images from S. C. Spanswick and R. J. Sutherland (2010). Object-context specific memory deficits associated with loss of hippocampal granule cells after adrenalectomy in rats. Learning and Memory, 17:241-245. Figure 2

Anxiety Disorders

We are all subject to anxiety, usually acutely in response to stress or less commonly as chronic reactivity—an increased anxiety response—even to seemingly minor stressors. Anxiety reactions certainly are not pathological; they are likely an evolutionary adaptation for coping with adverse conditions. But anxiety can become pathological and make life miserable. Anxiety disorders are among the most common psychiatric conditions. The DSM-5 lists 10 classes of anxiety disorders that together affect 15 percent to 35 percent of the population at some point in their life lives (see Figure 16-14).

Imaging studies of people with anxiety disorders record increased baseline activity in the cingulate cortex and parahippocampal gyrus and enhanced responsiveness to anxiety-provoking stimuli in the amygdala and prefrontal cortex. This finding suggests excessive excitatory neurotransmission in a circuit involving cingulate cortex, amygdala, and the parahippocampal region. Because drugs that enhance the inhibitory transmitter GABA are particularly effective in reducing anxiety, researchers hypothesize that excessive excitatory neurotransmission in this circuit is anxiety. But what causes it?

Considerable interest has developed in investigating why some people show pathological anxiety to stimuli to which others have a milder response. One hypothesis, covered earlier, in the section on depression, is that stressful experiences early in life increase susceptibility to a variety of behavioral disorders, especially anxiety disorders.

Although anxiety disorders used to be treated primarily with benzodiazepines, such as Valium, now they are also treated with SSRIs, such as Prozac, Paxil, Celexa, and Zoloft. Antidepressant drugs do not act immediately, however, suggesting that the treatments must stimulate some gradual change in brain structure, much as these drugs act in treating depression.

Cognitive-behavioral therapy is as effective as drugs in treating anxiety. The most effective behavioral therapies expose and re-expose patients to their fears. For example, treating a phobic fear of germs requires exposing the patient repeatedly to potentially germy environments, such as public washrooms, until the discomfort abates.

Focus 12-3 describes symptoms of anxiety disorders; Section 6-5, how stress-induced damage contributes to PTSD.

Figure 12-18 diagrams these limbic system structures and charts their major connections.

One more time: a pill is not a skill.

(16-4) REVIEW

Understanding and Treating Behavioral Disorders

Before you continue, check your understanding.

1. Schizophrenia is a complex disorder associated with neurochemical abnormalities in _____, _____, and _____.

2. Schizophrenia is associated with pronounced anatomical changes in the _____ and _____ cortices.

3. The monoamine-activating systems that have received the most investigation related to understanding depression are _____ and _____.

4. The most effective treatment for depression and anxiety disorders is _____.

5. Describe the main difficulty in linking genes to schizophrenia.

Answers appear at the back of the book.

For additional study tools, visit **LaunchPad**:
www.macmillanhighered.com/launchpad/kolb5e

(16-5) Is Misbehavior Always Bad?

You know this movie plot: a person sustains a blow to the head, then becomes a better person. Do pathological changes in brain and behavior sometimes lead to behavioral improvement in real life? A report by Jim Giles (2004) on Tommy McHugh's case is thought provoking.

To learn more and view McHugh's art, go to http://www.tommymchugh.co.uk.

McHugh (1949–2012), a heroin addict, committed multiple serious crimes and spent a great deal of time in jail. Later he had a cerebral hemorrhage (bleeding into the brain) from an aneurysm. The bleeding was repaired surgically with a metal clip on the leaking artery. After he recovered from the injury, McHugh's personality changed dramatically. He took up painting, which he had never done before, and became a successful artist.

McHugh's injury-induced brain changes appear to have been beneficial, but the exact nature of his brain injury has not been identified. The metal clip in his brain precluded the use of MRI. Aspects of his cognitive behavior suggest that he may have had frontal lobe damage.

The phenomenon in which an individual acquires a new skill after an injury is called *acquired savant syndrome*. There are other reports of people who have developed new musical or artistic talents after their injuries (Miller et al., 2000). Corrigan and colleagues (2012) propose that allied savant skills can be acquired by depressing inhibitory systems in the brain so that new skill strategies can be activated. In experiments, for example, depressing participants' left hemispheres with TMS briefly improved mathematical skills, which are subserved by the right hemisphere.

cognitive enhancement Brain function enhancement by pharmacological, physiological, or surgical manipulation.

In Focus 6-1, a brief history of cognitive enhancers is context for a trend: procuring medication prescribed for ADHD as a study aid.

The general idea of artificially manipulating the brain for the better is controversial (Heinz et al., 2012). Influencing brain function through a strategy loosely described as **cognitive enhancement** enlists current knowledge of pharmacology, brain plasticity, brain stimulation, neurogenetics, and other specialties to boost brain functioning. Of course, people already use drugs to alter brain function, and the basis of many therapies is to enhance brain function. Psychosurgical techniques such as frontal lobotomy were based on the general idea that brain function could be improved. As yet, however, evidence is lacking that cognitive enhancement for the average person is better than old-fashioned but readily available methods: learning, practice, and a healthy lifestyle.

■ SUMMARY

Contemporary understanding of brain and behavior is providing new insights, explanations, and treatments for brain disorders. Neurologists, who treat organic disorders, and psychiatrists, who treat behavioral disorders, are forging a unified understanding of mind and brain: neuropsychoanalysis.

16-1 Multidisciplinary Research on Brain and Behavioral Disorders

Most behavioral disorders have multiple causes—genetic, epigenetic, biochemical, anatomical, social–environmental variables—all of them interacting. Research methods directed toward these causes include family studies designed to find a genetic abnormality that might be corrected, biochemical anomalies that might be reversed by drug or hormone therapy, anatomical pathologies that might account for behavioral changes, and social–environmental variables.

Investigators rely increasingly on neuroimaging (fMRI, PET, TMS, ERP) to examine brain–behavior relations in vivo in healthy participants as well as in people with disorders. Interest in more refined behavioral measurements is growing, especially for cognitive behavior, the better to understand behavioral symptoms.

16-2 Classifying and Treating Brain and Behavioral Disorders

Disorders can be classified according to presumed etiology (cause), symptomatology, or pathology. The classification systems developed by psychologists, psychiatrists, and neurologists overlap, and each is revised from time to time. Clearly, better understanding the causes

of disorders will lead to better classification systems. Advances in genetics and brain imaging will aid this effort. The table summarizes the range of available treatments, from highly invasive neurosurgery to noninvasive electrophysiology, from moderately invasive pharmacology to behavioral treatments.

General Treatment Categories

Neurosurgical	Behavioral
Direct intervention	*Manipulation of experience*
DBS	Behavior modification
Stem cell transplantation	Cognitive, cognitive-behavioral therapy
Tissue removal or repair	Neuropsychological
Electrophysiological	Emotional therapy, psychotherapy
Noninvasive manipulation	Physical activity, music
ECT	rt-fMRI
TMS, rTMS	VR exposure and other computer-based simulations
Pharmacological	
Chemical administration	
Antibiotics or antivirals	
Psychoactive drugs	
Neurotrophic factors	
Nutrition	

(16-3) Understanding and Treating Neurological Disorders

If a disorder, such as depression, is presumably caused primarily by a biochemical imbalance, treatment is likely to be pharmacological, although brain activation with TMS also is effective and is noninvasive. If the disorder has a suspected anatomical cause, treatment may include removal of pathological tissue (as in epilepsy) or implanted electrodes to activate underactive regions (as in Parkinson disease and stroke). Many disorders require medical treatment concurrent with behavioral therapy, including physiotherapy or cognitive rehabilitation in patients with stroke and TBI, and cognitive-behavioral therapies for patients with depression and anxiety disorders.

(16-4) Understanding and Treating Behavioral Disorders

The number of people who endure hidden diseases of behavior, especially neurodegenerative disorders and stroke, is increasing as the population of the developed world ages. Like other plagues in human history, dementias affect not only the person with the disease but also the caregivers, about half of whom seek psychiatric care themselves.

(16-5) Is Misbehavior Always Bad?

In rare cases, people with a behavioral disorder also have some benefit. An individual who has a brain injury, for example, may suddenly display an artistic talent. The explanation for this acquired savant syndrome is that depressing the brain's inhibitory systems can activate new skill strategies. Artificially manipulating the brain with cognitive enhancers is a controversial approach to improving brain function.

■ KEY TERMS

akathesia, p. 586

autoimmune disease, p. 584

behavioral therapy, p. 575

bipolar disorder, p. 595

chronic traumatic encephalopathy (CTE), p. 579

cognitive enhancement, p. 598

cognitive therapy, p. 575

cognitive-behavioral therapy (CBT), p. 596

deep brain stimulation (DBS), p. 572

dementia, p. 584

diaschisis, p. 580

Diagnostic and Statistical Manual of Mental Disorders (DSM), p. 569

festination, p. 586

focal seizure, p. 583

generalized seizure, p. 583

HPA axis, p. 595

ischemia, p. 580

Lewy body, p. 590

magnetic resonance spectroscopy (MRS), p. 579

mania, p. 595

neuroprotectant, p. 580

neuropsychoanalysis, p. 565

phenylketonuria (PKU), p. 565

posttraumatic stress disorder (PTSD), p. 562

prion, p. 590

psychotherapy, p. 575

real-time fMRI (rt-fMRI), p. 576

tardive dyskinesia, p. 575

virtual reality (VR) exposure therapy, p. 562

CHAPTER 1

What Are the Origins of Brain and Behavior?

REVIEW 1-1

Neuroscience in the Twenty-First Century

1. Traumatic brain injury (TBI)

2. central nervous system (CNS); peripheral nervous system (PNS)

3. cerebrum; forebrain; hemispheres; brainstem

4. inherited; learning

5. Research on embodied behavior proposes that we understand each other not only by listening to words but also by observing gestures and other body language and that we think not only with silent language but also with overt gestures and body language.

REVIEW 1-2

Perspectives on Brain and Behavior

1. mentalism; dualism; Materialism

2. natural selection; Charles Darwin

3. minimally conscious state *or* MCS; persistent vegetative state *or* PVS

4. In formulating the theory of natural selection, Darwin relied on observation to conclude that living organisms are related and pass traits from parents to offspring. Mendel used experimentation to show that heritable factors underlie phenotypic variation among species.

REVIEW 1-3

Evolution of Brains and of Behavior

1. nervous systems

2. nerve net; bilaterally symmetrical; ganglia; chordate

3. cladogram

4. Humans possess the largest brain of all animals relative to body size and the most complex brain structure.

REVIEW 1-4

Evolution of the Human Brain and Behavior

1. common ancestor; chimpanzee

2. hominid; *Australopithecus; Homo habilis; Homo erectus*

3. encephalization quotient (EQ); counting brain cells (neurons)

4. *in any order:* climate changes; changes in lifestyle skills; physiological changes; delayed maturation *or* neoteny

5. Changes in climate may have driven many physical changes in hominids, including the nearly threefold increase in brain size from apes to modern humans. Evidence suggests that each new hominid species appeared after climate changes devastated old environments and produced new ones. Eventually, modern humans evolved adaptability sufficient to allow us to populate almost every climatic region on earth.

REVIEW 1-5

Modern Human Brain Size and Intelligence

1. species-typical behavior

2. culture; memes

3. *g;* multiple intelligences

4. In comparing different species, a larger brain correlates with more complex behavior. In comparing individuals within a species, brain size and intelligence are only remotely related. Rather, the complexity of different brain regions is related to behavioral abilities. Humans, for example, vary widely in body size and in brain size as well as in having different kinds of intelligence. All of these factors make any simple comparison of individuals' brain sizes and intelligence impossible.

CHAPTER 2

What Is the Nervous System's Functional Anatomy?

REVIEW 2-1

Overview of Brain Function and Structure

1. behavior; brain

2. *in any order:* frontal; temporal; parietal; occipital

3. neuroplasticity

4. white matter; gray matter

5. tracts; nerves

6. Compare your diagram with Figure 2-2B.

REVIEW 2-2

The Nervous System's Evolutionary Development

1. forebrain; midbrain; hindbrain

2. behavior

3. The forebrain has grown dramatically over the course of vertebrate evolution. But primitive forms have not been discarded and replaced as more complex nervous systems emerged. The forebrain's growth thus is an elaboration of functions already present in the other brain regions and leads to its functioning on multiple levels.

REVIEW 2-3

The Central Nervous System: Mediating Behavior

1. levels of function

2. spinal cord

3. hindbrain; midbrain; diencephalon

4. cerebellum

5. basal ganglia; limbic system

6. allocortex; neocortex; sensory; motor; integrative

7. The forebrain regulates cognitive activity, including thought and memory, and holds ultimate control over movement (behavior).

REVIEW 2-4

Somatic Nervous System: Transmitting Information

1. cranial nerves; spinal (peripheral) nerves

2. same

3. head; internal organs and glands

4. The law of Bell and Magendie states that sensory (afferent) spinal nerve fibers are dorsal (in humans, posterior) and motor (efferent) spinal fibers are ventral (in humans, anterior). This law is important because it allows neurologists to predict the location of spinal cord damage accurately according to changes in sensation or movement.

REVIEW 2-5

Autonomic and Enteric Nervous Systems: Visceral Relations

1. ganglia

2. sympathetic; parasympathetic; in opposition

3. The ANS operates largely outside our conscious awareness, whether we are awake or asleep, to regulate the vegetative functions essential to life.

4. numbers and types of neurons and glia and of chemical transmitters

5. microbiome; nutrients; chemicals

6. Psychobiotics are live organisms that, when ingested in adequate amounts, can benefit people with psychiatric illness.

REVIEW 2-6

Ten Principles of Nervous System Function

1. *in any order:* olfactory system; somatic nervous system; ANS; ENS

2. multiple levels of functioning

3. excitation; inhibition

4. Any individual's perceived reality is only a rough approximation of what is actually present. An animal's representation of the world depends on the nature of the information sent to the animal's brain.

CHAPTER 3

What Are the Nervous System's Functional Units?

REVIEW 3-1

Cells of the Nervous System

1. *in either order:* neurons; 86 billion; glia; 87 billion

2. *in either order:* exciting; inhibiting

3. *in any order:* sensory neurons; detect and convey incoming stimuli into the CNS; interneurons; form links between sensory and motor neurons; motor neurons; make muscles move

4. *in any order:* ependymal cells; astrocytes; microglia; oligodendroglia; Schwann cells; nourishing; removing waste; insulating; supporting; repairing

5. The main obstacle is duplicating the complexity of a mammalian brain and its ability to change (plasticity). Advances in artificial intelligence are bringing increasingly sophisticated robotic technology to fruition.

REVIEW 3-2

Internal Structure of a Cell

1. *in any order:* cell membrane; nucleus; endoplasmic reticulum (*or* ER); Golgi bodies; microtubules (*or* tubules); vesicles

2. proteins; *in any order:* channels; gates; pumps

3. DNA; RNA; protein

4. endoplasmic reticulum (*or* ER); Golgi bodies; microtubules; exocytosis

5. By using most of the proteins that it makes, a cell enables itself to interact with other cells and to modify their behavior. The collective action of cells mediates behavior.

REVIEW 3-3

Genes, Cells, and Behavior

1. 23; protein

2. alleles; proteins

3. mutation; Down syndrome; trisomy

4. recessive; dominant

5. Selective breeding; Cloning; transgenic

6. Gene methylation *or* DNA methylation

7. Mendelian genetics concentrates on inheritance patterns—on which genes parents pass to their offspring and offspring pass to succeeding generations. Epigenetics is the study of how the environment and experience can affect the inherited genome.

CHAPTER 4

How Do Neurons Use Electrical Signals to Transmit Information?

REVIEW 4-1

Searching for Electrical Activity in the Nervous System

1. René Descartes

2. stimulation; recording

3. *in any order:* how to record from the giant axons of the North Atlantic squid; how to use an oscilloscope to measure small changes in voltage; how to craft microelectrodes small enough to place on or in an axon

4. *in either order:* concentration gradient, from an area of relatively high concentration to an area of lower concentration; voltage gradient, from an area of relatively high charge to an area of lower charge

5. Ion channels in cell membranes may open to facilitate ion movement, close to impede ion movement, or pump ions across the membrane.

REVIEW 4-2

Electrical Activity of a Membrane

1. resting potential; ions

2. semipermeable; negative

3. hyperpolarization; depolarization

4. action potential; nerve impulse

5. Nerve impulses travel more rapidly on myelinated axons because of saltatory conduction: action potentials leap between the nodes separating the glial cells that form the axon's myelin sheath.

REVIEW 4-3

How Neurons Integrate Information

1. excitatory postsynaptic potentials (EPSPs); inhibitory postsynaptic potentials (IPSPs)

2. time; space; integrates

3. cell body; initial segment; axon

4. Some neurons have voltage-sensitive channels on their dendrites that allow the reverse movement of an action potential into the neurons' dendritic fields.

REVIEW 4-4

Into the Nervous System and Back Out

1. sensory system *or* sense

2. sensory receptor cell; voltage-sensitive

3. motor; muscles

4. autoimmune; acetylcholine

5. The varieties of membrane channels generate the transmembrane charge, mediate graded potentials, and trigger the action potential.

CHAPTER 5

How Do Neurons Communicate and Adapt?

REVIEW 5-1

A Chemical Message

1. chemical synapses; gap junction

2. experience; learning

3. axodendritic; axosomatic; axomuscular; axoaxonic; axosynaptic; axoextracellular; axosecretory; dendrodendritic

4. dendrite; cell body *or* soma

5. When an action potential reaches an axon terminal, (1) a chemical transmitter that has been synthesized and stored in the axon terminal (2) is released from the presynaptic membrane into the synaptic cleft. The transmitter (3) diffuses across the cleft and binds to receptors on the postsynaptic membrane. (4) The transmitter is deactivated.

REVIEW 5-2

Varieties of Neurotransmitters and Receptors

1. synthesis; release; receptor action; inactivation

2. *in any order:* small-molecule transmitters; peptide transmitters; gaseous transmitters; lipid transmitters

3. *in either order:* acetate, choline; acetylcholinesterase *or* AChE

4. lipid; postsynaptic

5. An ionotropic receptor's pore or channel can be opened or closed to regulate the flow-through of ions, directly effecting rapid and usually excitatory voltage changes on the cell membrane. Metabotropic receptors, which are generally inhibitory and slow acting, activate second messengers to indirectly produce changes in cell function and structure.

REVIEW 5-3

Neurotransmitter Systems and Behavior

1. neurotransmitter; neurotransmitter

2. acetylcholine *or* ACh; acetylcholine *or* ACh; acetylcholine *or* ACh; norepinephrine *or* NE

3. *in either order:* serotonin *or* 5-HT; dopamine *or* DA

4. *in any order:* cholinergic; dopaminergic; noradrenergic; serotonergic

5. This idea has been attractive for a long time, because a clear relationship exists between DA loss in the substantia nigra and Parkinson disease and because acetylcholine and norepinephrine are clearly related to somatic and autonomic behaviors. But for other neurotransmitter systems in the brain, establishing clear one-to-one relationships has proved difficult.

REVIEW 5-4

Adaptive Role of Synapses in Learning and Memory

1. synapse; learning

2. *in either order:* habituation; sensitization

3. presynaptic axon terminal; sensory; calcium; less

4. interneurons; potassium *or* K; calcium ions *or* Ca^{2+}

5. posttraumatic stress disorder *or* PTSD; sensitization

6. Permanent responses to frequently occurring stimuli are biologically (*or* behaviorally *and/or* metabolically) efficient, but if stimuli change suddenly, a lack of flexibility becomes maladaptive.

CHAPTER 6

How Do Drugs and Hormones Influence the Brain and Behavior?

REVIEW 6-1

Principles of Psychopharmacology

1. psychoactive drugs; psychopharmacology

2. blood–brain barrier; brain

3. synapses; agonists; antagonists

4. tolerance; sensitization

5. *in any order:* feces; urine; sweat; breath; breast milk

6. (a) Drug use at home is unlikely to condition drug-taking behavior to familiar home cues, so tolerance is likely to occur. (b) Novel cues in a work setting may enhance conditioning and so sensitize the occasional drug user.

REVIEW 6-2

Grouping Psychoactive Drugs

1. *in either order:* behavioral; psychoactive

2. GABA$_A$; Cl$^-$ *or* chloride ion

3. MAO inhibitors; SSRIs

4. endorphins

5. release; reuptake; D$_2$

6. Psychotropic drugs act on many neurotransmitters, including acetylcholine, anandamide, dopamine, epinephrine, glutamate, norepinephrine, and serotonin.

REVIEW 6-3

Factors Influencing Individual Responses to Drugs

1. disinhibition theory (also, impulse control); learning; behavioral myopia theory

2. Substance abuse; addiction *or* substance dependence

3. psychomotor activation; mesolimbic dopamine system

4. females; males

5. Behavioral myopia theory suggests that intoxicated individuals are unusually responsive to local and immediate cues, so the environment excessively influences their behavior, while consequences go ignored.

REVIEW 6-4

Explaining and Treating Drug Abuse

1. liking (pleasure); tolerance; wanting (craving); sensitization

2. frontal cortex; brainstem; mesolimbic dopamine system (pathways); basal ganglia

3. inheritance; epigenetics

4. drugs; other life experiences

5. A reasonable approach to treatment views drug addiction in the same way as chronic behavioral addictions and medical problems are viewed: as a lifelong challenge for most people.

REVIEW 6-5

Hormones

1. neurohormones; pituitary gland; releasing hormones; brain

2. *in either order:* steroids; peptides

3. homeostatic; gonadal; glucocorticoids

4. anabolic (*or* anabolic–androgenic) steroids; muscle mass; masculinizing

5. epinephrine; cortisol

6. The hippocampus is important in ending the stress response by regulating cortisol levels. If cortisol remains elevated by prolonged stress, eventually it damages the hippocampus.

CHAPTER 7

How Do We Study the Brain's Structures and Functions?

REVIEW 7-1

Measuring and Manipulating Brain and Behavior

1. *in either order:* brain function; behavior; *any one from among:* place learning, matching to place, landmark learning

2. sectioning and staining; multiphoton microscope

3. *in any order:* brain lesions; brain stimulation; drugs; optogenetics; chemogenetics

4. Brain stimulation methods include using electrical pulses, as in DBS; magnetic fields, as in TMS; chemicals, by administering drugs; or in the transgenic techniques of optogenetics, which employs light, and chemogenetics, which employs synthetic drugs to interact exclusively with designer receptors.

REVIEW 7-2

Measuring the Brain's Electrical Activity

1. *in any order:* single-cell recording; EEG; ERP; MEG

2. action potentials

3. graded potentials

4. magnetic activity of many neurons; three-dimensional localization of the cell groups generating the measured field

5. EEG is much less expensive than MEG.

REVIEW 7-3

Anatomical Imaging Techniques: CT and MRI

1. *in either order:* computed tomography *or* CT scan; magnetic resonance imaging *or* MRI

2. neural connections *or* fiber pathways; concentrations of brain metabolites

3. brain injury *or* brain damage

4. CT produces X-ray images of one object from many angles, then uses scanning software to combine them into a three-dimensional image of the brain.

REVIEW 7-4

Functional Brain Imaging

1. *in any order:* functional magnetic resonance imaging *or* fMRI; optical tomography *or* fNIRS; functional positron emission tomography *or* PET

2. radioactively labeled molecules; neurochemical

3. cerebral blood flow

4. Resting-state images in PET and rs-fMRI can identify abnormalities in brain function. rs-fMRI can also identify functional connections in the resting brain.

REVIEW 7-5

Chemical and Genetic Measures of Brain and Behavior

1. biochemical; *in either order:* microdialysis; voltammetry

2. concordance rates

3. DNA; gene expression

4. Epigenetic studies show that life experience can alter gene expression and that these changes are associated with changes in neuronal structure and connectivity. Altered neuronal organization in turn is associated with changes in behavior.

REVIEW 7-6

Comparing Neuroscience Research Methods

1. *in any order:* temporal resolution; spatial resolution; degree of invasiveness

2. *any one or more:* EEG, ERP, *and/or* fNIRS; inexpensive

3. The fundamental goal of neuroscience research is to gain an understanding of brain–behavior relationships.

REVIEW 7-7
Using Animals in Brain—Behavior Research

1. *any two in any order:* stroke; ADHD; Parkinson disease; schizophrenia

2. whether laboratory animals have the same symptoms that humans do

3. neural bases; treatments

4. Using laboratory animals in research leads to concerns about animal welfare and raises ethical issues about whether animals should be used in research and, if so, in what types of research.

CHAPTER 8
How Does the Nervous System Develop and Adapt?

REVIEW 8-1
Three Perspectives on Brain Development

1. behavior

2. neural circuits

3. *any three in any order:* hormones; sensory experience; injuries; genes

4. Behaviors cannot emerge until the requisite neural structures are sufficiently mature.

REVIEW 8-2
Neurobiology of Development

1. neural tube

2. neurogenesis; gliogenesis

3. *in either order:* cell adhesion molecules *or* CAMs; tropic factors

4. *in either order:* myelination; synaptic pruning

5. Dynamic changes in frontal lobe structure (morphology) are related to the development of intelligence.

REVIEW 8-3
Using Emerging Behaviors to Infer Neural Maturation

1. independent finger movements *or* the pincer grasp

2. vocabulary; sound processing

3. Piaget's stages of cognitive development

4. temporal lobe; basal ganglia

5. Correlation does not prove causation.

REVIEW 8-4
Brain Development and the Environment

1. chemoaffinity hypothesis

2. amblyopia

3. testosterone

4. critical periods *or* sensitive periods

5. Adolescence is a time of rapid brain change related to pubertal hormones and psychosocial stressors, both of which make the brain vulnerable to disorders.

CHAPTER 9
How Do We Sense, Perceive, and See the World?

REVIEW 9-1
Nature of Sensation and Perception

1. Sensory receptors

2. Receptive; density

3. target in the brain

4. subjective experience of sensation

5. Each modality has many receptors and sends information to the cortex to form topographic maps.

REVIEW 9-2
The Visual System's Functional Anatomy

1. retinal ganglion cells *or* RGCs

2. P *or* parvocellular; M *or* magnocellular

3. geniculostriate; tectopulvinar

4. facial agnosia *or* prosopagnosia

5. The dorsal stream to the parietal lobe processes the visual guidance of movements (the *how*). The ventral stream to the temporal lobe processes the visual perception of objects (the *what*).

REVIEW 9-3
Location in the Visual World

1. small size

2. photoreceptors; retinal ganglion cells, lateral geniculate neurons, cortical neurons

3. topographic map

4. corpus callosum

5. The fovea is represented by a larger area in the cortex than the visual field's periphery, and thus there is more processing of foveal information in region V1 than of peripheral information.

REVIEW 9-4
Neuronal Activity

1. bars of light

2. temporal

3. trichromatic theory

4. opponent

5. RGCs are excited by one wavelength of light and inhibited by another, producing two pairs of what seem to be color opposites—red versus green and blue versus yellow.

REVIEW 9-5
The Visual Brain in Action

1. hemianopia

2. scotomas

3. monocular blindness

4. optic ataxia

5. Damage to the dorsal stream produces deficits in visually guided movements. Damage to the ventral stream produces deficits in object recognition.

CHAPTER 10
How Do We Hear, Speak, and Make Music?

REVIEW 10-1
Sound Waves: Stimulus for Audition

1. air pressure waves *or* compression waves *or* sound waves

2. *in any order:* frequency; amplitude; complexity

3. *in any order:* loudness; pitch; prosody, quality *or* timbre

4. temporal

5. Delivery speed, or the number of sound segments that can be analyzed per second, distinguishes speech and musical sounds from other auditory inputs. Nonlanguage sounds faster than 5 segments per second are heard as a buzz, yet we are capable of understanding speech delivered at nearly 30 segments per second. Random or aperiodic sounds are noise.

REVIEW 10-2
Functional Anatomy of the Auditory System

1. ossicles *or, in any order,* hammer, anvil, and stirrup

2. inner hair cells; cochlea

3. *in either order:* basilar; tectorial

4. auditory *or* cochlear; auditory vestibular *or* eighth

5. inferior colliculus; medial geniculate nucleus

6. The planum temporale is larger in the left hemisphere, and Heschl's gyrus is larger in the right. In most people, this anatomical asymmetry correlates to a functional asymmetry: the left temporal cortex analyzes language-related sounds, whereas the right temporal cortex analyzes music-related ones.

REVIEW 10-3
Neural Activity and Hearing

1. tonotopic

2. cochlea

3. superior olive; trapezoid body

4. audition for action

5. The brain detects a sound's location via two mechanisms. Neurons in the brainstem (hindbrain) compute the ITD, the time difference in a sound wave's arrival at each ear. Other neurons in the brainstem compute IID, the difference in sound amplitude (loudness) in each ear.

REVIEW 10-4
Anatomy of Language and Music

1. language; music
2. *in any order:* Broca's area; supplementary speech area; face area of motor cortex
3. Wernicke's
4. Broca's
5. *in either order:* perfect (*or* absolute) pitch; amusic *or* tone deaf
6. Three lines of evidence support the idea that language is innate: the universality of language, the natural acquisition by children, and the presence of syntax in all languages.

REVIEW 10-5
Auditory Communication in Nonhuman Species

1. epigenetic mechanisms
2. left
3. echolocation; sonar
4. Birdsong dialects demonstrate that the songs young birds hear influence how they sing.

CHAPTER 11

How Does the Nervous System Respond to Stimulation and Produce Movement?

REVIEW 11-1
A Hierarchy of Movement Control

1. hierarchy
2. prefrontal; premotor; motor cortex *or* M1
3. brainstem
4. spinal cord
5. Lower-level functions in the motor hierarchy can continue in the absence of higher-level ones, but the higher levels provide voluntary control over movements. When the brain is disconnected from the spinal cord then, movement can no longer be controlled at will.

REVIEW 11-2
Motor System Organization

1. topographic; homunculus; larger
2. motor map
3. corticospinal; lateral corticospinal; anterior corticospinal
4. trunk; arm; finger
5. muscles; *in either order:* flexes, extends

6. The motor cortex, M1, is organized into a set of functional categories that encode a movement lexicon, or dictionary. Used in different combinations, these few movements enable more complex movements.

REVIEW 11-3
Basal Ganglia, Cerebellum, and Movement

1. basal ganglia; force
2. hyperkinetic; hypokinetic
3. accuracy; skills
4. The cerebellum compares an intended movement with the actual movement, calculates any necessary corrections, and informs the cortex to correct the movement.

REVIEW 11-4
Somatosensory System Receptors and Pathways

1. hapsis; proprioception; nociception
2. posterior; anterior
3. pain gate
4. periaqueductal gray matter *or* PAG
5. vestibular; balance
6. Without proprioception, sensory information about body location and movement is lost and can be regained by only using vision.

REVIEW 11-5
Exploring the Somatosensory Cortex

1. primary; secondary
2. apraxia
3. dorsal visual; ventral visual
4. Pain perception does not depend simply on pain sensations but is a construct of the brain.

CHAPTER 12

What Causes Emotional and Motivated Behavior?

REVIEW 12-1
Identifying the Causes of Behavior

1. rewarding
2. minimum level of sensory stimulation
3. smell and taste *or* chemical senses
4. In general, behavior is controlled by neural circuits that are modulated by a wide range of factors.

REVIEW 12-2
The Chemical Senses

1. olfactory epithelium
2. flavor
3. pheromones
4. allele of the taste receptor gene *TAS2R38*; number of taste buds

5. Any given odorant stimulates a unique pattern of receptors, and the summed activity, or pattern of activity, produces our perception of a particular odor.

REVIEW 12-3
Evolution, Environment, and Behavior

1. rewards *or* reinforcers
2. taste aversion learning
3. innate releasing mechanisms *or* IRMs
4. tasting
5. When two unrelated events are experienced together, they may inadvertently become associated. For example, unexpected pain in the presence of a stranger may lead to a faulty association between the person and the pain.

REVIEW 12-4
Neuroanatomy of Motivated and Emotional Behavior

1. regulatory; nonregulatory
2. hypothalamus
3. *in any order:* hypothalamus; limbic system; frontal lobes
4. *in any order:* dorsolateral; orbitofrontal; ventromedial
5. amygdala
6. hormones
7. The limbic system stimulates emotional reactions and species-typical behaviors, whereas the frontal lobes generate the rationale for behavior at the right time and context, taking into account factors such as external events and internal information.

REVIEW 12-5
Control of Regulatory and Nonregulatory Behavior

1. *in any order:* lateral hypothalamus; ventromedial hypothalamus; paraventricular nucleus
2. *in either order:* hypothalamus; amygdala
3. *in either order:* organizing; activating
4. osmotic; hypovolemic
5. Variations in epigenetic effects could lead to different architecture and function of the hypothalamus among heterosexuals, homosexuals, and transgender individuals.

REVIEW 12-6
Reward

1. rewarding
2. wanting; liking
3. *in any order:* dopamine; opioid; benzodiazepine–GABA
4. Intracranial self-stimulation is a phenomenon whereby animals learn to turn on a stimulating electric current to their brain, presumably because it activates the neural system that underlies reward.

CHAPTER 13

Why Do We Sleep and Dream?

REVIEW 13-1

A Clock for All Seasons

1. circannual; circadian

2. free-running; Zeitgebers

3. *any 2:* light pollution; jet lag; working swing shifts; working night shifts

4. Circadian rhythm allows us to synchronize our behavior with our body's metabolic processes—so that we are hungry at optimal times for eating, for example, and tired at optimal sleep times.

REVIEW 13-2

Neural Basis of the Biological Clock

1. superchiasmatic nucleus *or* SCN

2. retinohypothalamic; melanopsin ganglion *or* photosensitive retinal ganglion

3. shell; chemical; anatomical

4. Experimental evidence suggests that the circadian rhythm can put a time stamp on a behavioral event, rendering it easier to re-call at the same time in the circadian cycle that it occurred in previously.

REVIEW 13-3

Sleep Stages and Dreaming

1. *in either order:* REM, rapid eye movement; NREM, non–rapid eye movement

2. EOG *or* electrooculogram; EMG *or* electro-myogram; EEG *or* electroencephalogram

3. five; lengthening

4. everyone; real time

5. Interpreting dreams is difficult because it is always possible that the interpreter will impose his or her own explanation, or spin, on the dreams.

REVIEW 13-4

What Does Sleep Accomplish?

1. biological; restorative; memories

2. Explicit; implicit

3. place cell; NREM

4. microsleep

5. If a memory can be stored during waking, sleep may not be essential for its storage.

REVIEW 13-5

Neural Bases of Sleep

1. reticular activating system *or* RAS; NREM

2. coma

3. REM sleep

4. subcoerulear

5. We have separate neural systems for keeping us awake while we are still (cholinergic) and awake when we move (serotinergic).

REVIEW 13-6

Sleep Disorders

1. insomnia; narcolepsy

2. drug-dependent insomnia

3. sleep paralysis; cataplexy

4. REM sleep behavioral disorder *or* REM without atonia; subcoerulear

5. Orexin is probably only one of many factors related to waking behavior, as animals with narcolepsy can be awake but then collapse into sleep.

CHAPTER 14

How Do We Learn and Remember?

REVIEW 14-1

Connecting Learning and Memory

1. Pavlovian *or* classical

2. operant *or* instrumental

3. implicit; explicit

4. Episodic

5. Memory is not localized to any particular brain circuit or region. Rather, multiple memory circuits vary with the require-ments of the memory task.

REVIEW 14-2

Dissociating Memory Circuits

1. *in either order:* hippocampus; amygdala

2. basal ganglia

3. Lashley searched for explicit memory in the perceptual and motor systems of his animal subjects using invasive tests designed mostly for implicit memory. Milner studied a patient with medial temporal removal and used behavioral tests of both explicit and implicit memory.

REVIEW 14-3

Neural Systems Underlying Explicit and Implicit Memories

1. *in either order:* hippocampus; neocortex (*or* cortex)

2. implicit

3. amygdala

4. consolidation

5. Emotional experiences stimulate hormonal and neurochemical activating systems that stimulate the amygdala. The amygdala in turn modulates the laying down of memory circuits in the rest of the brain.

REVIEW 14-4

Structural Basis of Brain Plasticity

1. long-term potentiation *or* LTP; long-term depression *or* LTD

2. GABAergic *or* inhibitory

3. *in either order:* synapse number; neuron number

4. hippocampus

5. behavioral sensitization

6. Plastic changes in neural networks can interfere with behavior, essentially by learning behaviors that interfere with healthy function. Examples are addiction and PTSD.

REVIEW 14-5

Recovery from Brain Injury

1. *in any order:* learn new ways to solve problems; reorganize the brain to do more with less; replace the lost neurons

2. *in either order:* direct cortical stimulation; deep brain stimulation *or* DBS

3. neurotrophic

4. Functional improvement after brain injury reflects compensation rather than recovery.

CHAPTER 15

How Does the Brain Think?

REVIEW 15-1

The Nature of Thought

1. *in order:* attending to; identifying; making meaningful responses to

2. language; flexibility

3. neuron

4. Much of human thought is verbal. Language allows us to categorize informa-tion and provides a way to organize our behavior around time.

REVIEW 15-2

Cognition and the Association Cortex

1. knowledge; cognition

2. temporal; parietal

3. *in either order:* plan movements; organize behavior over time

4. Mirror

5. Multimodal cortex allows the brain to combine characteristics of stimuli across different sensory modalities, whether we encounter them together or separately.

REVIEW 15-3

Expanding Frontiers of Cognitive Neuroscience

1. cognitive neuroscience

2. brain connectome

3. cerebellum

4. social interactions

5. theory of mind

6. decision making

7. *in any order:* understanding others; understanding oneself; self-regulation; social living

REVIEW 15-4
Cerebral Asymmetry in Thinking

1. *in either order:* spatial behavior; music
2. *in either order:* controlling voluntary movement sequences; language
3. corpus callosum
4. Because the hemispheres process information differently, they think differently. And the existence of language in the left hemisphere allows it to label computations and thus make inferences that the right cannot.

REVIEW 15-5
Variations in Cognitive Organization

1. *in either order:* sex; handedness
2. neural circuits
3. synesthesia
4. Gonadal hormones influence brain development and shape neural circuits in adulthood.

REVIEW 15-6
Intelligence

1. *g* factor *or* general intelligence; multiple intelligences; convergent and divergent; intelligence A; intelligence B
2. structural; functional
3. *any 3, in any order:* gyral patterns; cytoarchitectonics; vascular patterns; neurochemistry
4. epigenetic
5. Both fMRI and ERP studies show that the efficiency of prefrontal–parietal circuits is related to standard intelligence measures. "Executive" function is related to gray matter volume in the frontal lobe.

REVIEW 15-7
Consciousness

1. complex
2. Consciousness
3. consciousness
4. Movements in which speed is critical, such as hitting a pitched ball, cannot be controlled consciously.

CHAPTER 16
What Happens When The Brain Misbehaves?

REVIEW 16-1
Multidisciplinary Research on Brain and Behavioral Disorders

1. brainstem and limbic system; neocortex; dorsal frontal cortex
2. *in any order:* genetic errors; epigenetic mechanisms; progressive cell death; rapid cell death; loss of neural connections
3. PKU *or* phenylketonuria
4. subjective
5. Brain pathology can exist without obvious clinical symptoms and clinical symptoms without obvious pathology.

REVIEW 16-2
Classifying and Treating Brain and Behavioral Disorders

1. *any 3 in any order:* social, psychological, psychiatric, neurological
2. Epidemiology
3. genetics, neuroimaging
4. *in any order:* neurosurgical, electrophysiological, pharmacological, behavioral
5. deep brain stimulation *or* DBS
6. transcranial magnetic stimulation *or* TMS

7. Classification systems can be revised using new information such as that obtained from genetics and brain imaging.

REVIEW 16-3
Understanding and Treating Neurological Disorders

1. Alzheimer; Parkinson
2. TBI *or* traumatic brain injury
3. ischemia; stroke
4. loss of cells from the substantia nigra; accumulation of Lewy bodies
5. Aerobic exercise and brain training are strategies for enhancing or stimulating neuroplasticity as we age.

REVIEW 16-4
Understanding and Treating Psychiatric Disorders

1. *in any order:* dopamine, glutamate, GABA
2. *in either order:* temporal; frontal
3. *in either order:* norepinephrine; serotonin
4. cognitive-behavioral therapy *or* CBT
5. Many genetic and epigenetic influences contribute to every behavior, including schizophrenia.

A

absolutely refractory The state of an axon in the repolarizing period, during which a new action potential cannot be elicited (with some exceptions), because gate 2 of sodium channels, which are not voltage sensitive, are closed.

acetylcholine (ACh) First neurotransmitter discovered in the PNS and CNS; activates skeletal muscles in the SNS; may either excite or inhibit internal organs in the ANS.

action potential Large, brief reversal in the polarity of an axon membrane.

activating system Neural pathways that coordinate brain activity through a single neurotransmitter; its cell bodies lie in a brainstem nucleus; axons are distributed through a wide CNS region.

addiction Desire for a drug; manifested by frequent use, leading to physical dependence in addition to abuse; often associated with tolerance and unpleasant, sometimes dangerous, withdrawal symptoms on cessation. Per the DSM-5, called substance use disorder.

afferent Conducting toward a CNS structure.

agonist Substance that enhances synapse function.

akathesia Small, involuntary movements or changes in posture; motor restlessness.

allele Alternative form of a gene; a gene pair contains two alleles.

alpha rhythm Regular wave pattern in an electroencephalogram; found in most people when they are relaxed with eyes closed.

Alzheimer disease Degenerative brain disorder related to aging that first appears as progressive memory loss and later develops into generalized dementia.

amblyopia Condition in which vision in one eye is reduced as a result of disuse; usually caused by a failure of the two eyes to look in the same direction.

amnesia Partial or total loss of memory.

amphetamine Drug that releases the neurotransmitter dopamine into its synapse and like cocaine, blocks dopamine reuptake.

amplitude Stimulus intensity; in audition, roughly equivalent to loudness, graphed by the increasing height of a sound wave.

amusia Tone deafness—inability to distinguish between musical notes.

amygdala Almond-shaped collection of nuclei in the limbic system; plays a role in emotional and species-typical behaviors.

anabolic steroid Class of synthetic hormones related to testosterone that have both muscle-building (anabolic) and masculinizing (androgenic) effects; also called *anabolic–androgenic steroid.*

androgen Class of hormones that stimulates or controls masculine characteristics and level of sexual interest.

anencephaly Failure of the forebrain to develop.

anomalous speech representation Condition in which a person's speech zones are located in the right hemisphere or in both hemispheres.

anorexia nervosa Exaggerated concern with being overweight that leads to inadequate food intake and often excessive exercising; can lead to severe weight loss and even starvation.

antagonist Substance that blocks synapse function.

anterior spinothalamic tract Pathway from the spinal cord to the thalamus that carries information about pain and temperature.

anterograde amnesia Inability to remember events subsequent to a disturbance of the brain such as head trauma, electroconvulsive shock, or neurodegenerative disease.

antianxiety agent Drug that reduces anxiety, including minor tranquilizers such as benzodiazepines and sedative-hypnotic agents.

aphagia Failure to eat; may be due to an unwillingness to eat or to motor difficulties, especially with swallowing.

aphasia Inability to speak or comprehend language despite the presence of normal comprehension and intact vocal mechanisms. *Broca's aphasia* is the inability to speak fluently despite the presence of normal comprehension and intact vocal mechanisms. *Wernicke's aphasia* is the inability to understand or to produce meaningful language even though word production remains intact.

apoptosis Genetically programmed cell death.

apraxia Inability to make voluntary movements in the absence of paralysis or other motor or sensory impairment, especially an inability to make proper use of an object.

association cortex Neocortex outside primary sensory and motor cortices; functions to produce cognition.

associative learning Linkage of two or more unrelated stimuli to elicit a behavioral response.

astrocyte Star-shaped glial cell that provides structural support to CNS neurons and transports substances between neurons and blood vessels.

atonia Lacking tone; condition of complete muscle inactivity produced by motor neuron inhibition.

attention Narrowing or focusing awareness to a part of the sensory environment or to a class of stimuli.

attention-deficit/hyperactivity disorder (ADHD) Developmental disorder characterized by core behavioral symptoms, including impulsivity, hyperactivity, and/or inattention.

auditory flow Change heard as a person and a source of sound move relative to one another.

autism spectrum disorder (ASD) Range of cognitive symptoms from mild to severe that characterize autism; severe symptoms include greatly impaired social interaction, a bizarre and narrow range of interests, marked abnormalities in language and communication, and fixed, repetitive movements.

autoimmune disease Illness resulting from an abnormal immune response by the body against substances and tissues normally present in the body.

autonomic nervous system (ANS) Part of the PNS that regulates the functioning of internal organs and glands.

autoreceptor Self-receptor in a neuronal membrane; that is, it responds to the same transmitter released by the neuron.

axon Root, or single fiber, of a neuron that carries messages to other neurons.

axon collateral Branch of an axon.

axon hillock Juncture of soma and axon.

B

back propagation Reverse movement of an action potential into the soma and dendritic field of a neuron; postulated to play a role in plastic changes that underlie learning.

barbiturate Drug that produces sedation and sleep.

basal ganglia Subcortical forebrain nuclei that coordinate voluntary movements of the limbs and body; connected to the thalamus and to the midbrain.

basic rest–activity cycle (BRAC) Recurring cycle of temporal packets, about 90-minute periods in humans, during which an animal's level of arousal waxes and wanes.

basilar membrane Receptor surface in the cochlea that transduces sound waves into neural activity.

behavioral myopia "Nearsighted" behavior displayed under the influence of alcohol: local and immediate cues become prominent; remote cues and consequences are ignored.

behavioral neuroscience Study of the biological bases of behavior in humans and other animals.

behavioral sensitization Escalating behavioral response to the repeated administration of a psychomotor stimulant such as amphetamine, cocaine, or nicotine; also called *drug-induced behavioral sensitization.*

behavioral therapy Treatment that applies learning principles, such as conditioning, to eliminate unwanted behaviors.

beta (β) rhythm Fast brain wave activity pattern associated with a waking EEG.

bilateral symmetry Body plan in which organs or parts present on both sides of the body are mirror images in appearance. For example, the hands are bilaterally symmetrical, whereas the heart is not.

binding problem Philosophical question focused on how the brain ties single and varied sensory and motor events together into a unified perception or behavior.

biological clock Neural system that times behavior.

biorhythm Inherent timing mechanism that controls or initiates biological processes.

bipolar disorder Mood disorder characterized by periods of depression alternating with normal periods and periods of intense excitation, or mania.

bipolar neuron Sensory neuron with one axon and one dendrite.

blind spot Retinal region where axons forming the optic nerve leave the eye and blood vessels enter and leave; has no photoreceptors and is thus said to be blind.

blob Region in V1 that contains color-sensitive neurons, as revealed by staining for cytochrome oxidase.

blood–brain barrier Tight junctions between the cells that compose blood vessels in the brain, providing a barrier to the entry of an array of substances, including toxins, into the brain.

brain connectome Map of the complete structural and functional fiber pathways of the human brain in vivo.

brainstem Central structure of the brain; responsible for most unconscious behavior.

Broca's area Anterior left hemisphere speech area that functions with the motor cortex to produce movements needed for speaking.

C

carbon monoxide (CO) Gaseous neurotransmitter; activates cellular metabolism.

cataplexy State of atonia, as in REM sleep, occurring while a person is awake and active; linked to strong emotional stimulation.

cell adhesion molecule (CAM) A chemical molecule to which specific cells can adhere, thus aiding in migration.

cell assembly Hypothetical group of neurons that become functionally connected via common sensory inputs; proposed by Hebb as the basis of perception, memory, and thought.

cell body (soma) Core region of the cell containing the nucleus and other organelles for making proteins.

central nervous system (CNS) The brain and spinal cord, which together mediate behavior.

cerebellum Major brainstem structure specialized for learning and coordinating movements; assists the cerebrum in generating many behaviors.

cerebral cortex Thin, heavily folded film of nerve tissue composed of neurons that is the outer layer of the forebrain. Also called *neocortex.*

cerebral palsy Group of disorders that result from brain damage acquired perinatally (at or near birth).

cerebral voltammetry Technique used to identify the concentration of specific chemicals in the brain as animals behave freely.

cerebrospinal fluid (CSF) Clear solution of sodium chloride and other salts that fills the ventricles inside the brain and circulates around the brain and spinal cord beneath the arachnoid layer in the subarachnoid space.

cerebrum (forebrain) Major structure of the forebrain that consists of two mirror image hemispheres (left and right) and is responsible for most conscious behavior.

channel Opening in a protein embedded in the cell membrane that allows the passage of ions.

chemical synapse Junction at which messenger molecules are released when stimulated by an action potential.

chemoaffinity hypothesis Proposal that neurons or their axons and dendrites are drawn toward a signaling chemical that indicates the correct pathway.

chemogenetics Transgenic technique that combines genetics and synthetic drugs to activate targeted cells in living tissue.

cholinergic neuron Neuron that uses acetylcholine as its main neurotransmitter; *cholinergic* applies to any neuron that uses ACh as its main transmitter.

chordate Animal that has both a brain and a spinal cord.

chronic traumatic encephalopathy (CTE) Progressive degenerative disease caused by multiple concussions and other closed-head injuries, characterized by neurofibrillary tangles, plaques, cerebral atrophy, and expanded ventricles due to cell loss.

chronotype Individual differences in circadian activity.

circadian rhythm Day–night rhythm.

cladogram Phylogenetic tree that branches repeatedly, suggesting a taxonomy of organisms based on the time sequence in which evolutionary branches arise.

clinical trial Consensual experiment directed toward developing a treatment.

cochlea Inner ear structure containing the auditory receptor cells.

cochlear implant Electronic device implanted surgically into the inner ear to transduce sound waves to neural activity and allow a deaf person to hear.

cognition Act or process of knowing or coming to know; in psychology, refers to thought processes.

cognitive-behavioral therapy (CBT) Problem-focused, action-oriented, structured treatment for eliminating dysfunctional thoughts and maladaptive behaviors.

cognitive enhancement Brain function enhancement by pharmacological, physiological, or surgical manipulation.

cognitive neuroscience Study of the neural bases of cognition.

cognitive therapy Psychotherapy based on the perspective that thoughts intervene between events and emotions, and thus the treatment of emotional disorders requires changing maladaptive patterns of thinking.

color constancy Phenomenon whereby an object's perceived color tends to remain constant relative to other colors, regardless of changes in illumination.

coma Prolonged state of deep unconsciousness resembling sleep.

common ancestor Forebear of two or more lineages or family groups; ancestral to both groups.

compensation Following brain damage, neuroplastic ability to modify behavior from that used prior to the damage.

competitive inhibitor Drug, such as nalorphine and naloxone, that acts quickly to block opioid action by competing with the opioid for binding sites; used to treat opioid addiction.

computed tomography (CT) X-ray technique that produces a static three-dimensional image of the brain in cross section—a *CT scan*.

concentration gradient Difference in the relative abundance of a substance among regions of a container; allows the substance to diffuse from an area of higher concentration to an area of lower concentration.

conditioned response (CR) In Pavlovian conditioning, the learned response to a formerly neutral conditioned stimulus (CS).

conditioned stimulus (CS) In Pavlovian conditioning, an originally neutral stimulus that after association with an unconditioned stimulus (UCS) triggers a conditioned response (CR).

cone Photoreceptor specialized for color and high visual acuity.

connectome Comprehensive map of all structural connectivity (the physical wiring) in an organism's nervous system.

consciousness The mind's level of responsiveness to impressions made by the senses.

consolidation Process of stabilizing a memory trace after learning.

constraint-induced therapy Procedure in which restraint of a healthy limb forces a patient to use an impaired limb to enhance recovery of function.

contralateral neglect Ignoring a part of the body or world on the side opposite (contralateral to) that of a brain injury.

convergent thinking Form of thinking that searches for a single answer to a question (such as $2 + 2 = ?$); contrasts with divergent thinking.

corpus callosum Band of white matter containing about 200 million nerve fibers that connects the two cerebral hemispheres to provide a route for direct communication between them.

cortical column Anatomic organization that represents a functional unit six cortical layers deep and approximately 0.5 mm square, perpendicular to the cortical surface.

corticospinal tract Bundle of nerve fibers directly connecting the cerebral cortex to the spinal cord, branching at the brainstem into an opposite-side lateral tract that informs movement of limbs and digits and a same side anterior tract that informs movement of the trunk; also called *pyramidal tract*.

cranial nerve One of a set of 12 nerve pairs that control sensory and motor functions of the head, neck, and internal organs.

critical period Developmental window during which some event has a long-lasting influence on the brain; also, *sensitive period*.

cross-tolerance Reduction of response to a novel drug because of tolerance to a chemically related drug.

culture Learned behaviors that are passed on from one generation to the next through teaching and imitation.

cytoarchitectonic map Map of the neocortex based on the organization, structure, and distribution of the cells.

D

deafferentation Loss of incoming sensory input, usually due to damage to sensory fibers; also loss of any afferent input to a structure.

decibel (dB) Measure of the relative physical intensity of sounds.

declarative memory Ability to recount what one knows, to detail the time, place, and circumstances of events; often lost in amnesia.

deep brain stimulation (DBS) Neurosurgery in which electrodes implanted in the brain stimulate a targeted area with a low-voltage electrical current to facilitate behavior.

delta (δ) rhythm Slow brain wave activity pattern associated with deep sleep.

dementia Acquired and persistent syndrome of intellectual impairment characterized by memory and other cognitive deficits and impairment in social and occupational functioning.

dendrite Branching extension of a neuron's cell membrane; greatly increases the cell's surface area; collects information from other cells.

dendritic spine Protrusion that greatly increases the dendrite's surface area; typical point of dendritic contact with the axons of other cells.

depolarization Decrease in electrical charge across a membrane, usually due to the inward flow of sodium ions.

dermatome Body segment corresponding to a segment of the spinal cord.

***Diagnostic and Statistical Manual of Mental Disorders* (DSM)** The American Psychiatric Association's classification system for psychiatric disorders.

diaschisis Neural shock that follows brain damage in which areas connected to the site of damage show a temporary arrest of function.

dichotic listening Experimental procedure for simultaneously presenting a different auditory input to each ear through stereophonic earphones.

diencephalon The between brain, which integrates sensory and motor information on its way to the cerebral cortex.

diffusion Movement of ions from an area of higher concentration to an area of lower concentration through random motion.

diffusion tensor imaging (DTI) Magnetic resonance imaging method that can image fiber pathways in the brain by detecting the directional movements of water molecules.

dimer Two proteins combined into one.

disinhibition theory Explanation holding that alcohol has a selective depressant effect on the brain's frontal cortex, which controls judgment, while sparing subcortical structures responsible for more instinctual behaviors, such as desire.

diurnal animal Organism that is active chiefly during daylight.

divergent thinking Form of thinking that searches for multiple solutions to a problem (how many ways can a pen be used?); contrasts with convergent thinking.

dopamine (DA) Amine neurotransmitter involved in coordinating movement, attention, learning, and in reinforcing behaviors.

dopamine hypothesis of schizophrenia Idea that excess dopamine activity causes symptoms of schizophrenia.

dorsal stream Visual processing pathway from V1 to the parietal lobe; guides movements relative to objects.

dorsolateral prefrontal cortex (DLPFC) Brodmann areas 9 and 46; makes reciprocal connections with posterior parietal cortex and the superior temporal sulcus; responsible for selecting behavior and movement with respect to temporal memory.

Down syndrome Chromosomal abnormality resulting in intellecutal impairment and other abnormalities, usually caused by an extra chromosome 21.

drug dependence insomnia Condition resulting from continuous use of sleeping pills; drug tolerance also results in deprivation of either REM or NREM sleep, leading the user to increase the drug dosage.

dualism Philosophical position that both a nonmaterial mind and a material body contribute to behavior.

dyslexia Impairment in learning to read and write; probably the most common learning disability.

E

echolocation Identifying and locating an object by bouncing sound waves off it.

efferent Conducting away from a CNS structure.

electrical stimulation Passage of an electrical current from the uninsulated tip of an electrode through tissue, resulting in changes in the electrical activity of the tissue.

electrical synapse See **gap junction.**

electrocorticography (ECoG) Graded potentials recorded with electrodes placed directly on the brain's surface.

electroencephalogram (EEG) Graph that records electrical activity from the brain and mainly indicates graded potentials of many neurons.

electrographic seizures Abnormal rhythmic neuronal discharges; may be recorded by an electroencephalogram.

embodied behavior Theory that the movements we make and the movements we perceive in others are central to communication with others.

emotion Cognitive interpretation of subjective feelings.

emotional memory Memory for the affective properties of stimuli or events.

encephalization quotient (EQ) Jerison's quantitative measure of brain size obtained from the ratio of actual brain size to expected brain size, according to the principle of proper mass, for an animal of a particular body size.

end plate On a muscle, the receptor–ion complex that is activated by the release of the neurotransmitter acetylcholine from the terminal of a motor neuron.

endocannabinoid Class of lipid neurotransmitters, including anandamide and 2-AG, synthesized at the postsynaptic membrane to act on receptors at the presynaptic membrane; affects appetite, pain, sleep, mood, memory, anxiety, and the stress response.

endorphin Opioid peptide that acts as a neurotransmitter and may be associated with feelings of pain or pleasure; mimicked by opioid drugs such as morphine, heroin, opium, and codeine.

enteric nervous system (ENS) Mesh of neurons embedded in the lining of the gut, running from the esophagus through the colon; controls the gut.

entorhinal cortex Located on the medial temporal lobe surface; provides a major route for neocortical input to the hippocampal formation; often degenerates in Alzheimer disease.

entrain Determine or modify the period of a biorhythm.

ependymal cell Glial cell that makes and secretes CSF; found on the walls of the brain's ventricles.

epidermal growth factor (EGF) Neurotrophic factor; stimulates the subventricular zone to generate cells that migrate into the striatum and eventually differentiate into neurons and glia.

epigenetics Differences in gene expression related to environment and experience.

epinephrine (EP, or adrenaline) Chemical messenger that acts as a neurotransmitter in the CNS and as a hormone to mobilize the body for fight or flight during times of stress.

episodic memory Autobiographical memory for events pegged to specific place and time contexts.

estrogens Variety of sex hormones responsible for the distinguishing characteristics of the female.

event-related potentials (ERPs) Complex electroencephalographic waveform related in time to a specific sensory event.

evolutionary psychology Discipline that seeks to apply principles of natural selection to understand the causes of human behavior.

excitation Increase in the activity of a neuron or brain area.

excitatory postsynaptic potential (EPSP) Brief depolarization of a neuron membrane in response to stimulation, making the neuron more likely to produce an action potential.

explicit memory Conscious memory: subjects can retrieve an item and indicate that they know the retrieved item is the correct one.

extinction In neurology, neglect of information on one side of the body when presented simultaneously with similar information on the other side of the body.

extrastriate (secondary visual) cortex (V2–V5) Visual cortical areas in the occipital lobe outside the striate cortex.

eyeblink conditioning Experimental technique in which subjects learn to pair a formerly neutral stimulus with a defensive blinking response.

F

facial agnosia Face blindness—the inability to recognize faces; also called *prosopagnosia*.

fear conditioning Conditioned emotional response between a neutral stimulus and an unpleasant event, such as a shock, that results in a learned association.

festination Tendency to engage in a behavior, such as walking, faster and faster.

fetal alcohol spectrum disorder (FASD) Range of physical and intellectual impairments observed in some children born to alcoholic parents.

filopod (pl. filopodia) Process at the end of a developing axon that reaches out to search for a potential target or to sample the intercellular environment.

focal seizure Seizure that arises at a synchronous, hyperactive, localized brain region (at a focus).

forebrain Evolutionarily the newest part of the brain; coordinates advanced cognitive functions such as thinking, planning, and language; contains the limbic system, basal ganglia, and neocortex.

fovea Central region of the retina specialized for high visual acuity; its receptive fields are at the center of the eye's visual field.

free-running rhythm Rhythm of the body's own devising in the absence of all external cues.

frequency Number of cycles a wave completes in a given time.

frontal lobe Part of the cerebral cortex often generally characterized as performing the brain's executive functions, such as decision making; lies anterior to the central sulcus and beneath the frontal bone of the skull.

functional magnetic resonance imaging (fMRI) Magnetic resonance imaging in which changes in elements such as iron or oxygen are measured during the performance of a specific behavior; used to measure cerebral blood flow during behavior or resting.

functional near-infrared spectroscopy (fNIRS) Noninvasive technique that gathers light transmitted through cortical tissue to image oxygen consumption; form of optical tomography.

G

G protein Guanyl nucleotide–binding protein coupled to a metabotropic receptor; when activated, binds to other proteins.

gamma-aminobutyric acid (GABA) Amino acid neurotransmitter; typically inhibits neurons.

ganglia Collection of nerve cells that function somewhat like a brain.

gap junction (electrical synapse) Area of contact between adjacent cells in which ion channels form a pore that allows ions to pass directly from one cell to the next.

gate Protein embedded in a cell membrane that allows substances to pass through the membrane on some occasions but not on others.

gender identity The degree to which a person feels male or female.

gene DNA segment that encodes the synthesis of a particular protein.

gene (DNA) methylation Epigenetic process in which a methyl group attaches to the DNA sequence, suppressing or enabling gene expression.

generalized anxiety disorder Persistently high levels of anxiety often accompanied by maladaptive behaviors to reduce anxiety; thought to be caused by chronic stress.

generalized seizure Seizure that may start at a focal location then spread rapidly and bilaterally to distributed networks in both hemispheres.

geniculostriate system Projections from the retina to the lateral geniculate nucleus to the visual cortex.

genotype Particular genetic makeup of an individual.

glabrous skin Skin that does not have hair follicles but contains larger numbers of sensory receptors than do hairy skin areas.

glial cell Nervous system cell that provides insulation, nutrients, and support and that aids in repairing neurons and eliminating waste products.

glioblast Product of a progenitor cell that gives rise to different types of glial cells.

glucocorticoid One of a group of steroid hormones, such as cortisol, secreted in times of stress; important in protein and carbohydrate metabolism.

glutamate (Glu) Amino acid neurotransmitter; typically excites neurons.

gonadal (sex) hormone One of a group of hormones, such as testosterone, that control reproductive functions and bestow sexual appearance and identity as male or female.

graded potential Small voltage fluctuation across the cell membrane.

gray matter Areas of the nervous system composed predominantly of cell bodies and capillary blood vessels that either collect and modify information or support this activity.

growth cone Growing tip of an axon.

growth spurt Sporadic period of sudden growth that lasts for a finite time.

gyrus (pl. gyri) A small protrusion or bump formed by the folding of the cerebral cortex.

H

habituation Learned behavior in which the response to a stimulus weakens with repeated presentations.

hair cell Specialized neurons in the cochlea tipped by cilia; when stimulated by waves in the cochlear fluid, the cilia bend and generate graded potentials in inner hair cells, the auditory receptor cells.

hapsis Perceptual ability to discriminate objects on the basis of touch.

hemisphere Literally, half a sphere, referring to one side of the cerebrum.

hertz (Hz) Measure of sound wave frequency (repetition rate); 1 hertz equals 1 cycle per second.

heterozygous Having two different alleles for the same trait.

hindbrain Evolutionarily the oldest part of the brain; contains the pons, medulla, reticular formation, and cerebellum, structures that coordinate and control most voluntary and involuntary movements.

hippocampus From the Greek word for *seahorse*; distinctive allocortical structure lying in the medial temporal lobe; participates in species-specific behaviors, memory, and spatial navigation and is vulnerable to the effects of stress.

histamine (H) Neurotransmitter that controls arousal and waking; can cause the constriction of smooth muscles; when activated in allergic reactions, constricts airway and contributes to asthma.

homeostatic hormone One of a group of hormones that maintain internal metabolic balance and regulate physiological systems in an organism.

homeostatic mechanism Process that maintains critical body functions within a narrow, fixed range.

hominid General term referring to primates that walk upright, including all forms of humans, living and extinct.

homonymous hemianopia Blindness of an entire left or right visual field.

homozygous Having two identical alleles for a trait.

homunculus Representation of the human body in the sensory or motor cortex; also any topographical representation of the body by a neural area.

HPA axis Hypothalamic–pituitary–adrenal circuit that controls the production and release of hormones related to stress.

Huntington disease Hereditary disease characterized by chorea (ceaseless involuntary jerky movements) and progressive dementia, ending in death.

hydrocephalus Buildup of fluid pressure in the brain and, in infants, swelling of the head, if the flow of CSF is blocked; can result in intellectual impairment.

hydrogen sulfide (H$_2$S) Gaseous neurotransmitter; slows cellular metabolism.

hyperconnectivity Increased local connections between two related brain regions.

hyperkinetic symptom Excessive involuntary movement, as seen in Tourette syndrome.

hyperphagia Overeating that leads to significant weight gain.

hyperpolarization Increase in electrical charge across a membrane, usually due to the inward flow of chloride or sodium ions or the outward flow of potassium ions.

hypnogogic hallucination Dreamlike event as sleep begins or while a person is in a state of cataplexy.

hypokinesia Slowness or absence of movement.

hypokinetic symptom Paucity of movement, as seen in Parkinson disease.

hypothalamus Diencephalon structure that contains many nuclei associated with temperature regulation, eating, drinking, and sexual behavior.

hypovolemic thirst Thirst produced by a loss of overall fluid volume from the body.

I

implicit memory Unconscious memory: subjects can demonstrate knowledge, such as a skill, conditioned response, or recall of events on prompting but cannot explicitly retrieve the information.

imprinting Formation of an attachment by an animal to one or more objects or animals at a critical period in development.

inhibition Decrease in the activity of a neuron or brain area.

inhibitory postsynaptic potential (IPSP) Brief hyperpolarization of a neuron membrane in response to stimulation, making the neuron less likely to produce an action potential.

initial segment Area near or overlapping the axon hillock where the action potential begins.

innate releasing mechanism (IRM) Hypothetical mechanism that detects specific sensory stimuli and directs an organism to take a particular action.

insomnia Disorder of slow-wave sleep resulting in prolonged inability to sleep.

insula Multifunctional cortical tissue located within the lateral fissure; contains language and taste perception–related regions and neural structures underlying social cognition.

intelligence A Hebb's term for innate intellectual potential, which is highly heritable and cannot be measured directly.

intelligence B Hebb's term for observed intelligence, influenced by experience and other factors in the course of development; measured by intelligence tests.

interneuron Association cell interposed between a sensory neuron and a motor neuron; in mammals, interneurons constitute most of the brain's neurons.

ionotropic receptor Embedded membrane protein; acts as (1) a binding site for a neurotransmitter and (2) a pore that regulates ion flow to directly and rapidly change membrane voltage.

ischemia Lack of blood to the brain, usually as a result of a stroke.

J

jet lag Fatigue and disorientation resulting from rapid travel through time zones and exposure to a changed light–dark cycle.

K

Klüver-Bucy syndrome Behavioral syndrome, characterized especially by hypersexuality, that results from bilateral injury to the temporal lobe.

Korsakoff syndrome Permanent loss of the ability to learn new information (anterograde amnesia) and to retrieve old information (retrograde amnesia) caused by diencephalic damage resulting from chronic alcoholism or malnutrition that produces a vitamin B_1 deficiency.

L

lateralization Localization of function primarily on one side of the brain.

law of Bell and Magendie The principle that sensory fibers are dorsal and motor fibers are ventral.

learned taste aversion Acquired association between a specific taste or odor and illness; leads to an aversion to foods that have the taste or odor.

learning Relatively permanent change in behavior that results from experience.

learning set Rules of the game; implicit understanding of how a problem can be solved with a rule that can be applied in many different situations.

Lewy body Circular fibrous structure found in several neurodegenerative disorders; forms within the cytoplasm of neurons and is thought to result from abnormal neurofilament metabolism.

light pollution Exposure to artificial light that changes activity patterns and so disrupts circadian rhythms.

limbic system Disparate forebrain structures lying between the neocortex and the brainstem that form a functional system controlling affective and motivated behaviors and certain forms of memory; includes cingulate cortex, amygdala, and hippocampus, among other structures.

locked-in syndrome Condition in which a patient is aware and awake but cannot move or communicate verbally because of complete paralysis of nearly all voluntary muscles except the eyes.

long-term depression (LTD) Long-lasting decrease in synaptic effectiveness after low-frequency electrical stimulation.

long-term potentiation (LTP) Long-lasting increase in synaptic effectiveness after high-frequency stimulation.

luminance contrast Amount of light an object reflects relative to its surroundings.

M

magnetic resonance imaging (MRI) Technique that produces a static three-dimensional brain image by passing a strong magnetic field through the brain, followed by a radio wave, then measuring a radio frequency signal emitted from hydrogen atoms.

magnetic resonance spectroscopy (MRS) Magnetic resonance imaging method that uses the hydrogen proton signal to determine the concentration of brain metabolites.

magnetoencephalogram (MEG) Magnetic potentials recorded from detectors placed outside the skull.

magnocellular (M) cell Large visual system neuron sensitive to moving stimuli and black-white vision.

major depression Mood disorder characterized by prolonged feelings of worthlessness and guilt, disruption of normal eating habits, sleep disturbances, a general slowing of behavior, and frequent thoughts of suicide.

mania Disordered mental state of extreme excitement.

masculinization Process by which exposure to androgens (male sex hormones) alters the brain, rendering it identifiably male.

materialism Philosophical position that behavior can be explained as a function of the nervous system without recourse to the mind.

medial forebrain bundle (MFB) Tract that connects brainstem structures with various parts of the limbic system; forms the activating projections that run from the brainstem to basal ganglia and frontal cortex.

medial geniculate nucleus Major thalamic region concerned with audition.

medial pontine reticular formation (MPRF) Nucleus in the pons participating in REM sleep.

melatonin Hormone secreted by the pineal gland during the dark phase of the day–night cycle; influences daily and seasonal biorhythms.

meme An idea, behavior, or style that spreads from person to person within a culture.

memory Ability to recall or recognize previous experience.

Ménière disease Disorder of the middle ear resulting in vertigo and loss of balance.

meninges Three layers of protective tissue—dura mater, arachnoid, and pia mater—that encase the brain and spinal cord.

mentalism Explanation of behavior as a function of the nonmaterial mind.

metabolic syndrome Combinations of medical disorders, including obesity and insulin abnormalities, that collectively increase the risk of developing cardiovascular disease and diabetes.

metabotropic receptor Embedded membrane protein with a binding site for a neurotransmitter linked to a G protein; can affect other receptors or act with second messengers to affect other cellular processes, including opening a pore.

metaplasticity Interaction among different plastic changes in the brain.

microdialysis Technique used to determine the chemical constituents of extracellular fluid in freely moving animals.

microelectrode A microscopic insulated wire or a saltwater-filled glass tube whose uninsulated tip is used to stimulate or record from neurons.

microglia Glial cells that originate in the blood, aid in cell repair, and scavenge debris in the nervous system.

microsleep Brief sleep period lasting a second or so.

midbrain Central part of the brain; contains neural circuits for hearing and seeing as well as orienting movements.

mind Proposed nonmaterial entity responsible for intelligence, attention, awareness, and consciousness.

mind–body problem Difficulty of explaining how a nonmaterial mind and a material body interact.

minimally conscious state (MCS) Condition in which a person can display some rudimentary behaviors, such as smiling or uttering a few words, but is otherwise not conscious.

mirror neuron Cell in the primate premotor and parietal cortex that fires when an individual observes an action taken by another individual.

monoamine oxidase (MAO) inhibitor Antidepressant drug that blocks the enzyme monoamine oxidase from degrading such neurotransmitters as DA, NE, and 5-HT.

monosynaptic reflex Reflex requiring one synapse between sensory input and movement.

mood stabilizer Drug for treating bipolar disorder; mutes the intensity of one pole of the disorder, thus making the other pole less likely to recur.

motivation Behavior that seems purposeful and goal-directed.

motor neuron Cell that carries efferent information from the brain and spinal cord to make muscles contract.

motor sequence Movement modules preprogrammed by the brain and produced as a unit.

multiple sclerosis (MS) Nervous system disorder resulting from the loss of myelin around axons in the CNS.

mutation Alteration of an allele that yields a different version of its protein.

myelin Glial coating that surrounds axons in the central and peripheral nervous systems; prevents adjacent neurons from short circuiting.

N

narcolepsy Slow-wave sleep disorder in which a person uncontrollably falls asleep at inappropriate times.

natural selection Darwin's theory for explaining how new species evolve and how existing species change over time. Differential success in the reproduction of different characteristics (phenotypes) results from the interaction of organisms with their environment.

neocortex (cerebral cortex) Most recently evolved outer layer (*new bark*) of the forebrain, composed of about six layers of gray matter; constructs our reality.

neoteny Process in which juvenile stages of predecessors become adult features of descendants; idea derived from the observation that more recently evolved species resemble the young of their common ancestors.

nerve Large collection of axons coursing together *outside* the CNS.

nerve growth factor (NGF) Neurotrophic factor that stimulates neurons to grow dendrites and synapses and in some cases promotes the survival of neurons.

nerve impulse Propagation of an action potential on the membrane of an axon.

nerve net Simple nervous system that has no center but consists of neurons that receive sensory information and connect directly to other neurons that move muscles.

netrin Member of the only class of tropic molecules yet isolated.

neural Darwinism Hypothesis that the processes of cell death and synaptic pruning are, like natural selection in species, the outcome of competition among neurons for connections and metabolic resources in a neural environment.

neural network Functional group of neurons that connects wide areas of the brain and spinal cord.

neural plate Primitive neural tissue that gives rise to the neural tube.

neural stem cell Self-renewing multipotential cell that gives rise to any of the different types of neurons and glia in the nervous system.

neural tube Structure in the early stage of brain development from which the brain and spinal cord develop.

neuritic plaque Area of incomplete necrosis (dead tissue) consisting of a central protein core (amyloid) surrounded by degenerative cellular fragments; often seen in the cortex of people with dementias such as Alzheimer disease.

neuroblast Product of a progenitor cell that gives rise to any of the different types of neurons.

neuroeconomics Interdisciplinary field that seeks to understand how the brain makes decisions.

neuron Specialized nerve cell engaged in information processing.

neuropeptide Short (fewer than 100), multifunctional amino acid chain; acts as a neurotransmitter and can act as a hormone; may contribute to learning.

neuroplasticity The nervous system's potential for physical or chemical change to adapt to environmental change and to compensate for injury.

neuroprosthetics Field that develops computer-assisted devices to replace lost biological function.

neuroprotectant Drug used to try to block the cascade of poststroke neural events.

neuropsychoanalysis Movement within neuroscience and psychoanalysis to combine the insights of both to yield a unified understanding of mind and brain.

neuropsychology Study of the relations between brain function and behavior, especially in humans.

neurotransmitter Chemical with an excitatory or inhibitory effect when released by a neuron onto a target.

neurotrophic factor A chemical compound that supports growth and differentiation in developing neurons and may act to keep certain neurons alive in adulthood.

nitric oxide (NO) Gaseous neurotransmitter; acts, for example, to dilate blood vessels, aid digestion, and activate cellular metabolism.

nociception Perception of pain, temperature, and itch.

node of Ranvier The part of an axon that is not covered by myelin.

nonregulatory behavior Behavior unnecessary to the animal's basic survival needs.

noradrenergic neuron From *adrenaline*, Latin for *epinephrine*; a neuron containing norepinephrine.

norepinephrine (NE, or noradrenaline) Neurotransmitter that accelerates heart rate in mammals; found in the brain and in the sympathetic division of the ANS.

NREM (non-REM) sleep Slow-wave sleep associated with delta rhythms.

nuclei (sing. nucleus) A group of cells forming a cluster that can be identified with special stains to form a functional grouping.

obesity Excessive accumulation of body fat.

obsessive-compulsive disorder (OCD) Behavior characterized by compulsively repeated acts (such as hand washing) and repetitive, often unpleasant, thoughts (obsessions).

occipital lobe Part of the cerebral cortex where visual processing begins; lies at the back of the brain and beneath the occipital bone.

ocular dominance column Functional column in the visual cortex maximally responsive to information coming from one eye.

oligodendroglia Glial cells in the CNS that myelinate axons.

operant conditioning Learning procedure in which the consequences (such as obtaining a reward) of a particular behavior (such as pressing a bar) increase or decrease the probability of the behavior occurring again; also called *instrumental conditioning*.

opioid analgesic Drug such as morphine, with sleep-inducing (narcotic) and pain-relieving (analgesic) properties; originally called narcotic analgesic.

opponent process Explanation of color vision that emphasizes the importance of the apparently opposing color pairs: red versus green and blue versus yellow.

optic ataxia Deficit in the visual control of reaching and other movements.

optic chiasm Junction of the optic nerves, one from each eye, at which the axons from the nasal halves of the retinas cross to the brain's opposite side.

optic flow Streaming of visual stimuli that accompanies an observer's movement through space.

optogenetics Transgenic technique that combines genetics and light to excite or inhibit targeted cells in living tissue.

orbitofrontal cortex (OFC) Prefrontal cortex behind the eye sockets (the *orbits*); receives projections from the dorsomedial nucleus of the thalamus; central to a variety of emotional and social behaviors, including eating; also called *orbital frontal cortex*.

organizational hypothesis Proposal that hormonal action during development alters tissue differentiation; for example, testosterone masculinizes the brain.

orienting movement Movement related to sensory inputs, such as turning the head to see the source of a sound.

oscilloscope Device that serves as a sensitive voltmeter by registering changes in voltage over time.

osmotic thirst Thirst that results from a high concentration of dissolved chemicals, or *solutes*, in body fluids.

ossicle Bone of the middle ear; includes malleus (hammer), incus (anvil), and stapes (stirrup).

otoacousitic emissions Spontaneous or evoked sound waves produced within the ear by the cochlea and escape from the ear.

P

pain gate Hypothetical neural circuit in which activity in fine-touch and pressure pathways diminishes the activity in pain and temperature pathways.

panic disorder Recurrent attacks of intense terror that come on without warning and without any apparent relation to external circumstances.

parahippocampal cortex Cortex located along the dorsal medial temporal lobe surface.

paralysis Loss of sensation and movement due to nervous system injury.

paraplegia Paralysis of the legs due to spinal cord injury.

parasympathetic division Part of the autonomic nervous system; acts in opposition to the sympathetic division—for example, preparing the body to rest and digest by reversing the alarm response or stimulating digestion.

parietal lobe Part of the cerebral cortex that directs movements toward a goal or to perform a task, such as grasping an object; lies posterior to the central sulcus and beneath the parietal bone at the top of the skull.

Parkinson disease Disorder of the motor system correlated with a loss of dopamine from the substantia nigra and characterized by tremors, muscular rigidity, and a reduction in voluntary movement.

parvocellular (P) cell Small visual system neuron sensitive to differences in form and color.

Pavlovian conditioning Learning achieved when neutral stimulus (such as a tone) comes to elicit a response after its repeated pairing with some event (such as delivery of food); also called *classical conditioning* or *respondent conditioning*.

peptide hormone Chemical messenger synthesized by cellular DNA that acts to affect the target cell's physiology.

perception Subjective interpretation of sensations by the brain.

periaqueductal gray matter (PAG) Nuclei in the midbrain that surround the cerebral aqueduct joining the third and fourth ventricles; PAG neurons contain circuits for species-typical behaviors (e.g., female sexual behavior) and play an important role in the modulation of pain.

peribrachial area Cholinergic nucleus in the dorsal brainstem having a role in REM sleep behaviors; projects to medial pontine reticular formation.

period Time required to complete an activity cycle.

peripheral nervous system (PNS) All of the neurons in the body outside the brain and spinal cord; provides sensory and motor connections to and from the central nervous system.

perirhinal cortex Cortex lying next to the rhinal fissure on the ventral surface of the brain.

perseveration Tendency to emit repeatedly the same verbal or motor response to varied stimuli.

persistent vegetative state (PVS) Condition in which a person is alive but unaware, unable to communicate or to function independently at even the most basic level.

phenotype Set of individual characteristics that can be seen or measured.

phenotypic plasticity An individual's capacity to develop into more than one phenotype.

phenylketonuria (PKU) Behavioral disorder caused by elevated levels of the amino acid phenylalanine in the blood and resulting from a defect in the gene for the enzyme phenylalanine hydroxylase; the major symptom is severe developmental disability.

pheromone Odorant biochemical released by one animal that acts as a chemosignal and can affect the physiology or behavior of another animal.

phobia Fear of a clearly defined object or situation.

photoreceptor Specialized retinal neuron that transduces light into neural activity.

pituitary gland Endocrine gland attached to the bottom of the hypothalamus; its secretions control the activities of many other endocrine glands; associated with biological rhythms.

place cell Hippocampal neuron maximally responsive to specific locations in the world.

plasticity The nervous system's potential for physical or chemical change; enhances its adaptability to environmental change and its ability to compensate for injury. (Also called neuroplasticity.)

positron emission tomography (PET) Imaging technique that detects changes in blood flow by measuring changes in the uptake of compounds such as oxygen or glucose; used to analyze the metabolic activity of neurons.

posterior spinothalamic tract Pathway that carries fine-touch and pressure fibers.

postsynaptic membrane Membrane on the transmitter, or input, side of a synapse.

posttraumatic stress disorder (PTSD) Syndrome characterized by physiological arousal associated with recurrent memories and dreams arising from a traumatic event that occurred months or years earlier.

prefrontal cortex (PFC) Extensive frontal lobe area anterior to the motor and premotor cortex; key to controlling executive functions such as planning.

preparedness Predisposition to respond to certain stimuli differently from other stimuli.

presynaptic membrane Axon terminal membrane on the transmitter, or output, side of a synapse.

primary auditory cortex (area A1) Asymmetrical structures within Heschl's gyrus in the temporal lobes; receive input from the ventral region of the medial geniculate nucleus.

primary visual cortex (V1) Striate cortex in the occipital lobe that receives input from the lateral geniculate nucleus.

priming Using a stimulus to sensitize the nervous system to a later presentation of the same or a similar stimulus.

prion From *protein* and *infection*, an abnormally folded protein that causes progressive neurodegenerative disorders.

procedural memory Ability to recall a movement sequence or how to perform some act or behavior.

progenitor cell (precursor cell) Derived from a stem cell; it migrates and produces a neuron or a glial cell.

proprioception Perception of the position and movement of the body, limbs, and head.

prosody Melodic tone of the speaking voice.

protein Folded-up polypeptide chain that serves a particular function in the body.

psyche Synonym for *mind*, an entity once proposed to be the source of human behavior.

psychedelic drug Drug that can alter sensation and perception; examples are lysergic acid diethylamide (LSD), mescaline, and psilocybin.

psychoactive drug Substance that acts to alter mood, thought, or behavior; is used to manage neuropsychological illness; or is abused.

psychological construct Idea or set of impressions that some mental ability exists as an entity; memory, language, and emotion are examples.

psychomotor activation Increased behavioral and cognitive activity: at certain levels of consumption, the drug user feels energetic and in control.

psychopharmacology Study of how drugs affect the nervous system and behavior.

psychosurgery Any neurosurgical technique intended to alter behavior.

psychotherapy Talk therapy derived from Freudian psychoanalysis and other psychological interventions.

pump Protein in the cell membrane that actively transports a substance across the membrane.

Purkinje cell Distinctively shaped interneuron found in the cerebellum.

pyramidal cell Distinctively shaped interneuron found in the cerebral cortex.

Q

quadrantanopia Blindness of one quadrant of the visual field.

quadriplegia Paralysis of the legs and arms due to spinal cord injury.

quantum (pl. quanta) Amount of neurotransmitter, equivalent to the content of a single synaptic vesicle, that produces a just-observable change in postsynaptic electric potential.

R

radial glial cell Path-making cell that a migrating neuron follows to its appropriate destination.

rapidly adapting receptor Body sensory receptor that responds briefly to the onset of a stimulus on the body.

rate-limiting factor Any chemical in limited supply that restricts the pace at which another chemical can be synthesized.

real-time fMRI (rt-fMRI) Behavior-modification technique in which individuals learn to change their behavior by controlling their own patterns of brain activation.

receptive field Sensory region that stimulates a receptor cell or neuron.

reconsolidation Process of restabilizing a memory trace after the memory is revisited.

referred pain Pain that arises in one of the internal organs but is felt on the surface of the body.

regulatory behavior Behavior motivated to meet the animal's survival needs.

reinforcer In operant conditioning, any event that strengthens the behavior it follows.

relatively refractory The state of an axon in the later phase of an action potential during which increased electrical current is required to produce another action potential; a phase during which potassium channels are still open.

releasing hormone Peptide released by the hypothalamus that increases or decreases hormone release from the anterior pituitary.

REM sleep Fast brain wave pattern displayed by the neocortical EEG record during sleep.

resting potential Electrical charge across the insulating cell membrane in the absence of stimulation; a store of potential energy produced by a greater negative charge on the intracellular side relative to the extracellular side.

resting-state fMRI (rs-fMRI) Magnetic resonance imaging method that measures changes in elements such as iron or oxygen when the individual is resting (not engaged in a specific task).

reticular activating system (RAS) Large reticulum (mixture of cell nuclei and nerve fibers) that runs through the center of the brainstem; associated with sleep–wake behavior and behavioral arousal; also called the *reticular formation.*

reticular formation Midbrain area in which nuclei and fiber pathways are mixed, producing a netlike appearance; associated with sleep–wake behavior and behavioral arousal.

retina Light-sensitive surface at the back of the eye consisting of neurons and photoreceptor cells.

retinal ganglion cell (RGC) One of a group of retinal neurons with axons that give rise to the optic nerve.

retinohypothalamic tract Neural route formed by axons of photosensitive retinal ganglion cells (pRGCs) from the retina to the suprachiasmatic nucleus; allows light to entrain the SCN's rhythmic activity.

retrograde amnesia Inability to remember events that took place before the onset of amnesia.

reuptake Deactivation of a neurotransmitter when membrane transporter proteins bring the transmitter back into the presynaptic axon terminal for reuse.

rod Photoreceptor specialized for functioning at low light levels.

S

saltatory conduction Fast propagation of an action potential at successive nodes of Ranvier; *saltatory* means *leaping.*

schizophrenia Behavioral disorder characterized by delusions, hallucinations, disorganized speech, blunted emotion, agitation or immobility, and a host of associated symptoms.

Schwann cell Glial cell in the PNS that myelinates sensory and motor axons.

scotoma Small blind spot in the visual field caused by migraine or by a small lesion of the visual cortex.

scratch reflex Automatic response in which an animal's hind limb reaches to remove a stimulus from the surface of its body.

second-generation antidepressant Drug that acts similarly to tricyclics (first-generation antidepressants) but more selectively on 5-HT reuptake transporter proteins; also called atypical antidepressant.

second messenger Chemical that initiates a biochemical process when activated by a neurotransmitter (the first messenger).

segmentation Division into a number of parts that are similar; refers to the idea that many animals, including vertebrates, are composed of similarly organized body segments.

selective serotonin reuptake inhibitor (SSRI) Tricyclic antidepressant drug that blocks 5-HT reuptake into the presynaptic terminal.

sensation Registration by the sensory organs of physical stimuli from the environment.

sensitization Learned behavior in which the response to a stimulus strengthens with repeated presentations.

sensory deprivation Experimental setup in which a participant is allowed only restricted sensory input; participants generally have a low tolerance for deprivation and may even hallucinate.

sensory neuron Cell that detects or carries sensory information into the spinal cord and brain.

serotonin (5-HT) Amine neurotransmitter; helps to regulate mood and aggression, appetite and arousal, perception of pain, and respiration.

sexual dimorphism Differential development of brain areas in the two sexes.

sexual orientation A person's pattern of sexual attraction—to the opposite sex or to the same sex or to both sexes.

sleep apnea Inability to breathe during sleep, causing a sleeper to wake up to breathe.

sleep paralysis Atonia and dreaming occurring when a person is awake, usually just falling asleep or waking up.

slow-wave sleep NREM sleep.

slowly adapting receptor Body sensory receptor that responds as long as a sensory stimulus is on the body.

small-molecule transmitter Quick-acting neurotransmitter synthesized in the axon terminal from products derived from the diet.

social neuroscience Interdisciplinary field that seeks to understand how the brain mediates social interactions.

somatic marker hypothesis Proposal that marker signals arising from emotions and feelings act to guide behavior and decision making, usually in an unconscious process.

somatic nervous system (SNS) Part of the PNS that includes the cranial and spinal nerves to and from the muscles, joints, and skin, which produce movement, transmit incoming sensory input, and inform the CNS about the position and movement of body parts.

somatosensory neuron Brain cell that brings sensory information from the body into the spinal cord.

sound wave Mechanical displacement of molecules caused by changing pressure that possesses the physical properties of frequency, amplitude, and complexity. Also *compression wave.*

spatial summation Addition of one graded potential to another that occur close in space.

species Group of organisms that can interbreed.

species-typical behavior Behavior that is characteristic of all members of a species, such as walking in amphibians.

spinal cord Part of the central nervous system encased within the vertebrae (spinal column); provides most of the connections between the brain and the rest of the body.

split brain Surgical disconnection of the hemispheres by severing the corpus callosum.

stereotaxic apparatus Surgical instrument that permits the researcher to target a specific part of the brain.

steroid hormone Fat-soluble chemical messenger synthesized from cholesterol.

storage granule Membranous compartment that holds several vesicles containing a neurotransmitter.

stretch-sensitive channel Ion channel on a tactile sensory neuron that activates in response to stretching of the membrane, initiating a nerve impulse.

striate cortex Primary visual cortex (V1) in the occipital lobe; shows stripes (striations) on staining.

striatum Caudate nucleus and putamen of the basal ganglia.

stroke Sudden appearance of neurological symptoms as a result of severely interrupted blood flow.

substance abuse A pattern of drug use in which people rely on a drug chronically and excessively, allowing it to occupy a central place in their life.

subunit Protein molecule that assembles with other protein molecules.

subventricular zone Lining of neural stem cells surrounding the ventricles in adults.

sudden infant death syndrome (SIDS) Unexplained death while asleep of a seemingly healthy infant less than 1 year old.

sulcus (pl. sulci) A groove in brain matter; most are in the neocortex or cerebellum.

supplementary speech area Speech production region on the left frontal lobe dorsal surface.

suprachiasmatic nucleus (SCN) Master biological clock located in the hypothalamus just above the optic chiasm.

sympathetic division Part of the autonomic nervous system; arouses the body for action, such as mediating the involuntary fight-or-flight response to alarm by increasing heart rate and blood pressure.

symptomatic seizure Identified with a specific cause, such as infection, trauma, tumor, vascular malformation, toxic chemicals, very high fever, or other neurological disorders.

synapse Spatial junction between one neuron and another; forms the information transfer site between neurons.

synaptic cleft Gap separating the neuronal presynaptic membrane from the postsynaptic membrane.

synaptic vesicle Membranous compartment that encloses a quantum of neurotransmitter.

synesthesia Ability to perceive a stimulus of one sense as the sensation of a different sense, as when sound produces a sensation of color; literally, *feeling together.*

syntax Ways in which words are put together; proposed to be unique to human language.

synthetic biology Design and construction of biological devices, systems, and machines not found in nature.

tardive dyskinesia Inability to stop the tongue or other body parts from moving; motor side effect of neuroleptic drugs.

Tay-Sachs disease Inherited birth defect caused by the loss of genes that encode the enzyme necessary for breaking down certain fatty substances; appears 4 to 6 months after birth and results in intellectual disability, physical changes, and death by about age 5.

tectopulvinar system Projections from the retina to the superior colliculus to the pulvinar (thalamus) to the parietal and temporal visual areas.

tectum Roof (area above the ventricle) of the midbrain; its functions are sensory processing, particularly visual and auditory, and the production of orienting movements.

tegmentum Floor (area below the ventricle) of the midbrain; a collection of nuclei with movement-related, species-specific, and pain perception functions.

temporal lobe Part of the cerebral cortex that functions in connection with hearing, language, and musical abilities; lies below the lateral fissure, beneath the temporal bone at the side of the skull.

temporal summation Addition of one graded potential to another that occur close in time.

terminal button (end foot) Knob at the tip of an axon that conveys information to other neurons.

testosterone Sex hormone secreted by the testes and responsible for the distinguishing characteristics of the male.

thalamus Diencephalon structure through which information from all sensory systems is integrated and projected into the appropriate region of the neocortex.

theory of mind Ability to attribute mental states to others.

threshold potential Voltage on a neural membrane at which an action potential is triggered by the opening of sodium and potassium voltage-sensitive channels; about −50 mV relative to extracellular surround. Also called *threshold limit.*

tolerance Decrease in response to a drug with the passage of time.

tonotopic representation In audition, structural organization for processing of sound waves from lower to higher frequencies.

topographic map Spatially organized neural representation of the external world.

topographic organization Neural spatial representation of the body or areas of the sensory world perceived by a sensory organ.

Tourette syndrome Disorder of the basal ganglia characterized by tics, involuntary vocalizations (including curse words and animal sounds), and odd, involuntary movements of the body, especially of the face and head.

tract Large collection of axons coursing together *in* the CNS.

transcranial magnetic stimulation (TMS) Procedure in which a magnetic coil is placed over the skull to stimulate the underlying brain; used either to induce behavior or to disrupt ongoing behavior.

transgender Possessing personal characteristics that transcend traditional gender boundaries and corresponding sexual norms; a person's belief that he or she was born the wrong sex.

transgenic animal Product of technology in which one or more genes from one species is introduced into the genome of another species to be passed along and expressed in subsequent generations.

transmitter-activated receptor Protein that has a binding site for a specific neurotransmitter and is embedded in the membrane of a cell.

transmitter-sensitive channel Receptor complex that has both a receptor site for a chemical and a pore through which ions can flow.

transporter Protein molecule that pumps substances across a membrane.

traumatic brain injury (TBI) Wound to the brain that results from a blow to the head.

trichromatic theory Explanation of color vision based on the coding of three primary colors: red, green, and blue.

tricyclic antidepressant First-generation antidepressant; its chemical structure, characterized by three rings, blocks 5-HT reuptake transporter proteins.

tropic molecule Signaling molecule that attracts or repels growth cones.

tumor Mass of new tissue that grows uncontrolled and independent of surrounding structures.

unconditioned response (UCR) Unlearned, naturally occurring response to the unconditioned stimulus (UCS), such as salivation when food is in the mouth.

unconditioned stimulus (UCS) A stimulus that naturally and automatically (unconditionally) triggers an unconditioned response (UCR).

ventral stream Visual processing pathway from V1 to the temporal lobe for object identification and perceiving related movements.

ventricle One of four cavities in the brain that contain CSF to cushion the brain; may play a role in maintaining brain metabolism.

ventrolateral thalamus Part of the thalamus that carries information about body senses to the somatosensory cortex.

vertebrae (sing. vertebra) The bones that form the spinal column.

vestibular system Somatosensory system comprising a set of receptors in each inner ear that respond to body position and to movement of the head.

virtual-reality (VR) exposure therapy Controlled virtual immersion environment that, by allowing individuals to relive traumatic events, gradually desensitizes them to stress.

visual field Region of the visual world seen by the eyes.

visual-form agnosia Inability to recognize objects or drawings of objects.

visuospatial memory Use of visual information to recall an object's location in space.

voltage gradient Difference in charge between two regions that allows a flow of current if the two regions are connected.

voltage-sensitive channel Gated protein channel that opens or closes only at specific membrane voltages.

voltmeter Device that measures the flow and the strength of electrical voltage by recording the difference in electrical potential between two bodies.

wanting-and-liking theory Explanation holding that when a drug is associated with certain cues, the cues themselves elicit desire for the drug; also called incentive sensitization theory.

Wernicke's area Secondary auditory cortex (planum temporale) lying behind Heschl's gyrus at the rear of the left temporal lobe; regulates language comprehension. Also *posterior speech zone.*

white matter Areas of the nervous system rich in fat-sheathed neural axons that form the connections between brain cells.

wild type Typical allele (most common in a population).

withdrawal symptom Physical and psychological behavior displayed by an addict when drug use ends.

Z

Zeitgeber Environmental event that entrains biological rhythms: German for *time giver.*

REFERENCES

CHAPTER 1

Antón, S. C., Potts, R., & Aiello, L. C. (2014). Human evolution. Evolution of early Homo: An integrated biological perspective. *Science, 45,* 1236828.

Darwin, C. (1871). *The Descent of Man, and Selection in Relation to Sex.* London: J. Murray.

Darwin, C. (1963). *On the origin of species by means of natural selection, or the preservation of favored races in the struggle for life.* New York: New American Library. (Original work published 1859.)

Darwin, C. (1965). *The expression of the emotions in man and animals.* Chicago: University of Chicago Press. (Original work published 1872.)

Deary, I. J. (2000). *Looking down on human intelligence: From psychometrics to the brain.* Oxford Psychology Series, No. 34. New York: Oxford University Press.

Dennett, D. (1978). *The intentional stance.* Cambridge, MA: MIT Press.

Descartes, R. (1972). *Treatise on man* (T. S. Hall, Trans.). Cambridge, MA: Harvard University Press. (Original work published 1664.)

Dunbar, R. (1998). *Grooming, gossip, and the evolution of language.* Cambridge, MA: Harvard University Press.

Eibl-Eibesfeldt, I. (1970). *Ethology: The biology of behavior.* New York: Holt, Rinehart and Winston.

Flynn, J. R. (2012). *Are we getting smarter? Rising IQ in the twenty-first century.* Cambridge: Cambridge University Press.

Fonseca-Azevedo K., & Herculano-Houzel, S. (2012). Metabolic constraint imposes tradeoff between body size and number of brain neurons in human evolution. Proceedings of the *National Academy of Sciences United States of America,* 109:18571–18576.

Gardner, H. (2006). *Multiple intelligences: New horizons.* New York: Basic Books.

Gardner R. A., & Gardner B. T. (1969). Teaching sign language to a chimpanzee. *Science, 165,* 664–672.

Gillespie-Lynch, K., Greenfield, P. M., Lyn, H., & Savage-Rumbaugh, S. (2014). Gestural and symbolic development among apes and humans: Support for a multimodal theory of language evolution. *Frontiers in Psychology, 30,* 1228.

Gordon, A. D., Nevell, L., & Wood, B. (2008). The Homo floresiensis cranium (LB1): Size, scaling, and early Homo affinities. *Proceedings of the National Academy of Sciences of the United States of America, 105,* 4650–4655.

Gould, S. J. (1981). *The Mismeasure of a man.* New York: Norton.

Gross, C. G. (1995). Aristotle on the brain. *The Neuroscientist,* 1,4, 245–250.

Hampshire, A., Highfield, R. R., Parkin, B. L., & Owen, A. M. (2012). Fractionating human intelligence. *Neuron, 76,* 1225–1237.

Hebb, D. O. (1949). *The organization of behavior: A neuropsychological theory.* New York: Wiley.

Herculano-Houzel. S., Avelino-de-Souza, K., Neves, K., Porfirio, J., Messeder, D., Mattos Feijo, L., Maldonado, J., & Manger, P. R. (2014). The elephant brain in numbers. *Frontiers in Neuroanatomy.* 12, 8–46.

Heron, W. (1957). The pathology of boredom. *Scientific American,* 196(1), 52–56.

Herringa, R. J., Birn, R. M., Ruttle, P. L., Burghy, C. A., Stodola, D.E., Davidson, R. J., & Essex, M. J. (2013). Childhood maltreatment is associated with altered fear circuitry and increased internalizing symptoms by late adolescence. *Proceedings of the National Academy of Sciences of the United States of America, 110,* 19119–19124.

Jacobson, E. (1932). Electrophysiology of mental activities. *American Journal of Psychology, 44,* 677–694.

Jerison, H. J. (1973). *The evolution of the brain and intelligence.* New York: Academic Press.

Johanson, D., & Edey, M. (1981). *Lucy: The beginnings of humankind.* New York: Warner Books.

Kunz, A. R., & Iliadis, C. (2007). Hominid evolution of the arteriovenous system through the cranial base and its relevance for craniosynostosis. *Child's Nervous System, 23,* 1367–1377.

Lewin, R. (1998). *The Origin of Modern Humans.* New York: Scientific American Library.

Linge, F. R. (1990). Faith, hope, and love: Nontraditional therapy in recovery from serious head injury, a personal account. *Canadian Journal of Psychology, 44,* 116–129.

Maslin, M. A., Shultz, S., & Trauth, M. H. (2015). A synthesis of the theories and concepts of early human evolution. *Philosophical Transaction of the Royal Society of London, B Biological Sciences, 370,* 20140064.

Mesoudi, A., Whiten, A., & Laland, K. N. (2006). Towards a unified science of cultural evolution. *Behavioural and Brain Sciences 29,* 329–347.

Milton, K. (2003). The critical role played by animal source foods in human (Homo) evolution. *Journal of Nutrition, 133* (Suppl. 2), 3886S–3892S.

Owen, A. M. (2015). Using functional magnetic resonance imaging and electroencephalography to detect consciousness after severe brain injury. *Handbook of Clinical Neurology, 127,* 277–293.

Pickering, R., Dirks, P. H., Jinnah, Z., de Ruiter, D. J., Churchill, S. E., et al. (2011). *Australopithecus sediba* at 1.977 Ma and implications for the origins of the genus *Homo. Science, 333,* 1421–1423.

Potts, R., & Sloan, C. (2010). What does it mean to be human? Companion volume to the Smithsonian National Museum of Natural History's David H. Koch Hall of Human Origins. Washington, DC: National Geographic Society.

Prinz, J. (2008). Is consciousness embodied? In P. Robbins and. M. Aydede (Eds.), *Cambridge Handbook of Situated Cognition.* Cambridge: Cambridge University Press.

Sankararaman, S., Mallick S., Dannemann, M., Prüfer, K., Kelso, J., Pääbo, S., Patterson, N., Reich, D. (2014). The genomic landscape of Neanderthal ancestry in present-day humans. *Nature, 507,* 354–357.

Savage-Rumbaugh, S. (1999). Ape communication: Between a rock and a hard place in origins of language—What non-human primates can tell us. *School of American Research Press.*

Schiff, N. D., & Fins, J. J. (2007). Deep brain stimulation and cognition: Moving from animal to patient. *Current Opinion in Neurology, 20,* 638–642.

Stedman, H. H., Kozyak, B. W., Nelson, A., Thesier, D. M., Su, L. T., Low, D. W., Bridges, C. R., Shrager, J. B., Minugh-Purvis, N., & Mitchell, M. A. (2004). Myosin gene mutation correlates with anatomical changes in the human lineage. *Nature, 428,* 415–418.

Tagliatela, J. P., Russell, J. L., Schaeffer, J. A., & Hopkins, W. D. (2011). Chimpanzee vocal signaling points to a multimodal origin of human language. *PLoS One, 6,* e18852.

Terkel, J. (1995). Cultural transmission in the black rat: Pinecone feeding. *Advances in the Study of Behavior, 24,* 119–154.

Villmoare, B., Kimbel, W. H., Seyoum, C., Campisano, C. J., DiMaggio, E. J., Rowan, J., Braun, D. R., Arrowsmith, J. R., & Reed, K. E., (2015). Early Homo at 2.8 Ma from Ledi-Geraru, Afar, Ethiopia. *Science, 20,* 1352–1355.

Watson, S. K., Townsend, S. W., Schel, A. M., Wilke, C., Wallace, E. K., Cheng, L., West, V., & Slocombe, K. E. (2015). Vocal learning in the functionally referential food grunts of chimpanzees. *Current Biology, 5,* 495–499.

Weiner, J. (1995). *The beak of the finch.* New York: Vintage.

Workman, A. D., Charvet, C. J., Clancy, B., Darlington, R. B., & Finlay, B. L. (2013). Modeling transformations of neurodevelopmental sequences across mammalian species. *Journal of Neuroscience, 33,* 7368–7380.

Zollikofer, C. P. (2012). Evolution of hominid cranial ontogeny. *Progress in Brain Research, 195,* 273–292.

CHAPTER 2

Appireddy, R. M. R., Demchuk, A. M., Goyal, M., Menon, B. K., Eesa, M., Choi, P., et al. (2015). Endovascular therapy for ischemic stroke. *Journal of Clinical Neurology, 11,* 1–8.

Avetisyan, M., Schill, E. M., & Heuchkeroth, R. O. (2015). Building a second brain in the bowel. *Journal of Clinical Investigation, 125,* 899–907.

Barton, R. A. (2012). Embodied cognitive evolution and the cerebellum. *Philosophical Transactions of the Royal Society B, 367,* 2097–2107.

Baumann, O., Borra, R. J., Bower, J. M., Cullen, K. E., Habas, C., Ivry, R. B., et al. (2015). Consensus paper: The role of the cerebellum in perceptual processes. *Cerebellum, 14,* 197–220.

Brodmann, K. (1909). *Vergleichende Lokalisationlehr der Grosshirnrinde in ihren Prinzipien dargestellt auf Grund des Zellenbaues.* Leipzig: J. A. Barth.

Farmer, A. D., Randall, H. A., & Aziz, Q. (2014). It's a gut feeling: How the gut microbiota affects the state of mind. *Journal of Physiology, 592(14),* 2981–2988.

Fiorito, G., & Scotto, P. (1992). Observational learning in *Octopus vulgaris. Science, 256,* 545–547.

Gilbert, S. F., & Epel, D. (2009). *Ecological developmental biology: Integrating epigenetics, medicine, and evolution.* New York: Sinauer.

Hatcher, M. A., & Starr, J. A. (2011). Role of tissue plasminogen activator in ischemic stroke. *Annals of Pharmacotherapy, 45,* 364–371.

Langhorne, P., Bernhardt, J., & Kwakkel, G. (2011). Stroke rehabilitation. *Lancet, 277,* 1693–1702.

Papez, J. W. (1937). A proposed mechanism of emotion. *Archives of Neurology and Psychiatry, 38,* 724–744.

Schmahmann, J. D. (2010). The role of the cerebellum in cognition and emotion: Personal reflections since 1982 on the dysmetria of thought hypothesis, and its historical evolution from theory to therapy. *Neuropsychology Reviews, 20,* 236–260.

CHAPTER 3

Bainbridge, M. N., Wiszniewski, W., Murdock, D. R., Friedman, J., Gonzaga-Jauregui, C., et al. (2011). Whole-genome sequencing for optimized patient management. *Science Translational Medicine, 3,* 87re3.

Balaban, E. (2005). Brain switching: Studying evolutionary behavioral changes in the context of individual brain development. *International Journal of Developmental Biology, 49,* 117–124.

Bertram, R., Daou, A., Hyson, R. L., Johnson, F., & Wu, W. (2014). Two neural streams, one voice: Pathways for theme and variation in the songbird brain. *Neuroscience, 26,* 806–817.

Butte, P. V., Mamelak, A., Parrish-Novak, J., Drazin, D., Shweikeh, F., Gangalum, P. R., et al. (2014). Near-infrared imaging of brain tumors using the Tumor Paint BLZ-100 to achieve near-complete resection of brain tumors. *Neurosurgery Focus, 36(2),* E1.

Casano, A. M., & Peri, F. (2015). Microglia: Multitasking specialists of the brain. *Developmental Cell, 23,* 469–477.

Charney, E. (2012). Behavior genetics and postgenomics. *Behavioral Brain Sciences, 35(5),* 331–358.

Chen, J. L., Andermann, M. L., Keck, T., Xu, N. L., & Ziv, Y. (2013). Imaging neuronal populations in behaving rodents: Paradigms for studying neural circuits underlying behavior in the mammalian cortex. *Journal of Neuroscience, 33,* 17631–17640.

Eddy, C. M., & Rickards, H. E. (2015). Theory of mind can be impaired prior to motor onset in Huntington's disease. *Neuropsychology, 29,* 792–798.

Gill, J. M., & Rego, A. C. (2009). The R6 lines of transgenic mice: A model for screening new therapies for Huntington's disease. *Brain Research Reviews, 59,* 410–431.

Giorgi, E. E. (2015, April). From many, one. *The Scientist.*

Gu, X., Cantle, J. P., Greiner, E. R., Lee, C. Y., Barth, A. M., Gao, F., et al. (2015). N17 modifies mutant huntingtin nuclear pathogenesis and severity of disease in HD BAC transgenic mice. *Neuron, 85,* 726–741.

Guerrero-Bosagna, C., & Jensen, P. (2015). Globalization, climate change, and transgenerational epigenetic inheritance: Will our descendants be at risk? *Clinical Epigenetics, 7,* 8.

Herculano-Houzel, S., Manger, P. R., & Kaas, J. H. (2014). Brain scaling in mammalian evolution as a consequence of concerted and mosaic changes in numbers of neurons and average neuronal cell size. *Frontiers in Neuroanatomy, 8:77.*

Kaati, G., Bygren, L. O., Pembrey, M., & Sjöström, M. (2007). Transgenerational response to nutrition, early life circumstances and longevity. *European Journal of Human Genetics, 15,* 784–790.

Kusakari, S., Saitow, F., Ago, Y., Shibasaki, K., Sato-Hashimoto, M., Matsuzaki, Y., et al. (2015). Shp2 in forebrain neurons regulates synaptic plasticity, locomotion, and memory formation in mice. *Molecular and Cell Biology, MCB, 35,* 1557–1572.

Livet, J., Weissman, T. A., Kang, H., Draft, R. W., Lu, J., Bennis, R. A., et al. (2007). Transgenic strategies for combinatorial expression of fluorescent proteins in the nervous system. *Nature, 450,* 56–62.

Mimori, T., Nariai, N., Kojima, K., Sato, Y., Kawai, Y., Yamaguchi-Kabata, Y., et al. (2015). Estimating copy numbers of alleles from population-scale high-throughput sequencing data. *BMC Bioinformatics, 16(Suppl. 1),* S4.

Ostrom, Q. T., Gittelman, H., Liao, P., Rouse, C., Chen, Y., Dowling, J., et al. (2014). CBTRUS statistical report: Primary brain and central nervous system tumors diagnosed in the United States in 2007–2011. *Neuro-oncology, 16 (Suppl. 4),* iv1–iv63.

Persson, M. E., Roth, L. S., Johnsson, M., Wright, D., & Jensen, P. (2015). Human-directed social behaviour in dogs shows significant heritability. *Genes, Brain and Behavior, 14,* 337–344.

Ramón y Cajal, S. (1909–1911). *Histologie du systeme nerveux de l'homme et des vertebres.* Paris: Maloine.

Reeve, R., van Schaik, A., Jin, C., Hamilton, T., Torben-Neilsen, B., & Webb, B. (2007). Directional hearing in a silicon cricket. *Biosystems, 87,* 307–313.

Rojczyk-Gołębiewska, E., Palasz, A., Worthington, J. J., Markowski, G., & Wiaderkiewicz, R. (2015). Neurolight: Astonishing advances in brain imaging. *International Journal of Neuroscience, 125,* 91–99.

Rosenegger, D. G., & Gordon, G. R. (2015). A slow or modulatory role of astrocytes in neurovascular coupling. *Microcirculation, 22,* 197–203.

Rusielewicz, T., Nam, J., Damanakis, E., John, G. R., Raine, C. S., & Melendez-Vasquez, C. V. (2014). Accelerated repair of demyelinated CNS lesions in the absence of non-muscle myosin IIB. *Glia, 62,* 580–591.

Wahlsten, D., & Ozaki, H. S. (1994). Defects of the fetal forebrain in acallosal mice. In M. Lassonde & M. A. Jeeves (Eds.), *Callosal agenesis* (pp. 125–132). New York: Plenum.

Wang, X., & Guo, Z. (2015). Chlorotoxin-conjugated onconase as a potential anti-glioma drug. *Oncology Letters, 9,* 1337–1342.

Webb, B. (1996). A cricket robot. *Scientific American, 275*(6), 94–99.

Wittmeier, S., Alessandro, C., Bascarevic, N., Dalamagkidis, K., Devereux, D., Diamond, A., et al. (2013). Toward anthropomimetic robotics: Development, simulation, and control of a musculoskeletal torso. *Artificial Life, 19,* 171–193.

Wu, H., Wang, Y., Zhang, Y., Yang, M., Lv, J., Liu, J., et al. (2015). TALE nickase-mediated SP110 knockin endows cattle with increased resistance to tuberculosis. *Proceedings of the National Academy of Sciences United States of America, 112,* E1530–E1539.

CHAPTER 4

Allen, M. J., Lacroix, J. J., Ramachandran, S., Capone, R., Whitlock, J. L., et al. (2011). Mutant SOD1 forms ion channel: Implications for ALS pathophysiology. *Neurobiology of Diseases, 45,* 831–838.

Bano, S., Yadav, S. N., Chaudhary, V., & Garga, U. C. (2011). Neuroimaging in epilepsy. *Journal of Pediatrics and Neuroscience, 6,* 19–26.

Bartholow, R. (1874). Experimental investigation into the functions of the human brain. *American Journal of Medical Sciences, 67,* 305–313.

Bender, K. J., & Trussell, L. O. (2012). The physiology of the axon initial segment. *Annual Review of Neuroscience, 35,* 249–265.

Bhalla, D., Druet-Cabanac, M., Godet, B., & Preux, P.-M. (2011). Etiologies of epilepsy: A comprehensive review. *Expert Review of Neurotherapeutics, 11,* 861–876.

Cao, Z. F., Burdakov, D., & Sarnyai, Z. (2011). Optogenetics: Potentials for addiction research. *Addiction Biology, 16,* 519–531.

Crotty, P., Sangrey, T., & Levy, W. B. (2006). Metabolic energy cost of action potential velocity. *Journal of Neurophysiology, 96,* 1237–1246.

Debanne, D. (2011). The nodal origin of intrinsic bursting. *Neuron, 25,* 569–570.

Descartes, R. (1972). *Treatise on man* (T. S. Hall, Trans.). Cambridge, MA: Harvard University Press. (Original work published 1664.)

Duncan, J. S., Sander, J. W., Sisodiya, S. M., & Walker, M. C. (2006). Adult epilepsy. *Lancet, 367,* 1087–1100.

Eccles, J. (1965). The synapse. *Scientific American, 21*(1), 56–66.

Fenno, L., Yizhar, O., & Deisseroth, K. (2011). The development and application of optogenetics. *Annual Review of Neuroscience, 34,* 389–412.

Hodgkin, A. L., & Huxley, A. F. (1939). Action potentials recorded from inside nerve fiber. *Nature, 144,* 710–711.

Legenstein, R., & Maass, W. (2011). Branch-specific plasticity enables self-organization of nonlinear computation in single neurons. *Journal of Neuroscience, 31,* 10787–10802.

Liewald, J. F., Brauner, M., Stephens, G. J., Bouhours, M., Schultheis, C., Xhen, M., et al. (2008). Optogenetic analysis of synaptic function. *Nature Methods, 10,* 895–902.

Mohajerani, M. H., & Cherubini, E. (2006). Role of giant depolarizing potentials in shaping synaptic currents in the developing hippocampus. *Critical Reviews in Neurobiology, 18,* 13–23.

Rezania, K., Soliven, B., Baron, J., Lin, H., Penumalli, V., & van Besien, K. (2012). Myasthenia gravis, an autoimmune manifestation of lymphoma and lymphoproliferative disorders: Case reports and review of literature. *Leukemia and Lymphoma, 53,* 371–380.

Valdueza, J. M., Doepp, F., Schreiber, S. J., van Oosten, B. W., Schmierer, K., Paul, F., et al. (2013). What went wrong? The flawed concept of cerebrospinal venous insufficiency. *Journal of Cerebral Blood Flow and Metabolism, 33,* 657–668.

Zhang, F., Aravanis, A. M., Adamantidis, A., de Lecea, L., & Deisseroth, K. (2007). Circuit-breakers: Optical technologies for probing neural signals and systems. *Nature Reviews Neuroscience, 8,* 577–581.

CHAPTER 5

Bailey, C. H., Kandel, E. R., & Harris, K. M. (2015). Structural components of synaptic plasticity and memory consolidation. *Cold Spring Harbor Perspectives in Biology.* doi: 10.1101/cshperspect.a021758.

Ballard, A., Tetrud, J. W., & Langston, J. W. (1985). Permanent human parkinsonism due to 1-methyl-4-phenyl-1, 2, 3, 6-tetrahydropyridine (MPTP). *Neurology, 35,* 949–956.

Barbeau, A., Murphy, G. F., & Sourkes, T. L. (1962). Les catecholamines dans la maladie de Parkinson. In J. de Ajuriaguerva (Ed.), Monoamines et système nerveux central. pp. 247–262. Symposium Bel-Air, Geneva, 1961. Geneva: Georg et Ci.

Birkmayer, W., & Hornykiewicz, O. (1961). Der L-3, 4-Dioxyphenylalanin (L-DOPA) Effekt bei der Parkinson A Kinase. *Wiener Klinische, 73,* 787–789.

Bosch, M., & Hayashi, Y. (2012). Structural plasticity of dendritic spines. *Current Opinion in Neurobiology, 22,* 383–388.

Dere, E., & Zlomuzica, A. (2012). The role of gap junctions in the brain in health and disease. *Neuroscience and Biobehavioral Reviews, 36,* 206–217.

Ehringer, H., & Hornykiewicz, O. (1960/1974). Distribution of noradrenaline and dopamine (3-hydroxytyramine) in the human brain and their behavior in the presence of disease affecting the extrapyramidal system. In J. Marks (Ed.), *The treatment of Parkinsonism with L-dopa* (pp. 45–56). Lancaster, UK: MTP Medical and Technical Publishing.

Hamilton, T. J., Wheatley, B. M., Sinclair, D. B., Bachmann, M., Larkum, M. E., & Colmers, W. F. (2010). Dopamine modulates synaptic plasticity in dendrites of rat and human dentate granule cells. *Proceedings of the National Academy of Sciences United States of America, 107*(42): 18185–18190.

Hebb, D. O. (1949). *The organization of behavior.* New York: Wiley.

Herrmann, N., Chau, S. A., Kircanski, I., & Lanctôt, K. L. (2011). Current and emerging drug treatment options for Alzheimer's disease: A systematic review. *Drugs, 71,* 2031–2065.

Lane, E. L., Björklund, A., Dunnett, S. B., & Winkler, C. (2010). Neural grafting in Parkinson's disease unraveling the mechanisms underlying graft-induced dyskinesia. *Progress in Brain Research, 184,* 295–309.

Langston, J. W. (2008). *The case of the frozen addicts.* Pantheon Books, 1995. Original from the University of Michigan, digitized August 5, 2008.

Magee, J. C., & Cook, E. P. (2000). Somatic EPSP amplitude is independent of synapse location in hippocampal pyramidal neurons. *Nature Neuroscience, 3,* 895–903.

Mechoulam, R., Hanus, L. O., Pertwee, R., & Howlett, A. C. (2014). Early phytocannabinoid chemistry to endocannabinoids and beyond. *Nature Neuroscience Reviews 15,* 757–764.

Moore, T. J., Glenmullen, J., & Mattison, D. R. (2014). Reports of pathological gambling, hypersexuality and compulsive shopping associated with dopamine receptor agonist drugs. *JAMA Internal Medicine, 174,* 1930–1933.

Parkinson, J. (1817/1989). An essay on the shaking palsy. In A. D. Morris & F. C. Rose (Eds.), *James Parkinson: His life and times* (pp. 151–175). Boston: Birkhauser.

Sacks, O. (1976). *Awakenings.* New York: Doubleday.

Tréatikoff, C. (1974). Thesis for doctorate in medicine, 1919. In J. Marks (Ed.), *The treatment of Parkinsonism with L-dopa* (pp. 29–38). Lancaster, UK: MTP Medical and Technical Publishing.

Ungerstedt, U. (1971). Adipsia and aphagia after 6-hydroxydopamine induced degeneration of the nigrostriatal dopamine system in the rat brain. *Acta Physiologica (Scandinavia)*, 82 (Suppl. 367), 95–122.

Widner, H., Tetrud, J., Rehngrona, S., Snow, B., Brundin, P., Gustavii, B., et al. (1992). Bilateral fetal mesencephalic grafting in two patients with Parkinsonism induced by 1-methyl-4-phenyl-1, 2, 3, 6-tetrahydropyridine (MPTP). *New England Journal of Medicine*, 327, 1556–1563.

CHAPTER 6

Aagaard, L., & Hansen, E. H. (2011). The occurrence of adverse drug reactions reported for attention deficit hyperactivity disorder (ADHD) medications in the pediatric population: A qualitative review of empirical studies. *Neuropsychiatric Disorders and Treatments*, 7, 729–744.

Advokat, C. D., Comaty, J. E., & Julien, R. M. (2014). *A primer of drug action* (13th ed.). New York: Worth.

Asarnow, J. R., Porta, G., Spirito, A., Emslie, G., Clarke, G., et al. (2011). Suicide attempts and nonsuicidal self-injury in the treatment of resistant depression in adolescents: Findings from the TORDIA study. *Journal of the American Academy of Child and Adolescent Psychiatry*, 50, 772–781.

Barth, C., Villringer, A., & Sacher, J. (2015). Sex hormones affect neurotransmitters and shape the adult female brain during hormonal transition periods. *Frontiers in Neuroscience*, 20, 9–37.

Becker, J. B., Breedlove, S. M., Crews, D., & McCarthy, M. M. (2002). *Behavioral endocrinology* (2nd ed.). Cambridge, MA: Bradford.

Becker, J. B., & Hu, M. (2008). Sex differences in drug abuse. *Frontiers in Neuroendocrinology*, 29(1), 36–47.

Berninger, J. P., LaLone, C. A., Villeneuve, D. L., & Ankley, G. T. (2015). Prioritization of pharmaceuticals for potential environmental hazard through leveraging a large scale mammalian pharmacological dataset. *Environment and Toxicological Chemistry*. doi: 10.1002/etc.2965. [Epub ahead of print.]

Bourgin, J., Cachia, A., Boumezbeur, F., Djemaï, B., Bottlaender, M., Duchesnay, E., et al. (2015, March 11). Hyper-responsivity to stress in rats is associated with a large increase in amygdala volume: A 7T MRI study. *European Journal of Neuropsychopharmacology*. [Epub ahead of print.]

Brown, A. R., Owen, S. F., Peters, J., Zhang, Y., Soffker, M., Paull, G.C., et al. (2015). Climate change and pollution speed declines in zebrafish populations. *Proceedings of the National Academy of Science United States of America*, 112, 1237–1246.

Büttner, A. (2011). Review: The neuropathology of drug abuse. *Neuropathology and Applied Neurobiology*, 37, 118–134.

Clauss, J. A., Avery, S. N., & Blackford, J. U. (2015, March 14). The nature of individual differences in inhibited temperament and risk for psychiatric disease: A review and meta-analysis. *Progress in Neurobiology*, 127–128, 23–45.

Comer, R. J. (2011). *Fundamentals of abnormal psychology* (7th ed.). New York: Worth.

Cowan, R. L., Roberts, D. M., & Joers, J. M. (2008). Neuroimaging in human MDMA (Ecstasy) users. *Annals of the New York Academy of Sciences*, 1139, 291–298.

Czoli, C. D., Hammond, D., Reid, J. L., Cole. A. G., & Leatherdale. S. T. (2015). Use of conventional and alternative tobacco and nicotine products among a sample of Canadian youth. *Journal of Adolescent Health*, 57, 123–125. [Epub ahead of print.]

Di Forti, M., Sallis, H., Allegri, F., Trotta, A., Ferraro, L., Stilo, S. A., et al. (2014). Daily use, especially of high-potency cannabis, drives the earlier onset of psychosis in cannabis users. *Schizophrenia Bulletin*, 40, 1509–1517.

Durell, T. M., Kroutil, L. A., Crits-Christoph, P., Barchha, N., & Van Brunt, D. E. (2008). Prevalence of nonmedical methamphetamine use in the United States. *Substance Abuse Treatment, Prevention, and Policy*, 3, 19.

Everitt, B. J. (2014). Neural and psychological mechanisms underlying compulsive drug seeking habits and drug memories: Indications for novel treatments of addiction. *European Journal of Neuroscience*, 40, 2163–2182.

Fraioli, S., Crombag, H. S., Badiani, A., & Robinson, T. E. (1999). Susceptibility to amphetamine-induced locomotor sensitization is modulated by environmental stimuli. *Neuropsychopharmacology*, 20, 533–541.

Freud, S. (1974). *Cocaine papers* (R. Byck, Ed.). New York: Penguin.

Grande, I., & Vieta, E. (2015). Pharmacotherapy of acute mania: Monotherapy or combination therapy with mood stabilizers and antipsychotics? *CNS Drugs*, 29, 221–227.

Greely, H., Sahakian, B., Harris, J., Kessler, R. C., Gazzaniga, M., et al. (2008). Towards responsible use of cognitive-enhancing drugs by the healthy. *Nature*, 456, 702–705.

Griffin, J. A., Umstattd, M. R., & Usdan, S. L. (2010). Alcohol use and high-risk sexual behavior among collegiate women: A review of research on alcohol myopia theory. *Journal of American College Health*, 58, 523–532.

Hampson, E., & Kimura, D. (2005). Sex differences and hormonal influences on cognitive function in humans. In J. B. Becker, S. M. Breedlove, & D. Crews (Eds.), *Behavioral endocrinology* (pp. 357–398). Cambridge, MA: MIT Press.

Hardee, J. E., Weiland, B. J., Nichols, T. E., Welsh, R. C., Soules, M. E., Steinberg, D. B., et al. (2014). Development of impulse control circuitry in children of alcoholics. *Biological Psychiatry*, 76, 708–716.

Hill, A. S., Sahay, A., & Hen, R. (2015, April 2). Increasing adult hippocampal neurogenesis is sufficient to reduce anxiety and depression-like behaviors. *Neuropsychopharmacology*, 40, 2368–2378.

Hillemacher, T., Weinland, C., Lenz, B., Kraus, T., Heberlein, A., Glahn, A., et al. (2015). DNA methylation of the LEP gene is associated with craving during alcohol withdrawal. *Psychoneuroendocrinology*, 51, 371–377.

Isacsson, G., & Rich C. L. (2014). Antidepressant drugs and the risk of suicide in children and adolescents. *Paediatric Drugs*, 16, 115–122.

Isbell, H., Fraser, H. F., Wikler, R. E., Belleville, R. E., & Eisenman, A. J. (1955). An experimental study of the etiology of "rum fits" and delirium tremens. *Quarterly Journal of Studies on Alcohol*, 16, 1–35.

Kerr, D. C., Zava, D. T., Piper, W. T., Saturn, S. R., Frei, B., & Gombart, A. F. (2015). Associations between vitamin D levels and depressive symptoms in healthy young adult women. *Psychiatry Research*, 227, 46–51.

Lajud, N., & Torner, L. (2015). Early life stress and hippocampal neurogenesis in the neonate: Sexual dimorphism, long-term consequences and possible mediators. *Frontiers in Molecular Neuroscience*, 8, 3. doi: 10.3389/fnmol.2015.00003. eCollection 2015.

Landré, L., Destrieux, C., Baudry, M., Barantin, L., Cottier, J. P., et al. (2010). Preserved subcortical volumes and cortical thickness in women with sexual abuse-related PTSD. *Psychiatry Research*, 183, 181–186.

Lee, B. Y., Park, S. Y., Ryu, H. M., Shin, C. Y., Ko, K. N., Han, J. Y., et al. (2015). Changes in the methylation status of DAT, SERT, and MeCP2 gene promoters in the blood cell in families exposed to alcohol during the periconceptional period. *Alcohol and Clinical and Experimental Research*, 39, 239–250.

Liu, P., Lu, H., Filbey, F. M., Tamminga, C. A., Cao, Y., & Adinoff, B. (2014). MRI assessment of cerebral oxygen metabolism in cocaine-addicted individuals: Hypoactivity and dose dependence. *NMR Biomedicine, 27,* 726–732.

Lubman, D. I., Cheetham, A., & Yücel, M. (2015). Cannabis and adolescent brain development. *Pharmacology and Therapeutics, 148C,* 1–16.

MacAndrew, C., & Edgerton, R. B. (1969). *Drunken comportment: A social explanation.* Chicago: Aldine.

MacDonald, T. K., MacDonald, G., Zanna, M. P., & Fong, G. T. (2000). Alcohol, sexual arousal, and intentions to use condoms in young men: Applying alcohol myopia theory to risky sexual behavior. *Health Psychology, 19,* 290–298.

McCann, U. D., Lowe, K. A., & Ricaurte, G. A. (1997). Long-lasting effects of recreational drugs of abuse on the central nervous system. *The Neurologist, 3,* 399–411.

McGowan, P. O., Sasaki, A., D'Alessio, A. C., Dymov, S., Labonté, B., Szyf, M., et al. (2009). Epigenetic regulation of the glucocorticoid receptor in human brain associates with childhood abuse. *Nature Neurosciences, 12,* 342–348.

Mead, E. A., & Sarkar, D. K. (2014). Fetal alcohol spectrum disorders and their transmission through genetic and epigenetic mechanisms. *Frontiers in Genetics, 5,* 154–159.

Nguyen, B. M., Kim, D., Bricker, S., Bongard, F., Neville, A., Putnam, B., et al. (2014). Effect of marijuana use on outcomes in traumatic brain injury. *American Surgery, 80,* 979–983.

Nugent, B. M., Tobet, S. A., Lara, H. E., Lucion, A. B., Wilson, M. E., Recabarren, S. E., et al. (2012). Hormonal programming across the lifespan. *Hormone and Metabolic Research, 44,* 577–586.

Nugent, B. M., Wright, C. L., Shetty, A. C., Hodes, G. E., Lenz, K. M., Mahurkar, A., et al. (2015). Brain feminization requires active repression of masculinization via DNA methylation. *Nature Neuroscience, 18*(5), 690–697.

Popova, S., Lange, S., Bekmuradov, D., Mihic, A., & Rehm, J. (2011). Fetal alcohol spectrum disorder prevalence estimates in correctional systems: A systematic literature review. *Canadian Journal of Public Health, 102,* 336–340.

Pouget, J. G., Shams, T. A., Tiwari, A. K., & Müller, D. J. (2014). Pharmacogenetics and outcome with antipsychotic drugs. *Dialogues in Clinical Neuroscience, 16,* 555–566.

Reinstatler, L., & Youssef, N. A. (2015). Ketamine as a potential treatment for suicidal ideation: A systematic review of the literature. *Drugs, 15,* 37–43.

Roberts, N. P., Roberts, P. A., Jones, N., & Bisson, J. I. (2015). Psychological interventions for post-traumatic stress disorder and comorbid substance use disorder: A systematic review and meta-analysis. *Clinical Psychological Reviews, 38,* 25–38.

Robinson, T. E., & Becker, J. B. (1986). Enduring changes in brain and behavior produced by chronic amphetamine administration: A review and evaluation of animal models of amphetamine psychosis. *Brain Research Reviews, 11,* 157–198.

Robinson, T. E., & Berridge, K. C. (2008). Incentive sensitization theory. *Philosophical Transactions of the Royal Society of London, 363,* 3137–3146.

Roitman, P., Mechoulam, R., Cooper-Kazaz, R., & Shalev, A. (2014). Preliminary, open-label, pilot study of add-on oral Δ9-tetrahydrocannabinol in chronic post-traumatic stress disorder. *Clinical Drug Investigations, 34,* 587–591.

Sapolsky, R. M. (2004). *Why zebras don't get ulcers* (3rd ed.). New York: Henry Holt.

Sapolsky, R. M. (2005). The influence of social hierarchy on primate health. *Science, 308*(5722), 648–652.

Sevincer, A. T., & Oettingen, G. (2014). Alcohol myopia and goal commitment. *Frontiers in Psychology, 4,* 169–175.

Smith, A. D., Smith, S. M., de Jager, C. A., Whitbread, P., Johnston, C., et al. (2010). Homocysteine-lowering by B vitamins slows the rate of accelerated brain atrophy in mild cognitive impairment: A randomized controlled trial. *PLoS One, 8,* e12244.

Steen, E., Terry, B. M., Rivera, E. J., Cannon, J. L., Neely, T. R., Tavares, R., et al. (2005). Impaired insulin and insulin-like growth factor expression and signaling mechanisms in Alzheimer's disease: Is this type 3 diabetes? *Journal of Alzheimer's Disease, 7,* 63–80.

Teixeira-Gomes, A., Costa, V. M., Feio-Azevedo, R., Bastos, M. L., Carvalho, F., & Capela, J. P. (2015). The neurotoxicity of amphetamines during the adolescent period. *International Journal of Developmental Neuroscience, 41,* 44–62.

Vevelstad, M., Oiestad, E. L., Middelkoop, G., Hasvold, I., Lilleng, P., et al. (2012). The PMMA epidemic in Norway: Comparison of fatal and non-fatal intoxications. *Forensic Science International, 219,* 151–157.

Wenger, J. R., Tiffany, T. M., Bombardier, C., Nicholls, K., & Woods, S. C. (1981). Ethanol tolerance in the rat is learned. *Science, 213,* 575–577.

Whishaw, I. Q., Mittleman, G., & Evenden, J. L. (1989). Training-dependent decay in performance produced by the neuroleptic *cis*(Z)-flupentixol on spatial navigation by rats in a swimming pool. *Pharmacology, Biochemistry, and Behavior, 32,* 211–220.

Wilkinson, S. T., Radhakrishnan R., & D'Souza, D. C. (2014). Impact of cannabis use on the development of psychotic disorders. *Current Addiction Reports, 1*(2), 115–128.

Yager, L. M., Pitchers, K. K., Flagel, S. B., & Robinson, T. E. (2015). Individual variation in the motivational and neurobiological effects of an opioid cue. *Neuropsychopharmacology, 40,* 1269–1277.

CHAPTER 7

Brown, A. R., Antle, M. C., Hu, B., & Teskey, G. C. (2011). High frequency stimulation of the subthalamic nucleus acutely rescues neocortical movement representations and motor deficits following 6-hydroxydopamine administration in rats. *Experimental Neurology, 231,* 82–90.

Bueller, J. A., Aftab, M., Sen, S., Gomez-Hassan, D. Burmeister, M., & Zubieta, J.-K. (2006). BDNF Val66Met allele is associated with reduced hippocampal volume in healthy subjects. *Biological Psychiatry, 59,* 812–815.

Cacucci, F., Yi, M., Wills, T. J., Chapmans, P., & O'Keefe, J. (2008). Place cell firing correlates with memory deficits and amyloid plaque burden in Tg2576 Alzheimer mouse model. *Proceedings of the National Academy of Sciences United States of America, 105,* 7863–7868.

Caspi, A., Moffitt, T. E., Cannon, M., McClay, J., Murray, R., et al. (2005). Moderation of the effect of adolescent-onset cannabis use on adult psychosis by a functional polymorphism in the catechol-O-methyltransferase gene: Longitudinal evidence of a gene X environment interaction. *Biological Psychiatry, 57,* 1117–1127.

Damasio, H., & Damasio, A. R. (1989). *Lesion analysis in neuropsychology.* New York: Oxford University Press.

Fox, P. T., & Raichle, M. E. (1986). Focal physiological uncoupling of cerebral blood flow and oxidative metabolism during somatosensory stimulation in human subjects. *Proceedings of the National Academy of Sciences United States of America, 83,* 1140–1144.

Fraga, M. F., Ballestar, E., Paz, M. F., Ropero, S., Setien, F., Ballestar, M. L., et al. (2005). Epigenetic differences arise during the lifetime of monozygotic twins. *Proceedings of the National Academy of Sciences United States of America, 102,* 10604–10609.

Gonzalez, C. L. R., Gharbawie, O. A., & Kolb, B. (2006). Chronic low-dose administration of nicotine facilitates recovery and synaptic change after focal ischemia in rats. *Neuropharmacology, 50,* 777–787.

Haubensak, W., Kunwar, P. S., Cai, H., Ciocchi, S., Wall, N. R., Ponnusamy, R., et al. (2010). Genetic dissection of an amygdala microcircuit that gates conditioned fear. *Nature, 468,* 270–276.

Kolb, B., & Walkey, J. (1987). Behavioural and anatomical studies of the posterior parietal cortex of the rat. *Behavioural Brain Research, 23,* 127–145.

Kut, C., Chaichana, K. L., Xi, J., Raza, S. M., Ye, X., McVeigh, E. R., et al. (2015). Detection of human brain cancer infiltration ex vivo and in vivo using quantitative optical coherence tomography. *Science Translational Medicine 17,* 292ra100. doi: 10.1126/scitranslmed.3010611.

Kwong, K. K., Belliveau, J. W., Chesler, D. A., Goldberg, I. E., Weisskoff, R. M., Poncelet, B. P., et al. (1992). Dynamic magnetic resonance imaging of human brain activity during primary sensory stimulation. *Proceedings of the National Academy of Sciences United States of America, 89,* 5678.

Lecendreux, M., Konofal, E., Cortese, S., & Faraone, S. V. (2015). A 4-year follow-up of attention-deficit/hyperactivity disorder in a population sample. *Journal of Clinical Psychiatry, 76,* 712–719.

Lomber, S. G., & Payne, B. R. (1996). Removal of two halves restores the whole: Reversal of visual hemineglect during bilateral cortical or collicular inactivation in the cat. *Visual Neuroscience, 13,* 1143–1156.

May, L., Byers-Heinlein, K., Gervain, J., & Werker, J. F. (2011). Language and the newborn brain: Does prenatal language experience shape the neonate neural response to speech? *Frontiers in Psychology, 2,* 1–9.

McGowan, P. O., Sasaki, A., D'Alessio, A. C., Dymov, S., Labonté, B., Szyf, M., et al. (2009). Epigenetic regulation of the glucocorticoid receptor in human brain associates with childhood abuse. *Nature Neuroscience, 12,* 342–348.

Morris, R. G. M. (1981) Spatial localization does not require the presence of local cues. *Learning and Motivation, 12,* 239–260.

Mychasiuk, R., Schmold, N., Ilnytskyy, S., Kovalchuk, O., Kolb, B., & Gibb, R. (2011). Prenatal bystander stress alters brain, behavior, and the epigenome of developing rat offspring. *Developmental Neuroscience, 33,* 159–169.

National Research Council (1996). *The guide for the care and use of laboratory animals.* Washington, DC: National Academy Press.

Ogawa, S., Lee, T. M., Kay, A. R., & Tank, D. W. (1990). Brain magnetic resonance imaging with contrast dependent on blood oxygenation. *Proceedings of the National Academy of Sciences United States of America, 87,* 9868–9872.

O'Keefe, J. (2006). Hippocampal neurophysiology in the behaving animal. In P. Andersen, R. Morris, D. Amaral, T. Bliss, & J. O'Keefe (Eds.), *The Hippocampus Book.* (pp. 475–548). New York: Oxford University Press.

O'Keefe, J., & Dostrovsky, J. (1971). The hippocampus as a spatial map. *Brain Research, 34,* 171–175.

Penfield, W., & Jasper, H. H. (1954). *Epilepsy and the functional anatomy of the human brain.* Boston: Little, Brown.

Posner, M. I., & Raichle, M. E. (1997). *Images of mind.* New York: W. H. Freeman.

Reza, M. F., Ikoma, K., Ito, T., Ogawa, T., & Mano, Y. (2007). N200 latency and P300 amplitude in depressed mood post-traumatic brain injury patients. *Neuropsychological Rehabilitation, 17,* 723–734.

Schallert, T., Whishaw, I. Q., Ramirez, V. D., & Teitelbaum, P. (1978). Compulsive, abnormal walking caused by anticholinergics in akinetic, 6-hydroxydopamine-treated rats. *Science, 199,* 1461–1463.

Schlaepfer, T. E., Bewernick, B. H., Kayser, S., Mädler, B., & Coenen, V. A. (2013). Rapid effects of deep brain stimulation for treatment-resistant major depression. *Biological Psychiatry, 73* (12), 1204–1212.

Scoville, W. B., & Milner, B. (1957). Loss of recent memory after bilateral hippocampal lesions. *Journal of Neurology, Neurosurgery, and Psychiatry, 20,* 11–21.

Spinney, L. (2005). Optical topography and the color of blood. *The Scientist, 19,* 25–27.

Szyf, M., McGowan, P., & Meaney, M. J. (2008). The social environment and the epigenome. *Environmental Molecular Mutagenetics, 49,* 46–60.

Tisdall, M. M., & Smith, M. (2006). Cerebral microdialysis: Research technique or clinical tool. *British Journal of Anaesthesia, 97,* 18–25.

Van den Heuvel, M. P., & Hulshoff Pol, H. E. (2010). Exploring the brain network: A review on resting-state fMRI functional connectivity. *European Neuropsychopharmcology, 20,* 519–534.

Wess, J., Nakajima, K., Jain, S. (2013). Novel designer receptors to probe GPCR signaling and physiology. *Trends in Pharmacological Sciences, 34,* 385–392.

Whishaw, I. Q. (1989). Dissociating performance and learning deficits in spatial navigation tasks in rats subjected to cholinergic muscarinic blockade. *Brain Research Bulletin, 23,* 347–358.

Whishaw, I. Q., & Kolb, B. (2005). *The behavior of the laboratory rat.* New York: Oxford University Press.

CHAPTER 8

Agate, R. J., Grisham, W., Wade, J., Mann, S., Wingfield, J., Schanen, C., et al. (2003). Neural, but not gonadal, origin of brain sex differences in a gynandromorphic finch. *Proceedings of the National Academy of Sciences United States of America, 100,* 4873–4878.

Ames, E. W. (1997). The development of Romanian orphanage children adopted to Canada. Final report to Human Resources Development, Canada.

Anda, R. F., Felitti, V. J., Bremner, J. D., Walker, J. D., Whitfield, C., et al. (2006). The enduring effects of abuse and related adverse experiences in childhood: A convergence of evidence from neurobiology and epidemiology. *European Archives of Psychiatry and Clinical Neuroscience, 256,* 174–186.

Berens, A. E., & Nelson, C. A. (2015). The science of early adversity: Is there a role for large institutions in the care of vulnerable children? *Lancet, S0140-6736(14),* 61131–61134.

Blumberg, S. J., Bramlett, M. D., Kogan, M. D., Schieve, L. A., Jones, J. R., et al. (2013). Changes in prevalence of parent-reported autism spectrum disorder in school-aged US children: 2007 to 2011–2012. *National Health Statistics Reports, 65,* 1–11.

Bock, J., Rether, K., Grogerr, N., Xie, L., & Braun, K. (2014). Perinatal programming of emotional brain circuits: An integrative view from systems to molecules. *Frontiers of Neuroscience, 11,* 1–15. doi: 10. 3389/fnins. 2014. 00011.

Bourgeois, J.-P. (2001). Synaptogenesis in the neocortex of the newborn: The ultimate frontier for individuation? In C. A. Nelson & M. Luciana (Eds.), *Handbook of Developmental Cognitive Neuroscience.* Cambridge, MA: MIT Press.

Bunney, B. G., Potkin, S. G., & Bunney, W. E. (1997). Neuropathological studies of brain tissue in schizophrenia. *Journal of Psychiatric Research, 31,* 159–173.

Changeux, J.-P., & Danchin, A. (1976). Selective stabilization of developing synapses as a mechanism for the specification of neuronal networks. *Nature, 264,* 705–712.

Chen, R., Jiao, Y., & Herskovits, E. H. (2011). Structural MRI in autism spectrum disorder. *Pediatric Research, 69,* 63R–68R.

Clarke, R. S., Heron, W., Fetherstonhaugh, M. L., Forgays, D. G., & Hebb, D. O. (1951). Individual differences in dogs: Preliminary report on the effects of early experience. *Canadian Journal of Psychology, 5*(4), 150–156.

Cowan, W. M. (1979). The development of the brain. *Scientific American, 241*(3), 116.

Epstein, H. T. (1979). Correlated brain and intelligence development in humans. In M. E. Hahn, C. Jensen, & B. C. Dudek (Eds.), *Development and evolution of brain size: Behavioral implications* (pp. 111–131). New York: Academic Press.

Finegold, S. M., Molitoris, D., Song, Y., Liu, C., Vaisanen, M. L., Bolte, E., et al. (2002). Gastrointestinal microflora studies in late-onset autism. *Clinical Infective Diseases, 35*, S6–S16.

Gershon, E. S., & Rieder, R. O. (1992). Major disorders of mind and brain. *Scientific American, 267*(3), 126–133.

Geschwind, D. H., & Rakic, P. (2013). Cortical evolution: Judge the brain by its cover. *Neuron, 80*, 633–647.

Gibb, R., Gonzalez, C., & Kolb, B. (2014). Prenatal enrichment and recovery from perinatal cortical damage: Effects of maternal complex housing. *Frontiers in Behavioral Neuroscience, 8*, 223. doi: 10.3389/fnbeh.2014.00223.

Giussani, C., Roux, F. E., Lubrano, V., Gaini, S. M., & Bello, L. (2007). Review of language organization in bilingual patients: What can we learn from direct brain mapping? *Acta Neurochir (Wien), 149*, 1109–1116.

Goldstein, J. M., Seidman, L. J., Horton, N. J., Makris, N., Kennedy, D. N., Caviness, V. S., Jr., et al. (2001). Normal sexual dimorphism of the adult human brain assessed by in vivo magnetic resonance imaging. *Cerebral Cortex, 11*, 490–497.

Guerrini, R., Dobyns, W. B., & Barkovich, A. J. (2007). Abnormal development of the human cerebral cortex: Genetics, functional consequences and treatment options. *Trends in Neurosciences, 31*, 154–162.

Halliwell, C., Comeau, W., Gibb, R., Frost, D. O., & Kolb, B. (2009). Factors influencing frontal cortex development and recovery from early frontal injury. *Developmental Neurorehabilitation, 12*, 269–278.

Harker, A., Raza, S., Williamson, K., Kolb, B., & Gibb, R. (2015). Preconception paternal stress in rats alters dendritic morphology and connectivity in the brain of developing male and female offspring. *Neuroscience, 303*, 200–210.

Harlow, H. F. (1971). *Learning to love.* San Francisco: Albion.

Hebb, D. O. (1947). The effects of early experience on problem solving at maturity. *American Psychologist, 2*, 737–745.

Horn, G., Bradley, P., & McCabe, B. J. (1985). Changes in the structure of synapses associated with learning. *Journal of Neuroscience, 5*, 3161–3168.

Hsiao E. Y., McBride, S. W., Hsien, S., Sharon, G., Hyde, E. R., McCue, T., et al. (2013). Microbiota modulate behavioral and physiological abnormalities associated with neurodevelopmental disorders. *Cell, 155*, 1451–1463.

Huttenlocher, P. R. (1994). Synaptogenesis in human cerebral cortex. In G. Dawson & K. W. Fischer (Eds.), *Human behavior and the developing brain* (pp. 137–152). New York: Guilford Press.

Juraska, J. M. (1990). The structure of the cerebral cortex: Effects of gender and the environment. In B. Kolb & R. Tees (Eds.), *The cerebral cortex of the rat* (pp. 483–506). Cambridge, MA: MIT Press.

Kinney, H. C. (2009). Brainstem mechanisms underlying the sudden infant death syndrome: Evidence from human pathologic studies. *Developmental Psychobiology, 51*, 223–233.

Klein, D., Watkins, K. E., Zatorre, R. J., & Milner, B. (2006). Word and nonword repetition in bilingual subjects: A PET study. *Human Brain Mapping, 27*, 153–161.

Kolb, B., & Gibb, R. (1993). Possible anatomical basis of recovery of function after neonatal frontal lesions in rats. *Behavioral Neuroscience, 107*, 799–811.

Kolb, B., Mychasiuk, R., Muhammad, A., Li, Y., Frost, D. O., & Gibb, R. (2012). Experience and the developing prefrontal cortex. *Proceedings of the National Academy of Sciences United States of America.*

Kovelman, J. A., & Scheibel, A. B. (1984). A neurohistologic correlate of schizophrenia. *Biological Psychiatry, 19*, 1601–1621.

Kuhl, P. K. (2011). Early language learning and literacy: Neuroscience implications for education. *Mind, Brain and Education, 5*, 128–142.

Lenneberg, E. H. (1967). *Biological foundations of language.* New York: Wiley.

Lenroot, R. K., Gogtay, N., Greenstein, D. K., Wells, E. M., Wallace, G. L., Clasen, L. S., et al. (2007). Sexual dimorphism of brain development trajectories during childhood and adolescence. *NeuroImage, 36*, 1065–1073.

Levitin, D. J., & Rogers, S. E. (2005). Absolute pitch: Perception, coding, and controversies. *Trends in Cognitive Science, 9*, 26–33.

Lorenz, K. (1970). *Studies on animal and human behavior* (Vols. 1 and 2). Cambridge, MA: Harvard University Press.

Lu, L. H., Leonard, C. M., Thompson, P. M., Kan, E., Jolley, J., Welcome, S. E., et al. (2007). Normal developmental changes in inferior frontal gray matter are associated with improvement in phonological processing: A longitudinal MRI analysis. *Cerebral Cortex, 17*, 1092–1099.

Malanga, C. J., & Kosofsky, B. E. (2003). Does drug abuse beget drug abuse? Behavioral analysis of addiction liability in animal models of prenatal drug exposure. *Developmental Brain Research, 147*, 47–57.

Marin-Padilla, M. (1993). Pathogenesis of late-acquired leptomeningeal heterotopias and secondary cortical alterations: A Golgi study. In A. M. Galaburda (Ed.), *Dyslexia and development: Neurobiological aspects of extraordinary brains* (pp. 64–88). Cambridge, MA: Harvard University Press.

Minnes, S., Singer, L. T., Min, M. O., Wu, M., Lang, A., & Yoon, S. (2014). Effects of prenatal cocaine/polydrug exposure on substance abuse by age 15. *Drug and Alcohol Dependence, 134*, 201–210.

Moore, K. L. (1988). *The developing human: Clinically oriented embryology* (4th ed.). Philadelphia: Saunders.

Mychasiuk, R., Gibb, R., & Kolb, B. (2011). Prenatal stress produces sexually dimorphic and regionally specific changes in gene expression in hippocampus and frontal cortex of developing rat offspring. *Developmental Neuroscience, 33*, 531–538.

Mychasiuk, R., Muhammad, A., & Kolb, B. (2014). Environmental enrichment alters structural plasticity of the adolescent brain but does not remediate the effects of prenatal nicotine exposure. *Synapse, 68*, 293–305.

National Institute on Drug Abuse (2012). http://www.drugabuse.gov/publications/research-reports/tobacco/smoking-pregnancy—what-are-risks

Nelson, C. A., & Luciana, M. (Eds.) (2008). *Handbook of developmental cognitive neuroscience*, 2nd ed. Cambridge, MA: MIT Press.

Nelson, C. A., Zeanah, C. H., Fox, N. A., Marshall, P. J., Smyke, A. T., & Guthrie, D. (2007). Cognitive recovery in socially deprived young children: The Bucharest Early Intervention Project. *Science, 318*, 1937–1940.

Noble, K. G., Houston, S. M., Brito, N. H., Bartsch, H., Kan, E., Kuperman, J. M., et al. (2015). Family income, parental education and brain structure in children and adolescents. *Nature Neuroscience, 18*, 773–778.

Nordahl, C. W., Scholz, R., Yang, X., Buonocore, M. H., Simon, T., Rogers S., et al. (2012). Increased rate of amygdala growth in children aged 2 to 4 years with autism spectrum disorders: A longitudinal study. *Archives of General Psychiatry, 69*, 53–61.

Nyagu, A. I., Loganovsky, K. N., & Loganovskaja, T. K. (1998). Psychophysiological aftereffects of prenatal irradiation. *International Journal of Psychophysiology, 30*, 303–311.

O'Hare, E. D., & Sowell, E. R. (2008). Imaging developmental changes in gray and white matter in the human brain. In C. A. Nelson and M. Luciana (Eds.), *Handbook of developmental cognitive neuroscience* (pp. 23–38), Cambridge, MA: MIT Press.

Overman, W., Bachevalier, J., Schuhmann, E., & Ryan, P. (1996). Cognitive gender differences in very young children parallel biologically based cognitive gender differences in monkeys. *Behavioral Neuroscience, 110,* 673–684.

Overman, W., Bachevalier, J., Turner, M., & Peuster, A. (1992). Object recognition versus object discrimination: Comparison between human infants and infant monkeys. *Behavioral Neuroscience, 106,* 15–29.

Paterson, D. S., Trachtenberg, F. L., Thompson, E. G., Belliveau, R. A., Beggs, A. H., Dranall, et al. (2006). Multiple serotonergic brainstem abnormalities in sudden infant death syndrome. *Journal of the American Medical Association, 296,* 2124–2132.

Paus, T., Keshavan, M., & Giedd, J. N. (2008). Why do so many psychiatric disorders emerge during adolescence? *Nature Reviews Neuroscience, 9,* 947–957.

Payne, B. R., & Lomber, S. G. (2001). Reconstructing functional systems after lesions of cerebral cortex. *Nature Reviews Neuroscience, 2,* 911–919.

Petanjek, Z., Judas, M., Simic, G., Rasin, M. R., Uylings, H. B. M., et al. (2011). Extraordinary neoteny of synaptic spines in the human prefrontal cortex. *Proceedings of the National Academy of Sciences U S A, 108,* 13281–13286.

Piaget, J. (1952). *The origins of intelligence in children.* New York: Norton.

Purpura, D. P. (1974). Dendritic spine "dysgenesis" and mental retardation. *Science, 186,* 1126–1127.

Raizada, R. D. S., Richards, T. L., Meltzoff, A., & Kuhl, P. K. (2008). Socioeconomic status predicts hemispheric specialization of the left inferior frontal gyrus in young children. *NeuroImage, 40,* 1392–1401.

Rakic, P. (1974). Neurons in rhesus monkey cerebral cortex: Systematic relation between time of origin and eventual disposition. *Science, 183,* 425.

Raza, S., Harker, A., Richards, S., Kolb, B., & Gibb, R. (2015). Tactile stimulation improves neuroanatomical pathology but not behaviour in rats prenatally exposed to valproic acid. *Behavioural Brain Research, 282,* 25–36.

Riesen, A. H. (1982). Effects of environments on development in sensory systems. In W. D. Neff (Ed.), *Contributions to sensory physiology* (Vol. 6, pp. 45–77). New York: Academic Press.

Rutter, M. (1998). Developmental catch-up, and deficit, following adoption after severe global early privation. *Journal of Child Psychology and Psychiatry, 39,* 465–476.

Salm, A. K., Pavelko, M., Drouse, E. M., Webster, W., Kraszpulski, M., & Birkle, D. L. (2004). Lateral amygdala nucleus expansion in adult rats is associated with exposure to prenatal stress. *Developmental Brain Research, 148,* 159–167.

Schnack, H. G., van Haren, N. E., Brouwer, R. M., Evans, A., Durston, S., Boomsma, D. I., et al. (2014). Changes in thickness and surface area of the human cortex and their relationship with intelligence. *Cerebral Cortex, 25,* 1608–1617.

Shaw, P., Greenstein, D., Lerch, J., Clasen, L., Lenroot, R., et al. (2006). Intellectual ability and cortical development in children and adolescents. *Nature, 440,* 666–679.

Shingo, T., Gregg, C., Enwere, E., Fujikawa, H., Hassam, R., Greary, C., et al. (2003). Pregnancy-stimulated neurogenesis in the adult female forebrain mediated by prolactin. *Science, 299,* 117–120.

Smyke, A. T., Zeanah, C. H., Gleason, M. M., Drury, S. S., Fox, N. A., et al. (2012). A randomized controlled trial comparing foster care and institutional care for children with signs of reactive attachment disorder. *American Journal of Psychiatry, 169,* 508–514.

Sodhi, M. S., & Sanders-Bush, E. (2004). Serotonin and brain development. *International Review of Neurobiology, 59,* 111–174.

Sowell, E. R., Thompson, P. M., Leonard, C. M., Welcome, S. E., Kan, E., & Toga, A. W. (2004). Longitudinal mapping of cortical thickness and brain growth in normal children. *Journal of Neuroscience, 24,* 8223–8231.

Sowell, E. R., Thompson, P. M., & Toga, A. W. (2004). Mapping changes in the human cortex throughout the span of life. *The Neuroscientist, 10,* 372–392.

Sperry, R. W. (1963). Chemoaffinity in the orderly growth of nerve fiber patterns and connections. *Proceedings of the National Academy of Sciences United States of America, 50,* 703–710.

Suomi, S. J. (2011). Risk, resilience, and gene-environment interplay in primates. *Journal of the Canadian Academy of Child and Adolescent Psychiatry, 20,* 289–297.

Twitchell, T. E. (1965). The automatic grasping response of infants. *Neuropsychologia, 3,* 247–259.

Wallace, P. S., & Whishaw, I. Q. (2003). Independent digit movements and precision grip patterns in 1–5-month-old human infants: Hand-babbling, including vacuous then self-directed hand and digit movements, precedes targeted reaching. *Neuropsychologia, 41,* 1912–1918.

Weiss, S., Reynolds, B. A., Vescovi, A. L., Morshead, C., Craig, C. G., & van der Kooy, D. (1996). Is there a neural stem cell in the mammalian forebrain? *Trends in Neurosciences, 19(9),* 387–393.

Werker, J. F., & Tees, R. C. (1992). The organization and reorganization of human speech perception. *Annual Review of Neuroscience, 15,* 377–402.

Yakovlev, P. E., & Lecours, A.-R. (1967). The myelogenetic cycles of regional maturation of the brain. In A. Minkowski (Ed.), *Regional development of the brain in early life.* Oxford: Blackwell.

CHAPTER 9

Bálint, R. (1909). Seelenlähmung des "Schauens," optische Ataxie, räumliche Störung der Aufmerksamkeit. *Monatschrift für Psychiatrie und Neurologie, 25,* 51–81.

Farah, M. J. (1990). *Visual agnosia.* Cambridge, MA: MIT Press.

Geschwind, N. (1972). Language and the brain. *Scientific American, 226(4),* 78–83.

Goodale, M. A., Milner, D. A., Jakobson, L. S., & Carey, J. D. P. (1991). A kinematic analysis of reaching and grasping movements in a patient recovering from optic ataxia. *Nature, 349,* 154–156.

Hamilton, R. H., Shenton, J. T., & Coslett, H. B. (2006). An acquired deficit of audiovisual speech processing. *Brain and Language, 98,* 66–73.

Hasson, U., Nir, Y., Levy, I., Fuhrmann, G., & Malach, R. (2004). Intersubject synchronization of cortical activity during natural vision. *Science, 303,* 1634–1640.

Held, R. (1968). Dissociation of visual function by deprivation and rearrangement. *Psychologische Forschung, 31,* 338–348.

Hubel, D. H., & Weisel, T. N. (1977). Functional architecture of macaque monkey visual cortex. *Proceedings of the Royal Society of London B, 198,* Figure 23.

Jerison, H. J. (1973). *The evolution of the brain and intelligence.* New York: Academic Press.

Kline, D. W. (1994). Optimizing the visibility of displays for older observers. *Experimental Aging Research, 20,* 11–23.

Kuffler, S. W. (1952). Neurons in the retina: Organization, inhibition and excitatory problems. *Cold Spring Harbor Symposia on Quantitative Biology, 17,* 281–292.

Milner, A. D., & Goodale, M. A. (2006). *The visual brain in action* (2nd ed.). Oxford: Oxford University Press.

Sacks, O., & Wasserman, R. (1987). The case of the colorblind painter. *The New York Review of Books, 34,* 25–33.

Snowden, R., Thompson, P., & Troscianko, T. (2008). *Basic vision: An introduction to visual perception.* Oxford: Oxford University Press.

Szentagothai, J. (1975). The "module-concept" in cerebral cortex architecture. *Brain Research, 95,* 475–496.

Tanaka, K. (1993). Neuronal mechanisms of object recognition. *Science, 262,* 685–688.

Weizkrantz, L. (1986). *Blindsight: A case study and implications.* Oxford: Oxford University Press.

Wong-Riley, M. T. T., Hevner, R. F., Cutlan, R., Earnest, M., Egan, R., Frost, J., & Nguyen, T. (1993). Cytochrome oxidase in the human visual cortex: Distribution in the developing and the adult brain. *Visual Neuroscience, 10,* 41–58.

Zaidi, F. H., Hull, J. T., Peirson, S. N., Wulff, K., Aeschbach, D., et al. (2007). Short-wavelength light sensitivity of circadian, pupillary, and visual awareness in humans lacking an outer retina. *Current Biology, 17,* 2122–2128.

Zihl, J., von Cramon, D., & Mai, N. (1983). Selective disturbance of movement vision after bilateral brain damage. *Brain, 106,* 313–340.

CHAPTER 10

Bermudez, P., Lerch, J. P., Evans, A. C., & Zatorre, R. J. (2009). Neuroanatomical correlates of musicianship as revealed by cortical thickness and voxel-based morphometry. *Cerebral Cortex, 19,* 1583–1596.

Boonman, A., Bumrungsri, S., & Yovel, Y. (2014). Nonecholocating fruit bats produce biosonar clicks with their wings. *Current Biology, 24,* 2962–2967.

Bregman, A. S. (2005). Auditory scene analysis and the role of phenomenology in experimental psychology. *Canadian Psychology, 46,* 1, 32–40.

Chomsky, N. (1965). Aspects of the theory of syntax. Cambridge, MA: MIT Press.

Clarke, G. M. (2015). The multi-channel cochlear implant: Multi-disciplinary development of electrical stimulation of the cochlea and the resulting clinical benefit. *Hearing Research, 322,* 4–13.

Daniel, E. (2007). Noise and hearing loss: A review. *The Journal of School Health, 77,* 225–231.

Drake-Lee, A. B. (1992). Beyond music: Auditory temporary threshold shift in rock musicians after a heavy metal concert. *Journal of the Royal Society of Medicine, 85,* 617–619.

Geissmann, T. (2001). Gibbon songs and human music from an evolutionary perspective. In N. L. Wallin, B. Merker, & S. Brown (Eds.), *The origins of music* (pp. 103–124). Cambridge, MA: MIT Press.

Hyde, K. L., Lerch, J. P., Zatorre, R. J., Griffiths, T. D., Evans, A. C., & Peretz, I. (2007). Cortical thickness in congenital amusia: When less is better than more. *Journal of Neuroscience, 27,* 13028–13032.

Johansson, B. B. (2012). Multisensory stimulation in stroke rehabilitation. *Frontiers in Human Neuroscience, 6,* 60.

Kim, K. H. S., Relkin, N. R., Young-Min Lee, K., and Hirsch, J. (1997). Distinct cortical areas associated with native and second languages. *Nature* 388, 171–174.

Knudsen, E. I. (1981). The hearing of the barn owl. *Scientific American, 245*(6), 113–125.

Loeb, G. E. (1990). Cochlear prosthetics. *Annual Review of Neuroscience, 13,* 357–371.

Marler, P. (1991). The instinct to learn. In S. Carey and R. German (Eds.), *The epigenesis of mind: Essays on biology and cognition* (p. 39). Hillsdale, NJ: Erlbaum.

Nottebohm, F., & Arnold, A. P. (1976). Sexual dimorphism in vocal control areas of the songbird brain. *Science, 194,* 211–213.

Penfield, W., & Roberts, L. (1956). *Speech and brain mechanisms.* Oxford, London: Oxford University Press.

Peretz, I., Kolinsky, R., Tramo, M., Labrecque, R., Hublet, C., Demeurisse, G., et al. (1994). Functional dissociations following bilateral lesions of auditory cortex. *Brain, 117,* 1283–1301.

Pinker, S. (1997). *How the mind works.* New York: Norton.

Rauschecker, J. P. (2012). Ventral and dorsal streams in the evolution of speech and language. *Frontiers in Evolutionary Neuroscience, 4*:7. doi: 10.3389/fnevo.2012.00007.

Romanski, L. M., Tian, B., Fritz, J., Mishkin, M., Goldman-Rakic, P. S., & Rauschecker, J. P. (1999). Dual streams of auditory afferents target multiple domains in the primate prefrontal cortex. *Nature Neuroscience, 2,* 1131–1136.

Sunitha Suresh, B. S., De Oliveira, G. S. Jr., & Suresh, S. (2015). The effect of audio therapy to treat postoperative pain in children undergoing major surgery: A randomized controlled trial. *Pediatric Surgical International, 31,* 197–201.

Teie, P. U. (1998). Noise-induced hearing loss and symphony orchestra musicians: Risk factors, effects, and management. *Maryland Medical Journal, 47,* 13–18.

Teng, S., & Whitney, D. (2011). The acuity of echolocation: Spatial resolution in the sighted compared to expert performance. *Journal of Visual Impairment & Blindness, 105,* 20–32.

Thaler, L., Arnott, S. R., & Goodale, M. A. (2011). Neural correlates of natural human echolocation in early and late blind echolocation experts. *PLoS ONE, 6,* e20162.

Thompson, C. K., Meitzen, J., Replogle, K., Drnevich, J., Lent, K. L., et al. (2012). Seasonal changes in patterns of gene expression in avian song control brain regions. *PLoS One, 7,* e35119.

Trehub, S., Schellenberg, E. G., & Ramenetsky, G. B. (1999). Infants' and adults' perception of scale structures. *Journal of Experimental Psychology: Human Perception and Performance, 25,* 965–975.

Zatorre, R. J., Evans, A. C., & Meyer, E. (1994). Neural mechanisms underlying melodic perception and memory for pitch. *Journal of Neuroscience, 14,* 1908–1919.

Zatorre, R. J., Evans, A. C., Meyer, E., & Gjedde, A. (1992). Lateralization of phonetic and pitch discrimination in speech processing. *Science, 256,* 846–849.

Zatorre, R. J., Meyer, E., Gjedde, A., & Evans, A. C. (1996). PET studies of phonetic processing of speech: Review, replication, and reanalysis. *Cerebral Cortex, 6,* 21–30.

CHAPTER 11

Aflalo, T. N., & Graziano, M. S. (2007). Relationship between unconstrained arm movements and single-neuron firing in the macaque motor cortex. *Journal of Neuroscience, 127,* 2760–2780.

Alessandria, M., Vetrugno, R., Cortelli, P., & Montagna, P. (2011). Normal body scheme and absent phantom limb experience in amputees while dreaming. *Consciousness and Cognition, 20,* 831–834.

Alexander, R. E., & Critcher, M. D. (1990). Functional architecture of basal ganglia circuits: Neural substrates of parallel processing. *Trends in Neuroscience, 13,* 269.

Asanuma, H. (1989). *The motor cortex.* New York: Raven Press.

Blakemore, S. J., Wolpert, D. M., & Frith, C. D. (1998). Central cancellation of self-produced tickle sensation. *Nature Neuroscience, 1,* 635–640.

Bleton, J. P., Teremetz, M., Vidailhet, M., Mesure, S., Maier, M. A., Lindberg, P. G. (2014). Impaired force control in writer's cramp showing a bilateral deficit in sensorimotor integration. *Movement Disorders, 29,* 130–134.

Brinkman, C. (1984). Supplementary motor area of the monkey's cerebral cortex: Short- and long-term deficits after unilateral ablation and the effects of subsequent callosal section. *Journal of Neuroscience, 4,* 918–992.

Casile, A., Caggiano, V., & Ferrari, P. F. (2011). The mirror neuron system: A fresh view. *Neuroscientist, 17,* 524–538.

Castellanos, F. X., Cortese, S., & Proal, E. (2014). Connectivity. *Current Topics in Behavioral Neuroscience, 16,* 49–77.

Church, J. A., Fair, D. A., Dosenbach, N. U., Cohen, A. L., Miezin, F. M., Petersen, S. E., & Schlaggar, B. L. (2009). Control networks in paediatric Tourette syndrome show immature and anomalous patterns of functional connectivity. *Brain, 32,* 225–238.

Cole, J. (1995). *Pride and a daily marathon.* Cambridge, MA: MIT Press.

Corkin, S., Milner, B., & Rasmussen, T. (1970). Somatosensory thresholds. *Archives of Neurology, 23,* 41–58.

Critchley, M. (1953). *The parietal lobes.* London: Arnold.

Daly, J. J., & Huggins, J. E. (2015). Brain-computer interface: Current and emerging rehabilitation applications. *Archives of Physical and Medical Rehabilitation, 96* (3 Suppl.), S1–S7.

Davarpanah Jazi, S., Yau, M., Westwood, D. A., & Heath, M. (2015). Pantomime-grasping: The 'return' of haptic feedback supports the absolute specification of object size. *Experimental Brain Research, 233,* 2029–2040.

Evarts, E. V. (1968). Relation of pyramidal tract activity to force exerted during voluntary movement. *Journal of Neurophysiology, 31,* 14–27.

Foster, E., Wildner, H., Tudeau, L., Haueter, S., Ralvenius, W. T., Jegen, M., et al. (2015). Targeted ablation, silencing, and activation establish glycinergic dorsal horn neurons as key components of a spinal gate for pain and itch. *Neuron, 85,* 1289–1304.

Friedhoff, A. J., & Chase, T. N. (1982). Gilles de la Tourette syndrome. *Advances in Neurology, 35,* 1–17.

Friend, D. M., & Kravitz, A. V. (2014). Working together: Basal ganglia pathways in action selection. *Trends in Neuroscience, 37,* 301–303.

Hashimoto, Y., Honda, T., Matsumura, K., Nakao, M., Soga, K., Katano, K., et al. (2015). Quantitative evaluation of human cerebellum-dependent motor learning through prism adaptation of hand-reaching movement. *PLoS One.* (3):e0119376.

Hellman, R. B., Chang, E., Tanner, J., Helms Tillery, S. I., & Santos, V. J. (2015). A robot hand testbed designed for enhancing embodiment and functional neurorehabilitation of body schema in subjects with upper limb impairment or loss. *Frontiers in Human Neuroscience, 9,* 1–26.

Hess, W. R. (1957). *The functional organization of the diencephalon.* London: Grune & Stratton.

Imani, S., Zagari, Z., Rezaei Zarchi, S., Jorjani, M., Nasri, S. (2015). Functional recovery of carbon nanotube/nafion nanocomposite in rat model of spinal cord injury. *Artificial Cells Nanomedicine and Biotechnology, 10,* 1–6.

Kaas, J. H. (1987). The organization and evolution of neocortex. In S. P. Wise (Ed.), *Higher brain functions* (pp. 237–298). New York: Wiley.

Kaas, J. H., Stepniewska, I., & Gharbawie, O. (2012). Cortical networks subserving upper limb movements in primates. *European Journal of Physical and Rehabilitation Medicine, 48,* 299–306.

Kalueff, A. V., Aldridge, J. W., LaPorte, J. L., Murphy D. L., & Tuohimaa, P. (2007). Analyzing grooming microstructure in neurobehavioral experiments. *Nature Protocols, 25,* 38–44.

Kambi, N., Halder, P., Rajan, R., Arora, V., Chand, P., et al. (2014). Large-scale reorganization of the somatosensory cortex following spinal cord injuries is due to brainstem plasticity. *Nature Communications, 8:5,* 3602.

Kern, U., Busch, V., Rockland, M., Kohl, M., & Birklein, F. (2009). Prevalence and risk factors of phantom limb pain and phantom limb sensations in Germany: A nationwide field survey. *Schmerz, 23,* 479–488.

Lang, C. E., & Schieber, M. H. (2004). Reduced muscle selectivity during individuated finger movements in humans after damage to the motor cortex or corticospinal tract. *Journal of Neurophysiology, 91,* 1722–1733.

Lashley, K. S. (1951). The problem of serial order in behavior. In L. A. Jeffress (Ed.), *Cerebral mechanisms and behavior* (pp. 112–136). New York: Wiley.

Leonard, C. M., Glendinning, D. S., Wilfong, T., Cooper, B. Y., & Vierck, C. J., Jr. (1991). Alterations of natural hand movements after interruption of fasciculus cuneatus in the macaque. *Somatosensory and Motor Research, 9,* 61–75.

Lopez-Escamez. J. A., Carey, J., Chung, W. H., Goebel, J. A., Magnusson, M., Mandalà, M., et al. (2015). Diagnostic criteria for Ménière's disease. *Journal of Vestibular Research, 25,* 1–7.

Melzack, R. (1973). *The puzzle of pain.* New York: Basic Books.

Melzack, R., & Wall, P. D. (1965). Pain mechanisms: A new theory. *Science, 150,* 971–979.

Mountcastle, V. B. (1978). An organizing principle for cerebral function: The unit module and the distributed system. In G. M. Edelman & V. B. Mountcastle (Eds.), *The mindful brain* (pp. 7–50). Cambridge, MA: MIT Press.

Nudo, R. J., Wise, B. M., SiFuentes, F., & Milliken, G. W. (1996). Neural substrates for the effects of rehabilitative training on motor recovery after ischemic infarct. *Science, 272,* 1791–1794.

Panksepp, J. (2007). Neuroevolutionary sources of laughter and social joy: Modeling primal human laughter in laboratory rats. *Behavioural Brain Research, 4,* 231–244.

Penfield, W., & Boldrey, E. (1958). Somatic motor and sensory representation in the cerebral cortex as studied by electrical stimulation. *Brain, 60,* 389–443.

Pons, T. P., Garraghty, P. E., Ommaya, A. K., Kaas, J. H., Taum, E., & Mishkin, M. (1991). Massive cortical reorganization after sensory deafferentation in adult macaques. *Science, 252,* 1857–1860.

Roland, P. E. (1993). *Brain activation.* New York: Wiley-Liss.

Rothwell, J. C., Taube, M. M., Day, B. L., Obeso, J. A., Thomas, P. K., & Marsden, C. D. (1982). Manual motor performance in a deafferented man. *Brain, 105,* 515–542.

Sacks, O. W. (1998). *The man who mistook his wife for a hat: And other clinical tales.* New York: Touchstone Books.

Thach, W. T. (2007). On the mechanism of cerebellar contributions to cognition. *Cerebellum, 6,* 163–167.

Therrien, A. S., Bastian, A. J. (2015). Cerebellar damage impairs internal predictions for sensory and motor function. *Current Opinion in Neurobiology, 33,* 127–133.

Tinaz, S., Malone, P., Hallett, M., Horovitz, S. G. (2015). Role of the right dorsal anterior insula in the urge to tic in Tourette syndrome. *Movement Disorders,* doi: 10.1002/mds.26230.

von Holst, E. (1973). *The collected papers of Erich von Holst* (R. Martin, Trans.). Coral Gables, FL: University of Miami Press.

Williams, T. H., Gluhbegovic, N., & Jew, J. (2000). *The human brain: Dissections of the real brain* (CD-ROM). Brain University: brain-university.com.

Windt, J. M., Harkness, D. L., & Lenggenhager, B. (2015). Tickle me, I think I might be dreaming! Sensory attenuation, self-other distinction, and predictive processing in lucid dreams. *Frontiers in Human Neuroscience, 8,* 717.

CHAPTER 12

Ackerly, S. S. (1964). A case of paranatal bilateral frontal lobe defect observed for thirty years. In J. M. Warren & K. Akert (Eds.), *The frontal granular cortex and behavior* (pp. 192–218). New York: McGraw-Hill.

Adelmann, P. K., & Zajonc, R. B. (1989). Facial efferents and the experience of emotion. *Annual Review of Psychology, 40,* 249–280.

Bao, A.-M., & Swaab, D. F. (2011). Sexual differentiation of the human brain: Relation to gender identity, sexual orientation and neuropsychiatric disorders. *Frontiers in Neuroendocrinology, 32,* 214–226.

Bartoshuk, L. M. (2000). Comparing sensory experiences across individuals: Recent psychophysical advances illuminate genetic variation in taste perception. *Chemical Senses, 25,* 447–460.

Beatty, J. (1995). *Principles of behavioral neuroscience* (p. 339). Dubuque, IA: Brown & Benchmark.

Becker, J. B., Berkley, K. J., Geary, N., Hampson, E., Herman, J. P., & Young, E. A. (2008). *Sex differences in the brain: From genes to behavior.* New York: Oxford University Press.

Berridge, K. C. (1996). Food reward: Brain substrates of wanting and liking. *Neuroscience and Biobehavioral Reviews, 20,* 6.

Brunetti, M., Babiloni, C., Ferretti, A., Del Gratta, C., Merla, A., et al. (2008). *European Journal of Neuroscience, 27,* 2922–2927.

Buss, D. (2014). *Evolutionary psychology: The new science of the mind* (5th ed.). New York: Taylor & Francis.

Butler, R. A., & Harlow, H. F. (1954). Persistence of visual exploration in monkeys. *Journal of Comparative and Physiological Psychology, 47,* 257–263.

Daly, M., & Wilson, M. (1988). *Homicide.* New York: Aldine.

Damasio, A. R. (1999). *The feeling of what happens: Body and emotion in the making of consciousness.* New York: Harcourt Brace.

Davis, M., Walker, D. L., & Myers, K. M. (2003). Role of the amygdala in fear extinction measured with potentiated startle. *Annals of the New York Academy of Sciences, 985,* 218–232.

Day, J. J., & Sweatt, J. D. (2011). Cognitive neuroepigenetics: A role for epigenetic mechanisms in learning and memory. *Neurobiology of Learning and Memory, 96,* 2–12.

Dethier, V. G. (1962). *To know a fly.* San Francisco: Holden-Day.

Duffy, V. B., Hayes, J. E., Davidson, A. C., Kidd, J. R., Kidd, K. K., & Bartoshuk, L. M. (2010). Vegetable intake in college-aged adults is explained by oral sensory phenotypes and TAS2R38 genotype. *Chemosensory Perception, 3,* 137–148.

Eisenberger, N. I., Jarcho, J. M., Lieberman, M. D., & Naliboff, B. D. (2006). An experimental study of shared sensitivity to physical pain and social rejection. *Pain, 126,* 132–138.

Eisenberger, N. I., Lieberman, M. D., & Williams, K. D. (2003). Does rejection hurt? An fMRI study of social exclusion. *Science, 302,* 290–292.

Everitt, B. J. (1990). Sexual motivation: A neural and behavioral analysis of the mechanisms underlying appetitive and copulatory responses of male rats. *Neuroscience and Biobehavioral Reviews, 14,* 217–232.

Field, T. M., Woodson, R., Greenberg, R., & Cohen, D. (1982), Discrimination and imitation of facial expression by neonates. *Science, 218,* 179–181.

Fung, T. T., van Dam, R. M., Hankinson S. E., Stampfer, M., Willett, W. C., & Hu, F. B. (2010). Low-carbohydrate diets and all-cause and cause-specific mortality: Two cohort studies. *Annals of Internal Medicine, 153,* 289–298.

Garcia, J., & Koelling, R. A. (1966). Relation of cue to consequences in avoidance learning. *Psychonomic Science, 4,* 123–124.

Garrison, K. A., Zeffiro, T. A., Scheinost, D., Constable, R. T., & Brewer, J. A. (2015, Apr 23). Meditation leads to reduced default mode network activity beyond an active task. *Cognitive Affective Behavioral Neuroscience, 15,* 712–720.

Gerkin, R.C., & Castro, J. B. (2015). The number of olfactory stimuli that humans can discriminate is still unknown. *eLife* 4:e08127.

Glickman, S. E., & Schiff, B. B. (1967). A biological theory of reinforcement. *Psychological Review, 74,* 81–109.

Gorski, R. A. (1984). Critical role for the medial preoptic area in the sexual differentiation of the brain. *Progress in Brain Research, 61,* 129–146.

Heron, W. (1957). The pathology of boredom. *Scientific American, 196*(1), 52–56.

Insel, T. R., & Fernald, R. D. (2004). How the brain processes social information: Searching for the social brain. *Annual Review of Neuroscience, 27,* 697–722.

Jacob, S., Kinnunen, L. H., Metz, J., Cooper, M., & McClintock, M. K. (2001). Sustained human chemosignal unconsciously alters brain function. *Neuroreport, 12,* 2391–2394.

Jacobsen, C. F. (1936). Studies of cerebral function in primates. *Comparative Psychology Monographs, 13,* 1–68.

Janes, A. C., Farmer, S., Frederick, B. deB., Nickerson, L. D., & Lucas, S. E. (2014). An increase in tobacco craving is associated with enhanced medial prefrontal cortex network coupling. *PLoS One, 9,* e88228.

Janes, A. C., Nickerson, L. D., Frederick, B. deB., & Kaufman, M. H. (2012). Prefrontal and limbic resting state brain network functional connectivity differs between biotine-dependent smokers and non-smoking controls. *Drug and Alcohol Dependence, 125,* 252–259.

Klüver, H., & Bucy, P. C. (1939). Preliminary analysis of the temporal lobes in monkeys. *Archives of Neurology and Psychiatry, 42,* 979–1000.

Kross, E., Berman, M. G., Mischel, W., Smith, E. E., & Water, T. D. (2011). Social rejection shares somatosensory representations with physical pain. *Proceedings of the National Academy of Sciences United States of America, 108,* 6270–6275.

LeDoux, J. (1996). *The emotional brain.* New York: Simon & Schuster.

Lundstrom, J. N., Boyle, J. A., Zatorre, R. J., & Jones-Gotman, M. (2008). Functional neuronal processing of body odors differs from that of similar common odors. *Cerebral Cortex, 18,* 1466–1474.

MacLean, P. D. (1949). Psychosomatic disease and the "visceral brain": Recent developments bearing on the Papez theory of emotion. *Psychosomatic Medicine, 11,* 338–353.

McCarthy, M. M., Auger, A. P., Bale, T. L., De Vries, G. J., Dunn, G. A., et al. (2009). The epigenetics of sex differences in the brain. *Journal of Neuroscience, 29,* 12815–12823.

Money, J., & Ehrhardt, A. A. (1972). *Man and woman, boy and girl.* Baltimore: Johns Hopkins University Press.

Mozaffarinan, D., Tao Hao, M. P. H., Rimm, E. B., Willett, W. C., & Hu, F. B. (2011). Changes in diet and lifestyle and long-term weight gain in women and men. *New England Journal of Medicine, 364,* 2392–2404.

Olds, J., & Milner, P. (1954). Positive reinforcement produced by electrical stimulation of septal area and other regions of rat brain. *Journal of Comparative and Physiological Psychology, 47,* 419–427.

Olsson, S. B., Barnard, J., & Turri, L. (2006). Olfaction and identification of unrelated individuals: Examination of the mysteries of human odor recognition. *Journal of Chemical Ecology, 32,* 1635–1645.

Panagiotakos, D. B., Pitsavos, C., Polychronopoulos, E., Chrysohoou, C., Zampelas, A., & Trichopoulou, A. (2004). Can a Mediterranean diet moderate the development and clinical progression of coronary heart disease? A systematic review. *Medical Science Monitor, 10,* RA193–RA198.

Robinson, T. E., & Berridge, K. C. (2008). Incentive sensitization theory. *Philosophical Transactions of the Royal Society of London, 363,* 3137–3146.

Schroeder, M., Krebs, M. O., Bleich, S., & Frieling, H. (2010). Epigenetics and depression. *Current Opinion in Psychiatry, 23,* 588–592.

Seeley, R. J., & Woods, S. C. (2003). Monitoring of stored and available fuel by the CNS: Implications for obesity. *Nature Reviews Neuroscience, 4,* 885–909.

Shai, I., Schwarzfuchs, D., Henkin, Y., Shahar, D. R., Witkow, S., et al. (2008). Weight loss with a low-carbohydrate, Mediterranean, or low-fat diet. *New England Journal of Medicine, 359,* 229–241.

Skinner, B. F. (1938). *The behavior of organisms.* New York: Appleton-Century-Crofts.

Smith, D. V., & Shepherd, G. M. (2003). Chemical senses: Taste and olfaction. In L. R. Squire, F. E. Bloom, S. K. McConnell, J. L. Roberts, N. C. Spitzer, & M. J. Zigmond (Eds.), *Fundamental Neuroscience* (2nd ed., pp. 631–667). New York: Academic Press.

Stern, K., & McClintock, M. K. (1998). Regulation of ovulation by human pheromones. *Nature, 392,* 177–179.

Veldhuizen, M. G., Albrecht, J., Zelano, C., Boesveldt, S., Breeslin, P., & Lundstrom, J. N. (2011). Identification of human gustatory cortex by activation likelihood estimation. *Human Brain Mapping, 32,* 2256–2266.

Wise, R. A. (1996). Addictive drugs and brain stimulation reward. *Annual Review of Neuroscience, 19,* 319–340.

Woo, C.-W., Koban, L., Kross, E., Lindquist, M. A., Banich, M. T., Ruzic, L., et al. (2014). Separate neural representations for physical pain and social rejection. *Nature Communications, 5,* 5380. doi: 10.1038/ncomms6380

Woolley, C. S., Gould, E., Frankfurt, M., & McEwen, B. (1990). Naturally occurring fluctuation in dendritic spine density on adult hippocampal pyramidal neurons. *Journal of Neuroscience, 10,* 4035–4039.

World Health Organization (2000). *Obesity: Preventing and managing the global epidemic.* WHO Technical Report Series, No. 894, 1–253.

CHAPTER 13

Amariei, C., Tomita, M., & Murray, D. B. (2014). Quantifying periodicity in omics data. *Frontiers in Cellular Developmental Biology, 19,* 2:40.

Batterink, L. J., Oudiette, D., Reber, P. J., & Paller, K. A. (2014). Sleep facilitates learning a new linguistic rule. *Neuropsychologia, 65,* 169–179.

Bendix, C., Marshall, C. M., & Harmon, F. G. (2015). Circadian clock genes universally control key agricultural traits. *Molecular Plant, S1674-2052(15),* 171–179.

Binkley, S. (1990). *The clockwork sparrow.* Englewood Cliffs, NJ: Prentice Hall.

Blumberg, M. S. (2015). Developing sensorimotor systems in our sleep. *Current Directions in Psychological Science, 24,* 32–37.

Bosler, O., Girardet, C., Franc, J. L., Becquet, D., François-Bellan, A. M. (2015). Structural plasticity of the circadian timing system: An overview from flies to mammals. *Frontiers in Neuroendocrinology,* S0091-3022(15)00014-X.

Cain, S. W., McDonald, R. J., & Ralph, M. R. (2008). Time stamp in conditioned place avoidance can be set to different circadian phases. *Neurobiology of Learning and Memory, 89,* 591–594.

Cain, S. W., Verwey, M., Szybowska, M., Ralph, M. R., & Yeomans, J. S. (2007). Carbachol injections into the intergeniculate leaflet induce nonphotic phase shifts. *Brain Research, 1177,* 59–65.

Carter, K. A., Hathaway, N. E., & Lettieri, C. F. (2014). Common sleep disorders in children. *American Family Physician, 89,* 368–377.

Chang, A. M., Aeschbach, D., Duffy, J. F., Czeisler, C. A. (2015). Evening use of light-emitting eReaders negatively affects sleep, circadian timing, and next-morning alertness. *Proceedings of the National Academy of Sciences United States of America, 112,* 232–237.

Claustrat, B., Leston, J. (2015). Melatonin: Physiological effects in humans. *Neurochirurgie, 61(2–3),* 77–84.

Corrêa Cde, C., Blasca, W. Q., & Berretin-Felix, G. (2015). Health promotion in obstructive sleep apnea syndrome. *International Archives of Otorhinolaryngology, 19,* 166–170.

de Lavilléon, G., Lacroix, M. M., Rondi-Reig, L., & Benchenane, K. (2015). Explicit memory creation during sleep demonstrates a causal role of place cells in navigation. *Nature Neuroscience, 18,* 493–495.

Dement, W. C. (1972). *Some must watch while some must sleep.* Stanford, CA: Stanford Alumni Association.

Dissel, S., Angadi, V., Kirszenblat, L., Suzuki, Y., Donlea, J., Klose, M., et al. (2015). Sleep restores behavioral plasticity to *Drosophila* mutants. *Current Biology, 25,* 1270–1280.

Dubey, A. K., Handu, S. S., & Mediratta, P. K. (2015). Suvorexant: The first orexin receptor antagonist to treat insomnia. *Journal of Pharmacology and Pharmacothereputics, 6,* 118–121.

Edwards, C. L., Ruby, P. M., Malinowski, J. E., Bennett, P. D., & Blagrove, M. T. (2013). Dreaming and insight. *Frontiers in Psychology, 24,* 974–979.

Elliott, A. S., Huber, J. D., O'Callaghan, J. P., Rosen, C. L., & Miller, D. B. (2014). A review of sleep deprivation studies evaluating the brain transcriptome. *Springerplus, 3:*728.

Filevich, E., Dresler, M., Brick, T. R., & Kühn, S. (2015). Metacognitive mechanisms underlying lucid dreaming. *Journal of Neuroscience, 35,* 1082–1088.

Forloni, G., Tettamanti, M., Lucca, U., Albanese, Y., Quaglio, E., Chiesa, R., et al. (2015). Preventive study in subjects at risk of fatal familial insomnia: Innovative approach to rare diseases. *Prion, 9,* 75–79.

Foulkes, D., & Domhoff, G. W. (2014). Bottom-up or top-down in dream neuroscience? A top-down critique of two bottom-up studies. *Conscious Cognition, 27,* 168–171.

Freud, S. (1990). *The interpretation of dreams.* Leipzig and Vienna: Franz Deuticke.

Gangwisch, J. E. (2014). Invited commentary: Nighttime light exposure as a risk factor for obesity through disruption of circadian and circannual rhythms. *American Journal of Epidemiology, 180,* 251–253.

Gerhart-Hines, Z., Lazar, M. A. (2015). Circadian metabolism in the light of evolution. *Endocrinology Reviews, 36(3),* 289–304. er20151007.

Gerrard, J. L., Burke, S. N., McNaughton, B. L., & Barnes, C. A. (2008). Sequence reactivation in the hippocampus is impaired in aged rats. *Journal of Neuroscience, 30,* 7883–7890.

Hall, C. S., Domhoff, G. W., Blick, K. A., & Weesner, K. E. (1982). The dreams of college men and women in 1950 and 1980: A comparison of dream contents and sex differences. *Sleep, 5,* 188–194.

Hobson, J. A. (2002). Sleep and dream suppression following a lateral medullary infarct: A first-person account. *Consciousness and Cognition, 11,* 377–390.

Hobson, J. A. (2004). *13 dreams Freud never had: A new mind science.* New York: Pi Press.

Hughes, S., Jagannath, A., Hankins, M. W., Foster, R. G., & Peirson, S. N. (2015). Photic regulation of clock systems. *Methods in Enzymology, 552,* 125–143.

Jones, B. E. (1993). The organization of central cholinergic systems and their functional importance in sleep–waking states. *Progress in Brain Research, 98,* 61–71.

Jouvet, M. (1972). The role of monoamines and acetylcholine-containing neurons in the regulation of the sleep–waking cycle. *Ergebnisse der Physiologie, 64,* 166–307.

Kang, J. I., Park, C. I., Namkoong, K., & Kim, S. J. (2015). Associations between polymorphisms in the *NR1D1* gene encoding for nuclear receptor REV-ERBα and circadian typologies. *Chronobiology International, 32,* 568–572.

Kerr, D. C., Zava, D. T., Piper, W. T., Saturn, S. R., Frei, B., & Gombart, A. F. (2015). Associations between vitamin D levels and depressive symptoms in healthy young adult women. *Psychiatry Research, 227,* 46–51.

Klinger, E. (1990). *Daydreaming.* Los Angeles, CA: Tarcher (Putnam).

Kreutzmann, J., Havekes, R., Abel, T., & Meerlo, P. (2015). Sleep deprivation and hippocampal vulnerability: Changes in neuronal plasticity, neurogenesis and cognitive function. *Neuroscience.*

Labrecque, N., & Cermakian N. (2015). Circadian clocks in the immune system. *Journal of Biological Rhythms, 30 (4),* 277–290.

Lajoie, P., Aronson, K. J., Day, A., & Tranmer, J. (2015). A cross-sectional study of shift work, sleep quality and cardiometabolic risk in female hospital employees. *BMJ Open*, 10;5(3):e007327.

Lamberg, L. (2003). Scientists never dreamed finding would shape half-century of sleep research. *Journal of the American Medical Association*, 290, 2652–2654.

Lan, K. C., Chang, D. W., Kuo, C. E., Wei, M. Z., Li, Y. H., Shaw, F. Z., et al. (2015). Using off-the-shelf lossy compression for wireless home sleep staging. *Journal of Neuroscience Methods*, 246, 142–152.

Landgraf, D., Tsang, A. H., Leliavski, A., Koch, C. E., Barclay, J. L., Drucker, D. J., et al. (2015). Oxyntomodulin regulates resetting of the liver circadian clock by food. *eLife 4*, e06253.

Li, Y., Ma, W., Kang, Q., Qiao, L., Tang, D., Qiu, J., et al. (2015). Night or darkness, which intensifies the feeling of fear? *International Journal of Psychophysiology*, 97 (1), 46–57.

Lungato, L., Gazarini, M. L, Paredes-Gamero, E. J., Tufik, S., & D'Almeida, V. (2015). Paradoxical sleep deprivation impairs mouse survival after infection with malaria parasites. *Malaria Journal*, 14, 183.

Mahowald, M. W., & Schenck, C. H. (2015). REM sleep behaviour disorder: A window on the sleeping brain. *Brain*, 138, 1131–1133.

Malcolm-Smith, S., Koopowitz, S., Pantelis, E., & Solms, M. (2012). Approach/avoidance in dreams. *Consciousness and Cognition*, 21, 408–412.

Maquet, P., Laureys, S., Peigneux, P., Fuchs, S., Petiau, C., et al. (2000). Experience-dependent changes in cerebral activation during human REM sleep. *Nature Neuroscience*, 3, 831–836.

Mårtensson, B., Pettersson, A., Berglund, L., & Ekselius, L. (2015). Bright white light therapy in depression: A critical review of the evidence. *Journal of Affective Disorders*, 182, 1–7.

Mistlberger, R. E., & Antle, M. C. (2011). Entrainment of circadian clocks in mammals by arousal and food. *Essays in Biochemistry*, 49, 119–136.

Monecke, S., Brewer, J. M., Krug, S., & Bittman, E. L. (2011). Duper: A mutation that shortens hamster circadian period. *Biological Rhythms*, 26, 283–292.

Moruzzi, G., & Magoun, H .W. (1949). Brain stem reticular formation and activation of the EEG. *Electroencephalography and Clinical Neurophysiology*, 1, 455–473.

Mulder, C. K., Reckman, G. A., Gerkema, M. P., & Van der Zee, E. A. (2015). Time-place learning over a lifetime: Absence of memory loss in trained old mice. *Learning and Memory*, 22, 278–288.

Nelini, C., Bobbo, D., & Mascetti, G. G. (2012). Monocular learning of a spatial task enhances sleep in the right hemisphere of domestic chicks (*Gallus gallus*). *Experimental Brain Research*, 18, 381–388.

Nir, Y., & Tononi, G. (2010). Dreaming and the brain: From phenomenology to neurophysiology. *Trends in Cognitive Science*, 14, 88–100.

Nobunaga, M., Obukuro, K., Kurauchi, Y., Hisatsune, A., Seki, T., Tsutsui, M., et al. (2014). High fat diet induces specific pathological changes in hypothalamic orexin neurons in mice. *Neurochemistry International*, 78, 61–66.

Osorio, I., & Daroff, R. B. (1980). Absence of REM and altered NREM sleep in patients with spinocerebellar degeneration and slow saccades. *Annals of Neurology*, 7, 277–280.

Pellegrino, R., Kavakli, I. H., Goel, N., Cardinale, C. J., Dinges, D. F., Kuna, S. T., et al. (2015). A novel BHLHE41 variant is associated with short sleep and resistance to sleep deprivation in humans. *Sleep*, 37, 1327–1336.

Postuma, R. B., Gagnon, J. F., Tuineaig, M., Bertrand, J. A., Latreille, V., Desjardins, C., et al. (2013). Antidepressants and REM sleep behavior disorder: Isolated side effect or neurodegenerative signal? *Sleep*, 36, 1579–1585.

Quinlan, J., & Quinlan, J. (1977). Karen Ann: The Quinlans tell their story. Toronto: Doubleday.

Ralph, M. R., & Lehman, M. N. (1991). Transplantation: A new tool in the analysis of the mammalian hypothalamic circadian pacemaker. *Trends in Neurosciences*, 14, 363–366.

Rasch, B., & Born, J. (2013). About sleep's role in memory. *Physiological Reviews*, 93, 681–766.

Raven, P. H., Evert, R. F., & Eichorn, S. E. (1992). *Biology of plants*. New York: Worth Publishers.

Reiter, R. J. (1980). The pineal and its hormones in the control of reproduction in mammals. *Endocrinology Review*, 1, 120.

Richter, C. P. (1965). *Biological clocks in medicine and psychiatry*. Springfield, IL: Charles C Thomas.

Roffward, H. P., Muzio, J., & Dement, W. C. (1966). Ontogenetic development of the human sleep–dream cycle. *Science*, 152, 604–619.

Schenck, C. H., Bundlie, S. R., Ettinger, M. G., & Mahowald, M. W. (1986). Chronic behavioral disorders of human REM sleep: A new category of parasomnia. *Sleep*, 25, 293–308.

Schmal, C., Myung, J., Herzel, H., & Bordyugov, G. (2015). A theoretical study on seasonality. *Frontiers in Neurology*, 7(6), 94.

Siegel, J. (2004). Brain mechanisms that control sleep and waking. *Naturwissenschaften*, 91, 355–365.

Silver, R., LeSauter, J., Tresco, P. A., & Lehman, M. N. (1996). A diffusible coupling signal from the transplanted suprachiasmatic nucleus controlling circadian locomotor rhythms. *Nature*, 382, 810–813.

Smarr, B. L. (2015). Digital sleep logs reveal potential impacts of modern temporal structure on class performance in different chronotypes. *Journal of Biological Rhythms*, 30, 61–67.

Valli, K., & Revonsuo, A. (2009). The threat simulation theory in light of recent empirical evidence: A review. *American Journal of Psychology*, 122, 17–38.

Vanderwolf, C. H. (2002). *An odyssey through the brain, behavior and the mind*. Amsterdam: Kluwer Academic.

Webb, I. C., Antle, M. C., & Mistlberger, R. E. (2014). Regulation of circadian rhythms in mammals by behavioral arousal. *Behavioral Neuroscience*, 128, 304–325.

Weingarten, J. A., & Collop, N. A. (2013). Air travel: Effects of sleep deprivation and jet lag. *Chest*, 144, 1394–1401.

Wijemanne, S., & Jankovic, J. (2015). Restless legs syndrome: Clinical presentation diagnosis and treatment. *Sleep Medicine*, 16, (6), 678–690.

Wilson, M. A., & McNaughton, B. L. (1994). Reactivation of hippocampal ensemble memories during sleep. *Science*, 265, 676–679.

Wilson, S., & Argyropoulos, S. (2005). Antidepressants and sleep: A qualitative review of the literature. *Drugs*, 65, 927–947.

Zaidi, F. H., Hull, J. T., Peirson, S. N., Wulff, K., Aeschbach, D., et al. (2007). Short-wavelength light sensitivity of circadian, pupillary, and visual awareness in humans lacking an outer retina. *Current Biology*, 17, 2122–2128.

Zhang, R., Lahens, N. F., Balance, H. I., Hughes, M. E., & Hogenesch, J. B. (2014). A circadian gene expression atlas in mammals: Implications for biology and medicine. *Proceedings of the National Academy of Sciences United States of America*, 111 (45), 16219–16224.

CHAPTER 14

Bliss, T. V., & Lomo, T. (1973). Long-lasting potentiation of synaptic transmission in the dentate are of the anaesthetized rabbit following stimulation of the perforant path. *Journal of Physiology*, 232, 331–356.

Cahill, L., Babinsky, R., Markowitsch, H. J., & McGaugh, J. L. (1995). The amygdala and emotional memory. *Nature*, 377, 295–296.

Candia, V., Wienbruch, C., Elbert, T., Rockstroh, B., & Ray, W. (2003). Effective behavioral treatment of focal hand dystonia in musicians alters somatosensory cortical organization. *Proceedings of the National Academy of Sciences United States of America, 100,* 7942–7946.

Chang, F.-L. F., & Greenough, W. T. (1982). Lateralized effects of monocular training on dendritic branching in adult split-brain rats. *Brain Research, 232,* 283–292.

Corkin, S. (2002). What's new with the amnesic patient H. M.? *Nature Reviews Neuroscience, 3,* 153–160.

Corkin, S., Amaral, D. G., Gonzalez, R. G., Johnson, K. A., & Hyman, B. T. (1997). H. M.'s medial temporal lobe lesion: Findings from magnetic resonance imaging. *Journal of Neuroscience, 17,* 3964–3979.

Damasio, A. R., Tranel, D., & Damasio, H. (1989). Amnesia caused by herpes simplex encephalitis, infarctions in basal forebrain, Alzheimer's disease and anoxia/ischemia. In F. Boller & J. Grafman (Eds.), *Handbook of neuropsychology* (Vol. 3, pp. 149–166). New York: Elsevier.

Davis, M. (1992). The role of the amygdala in fear and anxiety. *Annual Review of Neuroscience, 15,* 353–375.

Day, J. J., Kennedy, A. J., & Sweatt, J. D. (2015). DNA methylation and its implications and accessibility for neuropsychiatric therapeutics. *Annual Review of Pharmacology and Toxicology, 55,* 591–611.

Eriksson, P. S., Perfilieva, E., Bjork-Eriksson, T., Alborn, A. M., Nordborg, C., Peterson, D. A., et al. (1998). Neurogenesis in the adult human hippocampus. *Nature Medicine, 4,* 1313–1317.

Fuster, J. M. (1995). *Memory in the cerebral cortex.* Cambridge, MA: MIT Press.

Fuster, J. M., Bodner, M., & Kroger, J. K. (2000). Cross-modal and cross-temporal association in neurons of frontal cortex. *Nature, 405,* 347–351.

Gazzaniga, M. S. (Ed.). (2000). *The new cognitive neurosciences.* Cambridge, MA: MIT Press.

Geschwind, N., & Galaburda, A. M. (1985). *Cerebral lateralization.* Cambridge, MA: MIT Press.

Gould, E., Tanapat, P., Hastings, N. B., & Shors, T. J. (1999). Neurogenesis in adulthood: A possible role in learning. *Trends in Cognitive Sciences, 3,* 186–191.

Gould, E., Tanapat, P., McEwen, B. S., Flugge, G., & Fuchs, E. (1998). Proliferation of granule cell precursors in the dentate gyrus of adult monkeys is diminished by stress. *Proceedings of the National Academy of Sciences United States of America, 95,* 3168–3171.

Hampson, E., & Kimura, D. (1988). Reciprocal effects of hormonal fluctuations on human motor and perceptual-spatial skills. *Behavioral Neuroscience, 102,* 456–459.

Hebb, D. O. (1947). The effects of early experience on problem solving at maturity. *American Psychologist, 2,* 737–745.

Hebb, D. O. (1949). *The organization of behavior: A neuropsychological theory.* New York: Wiley.

Jacobs, B., Schall, M., & Scheibel, A. B. (1993). A quantitative dendritic analysis of Wernicke's area in humans: II. Gender, hemispheric, and environmental factors. *Journal of Comparative Neurololgy, 327,* 97–111.

Jacobs, B., & Scheibel, A. B. (1993). A quantitative dendritic analysis of Wernicke's area in humans: I. Lifespan changes. *Journal of Comparative Neurology, 327,* 83–96.

Kaas, J. (2000). The reorganization of sensory and motor maps after injury in adult mammals. In M. S. Gazzaniga (Ed.), *The cognitive neurosciences* (pp. 223–236). Cambridge, MA: MIT Press.

Kempermann, G., Kuhn, H. G., & Gage, F. H. (1998). Experience-induced neurogenesis in the senescent dentate gyrus. *Journal of Neuroscience, 18,* 3206–3212.

Kolb, B., Cote, S., Ribeiro-da-Silva, A., & Cuello, A. C. (1997). Nerve growth factor treatment prevents dendritic atrophy and promotes recovery of function after cortical injury. *Neuroscience, 76,* 1146.

Kolb, B., & Gibb, R. (2014). Searching for principles of brain plasticity and behavior. *Cortex, 58,* 251–260.

Kolb, B., Gibb, R., & Gorny, G. (2003). Experience-dependent changes in dendritic arbor and spine density in neocortex vary with age and sex. *Neurobiology of Learning and Memory, 79,* 1–10.

Kolb, B., Gorny, G., Cote, S., Ribeiro-da-Silva, A., & Cuello, A. C. (1997). Nerve growth factor stimulates growth of cortical pyramidal neurons in young adult rats. *Brain Research, 751,* 289–294.

Kolb, B., Gorny, G., Li, Y., Samaha, A. N., & Robinson, T. E. (2003). Amphetamine or cocaine limits the ability of later experience to promote structural plasticity in the neocortex and nucleus accumbens. *Proceedings of the National Academy of Science United States of America, 100,* 10523–10528.

Kolb, B., Morshead, C., Gonzalez, C., Kim, N., Shingo, T., & Weiss, S. (2007). Growth factor–stimulated generation of new cortical tissue and functional recovery after stroke damage to the motor cortex of rats. *Journal of Cerebral Blood Flow and Metabolism, 27,* 983–397.

Lashley, K. S. (1960). In search of the engram. Symposium No. 4 of the Society of Experimental Biology. In F. A. Beach, D. O. Hebb, C. T. Morgan, & H. T. Nissen (Eds.), *The neuropsychology of Lashley* (pp. 478–505). New York: McGraw-Hill. (Reprinted from R. Sutton (Ed.), *Physiological mechanisms of animal behavior,* pp. 454–482, 1951. Cambridge: Cambridge University Press.)

LeDoux, J. E. (1995). In search of an emotional system in the brain: Leaping from fear to emotion and consciousness. In M. S. Gazzaniga (Ed.), *The cognitive neurosciences* (pp. 1047–1061). Cambridge, MA: MIT Press.

Lepage, M., McIntosh, A. R., & Tulving, E. (2001). Transperceptual encoding and retrieval process in memory: A PET study of visual and haptic objects. *Neuroimage, 14,* 572–584.

LePort, A. K., Mattfeld, A. T., Dickinson-Anson, H., Falon, J. H., Stark, C. E., Kruggle, F., et al. (2012). Behavioral and neuroanatomical investigation of Highly Superior Autobiographical Memory (HSAM). *Neurobiology of Learning and Memory, 98,* 78–92.

Loftus, E. F. (1997). Creating false memories. *Scientific American, 277*(3), 70–75.

MacDougall, M., & Fine, A. (2014). The expression of long-term potentiation: reconciling the preists and the postivists. *Philosophic Transactions of the Royal Society B Biological Science, 269,* 20130135. doi: 10.1098/rstb.

Maguire, E. A., Gadian, D. G., Johnsrude, I. S., Good, C. D., Ashburner, J., Frackowiak, R. S., et al. (2000). Navigation-related structural change in the hippocampi of taxi drivers. *Proceedings of the National Academy of Sciences United States of America, 97,* 4398–4403.

Mahncke, H. W., Bronstone, A., & Merzenich, M. M. (2006). Brain plasticity and functional losses in the aged: Scientific bases for a novel intervention. *Progress in Brain Research, 157,* 81–109.

Markowitsch, H. J., & Staniloiu, A. (2013). The impairment of recollection in functional amnesic states. *Cortex, 49,* 1494–1510.

Markowitsch, H. J. (2003). Psychogenic amnesia. *Neuroimage, 20* (Suppl. 1), S132–S138.

Martin, A., Haxby, J. V., Lalonde, F. M., Wiggs, C. L., & Ungerleider, L. G. (1995). Discrete cortical regions associated with knowledge of color and knowledge of action. *Science, 270,* 102–105.

Martin, P. R. (1985). Cover, *Alcohol Health & Research World, 9* (Spring 1985).

McGaugh, J. (2004). The amygdala modulates the consolidation of memories of emotionally arousing experiences. *Annual Review of Neuroscience, 27,* 1–28.

McKenzie, S., & Eichenbaum, H. (2011). Consolidation and reconsolidation: Two lives of memories? *Neuron, 71,* 224–233.

Meloni, E. G., Gillis, T. E., Manoukian, J., & Kaufman, M. J. (2014). Xenon impairs reconsolidation of fear memories in a rat model of post-traumatic stress disorder (PTSD). *PLoS ONE, 9*(8): e106189. doi:10.1371 /journal.pone.0106189.

Miller, C. A., Gavin, C. F., White, J. A., Parrish, R. R., Honasoge, A., Yancey, C. R., et al. (2010). Cortical DNA methylation maintains remote memory. *Nature Neuroscience, 13,* 664–666.

Milner, B., Corkin, S., & Teuber, H. (1968). Further analysis of the hippocampal amnesic syndrome: 14-year follow-up study of HM. *Neuropsychologia, 6,* 215–234.

Mishkin, M. (1982). A memory system in the brain. *Philosophical Transactions of the Royal Society of London, Biological Sciences, 298,* 83–95.

Mishkin, M., Suzuki, W. A., Gadian, D. G., & Vargha-Khadem, F. (1997). Hierarchical organization of cognitive memory. *Philosophical Transactions of the Royal Society of London, Biological Sciences, 352,* 1461–1467.

Murray, E. (2000). Memory for objects in nonhuman primates. In M. S. Gazzaniga (Ed.), *The new cognitive neurosciences* (pp. 753–763). Cambridge, MA: MIT Press.

Mychasiuk, R., Muhammad, A., Ilnystskyy, S., & Kolb, B. (2013). Persistent gene expression changes in NAc, mPFC, and OFC associated with previous nicotine or amphetamine exposure. *Behavioural Brain Research, 256,* 655–661.

Mychasiuk, R., Muhammad, A., Ilnystskyy, S., Kovalchuk, O., & Kolb, B. (2015). Persistent gene expression changes in mPFC, OFC, and hippocampus associated with adult stress. Manuscript in submission.

Nudo, R. J., Plautz, E. J., & Milliken, G. W. (1997). Adaptive plasticity in primate motor cortex as a consequence of behavioral experience and neuronal injury. *Seminars in Neuroscience, 9,* 13–23.

O'Keefe, J. (2006). Hippocampal neurophysiology in the behaving animal. In P. Andersen, R. Morris, D. Amaral, T. Bliss, & J. O'Keefe (Eds.), *The Hippocampus Book* (pp. 475–548). New York: Oxford University Press.

O'Keefe, J., & Nadel, L. (1978). *The hippocampus as a spatial map.* New York: Oxford University Press.

Patihis, L., Frenda, S. J., LePort, A. K. R., Petersen, N., Nichols, R. M., Stark, C. E. L., et al. (2013). False memories in highly superior autobiographical memory individuals. *Proceedings of the National Academy of Sciences United States of America, 110,* 20947–20952.

Purves, D., & Voyvodic, J. T. (1987). Imaging mammalian nerve cells and their connections over time in living animals. *Trends in Neurosciences, 10,* 398–404.

Ragert, P., Schmidt, A., Altenmuller, E., & Dinse, H. R. (2003). Superior tactile performance and learning in professional pianists: Evidence for meta-plasticity in musicians. *European Journal of Neuroscience, 19,* 473–478.

Ramachandran, V. S. (1993). Behavioral and magnetoencephalographic correlates of plasticity in the adult human brain. *Proceedings of the National Academy of Sciences United States of America, 90,* 10413–10420.

Ramón y Cajal, S. (1928). *Degeneration and regeneration of the nervous system.* London: Oxford University Press.

Reynolds, B., & Weiss, S. (1992). Generation of neurons and astrocytes from isolated cells of the adult mammalian central nervous system. *Science, 255,* 1707–1710.

Robinson, T. E., & Kolb, B. (1997). Persistent structural adaptations in nucleus accumbens and prefrontal cortex neurons produced by prior experience with amphetamine. *Journal of Neuroscience, 17,* 8491–8498.

Robinson, T. E., & Kolb, B. (2004). Structural plasticity associated with drugs of abuse. *Neuropharmacology, 47*(Suppl. 1), 33–46.

Sainsbury, R. S., & Coristine, M. (1986). Affective discrimination in moderately to severely demented patients. *Canadian Journal on Aging, 5,* 99–104.

Sapolsky, R. M. (1992). *Stress, the aging brain, and the mechanisms of neuron death.* Cambridge, MA: MIT Press.

Schacter, D. L. (1983). Amnesia observed: Remembering and forgetting in a natural environment. *Journal of Abnormal Psychology, 92,* 236–242.

Sherry, D. F., Jacobs, L. F., & Gaulin, S. J. C. (1992). Spatial memory and adaptive specialization of the hippocampus. *Trends in Neuroscience, 15,* 298–303.

Sirevaag, A. M., & Greenough, W. T. (1987). Differential rearing effects on rat visual cortex synapses: III. Neuronal and glial nuclei, boutons, dendrites, and capillaries. *Brain Research, 424,* 320–332.

Sirevaag, A. M., & Greenough, W. T. (1988). A multivariate statistical summary of synaptic plasticity measures in rats exposed to complex, social and individual environments. *Brain Research, 441,* 386–392.

Skinner, B. F. (1938). *The behavior of organisms.* New York: Appleton-Century-Crofts.

Squire, L. R., Genzel, L., Wixted, J. T., & Morris, R. G. (2015). Memory consolidation. *Cold Spring Harbor Perspectives in Biology, 7.* pii: a021766. doi: 10.1101/cshperspect.a021766

Stewart, J., & Kolb, B. (1994). Dendritic branching in cortical pyramidal cells in response to ovariectomy in adult female rats: Suppression by neonatal exposure to testosterone. *Brain Research, 654,* 149–154.

Sutherland, R. J., Sparks, F. T., & Lehmann, H. (2010). Hippocampus and retrograde amnesia in the rat model: A modest proposal for the situation of systems consolidation. *Neuropsychologia, 48,* 2357–2369.

Temple, E., Deutsch, G. K., Poldrack, R. A., Miller, S. L., Tallal, P., Merzenich, M. M., et al. (2003). Neural deficits in children with dyslexia ameliorated by behavioral remediation: Evidence from functional MRI. *Proceedings of the National Academy of Sciences United States of America, 100,* 2860–2865.

Thorndike, E. L. (1898). Animal intelligence: An experimental study of the associative processes in animals. *Psychological Review Monograph Supplements, 2,* 1–109.

Tulving, E. (2002). Episodic memory: From mind to brain. *Annual Review of Psychology, 53,* 1–25.

Turner, A., & Greenough, W. T. (1985). Differential rearing effects on rat visual cortex synapses: I. Synaptic and neuronal density and synapses per neuron. *Brain Research, 329,* 195–203.

Walker, L. C., & Jucker, M. (2015). Neurodegenerative diseases: Expanding the prion concept. *Annual Review of Neuroscience, 38,* 87–103.

Wise, R. A. (2004). Dopamine, learning and motivation. *Nature Neuroscience Reviews, 5,* 483–494.

Wisniewski, T., & Goni, F. (2015). Immunotherapeutic approaches for Alzheimer's disease. *Neuron, 85,* 1162–1176.

Woollett, K., & Maguire, E. A. (2011). Acquiring "the Knowledge" of London's layout drives structural brain changes. *Current Biology, 21,* 2109–2014.

Woolley, C. S., Gould, E., Frankfurt, M., & McEwen, B. S. (1990). Naturally occurring fluctuation in dendritic spine density on adult hippocampal pyramidal neurons. *Journal of Neuroscience, 10,* 4035–4039.

CHAPTER 15

Adolphs, R., Gosselin, F., Buchanan, T. W., Tranel, D., Schyns, P., & Damasio, A. R. (2005). A mechanism for impaired fear recognition after amygdala damage. *Nature, 433,* 68–72.

Baumann, O., Borra, B. J., Bower, J. M., Cullen, K. E., Habas, C., Ivry, R. B., et al. (2015) Consensus paper: The role of the cerebellum in perceptual processes. *Cerebellum, 14,* 197–220.

Barton, R. A. (2012). Embodied cognitive evolution and the cerebellum. *Philosophical Transactions of the Royal Society B, 367*, 2097–2107.

Boria, S., Fabbri-Destro, M., Cattaneo, L., Sparaci, L., Sinigaglia, C., Santelli, E., et al. (2009). Intention understanding in autism. *PLoS ONE, 4*, e5596.

Calvin, W. H. (1996). *How brains think*. New York: Basic Books.

Carr, L., Iacoboni, M., Dubeau, M. C., Mazziotta, J. C., & Lenzi, G. L. (2003). Neural mechanisms of empathy in humans: A relay from neural systems for imitation to limbic areas. *Proceedings of the National Academy of Sciences United States of America, 100*, 5497–5502.

Castiello, U., Paulignan, Y., & Jeannerod, M. (1991). Temporal dissociation of motor responses and subjective awareness. *Brain, 114*, 2639–2655.

Chalmers, D. J. (1995). *The conscious mind: In search of a fundamental theory*. Oxford: Oxford University Press.

Crick, F., & Koch, C. (1998). Consciousness and neuroscience. *Cerebral Cortex, 8*, 97–107.

Csibra, G. (2007). Action mirroring and action understanding: An alternative account. In P. Haggard, Y. Rosetti, & M. Kawato (Eds.) *Sensorimotor foundations of higher cognition: Attention and Performance XII* (pp. 453–459). Oxford: Oxford University Press.

Cytowic, R. E. (1998). *The man who tasted shapes*. Cambridge, MA: MIT Press.

Diamond, M. C., Scheibel, A. B., Murphy, G. M., Jr., & Harvey, T. (1985). On the brain of a scientist: Albert Einstein. *Experimental Neurology, 88*, 198–204.

Duncan, J., Seitz, R. J., Kolodny, J., Bor, D., Herzog, H., Ahmed, A., Newell, F. N., & Emslie, H. (2000). A neural basis for general intelligence. *Science, 289*, 457–459.

Gardner, H. (1983). *Frames of mind*. New York: Basic Books.

Gaulin, S. J. (1992). Evolution of sex differences in spatial ability. *Yearbook of Physical Anthropology, 35*, 125–131.

Gazzaniga, M. S. (1970). *The bisected brain*. New York: Appleton-Century-Crofts.

Gazzaniga, M. S. (1992). *Nature's mind*. New York: Basic Books.

Gazzaniga, M. S., Ivry, R. B., & Mangun, G. R. (1999). *Cognitive science: The biology of the mind*. New York: Norton.

Ghanzanfar, A. A., & Schroeder, C. E. (2006). Is neocortex essentially multisensory? *Trends in Cognitive Science, 10*, 278–285.

Goldstein, J. M., Seidman, J. L., Horton, N. J., Makris, N., Kennedy, D. N., et al. (2001). Normal sexual dimorphism of the adult human brain assessed by in vivo magnetic resonance imaging. *Cerebral Cortex, 11*, 490–497.

Gray, J. R., & Thompson, P. M. (2004). Neurobiology of intelligence: Science and ethics. *Nature Reviews Neuroscience, 5*, 471–482.

Guilford, J. P. (1967). *The nature of human intelligence*. New York: McGraw-Hill.

Hebb, D. O. (1949). *The Organization of Behavior*. New York: McGraw-Hill.

Hebb, D. O. (1980). *Essay on mind*. Hillsdale, NJ: Lawrence Erlbaum.

Hickok, G. (2013). Do mirror neurons subserve action understanding? *Neuroscience Letters, 540*, 56–58.

Hickok, G. (2014). *The myth of motor neurons*. New York: Norton.

Hubbard, E. W. (2007). Neurophysiology of synesthesia. *Current Psychiatry Reports, 9*, 193–199.

Iacoboni, M., & Dapretto, M. (2006). The mirror neuron system and the consequences of its dysfunction. *Nature Neuroscience Reviews, 7*, 942–951.

Ingalhalikar, M., Smith, A., Parker, D., Satterthwaite, P. D., Elliott, M. A., Ruparel, K., et al. (2013). Sex differences in the structural connectome of the human brain. *Proceedings of the National Academy of Sciences United States of America, 111*, 823–828.

James, W. (1890). *Principles of psychology*. New York: Henry Holt.

Kelly, C., Biswal, B. B., Craddock, R. C., Castellanos, F. X., & Milham, M. P. (2012). Characterizing variation in the functional connectome: Promise and pitfalls. *Trends in Cognitive Science, 16*, 181–188.

Kimura, D. (1967). Functional asymmetry of the brain in dichotic listening. *Cortex, 3*, 163–178.

Kimura, D. (1973). The asymmetry of the human brain. *Scientific American, 228*(3), 70–78.

Kimura, D. (1999). *Sex and cognition*. Cambridge, MA: MIT Press.

Kolb, B., & Stewart, J. (1991). Sex-related differences in dendritic branching of cells in the prefrontal cortex of rats. *Journal of Neuroendocrinology, 3*, 95–99.

Kranz, G. S., Hahn, A., Kaufmann, U., Kublbock, M., Hummer, A., Ganger S., et al. (2014). White matter microstructure in transsexuals and controls investigated by diffusion tensor imaging. *Journal of Neuroscience, 34*, 15466–15474.

Langer, N., Pedroni, A., Gianotti, L. R., Hanggi, J., Knoch D., & Jancke, L. (2009). Functional brain network efficiency predicts intelligence. *Human Brain Mapping, 4*, 299–307.

Lieberman, M. D. (2007). Social cognitive neuroscience: A review of core processes. *Annual Review of Psychology, 58*, 259–289.

Lieberman, M. D., Berkman, E. T., & Wager, T. D. (2012). Correlations in social neuroscience aren't voodoo. *Perspectives on Psychological Science, 33*, 1393–1406.

Loui, P., Li, H. C., Hohmann, A., & Schlaug, G. (2011). Enhanced cortical connectivity in absolute pitch musicians: A model for local hyperconnectivity. *Journal of Cognitive Neuroscience, 23*, 1015–1026.

McClure, S. M., Li, J., Tomlin, D., Cypert, K. S., Montague, L. M., & Montague, P. R. (2004). Neural correlates of behavioral preferences for culturally familiar drinks. *Neuron, 44*, 379–387.

Mlodinow, L. (2009). *The drunkard's walk: How randomness rules our lives*. New York: Vintage Books.

Moran, J., & Desimone, R. (1985). Selective attention gates visual processing in the extrastriate cortex. *Science, 229*, 782–784.

Mukerjee, M. (1996). Interview with a parrot [field note]. *Scientific American, 274*(4), 24.

Newsome, W. T., Shadlen, M. N., Zohary, E., Britten, K. H., & Movshon, J. A. (1995). Visual motion: Linking neuronal activity to psychophysical performance. In M. Gazzaniga (Ed.), *The cognitive neurosciences* (pp. 401–414). Cambridge, MA: MIT Press.

Olulade, O. A., Jamal, N. I., Koo, D. S., Perfetti, C. A., LaSasso, C., & Eden, G. F. (2015). Neuroanatomical evidence in support of the bilingual advantage theory. *Cerebral Cortex*, Jul 16. pii: bhv152. [Epub ahead of print.]

Pepperberg, I. M. (1990). Some cognitive capacities of an African grey parrot (*Psittacus erithacus*). In P. J. B. Slater, J. S. Rosenblatt, & C. Beer (Eds.), *Advances in the study of behavior* (Vol. 19, pp. 357–409). New York: Academic Press.

Pepperberg, I. M. (1999). *The Alex studies*. Cambridge, MA: Harvard University Press.

Pepperberg, I. M. (2006). Ordinality and inferential ability of a grey parrot (*Psittacus erithacus*). *Journal of Comparative Psychology, 120*, 205–216.

Ramachandran, V. S., & Oberman, L. M. (2006). Broken mirrors: A theory of autism. *Scientific American, 295*, 62–69.

Rameson, L. T., Morellis, S. A., & Lieberman, M. D. (2012). The neural correlates of empathy: Experience, automaticity, and prosocial behavior. *Journal of Cognitive Neuroscience, 24*, 235–245.

Rasmussen, T., & Milner, B. (1977). The role of early left brain injury in determining lateralization of cerebral speech functions. *Annals of the New York Academy of Sciences, 299*, 355–369.

Rizzolatti, G. (2007). *Mirrors on the mind.* New York: Oxford University Press.

Rizzolatti, G., & Craighero, L. (2004). The mirror-neuron system. *Annual Review of Neuroscience, 27,* 169–192.

Rizzolatti, G., & Fabbri-Destro, M. (2010). Mirror neurons: From discovery to autism. *Experimental Brain Research, 200,* 223–237.

Sacks, O. (1989). *Seeing voices.* Los Angeles: University of California Press.

Sala-Llonch, R., Bartres-Faz, D., & Junque, C. (2015). Reorganization of brain networks in aging: A review of functional connectivity studies. *Frontiers in Psychology.* doi: 10.3389/fpsyg.2015.00663.

Sawamoto, N., Honda, M., Okada, T., Hanakawa, T., Kanda, M., et al. (2000). Expectation of pain enhances responses to nonpainful somatosensory stimulation in the anterior cingulate cortex and parietal operculum/posterior insula: An event-related functional magnetic resonance imaging study. *Journal of Neuroscience, 20,* 7438–7445.

Sperry, R. (1968). Mental unity following surgical disconnection of the cerebral hemispheres. *Harvey Lectures, 62,* 293–323.

Stein, B. E., & Rowland, B. A. (2011). Organization and plasticity in multisensory integration: Early and late experience affects its governing principles. *Progress in Brain Research, 191,* 145–163.

Stewart, J., & Kolb, B. (1994). Dendritic branching in cortical pyramidal cells in response to ovariectomy in adult female rats: Suppression by neonatal exposure to testosterone. *Brain Research, 654,* 149–154.

Takeuchi, H., Sugiura, M., Sassa, Y., Sekiguchi, A., Yomogida, Y., et al. (2012). Neural correlates of the differences between working memory speed and simple sensorimotor speed: An fMRI study. *PLoS One, 7,* e30579.

Vul, E., Harris, C., Winkielman, P., & Pashler, H. (2009). Puzzlingly high correlations in fMRI studies of emotion, personality, and social cognition. *Perspectives on Psychological Science, 4,* 274–290.

Vul, E., & Pashler, H. (2012). Voodoo and circularity errors. *Neuroimage, 62,* 945–948.

Wada, J., & Rasmussen, T. (1960). Intracarotid injection of sodium amytal for the lateralization of cerebral speech dominance: Experimental and clinical observations. *Journal of Neurosurgery, 17,* 266–282.

Witelson, S. F., & Goldsmith, C. H. (1991). The relationship of hand preference to anatomy of the corpus callosum in men. *Brain Research, 545,* 175–182.

Witelson, S. F., Kigar, D. L., & Harvey, T. (1999). The exceptional brain of Albert Einstein. *Lancet, 353,* 2149–2153.

Yeo, B. T. T., Fienen, F. M., Sepulcre, J., Sabuncu, M. R., Lashkari, D., Hollinshead, M., et al. (2011). The organization of the human cerebral cortex estimated by intrinsic functional connectivity. *Journal of Neurophysiology, 106,* 1125–1165.

CHAPTER 16

American Psychiatric Association. (2013). *Diagnostic and Statistical Manual of Mental Disorders* (5th ed.). Washington, DC: American Psychiatric Association.

Arnold, S. E., Rushinsky, D. D., & Han, L. Y. (1997). Further evidence of abnormal cytoarchitecture in the entorhinal cortex in schizophrenia using spatial point analyses. *Biological Psychiatry, 142,* 639–647.

Asante, E. A., Smidak, M., Grimshaw, A., Houghton R., Tomlinson A., Jeelani, A., et al. (2015). A naturally occurring variant of the human prion protein completely prevents prion disease. *Nature, 522*(7557), 478–481.

Birbaumer, N., Ruiz, S., & Sitaram, R. (2013). Learned regulation of brain metabolism. *Trends in Cognitive Science, 17,* 295–302.

Block, C., West, S., & Goldin, Y. (2015). Misconceptions and misattributions about traumatic brain injury: An integrated conceptual framework. *PM&R,* S1934-1482(15)00279-8.

Calne, D. B., & Mizuno, Y. (2004). The neuromythology of Parkinson's disease. *Parkinsonism and Related Disorders, 10,* 319–322.

Charney, D. S., Nestler, E. J., & Bunney, B. S. (Eds.). (1999). *The Neurobiology of Mental Illness.* New York: Oxford University Press.

Cho, R. Y., Gilbert, H., & Lewis, D. A. (2004). The neurobiology of schizophrenia. In D. S. Charney & F. J. Nestler (Eds.), *The Neurobiology of Mental Illness* (2nd ed., pp. 299–310). New York: Oxford University Press.

Claes, S., Tang, Y. L., Gillespie, C. F., & Cubells, J. F. (2012). Human genetics of schizophrenia. *Handbook of Clinical Neurology, 106,* 37–52.

Cleary, D. R., Ozpinar, A., Raslan, A. M., & Ko, A. L. (2015). e *Neurosurgical Focus,* 38, E2.

Corrigan, N. M., Richards, T. L., Treffert, D. A., & Dager, S. R. (2012). Toward a better understanding of the savant brain. *Comprehensive Psychiatry, 53,* 706–717.

Costa, V., Lugert, S., & Jagasia, R. (2015). Role of adult hippocampal neurogenesis in cognition in physiology and disease: Pharmacological targets and biomarkers. *Handbook of Experimental Pharmacology, 228,* 99–155.

Costanzo, M. E., Chou, Y. Y., Leaman, S., Pham, D. L., Keyser, D., Nathan, D. E., et al. (2014). Connecting combat-related mild traumatic brain injury with posttraumatic stress disorder symptoms through brain imaging. *Neuroscience Letters, 577,* 11–15.

deCharms, R. C. (2008). Applications of real-time fMRI. *Nature Reviews Neuroscience, 9,* 720–729.

Drevets, W. C., Kishore, M. G., & Krishman, K. R. R. (2004). Neuroimaging studies of mood disorders. In D. S. Charney & E. J. Nestler (Eds.), *The Neurobiology of Mental Illness* (2nd ed., pp. 461–490). New York: Oxford University Press.

Duman, R. S. (2004). The neurochemistry of depressive disorders. In D. S. Charney & E. J. Nestler (Eds.), *The Neurobiology of Mental Illness* (2nd ed., pp. 421–439). New York: Oxford University Press.

Fereshtehnejad, S. M., Romenets, S. R., Anang, J. B., Latreille, V., Gagnon, J. F., & Postuma, R. B. (2015). New clinical subtypes of Parkinson disease and their longitudinal progression: A prospective cohort comparison with other phenotypes. *JAMA Neurology, 72*(8), 863–873.

Foroozani, H., Abiri, M., Salehpour, S., Bagherian, H., Sharifi, Z., Alaei, M. R., et al. (2015). Molecular characterization of QDPR gene in Iranian families with BH4 deficiency: Reporting novel and recurrent mutations. *JIMD Reports, 21,* 123–128.

François, C., Grau-Sánchez, J., Duarte, E., & Rodriguez-Fornells, A. (2015). Musical training as an alternative and effective method for neuro-education and neuro-rehabilitation. *Frontiers in Psychology, 6,* 475–485.

Gebicke-Haerter, P. J. (2012). Epigenetics of schizophrenia. *Pharmacopsychiatry, 45,* Suppl. 1, S42–S48.

Giles J. (2004). Neuroscience: Change of mind. *Nature, 430,* 14.

Gogtay, N., Lu, A., Leow, A. D., Klunder, A. D., Lee, A. D., Chavez, A., et al. (2008). Three-dimensional brain growth abnormalities in childhood-onset schizophrenia visualized by using tensor-based morphometry. *Proceedings of the National Academy of Sciences U S A, 105,* 15979–15984.

Gonçalves, R., Pedrozo, A.L., Coutinho, E.S., Figueira, I., & Ventura, P. (2012). Efficacy of virtual reality exposure therapy in the treatment of PTSD: A systematic review. *PLoS One, 7*(12), e48469.

Gross, C., & Hen, R. (2004). The developmental origins of anxiety. *Nature Reviews Neuroscience, 5*, 545–552.

Gubbi, J., Kusmakar, S., Rao, A., Yan, B., O'Brien, T., & Palaniswami, M. (2015). Automatic detection and classification of convulsive psychogenic non-epileptic seizures using a wearable device. *IEEE Journal of Biomedical and Health Information.* [Epub ahead of print.]

Heinz, A., Kipke, R., Heimann, H., & Wiesing, U. (2012). Cognitive neuroenhancement: False assumptions in the ethical debate. *Journal of Medical Ethics, 38*, 372–375.

Heninger, G. R. (1999). Special challenges in the investigation of the neurobiology of mental illness. In D. S. Charney, E. J. Nestler, & B. S. Bunney (Eds.), *The Neurobiology of Mental Illness* (pp. 89–98). New York: Oxford University Press.

Holmstrom, L. L., & Burgess, A. W. *The victim of rape: Institutional reactions.* Wiley-Interscience, 1978.

Jorge, R. E. (2015). Posttraumatic stress disorder. *Behavioral Neurology and Neuropsychiatry, 21*, 789–805.

Kaufer, D. I., & DeKosky, S. T. (1999). Diagnostic classifications: Relationship to the neurobiology of dementia. In D. S. Charney, E. J. Nestler, & B. S. Bunney (Eds.), *The Neurobiology of Mental Illness* (p. 642). New York: Oxford University Press.

Khachaturian, Z. S., & Khachaturian, A. S. (2015, June 5). Politics of science: Progress toward prevention of the dementia-Alzheimer's syndrome (review). *Molecular Aspects of Medicine, 43-44*, 3-15.

Knight, E. J., Testini, P., Min, H. K., Gibson, W. S., Gorny, K. R., Favazza, C. P., et al. (2015). Motor and nonmotor circuitry activation induced by subthalamic nucleus deep brain stimulation in patients with Parkinson disease: Intraoperative functional magnetic resonance imaging for deep brain stimulation. *Mayo Clinic Proceedings, 90*, 773-785.

Kong, L., Herold, C., Stieltjes, B., Essig, M., Seidl, U., et al. (2012). Reduced gray to white matter tissue intensity contrast in schizophrenia. *PLoS One, 7*, e37016.

Kornek, B. (2015). An update on the use of natalizumab in the treatment of multiple sclerosis: Appropriate patient selection and special considerations. *Patient Preference and Adherence, 9*, 675–684.

Kumar, J., Namsechi, R., & Sim, V. L. (2015). Structure-based peptide design to modulate amyloid beta aggregation and reduce cytotoxicity. *PLoS One, 12*;10(6).

Kuo, H.-K., Jones, R. N., Milberg, W. P., Tennstedt, S., Talbot, L., et al. (2005). Effect of blood pressure and diabetes mellitus on cognitive and physical functions in older adults: A longitudinal analysis of the advanced cognitive training for independent and vital elderly cohort. *Journal of the American Geriatrics Society, 53*, 1154–1161.

Kwakkel, G., Veerbeek, J. M., van Wegen, E. E., & Wolf, S. L. (2015). Constraint-induced movement therapy after stroke. *Lancet Neurology, 14*, 224–234.

Laver, K. E., George, S., Thomas, S., Deutsch, J. E., & Crotty, M. (2015). Virtual reality for stroke rehabilitation. *Cochrane Database Systems Review,* Sep 7;(9):CD008349.

Leritz, E. C., Salat, D. H., Williams, V. J., Schnyer, D. M., Rudolph, J. L., et al. (2011). Thickness of the human cerebral cortex is associated with metrics of cerebrovascular health in a normative sample of community dwelling older adults. *Neuroimage, 54*, 2659–2671.

Malberg, J. E., Eisch, A. J., Nestler, E. J., & Duman, R. S. (2000). Chronic antidepressant treatment increases neurogenesis in adult rat hippocampus. *Journal of Neuroscience, 20*, 9104–9110.

Martin, J. P. (1967). *The basal ganglia and posture.* London: Ritman Medical.

Mateer, C. A., & Sira, C. S. (2006). Cognitive and emotional consequences of TBI: Intervention strategies for vocational rehabilitation. *NeuroRehabilitation, 21*, 315–326.

McGowan, P. O., & Szyf, M. (2010). Environmental epigenomics: Understanding the effects of parental care on the epigenome. *Essays in Biochemistry, 48*, 275–287.

Miller, B. L., Boone, K., Cummings, J. L., Read, S. L., & Mishkin, F. (2000). Functional correlates of musical and visual ability in frontotemporal dementia. *British Journal of Psychiatry, 176*, 458–463.

National Institute of Mental Health Web site: http://www.nimh.nih.gov/health/publications/the-numbers-count-mental-disorders-in-america/index.shtml

Nevler, N., Ash, E.L. (2015). TMS as a tool for examining cognitive processing. *Current Neurological and Neuroscience Reports, 15*, 575.

Olanow, C. W., & Brundin, P. (2013). Parkinson's disease and alpha synuclein: Is Parkinson's disease a prion-like disorder? *Movement Disorders, 28*, 31–40.

Ostergard, T., & Miller, J. P. (2014). Deep brain stimulation: New directions. *Journal of Neurosurgical Science, 58*, 191–198.

Pannese, R., Minichino, A., Pignatelli, M., Delle Chiaie, R., Biondi, M., & Nicoletti, F. (2012). Evidences on the key role of the metabotropic glutamatergic receptors in the pathogenesis of schizophrenia: A "breakthrough" in pharmacological treatment. *Reviews in Psychiatry, 47*, 149–169.

Politis, M., & Lindvall, O. (2012). Clinical application of stem cell therapy in Parkinson's disease. *BMC Medicine, 10*, 1.

Rao, J., Chiappelli, J., Kochunov, P., Regenold, W. T., Rapoport, S. I., & Hong, L. E. (2015). Is schizophrenia a neurodegenerative disease? Evidence from age-related decline of brain-derived neurotrophic factor in the brains of schizophrenia patients and matched nonpsychiatric controls. *Neurodegenerative Diseases, 15*, 38–44.

Rapoport, J. L., Giedd, J. N., & Gogtay, N. (2012). Neurodevelopmental model of schizophrenia: Update 2012. *Molecular Psychiatry, 17*, 1228–1238.

Reis, C., Wang, Y., Akyol, O., Ho, W. M., Ii, R. A., Stier, G., et al. (2015). What's new in traumatic brain injury: Update on tracking, monitoring and treatment. *International Journal of Molecular Science, 16*, 11903–11965.

Rizzo, A., Buckwalter, J. G., John, B., Newman, B., Parsons, T., Kenny, P., et al. (2012). STRIVE: Stress Resilience in Virtual Environments: A pre-deployment VR system for training emotional coping skills and assessing chronic and acute stress responses. *Studies in Health and Technology Information, 173*, 379–385.

Rose, S. C., Weber, K. D., Collen, J. B., & Heyer, G. L. (2015). The diagnosis and management of concussion in children and adolescents. *Pediatric Neurology, 53*, 108–118.

Sacks, O. (1998). *The man who mistook his wife for a hat: And other clinical tales.* New York: Touchstone.

Santarelli, L., Saxe, M., Gross, C., Surget, A., Battaglia, F., et al. (2003). Requirement of hippocampal neurogenesis for the behavioral effects of antidepressants. *Science, 301*, 805–809.

Savitz, S. I. (2015). Developing cellular therapies for stroke. *Stroke, 46*, 2026–2031.

Serafini, G., Pompili, M., Belvederi, M. M., Respino, M., Ghio, L., Girardi, P., et al. (2015). The effects of repetitive transcranial magnetic stimulation on cognitive performance in treatment-resistant depression. A systematic review. *Neuropsychobiology, 71*, 125–139.

Shi, Q., Chen, L. N., Zhang, B. Y., Xiao, K., Zhou, W., Chen, C., et al. (2015). Proteomics analyses for the global proteins in the brain tissues of different human prion diseases. *Molecular Cell Proteomics, 14*, 854–869.

Shin, J. H., Bog, G., Park, S., Ho, G., & Jang, S. (2015). Effects of game-based virtual reality on health-related quality of life in chronic stroke patients: A randomized, controlled study. *Computational Biological Medicine, 63*, 92–98.

Shorter, K. R., & Miller, B. H. (2015). Epigenetic mechanisms in schizophrenia. *Progress in Biophysics and Molecular Biology, 118*, 1–7.

Sohlberg, M. M., & Mateer, C. (1989). *Introduction to Cognitive Rehabilitation.* New York: Guilford.

Sundström, P., & Salzer, J. (2015). Vitamin D and multiple sclerosis: From epidemiology to prevention. *Acta Neurology Scandanavia Supplement, 132,* 56–61.

Tsivgoulis, G., Faissner, S., Voumvourakis, K., Katsanos, A. H., Triantafyllou, N., Grigoriadis, N., et al. (2015). "Liberation treatment" for chronic cerebrospinal venous insufficiency in multiple sclerosis: The truth will set you free. *Brain and Behavior, 5*, 3–12.

Wang, J., Zhao, X., & He, M. (2012). Is BDNF a biological link between depression and type 2 diabetes mellitus? *Medical Hypotheses, 79*, 255–258.

Wassermann, E. M., & Zimmermann, T. (2012). Transcranial magnetic brain stimulation: Therapeutic promises and scientific gaps. *Pharmacology and Therapeutics, 133*(1), 9.

Wingenfeld, K., & Wolf, O. T. (2014). Stress, memory, and the hippocampus. *Frontiers in Neurological Neuroscience. 34*, 109–120.

Note: Page numbers followed by *f* indicate figures; those followed by *t* indicate tables.

Study Smarter with LearningCurve!

A link to the e-Book makes it easy to review.

What is ?

LearningCurve is a cutting-edge study tool designed to increase your understanding and memory of the core concepts in every chapter. Based on insights from the latest learning and memory research, the LearningCurve system pairs multiple-choice and fill-in-the-blank questions with instantaneous feedback and a rich array of study tools including videos, animations, and lab simulations.

The LearningCurve system is adaptive, so the quiz you take is customized to your level of understanding. The more questions you answer correctly, the more challenging the questions become. Best of all, the e-Book of *An Introduction to Brain and Behavior,* **Fifth Edition,** is fully integrated, so you can easily review the text as you study and answer questions.

LearningCurve is a smart and fun way to master each chapter and prepare for your exam.

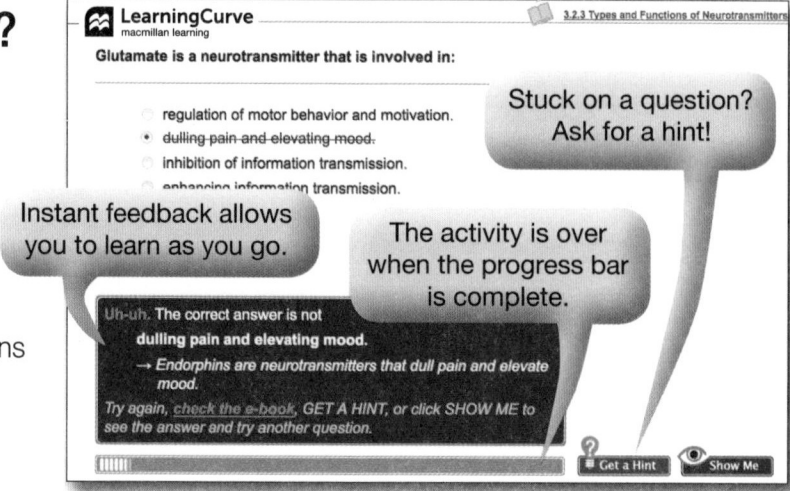

Stuck on a question? Ask for a hint!

Instant feedback allows you to learn as you go.

The activity is over when the progress bar is complete.

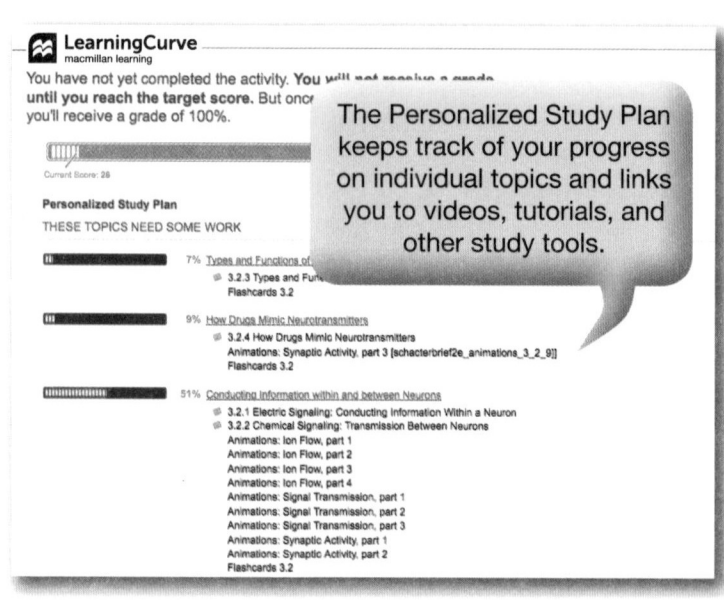

The Personalized Study Plan keeps track of your progress on individual topics and links you to videos, tutorials, and other study tools.